Y0-BXQ-633

CHEMICAL ANALYSIS

Vol. I: **The Analytical Chemistry of Industrial Poisons, Hazards, and Solvents**
Second Edition. By Morris B. Jacobs

Vol. II: **Chromatographic Adsorption Analysis**
By Harold H. Strain

Vol. III: **Colorimetric Determination of Traces of Metals**
Third Edition. By E. B. Sandell

Vol. IV: **Organic Reagents Used in Gravimetric and Volumetric Analysis**
By John F. Flagg

Vol. V: **Aquametry. Application of the Karl Fischer Reagent to Quantitative Analyses Involving Water**
By John Mitchell, Jr., and Donald Milton Smith

Vol. VI: **Analysis of Insecticides and Acaricides**
By Francis A. Gunther and Roger C. Blinn

Vol. VII: **Chemical Analysis of Industrial Solvents**
By Morris B. Jacobs and Leopold Scheflan

Vol. VIII: **Colorimetric Determination of Nonmetals**
Edited by David F. Boltz

Vol. IX: **Analytical Chemistry of Titanium Metals and Compounds**
By Maurice Codell

Vol. X: **Chemical Analysis of Air Pollutants**
By Morris B. Jacobs

Vol. XI: **X-Ray Spectrochemical Analysis**
By L. S. Birks

Vol. XII: **Systematic Analysis of Surface-Active Agents**
By Milton J. Rosen and Henry A. Goldsmith

Vol. XIII: **Alternating Current Polarography**
By B. Breyer and H. H. Bauer

Vol. XIV: **Chemical Analysis by Flame Photometry**
Second Edition. By Roland Herrmann and C. T. J. Alkemade. Translated by Paul T. Gilbert, Jr.

Vol. XV: **Titrimetric Organic Analysis—Parts I and II**
By M. R. F. Ashworth

Vol. XVI: **Complexation in Analytical Chemistry: A Guide for the Critical Selection of Analytical Methods Based on Complexation Reactions**
By Anders Ringbom

Vol. XVII: **Electron Probe Microanalysis**
By L. S. Birks

Other volumes in preparation

CHEMICAL ANALYSIS

A SERIES OF MONOGRAPHS ON ANALYTICAL CHEMISTRY AND ITS APPLICATIONS

Volume XV

Titrimetric Organic Analysis

Part II—Indirect Methods

by M. R. F. Ashworth

INTERSCIENCE PUBLISHERS

A division of John Wiley & Sons Inc.

NEW YORK - LONDON - SYDNEY

TITRIMETRIC ORGANIC ANALYSIS

PART II: INDIRECT METHODS

M. R. F. ASHWORTH
Professor of Applied and Analytical Organic Chemistry
University of the Saar, Saarbrücken, Germany

1965

INTERSCIENCE PUBLISHERS
A division of John Wiley & Sons Inc.
NEW YORK - LONDON - SYDNEY

Library of Congress Catalog Card Number 64-13477

*Made and printed in Great Britain by
Willmer Brothers Limited, Birkenhead.*

INTRODUCTION

The first titrations were carried out over 100 years ago and, together with gravimetric determinations, titration belongs to the classical procedures of chemical analysis. Analytical methods based on titration have always found and continue to find extensive application, with the modern accent on procedures with micro and submicro quantities. It is customary to distinguish between direct and indirect titration procedures. Direct titration has been treated in Part I of this book and indirect procedures are dealt with here in Part II.

CONTENTS

SECTION 2: REAGENTS USED IN INDIRECT TITRATION OF ORGANIC COMPOUNDS

SECTION 3: INDEX TO FUNCTIONAL GROUPS AND COMPOUND CLASSES

SECTION 1

INDIRECT TITRATION PROCEDURES

Indirect titration is defined here as a method of determination involving two or more operations, of which the concluding, measuring operation is a direct titration. The operations may be chemical or purely physical treatments. Where the latter are operations accompanying a chemical method (such as filtration of a precipitate or distillation of a volatile reaction product) they are not considered here. Mention is made below (p. 3) of methods in which titration has concluded a purely physical treatment.

The general equation for determination of a component A of a mixture containing other components B, C, etc., by reaction with a reagent X to yield reaction products A′, A″, etc., is

$$\underbrace{A + B + C + \ldots}_{} + \underset{\text{Reagent}}{X} \rightarrow \underset{\text{Products}}{A' + A''} + \underset{\text{Unchanged components}}{B + C + \ldots} + \underset{\text{Excess unused reagent}}{X}$$

Three types of analytical procedure are based on this chemical equation, namely:

(1) determination of unused reagent X; this has usually been referred to as 'back titration' and is the most familiar type of indirect titration.

(2) determination of a reaction product A′, A″, etc.

(3) determination of unchanged B + C + . . ; from a control determination giving A + B + C + . . , the amount of A is obtained by difference.

REQUIREMENTS OF THE PROCEDURES

Some general requirements are common to all 3 types of procedure:

(a) The reagent X must be present in excess.

(b) Adequate time must be allowed for complete reaction. If functional group totals are being determined, all the groups contributing to the total must be given this necessary time.

(c) The reaction must be stoichiometric or at least reproducible under conditions varying within fairly wide limits. For example, if reaction time and temperature and, particularly, amount of X in excess, influence the conversion, the method will be valueless.

The individual procedures demand for success the fulfilment of certain conditions:

Procedure Type 1

(a) The amount of X added must be accurately measured.

(b) Only the component A, which is to be determined, must react with X.

(c) The unreacted amount of X must be accurately measured. This requires amongst other things that the determination of X must be influenced unfavourably neither by the unchanged components of the sample (B, C, etc.) nor by the reaction products A′, A″, etc.

Procedure Type 2

(a) The amount of X need not be accurately known.

(b) Other components of the sample (B, C, etc.) can react with X, provided that no reaction product is formed during this side reaction which interferes with the final stage of determination of reaction product A′ or A″, and provided that so much X is not consumed that the general condition (a) is unfulfilled.

(c) The determination of A′ or A″ etc. must be uninfluenced by the other components of the reaction mixture. If this condition is unlikely to be fulfilled, a partial or total separation procedure may precede the final determination. Usually A′ or A″ is separated but the potentially interfering compound may be removed. The usual separation procedures are available for this, namely, distillation, filtration, extraction, etc.

Procedure Type 3

(a) As in procedure 2, the amount of X need not be accurately known.

(b) The component A must not react with X.

(c) The determination of unchanged B + C etc., must be uninfluenced by the other components of the reaction mixture.

The procedures types 1 and 3 are differential, since the amount of reagent equivalent to the component to be determined is given by the difference between an initial and a final measured value. This introduces an increased uncertainty into the determination, an uncertainty from which type 2 procedures do not suffer. Moreover, in type 2 procedures, a large excess of X may be used in order to accelerate the reaction if desired. Type 1 procedures have, however, a practical advantage over those of type 2. The consumption of reagent is independent of the reaction occurring. Certain versatile reagents, such as halogens, which enter into several types of reaction, are eminently suitable for such procedures and determinations of a variety of functional groups and compound classes can be carried out conveniently using always the same reagent for standardization and back titration. Type 2 procedures are restricted to reactions yielding the particular reaction product which is titrated.

The complete analytical method may comprise several successive procedures of the above types. A few examples will illustrate this:

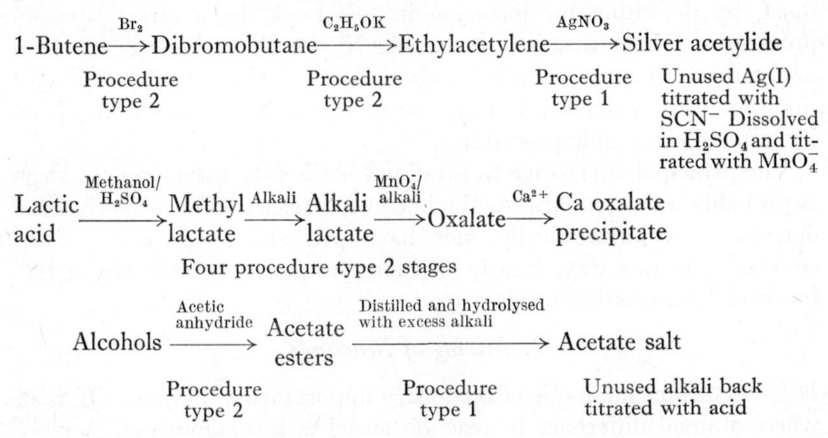

PHYSICAL METHODS

There are few methods in which titration has followed purely physical treatment of the sample. The treatment brings about separation of the components of the sample and the separation may be complete, such as in some distillations; or partial, such as in some methods of partition between solvents. Some examples are given in Sect. 2 under the heading 'Physical Methods'.

TITRATION FEATURES

Some comments are made here about various aspects of the titration procedures. For the most part, these comments are closely similar to those made in Part I on direct titration on the same topics, to which reference can be made.

1. *Measurement of the Amount of Reagent X (for Procedure Type 1) and of Sample*

Solid, liquid and gaseous samples have been analysed and solid and liquid reagents used (there appears to be no example of a gaseous reagent in procedures of type 1). The customary measurement techniques have been used, i.e. volume and weight. Electrolytically generated reagents have been used but less often than in direct titration.

2. *Measurement of Unused X (Procedure Type 1), Reaction Product A′ or A″, etc., or Unchanged Components B or C*

Where this measurement is the final stage of the determination, it must, by definition for inclusion in this book, be a direct titration procedure. Direct titration of organic X, A′, B, etc. has been given under the relevant reagent heading in Part I and the reader can refer there for further details. Titration of inorganic X, A′, B, etc. has been by standard inorganic procedures.

The principal alternative to titration for the final measurement stage is probably a colorimetric method. Unused reagent X has rarely been determined colorimetrically, nor have procedures of type 3 been concluded in this way. Nearly all examples are of colorimetric determination of a reaction product.

3. *Mixing of Reactants*

Highly efficient mixing is of secondary importance in indirect titration, where a small difference in reaction speed is less significant. A more important factor is the order of mixing and there are cases where this has been claimed to have an appreciable influence on the result. In general this is related to side reactions which may take place with one component of a complex reagent. A notable example is the determination of aldoses by oxidation with alkali/iodine. There has been disagreement about the sequence of addition of the alkali and iodine parts of the reagent and small, successive, alternate additions have also been proposed.

4. *Speed of Reaction*

The content of the corresponding section in Part I (p. 8) is valid for indirect titration also. Catalysts have been used in indirect as in direct titration although the pattern of use differs. The same oxidation, reduction and addition catalysts are encountered for the most part, but the principal catalysed reactions are those which were scarcely or not at all found in direct procedures. Chief place is held by hydrolysis, with examples also of esterification, dehydration, decarboxylation and depolymerization. These are evidently reactions which proceed in general very slowly but which, with the aid of catalysts, can be accelerated sufficiently to be available at least for indirect titration.

The following table, similar to that in Part I (p. 9), summarizes the principal catalysts. Cross-references are given in the last column to the citations under the relevant reagent heading in Sect. 2. The word 'many' signifies that there are *ca* 10 or more such sources in Sect. 2, or that the catalyst is so familiar that its use has usually not even been given in the tables in Sect. 2 (e.g. Mn(II) in permanganate oxidations, Br^- in nitrosation, Cu(II) or Hg(II) in Kjeldahl nitrogen determinations).

Catalyst	Reagent and heading in Sect. 2	Reaction	Determination of	Ref.
Acetic acid	Amines	Addition	α,β-Unsaturated nitriles and carbonyl compounds	61
Acetate (K)	Lead (IV)	Oxidation	Formate	6
Alkalies	Water (under the heading 'Alkalies')	Hydrolysis	E.g. esters, anhydrides, amides, halides	Many
	Mercaptans	Addition	α,β-Unsaturated nitriles	3, 4, 5, 11
	Nitriles	Addition	Mercaptans, alcohols	1, 2, 3, 4, 6
Barium chloride	Hydrochloric acid	Addition	C_4 olefines	46
Bisulphate	Bisulphate	Dehydration	Hydroxy compounds	1, 2
Boron trifluoride	Alcohols	Esterification	Carboxylic acids	19
	Carboxylic acids	Esterification	Alcohols	15
	Phenols	Condensation	Methylol groups	3
	Water	Hydrolysis	Anhydrides	6
Bromide	Cerium (IV)	Oxidation	Formic acid	54
	Nitrite	Nitrosation	Amines, amino acids, amides, hydrazines	Many

Catalyst	Reagent and heading in Sect. 2	Reaction	Determination of	Ref.
Calcium (II)	Permanganate	Oxidation	Some hydroxy acids	112
Cerium (IV)	Bichromate	Oxidation	Cholesterol	86
Chromium (III)	Cerium (IV)	Oxidation	Formic acid	39, 44, 45
Copper (II)	Kjeldahl nitrogen determination	Reduction and oxidation	Nitrogen-containing compounds	Many
	Permanganate	Oxidation	Hydroxy compounds	137
Cyanide	Alkalies	Hydrolysis	Alloxan	167
Fluoroboric acid	Anhydrides	Esterification	Alcohols	86
Hydrobromic acid	Water (under the heading 'Hydrobromic acid')	Hydrolysis	Acetals, ketals, vinyl ethers; tributyl phosphate	11 15
Hydrochloric acid	Alcohols	Esterification	Carboxylic acids	33
	Alcohols	Transesterification	Esters	21, 35, 53, 63
	Water (under the heading 'Hydrochloric acid')	Hydrolysis	E.g. esters, amides, polysaccharides, nitriles, etc.	Many
		Dehydration	Pentoses	Many
		Depolymerization	Aldehyde polymers	4
		Decarboxylation	Uronic acids	15, 26, 29, 64, 81, 115, 124
		Addition	Isocyanates	104
Hydrofluoric acid	Titanium (III)	Reduction	Azo, nitro, nitroso compounds, etc.	Many
Iodide	Cerium (IV)	Oxidation	Antabuse	46
	Water	Hydrolysis	Anhydrides	7, 9
Iodine monochloride	Cerium (IV)	Oxidation	Oxalic acid	7
Iron (III)	Water (under heading 'Hydrochloric acid')	Hydrolysis	Glucose	48

Catalyst	Reagent and heading in Sect. 2	Reaction	Determination of	Ref.
	Hydrogen peroxide	Oxidation	Butyric, isobutyric acids	10, 12
	Iodide	Reduction	Peresters, peracids	206, 231
Manganese (II)	Cerium (IV)	Oxidation	Polyalcohols	53
	Iodine	Oxidation	Acetone	245
	Manganese (IV)	Oxidation	Lactic acid	1, 6
	Permanganate	Oxidation	Lactic, oxalic acids	Many
Mercury (II)	Bromine reagents	Addition	Olefines	235, 346, 354, 361, 503
		Addition	Unsaturated acids	483, 484, 498
		Addition	Acetylenes	145
		Addition	α,β-Unsaturated nitriles	426
		Oxidation	Camphoquinone	360
	Iodine reagents	Addition	Olefines	258, 299, 330, 352
		Oxidation	Vicinal dioximes	373
	Iodine chlorides	Addition	Olefines	Many
	Kjeldahl nitrogen determination	Oxidation and reduction	Nitrogen-containing compounds	Many
	Thiocyanogen	Addition	Olefines	20
	Water	Addition	Acetylenes	19
Molybdenum (VI) (molybdate, MoO_3)	Bromine reagents	Addition	Furfuraldehyde	66, 203, 253, 265
			Unsaturated compounds	503, 532, 533
		Oxidation	Urea	508
	Hydrogen peroxide	Oxidation	Acetaldehyde	25
	Iodide	Reduction	Peroxides, peracids	218

Catalyst	Reagent and heading in Sect. 2	Reaction	Determination of	Ref.
	Iron (II)	Reduction	Nitrate esters	10
Nickel	Hydrogen gas	Reduction	Chloropicrin	3
Nitrate	Mercury (II)	Addition	Olefines	107
Nitric acid	Water (under the heading 'Nitric acid')	Hydrolysis	Halides, urea	Many
Osmium tetroxide	Cerium (IV)	Oxidation	Oxalic acid	7
	Chlorine reagents	Oxidation	Aldehydes	25
	Ferricyanide	Oxidation	Thiourea	103, 107
		Oxidation	Formate	125
		Oxidation	Xanthate	128
Palladium	Halides ('Active')	Oxidation	Amino acids	71
	Hydrogen gas	Reduction	Phenazines, carbo-benzyloxy groups	4, 5
			Nitriles	6
Perchloric acid	Anhydrides	Esterification	Alcohols	114, 132, 137, 154, 162, 163, 164, 165, 168
	(under the heading 'Perchloric acid')	Dehydration	Alcohols, ethers	12, 13
	Mercury (II)	Addition	Olefines	144, 150
Phosphoric acid	(under the heading 'Alcohols')	Transesterification	Esters	2
	(under the heading 'Phosphoric acid')	Dehydration	Pentoses	10, 12
Platinum	Aluminium hydride and borohydride	Reduction	Olefines	8
	Hydrogen gas	Reduction	Vinyl ethers	2

Catalyst	Reagent and heading in Sect. 2	Reaction	Determination of	Ref.
			Nitriles	6
	Hydrogen peroxide	Oxidation	Halides	23
Polyhydroxy compounds	Titanium (III)	Reduction	Azo, nitro, nitroso compounds, etc.	Many
Pyridine	Water	Hydrolysis	Anhydrides	10, 11, 20, 21, 22, 25
			Acid chlorides	16
Selenium dioxide	Bichromate	Oxidation	Sewage	146
	Kjeldahl nitrogen determination	Oxidation and reduction	Nitrogen-containing compounds	Many
Silver (I)	Bichromate	Oxidation	Sewage, etc.	198, 199, 226
			Fatty acids, lipids	42, 45, 110, 140, 163
	Cerium (IV)	Oxidation	Polyalcohols	16, 53
	Persulphate	Oxidation	Organic matter	5, 6, 7, 8
Sulphonic acids	Alcohols	Esterification	Carboxylic acids	41, 50
		Trans-esterification	Esters	5, 7, 10, 13, 14, 29
	Anhydrides	Esterification	Alcohols	101, 103, 124, 147, 149, 152, 160
	Carboylic acids	Esterification	Alcohols	25
	Phenols	Condensation	Methylol groups	2
	Water (under the heading 'Sulphonic acids')	Hydrolysis	Esters, amides, especially of acetic acid	Many
	(under the 'Sulphonic acids')	Dehydration	Alcohols, especially tertiary	14, 15, 16
Sulphuric acid	Alcohols	Esterification	Carboxylic acids	37, 46
	Alcohols	Trans-esterification	Esters	23, 54

Catalyst	Reagent and heading in Sect. 2	Reaction	Determination of	Ref.
	Anhydrides	Esterification	Alcohols	114, 134, 162
	Carboxylic acids	Esterification	Alcohols	27, 31
	Carboxylic acids	Addition	Olefines (yielding esters)	10, 14, 23, 31
	Water (under the heading 'Sulphuric acid')	Hydrolysis	Esters, amides, polysaccharides, hydrazines, nitriles, etc.	Many
	(under the heading 'Sulphuric acid')	Addition	α-Epoxides	38, 91, 107, 124
		Decarboxylation		123, 134, 135
		Depolymerization	Aldehyde polymers	31, 44, 48, 115, 122
		Dehydration	Alcohols, ethers	128, 129
Tartaric acid	Carboxylic acids	Hydrolysis	Hexamine	17
Tin (II)	Isothiocyanates and isocyanates	Addition	Hydroxy compounds	6
Vanadium pentoxide	Hydrogen peroxide	Oxidation	Acetaldehyde	25
	Kjeldahl nitrogen determination	Oxidation and reduction	Nitrogen-containing compounds	14
Zinc (II)	Permanganate	Oxidation	Coumarin	18

The inconvenience of very slow reactions can sometimes be circumvented by extrapolation procedures. Aliquots of the reaction mixture are removed at intervals, the concluding titration (or other measurement) carried out and the data extrapolated to the asymptotic end-value. This has been tried notably to determine unsaturation of hydrocarbon mixtures like rubber products or petroleum fractions. An excessively long reaction time renders the method susceptible to side or consecutive reactions (e.g. in the example mentioned, substitution) so that these extrapolation data need careful interpretation.

In recent years especially, there has been increasing interest in the determination of mixtures of compounds with the same functional group by making use of their different speeds of reaction with a reagent. This will not be described in detail here because the technique is by no means restricted to indirect titration. The faster reacting component reacts only at the beginning of the determination; later, when it has sensibly disappeared, only the slower reacting component undergoes reaction. An analytical result can be worked out from data taken from the earlier or later parts of a curve of overall, total reaction; or calculated or otherwise worked out from the knowledge of the rates of reaction of the pure compounds under the same conditions. Where only one of the components can satisfactorily be determined in one of these ways, the second can be determined by difference from a total obtained in an accelerated procedure (e.g. at higher temperature) or by waiting until reaction is complete. Two articles in which the techniques, including those based on titration and for analysis of mixtures of organic compounds, are described, are:

Laitinen, H. A., 'Reaction rates in chemical analysis', *Chemical Analysis*, McGraw-Hill Book Co., New York, 1960, pp. 452-460.

Mark, H. B., Papa, L. J. and Reilley, C. N., 'Reaction rate methods', *Advances in Analytical Chemistry and Instrumentation, Volume* 2, Interscience Publishers, New York, 1963, pp. 255-385, especially 332-359.

5. *End-point Determination*

Most of the direct titration procedures that conclude an indirect determination are inorganic, since inorganic reagents predominate and, even where a reaction product is titrated at the end, it is often inorganic, such as Fe(II) from oxidations with Fe(III). No details are given of these procedures since they belong to inorganic analysis. As already mentioned (p. 4), where the directly titrated product at the end was organic, the titration has been given in Part I under the titrant used.

REACTIONS USED IN THE INDIRECT TITRATION OF ORGANIC COMPOUNDS

Most of the reactions known to direct titration appear also in indirect titration, but with a different distribution, occasioned by the different importance of reaction speed. Thus the reactions of 'neutralization' of acid/base titration are nearly always so fast that direct titration is possible and indirect titration scarcely ever needed. On the other hand, slower reactions like, say, condensation, meagrely represented in direct titration, have been fairly widely employed as a basis of indirect titration methods. Moreover, since smaller reaction speeds can be tolerated in indirect procedures, the list of adaptable reactions and also of available reagents is markedly larger than that for direct titration.

While some reactions like oxidation, reduction, hydrolysis, and condensation are clearly defined, some confusion and unclarity reigns in other cases. This can bring about difficulty of classification and some examples of this are given here, arranged as a small table:

Reaction	Possible headings for classification	Heading adopted here
—OH, —SH, ≡CH, =NH groups with Ag(I) and Hg(II) reagents, e.g. mercaptans	Ion/ion combination, $RS^- + Ag^+ \rightarrow RSAg$ or hydrogen replacement, $RSH + Ag^+ \rightarrow RSAg + H^+$	Former in clearly alkaline solution; latter if acid
Precipitation of bases with acids, e.g. with picric acid	Addition, Base + HX $\rightarrow$ (Base.H^+)X Ion/molecule combination, Base + H^+ + X^- $\rightarrow$ (Base.H^+)X^- Ion/ion combination, if fast reaction, Base + H^+ $\rightarrow$ (Base.H^+) followed by (Base.H^+) + X^- $\rightarrow$ (Base.H^+)X^- Complex formation if a more complex stoichiometry is followed	The distinction turns on the degree of dissociation of the acid and on the relative speeds of the two reactions in the third possibility. Ion/ion and ion/molecule combination are classed together here
Acid/base titrations, of 'neutralization' or 'displacement'	Ion/ion or ion/molecule combination	Classified under this dual heading (very few examples in any case in indirect titration)
Nitriles, $RCN + H_2O \rightarrow RCONH_2 \rightarrow RCOOH + NH_3$	Addition or hydrolysis?	Hydrolysis, since the reaction does not stop at the amide stage in quantitative methods
'Zeisel' reaction, $ROR' + HI \rightarrow ROH + R'I$	Reduction, dealkylation, hydrolysis?	Dealkylation

Reaction	Possible headings for classification	Heading adopted here
Halides with acids or alkalies, X—Hal + H_2O → X—OH + HY	Hydrolysis or halogen replacement?	Hydrolysis
ROH + R′COCl → R′COOR + HCl	Ester formation or hydrogen replacement?	Both
RNH_2 + R′COCl → R′CONHR + HCl	Amide formation or hydrogen replacement?	Both
—C=C— + H_2 → —CH—CH—	Addition or reduction?	Both
—C=C— + O_3 → —C—O—C— (with O—O bridge); and —C=C— + RCOOOH → —C—C— (with O bridge)	Addition or oxidation?	Both
=N— + R—Hal → $(=\overset{+}{N}R—)Hal^-$; —S— + R—Hal → $(—\overset{+}{S}R—)Hal^-$; Naphthalene + picric acid → naphthalene 'picrate'; Cholesterol + digitonin → 'addition' product	Addition or complex formation?	Addition for the first two; complex formation for the others

Despite such ambiguities, an attempt is made here to classify and comment on the reactions on which indirect organic titration has been based.

Tables are given below under most of the reaction headings, which show the relative frequency of use of the various reagents and enable a comparison of indirect and direct titration to be made in this connection.

1. *Oxidation*

This reaction is the most widely used in indirect titration and *ca* 1500 examples are quoted in this book.

Approx. no of refs	Indirect titration	Direct titration
Over 250	Iodine reagents	
200–250	Bichromate	
150–200	Copper (II)	
100–150	Bromine reagents; Ferricyanide; Periodate and periodic acid; Permanganate	Copper (II)
50–100	Cerium (IV); Iodate; Mercury (II)	Bromine reagents; Cerium (IV); Ferricyanide; Iodate; Iodine; Permanganate
25–50	Hydrogen peroxide; Silver (I)	Bichromate; Tillmans' reagent
10–25	Halides ('Active'); Lead (IV); Molybdenum and tungsten (VI); Percarboxylic acids; Vanadate; Ninhydrin	Chlorine reagents (including hypochlorite); Dyes; Halides ('active'); Iodine monochloride; Iron (III)
5–10	Chlorate; Chlorite; Chlorine; Dyes; Iron (III); Manganese (IV); Persulphate; Selenium dioxide	Gold trichloride; Copper (III); Periodate
Under 5	Arsenic (V); Copper (III); Iodine Chlorides etc.; Iodosobenzoate; Manganate; Manganese (III); Ozone; Tillmans' reagent; Tetrathionate	

As might be anticipated, bichromate, bromine reagents, cerium (IV), copper (II), ferricyanide, iodate, iodine reagents and permanganate have all found considerable use in indirect as well as in direct titration.

Marked contrasts are shown, operating in each direction. Thus periodate, mercury (II), hydrogen peroxide and silver (I) have been used far more in indirect than in direct titration as oxidizing agents (in fact, the last named two appear not to have been used at all in direct titration). On the other hand, Tillmans' reagent and iodine monochloride have been used almost only in the direct procedures.

A rather wider range of functional group and compound class has naturally been determined by indirect titration than by direct. These include: alcohols; polyalcohols; polyphenols; carboxylic, polycarboxylic, and hydroxycarboxylic acids; aldehydes (including sugars); hydrazine derivatives; and many sulphur-containing compounds like mercaptans.

2. *Reduction*

About 400 references to determinations based on reduction are cited.

Approx. no. of refs	Indirect titration	Direct titration
150–200	Iodides and hydriodic acid	
100–150	Metals	
50–100	Titanium (III)	
25–50	Tin (II)	Titanium (III)
10–25	Iron (II); Thiosulphate	Dithionite; Iron (II); Thiosulphate; Vanadium (II)
5–10	Arsenic (III); Chromium (II); Hydrogen gas; Vanadium (II)	Ascorbic acid; Chromium (II); Electrolytic reduction; Hydrogen gas; Lithium aluminium hydride; Sulphide; Tin (II)
Under 5	Aluminium hydride and borohydride; Carboxylic acids; Dithionite; Electrolytic reduction; Mercaptans; Molybdenum (III); Sulphides	

From the table the predominant position of titanium (III) and, to a lesser extent, iron (II), in both types of titration is seen. Tin (II), metals, and, above all, hydriodic acid, have been far more frequently employed in indirect titration—in fact, the last two have evidently not been used at all in direct procedures (metals scarcely lend themselves to direct titration procedures!).

The functional groups and compound classes determined by indirect titration are those amenable to the direct methods (e.g. quinones; nitro, nitroso and azo compounds, including dyes; periodides) together with, notably, peroxides, halides and sulphur-containing materials like disulphides and sulphoxides).

3. *Addition*

More indirect titrations have depended on addition reactions (bracketed approximately with hydrolysis) than on any other reaction apart from oxidation. Between 600 and 700 references are given.

Approx. no. of refs	Indirect titration	Direct titration
150–200	Bromine reagents; Bisulphite and sulphite	
50–100	Iodine chlorides, etc.	Bromine reagents
25–50	Hydrochloric acid; Maleic anhydride; Alcohols	Inorganic halides (in non-aqueous solution)
10–25	Amines; Cyanide; Iodine; Mercury (II); Percarboxylic acids; Thiocyanogen	
5–10	Ammonia; Carboxylic acids; Chlorine reagents; Hydrobromic acid; Iodides and hydriodic acid; Mercaptans; Nitriles; Quinones; Thiosulphate	Chlorine reagents
Below 5	Thiourea	

The comparison with direct titration is again interesting. Bromine reagents have been frequently used in both types of titration (almost exclusively the titration of olefines). The adaptation of other types of addition reaction to indirect titration accounts for the major differences shown in the above table. Thus bisulphite/sulphite reagent (addition mainly to C=O), hydrochloric acid (mainly to α-epoxides), maleic anhydride and quinones (to C=C—C=C—), hydrocyanic acid (to C=O), alcohols (to C=S in carbon disulphide), and ammonia and amines (to C=O and the N=C groups of isocyanates and isothiocyanates) are scarcely or not at all represented in direct titration. Further, one notes that some reagents for olefine determination such as iodine monochloride, etc., iodine, mercury (II), percarboxylic acids and thiocyanogen, have been far more employed in the indirect procedures.

The direct titrations with inorganic halides in non-aqueous solution were mainly physicochemical studies rather than analytical procedures; it is therefore not surprising that there are no examples in indirect titration.

4. *Hydrolysis*

As mentioned in the previous section (3), hydrolysis is, together with addition, the reaction most frequently adapted to indirect titration after oxidation. Well over 600 examples are cited below. In only a limited number of cases (highly reactive materials like acid anhydrides) has water itself or a sensibly neutral solution been used. Some 20 examples of this sort are given. Most hydrolyses have been alkaline (*ca* 500 references, classified under 'Alkalies'); or acid, with the common inorganic acids (hydrochloric, nitric, phosphoric and sulphuric—about 200 examples) or sulphonic acids (*ca* 15 examples) as catalysts.

The principal covalent links undergoing hydrolysis in indirect titrimetric methods are:

C—O	esters, some ethers, anhydrides, acetals and ketals, polysaccharides
C—N	amides
C—Hal	many halides
C=N	condensation products of carbonyl compounds with reagents containing $—NH_2$ groups like hydroxylamine and hydrazine derivatives
C≡N	nitriles

Others, less often hydrolysed are:

C—S	some sulphonic acids
C—Metal	many metal–organic compounds of arsenic, bismuth, germanium, lead, mercury and also silicon
S—N	sulphonamides
S—Cl	sulphonyl chlorides

There are practically no examples of direct titration depending on hydrolysis, which, as stated in Part I, is surprising. More examples might have been expected of direct titration of reactive acid halides, anhydrides or easily hydrolysed esters like oxalates. In the event, probably the greatest contrast between the reactions of direct and indirect titration methods is shown here.

5. *Ion/Ion and Ion/Molecule Combination*

On p. 12 above, this double heading has been mentioned, and has been adopted mainly to circumvent difficulties of distinction between the two. In the table below, the 'neutralization' and displacement' reactions of Part I are given for comparison.

Approx. no. of refs	Indirect titration	Direct titration
Over 300		Perchloric acid
150–200		Alkalies; Silver (I)
100–150		Alkoxides
50–100	Iodine (I_3^-); Silver (I)	Hydrochloric acid
25–50	Calcium (II); Nitrophenols; Thiocyanate	Mercury (II); Quaternary ammonium hydroxides; Sulphonic acids; Surface-active materials
10–25	Amines; Bichromate; Bismuth (III); Cadmium (II); Copper (II); Nickel (II); Perchloric acid; Potassium (I); Tetraphenylborate	Amines; Carboxylic acids; Copper (II); Dyes; Halides in non-aqueous solution; Lead (II); Picric acid; Zinc (II)
5–10	Ammonium hydroxide; Barium (II); Carboxylic acids; Ferricyanide; Lead (II); Mercury (II); Phosphoric acid; Sulphuric acid; Zinc (II)	Ammonium hydroxide; Barium (II); Electrolytically generated acid and base; Halide complex anions; Iodine (I_3^-); Iron (III); Nickel (II); Sulphuric acid; Tetraphenylborate
Under 5	Alkalies; Ferrocyanide; Hydrazines; Hydrobromic acid; Hydrochloric acid; Iodate; Iron (III); Mercury (I) Periodate; Sodium (I); Sulphide; Surface-active materials	

The fast reactions of 'neutralization' and 'displacement' for determination of acids, bases and salts of weak acids and strong bases or vice versa, are ideally suited to direct titration and the few examples in indirect titration are mostly related to poor solubility of the sample which had therefore to be left in contact with the reagent for a sufficient period.

Most of the other ion/ion or ion/molecule reactions result in the formation of a product, separable from the reaction mixture by filtration or distillation or which even decomposes spontaneously (e.g. xanthic acids). Silver (I) is highly placed in both the lists in the table above. Iodine (strictly, the triiodide ion) has been the most widely used reagent in indirect procedures of this sort and mercury (II) and surface-active materials in direct procedures. Ions of opposite charge have been thus determined.

The blurred distinction between ion/ion and ion/molecule combination, hydrogen replacement and even addition and complex formation, already mentioned above (table, p. 12–13), unfortunately at least partially invalidates comparison and classification especially with reagents such as bismuth (III), mercury (II), silver (I) and thiocyanate.

About 450 references have been quoted, approximately the same as for reduction.

6. *Hydrogen Replacement* (*Substitution*)

Allowing for the uncertainties of classification under this heading, to which references has been made several times already, an estimated total of 350–400 examples has been tabulated for indirect titration, distributed as follows:

Approx. no. of refs	Indirect titration	Direct titration
150–200	Bromine reagents	
50–100		Bromine reagents
25–50	Halides ('active'); Iodine; Silver (I)	
10–25	Copper (II), Iodine chlorides, etc.; Mercury (II)	Silver (I)
5–10	Aluminium hydride and borohydride; Calcium (II); Chlorine reagents; Copper (I)	Iodine
Under 5	Sodamide; Thiocyanogen	

The classification difficulties militate against a reliable comparison but no outstanding differences are observable except possibly the more extensive use in indirect titration of active halides like acid chlorides and chloramines.

=CH— (especially in aromatic and heterocyclic nuclei); —OH (in alcohols and phenols); —SH (especially in mercaptans); and —NH— (in amines) are the groups which have been determined by hydrogen replacement.

7. *Condensation*

(This does not include methods of direct ester formation which are classified under that heading.)

Approx. no. of refs	Indirect titration	Direct titration
150–200	Hydroxylamine	
25–50	Carbonyl compounds; Hydrazines	
10–25	Xanthydrol	
5–10	Ammonia	Hydrazines
Under 5	Amines; Phenols	Aldehydes; Amines; Hydroxylamine

It is at once evident that condensation reactions, largely involving the carbonyl group as either the determined group or as reagent, have been much more used in indirect titration. About 250 references are quoted.

8. *Esterification and Transesterification*

These reactions are too slow to be represented in direct titration. Indirect titrimetric determinations have been based on the equations:

$$ROH + R'COOH \rightarrow R'COOR + H_2O$$
$$\text{(alcohols} + R'COCl \rightarrow R'COOR + HCl$$
$$\text{or}$$
$$\text{phenols)} + (R'CO)_2O \rightarrow R'COOR + R'COOH$$

Either reaction partner has been used as reagent in order to determine the other.

Esterification is the basis of some determinations of alcohols (mostly lower aliphatic) with hydrobromic, hydrochloric and nitrous acids.

Some 200 references are summarized in the tables, of which about two-thirds are based on the use of anhydride reagents.

In transesterification (*ca* 15 examples), a volatile ester is formed in the determination of a higher ester by reaction with a lower alcohol in the presence of an acid catalyst:

$$RCOOR' + R''OH \rightleftharpoons RCOOR'' + R'OH$$

(usually a methyl or ethyl ester)

The volatile ester is continuously distilled out and determined.

9. *Complex Formation*

Some of the reagents in the following table for indirect titration have been classified under other headings on the basis of the same reaction. This is because the nature of the reaction is so often uncertain.

Approx. no. of refs	Indirect titration	Direct titration
25–50	Mercury (II); Nitrophenols; Thiocyanate	Halides (Inorganic) in non-aqueous solution; Heteropoly acids (equivalent to molybdenum and tungsten (VI))
10–25	Bismuth (III); Cadmium (II); Copper (II); Silver (I)	Copper (II); Mercury (II)
5–10	Digitonin; Molybdenum and tungsten (VI)	Iodine; Iron (III)
Under 5	Copper (I); Ferrocyanide; Iodine; Iodine monochloride, etc.; Iron (III)	

Little can be said about this miscellaneous and even controversial group of about 200 quoted examples.

10. *Amide Formation*

Like esterification, this reaction has been used to determine either reaction partner in the equations:

$$RNH_2 + R'COCl \rightarrow R'CONHR + HCl$$
$$(NH_3) \qquad\qquad (R'CONH_2)$$
$$RNH_2 + (R'CO)_2O \rightarrow R'CONHR + R'COOH$$

In contrast to the modest total of 4 examples in direct titration, over 50 references are given to methods based on amide formation in indirect titration (mostly determinations of acid chlorides and anhydrides with amines).

11. *Dealkylation* (*of ethers*)

The widespread and important determination of ethers containing lower alkyl groups (methyl to butyl) by dealkylation with hydriodic acid is regarded as justification for a separate heading, rather than attempting to squeeze it in under 'reduction' or 'hydrolysis' for example. Over 60 references are mentioned in the tables.

12. *Dehydration*

Under this heading, the elimination of water from one compound is understood. Condensation and esterification reactions are separately grouped. Some 30 examples of this reaction are quoted, of which about two-thirds were catalysed with hydrochloric acid and the remainder by other acids or acidic agents. Most of the determinations were of pentoses, dehydrated to furfuraldehyde, but some alcohols have been determined also, by conversion to olefines.

There appears to be no example in direct titration.

13. *Reduction and Oxidation* (*concurrently*)

Two determinations are grouped together here: the Kjeldahl nitrogen method, in which organic matter is oxidized with formation of NH_4^+ (*ca* 20 examples given); and the Cannizzaro reaction, used in about 10 cases to determine aldehydes with alkali catalyst.

14. *Halogen Replacement*

The halogen atoms of halides have often served as the nucleus of attack in a replacement reaction for the determination of these compounds. Such a reaction with alkalies or with water, catalysed with acids, has been often used, but has been classified under the heading of 'Hydrolysis'. Some other reagents have been used to split out halogen, such as: alcohols; ammonia; amines; bisulphite; copper (I); mercaptans; and thiosulphate. Between 20 and 25 references are given, of which over half are to the use of amines.

The fission of C—Hal links is usually too slow to permit direct titration and the 4 examples in Part I are of the determination of Si—Hal or Hg—Hal links.

15. *Nitrosation*

This includes reactions of diazotization, deamination (e.g. of amino acids, aliphatic primary amines, amides and even hydrazines) and nitrosation, e.g. of secondary amines and phenols (classified here rather than under hydrogen replacement). Since all these reactions evidently depend on the attack of NO^+ and require nitrite/acid reagent, it is convenient to collect them under a single heading.

There are about 20 examples given for indirect titration, contrasted with *ca* 150 for direct titration (especially practicable for the comparatively fast diazotisation reactions).

16. *Decarboxylation*

About 15 examples of determinations (nearly all of uronic and related acids) via decarboxylation using acid catalysts (chiefly hydrochloric acid) are given.

17. *Fission of* S—S *bonds*

Disulphides, dithiocarbamates and other compound classes containing the S—S group have been determined through reaction with cyanide or sulphite according to the equations:

$$RS{-}SR + CN^- \rightarrow RSR + SCN^-$$
$$RS{-}SR + SO_3^{2-} \rightarrow RS^- + RSSO_3^-$$

About 20 examples altogether are given.

18. *Fission of* C—S *bonds*

Bisulphite compounds, formed as an intermediate stage in the determination of carbonyl compounds, have been determined via C—S fission with cyanide or hydroxylamine:

$$\underset{\displaystyle SO_3^-}{\underset{|}{RCHOH}} + CN^- \rightarrow \underset{\displaystyle CN}{\underset{|}{RCHOH}} + SO_3^{2-}$$

or

$$+NH_2OH \rightarrow RCH{=}NOH + HSO_3^- + H_2O$$

19. *Xanthate Formation*

This reaction occurs in the determination of alcohols with alkali/carbon disulphide reagent:

$$ROH + CS_2 + OH^- \rightarrow RO\underset{\displaystyle S}{\underset{\|}{C}}S^- + H_2O$$

The reverse determination, in which carbon disulphide is determined with alcohol/alkali reagent, has been classified as addition, since the carbon disulphide suffers addition.

Amine determination by the analogous reaction with carbon disulphide to yield dithiocarbamates can be grouped here also.

20. *Other Reactions*

There are fewer than 10 quoted examples based on the following reactions:

Alkylation: Dimethyl sulphate has been used in three alkylation reactions, one of phenols and two of substituted pyridine derivatives which suffered splitting of the ring in the process.

Coupling: With diazonium salt reagents, to determine principally phenols. About 25 examples of direct titration based on coupling were cited in Part I.

Depolymerization: Using inorganic acids (hydrochloric, phosphoric, and sulphuric) for determination of aldehyde polymers.

Halogen interchange: Some chlorides or bromides react with iodide to liberate iodine via formation of unstable iodides and this has been the basis of a few determinations.

Meerwein–Ponndorf–Verley reaction:	One example of this is given, for determination of acetophenone and benzaldehyde derivatives and using aluminium isopropylate.
Nitration:	The nitric/sulphuric acid nitration reagent appears to have been used to determine only benzene. The nitration reaction occurs in determination of nitrate esters by treatment with sulphuric acid/salicylic acid but it is a reaction secondary to the hydrolysis of the ester to nitric acid.
Sulphonation:	In most cases, sulphonation has been carried out to improve solubility of certain compounds before they are treated with other reagents.

Some references to methods depending on reactions which are unclear or composite, have necessarily been omitted from the classification above. Most of these concern metal organic compounds like lead tetraethyl, mercury organic compounds and lithium alkyls.

In addition to the chemical reactions, the physical process of racemate formation has been the basis of determinations of *d*- or *l*-tartrate by using the antimer + Ca^{2+} as reagent, giving the insoluble calcium racemate. The physical operations of distillation, filtration and extraction have also been frequently used in non-chemical methods although only a small selection of examples has been made.

EXAMPLES OF INDIRECT TITRATION OF ORGANIC COMPOUNDS

Material and Literature Covered

The data collected together are given in Sect. 2 in the following pages. As much as possible of the literature has been covered up to the end of 1963 and, for the more widely circulating journals of analytical chemistry, to the middle of 1964.

The examples have been chosen, as in Part I, to illustrate mainly the range of functional groups and compound classes determined and the fields in which the methods have been applied (e.g. medicine, pharmacy, industry such as the petroleum industry, agriculture, etc.). There has been a tendency to concentrate on older (*ca* pre-1910) and more modern methods (*ca* post-1945) in the bibliography. This serves to delineate both the similarities (e.g. use of the same reactions and reagents) and the differences (e.g. the replacement of gravimetric procedures by methods like dissolving the precipitate and determining it titrimetrically).

Clearly, it has not been possible to include all references to a method, especially with the more extensively used reagents. A selection has therefore been made from the large number of publications on determinations such as: unsaturation, using halogen reagents, in particular bromine; carbonyl compounds, using hydroxylamine; esters by saponification with alkalies; many compounds by oxidation with bichromate. A similar restriction was necessary in Part I for direct titration of, say, dyes with titanium (III), or of ascorbic acid with Tillmans' reagent.

The following list of deliberate omissions indicates a further attempt to limit the total of examples within reasonable dimensions:

Methods of element analysis are not included, except for a short list of titrimetrically concluded Kjeldahl nitrogen determinations, used to determine a nitrogen-containing compound in the presence of other materials.

Very few examples are given of applied analysis of vaguely defined materials such as organic matter of soils, sewage, etc.; ketone bodies in biological fluids; solids, not fat, in milk, etc.

Polemical cross-references have been either omitted or very sparsely given.

Methods based on biological treatment, e.g. decomposition with enzymes, have not been considered.

Methods based on chromatographic separations are not considered as a rule, because many monographs and books are available which deal with this subject. Comparatively few methods of this type are concluded by titration, in any case.

Classification of Data

The classification has been based on the same principle as in Part I, namely, alphabetically according to reagent, with chronological arrangement of the bibliography under each reagent separately. Within each calendar year, the references are alphabetically ranged, according to the first author's name. In the years 1961–4, this order has sometimes been abandoned, because extra references have been added at the last minute in order to keep the contents as up to date as possible.

Under many of the reagent headings, summaries have been made of: the reagents; the materials determined; the reactions on which the determinations depended; the reaction conditions; subsequent treatment; and the final direct titration stage. Where the subsequent treatment has consisted of several further reaction stages before the concluding titration was carried out, the reference is given under each reagent employed, provided that an organic compound was being determined. Two examples will explain this:

$$\underset{(sec\text{- or } tert\text{-})}{ROH} \xrightarrow{HCl} RCl \xrightarrow{\text{Thiourea/KI}} \left(R{-}S{-}C\begin{matrix}{=}NH_2\\ \diagdown NH_2\end{matrix}\right)^+ Cl^- \xrightarrow{\text{3, 5-Dinitrobenzoate}}$$

$$\left(R{-}S{-}C\begin{matrix}{=}NH_2\\ \diagdown NH_2\end{matrix}\right)^+ \left(C_6H_3(NO_2)_2COO\right)^- \xrightarrow{\text{Ti (III)}} \text{Corresponding amine (unreacted Ti (III) back titrated)}$$

The successive stages are given under 'Hydrochloric acid'; both 'Thiourea' and 'Iodide'; 'Carboxylic acids and carboxylates'; and 'Titanium (III)'.

$$ROCH_3 \xrightarrow{HI} CH_3I \xrightarrow{\text{Bromine}} IO_3^- \xrightarrow{I^-/\text{acid}} I_2 \text{ Titrated with thiosulphate.}$$

The successive stages are given under 'Iodides and hydriodic acid' and 'Bromine reagents' but not the last stage under 'Iodides etc.' because the iodate determined is inorganic. The last two operations are therefore both briefly summarized under 'Bromine reagents'.

The latter example illustrates another feature of the classified data. Where a reagent consisting of two (or more—this is rare) directly participating components has been used, the example has generally been put under both component headings. One or two other examples can be mentioned in addition to the thiourea/potassium iodide example above: alcohols/certain acids for determinations based on trans-esterification; copper (II)/thiocyanate and silver (I)/picric acid for determination by precipitation of bases. Naturally a reasonable limit has had to be drawn; for instance, the many oxidation and reduction methods are not classified also under the headings of the acids or alkalies used in conjunction with them.

Related reagents have been grouped together where possible. Thus 'Bromine reagents' includes bromine, bromate/bromide, bromine chloride and hypobromite; 'Halides ("active")', includes the chloramines, acid chlorides, sulphonyl chlorides, *N*-bromsuccinimide, etc.; bisulphite and sulphite form one section and so on.

Included in Sect. 2 are also the headings 'Electrolytic reduction', 'Kjeldahl nitrogen determination', 'Physical methods', and 'Pyrolysis'. Although not reagents, these headings permit related methods to be grouped together, justifying their use. Further, many examples of hydrolysis, dehydration, decarboxylation and depolymerization have been included under the headings 'Alkalies' and various acids like 'Hydrochloric acid', 'Sulphuric acid', etc. The heading is then strictly catalyst rather than reagent, but as mentioned above in this paragraph, the usage is considered justified by the convenience of classification.

Details in the tables of examples have necessarily had to be kept to a minimum in order to save space. Preliminary treatment such as deproteinization of samples of biological fluids or solvent extraction of materials, are not given. (Under 'Physical Methods' in Sect. 2 a few examples of preliminary treatment of the latter type are mentioned.) Under the column heading 'Reagent and reaction conditions', concentrations have not as a rule been given, although as far as known, reaction time and temperature have been quoted. No details of end-point determination have been given in the last column of the tables, beyond mention of the method used and the indicator, if any.

The determination of the reagent concentration (in methods of back titration) or the carrying out of a blank or control determination without the sample, are regarded as self-evident and this has thus not usually been mentioned under each separate reagent heading.

Full details have not always been available about a particular method but some examples have been quoted despite this if they illustrate an unusual determination or other point of special interest.

As in Part I, the data arranged under the reagent headings are followed by an 'Index to Functional Groups and Compound Classes'. In this, the groups and classes have been classified alphabetically with cross-references to the reagents used.

Finally comes an 'Index to Individual Compounds', covering both Parts I and II, in which cross-reference is made to this 'Index to Functional Groups and Compound Classes'.

SECTION 2

REAGENTS USED IN INDIRECT TITRATION OF ORGANIC COMPOUNDS

1. Acids

About 30 acids (in the Arrhenius sense) have been used as reagents or components of reagents in indirect titration. These include inorganic acids; organic carboxylic and sulphonic acids; and certain phenols. These acids have not been grouped all together, although separate classification has necessarily involved some repetition. Such a single group would be inconveniently large. Some general remarks are made here about acid reagents.

Acids take part in many, indeed almost all types of reaction. Two broad types may be distinguished:

I. Catalytic reactions in which the anion has usually only a secondary effect (e.g. on the rate of reaction). The stronger mineral (and sulphonic) acids have been used here and can be interchanged without marked influence on the result. Acid is not consumed in these catalytic reactions (except in a limited number of cases where a product of reaction takes up acid) so that the determination has not usually been concluded by back titration.

Such catalysed reactions include:

1. Hydrolysis of a number of bonds. Some of these have been enumerated under the headings of 'Hydrochloric acid' and 'Sulphuric acid', the two principally used reagents. The most important are summarized here:

C—O	esters, acetals, polysaccharides
C—N	amides, polyamides, hydrazides, hexamine
C=N	condensation products of carbonyl compounds with hydroxylamine, hydrazines, etc.
C≡N	nitriles
C—Hal	
C—Metal	

(2) Depolymerization, e.g. of metaldehyde.

(3) Dehydration, e.g. of pentoses or of alcohols, especially tertiary alcohols.

(4) Decarboxylation, e.g. of uronic acids.

(5) Addition (of water) to, for example, α-epoxides.

(6) Esterification and transesterification, in combination with an alcohol.

II. Reactions in which acid is consumed and the anion or unionized (weak) acid usually plays a direct part. Examples of such reactions are:

(1) Sulphonation.

(2) Nitration.

(3) Addition (of the acid molecule, e.g. of HCl or HBr to olefines or α-epoxides).

(4) Ion/ion or ion/molecule combination, including 'neutralization' reactions in determination of bases.

(5) Ester formation (direct formation, yielding the ester of the acid reagent).

(6) Hydration, e.g. in determination of acetic anhydride with oxalic acid.

(7) Oxidation, e.g. with periodic acid or percarboxylic acids.

(8) Reduction, e.g. with hydriodic acid.

(9) Condensation, e.g. of benzyl ethers with HCl.

The anion may enter into the molecule of the compound determined (as, for example, in the first three reactions given); or may appear, wholly or partly, as a reaction product (e.g. reductions with HI yielding iodine). Since acid or anion is consumed, back titration of the unused part is often possible; alternatively, the reaction product from the anion (like the iodine mentioned) can be titrated.

In some cases, the acid has been formed 'in situ' by using a salt + a suitable mineral acid as reagent. Hydriodic and periodic acids are the chief examples of this and for these the double section headings of 'Iodides and hydriodic acid' and 'Periodates and periodic acid' have been used. For convenience of classification, the heading 'Carboxylic acids and carboxylates' has been adopted.

Acids have been frequently used in conjunction with (and to stabilize) many reagents, especially those used for oxidation and reduction methods, like $Cr_2O_7^{2-}$, MnO_4^-, $S_2O_8^{2-}$, V(II), Fe(II), Ti(III) and Ce(IV). These have been classified under the respective cation or anion.

2. Alcohols

Reagent. Methanol or ethanol, with rare examples of the use of higher alcohols.

Reactions, materials titrated and subsequent treatment.

(1) Addition (xanthate formation) in determination of CS_2 (also COS).

$$CS_2 + ROH + OH^- \rightarrow RO.\underset{\underset{S}{\|}}{C}.S^- + H_2O$$

This is a fast reaction and has usually been carried out at ordinary temperatures with reaction periods of a few minutes only.

The xanthate has been determined in weakly acid solution by direct titration with iodine or copper (II) (see under these reagent headings in Part I); or by using either of these, or chloramine T in excess and determining the unused part (see under these reagent headings in the present volume).

$$2\,RO.\underset{\underset{S}{\|}}{C}.S^- \begin{cases} + I_2 \rightarrow RO.\underset{\underset{S}{\|}}{C}.S.S.\underset{\underset{S}{\|}}{C}.OR + 2\,I^- \\ \text{or} \\ + Cu^{2+} \rightarrow (RO.\underset{\underset{S}{\|}}{C}.S.)_2Cu \end{cases}$$

The alternative colorimetric determination of the brown copper salt appears seldom to have been used.

(2) Ester formation in determination of RCO— (notably acetyl) groups. Three types are encountered.

(a) Acid chlorides and anhydrides, reacting:

$$RCOCl + R'OH \rightarrow RCOOR' + HCl$$

$$\text{or} \quad (RCO)_2O + R'OH \rightarrow RCOOR' + RCOOH$$

These reactions are fairly fast and reaction times have rarely exceeded 30 minutes at ordinary temperature. One equivalent of acid formed is titrated with standard alkali. To allow for hydrochloric or carboxylic acid present as impurities, a parallel control titration with alkali is made directly on the acid chloride or anhydride or after having hydrolysed it with water (see under 'Water' below). The difference between the two alkali titrations is equivalent to the chloride or anhydride.

$$RCOCl + H_2O \rightarrow RCOOH + HCl$$
$$(RCO)_2O + H_2O \rightarrow 2\ RCOOH \quad \text{(2 equivalents acid formed)}$$

(b) Carboxylic acids and their salts, reacting:

$$RCOOH + R'OH \rightarrow RCOOR' + H_2O$$

An acid catalyst like hydrochloric, sulphuric, phosphoric or a sulphonic acid or boron trifluoride is used and the equilibrium displaced to the right by continuous distillation of the ester or of the water formed. This is sometimes preceded by a period of reflux where the esterification reaction is slower. The determination has been concluded in several ways:

(i) Saponification of the distilled ester with measured excess of alkali and back titration of the unused part. This is the most usual method. (See Alkalies.)

(ii) Saponification of the distilled ester, followed by an oxidation procedure. Examples are:

Lactate—oxidation with alkaline permanganate to oxalate, precipitation as Ca salt and titration of this salt with permanganate in acid solution

Formate—oxidation with Hg(II) with ensuing iodometric titration of the Hg(I) formed

Oxalate—titration with permanganate

Acetate—differential oxidation with two bichromate reagents, one of which attacks all components of the distillate except acetate and the other attacking the acetic acid also.

(iii) Titration of the water formed using the Karl Fischer reagent.

(iv) Determination of the loss of acidity of the sample by alkali titration of sample + reagent before and after ester formation.

(c) Acetyl groups in esters and amides in transesterification with a volatile alcohol:

$$\begin{array}{cccc} X.O.COCH_3 & + \; CH_3OH \rightarrow & X.OH & + \; CH_3COOCH_3 \\ \text{or} & \text{or} & \text{or} & \text{or} \\ X.N.COCH_3 & C_2H_5OH & X.NH & CH_3COOC_2H_5 \\ | & & | & \end{array}$$

As with carboxylic acids and salts, an acid catalyst is generally needed although there are some examples of the use of alkoxides. Reaction time depends on the nature of the residual part of the molecule denoted above by X. In some cases a slow distillation of the acetate ester is begun early but generally authors recommend preliminary reflux. *N*-Acetyl groups are resistant to hydrolysis and reflux periods of up to 3 hours have been used. The conclusion of the determination appears to be always by method (i) under (b) above.

(3) Addition, in determination of acetylenes:

$$RC{\equiv}CR + 2\ CH_3OH \rightarrow RCH_2.C(OCH_3)_2R$$

or

$$RC{\equiv}CH + 2\ CH_3OH \rightarrow CH_3.C(OCH_3)_2R$$

The ketals were hydrolysed to ketones which were then determined by a hydroxylamine procedure.

(4) Alcoholysis of alkyl silane thiocyanates:

$$(C_2H_5)_nSi(SCN)_{4-n} + (4-n)\ ROH \rightarrow (C_2H_5)_nSi(OR)_{4-n} + (4-n)\ HSCN$$

The thiocyanic acid was then titrated with alkali.

(5) Dehydration in determination of methylol groups:

$$X.CH_2OH + ROH \rightarrow X.CH_2.O.R + H_2O$$

The water formed was titrated with the Karl Fischer reagent.

Examples

Material titrated	Reagent and reaction conditions	Subsequent treatment and final titration stage	Ref.
CS_2	Absorbed in KOH/ ethanol	+ acetic acid and titrated with iodine (see Part I, Iodine, ref. 3)	1
O- and *N*-Acetyl groups	Slowly distilled with H_2SO_4/excess ethanol (*ca* 45 min duration with *O*-acetyl, longer with *N*-)	Distillate (ethyl acetate) + excess standard KOH; back titrated with H_2SO_4 (see Alkalies, refs 11, 12 and 14)	2
CS_2 in benzene solution or coal gas	+ KOH/ethanol; 30 min	+ acetic acid + excess copper acetate; unused Cu(II) determined iodometrically (see Copper (II), ref. 16)	3

Materials titrated	Reagent and reaction conditions	Subsequent treatment and final titration stage	Ref.
CS_2 in CCl_4	+ KOH/ethanol; 5 min	+ acetic acid to phenolphthalein, + $NaHCO_3$ and titrated with iodine (see Part I, Iodine, ref. 18)	4
O- and *N*-Acetyl groups	+ excess ethanol + *p*-toluenesulphonic acid + silver *p*-toluenesulphonate if halogen present. Refluxed and then distilled	Distillate (ethyl acetate) + excess standard NaOH; back titrated with acid (see Alkalies, refs 35 and 42)	5, 7
CS_2 (from acid hydrolysis, in determination of dithiocarbamates: and from reduction, in determination of thiuram disulphides)	Led into KOH/ethanol	Titrated with iodine	6
CS_2 in gas streams	Absorbed in KOH/ethanol	+ acetic acid + excess standard copper acetate; unused Cu(II) determined iodometrically	8
Anhydrides	+ methanol; 30 min reflux (control, + water)	Titrated with NaOH (also titrated with NaOH)	9
O-Acetyl groups	+ excess ethanol + *p*-toluenesulphonic acid; 15 min reflux, then distilled	Distillate (ethyl acetate) + excess standard NaOH; back titrated with acid (see Alkalies, ref. 75)	10
CS_2	+ KOH/ethanol	+ acetic acid till just acid to phenolphthalein; titrated with iodine to starch (see Part I, Iodine, ref. 33)	11
Acetyl groups in nitroacetylcellulose: formyl groups in formylcellulose	+ excess ethanol/phosphoric acid. Refluxed and distilled	Distillate (ethyl formate or acetate) determined by saponification (see Alkalies, ref. 86)	12
O-Acetyl groups	+ excess ethanol + *p*-toluenesulphonic acid. 15 min reflux, then distilled	Distillate + excess standard NaOH; back titrated with acid (see Alkalies, ref. 94)	13
O-Acetyl groups in fats	+ excess ethanol + *p*-toluenesulphonic acid	Distillate + excess standard NaOH; back titrated with acid	14

Materials titrated	Reagent and reaction conditions	Subsequent treatment and final titration stage	Ref.
CS_2	+ KOH/ethanol	Titrated with iodine	15
O- and *N*-Acetyl groups in osazones	Method of ref. 5		
CS_2 in blood	+ KOH/ethanol	Titrated with iodine	17
CS_2	+ KOH/ethanol; 30 min	+ H_2SO_4 to phenolphthalein; + excess iodine and back titrated with thiosulphate (see Iodine reagents, ref. 176)	18
Carboxylic acids	In dioxan, + methanol/BF_3	Titrated with Karl Fischer reagent	19
CS_2 in mixtures	+ KOH/methanol or ethanol	+ acetic acid to phenolphthalein; titrated with iodine to starch	20
Acetyl groups	+ excess ethanol + HCl. Distilled	Distillate + excess NaOH; back titrated with acid (see Alkalies, ref. 133)	21
Acetic acid in body fluids	+ excess methanol. Distilled	Distillate (methyl acetate) + NaOH giving sodium acetate; oxidized with $Ag_2Cr_2O_7$/H_2SO_4 and $K_2Cr_2O_7$/H_2SO_4. Difference in oxidation (back titration of unused) equivalent to acetate (see Alkalies, ref. 140, and Bichromate, ref. 110)	22
Acetyl groups	+ ethanol/H_2SO_4; distilled	Distillate hydrolysed with NaOH, passed through an ion exchanger and the acetic acid in the effluent titrated (see Alkalies, ref. 148 and Ion exchangers, ref. 1)	23
Acetyl groups in esters of cellulose and other polyhydroxy compounds	In methanol, + CH_3ONa/methanol; 3 h reflux	+ excess *p*-toluenesulphonic acid; methyl acetate distilled into excess standard alkali; back titrated unused (see Alkalies, ref. 151)	24
CS_2 in benzene	+ KOH/ethanol	Titrated with iodine	25

Materials titrated	Reagent and reaction conditions	Subsequent treatment and final titration stage	Ref.
Acetic anhydride	+ ethanol	Titrated with C_2H_5ONa/ethanol to phenolphthalein (control, titrated directly with alkali)	26
CS_2, COS in coal gas	Absorbed in KOH/alcohol	Determined iodometrically	27
Acetyl groups in carbohydrate esters	In methanol + CH_3ONa/methanol; *ca* 15 min. Distilled	+ excess H_2SO_4; methyl acetate distilled into excess standard alkali; unused back titrated (see Alkalies, ref. 156)	28
Sodium acetate in dyes	+ ethanol+ *p*-toluene-sulphonic acid; distilled	Distillate (ethyl acetate) + excess standard alkali; unused back titrated.	29
CS_2 in CCl_4	+ KOH/ethanol; 30 min	+ acetic acid to phenol-phthalein; + ethanol and titrated with iodine to a biamperometric end-point (see Part I, Iodine, ref. 53)	30
CS_2, COS in coal gas	Absorbed in KOH/alcohol	Determined iodometrically	31
Acetylsalicylic acid	+ NaOH/ethanol. Distilled	Distillate + excess standard NaOH. Unused back titrated	32
Formic acid in wine	+ methanol/HCl. Distilled slowly	Distillate (methyl formate) + excess NaOH; evaporated and formate determined via oxidation with $HgCl_2$ and iodometric titration of HgCl formed (see Mercury (II), ref. 95, and Alkalies, ref. 192)	33
Acetic anhydride	+ methanol (control, + water)	Titrated with alkali (also titrated with alkali)	34
O- and *N*-Acetyl groups	+ ethanol/HCl. 2 h reflux for *O*-acetyl; longer for *N*-acetyl. Distilled	Distillate + excess standard alkali; unused back titrated (see Alkalies, ref. 203)	35
Acetylenes, RC≡CH and RC≡CR′	+ methanol/BF_3/HgO; 75–110 min/25° giving ketals	Ketals hydrolysed to ketones, then determined with hydroxylamine (see Hydroxylamine, ref. 73)	36

Materials titrated	Reagent and reaction conditions	Subsequent treatment and final titration stage	Ref.
Lactic acid in sugar industrial products	+ methanol/H_2SO_4. Distilled	Distillate (methyl lactate) saponified, oxidized with permanganate to oxalate, precipitated as Ca salt and titrated with permanganate (see Permanganate, ref. 87, Calcium(II), ref. 23, and Alkalies, ref. 221)	37
$(C_2H_5)_nSi(SCN)_{4-n}$ ($n = 1$, 2 or 3)	+ 95% ethanol, giving HSCN	Titrated with NaOH to phenolphthalein	38
CS_2 in light oil forerunning	+ KOH/alcohol/ benzene; 3 h	Aqueous layer containing xanthate + excess standard iodine + acetic acid. Back titrated with thiosulphate (see Iodine, ref. 270)	39
CS_2 in water	+ KOH/ethanol; 30 min	Acidified, + excess standard iodine and back titrated with thiosulphate (see Iodine, ref. 272)	40
Fatty acids in presence of rosin acids	+ n-butanol/benzene/ benzenesulphonic acid. 60–90 min/125°. Water formed removed in a trap to force equilibrium to completion	Titrated with KOH potentiometrically or to an indicator. Control titration.	41
Phthalic anhydride in glyptal resins	In 5% acetone + methanol	Titrated with KOH/alcohol to phenolphthalein. Control titration	42
CS_2 from acid hydrolysis of dithiocarbamates in their determination	Distilled into KOH/ methanol	+ acetic acid to phenolphthalein and titrated with iodine to starch (see Part I, Iodine, ref. 66)	43
Anhydrides, e.g. acetic, maleic, phthalic in presence of the corresponding acids	In acetone + methanol (control, + excess KOH/water)	Titrated with KOH/alcohol (titrated with HCl)	44
Chrysanthemum monocarboxylic acid chloride	+ methanol. Not over 5 min	Titrated HCl formed with KOH/methanol to dimethyl yellow/methylene blue	45
Oxalic acid in plants	+ alcohol/H_2SO_4. Distilled	Ester in distillate saponified and the alkali oxalate titrated in acid solution with permanganate	46

Materials titrated	Reagent and reaction conditions	Subsequent treatment and final titration stage	Ref.
Anhydrides	+ dry methanol + dry pyridine; 30 min, some refluxed 15 min (control, + pyridine + water)	Titrated with NaOH to phenolphthalein (also titrated with NaOH)	47
CS_2 from acid hydrolysis of dithiocarbamates in their determination	Method of ref. 43		48
CS_2	+ KOH/ethanol	Titrated with copper acetate at pH 5·8–7 (dilute acetic acid added) (see Part I, Copper (II), ref. 123)	49
Fatty acids in presence of rosin acids	+ butanol/benzene/ H_2SO_4; 30 min reflux (modification of method of ref. 41)	Titrated with KOH	50
CS_2 from acid hydrolysis of dithiocarbamates and reduction of thiuram disulphides in their determination	+ KOH/alcohol	Titrated with iodine to starch (see Part I, Iodine, ref. 103)	51
CS_2 from acid hydrolysis of dithiocarbamates in their determination	+ KOH/alcohol	Titrated with iodine	52
Methylol groups in amine/HCHO resins	+ methanol/HCl; 10 min	+ dry methanol. Titrated with Karl Fischer reagent	53
Acetyl groups in aspirin and other medicines	+ ethanol/H_2SO_4; 1 h reflux; distilled	Distillate + excess standard KOH; back titrated with acid (see Alkalies, ref. 370)	54
Acid chlorides (in dioxan solution)	+ ethanol; 5–10 min/ 80°	Titrated with CH_3ONa/ methanol/benzene to thymol blue	55
Purity of acid chlorides	+ dry ethanol; 5 min/100°	Cooled in ice and titrated free HCl to methyl red and free carboxylic acid to phenolphthalein. Excess alkali added, heated and unused back titrated giving the ester formed (see Alkalies, refs 402, 424)	56, 59

Materials titrated	Reagent and reaction conditions	Subsequent treatment and final titration stage	Ref.
CS_2 in benzene	+ KOH/alcohol; 10–15 min	Water extract + acetic acid to phenolphthalein; titrated with iodine to starch	57
CS_2	+ KOH/ethanol	+ excess chloramine T; back titrated iodometrically (see Halides ('active'), ref. 65)	58
CS_2	+ KOH/alcohol	+ acetic acid giving pH 5·4–5·8; titrated with iodine to starch (see Part I, Iodine, ref. 123)	60
Acetic anhydride	+ n-propanol/pyridine, 85/15. A few min	Titrated with NaOH to phenolphthalein	
	(control, + water/pyridine, 85/15)	(also titrated with NaOH)	61
Acetic anhydride + acetic acid + excess triethylamine in toluene	+ ethanol; 1 min	Titrated with H_2SO_4 potentiometrically	61
	(control, + water)	(also titrated with H_2SO_4	
CS_2 from acid hydrolysis of dithiocarbamates and reduction of thiuram disulphides in their determination in crude products	+ KOH/methanol	+ acetic acid to phenolphthalein; titrated with iodine to starch (see Part I, Iodine, ref. 125)	62
Acetyl groups in acetylated polyformaldehyde	+ methanol/HCl	Methyl acetate distilled and determined by saponification with excess NaOH	63
Phosgene in mixtures with $CHCl_3$ etc	+ ethanol	Liberated HCl titrated with pyramidone/benzene	64
(free HCl previously titrated directly with the same reagent);			
Acid chlorides	In benzene, + dry methanol; 10 min/60–65°	Titrated with pyramidone/benzene to dimethyl yellow	65
CS_2 from determination of dithiocarbamate by acid hydrolysis	Method of ref. 43		66

Materials titrated	Reagent and reaction conditions	Subsequent treatment and final titration stage	Ref.
2,4-Dinitrophenyl thioethers from determination of mercaptans in petroleum products by reaction with 2,4-dinitrochlorobenzene	+ isopropanol, liberating the original mercaptans	Titrated with Ag^+ in ammoniacal solution	67
CS_2	+ KOH/ethanol 30–60 min	Aliquot (2N in KOH) + excess ferricyanide; 5 min/20°, acidified to pH 7–10 and titrated with $FeSO_4$ to dimethylglyoxime	68

References

1. Gastine, M., *Compt. rend.* **98**, 1588 (1884).
2. Perkin, A. G., *Proc. Roy. Soc.* **20**, 171 (1904); *J. Chem. Soc.* **85**, 1462 (1904); ibid. **87**, 107 (1905).
3. Harding, E. P. and Doran, J., *J. Am. Chem. Soc.* **29**, 1476 (1907).
4. Radcliffe, L. G., *J. Soc. Chem. Ind., London* **28**, 229, (1909).
5. Freudenberg, R. and Harder, M., *Ann.* **433**, 230 (1923).
6. Callan, T. and Strafford, N., *J. Soc. Chem. Ind., London* **43**, 1T (1924).
7. Freudenberg, R. and Weber E., *Angew. Chem.* **38**, 280 (1925).
8. Huff, W. J., *J. Am. Chem. Soc.* **48**, 81 (1926).
9. Lukashevich, V. O., *J. Chem. Ind.* (*USSR*) **8**, 1086 (1931).
10. Bredereck, H., *Angew. Chem.* **45**, 241 (1932).
11. Matuszak, M. P., *Ind. Eng. Chem., Anal. Ed.* **4**, 98 (1932).
12. Ezrielev, I. M. and Soloveichik, L. S., *Plasticheskie Massui*, No. 5, **27**, and No. 3, **40** (1934).
13. Phillips, M., *Ind. Eng. Chem., Anal. Ed.* **6**, 321 (1934).
14. Täufel, K., Thaler, H. and de Mengo, M., *Fettchem. Umschau* **41**, 156 (1934).
15. Damon, W. A., *72nd Ann. Rept. Alkali Etc. Works* 29 (1936).
16. Wolfrom, M. L., Konigsberg, M. and Salzberg, S., *J. Am. Chem. Soc.* **58**, 490 (1936).
17. Harrower, J. R. and Wiley, F. H., *J. Ind. Hyg. Toxicol.* **19**, 486 (1937).
18. Magidova, S. S., Divinskaya, E. K., Andreeva, E. F. and Ivashkevich, K. D., *Zavodskaya Lab.* **6**, 693 (1937).
19. Mitchell, J., Smith, D. M. and Bryant, W. M. D., *J. Am. Chem. Soc.* **62**, 4 (1940).
20. Bell, R. T. and Agruss, M. S., *Ind. Eng. Chem., Anal. Ed.* **13**, 297 (1941).

21. Matchett, J. R. and Levine, J., *Ind. Eng. Chem., Anal. Ed.* **13** 98 (1941).
22. Caselli, P. and Cearanfi, E., *Biochem. Z.* **313**, 11 (1942).
23. Wiesenberger, E., *Mikrochemie ver. Mikrochim. Acta* **30**, 241 (1942).
24. Cramer, F. B., Gardner, T. S. and Purves, C. B., *Ind. Eng. Chem., Anal. Ed.* **15**, 319 (1943).
25. Pieters, H. A. J. and Popelier, C., *Chem. Weekblad* **40**, 2 (1943).
26. Reti, L. and Lando, E., *Industria y quim* **5**, 79 (1943).
27. Riesz, C. H. and Wohlberg, C., *Am. Gas Assoc. Proc.* **25**, 259 (1943).
28. Whistler, R. L. and Jeanes, A., *Ind. Eng. Chem., Anal. Ed.* **15**, 317 (1943).
29. Sclar, R. N. and Clark, G. R., *J. Assoc. Offic. Agr. Chem.* **27**, 472 (1944).
30. Bishop, R. L. and Wallace, E. L., *Ind. Eng. Chem., Anal. Ed.* **17**, 563 (1945).
31. Hakewill, H. and Rueck, E. M., *Am. Gas. Assoc. Proc.* **28**, 529 (1946).
32. Toffoli, C. and Marzadco, M., *Ann. chim. applicata* **36**, 370 (1946).
33. Bastrup, T., *Acta Pharmacol. Toxicol.* **3**, 303 (1947).
34. Johansen, A., *Svensk Papperstidn* **50**, 527 (1947).
35. Stuart, A. G., *Analyst* **72**, 235 (1947).
36. Wagner, C. D., Goldstein, T. and Peters, E. D., *Anal. Chem.* **19**, 103 (1947).
37. Hummel, V., *Listy Cukrovar* **64**, 229 (1948).
38. Anderson, H. H., *J. Am. Chem. Soc.* **71**, 1801 (1949).
39. Hansen, H., *Brennstoffchem.* **30**, 419 (1949).
40. Hofman-Bang, N. and Szybalski, W., *Acta Chem. Scand.* **3**, 926 (1949).
41. Linder, A. and Persson, V., *Svensk Papperstidn* **52**, 331 (1949).
42. Shkol'man, E. E. and Popova, I. A., *Zhur. Priklad Khim.* (*J. Appl. Chem., USSR*) **22**, 135 (1949).
43. Clarke, D. G., Baum, H., Stanley, E. L. and Hester, W. F., *Anal. Chem.* **23**, 1842 (1951).
44. Nicolas, L. and Burel, R., *Chim. anal.* **33**, 341 (1951).
45. Hogsett, J. N., Kacy, H. W. and Johnson, J. B., *Anal. Chem.* **25**, 1207 (1953).
46. Lehmann, E. and Grütz, W., *Z. Pflanzernähr. Düng. u. Bodenk.* **61**, 77 (1953).
47. Dal Nogare, S., Montague, B. A. and Mitchell, J., *Division of Anal. Chem.*, 125th meeting A.C.S., Kansas City, U.S.A., March 30th (1954).
48. Iijima, T., *J. Soc. Rubber Ind., Japan* **29**, 14, (1956).
49. Maurice, M. J., *Anal. Chim. Acta* **14**, 583 (1956).
50. Linder, A. and Persson, V., *J. Am. Oil Chemists' Soc.* **34**, 24 (1957).
51. Roth, H. and Beck, W., *Mikrochim. Acta* **6**, 845 (1957).
52. Cartoni, L., *Ricerca Sci.* **28**, 1639 (1958).
53. Morath, J. C. and Woods, J. T., *Anal. Chem.* **30**, 1437 (1958).
54. Pinguet, *Pharm. Acta Helv.* **33**, 114 (1958).
55. Patchornik, A. and Rogozinski, S. E., *Anal. Chem.* **31**, 985 (1959).

56. Burger, K. and Schulek, E., *Talanta* **4**, 120 (1960).
57. Idel'son, E. M., *Zavodskaya Lab.* **26**, 947 (1960).
58. Satyanarayana Rao, V. R. and Vasudeva Murthy, A. R., *Talanta* **4**, 206 (1960).
59. Burger, K. and Schulek, E., *Magyar Kem. Folyóirat* **67**, 59 (1961).
60. Eusuf, M. and Khundkar, M. H., *Anal. Chim. Acta* **24**, 419 (1961).
61. Görög, S. and Trischler, F., *Acta Chim. Acad. Sci. Hung.* **26**, 437 (1961).
62. Roth, H., *Angew. Chem.* **73**, 167 (1961).
63. Kosinska, V. and Feigin, E., *Plasticheskie Massy* No. 6, 8 (1961).
64. Schulek, E. and Barcza, L., *Acta Pharm. Hung.* **32**, 1 (1962).
65. Barcza, L., *Talanta* **10**, 503 (1963).
66. Bighi, C. and Penzo, L., *Ann Chim. (Rome)* **53**, 1068 (1963).
67. Dahmen, E. A. M. F., Dijkstra, R. and Verjaal, A. J., *Erdöl u. Kohle* **16**, 768 (1963).
68. Kiboku, M., *Bunseki Kagaku* **12**, 797 (1963).

3. Alkalies

Reagent. Alkali reagents classified here are alkali and alkaline earth hydroxides and carbonates, together with alkoxides of lower alcohols. They have been used in aqueous solution or in alcohol or polyalcohol solvents in most cases. NaOH and KOH account for about 90% of the examples.

Ammonium hydroxide is included under a separate heading.

Sometimes a sodium/alcohol reagent has been used, especially for halide determination. This has been classified also under 'Metals' since the essential reagent may be regarded as the sodium metal or the alkoxide formed.

Alkalies have been used extensively in conjunction with other reagents which require a higher pH for their function. To give a few examples: permanganate; halogens (to yield hypohalites); alcohols (to yield xanthates with CS_2); hydroxylamine hydrochloride (when working in neutral or alkaline solution). These applications are not included here but only under the other component of the reagent mixture.

Reactions and materials titrated. 1. Hydrolysis of various organic bonds is the reaction of alkalies most extensively adapted to organic analysis. Some examples are given below, grouped under the bond hydrolysed:

C—O: Esters (organic and inorganic), anhydrides and lactones have been determined in this way, e.g.

$$RCOOR' + OH^- \rightarrow RCOO^- + R'OH$$
$$(RCO)_2O + 2\ OH^- \rightarrow 2\ RCOO^- + H_2O$$

This determination is the most extensively used method for esters and is moreover the principal application of alkalies in organic titration. About 200 or approaching 50% of the examples tabulated below are of determination of esters or 'saponification numbers' or 'values'.

C—N: Amides have been determined principally by alkali hydrolysis:

$$RCONH_2 + OH^- \rightarrow RCOO^- + NH_3$$

The determination of penicillin by treatment with alkali and then with iodine is a prominent recent example depending on this hydrolysis reaction (and also with fission of C—S).

C≡N: The first reaction taking place in the determination of nitriles with alkalies, is probably addition of water to form amides, which are then hydrolysed as above. It is convenient to regard the overall reaction as one of hydrolysis.

C—Hal: Alkali hydrolysis is undoubtedly the reaction on which the majority of halide determinations depend:

$$X\text{—}Hal + OH^- \rightarrow X\text{—}OH + Hal^-$$

Probably the most common examples are of the determination of volatile halides in air (e.g. CH_3Br, CH_2Cl_2, $CHCl_3$, $COCl_2$); of halogen-containing insecticides like DDT and BHC; and of some specific compounds like chloral and iodoform. Over 100 of the examples in the tables are determinations of halides, the next most prolific example to ester determination.

Other bonds: These include C—S in *S*-alkylthioureas, S—N (sulphonamides), S—Cl (sulphonyl chlorides) and carbon bonds with Si, As and Ge.

2. 'Neutralization' reactions, though very widely adapted to direct titration, have been used in indirect titration only in cases where

reaction has been retarded by low solubility (*cf.* Perchloric acid). In fact, only two examples are quoted.

3. The Cannizzaro reaction,

$$2\ RCHO + OH^- \rightarrow RCOO^- + RCH_2OH$$

has been the basis of a number of determinations of aldehydes.

4. One or two compounds have been determined by methods depending on reactions other than those mentioned above. E.g. tetramethylammonium salts by heating with alkali to yield trimethylamine; or trichloracetate by decarboxylation in presence of alkali (yielding the carbonate + $CHCl_3$).

Reaction conditions. With between four and five hundred examples in the tables, it is virtually impossible to say anything general. Most reactions have been carried out in water, alcohols or glycols (or mixtures of these) the last named being used where higher temperatures were desired to accelerate reaction.

Subsequent treatment and final titration stage. (i) Back titration with acid of unreacted alkali has been used in many determinations based on hydrolysis and also on some other reactions like neutralization and the Cannizzaro reaction. Nearly always HCl or H_2SO_4 have been used as titrants and esters, anhydrides, amides, halides and aldehydes have been extensively determined in this way. About 40% of the methods below in the tables were thus concluded.

(ii) In the remaining methods, a reaction product has been determined and some of the more commonly formed products and the titrimetric procedures for their determination are summarized below:

1. Halide ion from determination of halides, has been titrated in one of three ways:
   (a) with Ag(I) reagent, either directly or by using excess and back titrating, usually with SCN^-.
   (b) with Hg(II) to nitroprusside or diphenylcarbazone indicators.
   (c) by oxidation (of Br^- or I^-) with chlorine or hypochlorite, giving bromate or iodate, then determined by reaction with I^-/acid and titration with thiosulphate.
2. Carboxylate anion, $RCOO^-$, from hydrolysis of esters, amides, nitriles and halides chiefly. Three general procedures may then be distinguished:

(a) the free acid has been isolated, by acidification followed by distillation or extraction with a suitable solvent; or by passing through an ion exchanger. The acid was then titrated with alkali or determined by adding iodate/iodide and titrating with thiosulphate.

(b) the anion has been separated by precipitation, e.g. with Hg(I) (fumarate), Ca(II) (oxalate) or K^+H^+ (phthalate), followed by determination of excess precipitant (e.g. Ca(II) with EDTA) or of the precipitated salt (e.g. KH phthalate with $HClO_4$).

(c) in most cases, the anion has been directly determined without separation from the reaction mixture, by an oxidation method. Thus salicylate has been determined with alkali/iodine, bromine and ICl reagents; formate with Hg(II); oxalate, lactate and phthalate with MnO_4^-; and penicilloate with alkali/iodine. Some anions, e.g. acetoacetate, decompose in alkaline solution yielding CO_2, which was titrimetrically determined.

Carboxylate has also been determined in the reaction mixture by a 'double indicator' method, via acid titration from pH *ca* 10 (e.g. phenolphthalein) to pH *ca* 4 (e.g. bromophenol blue).

3. Alcohols, phenols or thiophenols from ester hydrolysis, determined with bromine reagent (substitution of phenols; addition to allyl alcohol, for example); with Cr(VI) reagent (bichromate or chromic oxide, used in several cases for ethanol determination); with iodine (e.g. thiophenol) or with Hg(II).

4. Ammonia or lower aliphatic amines, chiefly from hydrolysis of nitrogen-containing compounds including amides (e.g. urea), nitriles, urethanes, carbamates, semicarbazones, sulphonamides, pyramidone and derivatives and proteins; some nitrate esters and nitro compounds have been determined with the same final stage but after an additional reduction. The ammonia or amines have been distilled out and titrated with acid.

5. Aromatic amines, from hydrolysis of sulphonamides, have been titrated with nitrite.

6. Some carbonyl compounds (e.g. HCHO or acetone), resulting mainly from hydrolyses, have been determined by the standard methods such as reaction with bisulphite or hydroxylamine.

Examples

Materials titrated	Reagent and reaction conditions	Subsequent treatment and final titration stage	Ref.
Chloral	+ excess NaOH	Unused titrated with HCl to litmus	1
Esters added to butter	In ethanol, + excess KOH; 15 min boiling	Unused titrated with HCl to phenolphthalein	2
HCHO	+ excess NaOH; 2 days gentle warming, then a few hours/80°	Unused titrated with H_2SO_4	3
Acetyl, benzoyl groups in fats	In methanol or ethanol, + KOH/alcohol; 30 min–1 h warming	Unused titrated with HCl to phenolphthalein	4
Urea	+ $BaCO_3$; 1 h/180° in sealed tube	Extracted with HCl, $Ba(OH)_2$ added and NH_3 distilled into excess standard acid; back titrated with alkali	5
Saponification numbers of dark coloured oils	+ excess alcoholic alkali	Unused precipitated with CO_2; residue of alkali salt heated with NH_4Cl, giving NH_3; $RCOONa + NH_4Cl \rightarrow NH_3 + NaCl + RCOOH$. Distilled into standard HCl and back titrated with alkali (see Ammonium hydroxide and ammonium salts, ref. 3)	6
Esters in fats and waxes	In petroleum ether, + KOH/alcohol; 12–24 h/room temp.	Unused titrated with HCl	7
Acetyl, benzoyl groups	+ KOH/methanol; 1 h reflux	+ phosphoric acid and acetic or benzoic acid distilled and titrated with NaOH to aurin	8, 13
Iodoform from determination of acetone with iodine/alkali	+ KOH/alcohol; A few min boiling	+ acetic acid and titrated with $AgNO_3$ to chromate	9
Saponification number of waxes	+ alkali/amyl alcohol; 30 min/100°	Unused titrated with HCl to phenolphthalein	10
Ethyl acetate from determination of acetyl groups by distillation with ethanol/H_2SO_4	+ excess KOH; a few min	Unused titrated with H_2SO_4	11, 12, 14

Materials titrated	Reagent and reaction conditions	Subsequent treatment and final titration stage	Ref.
Trichloroacetic acid	+ excess KOH. Boiled, giving $CHCl_3$ + CO_2	Carbonate precipitated with Ba^{2+} and unused alkali titrated with acid	15
Chloroform	+ KOH/alcohol; 1 h reflux	Neutralized and Cl^- titrated with Ag^+ to chromate	16
Chloral	In ethanol, + NaOH; 3 h reflux, giving NaCl + HCOONa	Neutralized with H_2SO_4 and Cl^- titrated with Ag^+	17
Acetate ester formed in determination of terpene tertiary alcohols by reaction with acetic anhydride/sodium acetate	+ excess alkali	Unused titrated with acid	18, 38
Chloral	In water, + KOH; 15–20 min/not above 15°	Unused titrated with H_2SO_4 to phenolphthalein	19
Acetyl groups	+ excess KOH/water/glycerol	Unused titrated with acid	20
Acetyl groups in cellulose acetate	In 75% ethanol (pre-heated solution), + NaOH; 15 min/50°, then 24–48 h/room temp.	Unused titrated with HCl to phenolphthalein	21
Iodoform	+ KOH/ethanol; 2 h reflux	Acidified with HNO_3, excess $AgNO_3$ added and back titrated with SCN^-	22
Saponification number of fats	+ KOH/water/glycerol	Unused titrated with acid	23
Saponification number of oils	+ alkali/n-propanol (higher boiling point gave faster hydrolysis)	Unused titrated with acid	24
Acetate ester formed in determination of —OH groups by acetylation with acetic anhydride	+ KOH/alcohol	Unused titrated with HCl	25
Fructose pentaacetates	+ NaOH; 2–3 h/0°	Unused titrated with H_2SO_4 to phenolphthalein	26
Ester in fats, oils and waxes	+ KOH/benzyl alcohol; 5 min boiling	Unused titrated with HCl to phenolphthalein	27

Materials titrated	Reagent and reaction conditions	Subsequent treatment and final titration stage	Ref
Aromatic sulphonyl chlorides	+ water and free acid titrated with NaOH; then + excess NaOH; 5–15 min reflux	Unused titrated with HCl	28
Esters	+ alkali/butanol/a little water (higher boiling point gave faster hydrolysis; also better solvent)	Unused titrated with acid	29
Saponification number of montan wax	+ KOH/ethanol/xylene; 5 h reflux	+ Ba^{2+} to precipitate the fatty acids, then titrated with HCl to phenolphthalein	30
Cellulose acetates	In acetone, + NaOH; 24 h/room temp.	+ water and titrated with acid to phenolphthalein	31
Pyramidone	Boiled with alkali in hydrogen current, giving dimethylamine	Amine carried into excess standard H_2SO_4 and back titrated with alkali to methyl orange	32
Acetic anhydride	+ excess alkali; a few min/room temp.	+ excess acid and finally titrated with alkali	33
Esters derived from alcohols by reaction with acetic anhydride	+ excess KOH/alcohol; 15–20 min/50–60° or left overnight/room temp.	Unused titrated with acid	34
Ethyl acetate from determination of acetyl groups by distillation with ethanol/*p*-toluene-sulphonic acid	Distilled into excess NaOH; 10 min boiling at end	Titrated with H_2SO_4 to phenolphthalein	35, 42
Ester formed in determination of —OH groups in essential oils by reaction with HCOOH/acetic anhydride	+ excess NaOH	Unused titrated with acid	36
Chloral hydrate	+ alkali/ethanol; 2 h/90–100° in sealed tube	Cl^- determined by acidifying, adding excess $AgNO_3$ and titrating the unused with SCN^-	37
Phosgene	+ excess KOH, giving KCl + K_2CO_3	+ excess HCl and back titrated with $Ba(OH)_2$	39

Materials titrated	Reagent and reaction conditions	Subsequent treatment and final titration stage	Ref
Acetyl groups	+ $Ba(OH)_2$/water 30 min–2 h reflux	+ phosphoric acid, acetic acid distilled out and titrated with NaOH to phenolphthalein	40
Phosgene	+ NaOH/water, giving NaCl + Na_2CO_3	+ water and unused titrated with HCl	41
Methyl or ethyl formate from determination of methanol or ethanol by heating with formic acid/H_2SO_4	+ NaOH	Unused titrated with acid	43
Chloral in syrup of chloral	+ water + excess NaOH; 10 min/room temp.	Unused titrated with H_2SO_4 to phenolphthalein	44, 51
Anhydride (+ acid) in lactic acid	+ NaOH; 10 min/100° (acid alone determined by direct NaOH titration)	+ excess acid and back titrated with NaOH to methyl red	45
Acetyl groups in neolactose β-octaacetate and α-chloroacetyl neolactose	In acetone, + KOH/water; 2 h/below 0°	Unused titrated with HCl	46
Saponification number (micro) of fats	+ KOH/water + drops ethanol	Dissolved in alcohol and titrated with acid to phenolphthalein	47
Pyramidone	Method of ref. 32 tried but found unsatisfactory		48
Aromatic nitroamines, e.g. nitroanilines, nitronaphthylamines	+ alkali and boiled giving NH_3	Distilled into acid and back titrated with alkali to methyl red	49
Acetate formed in determination of the acetylizable content of oils by reaction with acetic anhydride/sodium acetate	+ KOH/alcohol; 1 h/reflux	Unused titrated with H_2SO_4	50
Chloral	Critical examination of method of refs 44, 51, 53		52
Chloral in syrup of chloral	+ NaOH; 1 min/room temp.	Unused titrated with H_2SO_4	53
Methyl bromide in air	Passed through CH_3ONa solution	Acidified, excess $AgNO_3$ added and back titrated with SCN^-	54

Materials titrated	Reagent and reaction conditions	Subsequent treatment and final titration stage	Ref.
Iodoform	Method of ref. 22		55
Santonin in pharmaceutical preparations	In ethanol, + KOH/ethanol; 45 min reflux	Unused titrated with HCl to phenolphthalein	56
Bromine addition product formed in determination of oleic/linoleic acid mixture in an oil by reaction with bromine/ether	+ KOH; 5 h/100°	Acidified, excess $AgNO_3$ added and back titrated with SCN^- (result got by interpolation)	57
Cellulose acetates	In pyridine, + NaOH; 30 min shaking	Unused titrated with acid to phenolphthalein	58
Anhydride (+ acid) in lactic acid	+ NaOH; 20 min boiling (acid alone determined by direct titration with NaOH)	Unused titrated with acid to neutral red	59
Sulphonamides $Ar.SO_2NH.Ar$	Dissolved in excess NaOH	Titrated with HCl to phenolphthalein or to slight turbidity with $BaCl_2$ indicator	60
Saponification values of oil	+ KOH/benzyl alcohol; 5 min reflux	Unused titrated with acid	61
Organic nitrate esters	In acetone, + NaOH + Na perborate + water. Left overnight, giving NO_3^-	Reduced to NH_3 with Devarda's alloy, distilled into excess H_2SO_4 and back titrated with ammonium hydroxide to methyl red	62
Iodoform	Melted with solid KOH, giving I^-	Acidified, oxidized to IO_3^- with chlorine water, unused chlorine boiled off, I^- added and iodine liberated titrated with thiosulphate	63
Diphenylchlorarsine, $(C_6H_5)_2AsCl$	+ NaOH/ethanol/water, giving Cl^-	+ HNO_3 + excess $AgNO_3$ and back titrated with SCN^- to Fe(III)	64
Anhydride (+ acid) in lactic acid	+ NaOH; 30 min/room temp. (free acid separately titrated with NaOH)	Unused titrated with acid	65
Saponification number (semimicro) of vegetable oils	+ $i\text{-}C_3H_7ONa$ solution; 30 min reflux	Unused titrated with H_2SO_4 to phenolphthalein	66

Materials titrated	Reagent and reaction conditions	Subsequent treatment and final titration stage	Ref.
Saponification number of oil mixtures with asphalt	In anisole, + KOH/ethanol; 1 h reflux	Unused titrated with HCl potentiometrically	67
Hexamine methylene-citrate in presence of hexamine	+ NaOH, giving HCHO (hexamine not attacked)	HCHO determined with alkali/excess iodine (see Iodine reagents, ref. 119)	68
Cellulose acetate	In 75% ethanol, + NaOH; 15 min/50°, then 24–48 h/room temp. (slight modification of method of ref. 21)	Unused titrated with acid to phenolphthalein	69
Chloral	In water, + NaOH; 1 min/room temp.	Unused titrated with H_2SO_4 or HCl to phenolphthalein	70
Acetyl groups in substituted acetamides	+ KOH/benzyl alcohol; 90 min reflux	+ ethanol and titrated with HCl to phenolphthalein	71
Lactones like narcotine, santonin	+ KOH/ethanol. Alcohol evaporated off	+ water + ether and titrated with HCl to phenolphthalein or alkali blue	72
Pyrethrin I	In kerosene, + NaOH/methanol; 3–4 h total reflux, giving salt of chrysanthemum-monocarboxylic acid	Acidified alcohol layer with H_2SO_4, distilled out organic acid in steam and titrated with NaOH to phenolphthalein	73
Tetramethylammonium sulphate or nitrate	+ NaOH. Heated giving trimethylamine	Distilled into standard H_2SO_4 and back titrated with NaOH	74
Ethyl acetate from determination of acetyl groups by distillation with ethanol/*p*-toluene-sulphonic acid	Distilled into excess NaOH; 10 min boiling at end	Unused titrated with H_2SO_4	75
Benzyl acetate formed in determination of benzyl cellulose by reaction with acetic anhydride/H_2SO_4	+ NaOH/water; 1 h/100°	Unused titrated with acid to phenolphthalein	76
Saponification number of shellac	+ KOH/alcohol; 2 h reflux	Unused titrated with HCl to thymol blue	77
Chloroform	+ KOH/alcohol; 4 h reflux	+ HNO_3 + excess $AgNO_3$ and back titrated with SCN^- to Fe(III)	78

Materials titrated	Reagent and reaction conditions	Subsequent treatment and final titration stage	Ref.
Acetate ester formed in determination of sugars and carbohydrates by reaction with acetic anhydride/sodium acetate in toluene or xylene	+ excess alkali	Unused titrated with acid	79
O-Acetyl and benzoyl groups; *N*-acetyl groups	+ NaOH/methanol–water, 1:1 or water. Usually 15 min reflux; 3 h for *N*-acetyl	Acidified with H_2SO_4, acetic acid distilled and titrated with NaOH to phenolphthalein	80
Some aldehydes, e.g. isobutyraldehyde, isovaleraldehyde, heptaldehyde	+ KOH/benzyl alcohol; *ca* 15 min reflux	Unused titrated with acid	81
Methoxyl groups in pectin	+ NaOH; 15 min/room temp.	+ excess H_2SO_4 and back titrated with alkali to phenolphthalein	82
Chloroform	In toluene, + KOH/alcohol. Refluxed, giving Cl^-	+ HNO_3 + $AgNO_3$ and back titrated with SCN^-	83, 84
Acetyl groups	+ NaOH; 12–15 h reflux	Unused titrated with HCl to phenolphthalein	85
Ethyl acetate or formate formed in determination of acetyl groups in nitroacetylcellulose or of formyl groups in formylcellulose by reaction with ethanol/phosphoric acid	Distilled into excess alkali	Unused titrated with acid	86
Acetate ester formed in determination of hydroxyl groups in fatty materials by reaction with acetic anhydride	+ KOH/alcohol; 2 h reflux	Acidified with *p*-toluenesulphonic acid, the acetic acid distilled and determined by reaction with IO_3^-/I^- and titration with thiosulphate (see Iodate, ref. 29)	87
Anhydride (+ acid) in lactic acid	+ NaOH; 1 h/room temp.	Unused titrated with H_2SO_4 to methyl orange	88
Degree of unsaturation of oils	+ KOH/alcohol. Refluxed	Neutralized with HCl, alcohol evaporated, $NaOCl/H_2SO_4$ added and unused determined iodometrically (see Chlorine reagents, ref. 7)	89

Materials titrated	Reagent and reaction conditions	Subsequent treatment and final titration stage	Ref.
Methyl salicylate	+ KOH/methanol; 2 h reflux	Most methanol evaporated, water added and titrated with HCl	90
Menthol acetate from determination of menthol by reaction with acetic anhydride/ sodium acetate	+ KOH/methanol; 1 h reflux	+ water and titrated with HCl	
Pentabromoacetone formed in determination of citric acid by reaction with $Br^-/H_2SO_4/MnO_4^-$	+ KOH/alcohol/ water, giving Br^-	+ HNO_3 + excess $AgNO_3$ and back titrated with SCN^-	91
Study of effect of chloroform on determination of phosgene	Chloroform samples absorbed in NaOH/ 85% ethanol	+ HNO_3 + $NaHCO_3$ to give pH *ca* 9; titrated with $AgNO_3$ to chromate (showed negligible interference of chloroform)	92
Aldehydes in oil of bitter almonds	Method of ref. 81		93
Ethyl acetate from determination of acetyl groups by distillation with ethanol/*p*-toluene-sulphonic acid	Distilled into excess KOH/alcohol	Unused titrated with acid to phenolphthalein	94
Esters in lacquer thinners	+ NaOH/ethanol; 90 min reflux	Unused titrated with acid	95
Pentabromoacetone from determination of citric acid by reaction with Br^-/MnO_4^-/acid	+ NaOH excess; 30 min/85–90°	Unused titrated with HCl to methyl red	96
Aromatic nitro compounds	Fused with KOH/ NaOH/Zn or Al powder in an iron tube, giving ammonia	Carried into excess H_2SO_4 and back titrated with alkali	97
Ethyl acetate	+ KOH/water	Unused titrated with HCl to phenolphthalein	98
Acetyl groups	+ KOH/ethanol; 4 min reflux. For *N*-acetyl groups, + KOH/nbutanol; 1 h reflux	+ conc. $MgSO_4$ solution + a little H_2SO_4; acetic acid distilled and titrated with NaOH to phenol red	99

Materials titrated	Reagent and reaction conditions	Subsequent treatment and final titration stage	Ref.
Benzonaphthol (2-naphthyl benzoate) in medicines	+ KOH/alcohol; 5 min reflux	+ water, alcohol distilled out and unused alkali titrated with HCl to phenolphthalein	100
Ethyl acetate from determination of ethanol by reaction with acetic anhydride	+ KOH. Warmed on water bath	Unused titrated with acid	101
Chlorbutanol, $(CH_3)_2C(OH)—CCl_3$	+ KOH; 30 min reflux	+ HNO_3 + excess $AgNO_3$ and back titrated with SCN^-	102
O- and *N*-Acetyl groups	Total determined by method of ref. 35 *O*-Acetyl by method of ref. 46 but with 1 h reaction time		103
Isatin	Dissolved in excess NaOH	Unused titrated with HCl to phenolphthalein	104
Esters	+ KOH/diethylene glycol; 3 min/120–130°	+ water and titrated with HCl to phenolphthalein	105
Benzyl benzoate	+ alkali/alcohol. Refluxed	Alcohol distilled off, acidified with H_2SO_4, benzoic acid extracted with $CHCl_3$ and titrated with alkali	106
Chloral	+ NaOH; 10 min boiling, giving formate	+ sodium acetate and titrated formate at 100° with permanganate	107
p-Dichlorobenzene in hide (extracted with ether)	+ CaO; fused at a bright red heat, giving Cl^-	+ HNO_3 and determined argentometrically	108
Saponification number of rosin	In alcohol solvent, + alkali/same solvent; 1 h reflux (results varied with solvent; several lower aliphatic alcohols tried)	Unused titrated with HCl	109
Methyl bromide in air	Absorbed in KOH/ethanol/ether, giving Br^-	Oxidized with NaOCl/NaCl/boric acid in *ca* 15 min/100°, to bromate; + I^- + ammonium molybdate and titrated with thiosulphate	110
Ethyl acetate	+ KOH; 3 h reflux	Unused titrated with HCl to phenolphthalein	111

Materials titrated	Reagent and reaction conditions	Subsequent treatment and final titration stage	Ref.
Esters	+ KOH/ethanol. Mostly 1 h reflux but some up to 50 h	Unused titrated with H_2SO_4 to α-naphtholphthalein	112
Acetates from determination of glycol or glycerol in tobacco by reaction with acetic anhydride/sodium acetate	+ KOH	Unused titrated with HCl	113
Acetyl, benzoyl groups	+ KOH/water; 15–60 min reflux	Acidified with phosphoric or *p*-toluenesulphonic acid, acetic or benzoic acid distilled and titrated with alkali	114
Ethyl acetate in wines	+ NaOH; 2 h/room temp.	+ H_2SO_4, the acetic acid distilled and titrated with NaOH	115
Ethyl *p*-hydroxybenzoate	+ NaOH; 15 min/room temp.	Acid determined with excess BrO_3^-; unused part measured by adding I^- and titrating with thiosulphate	116
Difficulty saponifiable esters, e.g. methyl abietate or bornyl phthalate	+ CH_3ONa/cyclohexanol/some methanol; 16 h/150° (also *t*-C_4H_9ONa/*t*-C_4H_9OH used)	Unused titrated with H_2SO_4 to phenolphthalein or thymol blue	117
Benzonaphthol (2-naphthyl benzoate)	+ KOH/ethanol; 5 min reflux	Neutralized with HCl, $NaHCO_3$ added and the naphthol determined by iodine titration to starch	118
Iodoform	+ KOH/ethanol; 2 h reflux	+ HNO_3 + excess $AgNO_3$ and back titrated with SCN^-	119
Diethylamides of nicotinic, phthalic acids	+ NaOH; 20 min reflux, giving diethylamine	Amine passed into HCl and back titrated with NaOH or borax to methyl red	120
Chloral hydrate	+ NaOH	Unused titrated with HCl to phenolphthalein	121
Aspirin	+ NaOH. Left overnight; some heating	Salicylate determined with Na_2CO_3/excess iodine and back titration of the unused with thiosulphate (see Iodine reagents, ref. 196)	122

Materials titrated	Reagent and reaction conditions	Subsequent treatment and final titration stage	Ref.
Dichloroethane in air	Absorbed in C_2H_5ONa/ ethanol; 2 h reflux, giving Cl^-	Just acidified with HNO_3, and Cl^- titrated with Hg(II) to turbidity of nitroprusside indicator	123
Amides, nitriles	+ KOH/an alcohol (best was benzyl alcohol); 1 h reflux, giving NH_3	Ammonia distilled and titrated with H_2SO_4 to methyl orange	124
Ureas, semicarbazones, urethanes, allophanic acid and esters, etc.	+ KOH/glycerol. Up to 2 h reflux, giving NH_3	Distilled in nitrogen stream and titrated with acid	125
Lobeline	Distilled with NaOH, giving acetophenone	Determined with NaOH/ excess iodine, unused being titrated with thiosulphate (see Iodine reagents, ref. 203)	126
Esters in fermented beverages, e.g. ethyl acetate or lactate	+ NaOH; 20 min/60°	+ excess H_2SO_4 and back titrated with NaOH; also acidified with phosphoric acid, distilled out acetic acid and titrated with alkali, giving the acetate ester content	127
Chloral hydrate	In water, + excess NaOH; 1–3 min	Unused titrated with HCl	128
Menthol acetate from determination of menthol by reaction with acetic anhydride/ sodium acetate	+ KOH/ethanol. Up to 3 h reflux; or + KOH/diethylene glycol, up to 30 min reflux	Unused titrated with HCl	129
Benzocaine	+ NaOH; 20 min reflux	Unused titrated with HCl to phenolphthalein	130
Total acyl groups in cellulose esters	Several methods tried out, including two based on alkali saponification; (a) slight modification of method of ref. 21 (b) + NaOH/95% ethanol; 16–24 h/not above 30°	Unused determined by HCl titration to phenolphthalein	131
Trichloroethylene	+ KOH; 1 h/150° in sealed tube	+ HNO_3 + excess $AgNO_3$ and back titrated with SCN^-	132

Materials titrated	Reagent and reaction conditions	Subsequent treatment and final titration stage	Ref.
Ethyl acetate formed in determination of acetyl groups by reaction with ethanol/HCl	Distilled into alkali; 30 min reflux	Unused titrated with acid to phenolphthalein	133
Esters of *p*-hydroxy-benzoic acid	Method of ref. 116		134
Esters, including nitrate esters	+ NaOH/alcohol/water. Boiled, then left in the cold overnight or longer	Unused titrated with HCl	135
Amides	+ NaOH. Boiled for various periods	Unused titrated with HCl	136
Ethyl chloride	+ KOH/alcohol; 15 min 120° in sealed vessel	Unused titrated with HCl	137
Esters in peppermint oil; also menthol acetate from determination of menthol in it by reaction with acetic anhydride/sodium acetate	+ KOH/alcohol; 1 h reflux	Unused titrated with H_2SO_4 to phenolphthalein	138
Santonin	+ ethanol + $Ba(OH)_2$; 15 min/100°	+ water, titrated with HCl to phenolphthalein; 15 min/100° with excess HCl and finally back titrated with alkali	139
Methyl acetate from determination of acetic acid in body fluids by reaction with methanol	Distilled into NaOH, giving sodium acetate	Oxidized with H_2SO_4/$Ag_2Cr_2O_7$ and H_2SO_4/$K_2Cr_2O_7$ and difference in oxidation values gave acetate (see Bichromate and chromic oxide, ref. 110)	140
Prostigmine (neostigmine)	+ alkali. Heated giving dimethylamine	Distilled into excess acid and back titrated with alkali to methyl red	141
Cellulose mixed esters	+ NaOH; 48–72 h/40°	+ phosphoric acid and acid mixture of acetic, propionic and butyric acid distilled out; determined by partition between butyl acetate and water and titration of the layer acidities	142

Materials titrated	Reagent and reaction conditions	Subsequent treatment and final titration stage	Ref.
Terpinyl acetate	In methyl cellosolve, + KOH/ethyl cellosolve; 30 min reflux	Unused titrated with HCl to phenolphthalein	143
Esters (methyl, ethyl, propyl) of *p*-hydroxybenzoic acid	+ NaOH; 15 min/100°	*p*-Hydroxybenzoate determined with excess bromate and iodometric back titration (see Bromine reagents, ref. 215)	144
1,2-Dibromobutane from determination of 1-butene in presence of 2-butene by reaction with bromine	+ C_2H_5OK; 1 h/100–110°, giving $C_2H_5C{\equiv}CH$	Ethylacetylene determined argentometrically by precipitating with excess Ag^+ and back titrating with SCN^- (see Silver (I), ref. 75)	145
Chloropicrin in air	Passed through NaOH/ Na_2SO_3/alkali; solution then refluxed	Cl^- determined with excess Ag^+ and back titration with SCN^-	146
Methyl bromide (+ inorganic Br^-) in foods fumigated with methyl bromide	+ KOH/alcohol. Evaporated to dryness after 1 h reflux. Then + NaOH and heated to 600°	Br^- determined by oxidation to BrO_3^- with NaOCl; + I^- + H_2SO_4 and titrated with thiosulphate	147
Ethyl acetate from determination of acetyl groups by reaction with ethanol/H_2SO_4	+ NaOH; 15 min reflux	Passed through ion exchanger Wofatite K or KS and acetic acid in eluate titrated with alkali to phenolphthalein (see Ion exchangers, ref. 1)	148
Monochloroacetic acid in drinks (extracted with ether)	+ NaOH. At least 2 h reflux	Cl^- determined with excess Ag^+ and back titration with SCN^-	149
Chlorobutanol	+ KOH/methanol. Left overnight/room temp.	+ HNO_3 + excess $AgNO_3$ and unused titrated with SCN^-	150
Methyl acetate from determination of acetyl groups in cellulose acetate by transesterification with methanol/CH_3ONa, then *p*-toluenesulphonic acid	+ NaOH; 1 h reflux	Unused titrated with HCl to phenolphthalein	151
Monochloroacetic acid in wine	Modification of method of ref. 149		152

Materials titrated	Reagent and reaction conditions	Subsequent treatment and final titration stage	Ref.
Amides	+ KOH/ethylene glycol; 6 h reflux	+ ether and titrated with HCl to bromophenol blue	153
Sodium alkyl sulphates, from $C_2H_5OSO_3Na$ to $C_{14}H_{29}OSO_3Na$	+ KOH/benzyl alcohol; 1 h reflux	Unused titrated with HCl to phenol red	154
Saponification number of fats, oils, etc.	+ KOH/alcohol	Titrated with HCl to pH *ca* 10 (unused alkali) and pH *ca* 4 (salt of organic acid saponification product); difference thus gives titration of salt. Done potentiometrically or with phenolphthalein + bromophenol blue; benzene added for second titration to dissolve freed organic acid	155
Methyl acetate from determination of acetyl groups in carbohydrate esters by transesterification with methanol/CH_3ONa	Distilled into NaOH; 15 min reflux	Unused titrated with HCl to phenolphthalein	156
DDT in kerosene	+ KOH/99% ethanol. Refluxed, converting all Cl to Cl^-	+ HNO_3 + excess $AgNO_3$ and back titrated with SCN^-	157
Saponification numbers (micro)	+ KOH/ethanol; 10 min/125°	Unused titrated with HCl to alkali blue	158
Ethyl acetate + acetaldehyde	+ alkali + H_2O_2 (to oxidize aldehyde); 15 min/80° then 1 h/ room temp. (aldehyde separately determined with bisulphite —see Bisulphite and sulphite, ref. 74)	Unused titrated with HCl to phenolphthalein	159
Trichloroacetonitrile	+ NaOH; 7 h, giving NH_3	Distilled into boric acid and titrated with HCl to methyl red/bromocresol green	160
Acyl groups in cellulose esters	In various mixtures of water, pyridine, acetone and methanol, + alkali 6–16 h/20–55°	Unused titrated with HCl to phenolphthalein	161
Saponification numbers (micro)	+ NaOH/methanol/ water; 30 min/60°	Unused titrated with HCl to phenolphthalein	162

Materials titrated	Reagent and reaction conditions	Subsequent treatment and final titration stage	Ref.
Propionyl groups	Method of ref. 80		163
Acrylonitrile in air (absorbed in conc. H_2SO_4)	+ NaOH + H_2O_2 + Cu acetate (to prevent polymerization); 30 min reflux, giving ammonia	Distilled into H_2SO_4 and back titrated with NaOH to methyl red	164
Ethyl acetate from determination of sodium acetate by reaction with ethanol/*p*-toluenesulphonic acid	+ alkali	Unused titrated with acid	165
Acetic anhydride + free acid	+ excess NaOH; heated to 100°	Unused titrated with acid	166
Alloxan	+ KCN/water; 5 min/ room temp. giving dialurate, oxalurate and CO_2 (CN^- catalyst)	Dialurate titrated with Ce (IV)	167
Dichloroacetic acid in food products	Heated with KOH/ ethanol or fused with Na_2CO_3	Cl^- determined with excess Ag^+ and back titration with SCN^-	168
Acetyl groups in acetates of sugars and glycosides	In 95% ethanol, + NaOH/ethanol; 4–24h/room temp.	Unused titrated with H_2SO_4 to phenolphthalein	169
Menthol acetate from determination of menthol in mint essence by acetylation	+ KOH/ethanol; 90 min reflux	Unused titrated with H_2SO_4	170
DDT	+ KOH/alcohol 30 min reflux, giving one Cl^-	+ HNO_3 + nitrobenzene + excess Ag^+ and back titrated with SCN^-	171
Methyl ester content of pectin	In water at pH 7·5, + NaOH; 30 min/room temp.	+ H_2SO_4 equivalent to the original NaOH added, then titrated with NaOH to pH 7·5 potentiometrically	172
Methyl bromide in air	Absorbed in CH_3ONa/ methanol	Acidified and titrated with Ag^+ to eosin; or + excess Ag^+ and back titrated with SCN^-	173

Materials titrated	Reagent and reaction conditions	Subsequent treatment and final titration stage	Ref.
DDT	+ KOH/ethanol; 30 min reflux	Neutralized with H_2SO_4 and Cl^- titrated with Ag^+ to dichlorofluorescein	174
Halogen-containing compounds	+ KOH/diethylene glycol. At 150–160°	+ HNO_3 + excess $AgNO_3$ and back titrated with SCN^-	175, 188
Monochloroacetic acid in commercial preservatives	+ NaOH; 30 min reflux or 2 h/100°	+ HNO_3 + excess $AgNO_3$ and back titrated with SCN^-	176
Penicillins	+ NaOH; 15 min/room temp.	Neutralized with HCl, determined with excess iodine and back titration with thiosulphate (see Iodine reagents, ref. 237)	177
DDT	+ KOH/ethanol; 5 min reflux, giving one Cl^-	+ HNO_3 + $AgNO_3$ excess and back titrated with SCN^-	178
Chloral	+ alkali. Less than 5 min/room temp. Also + $Ca(OH)_2$; 10 min boiling	Unused titrated with acid to phenolphthalein; unreacted precipitated with Na_2CO_3, excess MnO_4^- added and unused determined with oxalic acid in acid solution (see Permanganate, ref. 81)	179
Saponification number	+ KOH/absolute or 95% ethanol; 30 min–3 h reflux	Titrated with HCl to phenolphthalein and then to bromophenol blue; difference equivalent to salt of organic acid from saponification	180
DDT	+ KOH/ethanol; 30 min reflux, giving one Cl^-	+ HNO_3 + excess $AgNO_3$ and unused titrated with SCN^-	181
p,p'-DDT	+ NaOH/95% ethanol; 15 min/room temp.	+ HNO_3 + excess $AgNO_3$ + nitrobenzene and unused Ag^+ titrated with SCN^-	182
Saponification numbers (micro) of fats and oils	+ KOH/ethanol; 30 min reflux	Titrated with HCl to phenolphthalein, then to bromophenol blue in presence of benzene (compare ref. 155)	183
High boiling esters	+ KOH/diethylene glycol; 15 min/125°	Unused titrated with HCl to phenolphthalein	184

Materials titrated	Reagent and reaction conditions	Subsequent treatment and final titration stage	Ref.
Penicillin G	+ NaOH	Neutralized with HCl and determined with excess iodine and back titration with thiosulphate (see Iodine reagents, ref. 241)	185
Phenyl ether of salicylic acid	+ alkali. Evaporated to dryness	Dissolved in water and determined with alkali/excess iodine (see Iodine reagents, ref. 244)	186
Ethyl acetate from determination of aspirin by heating with ethanol/NaOH	Distilled into excess alkali	Unused titrated with acid	187
Ethylene chlorohydrin	+ KOH/water; 1 h reflux	+ HNO_3 + excess $AgNO_3$ and back titrated with SCN^-	189
Saponification numbers of fatty oils, e.g. olive, linseed oils	+ KOH/alcohol. Various lower alcohols tried and propanol found best. 30–120 min reflux	Unused titrated with acid	190
Saponification numbers of vegetable and ash oils	Method of ref. 190; isopropanol again found best		191
Methyl formate from determination of formic acid in urine by reaction with HCl/methanol	Distilled into excess NaOH	Alkali formate determined with excess Hg(II) (see Mercury (II), ref. 95)	192
Sulphonamides	Heated with alkali, giving aromatic amines	+ acid and titrated with nitrite to starch/iodide (see Part I, Nitrite, ref. 46)	193
Benzene hexachloride in impregnated clothing	+ NaOH/acetone/water; 2 h reflux	+ HNO_3 + excess $AgNO_3$ and unused titrated with SCN^-	194
Mono- and dichloromethyl chloroformate	+ NaOH; 5 min/room temp., giving HCHO and $HCOO^-$	Determined with excess Hg(II) and back titration with iodine (see Mercury (II), ref. 97)	195
Physostigmine (Eserine)	+ NaOH, giving methylamine	Distilled into excess H_2SO_4 and back titrated unused	196

Materials titrated	Reagent and reaction conditions	Subsequent treatment and final titration stage	Ref.
Acetate of linalool in its determination by reaction with acetic anhydride	+ KOH/alcohol	Unused titrated with acid	197
Some methyl and ethyl esters, e.g. methyl salicylate, ethyl carbamate	+ KOH, giving methanol or ethanol	Distilled out and titrated with CrO_3/H_2SO_4 to external indicator of leucobase of methylene blue (see Part I, Bichromate and chromic acid, ref. 14)	198
Saponification number of natural waxes	+ KOH/ethanol + carbitol; 1 h reflux	Unused titrated with HCl to phenolphthalein	199
Chloroform, bromoform	+ KOH/alcohol/acetone. Less than 1 h/room temp. (5 min for bromoform)	Cl^- determined with excess Ag^+ and back titration with SCN^-	200
	$(CH_3)_2CO + CHCl_3 = (CH_3)_2C(OH).CCl_3 \xrightarrow{4\,KOH} (CH_3)_2CO + 3\,KCl + HCOOK + 2\,H_2O$		
DDT	+ KOH/alcohol/acetone; 30 min/room temp.	+ HNO_3 + excess $AgNO_3$ and unused titrated with SCN^-	201
Polyvinyl acetate in polyvinyl acetal ketal resins (safety glass)	Heated in methanol/butanol, + excess NaOH	+ excess H_2SO_4 and back titrated with NaOH to bromothymol blue	202
Ethyl acetate from determination of acetyl groups by trans-esterification with ethanol/HCl	Distilled into excess alkali	Unused titrated with acid	203
DDT	+ KOH/diethylene glycol; 150–160°, giving one Cl^-	Determined with excess Ag^+ and back titration with SCN^-	204
DDT	+ alkali; recommended 30–60 min with 0·1N (studied effect of different alkali concentrations)	Cl^- titrated argentometrically	205
O-Acetyl in presence of *N*-acetyl groups	+ NaOH/water/acetone; 2 h/room temp.	Unused titrated with acid to phenol red	206

Materials titrated	Reagent and reaction conditions	Subsequent treatment and final titration stage	Ref.
Ethyl carbamate in blood	+ NaOH, giving NH_3,CO_2 and ethanol	Distilled into excess $Cr_2O_7^{2-}/H_2SO_4$ and determined unused iodometrically	207
5,6-Dicyclopentenyl formate formed in determination of dicyclopentadiene by reaction with formic acid	In benzene, + KOH/95% ethanol; 6 h reflux	Unused titrated with HCl to phenolphthalein	208
1-Benzoylglucuronic acid in urine	+ NaOH; 2 h boiling	Acidified, benzoic acid extracted with toluene and titrated with C_2H_5ONa to phenolphthalein	209
Diethyl phthalate in smokeless powder	+ KOH/water; 1 h reflux, then + H_2O_2 to oxidize aldehydes present and refluxed 1 further hour	+ water and ethanol distilled into $Cr_2O_7^{2-}/H_2SO_4$; unused determined iodometrically	210
Dichloroacetic acid	+ NaOH; 1 h reflux; $CHCl_2COO^- + 2\ OH^- \rightarrow CHO.COO^- + 2\ Cl^- + H_2O$; $2\ CHO.COO^- + OH^- \rightarrow CH_2OH.COO^- + COO^-.COO^-$	+ ammonia + Ca acetate, giving precipitate of Ca oxalate; dissolved in H_2SO_4 and titrated with MnO_4^-	211
Pectin	+ NaOH; 30 min/room temp.	+ excess H_2SO_4 and back titrated with NaOH	212
Tetraethyl pyrophosphate	In benzene (from extraction procedure), + NaOH; 1 h shaking/room temp.	Unused titrated with HCl to bromothymol blue	213
Saponification number of fats and waxes	+ alkali/alcohol (ethanol or propanol best; dissolving power of methanol too poor)	Unused titrated with acid	214
Halides in air	In ethanol or propanol, + KOH. Left overnight/50°	+ acetic acid and Hal^- titrated with $AgNO_3$ using Liebig's method	215
Saponification number of cottonseed oil	+ KOH/isopropanol; 30 min reflux	+ ethylene or propylene glycol and titrated with HCl/glycol/isopropanol to aniline blue	216

Materials titrated	Reagent and reaction conditions	Subsequent treatment and final titration stage	Ref.
Diphenyl carbonate in cloth	Evaporated ether extract, + K_2CO_3/water; 20–30 min heating, giving phenol	Determined with excess bromate/bromide and iodometric back titration (see Bromine reagents, ref. 275)	217
Dimalone (insect repellent) in cloth	+ KOH/alcohol; 90 min reflux	Unused titrated with H_2SO_4 to phenolphthalein	218
Penicillin G	+ NaOH; 15 min/room temp.	Neutralized and determined with excess iodine and back titration with thiosulphate (see Iodine reagents, ref. 259)	219
Anhydride + acid in lactic acid	+ alkali; 3 min boiling	Unused titrated with acid	220
Methyl lactate from determination of lactic acid by reaction with methanol/H_2SO_4	Hydrolysed with alkali	Lactate determined by oxidation with MnO_4^-/alkali to oxalate, precipitation with Ca^{2+} and final titration of the Ca oxalate with MnO_4^- (see Permanganate, ref. 87, and Calcium (II), ref. 23)	221
Chlorobutanol	+ KOH/alcohol	Unused titrated with HCl to methyl orange	222
	also + KOH/$Ca(OH)_2$/ Fehlings reagent. Digested, giving acetone	distilled and determined with alkali/excess iodine and back titration with thiosulphate (see Iodine reagents, ref. 262)	
Phthalate esters in propellants	+ KOH/ethanol; refluxed	Unused titrated with HCl to phenolphthalein	223
Benzene hexachloride isomers	+ KOH/alcohol; 20 min reflux (all isomers react); also 15 min/0° and 50 min/0° (difference equivalent to γ-isomer)	+ HNO_3 + nitrobenzene + excess $AgNO_3$ and back titrated with SCN^-	224
Na penicillin	+ NaOH; 20 min/room temp.	Neutralized and determined with excess iodine with back titration using thiosulphate	225
Benzene hexachloride in commercial products	+ KOH/alcohol	+ HNO_3 + excess $AgNO_3$ unused determined with SCN^-	226

Materials titrated	Reagent and reaction conditions	Subsequent treatment and final titration stage	Ref.
Hydrolysable organic halides, e.g. chlorohydrins	+ NaOH, 1 h reflux; or + $NaHCO_3$, 30 min reflux	Neutralized and Hal^- titrated with $AgNO_3$ to chromate	227
Penicillin	In phosphate buffer, pH 7, + NaOH; 30 min/room temp.	Neutralized and determined with excess iodine and back titration using thiosulphate (see Iodine reagents, ref. 266)	228
Alkylsilicon isothiocyanates	+ slightly less than equivalent of alkali	Completed titration with alkali to phenolphthalein	229
Methyl bromide in air	Passed through KOH/ ethanol; 2 h/room temp.	+ water + acetic acid and Br^- titrated with Ag^+ to eosin	230
Penicillin	+ NaOH; 30 min/30°	Made slightly acid and determined with excess iodine, back titrating with thiosulphate (see Iodine reagents, ref. 267)	231
Glutamine in blood or plasma	+ KOH/borax. Left overnight/38°	Ammonia diffused into excess H_2SO_4 and back titrated with NaOH	232
Monochloroacetic acid in wines, etc.	+ NaOH; 2 h/80°	+ HNO_3 + excess $AgNO_3$ back titrated with SCN^-	233
Saponification number of an olive oil	+ KOH/ethanol (study of conditions)	Unused titrated with HCl potentiometrically or to phenolphthalein	234
Vinyl acetate	+ NaOH/ethanol; 30 min/45–50°	Unused titrated with acid	235
Phenyl thioacetate, $C_6H_5SCOCH_3$	+ KOH/alcohol; 20 min/room temp., giving thiophenol	+ acetic acid + drops pyridine and titrated with iodine (see Part I, Iodine, ref. 63)	236
Penicillin	+ NaOH. Heated to boiling	Slightly acidified and determined with excess iodine (see Iodine reagents, ref. 273)	237
p,p′-DDT in crude DDT	+ KOH; 1 h/1–5°	+ HNO_3 + excess $AgNO_3$ and titrated with SCN^-	238
Malic acid in green tobacco leaves	+ NaOH; 3 h/130°, giving fumaric acid	+ water and precipitated as Hg(I) salt; oxidized to Hg(II) and determined with SCN^- (see Mercury (I), ref. 2)	239

Materials titrated	Reagent and reaction conditions	Subsequent treatment and final titration stage	Ref.
Benzene hexachloride in pharmaceutical preparations	Refluxed 1 h with KOH/ethanol	+ HNO_3, trichlorobenzene extracted with ether and Cl^- determined argentometrically	240
p,p'-DDT	+ KOH/alcohol; 40 min/40°, giving one Cl^-	Cl^- determined with excess $AgNO_3$ and back titration with SCN^-	241
Tetraethylpyrophosphate	+ NaOH/water; 30 min/room temp.	Unused titrated with HCl to methyl red or potentiometrically	242
Saponification numbers of waxes	+ KOH/ethylene glycol + a little xylene; 2 h/130°	Titrated with HCl to thymolphthalein and then to bromophenol blue; difference equivalent to the organic acid	243
Alkyl silicon isocyanates and isothiocyanates	+ excess NaOH (isocyanates) or + slightly less than equivalent of alkali (isothiocyanates)	Unused titrated with HCl or titration completed with alkali	244
Ethylgermanium formate, acetate and mercaptoacetate	+ *ca* 95% expected amount of NaOH/ethanol; 5 min/room temp.	Titration completed to bromophenol blue, phenolphthalein or phenol red respectively	245
Urethane in body fluids	+ NaOH giving ethanol	Carried into excess bichromate/H_2SO_4 and unused determined iodometrically (see Bichromate and chromic oxide, ref. 152)	246
Acetates of hydroxyethylcellulose	+ KOH/ethanol/water; 48–72 h/room temp.	Unused titrated with acid	247
Mono- and dimethylolurea	In water, + NaOH/NaH_2PO_4;15–60 min reflux, giving HCHO	Determined with bisulphite (see Bisulphite and sulphite, ref. 97)	248
Saponification numbers	+ KOH/ethylcellosolve–xylene, 1:1; 10 min/*ca* 90°	Unused titrated with HCl/ethylcellosolve to thymolphthalein	249
Esters in tall oil	+ KOH/methanol; 3 h reflux	Unused titrated with acid to thymol blue/thymolphthalein	250
Saponification values	+ KOH/glycol/a little benzene; 2 h/130°	Titrated with HCl to thymolphthalein and then bromophenol blue; difference equivalent to the organic acid	251

Materials titrated	Reagent and reaction conditions	Subsequent treatment and final titration stage	Ref.
Na, Ca or procaine salt of penicillin	+ NaOH; 20 min/room temp.	Brought to pH 2–6·5 and determined with excess iodine (see Iodine reagents, ref. 278)	252
Dimethyl sulphate	+ NaOH; 90 min/room temp., giving $CH_3O.SO_3Na$	Unused titrated with HCl to bromocresol green	253
Proteins in cows' milk (chiefly from glutamine and asparagine)	+ $NaOH/BaCl_2$; 10 min distillation, giving ammonia	Distilled into excess H_2SO_4 and back titrated with NaOH to methyl red/methylene blue	254
Penicillin	+ NaOH; various conditions studied, e.g. 15 min/22° or 10 min/100°	Determined with excess iodine (conditions studied) (see Iodine reagents, ref. 279)	255
DDT in surface sprays, etc.	+ KOH/water; 30 min/room temp. Or + KOH/alcohol; 30 min reflux	Unused alkali titrated with acid to methyl orange	256
Methyl salicylate	+ KOH/ethanol; 30 min reflux	Acidified; the salicylic acid extracted with ether and titrated with NaOH to phenol red	257
DDT	+ KOH/ethanol; 25–30 min reflux, giving one Cl^-	Unused titrated with acid to phenolphthalein	258
Esters in presence of aldehydes	Latter reacted with NH_2OH, then + NaOH; 30 min/60°	Unused titrated with HCl to thymolphthalein	259
Penicillins in industrial cultures	Butanone extract + NaOH; 10 min/room temp.	Brought to pH 4 and determined with excess iodine (see Iodine reagents, ref. 281)	260
Acetyl groups in pectin	+ NaOH. Left till dissolved and 1 h more	+ $H_2SO_4/MgSO_4$, distilled and titrated with NaOH to phenol red	261
Chlordan	In petroleum ether, + KOH/alcohol; 30 min reflux	Cl^- determined with excess Ag^+ and back titration with SCN^-	262
Benzene hexachloride isomers in technical products	+ NaOH/methanol. Various reaction conditions. E.g. 20 min/100°, reacting with all isomers; 20 min/30°, reacting with α-, γ- and δ-isomers	Cl^- titrated with $HgSO_4$ to diphenylcarbazone; simultaneous equations gave concentrations of all isomers	263

Materials titrated	Reagent and reaction conditions	Subsequent treatment and final titration stage	Ref.
Penicillin from determination of procaine salt after precipitation of the procaine with molybdo- or tungstosilicic acid	Method of ref. 228	(see Iodine reagents, ref. 287)	264
Alkyl silicon iodides R_xSiI_{4-x}	+ excess NaOH/ethanol	Unused titrated with acid	265
Isomers of benzene hexachloride after chromatographic separation	+ KOH/alcohol; 10 min reflux	+ HNO_3 and titrated with $AgNO_3$ potentiometrically	266
Diacetone alcohol and other keto alcohols	+ NaOH; 1–2 h/room temp., giving ketone	Steam distilled into $NH_2OH.HCl$ reagent and titrated HCl set free (see Hydroxylamine, ref. 96)	267
2-Thenyl salicylate (a miticide)	+ KOH/alcohol; 2 h reflux	Unused titrated with HCl to phenolphthalein, phenolphthalein/thymol blue or potentiometrically	268
	Also + KOH/water; 30 min reflux	Salicylic acid determined with BrO_3^-/Br^- excess and iodometric back titration (see Bromine reagents, ref. 325)	
Ca or Zn resinates	+ excess alkali	Titrated with HCl to thymolphthalein and bromophenol blue as in method of ref. 251	269
Ethyl chloride	+ KOH/alcohol; 2 h reflux	Unused titrated with acid	270
Acetate ester from determination of hydroxyl groups by reaction with acetic anhydride	+ KOH/alcohol; 30 min reflux	Unused titrated with HCl to phenolphthalein	271
DDT + benzene hexachloride	Acetone extract + KOH/alcohol; 12 min reflux (parallel colorimetric determination of DDT alone)	+ HNO_3 + excess $AgNO_3$ and back titrated with SCN^-	272
Demethylated pectin	+ NaOH; 15 min	+ excess HCl and back titrated with NaOH to phenolphthalein	273

Materials titrated	Reagent and reaction conditions	Subsequent treatment and final titration stage	Ref.
Copolymers of methyl and allyl methacrylates	+ KOH/alcohol; 2 h reflux	Alcohol distilled out with steam and the allyl alcohol determined with excess BrO_3^- (see Bromine reagents, ref. 330)	274
Benzyl chloride	In ethanol/water, + NaOH/27% ethanol; 30 min reflux	Unused titrated with acid	275
Difficulty saponifiable esters, e.g. of rosin	+ KOH/diethylene glycol/phenetole, 92:8 (latter to increase solvent power and give a blanket of vapour excluding oxygen); 2 h reflux (*ca* 175°)	Unused titrated with HCl to tetrabromophenol blue or potentiometrically to pH 3·5	276
Acetate esters from determination of alcohols by reaction with acetic anhydride	Neutralized solution + NaOH/alcohol. At least 2 h reflux	Unused titrated with H_2SO_4 to cresol red/thymol blue	277
Methyl nitrate	+ CH_3OK; 1 h/room temp., then 1 h reflux	Nitrate reduced to ammonia with Devarda's alloy and determined by acid titration	278
Esters (saponification numbers) (micro)	+ KOH/water, ethanol, ethylene glycol or diethylene glycol; 1 h/100° in sealed tubes	Unused titrated with HCl to cresol red/thymol blue	279
DDT	Various procedures to take out 1, 3 or 5 Cl^-, e.g. + Fe_2O_3/dil.NaOH, 30 min/250°; + KOH/ethylene glycol; 3 h/180°	Unused titrated with H_2SO_4 methyl orange Cl^- titrated with $AgNO_3$ potentiometrically	280
Esters from acetylation studies of corn starch, amylose and amylopectin	Methods of refs 131 and 161		281
Penicillin after preliminary extraction with amyl acetate	+ NaOH; 5 min/room temp.	Neutralized with HCl and determined with excess iodine (see Iodine reagents, ref. 296)	282
Methyl salicylate in liniment	+ KOH/ethanol	Ethanol evaporated, acidified, salicylic acid extracted with ether and titrated with alkali	283

Materials titrated	Reagent and reaction conditions	Subsequent treatment and final titration stage	Ref.
Halides (semimicro)	+ KOH/diethylene glycol; 3 h/150–160° in sealed tube	+ HNO_3 + nitrobenzene + excess $AgNO_3$ and back titrated with SCN^-	284
Bromoform in syrups and pills	Heated with solid NaOH	Br^- determined with excess Ag^+ and back titration with SCN^-	285
Anhydride + acid in lactic acid	+ NaOH; 20–30 min/ room temp.	Unused titrated with acid to phenolphthalein	286
p,p'-DDT in DDT emulsions	+ KOH/methanol; 40 min/40°	+ HNO_3, extracted with water and Cl^- determined with excess Ag^+ and back titration with SCN^-	287
Acetyl groups in cellulose acetate	+ 75% ethanol (heated 30 min/50–60°) + NaOH; 15 min/50°, then 48 h/room temp.	+ slight excess HCl; left overnight and back titrated with alkali	288
Aralkyl sulphonates	Fused with alkali at 350°	Dissolved in water, neutralized and phenols determined with excess bromine and iodometric back titration (see Bromine reagents, ref. 339)	289
3-(*p*-Chlorophenyl)-1,1-dimethylurea	+ KOH/water/ethanol/ glycerol; 2·5 h reflux, giving dimethylamine	Distilled into excess HCl and back titrated with alkali potentiometrically	290
Esters (semimicro)	+ NaOH; 30 min/60° in sealed tube	Unused titrated with HCl to phenolphthalein, thymolphthalein or thymol blue	291
Ethyl ester of phenylcarbamic acid	+ KOH/ethanol, giving aniline	Acidified and titrated with nitrite	292
Methyl bromide	+ NaOH/methanol; 15 min/*ca* 0°, then 1 h/55°	Br^- determined with excess Ag^+ and back titration with SCN^-	293
Benzoyl groups	+ NaOH/water/ pyridine; 5 h/140–150°; or + C_2H_5ONa/ ethanol/pyridine; 5 h/110–120°	Acidified, extracted benzoic acid with $CHCl_3$ and titrated with CH_3ONa to thymol blue	294
1,1-Bis-(*p*-ethoxyphenyl)-2-(bromophenyl) ethylene	Heated with Na_2CO_3	Br^- determined argentometrically	295

Materials titrated	Reagent and reaction conditions	Subsequent treatment and final titration stage	Ref.
Phthalic anhydride	+ KOH/ethanol; 15 min/70–75°	+ ether, neutralized to phenolphthalein with oleic acid, the potassium hydrogen phthalate filtered and determined with excess permanganate (see Permanganate, ref. 111)	296
Phthalate esters in propellant powders	Extract with methylene chloride saponified with KOH	Acidified with phosphoric acid, the phthalic acid extracted with ether and titrated with alkali	297
Methylenesalicylic acid	+ NaOH, giving salicylaldehyde	Determined with excess BrO_3^- and iodometric back titration	298
Amides in plant extracts (e.g. asparagine, glutamine)	+ alkali; 2–4 min heating, giving ammonia	Absorbed in boric acid and titrated with H_2SO_4	299
Proteins	Heated with NaOH/sodium acetate, giving ammonia	Absorbed in excess H_2SO_4 and back titrated with alkali	300
Chloramphenicol	Fused with K_2CO_3/Na_2CO_3	+ HNO_3 + excess $AgNO_3$ and back titrated with SCN^-	301
Monobromoacetic acid in musts, fruit juices	+ KOH/ether/water; added MgO to water layer, evaporated to dryness and heated 2 h/475°	Br^- oxidized with OCl^- at pH 6·5 to BrO_3^- and determined by adding I^-/acid and titrating with thiosulphate	302
Dichloro- or chlorobromoethane in air	Absorbed in ethanol, NaOH added and heated	Hal^- determined with excess Ag^+ and back titration with SCN^-	303
Acetyl groups in pectic substances	+ NaOH; 3 h/room temp.	Acidified, the acetic acid extracted and titrated with alkali	304
Esters in ethanol	+ NaOH; 1 h/room temp.	Unused titrated with H_2SO_4	305
Amide nitrogen in collagen and other proteins.	Heated to 70° with 2N NaOH, giving NH_3	Absorbed in boric acid and titrated at intervals during 6 h. Extrapolated straight line part to $t = 0$	306

Materials titrated	Reagent and reaction conditions	Subsequent treatment and final titration stage	Ref.
N,*N'*-Dibenzylethylenediaminedibenzylpenicillin	+ NaOH 10 min/room temp.	Neutralized and determined with excess iodine (see Iodine reagents, ref. 322)	307
Belladonna alkaloids	+ excess alkali. Boiled, giving tropic acid	Unused titrated with acid to phenolphthalein	308
Saponification values of drying oil products, e.g. copolymers with styrene or cyclopentadiene	+ $KOH/n\text{-}C_4HO_9H/$ 5% water	Unused titrated with acid	309
Acetyl, benzoyl groups	Heated with NaOH/ethanol	Passed through Amberlite IR-120 and titrated the organic acid in the effluent with NaOH	310
Acetyl groups, e.g. in carbohydrate derivatives	+ NaOH/methanol; 20 min/130–140°, then distilling out methanol	+ H_2SO_4 and the acetic acid distilled and titrated with NaOH	311
Benzyl benzoate + dibutyl phthalate	+ NaOH/ethanol; 1 h reflux	Unused titrated with H_2SO_4 potentiometrically	312
(combined with light absorption data, giving value for each)			
Trichloroethane in dichloroethane	+ $Ba(OH)_2$/methanol; 2–2·5 h/30–40° (latter reacts negligibly)	Unused titrated with HCl to methyl orange	313
Alkyl phthalates after separation from nitro compounds in propellants by reduction of latter with Ti(III) and extraction of former with petroleum ether	Evaporated extract + KOH/ethanol; 45 min reflux	Unused titrated with HCl to phenolphthalein	314
Dialdehyde content of periodate oxystarches	+ NaOH; 1 min/100°	+ excess H_2SO_4 and back titrated with alkali to phenolphthalein or potentiometrically	315
Rosin esters	+ KOH/n-hexyl alcohol/hydrazine hydrate (to give colourless solutions)	+ ethanol or isopropanol and titrated with HCl to phenolphthalein	316
Dibutyl phthalate in propellants	Evaporated ether extract + NaOH/ethanol; 45 min reflux	Unused titrated with HCl to thymol blue	317

Materials titrated	Reagent and reaction conditions	Subsequent treatment and final titration stage	Ref.
Diketopiperazines in polycondensation products of α-amino acids	+ NaOH; 1 h/40°, giving dipeptides	Titrated with $CuSO_4$ to colour change from red-violet to blue (see Part I, Copper (II), ref. 114)	318
Glyoxal in presence of glyoxylic acid	In water, + excess NaOH; 10 min/room temp.	Unused titrated with H_2SO_4 to phenolphthalein	319
γ-Benzene hexachloride in dusts, etc.	In ethanol, + KOH/alcohol. Two determinations with 13–17 and with 50 min/room temp.	+ HNO_3 + excess $AgNO_3$ and unused titrated with SCN^-; difference equivalent to γ-form	320
Chloroform; chloral	+ NaOH; refluxed or in cold respectively	Cl^- determined with excess Ag^+ and back titration with SCN^-; or unused alkali titrated with HCl	321
Chlorobutanol	+ NaOH/water/ethanol; 15 min reflux	+ HNO_3 and Cl^- titrated with $Hg(NO_3)_2$ to turbidity with nitroprusside indicator	322
'Altax' (dibenzothiazole disulphide) in the air of industrial plants	+ excess NaOH	Unused titrated with acid to phenolphthalein	323
Heptylpenicillin	+ NaOH; 15 min/room temp.	Determined with excess iodine at pH 6, using back titration with thiosulphate (see Iodine reagents, ref. 331)	324
Dichloroethane	+ KOH/water/ethanol; 2 h/125° under pressure	Cl^- determined with excess Ag^+ and back titration with SCN^-	325
Nitriles, amides	+ 40% NaOH, giving ammonia	Distilled into excess H_2SO_4 and back titrated with alkali	326
Benzene hexachloride from sprayed surfaces	In acetone, + KOH/alcohol; 15 min reflux	+ HNO_3 + excess $AgNO_3$; 15 min/100°, filtered and unused titrated with SCN^-	327
Dialkylphosphites, $(RO)_2PH{=}O$	In ethanol, + NaOH, giving Na monoalkylphosphites, $RO.PH(=O)O^-$	Unused titrated with HCl to phenolphthalein	328

Materials titrated	Reagent and reaction conditions	Subsequent treatment and final titration stage	Ref.
Chromones	+ excess NaOH/ethanol, splitting pyrone ring giving acid + ketone	Unused alkali titrated with acid	329
Methyl bromide in food	Passed into NaOH/H_2O_2	Br^- titrated with Ag^+ to brilliant yellow	330
3,5,5-Trimethylcyclohexyl mandelate ('Cyclospasmol')	In ethanol, + KOH/ethanol; 2 h reflux	Unused titrated with HCl	331
Benzene hexachloride on surfaces	Extract in ethanol, + NaOH; 15 min reflux	Unused titrated with HCl potentiometrically	332
Ethyl acetate from determination of ethanol by reaction with acetic anhydride	+ excess NaOH	Unused titrated with acid	333
Vinyl acetate in copolymer with vinyl chloride	In dioxan, + C_2H_5ONa; 1 h reflux in nitrogen atmosphere	+ H_2SO_4 + Ag_2SO_4 and the acetic acid distilled and titrated with NaOH to phenolphthalein	334
End carboxyl groups in polycaprolactam (precipitated from phenol solution with 96% ethanol)	+ excess KOH/KCl or NaOH/NaCl; 10–20 min/room temp.	Unused titrated with acid	335
Glyoxal	+ excess NaOH; 8 min/room temp.	+ HCl equivalent to the original NaOH and titrated with NaOH to phenol red	336
Saponification number of petroleum tar fractions	In benzene/ethanol, 2:5, + KOH/ethanol; 1 h reflux	Unused titrated with HCl/ethanol potentiometrically	337
Urea/HCHO resins in mixtures with melamine/HCHO resins	+ KOH/ethylene glycol; 1 h reflux, giving ammonia	Aspirated into excess H_2SO_4 and back titrated with NaOH to methyl purple	338
Methylene chloride in aqueous solutions	+ NaOH; 5 min heating in Parr-type bomb	+ H_2SO_4 and titrated with $AgNO_3$ to chromate	339
Pyramidone	Heated with NaOH/$KMnO_4$, giving dimethylamine	Distilled into excess HCl or H_2SO_4 and back titrated with NaOH to phenolphthalein	340

Materials titrated	Reagent and reaction conditions	Subsequent treatment and final titration stage	Ref.
Acetate esters from determination of ethylene glycol or methyl cellosolve by reaction with acetic anhydride	+ excess NaOH	Unused titrated with acid	341
Penicillin	+ NaOH; 30 min/50°	Determined with excess iodine (studied conditions) (see Iodine reagents, ref. 344)	342
Ester groups in polyesters, e.g. polyacrylates and polymethacrylates	In benzene/methanol, + KOH; 3–4 h/120–180° in sealed tube	Unused titrated with HCl to phenolphthalein	343
Linalool acetate from determination of linalool by reaction with acetic anhydride/acetyl chloride	+ excess alkali	Unused titrated with acid	344
Methyl or ethyl salicylate	Refluxed with KOH	Neutralized with H_2SO_4, excess ICl added and unused iodometrically determined (see Iodine chlorides, etc., ref. 92)	345
Esters of *p*-hydroxybenzoic acid	Hydrolysed with NaOH	Acidified and the aromatic acid determined with excess BrO_3^- and iodometric back titration (see Bromine reagents, ref. 428)	346
Thionyl groups in organic compounds, e.g. O←S(O—C—)(O—C—)	+ KOH; 1 h reflux, giving K_2SO_3	+ phosphoric acid and SO_2 distilled into excess iodine; back titrated with thiosulphate	347
Esters or chlorides of oxalic acid monoesters	+ NaOH/ethanol; 1 h reflux	+ acetic acid/sodium acetate and precipitated with Ca^{2+} excess; unused determined by titration with EDTA to eriochrome black (see Calcium (II), ref. 33)	348
Amides	+ KOH/alcohol; 1·5–4 h reflux	Unused titrated with acetic acid to thymolphthalein or potentiometrically	349

Materials titrated	Reagent and reaction conditions	Subsequent treatment and final titration stage	Ref.
Methyl phenyl-malonate in presence of methyl phenylethyl-malonate	In ethanol, + NaOH; 30 min/room temp. (second ester negligibly hydrolysed)	Unused titrated with H_2SO_4 to phenolphthalein	350
Dibromoethane in fumigated fruit	Extract in benzene, + NaOH/benzene/ethanol. Refluxed	Br^- determined by oxidation to BrO_3^- and iodometric titration	351
Esters of thiophos-phoric acid	In acetone, + NaOH; 90 min reflux	Solvent evaporated, Br^-/HCl/excess BrO_3^- added and unused determined iodo-metrically	352
Higher aldehydes in presence of ketones and fatty acids	+ excess NaOH + H_2O_2; 30–60 min/100°	+ ethanol and unused titrated with HCl to phenolphthalein	353
Amides	+ NaOH. Some re-fluxed 30 min–2 h	Ammonia or amine distilled into excess HCl and back titrated with alkali	354
Phthalate esters in propellants (after reduction of nitro and nitrate groups with Zn dust/acetic acid)	+ KOH/ethanol; 1 h/60–70°	+ ether, potassium hydrogen phthalate filtered and titrated with $HClO_4$ in acetic acid (see Part I, Perchloric acid, ref. 194)	355
Acetyl groups in fish oil	+ KOH/ethanol. Refluxed	Passed through ion exchanger, Diaion BK, giving acetic acid; titrated with alkali (see Ion exchangers, ref. 22)	356
Butyl acetate in water	+ excess NaOH; 40 min reflux	Unused titrated with H_2SO_4	357
Methyl salicylate in medicinal preparations	+ NaOH; 15 min reflux	Salicylic acid determined by adding HCl/Br^-/excess BrO_3^- and titrating unused iodometrically (see Bromine reagents, ref. 442)	358
Coumarin	In ethanol, + NaOH + some HgO; 15 min shaking/room temp.	Unused titrated with acid	359
Some alkyl halides and phosphorus- and sulphur-containing esters	+ C_3H_7ONa/propanol, KOH/propanol or KOH/methanol; 1 h reflux	Passed through Dowex 50 ion exchanger and titrated effluent acid with NaOH (see Ion exchangers, ref. 24)	360

Materials titrated	Reagent and reaction conditions	Subsequent treatment and final titration stage	Ref.
Pyrazine carboxamide	Heated with KOH giving ammonia	Distilled into excess acid and back titrated with alkali	361
Nicotinic and iso-nicotinic nitriles	Heated with NaOH, giving ammonia	Distilled into excess HCl and back titrated with alkali	362
Unsaturated polyesters, e.g. polyacrylates, poly-methacrylates	In acetone, + NaOH; stirred until saponified	Neutralized with HCl, acetone evaporated and residue determined with excess MnO_4^-; also determined by method of ref. 184, Bromine reagents	363
Acetyl groups in carbohydrates; amides, e.g. acetanilide	Best with 4–5N NaOH/methanol (33%); 30 min reflux	Acidified, the acetic acid distilled and titrated with alkali	364
1-Nitroso-1-methylurea	+ NaOH until no more evolution of diazomethane	Unused titrated with H_2SO_4 to phenolphthalein	365
$H_2NCON(NO)CH_3 + NaOH \rightarrow NaCNO + CH_2N_2 + 2\,H_2O$			
Dichloroacetaldehyde	+ excess KOH/ethanol; 3–4 h/100° in a closed bottle	(a) Unused alkali titrated with acid (b) Cl^- titrated with $AgNO_3$	366
Di- and trichloro-acetaldehyde	+ excess KOH. Conditions as in ref. 366	(a) Unused alkali titrated with acid (b) Cl^- titrated with $AgNO_3$	367
(in combination with colorimetric determination of CCl_3CHO)			
Malachite green	In water, + NaOH; 20 min/room temp., giving precipitate of the carbinol base	Product dissolved in H_2SO_4 and titrated with Ce(IV) potentiometrically (see Part I, Cerium (IV), ref. 66)	368, 391
Penicillin	+ NaOH; 20–30 min/room temp.	Neutralized with H_2SO_4, acetate buffer added and determined with excess iodine (see Iodine reagents, ref. 368)	369
Ethyl acetate from determination of acetyl groups in aspirin and other medicines by trans-esterification with ethanol/H_2SO_4	+ KOH/alcohol; 30 min reflux	Unused titrated with H_2SO_4	370

Materials titrated	Reagent and reaction conditions	Subsequent treatment and final titration stage	Ref.
Neostigmine bromide and methyl sulphate, $(CH_3)_3\overset{+}{N}—C_6H_4—O—CON(CH_3)_2$ Br^- or $CH_3SO_4^-$	In water, + NaOH, giving dimethylamine	Distilled into excess HCl and back titrated with KOH to methyl red	371
Saponins in horse chestnuts	Extract in methanol, + NaOH/methanol. Evaporated down, giving salt of aescinol	Dissolved in water and aescinol precipitated with HCl (5 min/40°); filtered and and titrated with NaOH to phenolphthalein	372
Anhydrides, lactones	In methanol or ethanol, + excess NaOH. Brought to boiling	Unused titrated with acid to to phenolphthalein	373
5-(Sodium acetylsulphonamido)-3,4-dimethylisoxazole	+ excess alkali	Unused titrated with acid	374
Phthivazide (isonicotinic acid vanillin hydrazone)	Dissolved in excess NaOH	Unused titrated with HCl to thymolphthalein	375
Saponification numbers	In benzene, + KOH/ethanol; 2 h reflux	Passed through Amberlite IR 120(H) ion exchanger and titrated effluent acid with KOH potentiometrically	376
Diamox (2-acetylamino-1,3,4-thiadiazole-5-sulphonamide)	+ NaOH; 30 min reflux	+ excess BrO_3^-/Br^- + acid and back titrated iodometrically (see Bromine reagents, ref. 465)	377
Nitriles	+ excess KOH + H_2O_2; 5 min/room temp., then warmed and partly evaporated	Unused titrated with H_2SO_4 to phenolphthalein	378
Ester from determination of camphene by reaction with $HCOOH/H_2SO_4$	+ excess KOH/ethanol; 1 h reflux	Unused titrated with H_2SO_4	379
Primary amino alkyl alkoxy silane coatings on glass	Fused with KOH, giving ammonia	Absorbed in boric acid and titrated with HCl to methyl red	380

Materials titrated	Reagent and reaction conditions	Subsequent treatment and final titration stage	Ref.
Carbamoyl groups (—NH_2CO— ⇌ NH=C(OH)—), e.g. in urecoline	In pyridine, + excess CH_3ONa/pyridine/ benzene/methanol; 1 h reflux	Unused titrated with benzoic acid to thymol blue	381
α,β-Unsaturated esters	+ KOH; 5–60 min/room temp.	Neutralized and salt determined by adding excess bromine/NaBr/methanol and back titrating iodometrically (see Bromine reagents, ref. 469)	382
Esters of amino alcohols	+ excess NaOH. Distilled	Titrated unused alkali and distillate with acid	383
Saponification numbers of oils (semimicro)	+ KOH/ethanol; 30 min reflux	Titrated with HCl/ethanol potentiometrically; difference between the two inflection points equivalent to the organic salt	384
Acetyl groups	Method of ref. 80, half automatized		385
Bromural (α-bromoisovalerylurea); carbromal (α-bromodiethylacetylurea)	Refluxed with NaOH	Heated with H_2O_2, weakly acidified with acetic acid and titrated coulometrically with Ag^+	386
Acetylated dark coloured fats	Refluxed with KOH/ethanol	+ excess HCl + petroleum ether; refluxed and aqueous layer titrated with NaOH	387
Phenoxymethylpenicillin	Method of ref. 177	(See Iodine reagents, ref. 378)	388
Proteins in food products	+ NaOH/Na acetate. Heated to *ca* 325°, giving ammonia	Passed into excess H_2SO_4 and back titrated with alkali to methyl orange	389
DDT (extracted from surfaces)	+ NaOH/ethanol; 15 min/room temp. for *p,p′*-compound; 10 min reflux for total	+ water + H_2SO_4 + excess $AgNO_3$ and unused titrated with NaCl potentiometrically	390
Acetyl groups, e.g. in acetylated sugars	Solution or suspension in dry methanol, + $KOCH_3$, reacting: $RCOCH_3 + KOCH_3 \rightarrow RC(CH_3)(OK)OCH_3$, then reacting with methanol giving RH + $CH_3COOCH_3 + KOCH_3$	+ water, hydrolysing the methyl acetate; back titrated unreacted base with HCl	392

Materials titrated	Reagent and reaction conditions	Subsequent treatment and final titration stage	Ref.
Penicillin	+ NaOH	Determined with excess iodine (see Iodine reagents, ref. 415)	393, 432
Penicillin in fermented broth samples	+ NaOH	Determined with excess iodine (see Iodine reagents, refs 380, 416)	394, 433
Tolbutamide $\left(\begin{array}{c} CH_3—C_6H_4—SO_2—NH \\ \vert \\ n\text{-}C_4H_9—NH—CO \end{array}\right)$	+ acetone + NaOH 2 min/ room temp.	Filtered, neutralized filtrate + excess Ag^+ and back titrated with SCN^-	395
4-Methyluracil	In water/acetone, + excess KOH	Unused titrated with HCl	396
Penicillin	Discussion of factors affecting the alkali/iodine method		397
Chloramphenicol	Heated with NaOH/ Na_2CO_3	+ water + HNO_3 + excess $AgNO_3$ and back titrated with SCN^- in presence of nitrobenzene	398
Glyoxals	+ NaOH/water/ methanol; 90 min reflux	Unused titrated with HCl potentiometrically	399
also bisulphite compounds of glyoxals		+ slight excess HCl,H_2O_2 added to oxidize to SO_4^{2-} (gave sharper end-point) and titrated with NaOH potentiometrically	
Acetyl and butyryl groups in cellulose acetobutyrate	+ KOH/ethanol; 72 h/room temp. or 15 h/40°	+ phosphoric acid, organic acids steam distilled out and titrated with KOH to phenolphthalein (combined with oxidation with bichromate)	400
Ichthyol in ointments and candles	Distilled with 50% NaOH, giving NH_3	Distilled into H_2SO_4 and back titrated with alkali	401
Ester from determination of acid chlorides by reaction with ethanol	Neutralized solution + NaOH; 1 h reflux	Unused titrated with H_2SO_4	402, 424

Materials titrated	Reagent and reaction conditions	Subsequent treatment and final titration stage	Ref.
Isophthalic and other dibasic acids in modified alkyd resins	In benzene, + KOH/ methanol or ethanol; 1–1·5 h reflux	+ more benzene, left 30 min/ ordinary temp. and dipotassium salts filtered; dissolved in glycol, excess HCl/ethanol added and back titrated with KOH/ methanol to *m*-cresol purple (volume between first and second colour changes)	403
Chlorendic acid in alkyd resins used in fire-retardant paint	In benzene, + KOH/ isopropanol; 1 h reflux giving precipitate of dipotassium salt	Precipitate + 1:1 H_2SO_4/ H_2O, freed acid extracted with ether and titrated with KOH/ methanol to *m*-cresol purple	404
Cellulose acetobutyrate	+ alkali/ethanol; 72 h/room temp.	Filtered, dissolved in water, passed through ion-exchanger to give the free fatty acids; titrated with alkali	405
Benzonaphthol	Saponified with alcoholic KOH	β-Naphthol determined by titration in acid solution with ICl/HCl (amperometrically) (see Part I, Iodine monochloride, ref. 20)	406
Penicillin in urine	Extract + alkali; 30 min/room temp., giving penicillinamine	Acidified with HCl, heated 1 h, borate buffer pH 9·23 added and titrated amperometrically with $HgCl_2$ (see Part I, Mercury (II), ref. 75)	407
Saponification numbers of waxes	In xylene/ethanol or isopropanol 1:1, + KOH/methanol	Back titrated with HCl to fluorescence indicators (e.g. β-methylumbelliferone) or to phenolphthalein (for comparison)	408
4-Acetamido-*N*-lauroyl-1-naphthalene-sulphonamide ('PANS')	+ NaOH; 30 min boiling	+ HCl + Br^- and determined by adding excess nitrite at 0° and back titration with sulphanilic acid to external starch/I^- (see Nitrite, ref. 27)	409
2,4-Dichloro-6-(*o*-chloroanilino)-*s*-triazine; cyanuric chloride	+ NaOH; 10 min reflux, hydrolysing 2 and 3 chlorine atoms respectively	Cl^- titrated with $AgNO_3$ potentiometrically	410

Materials titrated	Reagent and reaction conditions	Subsequent treatment and final titration stage	Ref.
Penicillin G or its Na salt	+ NaOH; 30 min/ room temp., giving penicillinamine (with —SH group)	+ HCl + NaN_3 + excess iodine; back titrated with arsenite after 1 min reaction; amount of mercapto compound read from a calibration curve (see Iodine reagents, ref. 399)	411
Saponification values of essential oils	+ KOH/alcohol; 2 h reflux	Back titrated with HCl to phenolphthalein	412
J acid–urea addition product	Refluxed 3 h with NaOH, giving salt of J acid (6-amino-1-naphthol-3-sulphonic acid)	+ HCl + Na *m*-xylene-sulphonate and titrated with nitrite potentiometrically or to starch/I^- (see Part I, Nitrite, ref. 138)	413
Acetyl groups in acetylated polyvinyl alcohol	+ KOH/n-propanol; 5 min boiling, then 2–3 h at room temp. and finally 30 min boiling	Warm liquid titrated with HCl to phenolphthalein	414
$CHCl_3$ (in presence of CCl_4 and CH_2Cl_2)	+ aqueous KOH; 6 h reflux or left overnight/ room temp.	Cl^- determined with excess $AgNO_3$ back titrating with SCN^-	415
BHC in mixture with DDT	Evaporated ether extract + KOH/ alcohol, giving trichlorobenzene	Extracted with petroleum ether, decomposed with Na /butanol the Cl^- titrated with $AgNO_3$ (see Metals, ref. 99)	416
Ethyl acetate	In alcohol/water (studied effect of hydrolysis conditions with alkali)	Back titrated with acid to to bromothymol blue	417
Milk proteins	Heated with NaOH, giving ammonia	Distilled out and titrated with acid	418
Diacetyl	+ excess NaOH + excess H_2O_2; 5 min/*ca* 40°	Back titrated with H_2SO_4 to thymol blue	419
Penicillins (natural and synthetic)	Method of ref. 237	(see Iodine reagents, ref. 408)	420
Some organophosphorus fluoridate and pyroester compounds, e.g. GB-Sarin, tetraethyl pyrophosphate	Rapidly neutralized solution (to methyl red/thymolphthalein) + excess NaOH; 2–5 min/room temp., hydrolysing the esters	Back titrated with HCl	421

Materials titrated	Reagent and reaction conditions	Subsequent treatment and final titration stage	Ref.
Penicillin in fermented media	Extract, + NaOH; 5 min/room temp.	+ slight excess HCl, then + iodine and titrated with thiosulphate after 5 min (see Iodine reagents, ref. 409)	422
4,7-Dichloroquinoline	+ $NaOCH_3$/dry methanol, replacing the 4-Cl atom by $—OCH_3$	Cl^- determined with excess $AgNO_3$, back titrating with SCN^-	423
3-Methylchromone	+ NaOH; 2 h reflux	Back titrated with acid to phenolphthalein	425
Nitrile moiety of copolymers of acrylonitrile and 5-vinyl-2-picoline	Hydrolysed with 40% KOH	NH_3 distilled into excess HCl and back titrated with alkali	426
Cresols	In acetone, + excess KOH/methanol	Back titrated with HCl/ methanol to high frequency end-point	427
N-(3,4,5-Trimethoxy-benzoyl)morpholine (Trioxazin)	+ 20% NaOH. Boiled 1 h, giving morpholine	Distilled out and titrated with HCl to methyl red	428
Penicillins	+ NaOH; 15 min/room temp.	+ slight excess HCl + acetate buffer, pH 4·6 + excess iodine; back titrated with thiosulphate (see Iodine reagents, ref. 410)	429
Primary and secondary nitro compounds, e.g. methyl, ethyl, iso-propyl, etc.	+ KOH/aqueous alcohol; 10 min/room temp.	+ HCl/I^- and titrated with thiosulphate	430
Methyl acetate from determination of acetate in acetylated polyformaldehyde via transesterification with HCl/methanol	+ excess NaOH; 2 h warming on water-bath	Cooled to −5°, excess HCl added and titrated with NaOH potentiometrically	431
Ethyl acrylate in mixture with acrylonitrile and dimethylformamide	+ KOH/ethanol; 5 min	Back titrated with HCl to phenolphthalein	434

Materials titrated	Reagent and reaction conditions	Subsequent treatment and final titration stage	Ref.
Vinyl acetate/vinyl chloride in copolymers	In tetrahydrofuran, + KOH/ethanol; 1–3 h/30°	Back titrated with H_2SO_4 to thymol blue; then + excess H_2SO_4 and Cl^- titrated with $AgNO_3$ potentiometrically or to chromate	435
Saponification equivalents of phenolic esters	+ NaOH/dioxan; at least 30 min reflux	+ excess HCl and back titrated with NaOH to phenol red or thymolphthalein	436
S-Alkylthioureas	+ NaOH + methanol if necessary and heated to boiling giving mercaptans	Titrated with *o*-hydroxy-mercuribenzoate to disappearance of blue of thio-fluorescein indicator	437
Saponification number of dark coloured fats and oils	+ KOH/alchohol; 1 h reflux, ether extracted, extract evaporated to dryness and residue again treated with KOH	Back titrated with HCl	438
Iodoform (containing ^{131}I)	+ KOH/isopentyl alcohol; 10 min/ 125–130°, then + KOH/ water and heated till alcohol layer clear	+ water, aqueous phase separated and I^- determined with excess Ag^+ and back titration with SCN^-	439
Xylenols in technical mixtures	Aliquot in acetone, + excess NaOH/methanol	Titrated with HCl/methanol to 'high frequency' end-points for excess NaOH and various xylenols	440
Chloroform	+ KOH/alcohol + toluene + acetone; 30 min reflux	+ HNO_3 + $AgNO_3$, filtered; filtrate + $K_2Ni(CN)_4$ + NH_4OH to pH 10 and liberated Ni^{2+} titrated with EDTA to murexide	441
Dimethylformamide in solutions or in textiles (preliminary extraction)	Aliquot + NaOH + water; distilled	Distilled dimethylamine into boric acid and titrated with HCl	442
Proteins in cheese (ether extract)	Boiled with NaOH, giving amino acids	+ HCHO at pH 8–8.5 and titrated with NaOH back to this pH (see Carbonyl compounds, ref. 30)	443

Materials titrated	Reagent and reaction conditions	Subsequent treatment and final titration stage	Ref.
Chloramphenicol	+ NaOH; 15 min boiling	+ HNO_3 + water, filtered and Cl^- in filtrate determined with excess Ag^+ and back titration with SCN^-	444
Trichloroethyl phosphate in pharmaceutical preparations	Aliquot of extract in pentyl alcohol, + KOH/ethanol; 2 h heating	+ HNO_3 + excess Ag^+ and back titrated with SCN^- to Fe(III)	445
Acetyl groups	Method of ref. 206, sometimes with more concentrated alkali for 24 h		446
1,2-Dibromoethane in air and as residue in fruits	+ NaOH/methanol; 15 min reflux (as in method of ref. 303)	+ HNO_3 and Br^- titrated coulometrically (method of ref. 351)	447
3,3-Di-(*p*-acetoxyphenyl) isatin	In KOH/ethanol, + conc. NaOH; 5–8 min, giving deacylation	Titrated potentiometrically with $Fe(CN)_6^{3-}$	448
Benzonitrile in by-products of coke production (in technical naphthalene)	+ NaOH; 45 min/140–145° in ampoule, giving NH_3	Absorbed in H_2SO_4 and back titrated with NaOH	449
Penicillin, e.g. in pure aqueous solution	+ NaOH; 30 min, giving pencillinamine	+ equivalent amount of HCl, 1 h/100°, borate buffer added and titrated amperometrically with $HgCl_2$	450
Tertiary amyl halides from determination of *t*-amylenes in presence of other amylenes by addition of HCl	+ KOH/alcohol; 90 min reflux	Back titrated with HCl/ethanol to phenolphthalein	451
Reineckates of aliphatic amines	+ NaOH/K tartrate; 2–3 min heating, giving SCN^-	+ acetic acid and titrated with $AgNO_3$ to dichlorofluorescein	452
Hexachlorophene; pentachlorophenol	Fused with solid NaOH	Dissolved in water, + HNO_3 and ultimately titrated with Ag^+ to CrO_4^{2-}	453
Saponiflcation values of Indian rosins	+ KOH/ethanol; 30 min reflux	Back titrated with acid electrometrically or to thymol blue or to a fluorescence indicator	454
Meprobamate	Boiled with KOH/alcohol	Back titrated with HCl to phenolphthalein/alizarin yellow	455

Materials titrated	Reagent and reaction conditions	Subsequent treatment and final titration stage	Ref.
Total combined lactic acid in lactic acid glyceride	+ KOH/alcohol; refluxed	+ water, titrated with HCl to methyl red; excess HCl added, extracted with hexane and organic layer titrated with KOH to phenolphthalein	456
Higher fatty acids, e.g. lauric, oleic, stearic	+ excess $KOCH_3$/ benzene/methanol	Back titrated with oxalic acid/benzene/methanol to phenol red/cresol red/ bromothymol blue, 3: 1: 1 (claimed better end-point than in direct titration)	457, 472
Ethyl acetate and heptoic acid esters in brandy	+ NaOH; 2·5 h/20° (hydrolysing former); and + NaOH, 30 min reflux (hydrolysing all)	Back titrated with H_2SO_4 to phenolphthalein	458
Oxamide in cellulose nitrate base propellants	Extract in CH_2Cl_2 evaporated, + NaOH and distilled	NH_3 distilled into excess HCl and back titrated with NaOH to methyl red	459
Formate from determination of ethyl orthoformate by treatment with water	+ excess NaOH	Back titrated with acid	460
Chloroformate from determination of —OH in polymers by reaction with phosgene	In solvent from previous stage (benzene, dichloroethane or ethylene glycol dimethyl ether), + NaOH/ water or alcohol or + $[(C_4H_9)_4N]$ OH/tetrahydrofuran for hydrophobic samples; refluxed or stirred until completely dissolved	Cl^- titrated with $AgNO_3$ potentiometrically	461
Ethyl mercurichloride in technical products and fungicides	In dimethylformamide, + NaOH to thymolphthalein	Cl^- titrated with $AgNO_3$ to chromate	462
Mixtures of chlorendic and maleic acids and anhydrides	+ excess KOH: 30–50 min/60°	+ excess HCl + acetone and potentiometrically titrated with KOH; 4 jumps, unused HCl, first hydrogen of maleic acid, chlorendic acid and second hydrogen of maleic acid	463

(combined with treatment with aniline and titration with KOH and with $HClO_4$—see Amines and heterocyclic bases, ref. 108)

Materials titrated	Reagent and reaction conditions	Subsequent treatment and final titration stage	Ref.
1,1-Bis(*p*-chlorophenyl)-2,2,2-trichloroethanol (CPCA)	+ KOH/methanol; brought to boiling in 45 min	+ HNO_3 and determined with excess Ag^+ and back titration with SCN^-	464
Cyanuric chloride, $C_3N_3Cl_3$	+ 20% KOH; 15–20 min reflux	+ HNO_3 + Ag^+ excess and back titrated with SCN^-	465
Acetoacetic ester; phenylethylcyanoacetic ethyl ester; esters of carbonic acid	+ $Ba(OH)_2$; 30–60 min/ca 100°	+ HCl, CO_2 distilled into standard $Ba(OH)_2$ and back titrated with HCl to thymol blue	466
Combined total acyl group in cellulose acetate	In 75% ethanol, + NaOH in nitrogen current; 1 h/55–60°	Back titrated with HCl, then with NaOH to phenolphthalein	467
Dichloroethane in water	+ NaOH or $KOCH_3$/methanol; 10–20 min in ampoule	+ HNO_3 + $AgNO_3$ and back titrated with SCN^-	468
Lactic acid in lactylated mono-glycerides	Saponified with alkali	+ HCl, fatty acid extracted with petroleum ether; lactic acid extracted from the petroleum ether with water and titrated with alkali	469
Succinyl sulphathiazole	+ 20% NaOH; 2 h reflux	Acidified and titrated with nitrite	470
1-Phenylpropane-1,2-dione ('acetyl-benzoyl')	H_2O_2 + sample + excess NaOH; 2 h/ca 20°, giving acetic and benzoic acids	Back titrated with HCl to phenolphthalein	471
Carbromal [(α-bromo-α-ethylbutyryl)urea]; bromisoval [(α-bromo-isovaleryl)urea]	Boiled with alcoholic KOH	+ HNO_3 and Br^- titrated with $AgNO_3$ containing ^{110}Ag radiometrically	473
ε-Caprolactam in aqueous solution	+ NaOH; 30 min reflux, then evaporated down for 15 min	Amino acid precipitated as Ba salt, HCl added, then HCHO and titrated with NaOH to phenolphthalein or potentiometrically (see Barium(II), ref. 7; Carbonyl compounds, ref. 35)	474

Materials titrated	Reagent and reaction conditions	Subsequent treatment and final titration stage	Ref.
Amides	+ large excess NaOH; 15–30 min reflux	+ water, passed through Dowex 50W–X8 ion exchanger in acid form and titrated effluent potentiometrically with NaOH (see Ion exchangers, ref. 50)	475
Methoxyl end-groups in paraformaldehyde	+ N NaOH/water; *ca* 1 min (until dissolved, then negligible Cannizzaro reaction)	+ acetic acid and methanol determined by conversion to methyl nitrite, hydrolysis and iodometric titration (see Nitrite, ref. 31)	476
Hydroxyl end-groups in paraformaldehyde	In methanol, + $NaOCH_3$/methanol; *ca* 4 h	+ acetic acid and water formed titrated with the Karl Fischer reagent	477
Binary mixtures of amides or nitriles	+ tetrahydrofuran/water + NaOH	Ammonia carried by nitrogen current into boric acid at pH 4 and continuously titrated with HCl maintaining this pH; kinetic plot gave both components	478
Amide nitrogen in plant extracts	+ KOH/water; 30 min/90°	Distilled into boric acid and titrated with $KH(IO_3)_2$ to methyl red/methylene blue	479

References

1. Meyer, V. and Haffter, H., *Ber.* **6**, 600 (1873).
2. Koettstorfer, J., *Z. anal. Chem.* **18**, 199, 431 (1879).
3. Legler, L., *Ber.* **16**, 1333 (1883).
4. Benedikt, R. and Ulzer, F., *Monatsh.* **8**, 41 (1887).
5. Schmied, *Archiv. f. Pysiologie von DuBois-Raymond* 552 (1892) (abstract in *Z. anal. Chem.* **34**, 484 (1895)).
6. McIlhiney, P. C., *J. Am. Chem. Soc.* **16**, 408 (1894).
7. Henriques, R., *Z. angew. Chem.* **8**, 721 (1895).
8. Meyer, R. and Meyer, H., *Ber.* **28**, 2965 (1895).
9. Argenson, G., *Bull. soc. chim., Paris* (3) **15**, 1055 (1896).
10. Einhorn, O., *Z. anal. Chem.* **39**, 640 (1900).
11. Perkin, A. G., *Proc. Roy. Soc.* **20**, 171 (1904).
12. Perkin, A. G., *J. Chem. Soc.* **85**, 1462 (1904).
13. Meyer, R. and Hartmann, E., *Ber.* **38**, 3956 (1905).

14. Perkin, A. G., *J. Chem. Soc.* **87**, 107 (1905).
15. Pool, J. F. A., *Pharm. Weekblad* **42**, 165 (1905).
16. Nicloux, M., *Compt. rend.* **142**, 163 (1906).
17. Wallis, T. E., *Pharm. J.* (4) **22**, 162 (1906).
18. Boulez, V., *Bull. soc. chim. France* (4) **1**, 117 (1907).
19. Garnier, J., *Bull. sci. pharm. Nancy* **15**, 77 (1908).
20. Siegfeld, M., *Chem.-Ztg.* **32**, 1128 (1908).
21. Eberstadt, O., *Dissertation über Acetylcellulose*, Heidelberg, 1909.
22. Gane, E. H. and Webster, M. H., *Pharm. J.*, (4) **28**, 555 (1909).
23. Kreis, H., *Chem.-Ztg.* **35**, 1053 (1911).
24. Winkler, L. W., *Z. angew. Chem.* **24**, 636 (1911).
25. Normann, W., *Chem. Rev. Fett u. Harz Ind.* **19**, 205 (1912).
26. Hudson, C. S. and Brauns, D. H., *J. Am. Chem. Soc.* **37**, 1283, 2736 (1915).
27. Slack, H. F., *Chemist & Druggist* **87**, 673 (1915).
28. Neitzel, F., *Chem.-Ztg.* **43**, 500 (1919).
29. Pardee, A. M. and Reid, E. E., *Ind. Eng. Chem.* **12**, 129 (1920); ibid. (+ Hasche, R. L.) 481.
30. Salvaterra, H., *Chem.-Ztg.* **44**, 129 (1920).
31. Barnett, W. L., *J. Soc. Chem. Ind., London* **40**, 9T (1921).
32. Olivieri-Mandalà, E. and Calderaro, E., *Gazz. Chim. Ital.* **51**, I 324 (1921).
33. Sage, C. E., *Perfumery Essent. Oil Record* **13**, 172 (1922).
34. Wolff, H., *Chem. Umschau* **29**, 2, 10 (1922).
35. Freudenberg, K. and Harder, M., *Ann.* **433**, 230 (1923).
36. Glichitch, L. S., *Bull. soc. chim. France* (4) **33**, 1284 (1923).
37. Kolthoff, I. M., *Pharm. Weekblad* **60**, 2 (1923).
38. Boulez, V., *Bull. soc. chim. France* **35**, 419 (1924).
39. Bredig, G. and von Goldberger, A., *Gas u. Wasserfach* **67**, 490 (1934).
40. Kögl, F. and Postowsky, J. J., *Ann.* **440**, 34 (1924).
41. Reeves, H. G., *J. Soc. Chem. Ind., London* **43**, 279T (1924).
42. Freudenberg, K. and Weber, E., *Angew. Chem.* **38**, 280 (1925).
43. Wimmer, J., *Angew. Chem.* **38**, 721 (1925).
44. Andron, P., *Bull. soc. pharm. Bordeaux* **64**, 199 (1926).
45. Eder, R. and Kutter, F., *Helv. Chim. Acta* **9**, 557 (1926).
46. Kunz, A. and Hudson, C. S., *J. Am. Chem. Soc.* **48**, 1982 (1926).
47. Matthes, E. and Ziegenspeck, H., *Botan. Archiv* **15**, 187 (1926).
48. Borloz, A., *Helv. Chim. Acta* **10**, 543 (1927).
49. Semiganowski, N., *Z. anal. Chem.* **72**, 27, 295 (1927).
50. Allan, J., *Perfumery Essent. Oil Record* **19**, 131 (1928)
51. Andron, P., *J. pharm. chim.* (8) **8**, 453 (1928).
52. Fleury, P. and Malmy, M., *J. pharm. chim.* (8) **8**, 537 (1928).
53. François, M., *J. pharm. chim.* (8) **7**, 54 (1928).

54. Glaser, E., *Deutsch. Z. ges. gerichtl. Med.* **12**, 470 (1928).
55. Jánský, A., *Časopis Českoslov Lékárnictva* **8**, 215 (1928).
56. Langer, A., *Apotheker-Ztg.* **43**, 815 (1928).
57. Volmar, Y. and Samdahl, B., *J. pharm. chim.* **7**, 106 (1928).
58. Battegay, M. and Penche, J., *Bull. soc. chim. France* **45**, 132 (1929).
59. Gehrke, M. and Willrath, H. H., *Z. physik. Chem.* **A 142**, 301 (1929).
60. Heller, K. and Fleischhans, Z., *J. prakt. Chem.* **123**, 146 (1929).
61. Kettle, S., *Chemist-Analyst* **18**, 7 (1929).
62. Muraour, H., *Bull. soc. chim. France* **45**, 1189 (1929).
63. Schulek, E. and Vastagh, G., *Magyar Gyógyszerésztud. Társaság Értesitöje* **5**, 43 (1929).
64. Frahm, E. D. G. and Boogaert, H. L., *Rec. trav. chim.* **49**, 623 (1930).
65. Brindle, H., *Quart. J. Pharm. Pharmacol.* **4**, 394 (1931).
66. Chargaff, E., *Z. physiol. Chem.* **199**, 221 (1931).
67. Demarest, J. V. and Rieman, W., *Ind. Eng. Chem., Anal. Ed.* **3**, 15 (1931).
68. Marotta, D. and DiStefano, F., *Ann. chim. applicata* **21**, 150 (1931).
69. Murray, T. F., Staud, C. J. and Gray, H. le B., *Ind. Eng. Chem., Anal. Ed.* **3**, 269 (1931).
70. Ramírez, C., *Rev. quím.* **6**, No. 10, 6 (1931).
71. Sabetay, S. and Sivadjian, J., *J. pharm. chim.* **13**, 530 (1931).
72. Snesarev, A. P., *J. Chem. Ind. (Moscow)* **8**, 161 (1931).
73. Vollmar, R. C., *Ind. Eng. Chem., Anal. Ed.* **3**, 110 (1931).
74. Bickerman, J. J., *Z. anal. Chem.* **90**, 335 (1932).
75. Bredereck, H., *Angew. Chem.* **45**, 241 (1932).
76. Meunier, L. and Gonfard, M., *Rev. gén. mat. plastiques* **8**, 427, 467 (1932).
77. Whitmore, W. F., Weinberger, H. and Gardner, W. H., *Ind. Eng. Chem., Anal. Ed.* **4**, 48 (1932).
78. Beal, G. D. and Szalkowski, C. R., *J. Am. Pharm. Assoc.* **22**, 540 (1933).
79. Boulez, V., *Zymologie* (2) **1**, 170 (1933).
80. Kuhn, R. and Roth, H., *Ber.* **66**, 1274 (1933).
81. Palfray, L., Sabetay, S. and Sontag, D., *Chimie et industrie, spec. No.* **29**, 1037 (1933).
82. Romeo, G., *Ann. chim. applicata* **23**, 530 (1933).
83. Shchigol, M., *Pharm. Zentralhalle* **74**, 529 (1933).
84. Shchigol, M., *Khim.-Prom. Farm.* 150 (1933).
85. Bailey, A. J. and Robinson, R. J., *Mikrochemie* **15**, 233 (1934).
86. Ezrielev, I. M. and Soloveichik, L. S., *Plasticheskie Massui* No. 5, 27 (1934).
87. Fürth, O., Kaunitz, H. and Stein, M., *Biochem. Z.* **268**, 189 (1934).
88. Girault, F., *Bull. sci. pharmacol.* **41**, 331 (1934).
89. Goswami, M. and Basu, K. L., *Analyst* **59**, 533 (1934).

90. Hosking, H. J., Snell, F. D. and Biffen, F. M., *Ind. Eng. Chem., Anal. Ed.* **6**, 254 (1934).
91. Kotnitz'kii, A. I. and Bogatirchuk, S. V., *Ukrain. Khim. Zhur.* **9**, 317 (1934).
92. Matuszak, M. P., *Ind. Eng. Chem., Anal. Ed.* **6**, 374 (1934).
93. Palfray, L., Sabetay, S. and Sontag, D., *Chimie et industrie, Spec. No.* 863 (1934).
94. Phillips, M., *Ind. Eng. Chem., Anal. Ed.* **6**, 321 (1934).
95. Watts, C. E., *Ind. Eng. Chem., Anal. Ed.* **6**, 262 (1934).
96. Korzheniovskii, G. A. and Rekeda, Ya. N., *Zavodskaya Lab.* **4**, 768 (1935).
97. Alekseevskii, E. V. and Gol'braikh, Z. E., *J. Appl. Chem., USSR* **9**, 1535 (1936).
98. Bohanes A., *Chem. Obzor* **11**, 71 (1936).
99. Clark, E. P., *Ind. Eng. Chem., Anal. Ed.* **8**, 487 (1936); **9**, 539 (1937).
100. Gengrinovich, A. I., *Farm. Zhur.* No. 4, 26 (1936).
101. Sagpir, I. N. and Frolova, R. A., *Sintet. Kauchuk USSR* No. 11–12, 17 (1936).
102. Sinton, F. C., *J. Assoc. Offic. Agr. Chem.* **19**, 535 (1936).
103. Wolfrom, M. L., Konigsberg, M. and Salzberg, S., *J. Am. Chem. Soc.* **58**, 490 (1936).
104. Andreevskaya, G. D., *Farmatsiya i Farmakol.* No. 11–12, 57 (1937).
105. Redeman, C. E. and Lucas, H. J., *Ind. Eng. Chem., Anal. Ed.* **9**, 521 (1937).
106. Reznek, S., *J. Assoc. Offic. Agr. Chem.* **20**, 560 (1937).
107. Schwicker, A., *Z. anal. Chem.* **110**, 161 (1937).
108. Shestakov, I. S., *Kozhev. Obuv. Prom* **16**, No. 12 54 (1937).
109. Smith, W. C., *Ind. Eng. Chem., Anal. Ed.* **9**, 469 (1937).
110. Busbey, R. L. and Drake, N. L., *Ind. Eng. Chem., Anal. Ed.* **10**, 390 (1938).
111. Butschewitz, E. and Vlk, A., *Ann. chim. anal. chim. appl.* **20**, 175 (1938).
112. Furter, M., *Helv. Chim. Acta* **21**, 601 (1938).
113. Lazar, O. and Meyling, A. H., *J. S. African Chem. Inst.* **21**, 8 (1938).
114. Merz, K. W. and Krebs, K. G., *Ber.* **71**, 302 (1938).
115. Peynaud, E., *Ann. fals.* **31**, 158 (1938).
116. Reimers, F., *Dansk Tids. Farm.* **12**, 203 (1938).
117. Shaefer, W. E. and Piccard, J., *Ind. Eng. Chem., Anal. Ed.* **10**, 515 (1938).
118. Belenits'ka, D. S., *Farm. Zhur.* **12**, No. 1, 19 (1939).
119. Funck, E., *Süddeut. Apotheker-Ztg.* **79**, 622 (1939).
120. Jackerott, K. A. and Reimers, F., *Z. anal. Chem.* **117**, 415 (1939).
121. Khait, G. Ya., *Ukrain. Gosudarst. Inst. Eksptl. Farm. (Kharkov), Konsul'tatsionnye Materialy* No. 3, 80 (1939).

122. Krüger, D., *Z. anal. Chem.* **117**, 318 (1939).
123. Mel'nikov, F. F. and Senilov, B. V., *Lab. Prakt.* (*USSR*) **14**, No. 9–10 18 (1939).
124. Palfray, L., Sabetay, S. and Rovira, S., *Compt. rend.* **209**, 483 (1939).
125. Rovira, S., *Compt. rend.* **209**, 754 (1939).
126. Tropp, M. Ya., *Ukrain. Gosudarst. Inst. Eksptl. Farm.* (*Kharkov*), *Konsul'tatsionnye Materialy* No. 2, 40 (1939).
127. Archinard, P., *Ann. fals.* **33**, 76 (1940).
128. Goretskii, L. M., *Farmatsiya* No. **6**, 31 (1940).
129. Hall, R. T., Holcomb, J. H. and Griffin, D. B., *Ind. Eng. Chem., Anal. Ed.* **12**, 187 (1940).
130. Sol'ts, L. M. and Kolik, E. M., *Ukrain. Gosudarst. Inst. Eksptl. Farm* (*Kharkov*), *Konsul'tatsionnye Materialy* No. 5, 162 (1940).
131. Genung, L. B. and Mallatt, R. C., *Ind. Eng. Chem., Anal. Ed.* **13**, 369 (1941).
132. Kelly, D. F., O'Connor, M. and Reilley, J., *Analyst* **66**, 489 (1941).
133. Matchett, J. R. and Levine, J., *Ind. Eng. Chem., Anal. Ed.* **13**, 98 (1941).
134. Reimers, F., *Z. anal. Chem.* **122**, 404 (1941).
135. Schoorl, N., *Pharm. Weekblad* **78**, 413 (1941).
136. Schoorl, N., *Pharm. Weekblad* **78**, 433 (1941).
137. Thorsell, P., *Svensk Farm. Tidskr.* **45**, 341 (1941).
138. Baldinger, L. H., *Ind. Eng. Chem., Anal. Ed.* **14**, 15 (1942).
139. Böhme, H., *Arch. Pharm.* **280**, 89 (1942).
140. Caselli, P. and Cearanfi, E., *Biochem. Z.* **313**, 11 (1942).
141. McNall, F. J., *J. Assoc. Offic. Agr. Chem.* **25**, 814 (1942).
142. Malm, C. J., Nadeau, G. F. and Genung, L. B., *Ind. Eng. Chem., Anal. Ed.* **14**, 292 (1942).
143. Perry, H. M. and West, T. F., *Analyst* **67**, 159 (1942).
144. Poethke, W., *Pharm. Zentralhalle* **83**, 1, 13 (1942).
145. Russo, F., *Ann. chim. applicata* **32**, 216 (1942).
146. Silver, S. D., Ferguson, R. L., McGrath, F. P. and Saldick, J., *War Dept., Chem. Warfare Service, Edgewood Arsenal, Md., EATR* 374 April 1942.
147. Shrader, S. A., Stenger, V. A. and Beshgetoor, A. W., *Ind. Eng. Chem., Anal. Ed.* **14**, 1 (1942).
148. Wiesenberger, E., *Mikrochemie ver. Mikrochim. Acta* **30**, 241 (1942).
149. Wilson, J. B., *J. Assoc. Offic. Agr. Chem.* **25**, 145 (1942).
150. Cowles, R. A., Ratcliffe, K., Miller, C. O. and Kelmme, C. J., *Proc. Am. Pharm. Mfrs. Assoc., Mid-year proc.* p. 64, 1943.
151. Cramer, F. B., Gardner, T. S. and Purves, C. B., *Ind. Eng. Chem., Anal. Ed.* **15**, 319 (1943).
152. Mallory, G. E. and Love, R. F., *Ind. Eng. Chem., Anal. Ed.* **15**, 207 (1943).

153. Olsen, S., *Die Chemie* **56**, 202 (1943).
154. Palfray, L. and Desseigne, G., *Compt. rend.* **217**, 213 (1943).
155. Rieman, W., *Ind. Eng. Chem., Anal. Ed.* **15**, 325 (1943).
156. Whistler, R. L. and Jeanes, A., *Ind. Eng. Chem., Anal. Ed.* **15**, 317 (1943).
157. Ferreira, C., *Anais fac. farm. odontol., Univ. Sao Paulo* **4**, 218 (1944–5).
158. Gorbach, G., *Anal. Mikrochem.* **31**, 319 (1944)
159. Lindeken, C. L., Clayton, J. O. and Skoog, D. A., *Ind. Eng. Chem., Anal. Ed.* **16**, 734 (1944).
160. Lubatti, O. F. and Harrison, A., *J. Soc. Chem. Ind., London* **63**, 140 (1944).
161. Malm, C. J., Genung, L. B., Williams, R. F. and Pile, M. A., *Ind. Eng. Chem., Anal. Ed.* **16**, 501 (1944).
162. Mitchell, J. Smith, D. M. and Money, F. S., *Ind. Eng. Chem., Anal Ed.* **16**, 410 (1944).
163. de Mittelman, D. G., *Anales asoc. quím. arg.* **32**, 84 (1944).
164. Petersen, G. W. and Radke, H. H., *Ind. Eng. Chem., Anal. Ed.* **16**, 63 (1944).
165. Sclar, R. N. and Clark, G. R., *J. Assoc. Offic. Agr. Chem.* **27**, 472 (1944).
166. Vais, O., *Chem. Listy* **38**, 15 (1944).
167. Archibald, R. M., *J. Biol. Chem.* **158**, 347 (1945).
168. Bruening, C. F., *J. Assoc. Offic. Agr. Chem.* **28**, 620 (1945).
169. Clarke, R. and Christensen, B. E., *Ind. Eng. Chem., Anal. Ed.* **17**, 334 (1945).
170. Ferreira, P. C. and Tucci, W., *Rev. quim. farm. (Rio de Janeiro)* **10**, No. 8 9 (1945).
171. Gunther, F. A., *Ind. Eng. Chem., Anal. Ed.* **17**, 149 (1945).
172. Hills, C. H., Ogg, C. L. and Speiser, R., *Ind. Eng. Chem., Anal. Ed.* **17**, 507 (1945).
173. Lewis, S. E., *J. Soc. Chem. Ind., London* **64**, 57 (1945).
174. Powning, R. F., *J. Council Sci. Ind. Research* **18**, 121 (1945).
175. Ubeda, F. B. and Puig, P. M., *Anales fis. y quim. (Madrid)* **41**, 518 (1945).
176. Wilson, J. B., *J. Assoc. Offic. Agr. Chem.* **28**, 302 (1945).
177. Alicino, J. F., *Ind. Eng. Chem., Anal. Ed.* **18**, 619 (1946).
178. Carter, R. H. and Hubanks, P. E., *J. Assoc. Offic. Agr. Chem.* **29**, 112 (1946).
179. Harrington, T., Boyd, T. H. and Cherry, G. W., *Analyst* **71**, 97 (1946).
180. Ketchum, D., *Ind. Eng. Chem., Anal. Ed.* **18**, 273 (1946).
181. Klein, A. K. and Wichman, H. J., *J. Assoc. Offic. Agr. Chem.* **29**, 191 (1946).
182. LaClair, J. B., *Ind. Eng. Chem., Anal. Ed.* **18**, 763 (1946).
183. Marcali, K. and Rieman, W., *Ind. Eng. Chem., Anal. Ed.* **18**, 144 (1946).
184. Maglio, M. M., *Chemist-Analyst* **35**, 39 (1946).
185. Mundell, M., Fischbach, H. and Eble, T. E., *J. Am. Pharm. Assoc.* **35**, 373 (1946).

186. Schuster, G., *Ann. chim. anal.* **28**, 146 (1946).
187. Toffoli, C. and Marzadro, M., *Ann. chim. applicata* **36**, 370 (1946).
188. Ubeda, F. B. and Puig, P. M., *Anales fis. y quim. (Madrid)* **42**, 1065 (1946).
189. Uhrig, K., *Ind. Eng. Chem., Anal. Ed.* **18**, 469 (1946).
190. André, E. and Maille, M., *Bull. soc. chim. France* **14**, 215 (1947).
191. André, E. and Maille, M., *Bull. soc. chim. France* **14**, 725 (1947).
192. Bastrup, T., *Acta Pharm. Toxicol.* **3**, 303 (1947).
193. Chapman, A. M. and Pierce, J. S., *Pharm. J.* **159**, 47 (1947).
194. Goldenson, J. and Sass, S., *Anal. Chem.* **19**, 320 (1947).
195, Gros, R., *Ann. pharm. franç.* **5**, 459 (1947).
196. Hellberg, H., *Svensk Farm. Tidskr.* **51**, 560 (1947).
197. Hoffmann, A. and Maffei, F. J., *Inst. pesq. tecnol. (Sao Paulo)*, separate No. 196, 93 (1947).
198. Ionescu-Matiu, A. and Popa, I., *Produits pharm.* **2**, 389 (1947).
199. Knight, B. H., *Anal. Chem.* **19**, 359 (1947).
200. Pesez, M., *Ann. pharm. franç.* **5**, 165 (1947).
201. Pesez, M., *Ann. pharm. franç* **5**, 167 (1947).
202. Ryan, J. D. and Shaw, F. B., *U.S. Patent No.* 2, 425, 568, Aug. 12, 1947.
203. Stuart, R. G., *Analyst* **72**, 235 (1947).
204. Ubeda, F. B. and Puig, M. M., *Inform. quím. anal. (Madrid)* **1**, 179 (1947).
205. Wain, R. L. and Martin, A. E., *Analyst* **72**, 1 (1947).
206. Alicino, J. F., *Anal. Chem.* **20**, 590 (1948).
207. Archer, H. E., Chapman, L., Rhoden, E. and Warren, F. L., *Biochem. J.* **42**, 58 (1948).
208. Bergmann, F. and Japhe, H., *Anal. Chem.* **20**, 146 (1948).
209. Borgstrom, B., *Acta Physiol. Scand.* **15**, 338 (1948).
210. Butts, P. G., Prine, G. B., Kouba, D. L. and Becker, W. W., *Anal. Chem.* **20**, 1066 (1948).
211. Dalin, G. A. and Haimsohn, J. N., *Anal. Chem.* **20**, 470 (1948).
212. Deschreider, A. R. and van den Driessche, S., *Food Manuf.* **23**, 77 (1948).
213. Dvornikoff, M. N. and Morrill, H. L., *Anal. Chem.* **20**, 935 (1948).
214. Elsner, E., *Pharmazie* **3**, 401 (1948).
215. Fahy, J. P., *J. Ind. Hyg. Toxicol.* **30**, 205 (1948).
216. Frampton, V. L. and Martin, G. N., *Anal. Chem.* **20**, 661 (1948).
217. Goldenson, J. and Sass, S., *Anal. Chem.* **20**, 730 (1948).
218. Goldenson, J. and Sass, S., *Anal. Chem.* **20**, 1118 (1948).
219. Gurmandi Robles, G., *Rev. facultad farm. y bioquím., Univ. nacl. mayor San Marcos (Lima)* **10**, 166 (1948).
220. Hickinbotham, A. R., *Analyst* **73**, 509 (1948).
221. Hummel, V., *Listy Cukrovar* **64**, 229 (1948).
222. Jensen, H. and Jannke, P., *J. Am. Pharm. Assoc., Sci. Ed.* **37**, 37 (1948).

223. Lamond, J., *Analyst* **73**, 674 (1948).
224. LaClair, J. B., *Anal. Chem.* **20**, 241 (1948).
225. Pedersen, V., *Arch. Pharm. Chemi* **55**, 625 (1948).
226. Raffaelli, D., *Ann. chim. applicata* **38**, 552 (1948).
227. Trafelet, L., *Anal. Chem.* **20**, 68 (1948).
228. Wild, A. M., *J. Soc. Chem. Ind., London* **67**, 90 (1948).
229. Anderson, H. H., *J. Am. Chem. Soc.* **71**, 1801 (1949).
230. Blinn, R. C. and Gunther, F. A., *Anal. Chem.* **21**, 1289 (1949).
231. Bond, C. R., *Analyst* **74**, 550 (1949).
232. Boulanger, P. and Osteux, R., *Bull. soc. chim. biol.* **31**, 1290 (1949).
233. do Campo, L. C., Copello, M. A., Jung, W. and Sernates, M. E., *Anales direc. gen. ofic. quím. nacl.* (*Buenos Aires*) **2**, 9 (1949).
234. Englis, D. T. and Reinschreiber, J. F., *Anal. Chem.* **21**, 602 (1949).
235. Gurvits, S. S. and Mel'nikova, P. A., *Zavodskaya Lab.* **15**, 672 (1949).
236. Harnish, D. P. and Tarbell, D. S., *Anal. Chem.* **21**, 968 (1949).
237. Korzybski, T. and Bagdasarian, G., *Med. Doświadczal. i Mikrobiol.* **1**, 632 (1949).
238. Pluchon, J. and Pille, G., *Med. trop.* **9**, 532 (1949).
239. Pyatnitskii, M. P. and Yur'eva, A. F., *Biokhimiya* **14**, 196 (1949).
240. Shaw, W. H. C., *J. Pharm. Pharmacol.* **1**, 813 (1949).
241. Takano, T. and Hamada, M., *Botyu Kagaku* No. 14, 26 (1949).
242. Wreath, A. R. and Zickefoose, E. J., *Anal. Chem.* **21**, 808 (1949).
243. Zöllner, W., *Farben, Lacke, Anstrichstoffe* **3**, 385 (1949).
244. Anderson, H. H., *J. Am. Chem. Soc.* **72**, 196 (1950).
245. Anderson, H. H., *J. Am. Chem. Soc.* **72**, 2089 (1950).
246. Beickert, A., *Arch. exptl. Path. Pharmakol.* **210**, 479 (1950).
247. Cohen, S. G. and Haas, H. C., *J. Am. Chem. Soc.* **72**, 3954 (1950).
248. Donnally, L. H., *Anal. Chem.* **22**, 365 (1950).
249. Hahn, F. L., *Anal. Chim. Acta* **4**, 577 (1950).
250. Hezel, E., *Fette u. Seifen* **52**, 149 (1950).
251. Hezel, E., *Farbe u. Lack* **56**, 10 (1950).
252. Ilva, K., Johansen, O. L. and Reimers, F., *Dansk Tids. Farm.* **24**, 253, (1950).
253. Jureček, M., *Chem. Listy* **44**, 134 (1950).
254. Kofrányi, E., *Die Milchwissenschaft* **5**, 51 (1950).
255. Korzybski, T. and Bagdasarian, G., *Med. Doświadczal. i Mikrobiol.* **2**, 468 (1950).
256. Mameli, E., *Atti ist. veneto sci., Classe sci., mat e nat.* **108**, 1 (1950).
257. McLachlan, T. and Smith, W. C., *Pharm. J.* **165**, 151 (1950).
258. Mellini, F., *Chimica* (*Milan*) **5**, 335 (1950).
259. Mitchell, J. and Smith, D. M., *Anal. Chem.* **22**, 746 (1950).
260. Pénau, H., Hagemann, G. and Saïas, E., *Ann. pharm. franç.* **8**, 100 (1950).

261. Pippen, E. L., McCready, R. M. and Owens, H. S., *Anal. Chem.* **22** 1457 (1950).
262. Romano, E., *Ann. staz. chim. agrar. sper., Roma*, Ser. 3, No. 26 (1950).
263. Roth, H., *Z. anal. Chem.* **131**, 347 (1950).
264. Wild, A. M., *Nature* **165**, 818 (1950).
265. Anderson, H. H., *J. Am. Chem. Soc.* **73**, 2351 (1951); and Anderson, H. H., Seaton, D. L. and Rudnicks, R. P. T., *J. Am. Chem. Soc.* 2144 (1951).
266. Belič, I., Štrauh, L. and Battestin, M., *Arhiv Kem.* **23**, 269 (1951).
267. Chaney, A. and Astle, M. J., *J. Org. Chem.* **16**, 57 (1951).
268. Goldenson, J. and Sass, S., *Anal. Chem.* **23**, 1170 (1951).
269. Hezel, E., *Fette u. Seifen* **53**, 82 (1951).
270. Kameswara Rao, G., Banerjee, J. N. and Bhattacharya, N. N., *Indian J. Pharm.* **13**, 6 (1951).
271. Meier, K., *Farbe u. Lack* **57**, 437 (1951).
272. Perkow, W., *Z. anal. Chem.* **134**, 267 (1951–2).
273. Rispoli, G. and Di Giacomo, A., *Boll. Lab. Chim. Provinciali (Bologna)* **2**, 55 (1951).
274. Rutovskii, B. N. and Shur, A. M., *Zhur. Priklad. Khim.* **24**, 1074 (1951).
275. Schiessler, R. W., Speck, R. M. and Dixon, J. A., *J. Am. Chem. Soc.* **73**, 3524 (1951).
276. Shaefer, W. E. and Balling, W. J., *Anal. Chem.* **23**, 1126, 1452 (1951).
277. Siggia, S. and Kervenski, I. R., *Anal. Chem.* **23**, 117 (1951).
278. Vandoni, R., *Mém. services chim. état (Paris)* **36**, No. 1, 19 (1951).
279. Vanetten, C. H., *Anal. Chem.* **23**, 1697 (1951).
280. Weber, E., *Z. anal. Chem.* **132**, 26 (1951).
281. Wolff, I. A., Olds, D. W. and Hilbert, G. E., *J. Am. Chem. Soc.* **73**, 346 (1951).
282. Beloff-Chain, A. and D'Accadia, F. D., *Analyst* **77**, 423 (1952).
283. Bhunvara, N. B. and Vadodaria, D. J., *Indian J. Pharm.* **14**, 86 (1952).
284. Buscarons, F. and Mir, P., *Anal. Chim. Acta* **7**, 185 (1952).
285. van Espen, J., *J. pharm. Belg.* **7**, 456 (1952).
286. Fetzer, W. R. and Jones, R. C., *Anal. Chem.* **24**, 835 (1952).
287. Hamada, M., Takano, T. and Ohno M., *Botyu Kagaku* **17**, 27 (1952).
288. Interlab. study, *Anal. Chem.* **24**, 400 (1952).
289. Jouslin, D., *Chim. anal.* **34**, 34 (1952).
290. Lowen, W. K. and Baker, H. M., *Anal. Chem.* **24**, 1475 (1952).
291. Smith, D. M., Mitchell, J. and Billmeyer, A. M., *Anal. Chem.* **24**, 1847 (1952).
292. Baskakov, Yu. A. and Mel'nikov, N. N., *Zhur. Anal. Khim.* **8**, 119 (1953).
293. Sato, R., Muta, I. and Ueshima, T., *Botyu Kagaku* **18**, 57 (1953).
294. v. Schivizhoffen, E. and Danz, H., *Z. anal. Chem.* **140**, 81 (1953).

295. Sina, A. and Sallam, M., *Proc. Pharm. Soc. Egypt, Sci. Ed.* **35**, No. 7 53 (1953).
296. Struszyński, M., Bellen, Z. and Bellen, N., *Przemysl Chem.* **9**, 243 (1953).
297. Tranchant, J., *Mém. poudres* **35**, 108 (1953).
298. Vaisman, G. A., *Aptechnoe Delo* **2**, No. 6, 25 (1953).
299. Varner, J. E., Bulen, W. A., Vanecko, S. and Burrell, R. C., *Anal. Chem.* **25**, 1528 (1953).
300. Babin, V. A. and Muserski, N. N., *Voprosy Pitaniya* **13**, No. 3, 34 (1954).
301. Boehm, T. and Horsch, *Pharm. Zentralhalle* **93**, 92 (1954).
302. Hansen, A., *Z. anal. Chem.* **143**, 17 (1954).
303. Kennett, B. H., *J. Agr. Food Chem.* **2**, 691 (1954).
304. Kertesz, Z. I. and Lavin, M. I., *Food Research* **19**, 627 (1954).
305. Klimovskii, D. N., Gryaznov, V. P. and Rzhechitskaya, G. V., *Spirtovaya Prom.* **20**, No. 3, 17 (1954).
306. Mellon, E. F., Viola, S. J. and Hoover, S. P., *J. Am. Leather Chem. Ass.* **49**, 710 (1954).
307. Parker, G. and Donegan, L., *J. Pharm. Pharmacol.* **6**, 167 (1954).
308. Revol, L., Nouvel, G. and Fosse, G., *Trans. soc. pharm. Montpellier* **14**, 284 (1954).
309. Shaw, J. N. and Fomo, M. W., *J. Am. Oil Chemists' Soc.* **31**, 448 (1954).
310. Tani, H. and Nara, A., *J. Pharm. Soc. Japan* **74**, 1309 (1954).
311. Wiesenberger, E., *Mikrochim. Acta* **127** (1954).
312. Davis, P. L. and Bowen, C. V., *Anal. Chem.* **27**, 1233 (1955).
313. Etlis, V. S. and Artyakhina, L. M., *Zavodskaya Lab.* **21**, 919 (1955).
314. Grodzinsky, J., *Anal. Chem.* **27**, 1765 (1955).
315. Hofreiter, B. T., Alexander, B. H. and Wolff, I. A., *Anal. Chem.* **27**, 1930 (1955).
316. Johnson, A. E. and Lawrence, R. V., *Anal. Chem.* **27**, 1345 (1955).
317. Mullaly, M. A. C., *Analyst* **80**, 237 (1955).
318. Poroshin, K. T., Kozarenko, T. D. and Khurgin, Ya. I., *Izvest. Akad. Nauk SSSR, Otdel Khim. Nauk* 773 (1955).
319. Salzer, F., *Z. anal. Chem.* **146**, 260 (1955).
320. Shogam, S. M. and Fen'kova, E. I., *Trudy Nauch. Inst. Udobren i Insektofungisid. im Ya. V. Samoilova*, No. 156, 30 (1955).
321. Stainier, C. and Grosjean, L., *Compt. rend. 27^e^ congr. intern. chim. ind., Brussels 1954*, published in *Ind. chim. belge* **20**, spec. No. 551 (1955).
322. Vach, S. and Horák, F., *Pharmazie* **10**, 596 (1955).
323. Vaskevich, D. N. and Khokhlova, R. V., *Khim. Prom.* 87 (1955).
324. Vladimirov, G. E., Klimov, A. N. and Zhukova, E. N., *Med. Prom. SSSR* No. 1, 19 (1955).
325. Abdulla-Zade, G. A., *Azerbaidzhan. Med. Zhur.* No. 10, 74 (1956).
326. Andrade, J. L. et al., *Rev. sanidad y asistencia social (Venezuela)* **21**, 231 (1956).

327. Bami, H. L., *Indian J. Malariol.* **10**, 305 (1956).
328. Bernhart, D. N. and Rattenbury, K. H., *Anal. Chem.* **28**, 1765 (1956).
329. DeLorenzi, F. and DaRe, P., *Boll. chim. farm.* **95**, 235 (1956).
330. Desbaumes, P. and Deshusses, J., *Mitt. Lebensm. u. Hyg.* **47**, 550 (1956)
331. Eijkel, G., Emsting, M. J. E., Rekker, R. F., and Nauta, W. T., *Pharm. Weekblad* **91**, 81 (1956).
332. Kolyakova, G. E., *Gigiena i Sanit.* **21**, No. 12, 46 (1956).
333. Kreshkov, A. P., Svyatsillo, S. V., Shemyatenkova, V. I. and Neshumova, A. M., *Zavodskaya Lab.* **22**, 660 (1956).
334. Lardero, M. R., Cernia, E. and Mori, A., *Ann. chim.* (*Rome*) **46**, 194 (1956).
335. Myagkov, V. A. and Pakshver, A. B., *Zhur. Priklad Khim.* **29**, 1703 (1956).
336. Salomaa, P., *Acta Chem. Scand.* **10**, 306, 311 (1956).
337. Sergienko, S. R., Galich, P. N., Izmailov, N. A. and Spivak, L. L., *Zhur. Anal. Khim.* **11**, 731 (1956).
338. Swann, M. H. and Esposito, G. G., *Anal. Chem.* **28**, 1984 (1956).
339. Templeman, B. M. and Juneau, J., *Anal. Chem.* **28**, 1324 (1956).
340. Yavorskii, N. P. and Romanyuk, Yu. F., *Aptechnoe Delo* **5**, No. 5, 27 (1956).
341. Yurist, I. M. and Firsova, Yu. F., *Zhur. Anal. Khim.* **11**, 205 (1956).
342. Banfield, J. E., *J. Chem. Soc.* 2578 (1957).
343. Drinberg, A. Ya., Yakovlev, A. D. and Sokolova, Z. S., *Zavodskaya Lab.* **23**, 26 (1957).
344. Fujita, Y., Ueda, T. and Kusumoto, N., *Koryo* No. 47, 42 (1957).
345. Gengrinovich, A. I. and Kadyrova, Ya. K., *Aptechnoe Delo* **6**, No. 2, 68 (1957).
346. Helou, J. H., *Anais farm. e quím., Sao Paulo* **8**, 7 (1957).
347. Hennart, C. and Merlin, E., *Chim. anal.* **39**, 429 (1957).
348. Hennart, C. and Merlin, E., *Anal. Chim. Acta* **17**, 534 (1957).
349. Ioffe, B. V. and Sergeeva, Z. I., *Zhur. Anal. Khim.* **12**, 540 (1957).
350. Jančik, F. and Buděšinský, B., *Československ. Farm.* **6**, 590 (1957).
351. Kennett, B. H. and Huelin, F. E., *J. Agr. Food Chem.* **5**, 201 (1957).
352. Meltzer, H., *Nachbrl. deut. Pflanzenschutzdienst* (*Berlin*) **11**, 178 (1957).
353. Metcalfe, L. D. and Schmitz, A. A., *Anal. Chem.* **29**, 1676 (1957).
354. Roth, H. and Schuster, P., *Mikrochim. Acta* **6**, 837 (1957).
355. Stalcup, H., McCollum, F. and Whitman, C. L., *Anal. Chem.* **29**, 1479 (1957).
356. Suzuki, K., *Kôgyô Kagaku Zasshi* **60**, 1128 (1957).
357. Turskii, Yu. I., Brik, A. N., Kumin, A. M. and Gal'pern, E. M., *Gazovaya Prom.* No. 9, 11 (1957).
358. Vaisman, G. A. and Benderskaya, S. N., *Aptechnoe Delo* **6**, No. 2, 32 (1957).

359. Valyashko, A. and Berdichevskii, E. G., *Zhur. Obshchei Khim.* **27**, 2302 (1957).
360. Baldwin, W. H. and Higgins, C. E., *Anal. Chem.* **30**, 446 (1958).
361. Blažek, J. and Stejskal, Z., *Českoslov. Farm.* **7**, 578 (1958).
362. Czerwiński, W., *Chem. Anal.* (*Warsaw*) **3**, 53 (1958).
363. Fijolka, P., Lenz, J. and Runge, F., *Makromol. Chem.* **26**, 61 (1958).
364. Inglis, A. S., *Mikrochim. Acta* 228 (1958).
365. Jančik, F., Kakáč, E., Vaníček, V. and Vrublovská, M., *Chem. Listy* **52**, 909 (1958).
366. Malhotra, O. P. and Anand, V. D., *Z. anal. Chem.* **159**, 285 (1958).
367. Malhotra, O. P. and Anand, V. D., *Z. anal. Chem.* **160**, 10 (1958).
368. Matrka, M. and Hanoušek, V., *Chem. Listy* **52**, 755 (1958).
369. Miss, A. and Conu, I., *Rev. chim.* (*Bucharest*) **9**, 268 (1958).
370. Pinguet, *Pharm. Acta Helv.* **33**, 114 (1958).
371. Poethke, W. and Wigert, R., *Pharmazie* **13**, 253 (1958).
372. Römisch, H., *Pharmazie* **13**, 707 (1958).
373. Roth, H., *Mikrochim. Acta* 766 (1958).
374. Štivić, I. and Marinov, V., *Acta Pharm. Jugoslav.* **8**, 93 (1958).
375. Suprun, P. P., *Med. Prom. SSSR* **12**, 50 (1958).
376. Swann, W. B., Zahner, R. J. and Milner, O. L., *Anal. Chem.* **30**, 1830 (1958).
377. Varga, E. and Vastagh, G., *Acta Pharm. Hung.* **28**, 44 (1958).
378. Whitehurst, D. H. and Johnson, J. B., *Anal. Chem.* **30**, 1332 (1958).
379. Błaskowicz, J., Roczniakowa, K., Wańtuch, S. and Bukała, M., *Chem. Anal.* (*Warsaw*) **4**, 719 (1959).
380. Bradley, H. B. and Neal, D. J., *Anal. Chem.* **31**, 1925 (1959).
381. Cerri, O., Spialtini, A. and Gallo, U., *Pharm. Acta Helv.* **34**, 13 (1959).
382. Critchfield, F. E., *Anal. Chem.* **31**, 1406 (1959).
383. Gélébart, F., *Ann. pharm. franç.* **17**, 278 (1959).
384. Gutiérrez Amo, P. A. and Martin, D., *Grasas y Aceites* **10**, 12 (1959).
385. Kainz, G., *Z. anal. Chem.* **166**, 32 (1959).
386. Kalinowski, K., *Acta Polon. Pharm.* **16**, 225 (1959).
387. Kartha, A. R. S., *J. Sci. Ind. Research* (*India*) **18B**, 217 (1959).
388. Kleiner, G. I. and Dendze-Pletman, B. Yu., *Med. Prom. SSSR* **13**, 42 (1959).
389. Kol'kovski, P. G. and Mitkova, N., *Khim. i Ind.* (*Sofia*) **31**, 55 (1959).
390. Kolyakova, G. E., *Gigiena i Sanit.* **24**, 72 (1959).
391. Matrka, M. and Hanoušek, V., *Collection Czechoslov. Chem. Communs.* **24**, 1347 (1959).
392. Mázor, L. and Meisel, T., *Anal. Chim. Acta* **20**, 130 (1959).
393. Mázor, L. and Pápay, M. K., *Acta Pharm. Hung.* **29**, 223 (1959).
394. Narasimhachari, N., Nayar, M. K. and Ramanarao, G., *Hindustan Antibiotics Bull.* **1**, 120 (1959).

395. Parikh, P. M. and Mukherji, S. P., *Indian J. Pharm.* **21**, 110 (1959).
396. Perel'man, Ya. M. and Krasulina, V. N., *Trudy Leningrad. Khim. Farm.* No. 6, 69 (1959).
397. Weiss, P. J., *Antibiotics and Chemotherapy* **9**, 660 (1959).
398. Andrey, M. and Mirimanoff, A., *Pharm. Acta Helv.* **35**, 276 (1960).
399. Baldinus, J. G. and Rothberg, I., *Anal. Chem.* **32**, 1176 (1960).
400. Bartels, U. and Hoyme, H., *Faserforsch. u. Textilchem.* **11**, 503 (1960).
401. Bostoganashvili, B. S., *Sb. Tr. Tbilissk. Nauch.-Issled. Khim.-Farmatseev. Inst.* **9**, 103 (1960).
402. Burger, E. and Schulek E., *Talanta* **4**, 120 (1960).
403. Esposito, G. G. and Swann, M. H., *Anal. Chem.* **32**, 49 (1960).
404. Esposito, G. G. and Swann, M. H., *Anal. Chem.* **32**, 680 (1960).
405. Franz, J., *Plaste u. Kautschuk* **7**, 493 (1960).
406. Gengrinovich, A. I., Kats, A. L. and Murtazaev, A. M., *Doklady Akad. Nauk Uzbek. S.S.R.*, No. 8, 44 (1960).
407. Grafnetterová, J., *Časopis lékařů ceských* **99**, 182 (1960).
408. Hessler, W. and Marsen, H., *Fette u. Seifen, Anstrichm ttel* **62**, 579 (1960).
409. Hsiao, Ch-Ch. and Wu, L-Ch., *Yao Hsueh Hsueh Pao* **8**, 229 (1960).
410. Kane, P. F. and Gillespie, K. G., *J. Agr. Food Chem.* **8**, 29 (1960).
411. Kurzawa, Z. and Suszka, A., *Chem. Anal.* (*Warsaw*) **5**, 897 (1960).
412. Lal, R. N. and Lal, J. B., *J. Proc. Oil Technol. Assoc., India Kanpur*, **15** Pt. 2, 15 (1960).
413. Matrka, M. and Navrátil, F., *Chem. průmysl* **10**, 361 (1960).
414. Prístavka, D., *Chem. zvesti* **14**, 472 (1960).
415. Robinson, E. A., *Anal. Chim. Acta* **23**, 305 (1960).
416. Shibasaki, J., *Bunseki Kagaku* **9**, 544 (1960).
417. Shul'man, M. S. and Gavrikova, O. F., *Tr. Tsentr. Nauchn.-Issled. Inst. Spirt. i Likero Vodochn. Prom.* No. 9, 74 (1960).
418. Stone, W. K., Cremers, L. F. and Thompson, N. R., *J. Dairy Sci.* **43**, 435 (1960).
419. Wolf, F., *Z. anal. Chem.* **172**, 413 (1960).
420. Alicino, J. F., *Anal. Chem.* **33**, 648 (1961).
421. Beach, L. K. and Sass, S., *Anal. Chem.* **33**, 901 (1961).
422. Bethel, M. M. and Bond, C. R., *Analyst* **86**, 448 (1961).
423. Bose, A., Chaudhuri, A. R. and Ghosh, T. N., *J. Proc. Inst. Chemists* (*India*) **33**, 16 (1961).
424. Burger, E. and Schulek, E., *Magyar Kem. Folyoirat* **67**, 59 (1961).
425. DeLorenzi, F. and DaRe, P., *Boll. chim. farm.* **100**, 23 (1961).
426. Emelin, E. A., Svistunova, G. and Tsarfin, Ya. A., *Zavodskaya Lab.* **27**, 283 (1961).
427. Ershov, B. N. and Pokrovskaya, V. L., *Plasticheskie Massy* No. 7, 65 (1961).

428. Floderer, I., Drozdik, G. and Toth, Z., *Acta Pharm. Hung.* **31**, 145 (1961).
429. Kerényi, I., *Magyar Kem. Folyoirat* **67**, 313 (1961).
430. Klimova, V. A. and Zabrodina, K. S., *Izvest. Akad. Nauk. SSSR, Otdel. Khim. Nauk* 176 (1961).
431. Kosinska, V. and Feigin, E., *Plasticheskie Massy* No. 6, 8 (1961).
432. Mázor, L. and Pápay, M. K., *Acta Chim. Acad. Sci. Hung.* **26**, 473 (1961).
433. Nayar, M. K. and Narasimhachari, N., *Hindustan Antibiotics Bull.* **3**, 101 (1961).
434. Philipp, B., Bartels, U. and Hayme, H., *Faserforsch., Textilchem.* **12**, 581 (1961).
435. Sodomka, J., *Chem. průmysl* **11**, 333 (1961).
436. Tobey, S. W., McGregor, S. D. and Cottrill, S. L., *J. Chem. Educ.* **38**, 611 (1961).
437. Wronski, M., *Chem. Anal. (Warsaw)* **6**, 859 (1961).
438. Baehler, B., Chams, G. and Cherbuliez, E., *Pharm. Acta Helv.* **36**, 338 (1961).
439. Bukharov, I. N. and Khusnutdinova, Z. S., *USSR Patent* 142, 801, Dec., 1961.
440. Ershov, B. N., Pokrovskaya, V. L. and Dvuglov, S. P., *Plasticheskii Massy* No. 10, 58 (1961)
441. Roushdi, I. M., Abdine, H. and El-Sheltawy, A. M., *Egypt. Pharm. Bull.* **42**, No. 4, 277 (1961).
442. Urbanowicz, S., *Chem. Anal. (Warsaw)* **6**, 855 (1961).
443. Armandola, P., *Latte* **36**, 709 (1962).
444. Awe, W. and Kienert, J., *Arch. Pharm.* **295**, 1962; *Mitt. Deut. Pharm. Ges.* **32**, 173 (1962).
445. Boon, P. F. G., *J. Pharm. Pharmacol.* **14**, 116T (1962).
446. Brancone, L. M., *Microchem. J. Symp. Ser.* **2**, 605 (1962).
447. Dumas, T., *J. Agr. Food Chem.* **10**, 476 (1962).
448. Dušinský, G. and Tyllová, M., *Ceskoslov. Farm.* **11**, 359 (1962).
449. Gorelov, P. N., *Zavodskaya Lab.* **28**, 668 (1962).
450. Grafnetterová, Y., *Antibiotiki* **7**, 736 (1962).
451. Karpov, O. N., *Zhur. Anal. Khim.* **17**, 1029 (1962).
452. Kuffner, F., Sattler-Dornbacher, S. and Humer, C., *Monatsh.* **93**, 99 (1962).
453. Lóránt, B., *Seifen, Öle, Fette, Wachse* **88**, 85 (1962).
454. Sharma, S. K. and Mathur, S., *Paintindia.* **12**, 108 (1962).
455. Solomon-Ionescu, I., Popescu, D. and Nicola, M., *Farmacia (Bucharest)* **10**, 627 (1962).
456. Stetzler, R. S. and Andress, T. B., *J. Am. Oil Chemists'. Soc* **39**, 509 (1962).

457. Tiwari, R. D., Srivastava, K. C. and Sharma, J. P., *Z. Anal. Chem.* **187**, 161 (1962); first 2 authors, *Proc. Natl. Acad. Sci. India* **A32**, 69 (1962).
458. Vysotskaya, L. E., *Vinodelie i Vinogradarstvo SSSR* 13 (1962).
459. Apatoff, J. B., Cohen, J. and Norwitz, G., *Anal. Chem.* **35**, 800 (1963).
460. Barcza, L. and Burger, K., *Magyar Kem. Folyoirat* **69**, 178 (1963).
461. Bush, D. G., Kunzelsauer, L. J. and Merrill, S. H., *Anal. Chem.* **35**, 1250 (1963).
462. Dragusin, I. and German, A., *Rev. Chim. (Bucharest)* **14**, 352 (1963).
463. Emelin, E. A., Smyslova, N. F. and Tsarfin, Ya. A., *Zavodskaya Lab.* **29**, 1169 (1963).
464. Katz, D., *Z. Anal. Chem.* **195**, 258 (1963).
465. Lyande, Yu. V. and Cherkasski, A. A., *Zavodskaya Lab.* **29**, 1050 (1963).
466. Maros, L., Molnár-Perl, I., Vajda, M. and Schulek, E., *Anal. Chim. Acta* **28**, 179 (1963).
467. Murakami, T. and Ishii, E., *Bunseki Kagaku* **12**, 657 (1963).
468. Nikolaeva, N. E., *Izv. Vysshikh Uchebn. Zavedenii, Pishchevaye Tekhnol.* 170 (1963).
469. Pohle, W. D., Gregory, R. L. and Van Giessen, B., *J. Am. Oil Chemists' Soc.* **40**, 549 (1963).
470. Ray, S. C., *Ann, Biochem. Exptl. Med. (Calcutta)* **23**, 411 (1963).
471. Ruzhentseva, A. K. and Larina, P. N., *Med. Prom. SSSR* 42 (1963).
472. Tiwari, R. D. and Sharma, J. P., *Z. Anal. Chem.* **195**, 267 (1963).
473. Tölgyessy, J. and Šaršimová, M., *Z. Anal. Chem.* **196**, 192 (1963).
474. Ziólkowski, Z., Respondek, J. and Przondo, J., *Chem. Anal. (Warsaw)* **8**, 273 (1963).
475. Bednarski, T. M. and Hume, D. N., *Anal. Chim. Acta* **30**, 1 (1964).
476. Přibyl, M. and Slovák, Z., *Z. Anal. Chem.* **200**, 23 (1964).
477. Přibyl, M. and Slovák, Z., *Z. Anal. Chem.* **202**, 112 (1964).
478. Siggia, S., Hanna, J. G. and Serencha, N. M., *Anal. Chem.* **36**, 227 (1964).
479. Barker, A. V. and Volk, R. J., *Anal. Chem.* **36**, 439 (1964).

4. Aluminium hydride and borohydride

Reagent. Both lithium aluminium hydride, $LiAlH_4$, and sodium borohydride, $NaBH_4$, have been used. Ethers have been used as solvents for these highly reactive agents.

Reactions and materials titrated. 1. Reduction in determination mainly of —CO— groups, and also of —CN, —S—S— and —C=C— groups

$$R_2CO \rightarrow R_2CH_2$$
$$RCONH_2 \rightarrow RCH_2NH_2$$
$$RCN$$
$$RSSR \rightarrow 2\ RSH$$
$$-\overset{|}{C}=\overset{|}{C}- \rightarrow -\overset{|}{C}H-\overset{|}{C}H-$$

2. Replacement of 'active hydrogen' in determination of alcohols, carboxylic acids, amines and other groups which contain it;

$$4\,X\text{—}H + LiAlH_4 \rightarrow LiAl(\text{—}X)_4 + 4\ H_2$$

Reaction conditions. Dry ether solvents (especially tetrahydrofuran) have mostly been used.

Reactions have generally been fairly fast and terminated in some minutes.

Subsequent treatment and final titration stage. Apart from the gasometric method for 'active hydrogen' determination by measurement of the volume of hydrogen evolved, several titrimetric procedures are known:

(i) Determination of unused reagent, which has been done in two ways:

1. Back titration (of $LiAlH_4$) with a titrant containing active hydrogen (usually a lower alcohol in benzene solution). End-point has been potentiometrically determined or with substituted aminoazobenzenes as colour indicators.
2. By oxidation with excess iodate and iodometric determination of the unused part:

$$3\ BH_4^- + 4\ IO_3^- \rightarrow 4\ I^- + 3\ H_2BO_3^- + 3\ H_2O$$

(ii) Determination of a reaction product, as for example:

1. Amines, by distillation and titration with acid.
2. Mercaptans by titration with $AgNO_3$.
3. Hydrogen by oxidation to water and titration with the Karl Fischer reagent; or by a complex series of reactions, namely, oxidation to water, conversion to CO, reaction with I_2O_5 to iodine, oxidation ultimately to iodate and titration with thiosulphate after adding I^-/acid.

Examples

Materials titrated	Reagent and reaction conditions	Subsequent treatment and final titration stage	Ref.
Hydroxy, amino, carbonyl compounds, esters	+ $LiAlH_4$/tetrahydro-furan. A few min reaction	Back titrated with ethanol or propanol/benzene potentiometrically	1
Hydroxy compounds	$LiAlH_4$/tetrahydro-furan, + sample; 15–30 min	Back titrated potentiometrically with propanol/benzene	2
Pharmaceuticals, e.g. alcohols, amines, acids, alkaloids, aldehydes, esters	Method of ref. 1		3
Compounds with 'active hydrogen', chiefly hydroxy compounds and carboxylic acids	Sample in tetrahydro-furan, + $LiAlH_4$/same solvent	Back titrated with butanol/benzene, trying out indicators (substituted aminoazobenzenes)	4
'Active hydrogen', e.g. benzoic acid, trimbromophenol	+ $LiAlH_4$/dipropyl ether, giving hydrogen	Hydrogen passed over CuO at 1100–1200°, giving water; converted by hot C to CO; passed through I_2O_5 at 120°, giving iodine: collected in NaOH and oxidized to iodate with bromine/acetic acid; unreacted bromine removed with formic acid, I^-/H_2SO_4 added and titrated with thiosulphate	5
Amides; some nitriles	+ $LiAlH_4$/diethyl ether; 15 min/room temp.	+ water + NaOH to destroy excess reagent; amines distilled into excess H_2SO_4 and back titrated with NaOH to methyl purple	6
Disulphides (aliphatic and aromatic)	+ $NaBH_4$/diethylene glycol + dimethyl ether + $AlCl_3$; 30 min/room temp.	+ NaOH to destroy excess reagent; + HNO_3 + NH_4OH and titrated the mercaptans formed with $AgNO_3$ potentiometrically (see Part I, Silver (I), ref. 125)	7
Unsaturation, e.g. unsaturated acids	+ dry methanol + $LiAlH_4$/ dibutyl ether, + PtO catalyst. Warmed for 10 min	Excess hydrogen oxidized with oxygen to water, then titrated with Karl Fischer reagent	8

Materials titrated	Reagent and reaction conditions	Subsequent treatment and final titration stage	Ref.
Carbonyl groups in cellulose (D-glucose or periodate cellulose)	At pH 12–12·3, + $NaBH_4$ reagent; 24–48 h/room temp.	Filtered, excess IO_3^- added, then NaOH, I^- and H_2SO_4 and titrated with thiosulphate	9
Acyl ferrocenes (determination of molecular weights)	+ $LiAlH_4/AlCl_3$, reducing to alkyl ferrocenes	Titrated potentiometrically with $Cr_2O_7^{2-}$/acetic acid	10
$R–S_x–R'$	+ suspension $LiAlH_4$/ tetrahydrofuran; 5 min reflux, reducing to H_2S and mercaptans	Unused reagent destroyed with water, H_2SO_4/water/pyridine added, heated 90 min/70–80° and H_2S carried into Cd acetate solution with nitrogen; precipitated CdS titrated with iodine; mercaptans distilled into $AgNO_3$/pyridine at −10° and titrated with NaOH to phenolphthalein; or mercaptide precipitate filtered and filtrate titrated (see Silver (I), ref. 207)	11

References

1. Higuchi, T., Lintner, C. J. and Schleif, R. H., *Science* **111**, 63 (1950).
2. Lintner, C. J., Schleif, R. H. and Higuchi, T., *Anal. Chem.* **22**, 534 (1950).
3. Lintner, C. J., Zuck, D. A. and Higuchi, T., *J. Am. Pharm. Assoc.* **39** 418 (1950).
4. Higuchi, T. and Zuck, D. A., *J. Am. Chem. Soc.* **73**, 2676 (1951).
5. Schöniger, W., *Z. anal. Chem.* **133**, 4 (1951).
6. Siggia, S. and Stahl, C. R., *Anal. Chem.* **27**, 550 (1955).
7. Stahl, C. R. and Siggia, S., *Anal. Chem.* **29**, 154 (1957).
8. Seaman, W., *Anal. Chem.* **30**, 1840 (1958).
9. Sugimatsu, A. and Yahara, S., *Kami-pa Gikyoshi* (*J. Jap. Tech. Assoc. Pulp Paper Ind.*) **14**, 516 (1960).
10. Peterlik, M. and Schoegl, K., *Z. anal. Chem.* **195**, 113 (1963).
11. Porter, M., Saville, B. and Watson, A. A., *J. Chem. Soc.* 346 (1963).

5. Aluminium isopropylate

A titrimetric application of the Meerwein–Ponndorf–Verley reaction is given below.

Materials titrated	Reagent and reaction conditions	Subsequent treatment and final titration stage
Carbonyl compounds, e.g. acetophenone and benzaldehyde derivatives	+ isopropanol + Al isopropylate; 15–60 min reflux, establishing the equilibrium: $(C_6H_5)(R)C{=}O + (CH_3)_2CHOH \rightleftharpoons (C_6H_5)(R)CHOH + (CH_3)_2C{=}O$ (R = H or CH_3)	The acetone (most volatile product) distilled into hydroxylamine hydrochloride; titrated with alkali to bromophenol blue, then to phenolphthalein, the difference giving the unreacted hydroxylamine and hence the acetone

Reference

Simonyi, I., Tokár, G. and Gál, G., *Acta Chem. Acad. Sci. Hung.* **16**, 217 (1956).

6. Amines and heterocyclic bases

Reagent. Aliphatic and aromatic; primary, secondary and tertiary; and mono- and diamines have been used. For halide determination, alcoholamines have been favoured because of their stronger basic properties.

Reactions, materials titrated and subsequent treatment. Indirect titration with amine reagents is based on several different reactions. The reaction conditions and subsequent treatment thus vary considerably. The final titration stage has been either back titration of unused amine in about one-third of the examples given; or determination of a reaction product. For back titration, acid reagents (hydrochloric, perchloric or sulphuric acids) have been used, or, with aromatic primary amine reagents, nitrite, bromate or diazonium salts also. Excess amine has nearly always been determined *in situ* and only rarely has the amine been first separated.

1. Amide formation with acid chlorides, anhydrides and, occasionally, esters:

$$RCOCl + R'NH_2 \rightarrow RCONHR' + HCl$$
$$(RCO)_2O + R'NH_2 \rightarrow RCONHR' + RCOOH$$

Comparatively mild reaction conditions have mostly been used, e.g. *ca* 15 min at room temperature. The determination has been concluded by back titration of excess amine or by alkali titration of the acid formed in the reaction (HCl or R′COOH). To allow for free acid(s) present as impurities, this second type of titration has generally been accompanied by a parallel alkali titration of the products of water hydrolysis of the chloride or anhydride sample. The difference between the two titrations corresponds to the chloride or anhydride. In a few cases, the amide has been isolated and titrimetrically determined.

2. Ion/ion/molecule combination, in determination of sulphonic and other strong acids which form salts, insoluble in water and soluble in organic solvents. Anionic surface-active agents are included here.

$$H^+ + RSO_3^- + R'NH_2 \rightarrow (R'NH_3)^+(RSO_3)^-$$

This is a fast reaction, but the reaction mixture has usually been left for a longer period to allow the precipitate to settle. In nearly all cases, the precipitate has subsequently been titrated with alkali and only rarely has excess amine been determined in the filtrate.

3. Halogen replacement and addition in determination of organic halides.

$$R\text{—}Hal + R'NH_2 \rightarrow RNHR' + Hal^- + H^+(+ \text{ excess base})$$

With lower alkyl iodides (from alkoxyl determination with HI reagent), quaternary iodides are formed with tertiary base reagents:

$$RI + R'_3N \rightarrow (RR'_3N)^+I^-$$

Reaction time clearly depends on the reactivity of the halide and reflux periods of up to several hours are quoted. The halide ion has mostly been determined with a silver reagent but some oxidation procedures have been used, e.g. of iodide with iodate to titratable iodine and of bromide with hypobromite to bromate. Recently, methylpyridinium iodide has been titrated with a quaternary hydroxide (ref. 92).

4. Addition to isocyanates and isothiocyanates; to α,β-unsaturated carbonyl compounds and nitriles; to carbon disulphide and oxysulphide.

$$RNCO + R'_2NH \rightarrow RNH.CONR'_2$$

$$CH_2{=}CH.CN + R'_2NH \rightarrow CH_3\text{—}\underset{\displaystyle NR'_2}{\underset{|}{CH}}.CN$$

$$CS_2 + R_2NH \rightarrow HS\text{—}\underset{\displaystyle NR_2}{\underset{|}{C}}{=}S$$

Isocyanate and isothiocyanate determinations have been concluded by titration of the unused amine. In the second example given, the tertiary amine addition product has been titrated with acid. The thiocarbamic acids resulting from reaction with carbon di- and oxy-sulphides have been titrated with alkali, silver or mercuric reagents.

5. Condensation with carbonyl or nitroso compounds.

$$R_2CO + R'NH_2 \rightarrow R_2C{=}NR'_2 + H_2O$$

$$RNO + R'NH_2 \rightarrow RN{=}NR'_2 + H_2O$$

Various final titration stages are encountered here, such as back titration of unused amine or titration of the water formed using the Karl Fischer reagent.

6. Single examples of other types of reactions of amines are given, such as coupling with diazonium salts. It may be mentioned here that amines have also been used as bases in certain analyses, e.g. in the determination of carbonyl compounds with hydroxylamine. The essential reaction is between the ketone or aldehyde and the hydroxylamine, so that there is a reduction of total base concentration.

Examples

Material titrated	Reagent and reaction conditions	Subsequent treatment and final titration stage	Ref.
Acetic anhydride	+ excess aniline	Titrated with alkali	1
Acetic anhydride in large excess acetic acid	+ 2,4-dichloroaniline. Left overnight	Extracted anilide with $CHCl_3$, converted to stable chloramine with bleaching powder/acetic acid, evaporated $CHCl_3$ and determined chloramine with KI and titration with thiosulphate	2
Methyl iodide from reaction with, in determination of methoxyl groups with hydriodic acid	Absorbed in pyridine	Titrated with $AgNO_3$ to chromate; or slight excess $AgNO_3$ added, then slight excess NaCl and finally titrated with $AgNO_3$	3
Acetic anhydride	+ aniline (control, + water)	Titrated with NaOH to phenolphthalein (also titrated with NaOH)	4

Materials titrated	Reagent and reaction conditions	Subsequent treatment and final titration stage	Ref.
Alkyl iodides from reaction with, in determination of alkoxyl groups with HI	Absorbed in pyridine	+ water and titrated with $AgNO_3$ to chromate	5
Diazotized *p*-aminophenol	+ excess *m*-phenylenediamine + sodium acetate at 25°	Titrated with benzenediazonium chloride (see Part I, Diazonium salts, ref. 5)	6
Acetic anydride	+ aniline	Acetanilide filtered, hydrolysed and the aniline determined bromometrically	7
Acetic anhydride	+ aniline/acetic acid (control, + excess NaOH)	Titrated with alkali (unused titrated with acid)	8
Acetic anhydride	+ 2,4-dichloroaniline in acetic acid at 25°	+ dilute HCl and titrated with nitrite to starch/iodide (see Part I, Nitrite, ref. 11)	9
Acetic anhydride	+ 2,4-dichloroaniline/ $CHCl_3$. Left overnight (control, + excess NaOH, overnight)	+ excess standard alkali and back titrated with acid (also back titrated with acid)	10, 13
Alkyl iodides from reaction with, in determination of alkoxyl groups with hydriodic acid	Absorbed in pyridine	Pyridinium iodide oxidized with iodate to iodine and then titrated with thiosulphate (see Iodate, ref. 15)	11
Small amounts of acetic anhydride in acetic acid	+ 2,4-dichloroaniline in acetic acid. Left overnight	+ HCl/water + excess bromate/bromide. Unused determined iodometrically (see Bromine reagents, ref. 55)	12
Acetate/sulphate (from determination of lead acetate via precipitation with measured excess H_2SO_4)	+ benzidine; 5 min	Filtered benzidine sulphate and titrated filtrate with NaOH to thymol blue or phenolphthalein	14
Alkyl sulphate detergents	+ benzidine hydrochloride	Dissolved precipitate in hot ethanol and titrated with alkali	15
Organic sulphate in commercial sulphated alcohols	In water, + benzidine hydrochloride; 10 min standing	Dissolved precipitate in hot ethanol and titrated with NaOH to bromocresol purple	16

Materials titrated	Reagent and reaction conditions	Subsequent treatment and final titration stage	Ref.
Acetic anhydride in cellulose esterification baths	+ excess standard aniline/acetic acid	Unused aniline titrated with a strong mineral acid	17
Naphthalenesulphonic acids	+ benzidine, β-naphthylamine or substituted anilines like *m*-nitroaniline	Precipitate titrated with NaOH to phenolphthalein	18
Acetic anhydride	+ excess anthranilic acid/acetic acid	Titrated with perchloric acid/acetic acid	19, 21
Methyl bromide in air	Absorbed in monoethanolamine. Not less than 15 min	Bromide determined via excess $AgNO_3$ and back titration with thiocyanate; or by hypochlorite oxidation to bromate, addition of KI/acid and titration with thiosulphate	20
Unused acetic anhydride after reaction with, in determination of non-basic hydrogen in amino acids	+ excess anthranilic acid; *ca* 3 h	Titrated with perchloric acid/acetic acid to crystal violet	22
Dichloroethane	+ monoethanolamine/dioxan; 1 h reflux	+ nitric acid + excess $AgNO_3$. Back titrated with thiocyanate to Fe(III)	23
HCHO in mixture with CH_3CHO	+ glycine	Remaining CH_3CHO, + $NaHSO_3$ followed by iodometric titration of combined bisulphite. Control on both aldehydes, giving HCHO by difference (see Bisulphite and sulphite, ref. 71)	24
Methyl bromide	Absorbed in monoethanolamine/wet sand (modification of method of ref. 20)	Br^- determined with excess Ag^+ or by hypobromite oxidation	25
Alkyl iodides from reaction with, in determination of alkoxyl groups with HI	Absorbed in pyridine	Distilled off pyridine, added water + Hg(OH)CN. Titrated liberated OH^- with H_2SO_4	26
Acetic anhydride	+ benzidine/nitrobenzene/benzene. At 0° (control, + water)	Titrated with alkali (also titrated with alkali)	27

Materials titrated	Reagent and reaction conditions	Subsequent treatment and final titration stage	Ref.
Methyl bromide in air	Absorbed in ethanol-amine/dioxan	Acidified. Titrated with $AgNO_3$ to eosin or with excess $AgNO_3$ and back titration with thiocyanate to Fe(III)	28
Aliphatic acid chlorides	+ aniline	+ HCl and aniline hydrochloride and unused HCl washed out. Remaining fatty acid titrated with alkali	29
Alkyl- and arylalkyl-sulphonates	+ *p*-toluidine hydrochloride/water/CCl_4; 5–10 min shaking	Amine sulphonate in CCl_4 layer titrated with alkali to *m*-cresol purple (see Part I, Alkali and alkaline earth hydroxides, ref. 45)	30
Excess acetic anhydride from determination of water in pyridine	+ aniline; 10 min (control, + water)	+ water and titrated with NaOH to phenolphthalein (also titrated with alkali)	31
Hexamethylene, benzyl and cyclohexyl isocyanates	In acetone, + piperidine/acetone	+ methanol + excess standard HCl. Unused acid titrated with alkali to methyl red/methylene blue. Control	32
Igepon T (Na salt of *N*-methyloleoyl-taurined	+ acid + benzidine hydrochloride; 3 h or left overnight	Precipitate dissolved in aqueous alcohol and titrated with NaOH to phenolphthalein (also gravimetric) (see Part I, Alkali and alkaline earth hydroxides, ref. 49)	33
Carbazole-3-sulphonic acid in mixture with isomeric sulphonic acids	In water, + benzidine hydrochloride. Boiled and cooled in ice	Precipitate titrated with NaOH to phenolphthalein (see Part I, Alkali and alkaline earth hydroxides, ref. 54)	34
Anhydrides of dibasic acids like tetrachlorophthalic anhydride	+ aniline/acetone; 30 min/room temp. or reflux	Titrated with alcoholic KOH to phenolphthalein	35, 36
Acid chlorides	In dioxan, + excess aniline	+ water. HCl titrated with NaOH to bromothymol blue. Also total Cl^- determined with excess $AgNO_3$ and back titration with thiocyanate. Difference equivalent to free acid chloride	37

Materials titrated	Reagent and reaction conditions	Subsequent treatment and final titration stage	Ref.
Sulphonate detergents	Extension of method of ref. 33	(see Part I, Alkali and alkaline earth hydroxides, ref. 58)	38
—NCO and —NCS groups	+ excess butylamine/ dry dioxan; 45 min/ room temp. for alkyl compounds. No delay for aryl compounds	+ water, and titrated with sulphuric acid to methyl red	39
Sulphoricinoleates	In water, + benzidine hydrochloride	Precipitate dissolved in hot ethanol and titrated with alcoholic KOH to bromocresol purple (see Part I, Alkali and alkaline earth hydroxides, ref. 62)	40
Isocyanates	In chlorobenzene, + excess butylamine/ chlorobenzene. Not over 5 min	+ methanol and titrated with aqueous HCl to bromophenol blue	41
Monohalides; mixtures	+ aniline or piperidine without solvent or in various solvents like nitrobenzene (components of mixtures react at different speeds)	+ acid and Cl^- determined with excess $AgNO_3$ and back titration with SCN^-	42
Salts of 2-nitro-1,3-indanedione	+ benzidine hydro-chloride; 24 h standing	Precipitate suspended in hot water and titrated with NaOH to phenolphthalein	43
Methyl bromide in chlorine-containing fumigants	+ ethanolamine	+ nitric acid and Cl^- titrated with Ag^+ potentiometrically	44
Anhydrides	+ excess aniline; 5–90 min/room temp. (15 min/100° for maleic anhydride)	+ isopropanol/ethylene glycol and titrated with HCl in same solvent potentiometrically (see Part I, Hydrochloric acid, ref. 26)	45
Anion-active materials	In water, + *p*-toluidine hydrochloride/ water + CCl_4 or ether; shaken 10 min.	Organic layer + ethanol, titrated with NaOH to cresol red (see Part I, Alkali and alkaline earth hydroxide, ref. 76)	46
Dibromomethane	+ ethanolamine. Study of conditions. 30 min/ 90° gave complete reaction	+ excess Ag^+ and back titration with SCN^- to Fe(III)	47

Materials titrated	Reagent and reaction conditions	Subsequent treatment and final titration stage	Ref.
Naphthalene-1,5- and -2,6-disulphonic acids	Neutral solution, + benzidine hydrochloride. Boiled and cooled	Precipitate titrated with NaOH to phenolphthalein (see Part I, Alkali and alkaline earth hydroxides, ref. 86)	48
—NCO groups in rubber bonding agents	+ excess isobutylamine/chlorobenzene. *Ca* 10 min	Titrated with HCl in chlorbenzene/methanol 3:10 potentiometrically (see Part I, Hydrochloric acid, ref. 29)	49
Allethrin (ester of chrysanthemum monocarboxylic acid)	+ ethylenediamine; 2 h/25–30° (yielding amine salt of the acid)	Titrated with $NaOCH_3$/pyridine to thymolphthalein	50
chrysanthemum monocarboxylic acid or anhydride	+ morpholine/methanol; 5 min/25–30°	titrated with HCl/methanol to dimethyl yellow/methylene blue	
Acetic anhydride	+ excess aniline in benzene; 5 min/0°, then 10 min/room temp.	+ CCl_4 + KBr + water and unused amine titrated with nitrite (see Part I, Nitrite, ref. 76)	51
Lignin sulphonic acids in sulphite waste liquors	+ excess polyamino-hydroxyethylchitosan or polymethylamino-chitosan	Unused titrated with potassium polyvinyl alcohol sulphate to toluidine blue	52
Aldehydes, e.g. HCHO, benzaldehyde, furfural, cinnamaldehyde, salicylaldehyde	+ excess laurylamine/isopropanol/ethylene glycol; 1 h/room temp.	Titrated with salicylic acid in same solvent potentiometrically (see Part I, Carboxylic acids, ref. 5)	53
Acetic anhydride	+ excess aniline/chlorobenzene	Unused titrated with perchloric acid/acetic acid to crystal violet (see Part I, Perchloric acid, ref. 68)	54
Anion-active synthetic tanning agents (sulphonates)	In water, + excess *p*-toluidine hydrochloride	Unused titrated with nitrite (see Part I, Nitrite, ref. 78	55
Unused propionic anhydride from reaction with in determination of —OH and —NH_2 groups	+ excess aniline/acetic acid/benzene; 5 min	Unused titrated with perchloric acid/acetic acid to crystal violet	56

Materials titrated	Reagent and reaction conditions	Subsequent treatment and final titration stage	Ref.
Anhydrides	+ excess morpholine/ methanol; 5–30 min	Titrated with HCl/methanol to dimethyl yellow/ methylene blue (see Part I, Hydrochloric acid, (ref. 41)	57
Unused propionic anhydride from reaction with, in determination of polyethylene glycol —OH groups	In acetic acid, + excess aniline/ benzene; 5 min	Titrated with $HClO_4$/acetic acid to crystal violet (see Part I, Perchloric acid, ref. 124)	58
Acetic anhydride	+ 3% aqueous aniline (control, + water)	Titrated with NaOH to phenolphthalein (also titrated with NaOH)	59
Sulphuric acid/ sulphonic acids in 'sour oil' from sulphonation of lubricating oils	Oil + $CHCl_3$ + aniline/ $CHCl_3$, giving aniline sulphate precipitate	Filtered and titrated sulphonic acids in filtrate with alcoholic KOH potentiometrically	60
α,β-Unsaturated nitriles and carbonyl compounds	+ morpholine/water/ acetic acid (catalyst); 5–240 min/25 or 98°	+ acetonitrile + acetic anhydride to react with unused morpholine. Titrated addition compound with HCl/ methanol to methyl orange/ xylene cyanol FF (see Part I, Hydrochloric acid, ref. 45)	61
Anhydrides	+ excess morpholine/ acetonitrile; 15 min	Neutralized to phenolphthalein, CS_2 added to convert unused amine to dithiocarbamic acid. Titrated with NaOH to thymolphthalein (see Part I, Alkali and alkaline earth hydroxides, ref. 117)	62
Benzene *o*- and *p*-disulphonic acids benzene *p*-disulphonic acid	+ β-naphthylamine + benzidine	Precipitate titrated in boiling solution with NaOH to phenolphthalein likewise determined (see Part I, Alkali and alkaline hydroxides, ref. 127)	63

Materials titrated	Reagent and reaction conditions	Subsequent treatment and final titration stage	Ref.
Acid chlorides and corresponding carboxylic acids	+ *m*-chloroaniline/acetone; 5 min/room temp.	+ water and titrated with NaOH potentiometrically. Break at pH 5–6 for amine hydrochloride and at 8–9·5 for the carboxylic acid	64
COS in petroleum gases	Absorbed in monoethanolamine/ethanol. Also in diamylamine at pH 10·6	+ CH_3COONa/acetic acid/ethanol or isopropanol. Titrated with $AgNO_3$/83% isopropanol potentiometrically (see Part I, Silver (I), ref. 109)	65
Acetic anhydride	+ excess aniline; 40–60 min	Unused titrated with $HClO_4$/acetic acid to crystal violet (see Part I, Perchloric acid, ref. 170)	66
Primary allyl-type chlorides in presence of isomeric tertiary type, e.g. 1-chloro-3-methyl-2-butene in presence 2-chloro-2-methyl-3-butene	+ hexamethylenetetramine/KI, giving $(RC_6H_{12}N_4)^+I^-$	Unused base titrated with HCl in presence formalin	67
Alkyl halides, esters of phosphoric and sulphuric acids (determination of equivalent weights)	+ ethanolamine; 1 or 2 h reflux or 1 h/100°	Passed through ion exchanger Dowex 50 and effluent titrated with NaOH (see Ion exchangers, ref. 24)	68
Unused phenyl isocyanate after reaction with, in determination of silanol groups	+ isobutylamine	Unused titrated with HCl	69, 74
Acetic anhydride	In acetic acid, + excess aniline; 15 min/100°	Unused titrated with $HClO_4$/acetic acid to methyl violet	70
CS_2	+ morpholine or diethanolamine in water/pyridine/isopropanol	Dithiocarbamic acid formed titrated with slight excess NaOH with final back titration with HCl to thymolphthalein	71
—NCO and —NCS groups	In chlorobenzene, + dibutylamine/chlorobenzene/methanol. A few min shaking	Unused titrated with HCl to bromophenol blue	72

Materials titrated	Reagent and reaction conditions	Subsequent treatment and final titration stage	Ref.
anhydrides	in acetic acid, + excess 2,4-dichloroaniline/acetic acid; 2 h	+ HCl + bromate/bromide excess, followed by iodometric determination of excess (see Bromine reagents, ref. 459)	72
—SO_3H groups in synthetic detergents, etc.	+ *p*-toluidine	Salt extracted with ether and titrated with NaOH	73
Alkylketene dimers	In ether, + ethylamine/ethanol	Unused titrated with HCl to bromocresol green (see Part I, Hydrochloric acid, ref. 69)	75
—NCO and —NCS groups	+ excess dibutylamine/dioxan; 15–45 min	Unused titrated with HCl to methyl red (see Part I, Hydrochloric acid, ref. 70)	76
Alkyl halides (reactive)	In dioxan, + aniline; 3–30 min reflux	+ aniline and titrated with CH_3ONa/benzene/methanol to thymol blue	77
Carbonyl compounds, e.g. aromatic aldehydes	+ aniline or *o*-toluidine/benzene	Water titrated with Karl Fischer reagent	78
CS_2	+ diethylamine	Dithiocarbamate titrated with $HgCl_2$/pyridine to Cu/EDTA (see Part I, Mercury (II), ref. 65)	79
Acrylonitrile	+ piperidine/dioxan + a little acetic acid; 30 min	+ acetic anhydride to acetylate excess piperidine. Titrated reaction product with HCl/methanol to methyl red/methylene blue (see Part I, Hydrochloric acid, ref. 72)	80
Reactive halide impurities in $CHCl_3$	+ piperidine; 2 h/60° in sealed ampoule	+ nitric acid + excess $AgNO_3$. Back titrated with SCN^- in presence nitrobenzene to Fe(III)	81
Unused propionic anhydride after reaction with, in determination of chloroamphenicol	+ excess aniline/benzene	Unused titrated with $HClO_4$/acetic acid to crystal violet or potentiometrically (see Part I, Perchloric acid, ref. 269)	82

Materials titrated	Reagent and reaction conditions	Subsequent treatment and final titration stage	Ref.
Aldehydes formed in determination of serine and threonine by oxidation with periodate	+ glycine to react with aldehydes and prevent formation of aldehyde–ammonia derivatives	Ammonia distilled and titrated with acid	83
N-Nitrosodiphenylamine	In 70% acetic acid, + excess α-naphthylamine/acetic acid; 30 min/60°	Unused titrated with $HClO_4$/acetic acid (see Part I, Perchloric acid, refs 309, 339)	84 89
Anion-active agents, e.g. sodium dodecylbenzenesulphonate	+ excess benzidine or *p*-toluidine (methods of refs 15, 30)	Unused titrated with nitrite (see Part I, Nitrite, ref. 136)	85
Anhydrides	+ moderate excess hexamethyleneimine or piperidine/dioxan; 5 min	+ ethanol and unused titrated with HCl/methanol to methyl red/methylene blue	86
Methyl bromide, dibromomethane and carbon tetrachloride in air	+ monoethanolamine (differential reaction with various reaction conditions)	Br^- and Cl^- titrated amperometrically with Ag^+	87
Anhydrides; acid chlorides	+ excess *m*-chloroaniline in acetic acid/benzene or nitrobenzene. Up to 1 h/65–70°	+ acetic acid + HCl + KBr and titrated with nitrite potentiometrically (see Part I, Nitrite, ref. 142)	88
Benzoyl, palmitoyl chlorides	+ morpholine/CCl_4 + mercuric acetate/acetic acid. Heated to boiling	Unused titrated with $HClO_4$/acetic acid to Tropeolin 00	90
Benzyl bromide, formed from, in determination of benzyl groups in esters by reaction with HBr	In benzene, + aniline; 5 min heating	Titrated with CH_3ONa/benzene/methanol to thymol blue	91
Phosgene	In toluene, + hexamethylenimine/toluene or dioxan. A few min reaction	Made alkaline, distilled unused amine into excess standard acid and titrated with standard alkali to methyl red/methylene blue	92

Materials titrated	Reagent and reaction conditions	Subsequent treatment and final titration stage	Ref.
Alkyl iodides from reaction with, in determination of alkoxyl and *S*-methyl groups with HI	Absorbed in pyridine; 2 h boiling	Titrated with tetrabutylammonium hydroxide in benzene/methanol potentiometrically or to azo violet. Difference between the breaks or colour changes equivalent to the quaternary iodide (see Part I, Quaternary ammonium hydroxides, ref. 50)	93
Unused phenyl isocyanate from determination of hydroxyl groups in unsaturated polyester resins	In chlorobenzene/acetone (from previous reaction) + diisobutylamine/chlorobenzene	Unused amine titrated with acid to bromophenol blue	94
Acetic anhydride in acetylation mixtures	+ excess aniline; 10 min/room temp.	+ diethylene glycol and back titrated with $HClO_4$/dioxan potentiometrically	95
Anionic surface-active agents	In dilute HCl (pH 1·5–2), + excess 4-amino-4′-chloro-biphenyl hydrochloride; 10 min/room temp., giving precipitate of salt	Filtered and filtrate titrated with nitrite to external starch/I^- (see Part I, Nitrite, ref. 147)	96
Anionic surface-active agents, e.g. sulphonates	In water, + *p*-toluidine hydrochloride + CCl_4	CCl_4 layer + ethanol and titrated with NaOH	97
Diisocyanates	In dry chlorobenzene, + hexamethylenimine/chlorobenzene; 20 min/room temp.	+ excess HCl + ethanol or isopropanol and titrated with NaOH to bromophenol blue	98
CS_2 in organic solvents	+ ethylenediamine/dimethylformamide; 2–3 min/room temp., then 30 sec/*ca* 100° giving β-aminoethyl-dithiocarbamate	+ NaOH/methanol and titrated with *o*-hydroxy-mercuribenzoic acid to disappearance of blue of thio-fluorescein	99
Unused propionic anhydride from determination of 'propionyl number' of essential oils	+ aniline/benzene, + acetic acid; 5 min/room temp.	Unused amine titrated with $HClO_4$ to crystal violet	100, 102
Isothiocyanates	+ excess piperidine/dioxan	Unused base titrated with acid	101

Materials titrated	Reagent and reaction conditions	Subsequent treatment and final titration stage	Ref
Unreacted phthalic anhydride from determination of water in formic acid	+ *N*-ethylaniline/ benzene; 5 min boiling	+ benzene/nitrobenzene and titrated potentiometrically with $HClO_4$/acetic acid	103
Aldehydes in mixtures with acetals	Method of ref 78		104
Acrylonitrile	+ methanol + hexamethyleneimine/ methanol + acetic acid; 4 h	+ acetic anhydride to remove unreacted imine and titrated with HCl/methanol to methyl red/methylene blue	105
Acid chlorides; sulphonyl chlorides	+ hexamethyleneimine/ methanol; 5–10 min/room temp.	Titrated with HCl/methanol to methyl red/methylene blue	106
Sulphonates	Modification of method of ref 30		107
Chlorendic acid/ chlorendic anhydride/ maleic acid/maleic anhydride	+ aniline/$CHCl_3$; 90 min	+ acetone; aliquot titrated with KOH potentiometrically, giving breaks for 1st H of maleic acid; for chlorendic acid + anilides; and for 2nd H of maleic acid; Also unreacted aniline back titrated with $HClO_4$	108
Cyanuric trichloride in presence of Cl^-	+ Na sulphanilate/ water; 25–30 min reflux	+ HCl and back titrated with nitrite to starch/I^-	109
Unreacted phenyl isocyanate from determination of hydroxyl equivalent weights of polyoxyalkylene compounds	In dimethylformamide/ toluene (from previous reaction), + dibutylamine/toluene; 15 min/room temp.	+ methyl cellosolve and titrated with $HClO_4$/methyl cellosolve to bromocresol green	110
Diazonium salts, e.g. tolyldiazonium chloride	+ excess hexamethyleneimine + Na_2CO_3; 5 min/room temp. also + Na acetate + *m*-toluidine; 15 min/ca room temp.	Made alkaline and unreacted amine distilled into boric acid and titrated with HCl to methyl red/methylene blue; unreacted amine similarly isolated and determined with excess bromate/bromide (see Bromine reagents, ref. 543)	111

Materials titrated	Reagent and reaction conditions	Subsequent treatment and final titration stage	Ref.
Unreacted *p*-tolyldiazonium chloride from determination of phenols	Method of ref 111		112

References

1. Menschutkin, N. and Vasilieff, M., *J. Russ. Phys. Chem. Soc.* **21**, 190 (1889).
2. Edwards, M. G. and Orton, K. J. P., *Analyst* **36**, 417 (1911); *J. Chem. Soc.* **99**, 1181 (1911).
3. Kirpal, A. and Bühn, T., *Ber.* **47**, 1084 (1914).
4. Radcliffe, L. G. and Medofski, S., *J. Soc. Chem. Ind., London* **36**, 628 (1917).
5. Melander, K. H. A., *Svensk Papperstidn.* **24**, 277 (1921).
6. Ermen, W. F. A., *Chem. & Ind. (London)* **42**, 538 (1923).
7. Spencer, G. C., *J. Assoc. Offic. Agr. Chem.* **6**, 493 (1923).
8. Porter, R., *Chem. Trade J.* **75**, 93 (1924).
9. Calcott, W. S., English, F. L. and Wilbur, O. C., *Ind. Eng. Chem.* **17**, 942 (1925).
10. Terlinck, E., *Ingénieur chimiste* **9**, 140 (1925).
11. Eaton, E. D. and West, E. S., *J. Biol. Chem.* **75**, 283 (1927).
12. Orton, K. J. P. and Bradfield, A. E., *J. Chem. Soc.* 983 (1927).
13. Terlinck, E., *Chem.-Ztg.* **53**, 814, 850 (1929).
14. Han, J. E. S. and Chu, T. L., *Ind. Eng. Chem., Anal. Ed.* **3**, 379 (1931).
15. Kling, W. and Püschel, F., *Melliand. Textilber.* **15**, 21 (1934).
16. Biffen, F. M. and Snell, F. D., *Ind. Eng. Chem., Anal. Ed.* **7**, 234 (1935).
17. Malm, C. J. and Nadeau, G. F., *U.S. Patent* 2,063,324, Dec. 8 (1936).
18. Zinkov, E. I., Damyushkevskii, Ya. L., Reinshtein, V. and Khomyakovskii, G. M., *J. Appl. Chem., USSR.* **9**, 1997 (1936).
19. Kilpi, S., *Suomen Kemistilehti* **11B**, 7 (1938).
20. Stenger, V. A., Shrader, S. A. and Beshgetoor, A. W., *Ind. Eng. Chem., Anal. Ed.* **11**, 121 (1939).
21. Kilpi, S., *Suomen Kemistilehti* **13B**, 19 (1940).
22. Toennies, G. and Kolb, J. J., *J. Biol. Chem.* **144**, 219 (1942).
23. Winteringham, F. P. W., *J. Soc. Chem. Ind., London* **61**, 187 (1942).
24. Shupe, I. S., *J. Assoc. Offic. Agr. Chem.* **26**, 249 (1943).
25. Chisholm, R. D. and Koblitsky, L., *Ind. Eng. Chem., Anal. Ed.* **16**, 538 (1944).
26. Ingram, G., *Analyst* **69**, 363 (1944).
27. Vais, O., *Chem. Listy* **38**, 15 (1944).

28. Lewis, S. E., *J. Soc. Chem. Ind., London* **64**, 57 (1945).
29. Bauer, S. T., *Oil & Soap* **23**, 1 (1946).
30. Marron, T. U. and Schifferli, J., *Ind. Eng. Chem., Anal. Ed.* **18**, 49 (1946).
31. Pesez, M., *Ann. pharm. franç.* **4**, 98 (1946).
32. Stagg, H. E., *Analyst* **71**, 557 (1946).
33. Shiraeff, D. A., *Proc. Am. Assoc. Text. Chem. Colorists* 313 (1947).
34. Borodkin, V. F. and Mal'kova, T. V., *Zhur. Anal. Khim.* **3**, 186 (1948).
35. Kappelmeier, C. P. A. and van Goor, W. R., *Verfkroniek* **21**, 136 (1948).
36. Kappelmeier, C. P. A. and van Goor, W. R., *Anal. Chim. Acta* **2**, 146 (1948).
37. Pesez, M. and Willemart, R., *Bull. soc. chim. France* 479 (1948).
38. Shiraeff, D. A., *Am. Dyestuff Reptr.* **37**, 411 (1948).
39. Siggia, S. and Hanna, J. G., *Anal. Chem.* **20**, 1084 (1948).
40. Robinet, M. and Chevron, N., *Bull. soc. chim. Belges* **58**, 324 (1949).
41. Siefkin, W., *Ann.* **562**, 99 (1949).
42. Salomon, G. and Ultée, A. J., *Rec. trav. chim.* **69**, 95 (1950).
43. Vanags, G. and Lipmanis, M., *Kim. Inst. Z. Raksti, Latvijas PSR Zinatnu Akad. Vestis* **1**, 78 (1950).
44. Winteringham, F. P. W., Bridges, R. G. and Harrison, A., *J. Sci. Food Agr.* **1**, 185 (1950).
45. Siggia, S. and Hanna, J. G., *Anal. Chem.* **23**, 1717 (1951).
46. Stüpel, H. and v. Segesser, A., *Helv. Chim. Acta* **34**, 1362 (1951).
47. Sinclair, W. B. and Crandall, P. R., *J. Econ. Entomol.* **45**, 80 (1952).
48. Spryskov, A. A. and Karavaev, B. I., *Zhur. Obshchei Khim.* **22**, 1620 (1952).
49. Williamson, A. G., *Analyst* **77**, 372 (1952).
50. Hogsett, J. N., Kacy, H. W. and Johnson, J. B., *Anal. Chem.* **25**, 1207 (1953).
51. Parravano, G., *Chim. anal.* **35**, 13 (1953).
52. Senju, R., *Bull. Chem. Soc., Japan* **26**, 143, 148 (1953).
53. Siggia, S. and Segal, E., *Anal. Chem.* **25**, 830 (1953).
54. Capitani, C. and Imperiale, P., *Chim. e Ind., Milan* **36**, 606 (1954).
55. Kilchler, H., *Österr. Lederztg., Festivalnr.* A 17 (1954).
56. Pesez, M., *Bull. soc. chim. France* 1237 (1954).
57. Johnson, J. B. and Funk, G. L., *Anal. Chem.* **27**, 1464 (1955).
58. Sezerat, A., *Ann. pharm. franç.* **13**, 516 (1955).
59. Zavarov, G. V., *Zavodskaya Lab.* **21**, 791 (1955).
60. Cali, L. J. and Loveland, J. W., *Anal. Chem.* **28**, 224 (1956).
61. Critchfield, F. E., Funk, G. L. and Johnson, J. B., *Anal. Chem.* **28**, 76 (1956).
62. Critchfield, F. E. and Johnson, J. B., *Anal. Chem.* **28**, 430 (1956).
63. Spryskov, A. A. and Starkov, S. P., *Zhur. Obshchei Khim.* **26**, 2607 (1956).

64. Stahl, C. R. and Siggia, S., *Anal. Chem.* **28**, 1971 (1956).
65. Bruss, D. B., Wyld, G. E. A. and Peters, E. D., *Anal. Chem.* **29**, 807 (1957).
66. Ellerington, T. and Nicholls, J. J., *Analyst* **82**, 233 (1957).
67. Leets, K. V., Pilevskaya, A. I. and Korovkina, M. I., *USSR. Patent* 106, 985 Aug. 25 (1957).
68. Baldwin, W. H. and Higgins, C. E., *Anal. Chem.* **30**, 446 (1958).
69. Damm, W. and Noll, K., *Kolloid Z.* **158**, 97 (1958).
70. Hryniewiecka, J. and Jaworska, J., *Chem. Anal.* (*Warsaw*) **3**, 163 (1958).
71. Romováček, J., *Chem. Listy* **52**, 1912 (1958).
72. Roth, H., *Mikrochim. Acta* 766 (1958).
73. Bespyatov, M. P., Preobrazhenskaya, E. A., Rits, O. V., Ovcharenko, V. B. and Storinskii, L. I., *Maslob.-Zhir. Prom.* **25**, 18 (1959).
74. Damm, W., Noll, K. and Krauss, W., *Farbe u. Lack* **65**, 17 (1959).
75. Imou, I., Wakabayashi, T., Yoshino, M., Komiya, S. and Kotera, K., *J. Japan Oil Chem. Soc.* **8**, 279 (1959).
76. Karten, B. S. and Ma, T. S., *Microchem. J.* **3**, 507 (1959).
77. Patchornik, A. and Rogozinski, S. E., *Anal. Chem.* **31**, 985 (1959).
78. Petrova, L. N., Novikova, E. N. and Skvortsova, A. B., *Zhur. Anal. Khim.* **14**, 347 (1959).
79. Šedivec, V. and Flek, J., *Collection Czechoslov. Chem. Communs.* **24**, 3643 (1959).
80. Terent'ev, A. P., Buzlanova, M. M. and Obtemperanskaya, S. I., *Zhur. Anal. Khim.* **14**, 506 (1959).
81. Williams, H., *J. Pharm. & Pharmacol.* **11**, 400 (1959).
82. Franchi, G. and Pellerano, C., *Ann. Chim.* (*Rome*) **50**, 134 (1960).
83. Maros, L., Molnar-Perl, I. and Schulek, E., *Acta Chim. Acad. Sci. Hung.* **24**, 213 (1960).
84. Marvillet, L. and Tranchant, J., *Mém. poudres* **42**, 261 (1960).
85. Nemoto, M., *Yukagaku* **9**, 65 (1960).
86. Terent'ev, A. P., Obtemperanskaya, S. I., Buzlanova, M. M. and Vlasova, T. E., *Vestn. Moskov. Univ. Ser. Khim. II* No. 4, 71 (1960).
87. Berck, B., *Can. Dept. Agr. Publ.* No. 1101 (1961).
88. Litvinenko, L. M., Aleksandrova, D. M. and Napadailo, V. G., *Zhur. Anal. Khim.* **16**, 226 (1961).
89. Marvillet, L. and Tranchant, J., *Chim. anal.* **43**, 169 (1961).
90. Ömböly, C. and Derzsi, E., *Z. anal. Chem.* **183**, 272 (1961).
91. Patchornik, A. and Ehrlich-Rogozinski, S., *Anal. Chem.* **33**, 803 (1961).
92. Terent'ev, A. P., Buzlanova, M. I. and Obtemperanskaya, S. I., *Zhur. Anal. Khim.* **16**, 743 (1961).
93. Cundiff, R. H. and Markunas, P. C., *Anal. Chem.* **33**, 1028 (1961).
94. Dreher, B., *Farbe u. Lack* **67**, 703 (1961).

95. Emelin, E. A. and Svistunova, G. P., *Zavodskaya Lab.* **27**, 971 (1961).
96. Izawa, Y., Tokumasu, K. and Kimura, W., *J. Jap. Oil Chem. Soc.* **10**, 205 (1961).
97. Podshibyakina, K. D., *Tekstil Prom.* **21**, No. 3, 63 (1961).
98. Strongin, G. M., Bodrova, A. N. and Smirnov, V. I., *Vestn. Tekhn. i Ekon. Inform. Nauch.—Issled. Inst. Tekhn.-Ekon. Issled. Gos. Kom. Soveta Min. SSSR. po Khim.* No. 5, 30 (1961).
99. Wronski, M., *Chem. Anal. (Warsaw)*, **6**, 865 (1961).
100. Franchi, G. and Franchi, R. R., *Boll. chim. farm.* **101**, 127 (1962).
101. Venkataraghavan, R. and Rao, C. N. R., *Chemist-Analyst* **51**, 48 (1962).
102. Franchi, G. and Franchi, R. R., *Congr. Sci. Farm., Conf. Comun.*, 21° *Pisa* 1961, 532 (1962).
103. Kiciak, S., *Chem. Anal. (Warsaw)* **7**, 847 (1962).
104. Skvortsova, A. B., Petrova, L. N. and Novikova, E. N., *Zhur. Anal. Khim.* **17**, 896 (1962).
105. Terent'ev, A. P., Buzlanova, M. I., Obtemperanskaya, S. I. and Volodz'ko, V. E., *Vestn. Mosk. Univ., Ser. Khim.* 83 (1962).
106. Terent'ev, A. P., Obtemperanskaya, S. I., Buzlanova, M. T., and Vlasova, T. E., *Zhur. Anal. Khim.* **17**, 900 (1962).
107. Bespyatov, M. A., Lipova, N. F., Dzyuba, L. Ya. and Ovcharenko, V. E., *Maslob.-Zhir. Prom.* **29**, 29 (1963).
108. Emelin, E. A., Smyslova, N. F. and Tsarfin, Ya. A., *Zavodskaya Lab.* **29**, 1169 (1963).
109. Lyande, Yu. U. and Cherkasskii, A. A., *Zavodskaya Lab.* **29**, 1050 (1963).
110. Reed, D. H., Critchfield, F. E. and Elder, D. K., *Anal. Chem.* **35**, 571 (1963).
111. Terent'ev, A. P. and Tubina, I. S., *Zhur. Anal. Khim.* **18**, 113 (1963).
112. Terent'ev, A. P. and Tubina, I. S., *Zhur. Anal. Khim.* **18**, 880 (1963).

Ammonium hydroxide and ammonium salts

Reagent. Mostly aqueous solutions, the chloride and sulphate being the salts used.

Reactions, materials titrated and subsequent treatment. There are three principal types:

1. Condensation, in determination of formaldehyde.

$$6\ HCHO + 4\ NH_3 \rightarrow (CH_2)_6N_4 + 6\ H_2O$$

After a reaction time of usually under an hour, the consumption of ammonia has been determined by titration of (i) the unused amount; (ii) unused alkali where used in combination with an ammonium salt;

or (iii) acid liberated from a neutral ammonium salt solution. In one case, the hexamine formed was determined via precipitation of its picrate.

2. Addition, in determination of allyl isothiocyanate.

$$C_3H_5N{=}C{=}S + NH_3 \rightarrow C_3H_5NH.CS.NH_2$$

The thiosinamine (allyl thiourea) has been then determined by oxidation titration, e.g. with iodine or iodate; or with a Ag^+ reagent (direct titration or use of excess and back titration)

$$C_3H_5NH.CS.NH_2 \rightleftharpoons C_3H_5NH.C(SH){=}NH$$

$$C_3H_5NH.C(SH){=}NH + Ag^+ \rightarrow C_3H_5NH.C(SAg){=}NH + H^+$$

In many cases, measured excess of silver reagent has been added together with the ammonia at the beginning and the two reaction stages carried out in one operation (see also under 'Silver (I)').

There are many references to this determination, especially in older literature and only a small selection has been given here.

3. Ion/ion combination, in determination of uric acid via precipitation as its insoluble salt. This is essentially a separation of the acid which was then regenerated in acid solution and determined by titration with oxidizing reagents such as iodine or permanganate.

Only one example of each of the following reactions is given in the tables:

4. Amide formation in determination of the free carboxylic acid in lauroyl chloride.

$$\begin{array}{lcl} R.COCl + 2\,NH_3 & \rightarrow & R.CONH_2 + NH_4Cl \\ + & & + \\ R.COOH & & R.COOH \text{ (as ammonium salt)} \end{array}$$

After acidification, the amide and carboxylic acid were extracted into an organic solvent and the acid titrated.

5. Halogen replacement, e.g. with DDT.

$$R.Cl + 2\,NH_3 \rightarrow R.NH_2 + NH_4^+ + Cl^-$$

The Cl^- was determined argentometrically.

6. 'Replacement' reaction with alkali salts of weak organic acids. E.g.

$$RCOOK + NH_4^+ \rightarrow RCOOH + K^+ + NH_3$$

The ammonia was distilled out and titrated.

7. Hydrolysis of a precipitated reineckate to yield thiocyanate. This was converted in an ion exchange column, to HSCN which was titrated.

Examples

Materials titrated	Reagent and reaction conditions	Subsequent treatment and final titration stage	Ref.
HCHO	+ excess NH_4OH. Up to 24 h tried—1 h found enough	Unused titrated with H_2SO_4 to rosolic acid	1, 8
Uric acid in urine	+ excess NH_4Cl; 2 h with frequent stirring	Insoluble salt added to water, uric acid precipitated with HCl and determined, e.g. with permanganate titration (see Part I, Permanganate, ref. 7)	2
Neutral salts of carboxylic acids	+ NH_4Cl + water	Ammonia distilled out into HCl and back titrated to methyl orange	3
HCHO	+ excess NH_4Cl + measured excess NaOH; 30 min	Titrated with acid to rosolic acid	4
Allyl isothiocyanate	+ ammonia + excess $AgNO_3$; 24 h/room temp.	+ HNO_3 and unused Ag^+ titrated with SCN^- to Fe(III)	5
HCHO	+ NH_4Cl or $(NH_4)_2SO_4$	Titrated with alkali to litmus	6
Uric acid	+ NH_4OH/NH_4Cl; 15 min	Insoluble salt dissolved in acetic acid, borax + $KHCO_3$ added and titrated with iodine (see Part I, Iodine, ref. 15)	7
HCHO	+ NH_4OH; 30 min	Unused NH_3 expelled by warming and derivative determined by precipitation with picric acid (see Nitrophenols, ref. 8)	9
HCHO	Method of ref. 4 criticized		10
Allyl isothiocyanate in mustard	Distilled into NH_4OH	+ H_2SO_4 + excess iodine, followed by back titration with thiosulphate (see Iodine reagents, ref. 74)	11

Materials titrated	Reagent and reaction conditions	Subsequent treatment and final titration stage	Ref.
Uric acid (micro)	Method of ref. 7	As in ref. 7 but with $NaHCO_3$ instead of borax/$KHCO_3$ (see Part I, Iodine, ref. 27)	12
Allyl isothiocyanate	+ NH_4OH; 15 min	Filtered, + H_2SO_4 + excess iodine; after 15 min + benzene and back titrated with thiosulphate	13
HCHO	+ neutralized NH_4Cl + measured excess NaOH	Titrated with acid to bromophenol blue	14
Allyl isothiocyanate in mustard oil	+ NH_4OH/alcohol; 10 min heating	+ KBr + HCl + $AuBr_3$, heated to 45° and titrated with bromate to yellow (see Part I, Bromate, ref. 40)	15
HCHO	+ NH_4OH. A few min standing	Unused ammonia distilled into excess standard H_2SO_4. Back titrated with alkali	16
HCHO in presence CH_3CHO	+ $(NH_4)_2SO_4$; 15 min	Titrated with NaOH to rosolic acid	17
Uric acid, urates	+ NH_4^+ salts	Precipitate dissolved in borax buffer and titrated with permanganate	18
Free lauric acid in lauroyl chloride	+ 6% NH_4OH; 20 min	+ HCl to methyl orange. Amide and acid extracted with ether/ethanol and extract titrated with NaOH to phenolphthalein	19
DDT in plant and other materials	Extract + benzene + NH_3/methanol; 16 h/45°	Cl^- determined with excess $AgNO_3$ and back titration with SCN^-	20
Uric acid in blood	+ NH_4^+ salts	Precipitate titrated with iodine	21
HCHO	Neutral solution + NH_4Cl + measured excess NaOH	Titrated with HCl to methyl red	22
Allyl isothiocyanate	+ NH_4OH/ethanol; 10 min/50°, then 10 min/70°	+ HCl and titrated with iodate potentiometrically (see Part I, Iodate, ref. 50)	23

Materials titrated	Reagent and reaction conditions	Subsequent treatment and final titration stage	Ref.
Chloropromazine reineckate, precipitated in determination of the base	In acetone/water + NH_4OH; 10 min/*ca* 100°	Passed through Wofatite F yielding HSCN. Titrated with alkali	24
Allyl isothiocyanate	+ NH_4OH/ethanol; 20 min heating	+ HNO_3 + excess $AgNO_3$. Unused Ag^+ determined by SCN^- titration to Fe(III) after filtration	25
Allyl isothiocyanate	+ aqueous NH_4OH; 10 min/40°	+ NH_4OH/NH_4NO_3 and titrated with $AgNO_3$ amperometrically	26
Allyl isothiocyanate in mustard seeds and their by-products	Distilled into NH_4OH	+$AgNO_3$; 1h/80°, filtered and filtrate titrated with SCN^- (see Silver (I), ref. 184)	27

References

1. Legler, L., *Ber.* **16**, 1333 (1883).
2. Hopkins, F. G., *Chemical News* **66**, 106 (1892); *Proc. Roy. Soc.* **52**, 96 (1892).
3. McIlhiney, P., *J. Am. Chem. Soc.* **16**, 408 (1894).
4. Smith, C. E., *Am. J. Pharm.* 86 (1898).
5. Gadamer, J., *Arch. Pharm.* **237**, 110, 372 (1899).
6. Schiff, H., *Chem.-Ztg.* **27**, 14 (1903).
7. Ronchèse, A., *J. pharm. chim.* (6) **23**, 336 (1906).
8. Legler, L., *Z. anal. Chem.* **44**, 442 (1909).
9. Kollo, C. and Lascar, O., *Bull. soc. chim. Romania* **3**, 3 (1921).
10. Mach, F. and Herrmann, R., *Z. anal. Chem.* **62**, 104 (1923).
11. Morvillez, F. and Meesemaecker, R., *J. pharm. chim.* **30**, 236 (1924).
12. Danet, R., *J. pharm. chim.* (8) **6**, 405 (1927).
13. Meesemaecker, R. and Boivin, J., *J. pharm. chim.* (8) **11**, 478 (1930).
14. Büchi, J., *Pharm. Acta Helv.* **6**, 1 (1931).
15. Madis, V., *Pharmacia* (*Estonia*) **18**, 252 (1939).
16. Foschini, A. and Talenti, M., *Z. anal. Chem.* **118**, 94 (1939).
17. Castiglioni, A., *Z. anal. Chem.* **119**, 287 (1940).
18. Malhada, *Arquiv. biol.* (*Sao Paolo*) **27**, 91 (1943).
19. Ackley, R. R. and Tesoro, G. C., *Ind. Eng. Chem., Anal. Ed.* **18**, 444 (1946).
20. Baier, W. E., Edmonds, E. J. Wilson, C. W., Elliot, M. I. and Gunther, F. A., *Science* **104**, 376 (1946).
21. Dobreva, N., *Ann. univ. Sofia, Fasc. med.* **27**, 801 (1947–8).

22. Casini, A., *Ann. chim. applicata* **39**, 600 (1949).
23. Berka, A. and Zýka, J., *Pharmazie* **13**, 88 (1958).
24. Howorka, K., *Pharm. Zentralhalle* **97**, 374 (1958).
25. Fürst, W. and Poethke, W., *Pharm. Zentralhalle* **99**, 674 (1960).
26. Fürst, W. and Poethe, W., *Pharm. Zentralhalle* **100**, 71 (1961).
27. Kerzner, I. L. and Ershova, M. S., *Masloboino-Zhirovaya Prom.* **27**, No. 11, 41 (1961).

8. Anhydrides

The anhydrides included here are those in which the anhydride group reacts with the component to be determined. The use of maleic anhydride in determination of conjugated olefines via Diels–Alder addition is considered under the heading of that reagent.

Reagent. Acetic anhydride in over 80% of the examples given. Next in frequency of use is phthalic anhydride. Other anhydrides which have been employed, are propionic, benzoic, 3-nitrophthalic and pyromellitic.

Reactions and materials titrated. 1. Ester formation in determination of hydroxyl compounds, which include alcohols, phenols, polyalcohols (glycols up to sugars) and the hydroxyl group concentration of materials like essential oils, tannins and lignins. This last named is sometimes referred to as the determination of the 'acetylation index'

$$R'OH + (RCO)_2O \rightarrow RCOOR' + RCOOH$$

Tertiary alcohols and phenols react less readily and many efforts have been made with only limited success to work out reaction conditions for complete reaction with these compounds. Phthalic anhydride is claimed not to react with phenols and has thus been used to determine alcohols in presence of phenols.

The determination of oximes by acylation can be included here.

2. Amide formation in determination of primary and secondary amine groups.

$$R'NH_2 + (RCO)_2O \rightarrow RCONHR' + RCOOH$$

This reaction has also been carried out to acylate these groups so that tertiary amines, which do not react, could subsequently be determined. In one case (ref. 135), amines were thus acetylated to prevent their interference in determination of olefines.

3. Two examples are given of acylation of an —SH group (refs 58 and 132); and one of dehydration of an alcohol to the corresponding olefine (ref. 122).

Reaction conditions. Usually in solution in pyridine or other tertiary base; also in other non-acylatable solvents like xylene, ethyl acetate or acetonitrile, and even without solvent. Sodium acetate has often been added especially where pyridine was not used.

Higher temperature and longer reaction times are needed for complete esterification of polyalcohols, but too high a temperature may be dangerous for some naturally occurring materials which suffer side reactions.

Acid catalysts like phosphoric, sulphonic, sulphuric, hydrochloric and perchloric acids have occasionally been used.

Subsequent treatment and final titration stage. (i) The esters formed from hydroxy compounds have been determined by saponification with measured excess alkali, followed by back titration of the unused part (see Alkalies). The ester has nearly always been first isolated by one of the following procedures:

(a) direct separation, especially with the water-insoluble esters of higher molecular weight materials such as menthol,
(b) extraction with a solvent like petroleum ether,
(c) distillation out, if volatile,
(d) as residue after distillation of acetic acid formed and unused acetic anhydride (as with (a), this is possible only with esters of higher alcohols).

Less usually, the reaction mixture has been neutralized and the ester then determined *in situ* by addition of the measured excess of alkali.

(ii) Unused anhydride has been determined by:
(a) direct titration with aniline,
(b) reaction with a measured excess of amine (e.g. aniline or anthranilic acid) followed by back titration of the unused amine with an acid like perchloric acid,
(c) reaction with a measured excess water, the unused part of which was back titrated with Karl Fischer reagent.

(iii) Carboxylic acid formed together with unreacted anhydride have been determined by titration with an alkali reagent. In the differential procedure usually employed, this titration is compared with that of a sample of anhydride reagent hydrolysed with water:

$$\underset{\text{(amine or hydroxy compound)}}{X\text{—}H} + (RCO)_2O \rightarrow X\text{—}COR + RCOOH \quad \text{Unreacted anhydride then hydrolysed}$$

$$H_2O + (RCO)_2O \rightarrow 2\ RCOOH$$

Any free acid in the reagent (which is difficult to obtain completely pure) is titrated in each case and the difference between the two alkali titrations is equivalent to the amine or hydroxy compound.

The stage of hydrolysis of unreacted anhydride before titration must be carefully controlled. It is catalysed by tertiary bases like pyridine and then usually takes place rapidly enough even in the cold. Numerous authors have warned against excessive heating which could hydrolyse some of the ester (less risk obtains with the stabler amides).

(iv) Where the acylation serves to remove certain components of the sample, the unattacked residue is subsequently titrated. The best-known example of this is mentioned under '2' of 'Reactions and materials titrated' above, namely the analysis of tertiary amines after acylation of primary and secondary. Perchloric or hydrochloric acids have been used for the titration.

Another example is titration with iodine monochloride of olefines after acetylation of potentially interfering amines (ref. 135).

(v) The olefines derived from dehydration of alcohols by acetic anhydride were determined bromometrically (ref. 122).

In some recent work (see refs 157, 158 and 159), binary mixtures of alcohols have been determined from kinetic data on the acetylation reaction (and of urethane formation with an isocyanate reagent).

Ref. 94 is to a review of methods of determining 'active hydrogen', and includes many acylation methods using anhydride reagents.

Examples

(The control titrations after hydrolysis with water, mentioned under (iii) above, are not mentioned individually in the tables.)

Material titrated	Reagent and reaction conditions	Subsequent treatment and final titration stage	Ref.
Aniline, *N*-methylaniline in presence of *N*-dimethylaniline	+ acetic anhydride; 30 min standing	+ water and titrated with NaOH to phenolphthalein	1
Alkylanilines e.g. monoethylaniline	+ acetic anhydride/xylene, *ca* 1:14; 1 h	+ water and titrated with $Ba(OH)_2$ to phenolphthalein	2
—OH in oil of citronella	+ phthalic anhydride/benzene; 2 h reflux	+ excess KOH and back titrated with H_2SO_4	3
Alcohols, phenols	+ acetic anhydride/pyridine, *ca* 1:7; 15 min/100°	+ water and titrated with NaOH to phenolphthalein	4

Materials titrated	Reagent and reaction conditions	Subsequent treatment and final titration stage	Ref.
Alcohols, phenols (determination of equivalent weight)	+ benzoic anhydride. Up to 2 h/100° or above	+ ether, benzene or $CHCl_3$ and + water. Titrated with K_2CO_3 to phenolphthalein	5
Terpene tertiary alcohols	+ acetic anhydride/ sodium acetate/oil of of turpentine; 3 h reflux	Ester isolated and determined by saponification	6
—OH groups	+ acetic anhydride alone	Acetic acid and excess anhydride distilled off and ester residue determined by saponification	7
—OH groups in essential oils	+ acetic anhydride/ formic acid, *ca* 2:1; 72–96 h/room temp.	Ester oil separated and determined by saponification with excess KOH (see Alkalies, ref. 36)	8
Terpene tertiary alcohols	+ acetic anhydride/ sodium acetate/ *m*-xylene; 9 h reflux	Ester isolated and determined by saponification with alcoholic NaOH (see Alkalies, ref. 38)	9
—OH groups in essential oils (determination of geraniol and citronellol)	+ phthalic anhydride/ pyridine. Left overnight/room temp. Also method of ref. 4	+ water and titrated with alkali	10
—OH groups in e.g. sugars, phenols	+ acetic anhydride/ pyridine, *ca* 1:2. Varied conditions; 16–120 h/37–90°	+ ice-water and titrated with NaOH to phenolphthalein	11
Acetylatable content of oils	+ acetic anhydride/ sodium acetate; 2 h reflux	Ester oil isolated and determined by saponification (see Alkalies, ref. 50)	12
Alcohols	+ acetic anhydride/ pyridine, 1:2, + *ca* 5% acetyl chloride; 1–4 h heating	+ water and titrated with NaOH to phenolphthalein	13, 14
—OH groups, e.g. in fats	+ acetic anhydride; 2 h/140°	Unused titrated with aniline thermometrically (see Part I, Amines and heterocyclic bases, ref. 3)	15
Ethanol, in industrial gases, after absorption on active charcoal	Method of ref. 4		16

Materials titrated	Reagent and reaction conditions	Subsequent treatment and final titration stage	Ref.
—OH groups, e.g. in phenols	Method of ref. 4 (tried also use of acetyl chloride and benzoyl chloride; see Halides ('active'), ref. 6)		17
—OH groups, e.g. in vanillin, β-naphthol, castor oil	+ acetic anhydride/ pyridine, 1:3; 15 min/ 100° or 24 h/ room temp.	+ ice water and titrated with alkali	18
—OH groups in fats	+ acetic anhydride/ pyridine, 1:2; 30–60 min heating	Titrated with NaOH to phenolphthalein	19
Benzylcellulose	+ acetic anhydride/ a few drops conc. H_2SO_4; 30–45 min reflux	+ water and benzyl acetate distilled out and determined by saponification with excess NaOH (see Alkalies, ref. 76)	20
—OH groups, e.g. in fats	+ acetic anhydride; 1–2 h/120–130° in sealed tube	+ water and titrated with KOH to phenolphthalein	21
Sugars, carbohydrates	+ acetic anhydride/ sodium acetate/xylene or toluene	Ester isolated and determined by saponification (see Alkalies, ref. 79)	22
—OH groups in essential oils	+ phthalic anhydride/ pyridine, 1:4; 18 h/room temp.	+ water and titrated with KOH to phenolphthalein	23
—OH groups	+ Acetic anhydride/ pyridine, 1:2; 1 h/100°	+ water and titrated with KOH to phenolphthalein	24
—OH groups in fatty materials	+ pure acetic anhydride in nitrogen atmosphere	Ester extracted with petroleum ether and determined by saponification with alcoholic KOH (see Alkalies, ref. 87)	25
Menthol	+ acetic anhydride/ sodium acetate; 1 h reflux	Ester separated and determined by saponification with NaOH (see Alkalies, ref. 90)	26
—OH groups in essential oils	+ acetic anhydride/ phosphoric acid; 15 min/over 50°	+ water, refluxed 10 min to destroy excess anhydride, ester isolated and determined by saponification	27

Materials titrated	Reagent and reaction conditions	Subsequent treatment and final titration stage	Ref.
—OH groups in fats and waxes, sterols, etc.	+ acetic anhydride/ pyridine, 1:7; 45–50 min/100° or 24 or more h/room temp.	+ hot water and butanol and titrated with alcoholic alkali	28
Primary and secondary alcohols, phenols; —OH groups in essential oils; amines	+ 2–3 fold excess acetic anhydride/ pyridine, 1:2; 30–60 min (benzoic anhydride found less good)	+ water, boiled 15 min and titrated with KOH/alcohol to to phenolphthalein	29
—OH groups	+ acetic anhydride/ acetonitrile or ether/ acetonitrile, + 2,4-dinitrobenzenesulphonic acid; 20 min (acetonitrile) or 1 day or more (ether)	+ water/acetonitrile and titrated with CH_3ONa/ methanol to thymol blue	32
—OH groups, e.g. hydroxy acids, carbohydrates, alcohols, phenols	+ acetic anhydride/ pyridine, *ca* 20% for sugars and 12% for phenols, fats, etc. Heated to boiling and refluxed 1 min	+ water and titrated with NaOH to phenolphthalein	33
—OH groups in fats, hydroxy acids, etc.	+ acetic anhydride/ 1:7; 75 min/100°	+ water and titrated with alkali	34
—OH groups in hydroxy fatty acids	+ acetic anhydride/ pyridine, 5N; 7 h/100°	Acetic acid + anhydride distilled under reduced pressure into standard KOH, then back titrated with HCl	35
—OH groups in sugars, flavonols, etc.	+ acetic anhydride/ pyridine; 30 min/100°	Titrated with NaOH to phenolphthalein	36
Ethanol	+ acetic anhydride; 1 h/100° in sealed ampoule	+ water and heated 30 min/ 50° to destroy excess anhydride. Ethyl acetate then determined with excess KOH (see Alkalies, ref. 101)	37
—OH groups in hydroxy fatty acids	+ acetic anhydride/ pyridine; 7 h reflux	+ water and titrated with NaOH to phenolphthalein	38
Primary alcohols	+ phthalic anhydride/ benzene; 2 h/100°	+ water/pyridine and heated 10 min. Titrated with KOH to phenolphthalein	39

Materials titrated	Reagent and reaction conditions	Subsequent treatment and final titration stage	Ref.
Primary and some secondary alcohols	+ phthalic anhydride/ pyridine, 2–4 fold excess; 1 h/100°	+ water and titrated with alkali to phenolphthalein	40
Glycol, glycerols	+ acetic anhydride/ pyridine, 1:7; 15–60 min boiling	+ water and titrated with NaOH to phenolphthalein	41
Micro —OH and —NH_2 groups in tubercle bacilli	+ acetic anhydride/ pyridine, 1:4; 1 h/100°	Titrated with alcoholic NaOH	42
Glycol or glycerol in tobacco	+ acetic anhydride/ sodium acetate; 90 min reflux	+ excess KOH and back titrated with acid	43
Glycol, glycerol	+ acetic anhydride/ pyridine, 12%; 10 or 60 min reflux respectively	Titrated with alkali to cresolphthalein	44
—OH groups	+ acetic anhydride/ pyridine, 1:7; 30 min reflux	+ water and titrated with alkali	45
Phenol, naphthol	+ benzoic anhydride/ pyridine, 1:1; 1 h/100°	+ water, heated 1 h/100° and titrated with KOH to phenolphthalein	46
Primary alcohols	+ phthalic anhydride/ pyridine; 1 h/100°	+ water (1 min hydrolysis to avoid saponification of the ester) and titrated with alkali to phenolphthalein	47
—OH groups, e.g. in polyhydric alcohols	+ acetic anhydride/ pyridine, 1:10; 3–6 h boiling	Titrated with alkali	48
Menthol	+ acetic anhydride/ sodium acetate; 2 h reflux	+ water, ester isolated and determined by saponification with excess KOH (see Alkalies, ref. 129)	49
—OH groups in hydrogenated lignin	+ acetic anhydride/ pyridine, 1:7; 4 h or overnight/90–100°	Titrated with NaOH to phenolphthalein	50
Menthol in peppermint oil	+ acetic anhydride/ pyridine, 1:2; (method of ref. 29)	Titrated with NaOH	51

Materials titrated	Reagent and reaction conditions	Subsequent treatment and final titration stage	Ref.
Mixtures of primary, secondary and tertiary amines	+ acetic anhydride; 3 h/*ca* 30°	Unreacted tertiary amine titrated with perchloric acid potentiometrically or to cresol red (see Part I, Perchloric acid, ref. 8)	52
Menthol in oil of peppermint	+ acetic anhydride/ di-n-butyl ether; 1 h reflux	Heated 30 min with water and titrated with KOH to phenolphthalein	53
—OH groups in essential oils, e.g., rosemary, sandalwood, peppermint		Tested several methods, e.g. of refs 4, 10 and 47. Suggested best acetylation procedure was 60–90 min with acetic anhydride/pyridine/xylene	54
Menthol in camphorated menthol	+ acetic anhydride/ pyridine, 1:4; 30 min/ 100°	Hydrolysed and titrated with KOH to phenolphthalein	55
Menthol in oil of peppermint	+ acetic anhydride/ sodium acetate; 1 h boiling	+ water, ester separated and determined by saponification (see Alkalies, ref. 138)	56
—OH groups in cellulose derivatives	+ acetic anhydride/ pyridine, 1:19, in large excess; 24 h/75–80°	Titrated with NaOH potentiometrically to pH 9, or to phenolphthalein	57
Non-basic hydrogen in amino acids, e.g. =NH in tryptophan or —SH in cysteine	+ acetic anhydride/ acetic acid/$HClO_4$; (basic hydrogen gives perchlorate salt and is not acetylated) 2 h/room temp.	+ measured excess anthranilic acid to react with $HClO_4$ and unused anhydride; after 3 h, unused titrated with $HClO_4$/ acetic acid to crystal violet (see Amines and heterocyclic bases, ref. 22)	58
Glucose	+ acetic anhydride/ pyridine, *ca* 50%; 10 min boiling	+ water and titrated with NaOH to phenolphthalein	59, 62
Glycerol	+ acetic anhydride/ pyridine, 1:7; 15–60 min boiling	Hydrolysed and titrated with alkali	60
—OH groups, e.g. in alcohols, phenols, sterols, carbohydrates, essential oils	+ acetic anhydride/ pyridine, *ca* 1:1; 24 h/room temp. in sealed tube	Titrated with alkali	61

Materials titrated	Reagent and reaction conditions	Subsequent treatment and final titration stage	Ref.
Primary and secondary amines	+ acetic anhydride/ pyridine; 30 min/room temp., then 30 min/60° with primary amines	+ excess water/NaI/pyridine and back titrated with Karl Fischer reagent (see Water, ref. 9)	63
Alcohols	+ acetic anhydride/ pyridine	Titrated with alcoholic KOH	64
Ethanol in mixtures with water, benzene and ether	Method of ref. 41		65
—OH groups in sugars and glucosides	+ acetic anhydride/ pyridine, 1:2; 48 h/ room temp. in sealed tube	Titrated with alkali	66
Menthol in mint essence	+ acetic anhydride/ sodium acetate; 2 h reflux	Neutralized and saponified with measured excess KOH (see Alkalies, ref. 170)	67
Primary and secondary alcohols; hydroxy acids	+ acetic anhydride/ pyridine 1:3; 45 min/100°	Titrated with alcoholic NaOH potentiometrically or to mixed indicator, changing at pH 9·8	68
Menthol in peppermint oil	+ acetic anhydride/ pyridine, 1:1; 48 h/room temp.	+ water and titrated with NaOH to phenolphthalein	69
Dodecyl alcohol	Method of ref. 68		70
Glycerol	+ acetic anhydride/ pyridine, 1:6; 30–40 min/100° (also tried other proportions and solvents)	+ water, heated 1–2 min, butanol added and titrated with KOH to phenolphthalein	71
—OH groups in alcohols and glycols	+ phthalic anhydride/ pyridine, *ca* 10%; 1 h/100° in sealed bottle	Titrated with NaOH to phenolphthalein	72
1,2,3,4-Tetrahydro-β-naphthol, extracted from impregnated clothing	+ acetic anhydride/ pyridine, *ca* 1:16; not under 2 h	Titrated with NaOH potentiometrically to pH 8·9 or to phenolphthalein/thymol blue	73
—OH groups	+ acetic anhydride; 1 h/180° in sealed tube	+ water, boiled and titrated with NaOH to phenolphthalein	74

Materials titrated	Reagent and reaction conditions	Subsequent treatment and final titration stage	Ref.
Linalool	+ acetic anhydride/ acetyl chloride/*N*-dimethylaniline; 30 min/ room temp. + 3 h/40° + acetic anhydride/ formic acid; 30 min/0° + 72 h/room temp. + acetic anhydride/ sodium acetate/xylene; 9 h reflux	Ester isolated and determined by saponification with excess alkali (see Alkalies, ref. 197)	75
—OH groups in essential oils	+ acetic anhydride/ pyridine, 100:3; 1 h/100°	Titrated with alcoholic alkali to thymolphthalein	76
Primary and secondary alcohols	+ acetic anhydride/ pyridine, 100:3; 15 min/ 100° for primary; 3 h/100° or 15 min/140° for secondary	Titrated with alcoholic alkali	77
Trimethylene glycol	+ acetic anhydride/ pyridine, 1:6; 30–40 min/100°	+ water/isobutanol and titrated with KOH to phenolphthalein	78
Vinyl alcohol content of polyvinyl acetal ketal resins	+ acetic anhydride/ pyridine	+ water + dichloroethane and titrated with alkali to phenolphthalein	79
Alcohol in vinyl ethers and acetals	+ acetic anhydride/ pyridine 1:3; 45–60 min/100° (phthalic anhydride if aldehydes present)	+ water + butanol, heated and titrated with alcoholic NaOH to cresol red/thymol blue or phenolphthalein (if phthalic anhydride used)	80
Mixtures of primary, secondary and tertiary amines	Method of ref. 52	Unreacted tertiary amine titrated with $HClO_4$/acetic acid (see Part I, Perchloric acid, ref. 16)	81
Primary and secondary alcohols	+ 3-nitrophthalic anhydride/benzene; 4 h reflux	Titrated with alkali	82
—OH groups	+ acetic anhydride/ pyridine, 1:3; 2 h reflux	+ water + butanol and titrated with alkali to cresol red/thymol blue	83

Materials titrated	Reagent and reaction conditions	Subsequent treatment and final titration stage	Ref.
—OCH_2CH_2OH groups in hydroxy-ethyl cellulose	+ phthalic anhydride/ pyridine; 1 h/room temp.	Titrated with NaOH	84
9,10-Octadecanediol-dicarboxylic acid	+ acetic anhydride/ xylene, 1:4; 1 h/100°	Unused anhydride distilled off with xylene and ester determined by saponification with excess alcoholic KOH	85
—OH groups	+ acetic anhydride/ dioxan + fluoroboric acid catalyst; 5 min/100°	Titrated with NaOH to phenolphthalein	86
Hydroxyethylcellulose (determination of equivalent weight per —OH group)	+ acetic anhydride/ pyridine, 1:20. Various times/75–80°; also + acetic anhydride/pyridine, 1:1; 24–48 h/90°	+ water and titrated with NaOH to phenolphthalein; ester precipitated and determined by hydrolysis with excess alkali (see Alkalies, ref. 247)	87
Menthol in peppermint leaves	In xylene + acetic anhydride/pyridine/ xylene, 1:1:10; 1 h/120°	Titrated with NaOH to phenolphthalein	88
Primary, secondary and tertiary amines	+ acetic anhydride; 15 min/room temp.	+ isopropanol/ethylene glycol and unreacted tertiary amine titrated with HCl potentiometrically (see Part I, Hydrochloric acid, ref. 25)	89
Glycerol monoethers	+ acetic anhydride/ pyridine, 15%; 2 h reflux	+ water and titrated with NaOH to phenolphthalein	90
—OH groups	+ acetic anhydride/ dry Na_2SO_4; 2 h reflux	+ water, ester extracted with petroleum ether and determined by saponification with with excess KOH (see Alkalies, ref. 271)	91
Alcohols	+ acetic anhydride/ formic acid, *ca* 2:1	+ water + pyridine and titrated with alcoholic NaOH	92
—OH groups in presence amines	+ acetic anhydride/ pyridine, 1:3; 45 min/100°	Neutralized and ester determined by saponification with excess alcoholic KOH (see Alkalies, ref. 277)	93

Materials titrated	Reagent and reaction conditions	Subsequent treatment and final titration stage	Ref.
Phenols	+ acetic anhydride/ pyridine, 5:12. Boiled, then 5 min/118° (some up to 1 h)	+ water + CCl_4 and titrated with NaOH to phenolphthalein	95
Phenols (semimicro)	+ acetic anhydride/ pyridine, 1:10; 2 h/100°	Titrated with KOH to phenolphthalein (excess anhydride hydrolysed in 3 min only, to prevent decomposition of the phenol ester)	96
Primary alcohols	+ acetic anhydride/ pyridine, 1:3; 1–2 h reflux	+ water and titrated with alkali to phenolphthalein	97
Alcoholic, phenolic and amine groups in coal hydrogenation products	Method of ref. 95		98
—OH groups in tannins, lignins and phenols	+ acetic anhydride/ pyridine, 1:3; 3–7 days/ room temp.	+ water + butanol at room temp. (not at 70–100°) and titrated with alkali	99
Tertiary alcohols in perfumery, e.g. in essential oils	+ acetic anhydride/ pyridine, 3:1; 15–20 min reflux	+ water, ester separated and determined by saponification	100
Primary, secondary and tertiary alcohols and primary and secondary amines	+ propionic anhydride/ acetic acid/*p*-toluene-sulphonic acid catalyst; 2 h/room temp. or 30 min/100°	Unused anhydride determined by reaction with measured excess aniline and titration of unused with $HClO_4$ (see Amines and heterocyclic bases, ref. 56)	101
Nicotine/nornicotine in tobacco alkaloids	In $CHCl_3$/benzene, + acetic anhydride	Unreacted nicotine titrated with $HClO_4$/acetic acid to crystal violet (sum of both determined in titration without acetylation) (see Part I, Perchloric acid, ref. 106)	102,
—OH groups in polyethylene glycols	+ propionic anhydride/ acetic acid/*p*-toluene-sulphonic acid catalyst. Left at room temp. to 60°	Unused anhydride determined by reaction with measured excess aniline and titration of unused with $HClO_4$ (see Amines and heterocyclic bases, ref. 58, and Part I, Perchloric acid, ref. 124)	103

Materials titrated	Reagent and reaction conditions	Subsequent treatment and final titration stage	Ref.
Phenol in methyl methacrylate	+ acetic anhydride/ pyridine, 1:1; 5 min/100°	+ water and titrated with alkali to cresol red/thymol blue	104
Primary and secondary alcohols	+ acetic anhydride/ pyridine, 1:10; 1 h/90–100°	+ water, and titrated with KOH to phenolphthalein	105
Ethanol	+ acetic anhydride/ pyridine, 1:1; 2 h/100°	Ethyl acetate distilled out and determined by saponification with excess alkali (see Alkalies, ref. 333)	106
Ethylene glycol; methyl cellosolve	+ acetic anhydride/ sodium acetate; 4·5–5 h reflux	+ water, neutralized and ester determined by saponification with excess NaOH (see Alkalies, ref. 341)	107
Amines in petroleum products, crude oil, coal tar and distillates	+ acetic anhydride	Unreacted tertiary amines titrated with $HClO_4$/acetic acid potentiometrically;	108
	+ phthalic anhydride	unreacted secondary and tertiary amines likewise titrated	
Linalool (semimicro)	+ acetic anhydride/ acetyl chloride/*N*-dimethylaniline; 4 h/50°	Ester isolated and determined by saponification (see Alkalies, ref. 344)	109
Glycerol in medicinals	+ acetic anhydride/ sodium acetate	Boiled with excess NaOH and back titrated	110
Alcohols	+ phthalic anhydride; 30–120 min reflux	Alkyl hydrogen phthalates separated on Celite 535 and titrated with NaOH	111
—OH groups	+ acetic anhydride/ pyridine; 24 h reaction time	+ water at 70–80° + acetone and titrated with NaOH	112
—OH groups in essential oils	+ acetic anhydride/ dioxan, 1:2, + drops phosphoric acid. Up to 24 h/room temp.	+ pyridine + water and titrated with NaOH	113

Materials titrated	Reagent and reaction conditions	Subsequent treatment and final titration stage	Ref.
—OH in epoxyresins	Tried acetic anhydride with: (a) pyridine/$HClO_4$; 30 min reflux (b) pyridine/HCl; 30 min reflux (c) acetic acid/trace H_2SO_4; (d) acetic acid/sodium acetate/pyridine; 6 h/100° (e) acetic acid, 2:1; 40–48 h	Titrated with KOH/ethanol or methanol; neutralized, H_2SO_4 added and acetic acid distilled out and titrated.	114
Amines	+ acetic anhydride. Refluxed + phthalic anhydride	Unreacted tertiary amines titrated with $HClO_4$/acetic acid potentiometrically; unreacted secondary and tertiary amines likewise titrated (see Part I, Perchloric acid, ref. 201)	115
Perfumery alcohols, e.g. benzyl and phenylethyl alcohols, geraniol	+ acetic anhydride/ sodium acetate + acetophenone (studied influence of latter at 80–140°)		116
'Phosphoric acetylation index' of essential oils	Method of ref. 113 based on 24 h/room temp.; higher values found than with pyridine/acetic anhydride acetylation mixtures, explained as due to reaction of tertiary alcohols, aldehydes, some olefinic compounds and ethers		117
Primary and secondary alcohols, glycols, sugars	+ acetic anhydride/ ethyl acetate or pyridine/$HClO_4$. At least 5 min/room temp.	+ water + pyridine and titrated with NaOH in water/ methanol or methyl cellosolve to cresol red/thymol blue or potentiometrically to pH 9·8	118
—OH groups in some raw materials for syntan production (diphenols)	+ acetic anhydride/ pyridine, 1:3; 45 min/100°	+ water and titrated with alcoholic NaOH to cresol red	119
Primary alcohols in essential oils, e.g. geraniol, phenylethyl alcohol	+ acetic anhydride/ pyridine, 1:3; 2 h	Titrated with alkali	120

Materials titrated	Reagent and reaction conditions	Subsequent treatment and final titration stage	Ref.
Sulphafurazole (sulphaisoxazole)	+ acetic anhydride/ pyridine; 10 min/0–2°	+ water, precipitate of *N*-acetyl derivative dissolved in acetone and titrated in HCl solution with nitrite to *N*-dimethylaminobenzaldehyde (see Part I, Nitrite, ref. 129)	121
1,1-Diphenylethanol; 1-(*p*-bromophenyl)-1-phenylethanol	+ acetic anhydride/ pyridine, 1:3; 90 min reflux	Olefine product determined with excess bromine/acetic acid and iodometric back titration (see Bromine reagents, ref. 481)	122
Chloramphenicol	+ propionic anhydride/ *p*-toluene sulphonic acid; 30 min/room temp.	Unused anhydride determined by reaction with measured excess of aniline and titration of unused with $HClO_4$ (see Amines and heterocyclic bases, ref. 82; Part I, Perchloric acid, ref. 269)	124
Aromatic amines	+ acetic anhydride/ pyridine, 1:3; 120°	Titrated with alkali to phenolphthalein or cresol red/thymol blue	125
Amine hydrochlorides	+ acetic anhydride/ acetic acid/mercuric acetate; 80–180 min/ room temp.	Unreacted tertiary amines titrated with $HClO_4$/acetic acid to crystal violet or cresol red (see Part I, Perchloric acid, ref. 238)	126
Amine mixtures	In acetic acid + acetic anhydride/ acetic acid	Aliquot + acetic acid and titrated with $HClO_4$/acetic acid to crystal violet	127
(studied rate of acetylation of primary and secondary amines and determined tertiary amines)			
Geraniol in oil of citronella	+ acetic anhydride/ pyridine, 1:3; 1 h/100°	+ water and titrated with KOH/ethanol to phenolphthalein	128
Citronellol	+ acetic anhydride/ formic acid; 72 h/0°	+ water + NaCl, ester separated and determined by saponification with excess KOH	129
Citronellol (after dehydration of geraniol with *p*-toluenesulphonic acid/xylene)	Method of ref. 128		130

Materials titrated	Reagent and reaction conditions	Subsequent treatment and final titration stage	Ref.
Di- and triallylamines	+ acetic anhydride/ Method of ref. 89	+ glycol + isopropanol and titrated unreacted triallylamine potentiometrically with HCl (method of Part I, Hydrochloric acid, ref. 25	131
Phenols, thiols, amines	Mostly with acetic anhydride/ethyl acetate or pyridine/$HClO_4$; 5 min/room temp. (By choice of reagent, more easily acetylizable compounds could be determined in presence of others). Compare method of ref. 118	+ water + pyridine and titrated with NaOH	132
Tri-n-octylamine in kerosene in presence of primary and secondary amines	+ acetic anhydride/ acetic acid, 10:1; 2 h	+ acetic acid and titrated with $HClO_4$/acetic acid potentiometrically (see Part I, Perchloric acid, ref. 316)	133
—OH groups in polyesters	In ethyl acetate + acetic anhydride + H_2SO_4 catalyst	Titrated with KOH/wzter/ methanol potentiometrically	134
—NH_2 or —NH— groups in high molecular weight fatty derivatives (determination of unsaturation of these compounds)	+ acetic anhydride; 5 min–1 h/100°	Unsaturation then determined with excess ICI (amines otherwise interfere) (see Iodine chlorides, etc., ref. 120)	135
Amine mixtures	+ acetic anhydride; 30 min/room temp.	Unreacted tertiary amine titrated with $HClO_4$/methyl cellosolve potentiometrically	136
Ketoximes, vicinal dioximes, some aldoximes	+ acetic anhydride/ pyridine/$HClO_4$; 5–10 min for ketoximes, 10–70 min for aldoximes and vicinal dioximes	+ water and titrated with NaOH to cresol red/thymol blue; or with CH_3ONa/methanol/ benzene to thymol blue, after adding dimethylformamide	137
Alcohol mixtures (e.g. isomers)	+ acetic anhydride/ pyridine, 1:24. Various reaction times	Aliquot + water and titrated with KOH/alcohol to phenolphthalein/Nile blue sulphate Kinetic plot yielded both components of mixture	138

Materials titrated	Reagent and reaction conditions	Subsequent treatment and final titration stage	Ref.
—OH, —NH_2 and —NH— groups	+ pyromellitic anhydride/tetrahydrofuran/pyridine; 2 min/100°, then most tetrahydrofuran boiled off	+ water and titrated with NaOH to phenolphthalein	139
Piperazine + its *N*-hydroxyethyl derivative	In acetonitrile, + acetic anhydride/acetic acid, 4:1; 100 min	Unreacted derivative titrated with $HClO_4$ to crystal violet	140
Residual alcohol in defatted, alcohol-washed soybean flakes	+ acetone + M phthalic anhydride/pyridine in *ca* 5-fold excess; 2 h	+ water, refluxed 10 min and titrated with NaOH	141
3-Methyl-2-penten-4-yn-1-ol in presence of the corresponding -3-ol (a tertiary alcohol)	+ acetic anhydride/dry pyridine; room temp.	+ water and titrated with KOH	142
Hydroxyl number of primary and secondary alcohols	Method of ref. 132		143
Phenylethyl alcohol	+ phthalic anhydride/pyridine; 1 h reflux	+ water, left 15 min and titrated with NaOH to phenolphthalein	144
Phenylethyl alcohol	+ phthalic anhydride/benzene; 1–2 h reflux	+ pyridine/water and titrated with NaOH	145
Amines	Tested and discussed 2 methods: (i) + pyridine/acetic anhydride, 3:1; 5 h/room temp. (ii) + acetic anhydride/dioxan, 1:2, + some drops phosphoric acid	+ water and titrated with NaOH to phenolphthalein	146
Hydroxyl number of polyoxyalkylene polyols	+ acetic anhydride/ethyl acetate/acetic acid/*p*-toluenesulphonic acid; 30 min/60°	+ water/pyridine and after 5 min titrated with KOH to cresol red/thymol blue	147
Primary amines in polynuclear polyamines	In acetic acid/formic acid, + phthalic anhydride; 1 h/90° (separate titration gave sum of primary and secondary)	+ acetone + Hg acetate and titrated unreacted secondary amines with $HClO_4$/acetic acid potentiometrically	148

Materials titrated	Reagent and reaction conditions	Subsequent treatment and final titration stage	Ref.
'Propionyl number' of essential oils	+ propionic anhydride/ *p*-toluenesulphonic acid/acetic acid; 7–8 h/room temp.	Unused anhydride determined by adding aniline/benzene/ acetic acid and back titrating unused aniline with $HClO_4$ (see Amines and heterocyclic bases, refs. 100 and 102)	149
Water in HCOOH	+ phthalic anhydride/ dioxan; 10 min heating	+ *N*-ethylaniline, heated 5 min, nitrobenzene/benzene added and unreacted amine titrated with $HClO_4$/acetic acid (see Amines and heterocyclic bases, ref. 103)	150
Theophylline + 7-(2-hydroxyethyl)-theophylline	+ acetic anhydride; 5 min reflux, acetylating	Titrated potentiometrically with $HClO_4$/dioxan, giving 2 jumps, first for the derivative from the second compound, then for that from the theophylline	151
Hydroxyl groups in alcohols and phenols	+ acetic anhydride/ dioxan/*p*-toluenesulphonic acid, some + phosphoric acid; 3 h/room temp. (up to 24 h in presence of phosphoric acid) (tested many compounds)	+ pyridine and titrated with NaOH	152
Primary alcohols	+ acetic anhydride/ pyridine, 1:3; 1–2 h	+ water and titrated with NaOH potentiometrically to pH 7·6	153
Hydroxyl groups	+ acetic anhydride/ ethyl acetate/$HClO_4$; 10–20 min (modification of reagent of ref. 132)	Titrated with NaOH	154
—OH groups (alcohols, phenols, alcoholic esters, essential oils)	+ stearic anhydride + *m*-xylene; 15–30 min reflux	+ pyridine or Na stearate, boiled 15 min and titrated hot with NaOH to phenolphthalein	155
Monosodium glutamate	+ acetic anhydride; 2 min reflux, acetylating the —NH_2 group	+ dioxan and titrated with $HClO_4$/acetic acid potentiometrically	156

Materials titrated	Reagent and reaction conditions	Subsequent treatment and final titration stage	Ref.
Ratio of primary —OH/secondary —OH in ethylene oxide polyethers	Reaction with phthalic anhydride and with phenyl isocyanate reagents; conversion to ester or urethane measured at intervals (in the case of phthalation, by back titrating aliquots, removed at intervals, with alkali)		157 158
n- and *sec*-Butanol in mixtures	In pyridine, + acetic anhydride/pyridine; various times/25·5° (Kinetic plot gave the amount of both alcohols)	+ water and titrated with KOH/alcohol to nile blue A/ phenolphthalein	159
Hydroxyl number of polyoxyalkylene ethers	+ acetic anhydride/ ethyl acetate/*p*-toluene-sulphonic acid; 15 min/50± 1°	+ water/pyridine and titrated with KOH/methanol to cresol red/thymol blue	160
Hydrochlorides of tetracaine and ephedrine	+ acetic anhydride, acetylating the latter	Extracted with $CHCl_3$ and tetracaine titrated with $HClO_4$	161
Free —OH groups in polyesters	+ acetic anhydride/ acetone/$HClO_4$ or H_2SO_4; 2 min shaking, then 5 min/5°	Titrated with NaOH to phenolphthalein	162
Primary and secondary alcohols, phenols	Slight modification of method of ref. 132		163
Alkoxy groups in alkoxysilanes	+ acetic anhydride/ ethyl acetate/$HClO_4$; 5 mins, reacting: $-\mathrm{SiOR} + (\mathrm{CH_3CO})_2\mathrm{O} \rightarrow -\mathrm{SiOCOCH_3} + \mathrm{ROCOCH_3}$; $-\mathrm{SiOCOCH_3} \xrightarrow{\text{hydrolysis}} -\mathrm{SiOH} + \mathrm{CH_3COOH}$	+ water + pyridine and subsequently titrated with KOH/methanol to cresol red/ thymol blue	164
β-phenylethyl alcohol	+ acetic anhydride/ pyridine/$HClO_4$; 10 min/room temp.	+ water and titrated with NaOH to phenolphthalein	165
Nicotinic acid hydrazide	+ acetic anhydride; 15 min/*ca* 100°	Titrated with $HClO_4$/dioxan to crystal violet	166
Mixtures of primary, secondary and tertiary amines	Aliquot in acetic acid, + acetic anhydride + Hg acetate; 1 h/80–90° (combined with determination of total amines and secondary + tertiary after reaction with salicylaldehyde; see Carbonyl compounds, ref. 34)	+ acetone and titrated residual tertiary amines potentiometrically with $HClO_4$/acetic acid	167

Materials titrated	Reagent and reaction conditions	Subsequent treatment and final titration stage	Ref.
Mercaptosilanes	+ acetic anhydride/ethyl acetate/$HClO_4$; 5 min, probably reacting:	+ pyridine/water, 3:1, left over 5 min and titrated with KOH/alcohol to cresol red/thymol blue	168
Dimethylhydrazine in presence of monomethyl or unsubstituted hydrazine	+ acetic anhydride/acetic acid; 1 min	Titrated with $HClO_4$/acetic acid to quinaldine red	169

$$-SiSR + (CH_3CO)_2O \rightarrow -SiOCOCH_3 + RSCOCH_3 \xrightarrow{\text{hydrolysis}} -SiOH + CH_3COOH$$

References

1. Reverdin, F. and de la Harpe, C., *Ber.* **22**, 1004 (1889).
2. Vaubel, W., *Chem.-Ztg.* **17**, 465 (1893).
3. Schimmel & Co., *Berichte*, Oct.-Nov. 1899.
4. Verley, A. and Bölsing, F., *Ber.* **34**, 3354 (1901).
5. Gascard, A., *J. pharm. chim.* (6) **24**, 97 (1906).
6. Boulez, V., *Bull. soc. chim. France* (4) **1**, 117 (1907).
7. Normann, W., *Chem. Rev. Fett u. Harz Ind.* **19**, 205 (1912).
8. Glichitch, L. S., *Bull. soc. chim. France* (4) **33**, 1284 (1923); *Compt. rend.* **177**, 268 (1923).
9. Boulez, V., *Bull. soc. chim. France* (4) **35**, 419 (1924).
10. Radcliffe, L. G. and Chadderton, E., *Perfumery Essent. Oil Record* **17** 254, 350 (1926).
11. Peterson, V. L. and West, E. S., *J. Biol. Chem.* **74**, 379 (1927).
12. Allan, J. et al., *Perfumery Essent. Oil Record* **19**, 131 (1928).
13. Verley, A., *Bull. soc. chim. France* **43**, 469 (1928).
14. Verley, A., *Am. Perfumer* **24**, 233 (1929).
15. Somiya, T., *J. Soc. Chem. Ind., Japan, Suppl. Bdg.* **33**, 140 (1930).
16. Connerade, E., *Chimie et Industrie*, Spec. No. 696 (1931).
17. Huppmann, *Pharm. Ztg.* **76**, 113, 329 (1931).
18. Marks, S. and Morrell, R. S., *Analyst* **56**, 428 (1931).
19. Delaby, R. and Breugnot, Y., *Bull. sci. pharm.* **39**, 354 (1932).
20. Meunier, L. and Gonfard, M., *Rev. gén. mat. plastiques* **8**, 427, 467, 591 (1932).
21. Roberts, W. L. and Schuette, H. A., *Ind. Eng. Chem. Anal., Ed.* **4**, 257 (1932).

22. Boulez, V., *Ann. zymologie* (2) **1**, 170 (1933).
23. Glichitch, L. S. and Naves, Y.-R., *Chimie et industrie, Spec. No.* 1024 (1933).
24. Normann, W. and Schildknecht, E., *Fettchem. Umschau* **40**, 194 (1933).
25. Fürth, O., Kaunitz, H. and Stein, H., *Biochem. Z.* **268**, 189 (1934).
26. Hosking, H. J., Snell, F. D. and Biffen, F. M., *Ind. Eng. Chem., Anal. Ed.*, **6**, 254 (1934).
27. Sabetay, S., *Compt. rend.* **199**, 1419 (1934).
28. West, E. S., Hoagland, C. L. and Curtis, G. H., *J. Biol. Chem.* **104** 627 (1934).
29. Delaby, R. and Sabetay, S., *Bull. soc. chim. France* (5) **2**, 1716 (1935).
30. Roberts, W. L., *J. Assoc. Offic. Agr. Chem.* **18**, 434 (1935).
31. Täufel, K., de Mingo, M. and Thaler, H., *Fettchem. Umschau* **42**, 141 (1935).
32. Toennies, G. and Elliot, M., *J. Am. Chem. Soc.* **57**, 2136 (1935).
33. Freed, M. and Wynne, A. M., *Ind. Eng. Chem., Anal. Ed.* **8**, 278 (1936).
34. Hafner, P. G., Swinney, R. H. and West, E. S., *J. Biol. Chem.* **116**, 691 (1936).
35. Hinsberg, K., *Biochem. Z.* **285**, 125 (1936).
36. Rabaté, J., *Bull. soc. chim. France* (5) **3**, 2112 (1936).
37. Sagpir, I. N. and Frolova, R. A., *Sintet. Kautschuk USSR* No. 11–12, 17 (1936).
38. Hinsberg, K., *Biochem. Z.* **289**, 294 (1937).
39. Sabetay, S. and Naves, Y.-R., *Ann. chim. anal. chim. appl.* **19**, 35 (1937).
40. Sabetay, S. and Naves, Y.-R., *Ann. chim. anal. chim. appl.* **19**, 285 (1937).
41. Shaefer, W. E., *Ind. Eng. Chem., Anal. Ed.* **9**, 449 (1937).
42. Stodola, F. H., *Mikrochemie* **21**, 180 (1937).
43. Lazar, O. and Meyling, A. H., *J. S. African Chem. Inst.* **21**, 8 (1938).
44. Öhman, V. and Laurent, G., *Svensk Kem. Tidskr.* **50**, 35 (1938).
45. Bergström, H. and Trobeck, K. G., *IVA* 10 (1939).
46. Leman, A., *Compt. rend.* **208**, 357 (1939).
47. Sabetay, S., *Ann. chim. anal. chim. appl.* **21**, 289 (1939).
48. Wilson, H. N. and Hughes, W. C., *J. Soc. Chem. Ind., London* **58**, 74 (1939).
49. Hall, R. T., Holcomb, J. H. and Griffin, D. B., *Ind. Eng. Chem., Anal. Ed.* **12**, 187 (1940).
50. Adkins, H., Frank, R. L. and Bloom, E. S., *J. Am. Chem. Soc.* **63**, 554 (1941).
51. Angren, A. and Bengtsson, E., *Farm. Revy* **40**, 57, 173 (1941).
52. Blumrich, K. and Bandel, G., *Angew. Chem.* **54**, 374 (1941).
53. Brignall, T. W., *Ind. Eng. Chem., Anal. Ed.* **13**, 166 (1941).
54. Grove, D. C., *J. Assoc. Offic. Agr. Chem.* **24**, 465 (1941).
55. Wilson, C. O., *Bull. Natl. Formulary Comm.* **9**, 350 (1941).

56. Baldinger, L. H., *Ind. Eng. Chem., Anal. Ed.* **14**, 15 (1942).
57. Malm, C. J., Genung, L. B. and Williams, R. E., *Ind. Eng. Chem., Anal. Ed.* **14**, 935 (1942).
58. Toennies, G. and Kolb, J. J., *J. Biol. Chem.* **144**, 219 (1942).
59. Leman, O., *Bull. soc. chim. France* **10**, 235 (1943).
60. Moore, J. C. and Blank, E. W., *Oil & Soap* **20**, 178 (1943).
61. Peterson, J. W., Hedberg, K. W. and Christensen, B. E., *Ind. Eng. Chem., Anal. Ed.* **15**, 225 (1943).
62. Leman, A., *Bull. soc. chim. France* **11**, 354 (1944).
63. Mitchell, J., Hawkins, W. and Smith, D. M., *J. Am. Chem. Soc.* **66**, 782 (1944).
64. Nobori, H. and Yamade, T., *J. Soc. Chem. Ind. Japan* **47**, 15 (1944).
65. Shaefer, W. E., *Ind. Eng. Chem., Anal. Ed.* **16**, 432 (1944).
66. Christensen, B. E. and Clarke, R. A., *Ind. Eng. Chem., Anal. Ed.* **17**, 265 (1945).
67. Ferreira, P. C. and Tucci, W., *Rev. quím. farm.* (*Rio de Janeiro*) **10**, No. 8, 9 (1945).
68. Ogg, C. L., Porter, W. L. and Willits, C. R., *Ind. Eng. Chem., Anal. Ed.* **17**, 394 (1945).
69. Jones, J. S. and Fang, S. C., *Ind. Eng. Chem., Anal. Ed.* **18**, 130 (1946).
70. McFarlane, S. B., *Oil & Soap* **23**, 237 (1946).
71. Pohle, W. D. and Mehlenbacher, V. C., *Oil & Soap* **23**, 48 (1946).
72. Elving, P. J. and Warshowsky, B., *Anal. Chem.* **19**, 1006 (1947).
73. Goldenson, J. and Sass, S., *Anal. Chem.* **19**, 322 (1947).
74. Helrich, K. and Rieman, W., *Anal. Chem.* **19**, 691 (1947).
75. Hoffmann, A. and Maffei, F. J., *Inst. pesq. tecnol.* (*Sao Paulo*), separate No. 196, 93 (1947).
76. Naves, Y.-R., *Helv. Chim. Acta* **30**, 796 (1947).
77. Naves, Y.-R., *Helv. Chim. Acta* **30**, 1613 (1947).
78. Pohle, W. D. and Mehlenbacher, V. C., *J. Am. Oil Chemists' Soc.* **24**, 155 (1947).
79. Ryan, J. D. and Shaw, F. B., *US Patent* 2,425,568, Aug. 12th 1947.
80. Siggia, S., *Anal. Chem.* **19**, 1025 (1947).
81. Wagner, C. D., Brown, R. H. and Peters, E. D., *J. Am. Chem. Soc.* **69**, 2609 (1947).
82. de Graef, H. and Pierret, J., *Bull. soc. chim. Belge* **57**, 307 (1948).
83. Hawke, F., *J. S. African Chem. Inst.* (*N.S.*) **1**, 85 (1948).
84. Senju, R., *J. Agr. Chem. Soc. Japan* **22**, 58 (1948).
85. Césaire, G., *Bull. soc. chim. France* **16**, 704 (1949).
86. Valentin, F. H. H., *J. S. African Chem. Inst.* (*N.S.*) **2**, 59 (1949).
87. Cohen, S. G. and Haas, H. C., *J. Am. Chem. Soc.* **72**, 3954 (1950).
88. Mitsui, T., Nakayama, H., Tanaka, J. and Fujiwara, H., *J. Agr. Chem. Soc. Japan* **24**, 82 (1950).

89. Siggia, S., Hanna, J. G. and Kervenski, I. R., *Anal. Chem.* **22**, 1295 (1950).
90. Stross, P. and Stuckey, R. E., *J. Pharm. Pharmacol.* **2**, 549 (1950).
91. Meier, K., *Farbe u. Lack* **57**, 437 (1951).
92. Sabetay, S., *Intern. Perfumer* **1**, No. 2, 11 (1951).
93. Siggia, S. and Kervenski, I. R., *Anal. Chem.*, **23**, 117 (1951).
94. Olleman, E. D., *Anal. Chem.* **24**, 1425 (1952).
95. DeWalt, C. W. and Glenn, R. A., *Anal. Chem.* **24**, 1789 (1952).
96. Brunner, H. and Thomas, H. R., *J. Appl. Chem. London* **3**, 49 (1953).
97. Petrova, L. N., *Zhur. Anal. Khim.* **8**, 61 (1953).
98. Glenn, R. A. and Olleman, E., *Anal. Chem.* **26**, 350 (1954).
99. Hillis, W. E., *J. Soc. Leather Trades Chem.* **38**, 177 (1954).
100. Ott, H., *Helv. Chim. Acta* **37**, 786 (1954).
101. Pesez, M., *Bull. soc. chim. France* 1237 (1954).
102. Cundiff, R. H. and Markunas, P. C., *Anal. Chem.* **27**, 1650 (1955).
103. Sezerat, A., *Ann. pharm. franç.* **13**, 516 (1955).
104. Takeuchi, T., Furasawa, M. and Takayama, Y., *Japan Analyst* **4**, 568 (1955).
105. Hauschild, R., Singer, K. and Petit, J., *Bull. soc. chim. France* 768 (1956).
106. Kreshkov, A. P., Svyatsillo, S. V., Shemyatenkova, V. I. and Neshumova, A. M., *Zavodskaya Lab.* **22**, 660 (1956).
107. Yurist, I. M. and Firsova, Yu. F., *Zhur. Anal. Khim.* **11**, 205 (1956).
108. Bezinger, N. N., Gal'pern, G. D. and Savost'yanova, T. I., *Khim. Tekhnol. i Primenenie Proizvodnykh. Piridina i Khinolina, Materialy Soveshchaniya, Inst. Khim. Akad. Nauk, Latv. SSR, Riga* 53, 1957.
109. Fujita, Y., Ueda, T. and Kusumoto, N., *Koryo* No. **47**, 42 (1957).
110. Gallo, U., Boll. chim. farm. **96**, 458 (1957).
111. Shichiji, S. and Hayashi, M., *Kogyo Gijutsuin Hakko Kenyushko Kenkyu Hokoku* No. 14, 19 (1957).
112. Shuter, L. M. and Berkman, Ya. P., *Ukr. Khim. Zhur.* **23**, 669 (1957).
113. Bertucat, M. and Mesnard, P., *Bull. soc. pharm. Bordeaux* **97**, 117 (1958).
114. Bring, A. and Kadlecek, F., *Plaste u. Kautschuk* **5**, 43 (1958).
115. Gal'pern, G. D. and Bezinger, N. N., *Zhur. Anal. Khim.* **13**, 603 (1958).
116. Lal, J. B., Mathur, A. P. and Patwardhan, V. M., *J. Oil Technol. An., India* **4**, 9 (1958).
117. Mesnard, P. and Bertucat, M., *Compt. rend.* **246**, 2793 (1958); *Bull. soc. chim. France* 307 (1959).
118. Fritz, J. S. and Schenk, G. H., *Anal. Chem.* **31**, 1808 (1959).
119. Langmaier, F. and Symovský, P., *Kožařství* **9**, 241 (1959).
120. Petrova, L. N. and Novikova, E. N., *Masloboino-Zhirovaya Prom.* **25**, No. 8 21 (1959).
121. Uno, T., Kono, M., Miyai, T. and Yasuda, H., *Yakugaku Zasshi* **79**, 113 (1959).

122. Buděšinský, B. and Aixnerová, M., *Českoslov. Farm.* **9**, 312 (1960).
123. Cundiff, R. H. and Markunas, P. C., *J. Assoc. Offic. Agr. Chem.* **43**, 519 (1960).
124. Franchi, G. and Pellerano, C., *Ann. chim. (Rome)* **50**, 134 (1960).
125. Goupil, R., *Chim. anal.* **42**, 300 (1960).
126. Gyenes, I., *Magyar Kem. Folyóirat* **65**, 264 (1959).
127. Nicksic, S. W. and Judd, S. H., *Anal. Chem.* **32**, 998 (1960).
128. van Os, F. H. L. and Sissing, J., *Pharm. Weekblad* **95**, 686 (1960).
129. van Os, F. H. L. and de Boer, G. D., *Pharm. Weekblad* **95**, 735 (1960).
130. van Os, F. H. L. and Elema, E. T., *Pharm. Weekblad* **95**, 761 (1960).
131. Parrish, J. R. and Stevenson, R., *Chem. & Ind. (London)* 531 (1960).
132. Schenk, G. H. and Fritz, J. S., *Anal. Chem.* **32**, 987 (1960).
133. Deptula, C., *Chem. Anal. (Warsaw)* **6**, 91 (1961).
134. Emelin, E. A. and Tsarfin, Ya. A., *Plasticheskie Massy* No. 3, 75 (1961).
135. Milun, A. J., *Anal. Chem.* **33**, 123 (1961).
136. Ruch, J. E. and Critchfield, F. E., *Anal. Chem.* **33**, 1569 (1961).
137. Schenk, G. H., *Anal. Chem.* **33**, 299 (1961).
138. Siggia, S. and Hanna, J. G., *Anal. Chem.* **33**, 896 (1961).
139. Siggia, S., Hanna, J. G. and Culmo, R., *Anal. Chem.* **33**, 900 (1961).
140. Toldy, E., Csillog, F., Bobák, T. and Gyenes, I., *Magyar Kem. Folyóirat* **67**, 180 (1961).
141. Black, L. T., Kirk, L. D. and Mustakas, G. C., *J. Am. Oil Chemists' Soc.* **38**, 483 (1961).
142. Solunina, I. A., Sorokina, R. A. and Devyatin, V. A., *Med. Prom SSSR* **15**, No. 5, 60 (1961).
143. Il'ina, A. I. and Nedavnyaya, V. G., *Masloboino- Zhirovaya Prom.* **27**, No. 10, 31 (1961).
144. Kishore, I. and Lal, J. B., *Indian Oil and Soap J.* **26**, 255 (1961).
145. Kishore, I. and Lal, J. B., *Riechstoffe u. Aromen* **11**, 221 (1961).
146. Mesnard, P. and Bertucat, M., *Bull. soc. chim. France* 611 (1961).
147. Madeline, P. and Debourg, G., *Mem. Poudres* **43**, 143 (1961).
148. Emelin, E. A. and Tsarfin, Ya. A., *Zhur. Anal. Khim.* **17**, 759 (1962).
149. Franchi G. and Franchi, R. R., *Boll. Chim. Farm.* **101**, 127 (1962).
150. Kiciak, S., *Chem. Anal. (Warsaw)* **7**, 847 (1962).
151. Linek, K. and Peciar, C., *Chem. Zvesti* **16**, 692 (1962).
152. Mesnard, P. and Bertucat, M., *Boll. Chim. Farm.* **101**, 519 (1962).
153. Quattrone, J. J. and Choy, T., *Microchem. J.* **6**, 259 (1962).
154. Schenk, G. H. and Santiago, M., *Microchem. J.* **6**, 77 (1962).
155. Sully, B. D., *Analyst* **87**, 940 (1962).
156. Adler, N., *Anal. Chem.* **34**, 1668 (1962).
157. Budd, M. S., *Anal. Chem.* **34**, 1343 (1962).
158. Hanna, J. G. and Siggia, S., *J. Polymer Sci.* **56**, 297 (1962).
159. Reilley, C. N. and Papa, L. J., *Anal. Chem.* **34**, 801 (1962).

160. Stetzler, R. S. and Smullin, C. F., *Anal. Chem.* **34**, 194 (1962).
161. Dupcza, K. and Kelemen-Kuttel, I, *Acta Pharm. Hung.* **33**, 202 (1963).
162. Khoroshaya, E. S., Lykova, A. N., Liberova, R. A. and Polinskii, S. L., *Zavodskaya Lab.* **29**, 549 (1963).
163. Klouček, B., Gasparic, J. and Obruba, K., *Collection Czechoslov. Chem. Communs.* **28**, 1606 (1963).
164. Magnuson, J. A., *Anal. Chem.* **35**, 1487 (1963).
165. Moiseeva, N. V. and Merzlikina, M. N. *Zavodskaya Lab.* **29**, 1437 (1963).
166. Solomon-Ionescu, I., Popescu, D. and Enache, S., *Rev. Chim. (Bucharest)* **14**, 532 (1963).
167. Strepikheev, Yu. A., Zalikin, A. A. and Chimishkyan, A. L., *Zhur. Anal. Khim.* **18**, 1262 (1963).
168. Berger, A. and Magnuson, J. A., *Anal. Chem.* **36**, 1156 (1964).
169. Malone, H. E. and Biggers, R. A., *Anal. Chem.* **36**, 1037 (1964).

9. Arsenate (Arsenic(V))

Two examples are given, based on oxidation; the phenylhydrazine determined reacts according to the equation:

$$C_6H_5NH.NH_2 + As_2O_5 \rightarrow C_6H_5OH + N_2 + H_2O + As_2O_3$$

A gasometric determination of organic hydrazines (measurement of the evolved nitrogen) based on this reaction, is also known.

Examples

Materials titrated	Reagent and reaction conditions	Subsequent treatment and final titration stage	Ref.
Phenylhydrazine; phenylhydrazones of some aldehydes	+ arsenate + HCl + acetic acid + Pt wire. Heated until nitrogen evolution ceased and then boiled 40 min longer	Made sensibly neutral, $NaHCO_3$ added and the arsenite formed titrated with iodine to starch	1
Phenylhydrazine	Heated with arsenate	Back titrated with chloramine T	2

References

1. Causse, H., *Compt. rend.* **125**, 712 (1897).
2. Afanas'ev, B. N., *Zavodskaya Lab.* **15**, 1271 (1949).

10. Arsenic (III)

An arsenite reagent has usually been used, but there is an example of triethylarsine $As(C_2H_5)_3$ as reagent.

The determinations are based on reduction and have been used for peroxides.

The conclusion has usually been titration of unused As(III).

Examples

Materials titrated	Reagent and reaction conditions	Subsequent treatment and final titration stage	Ref.
Xanthate	+ arsenite; 15 min	+ acetic acid, extracted with benzene; aliquot of aqueous layer + $NaHCO_3$ titrated with thiosulphate	1
Benzoyl peroxide in organic media	+ As_2O_3 + $NaHCO_3$ solution + ethanol if necessary. Boiled (until organic solvent boiled off)	Just acidified with H_2SO_4, $NaHCO_3$ added and titrated with iodine	2
Hydroperoxides in pertroleum products	+ Na arsenite + NaOH + some ethanol. Refluxed 45 min in a nitrogen atmosphere	+ $NaHCO_3$ and titrated with iodine to starch or potentiometrically	3
Peroxides	Compared method of ref. 2 with the iodometric method (ref. 78 under Iodides and hydriodic acid)		4
Dialkyl peroxides in presence of diacyl and alkyl hydrogen peroxides and peracids	+ $As(C_2H_5)_3$ in nitrogen atmosphere. 10 min. Last three react giving arsine oxide	Unreacted dialkyl peroxides determined by adding I^- + acetic acid and titrating with thiosulphate (see Iodides and hydriodic acid, ref. 199)	5
Hydroperoxides (in polymer latex)	+ slight excess As(III) in alkaline solution	Back titrated with excess hydroperoxide, concluding amperometrically with iodine	6

References

1. Tarugi, N. and Sorbini, F., *Boll. Chim. Farm.* **51**, 361 (1912).
2. Siggia, S., *Anal. Chem.* **19**, 872 (1947).
3. Walker, D. C. and Conway, H. S., *Anal. Chem.* **25**, 923 (1953).
4. Radford, A. J., *Analyst* **79**, 501 (1954).
5. Horner, L. and Jürgen, E., *Angew. Chem.* **70**, 266 (1958).
6. Kolthoff, I. M., Meehan, E. J., Bruckenstein, S. and Minato, H., *Microchem. J.* **4**, 53 (1960).

11. Barium (II)

Some organic polycarboxylic acids have been determined by precipitation as barium salts. While the conclusion has usually been gravimetric, some titrimetric procedures have been published and are given below.

Since many acids, often those occurring together, give poorly soluble barium salts, reaction conditions must be adjusted as far as possible to favour specific precipitation of the acid to be determined. This is not always easy and accuracy is therefore not high.

Examples

Materials titrated	Reagent and reaction conditions	Subsequent treatment and final titration stage	Ref.
Citric acid in biological mixtures	Concentrated solution + $BaCl_2$. Heated 5 min	Ba citrate centrifuged, oxidized to acetone with MnO_4^- and the acetone determined with alkali/excess iodine (see Iodine reagents, ref. 232, and Permanganate, ref. 79)	1
Citric acid in port wines	+ Ba(II) reagent	Ba citrate oxidized with acid/MnO_4^- to acetone, then determined with alkali/excess alkali (see Iodine reagents, ref. 312, and Permanganate, ref. 109)	2
Sulphonate in sulphonation reaction mixtures	+ $Ba(OH)_2$ to precipitate sulphate; 30 min/100°	Filtered, passed filtrate through Dowex 50 column and titrated effluent with NaOH (see Ion exchangers, ref. 21)	3
Tartaric acid in wine	+ Ba(II) reagent at pH 4·7 or 7	Ba tartrate determined by periodate oxidation	4
Succinic acid in wines	Neutral solution, + $BaCl_2$ + ethanol to bring to 66% ethanol; 2 h/10°; the same, but bringing to 76% ethanol and 4 h reaction time	Filtered and titrated filtrate with NaOH. Difference between the two titrations equivalent to the succinate	5
Sulphates of alkaloids, e.g. of atropine, strychnine, quinine	+ $BaCl_2$ + Cu(II) derivative of EDTA	Back titrated with EDTA to 1-(2-pyridylazo)-2-naphthol	6

Materials titrated	Reagent and reaction conditions	Subsequent treatment and final titration stage	Ref.
ε-Aminocaproic acid, from determination of ε-caprolactam by hydolysis with NaOH	+ $BaCl_2$ + $Ba(OH)_2$; 15 min, yielding precipitate of Ba salt	Neutralized with HCl, neutralized HCHO added and titrated with NaOH to phenolphthalein, or potentiometrically (see Carbonyl compounds, ref. 35)	7

References

1. de Saint-Rat, L. and Hatey, J., *Bull. assoc. chim.* **61**, 285 (1944).
2. Ramos, M. da C. and Guimarães, A. F., *Anais inst. vinho Porto* 9 (1953).
3. Houff, W. H., Christie, D. R. and Beaumont, R. H., *Anal. Chem.* **29**, 1866 (1957).
4. Mareca Cortes, I. and de Bethancourt, C. D., *Inds. aliment. et agr.* (*Paris*) **75**, 563 (1958).
5. Procopio, M. and Antona, M., *Vini. Ital.* **3**, 217 (1961).
6. Fulop, L., Vereph, I. and Martonfi, L., *Farmacia* (*Bucharest*) **11**, 301 (1963).
7. Ziólkowski, Z., Respondek, J. and Przondo, J., *Chem. Anal.* (*Warsaw*) **8**, 273 (1963).

12. Bichromate and chromic oxide (Chromium (VI))

Reagent. Usually prepared from an alkali bichromate; sometimes from chromic oxide.

Reactions and materials titrated. 1. Oxidation of a variety of functional groups and compound classes according to the equation:

$$Cr_2O_7^{2-} + 14\,H^+ + 6\epsilon \rightarrow 2\,Cr^{3+} + 7\,H_2O$$
$$\text{i.e. } Cr(VI) + 3\epsilon \rightarrow Cr(III)$$

(i) Hydrocarbons and *C*-methyl groups, including rubber hydrocarbons. The extent of oxidation of the *C*-methyl groups (to acetic acid) in many types of compound has been extensively studied.

(ii) Hydroxy compounds. These include lower alcohols such as methanol and ethanol; polyhydroxy compounds, ranging from glycol and glycerol to mannitol, sugars, celluloses and starches; phenols; sterols like cholesterol; and lignin. There are many examples of the determination of ethanol in biological fluids and only a selection is given here avoiding the polemical discussions which have developed. Refs 218 and 250 are to a study of the oxidation of alcohols; ref. 244 to a kinetic study of the oxidation of cyclohexanone.

(iii) Carboxylic acids, principally aliphatic from formic to butyric (but excluding acetic acid which is relatively resistant to oxidation) and including hydroxy- and polycarboxylic acids such as lactic, adipic, tartaric, salicylic and β-hydroxybutyric acids.

(iv) Ethers like diethyl ether, dioxan, cellosolves and polyalkylene glycols. Most frequently encountered of these are determinations of ethyl ether in biological fluids.

(v) Aldehydes like benzaldehyde (the sugars mentioned under (ii) could be classified here).

(vi) Various miscellaneous, compounds, usually of higher molecular weight. For example; indigo, proteins, carbazole, naphthalene sulphonic acids, trinitrotoluene, diphenylamine. These include insoluble reaction products formed as the first stage of an analysis; e.g. determination of cholesterol after precipitation of the 'digitonide', or of urea after precipitation of dixanthydryl. The determination of 'chemical oxygen demand' or 'oxygen-consumption' of materials like sewage or effluents has often been done by a standardized treatment with a bichromate reagent. This has not been considered in any detail here but a few references are given.

The end-products of oxidation are usually carbon dioxide and water. In some cases, acetic acid is the stable product, especially from ethanol and from *C*-methyl groups.

2. Ion/ion combination with formation of insoluble bichromate salts in determination of many large cations such as of atebrin, rivanol, methylene blue, quaternary ammonium antiseptics, strychnine, etc.

Reaction conditions. Oxidations have been carried out in acid solution (generally sulphuric acid but also with other acids like nitric) and frequently at higher temperatures. A silver catalyst has sometimes been used to ensure complete oxidation, even of acetic acid, to carbon dioxide. Ref. 194 compares different procedures for blood alcohol. One example (ref. 157) is given of oxidation in alkaline solution.

Formation of insoluble bichromate salts has mostly been in weak acid or neutral solution.

Subsequent treatment and final titration stage. (i) In the majority of cases, unused bichromate has been determined, using one of the following methods:

1. Addition of iodide (and acid where the solution is neutral or only weakly acid) and titration of the liberated iodine with thiosulphate, generally using a starch indicator.

2. Direct titration with a Fe(II) reagent.

3. Addition of measured excess of a Fe(II) reagent and back titration of the unused portion, generally with permanganate.

4. Direct titration with ferrocyanide.

5. Titration with Pb(II) or hydroquinone.

(ii) Determination of a reaction product, which includes:

1. Carbon dioxide from a complete oxidation, by absorption in a $Ba(OH)_2$ reagent and back titration of the unused part.

2. Acetone from isopropanol or β-hydroxybutyric acid, or other ketones from other secondary alcohols. These have been determined by reaction with excess iodine/alkali or with hydroxylamine.

3. Acetic acid, usually distilled from the oxidation mixture and titrated with alkali, generally to phenolphthalein.

4. Chlorine from chlorides, determined iodometrically.

Examples

Two simplifications are used in the following tables:

1. The reagent composition is not given where it is the usual mixture of sulphuric acid/bichromate or chromic oxide, unless some special feature is illustrated.

2. The determination of unused reagent by the commonly used principle of (i) 1 is abbreviated in the last column with 'I^-/thiosulphate'.

Materials titrated	Reaction conditions	Subsequent treatment and final titration stage	Ref.
Formic/acetic acid mixture	Refluxed	Unchanged acetic acid distilled and titrated	1
Alcohols, aldehydes	Heated 2–3 h in sealed tube	I^-/thiosulphate	2
Glycerol	2 h/100°	Unused back titrated with ferrous ammonium sulphate to $Fe(CN)_6^{3-}$ external indicator	3
Methanol in formalin solution	12 h standing	I^-/thiosulphate (both components oxidized and result obtained by interpolation)	4
Lactic acid	1 h boiling giving acetic acid + CO_2	I^-/thiosulphate	5
Glycerol	2 h/100°	I^-/thiosulphate	6
Ethanol in essences, tinctures, etc.	2–3 h	I^-/thiosulphate	7
β-Hydroxybutyric acid	Oxidized to acetone	Acetone distilled into iodine/alkali (see Iodine reagents, ref. 58)	8

Materials titrated	Reagent and reaction conditions	Subsequent treatment and final titration stage	Ref.
Ethanol in air	Absorbed in reagent; 15 min reflux	I^-/thiosulphate	9
Blood ethanol	Distilled into reagent (2 h duration)	I^-/thiosulphate	10
Celluloses	5 h boiling giving $CO_2 + H_2O$	Unused back titrated with ferrous ammonium sulphate to $Fe(CN)^{3-}$	11
Glycerol	2–3 h/*ca* 100°	I^-/thiosulphate	12
Ether in air or blood	Absorbed in 50% H_2SO_4, diluted to 40%, $Cr_2O_7^{2-}$ added and heated 30 min/100°	I^-/thiosulphate	13
Fatty acids	30 min/*ca* 100°	I^-/thiosulphate	14
Blood ethanol	Method of ref. 10		15
Propionic, butyric acid	1 h boiling	I^-/thiosulphate	16
Ethanol	Oxidized to acetic acid	Unused back titrated with Fe(II)	17
Sugars in blood	30 min/90°	I^-/thiosulphate	18
Alcohol in beer	Distilled into reagent; 1 h/80°	I^-/thiosulphate	19
Lactic acid, lactates	1 h/70°	I^-/thiosulphate	20
Ethanol	Distilled into reagent, hot from mixing	I^-/thiosulphate	21
Tartaric, phthalic, salicylic acids, sucrose, β-naphthol	*Ca* twofold amount of reagent in excess High $[H_2SO_4]$, giving oxidation to CO_2 15 min/100°	I^-/thiosulphate	22
Organic matter in water	2 h/100–110°, giving CO_2	Unused back titrated with Fe(II)	23
Ethanol, ether	6 h/room temp. or 2 h/60° for ethanol. Ether with a more concentrated reagent	I^-/thiosulphate	24

Materials titrated	Reagent and reaction conditions	Subsequent treatment and final titration stage	Ref.
Propionic acid in acetic acid	3 h reflux, oxidizing former to acetic acid	I^-/thiosulphate	25
Isopropanol, *sec*-butanol	Oxidized to acetone and butanone respectively	Ketones determined with iodine reagent (see Iodine reagents, ref. 88)	26
Ethanol in tissues	Oxidized to acetic acid	Distilled and titrated with NaOH to phenolphthalein	27
Benzaldehyde in cherry-laurel water	90 min, oxidizing to benzoic acid	Extracted with $CHCl_3$ and titrated	28
Isopropanol in presence of ethanol	Oxidized to acetone	Determined with hydroxylamine (see Hydroxylamine, ref. 10)	29
Dixanthydrylurea, formed in determination of urea	Oxidized to CO_2	Absorbed in $Ba(OH)_2$ and back titrated with acid	30
Dixanthydrylurea, formed in determination of urea	Oxidized to CO_2	Unused back titrated with Fe(II) to $Fe(CN)^{3-}$	31
Glycerol in wines and liqueurs	Distilled into reagent; 2 h boiling	+ excess ferrous ammonium sulphate and back titrated with permanganate	32
Hexamethylenetetramine	1 h/100°	I^-/thiosulphate	33
Strychnine	+ bichromate/dilute H_2SO_4 giving insoluble salt; 30 min	Filtrate + HCl/KI and titrated with thiosulphate	34
Carbazole in technical material	+ acetic acid + CrO_3 + water; 1 h digestion	Acetic acid distilled out, then Zn/NaOH added and ammonia distilled into excess standard HCl; back titrated with NaOH to methyl red	35
Ether in mixtures with ethanol	Modification of method of ref. 24 (different absorption technique)		36
Ethanol in presence of isopropanol and acetone	30 min/room temp. Oxidized to acetic acid (isopropanol to acetone)	+ excess $FeSO_4$, distilled and titrated with alkali to phenolphthalein	37

Materials titrated	Reagent and reaction conditions	Subsequent treatment and final titration stage	Ref.
Ethanol in urine, blood, etc.		I^-/thiosulphate	38
Nitro and amino compounds like diphenylamine and trinitrotoluene	*Ca* 20 min boiling with reagent *ca* 20% in excess	I^-/thiosulphate	39
Methanol in ethanol	Oxidized to CO_2 and acetic acid respectively	Absorbed in $BaCl_2/NH_4OH$, $BaCO_3$ filtered and titrated with HCl	40
Ethanol	5–10 min, giving acetic acid and no acetaldehyde	Unused titrated with ferrous ammonium sulphate to external $Fe(CN)_6^{3-}$	41
Cholesterol 'digitonide', precipitated in determination of former	+ reagent + $Ag_2Cr_2O_7$; 15 min/124° or 90 min/100°	I^-/thiosulphate	42
Glycerol in wines and fermented beverages	Distilled into reagent; 3 h duration	Unused titrated with Fe(II)	43
Lactic acid in blood	1 h/100°	I^-/thiosulphate	44
Fatty acids in blood (after preliminary extraction)	+ reagent + silver bichromate catalyst; 90 min/100°	I^-/thiosulphate	45
Ethanol in blood, etc.	15 min or more digestion	I^-/thiosulphate	46
C-Methyl groups	Oxidized to acetic acid	Excess reagent reduced with hydrazine, solution partly neutralized and acetic acid distilled and titrated with alkali to phenolphthalein	47, 59
Determination of oxygen consumption of sewage and industrial wastes	$CrO_3/H_2SO_4/H_3PO_4$; 2 h boiling, giving CO_2	Absorbed in excess $Ba(OH)_2$ and back titrated with HCl to phenolphthalein	48
Methanol, ethanol, ether, glycerol	1 h/85°. Ethanol oxidized to acetic acid; the others to CO_2	Excess Fe(II) added and back titrated with permanganate	49
Ethanol in blood or exhaled air	Modification of method ref. 10, oxidizing to acetic acid	I^-/thiosulphate	50

Materials titrated	Reagent and reaction conditions	Subsequent treatment and final titration stage	Ref.
Ethanol/n-butanol mixtures	+ bichromate/H_3PO_4, giving acetic acid and butyric acid	Distilled and partitioned between water and isopropyl ether; titrated with alkali	51
Ethanol/butanol mixtures	Oxidized to acetic and butyric acids	Distilled out in accordance with the Duclaux method and titrated with $Ba(OH)_2$ to phenol red	52
Ethanol in vinasses	Distilled into reagent. Method of ref. 21	I^-/thiosulphate	53
Ether (after separation from ethanol and aldehydes with permanganate)	Aspirated into reagent; 3 h	I^-/thiosulphate	54
Naphthalenemono-, -di-, -tri- and -tetrasulphonic acids	45 min/100°, giving CO_2 and SO_3	I^-/thiosulphate	55
Ethanol	+ bichromate/H_3PO_4, giving acetic acid	I^-/thiosulphate	56
Ethanol in milk	Distilled about one-half at 50° under reduced pressure into reagent	I^-/thisulphate	57
Lactic acid in wines and fruit juices	1 h reflux, oxidizing to acetic acid	Distilled and titrated	58
Ether	Absorbed in reagent (5 h duration)	I^-/thiosulphate	60
Isopropanol	4 h, giving acetone	+ $FeSO_4$ and acetone distilled into hydroxylamine hydrochloride, titrating the HCl set free (see Hydroxylamine, ref. 27)	61
Ethanol in chloroform	1 h/85°	+ excess ferrous ammonium sulphate and back titrated with permanganate	62
Strychnine, brucine	+ bichromate/dilute acid, giving an insoluble salt	Precipitate dissolved in excess $FeSO_4/H_2SO_4$ and back titrated with bichromate to diphenylamine/H_2SO_4	63
Organic matter in muds and sludges	Best with 50% H_2SO_4	Unused titrated with Fe(II)	64

Materials titrated	Reagent and reaction conditions	Subsequent treatment and final titration stage	Ref.
Ethanol/n-butanol mixtures	10 min/100°. Two determinations: with two reagents, of different acid concentration; or before and after extraction with CCl_4	I^-/thiosulphate	65
Methanol or ethanol in biological materials	Distilled into reagent	Unused titrated with Fe(II) to methyl orange	66
Ethanol	1 h/40°	I^-/thiosulphate	67
Acetone bodies like β-hydroxybutyric acid in blood, urine, etc.	Oxidized to acetone	Determined iodometrically (see Iodine reagents, ref. 137)	68
Many compounds with —OH and —COOH groups, e.g. mannitol, sucrose, adipic, benzoic and succinic acids	15 or more min/100°	Partly neutralized, then I^-/thiosulphate	69
Ethanol	5 min boiling	I^-/thiosulphate	70
Ethanol in rectified butadiene	1 h boiling		71
Ethanol in beer	Distilled into reagent	I^-/thiosulphate	72
Isopropanol	24 h/room temp., giving acetone	Neutralized, acetone distilled and determined iodometrically (see Iodine reagents, ref. 166)	73
Ethanol in body fluids	5 min/room temp.	I^-/thiosulphate	74
Ethanol	1 h/85°, giving acetic acid	+ excess ferrous ammonium sulphate and back titrated with permanganate	75
Binary mixtures, e.g. of benzoic, succinic or adipic acids/mannitol, sucrose or salicylic acid	Two determinations with reagents containing 40% sulphuric acid and 80% acid	I^-/thiosulphate	76
Ethanol, butanol, hexanol in fusel-oil water	30 min	I^-/thiosulphate	77

Materials titrated	Reagent and reaction conditions	Subsequent treatment and final titration stage	Ref.
Acetone bodies in urine	Oxidized to acetone	Acetone distilled and determined iodometrically (see Iodine reagents, ref. 170)	78
Atebrin dihydrochloride; rivanol lactate	+ acetate buffer + excess bichromate, giving insoluble salts	Filtered, filtrate + HCl/KI and titrated with thiosulphate	79
Many compounds, e.g. sugars, succinic acid, acetanilide, quinoline	20 min/165°; more acid added and 5 min further boiling	I^-/thiosulphate	80
α-Cellulose (separated from β- and γ-)	10 min boiling	I^-/thiosulphate	81
Methanol + ethanol	(1) 25 min/100°, giving formic and acetic acids respectively. (2) 15 min with more concentrated reagent, giving CO_2	(1) + excess ferrous ammonium sulphate and back titrated with bichromate. (2) I^-/thiosulphate	82
Rubber hydrocarbons	Oxidation of method of refs 47, 59, giving acetic acid	Distilled and titrated with alkali	83
Glycerol	2 h/90–100°	Unused titrated with Fe(II) potentiometrically	84
Glycerol in soaps, etc. (after preliminary separation)	90 min/100°	Titrated into ferrous ammonium sulphate with diphenylamine/H_2SO_4 indicator	85
Cholesterol in blood	Reagent + Ce(IV) catalyst	I^-/thiosulphate	86
Ethanol in presence of methanol, isopropanol	Oxidized in presence of Hg(II) to acetic acid	Distilled and titrated with NaOH to phenolphthalein	87
Ethanol	+ bichromate/HNO_3	I^-/thiosulphate	88
α-Cellulose	5 min boiling (modification of method of ref. 81)	I^-/thiosulphate	89
Ether; $(C_2D_5)_2O$	Method of ref. 10		90
Oxidizability of waters	15–20 min/100°	I^-/thiosulphate	91

Materials titrated	Reagent and reaction conditions	Subsequent treatment and final titration stage	Ref.
Ethanol	10 min/100°	I^-/thiosulphate	92
Ethanol	Oxidized to acetic acid	I^-/thiosulphate	93
Isopropanol in flavouring matters	Oxidized to acetone	I^-/thiosulphate	94, 102, 113
Ethanol		Unused titrated with ferrocyanide to diphenylamine	95
Glycerol/ethylene glycol/diethylene glycol	20–30 min reflux (in combination with periodate oxidation giving the first two—see Periodate and periodic acid, ref. 14)	I^-/thiosulphate	96
Blood ether	Aerated into reagent and oxidized to acetic acid	I^-/thiosulphate	97
Ethanol traces (not over 0·6%) in presence of acetone and benzene	10 min	I^-/thiosulphate	98
Ethanol in blood or urine	Method of ref. 66, with oxidation to acetic acid	Unused titrated with Fe(II) to methyl orange	99
n-Butanol from phosphoric acid hydrolysis used in analysis of resins from HCHO/urea/butanol	Distilled into reagent; 45 min reflux, giving acetic acid	Distilled out and titrated with NaOH to phenolphthalein	100
Paraldehyde in biological fluids	Oxidized to acetic acid	I^-/thiosulphate	101
Methylene blue	In water + bichromate, giving insoluble salt	Unused determined in filtrate with I^-/thiosulphate	103
Ethanol, ether in air	Passed through reagent; 1–2 h/100° or 1–18 h/room temp. (depending on reagent concentrations; higher H_2SO_4 concentration for ether determination)	I^-/thiosulphate	104
Ethanol	Distilled into reagent; 20 min/100°	I^-/thiosulphate	105
Ethanol	Oxidized to acetic acid (modification of method of ref. 53)	+ excess Fe(II) and back titrated with permanganate	106

Materials titrated	Reagent and reaction conditions	Subsequent treatment and final titration stage	Ref.
Glucose	60–80 min/100°	I^-/thiosulphate or + excess Fe(II) and back titration with permanganate	107
Dixanthydrylurea, formed in determination of urea		Unused titrated with ferrocyanide to diphenylamine	108
Glycerol (micro)	+ bichromate/HNO_3; 20 min/100°	Unused titrated with ferrocyanide to diphenylamine	109, 114
Sodium acetate in presence of salts of other organic acids (in analysis of acid mixture by ester formation with methanol, followed by alkali saponification)	Two determinations: with bichromate/50% H_2SO_4, oxidizing all except the acetate and with silver bichromate/60% acid, oxidizing acetate also	I^-/thiosulphate; difference equivalent to acetate	110
Some quaternary ammonium salts in antiseptics	+ bichromate/dilute acid; 24 h	Unused determined in filtrate with I^-/thiosulphate	111
Cellulose in raw fibre (after preliminary extraction)	1 h boiling	Unused titrated with ferrous ammonium sulphate to ferroin	112
Ethanol in wine	5 min boiling	I^-/thiosulphate	115
Ethanol in blood or urine	Diffused into reagent; 2 h/50°, 6 h/37° or 10 h/25°	I^-/thiosulphate	116
Rubber hydrocarbons	1 h/100°, giving 75% yield of acetic acid; 1 mole isoprene → 1 acid	Distilled and titrated with NaOH to phenolphthalein	117
Ethanol in blood	+ bichromate/HNO_3 giving acetic acid; 1 h	I^-/thiosulphate	118
β-Hydroxybutyric acid	45 min distillation giving acetone	Acetone determined iodometrically (see Iodine reagents, ref. 223)	119
Glucose	30 min/100° giving CO_2	Unused titrated with ferrous ammonium sulphate to external ferrocyanide	120

Materials titrated	Reagent and reaction conditions	Subsequent treatment and final titration stage	Ref.
Glycerol	+ bichromate/HNO_3; 20 min/100°, giving CO_2	Unused titrated with ferrocyanide to diphenylbenzidine	121
Alkyl cellosolves, $HOCH_2.CH_2OR$ in vapour or dilute aqueous solution	15 min/100° for R = CH_3 or C_2H_5 120 min/100° for R = C_4H_9 240 min/100° for R = C_3H_7	I^-/thiosulphate	122
Certain terminal methyl groups, e.g. in crotonic acid or methylcyclohex-1-en-3-one	90 min reflux, giving acetic acid	Distilled and titrated with $Ba(OH)_2$ to phenolphthalein, or determined iodometrically with iodate/iodide	123
C-Methyl groups	Modified oxidation of refs 47 and 59, giving 75–85% theoretical yield of acetic acid	Distilled and titrated with alkali	124
Quinacrine hydrochloride	In acetate buffer + bichromate, giving insoluble salt	Unused determined in filtrate with I^-/thiosulphate	125
Ethanol in chloroform	+ bichromate/HNO_3; 3 min shaking, giving acetic acid	I^-/thiosulphate	126
Total flavines in trypaflavine	+ acetate buffer + bichromate; 1 h/room temp.	Unused determined in filtrate with I^-/thiosulphate	127
Rubber hydrocarbons	Method of ref. 117 (found satisfactory)		128
Salicylic and benzoic acids	Two determinations: with bichromate/40% H_2SO_4, oxidizing former only; and with bichromate/80% acid, oxidizing both	I^-/thiosulphate or unused back titrated with Fe(II)	129
Glycerol (after separation by precipitation with sodium tungstate)	20 min/100°	Unused titrated with ferrous ammonium sulphate to diphenylamine/H_2SO_4	130
Isopropanol	Oxidized to acetone	Determined iodometrically	131
Glycerol in suppositories	1 h/100°	I^-/thiosulphate	132

Materials titrated	Reagent and reaction conditions	Subsequent treatment and final titration stage	Ref.
Ethanol in gastric or intestinal contents	30 min/100°	Unused titrated with ferrous ammonium sulphate to congo red → pale violet	133
Dioxan	1 h/100° in sealed tube	I^-/thiosulphate	134
Blood alcohol	25–30 sec (modification of method of ref. 75)	+ excess ferrous ammonium sulphate and back titrated with permanganate	135
β- and γ-Cellulose in wood pulp after removal of α-form		Unused titrated with ferrous ammonium sulphate to diphenylamine/H_2SO_4	136
Ethanol, ether	Aspirated into reagent; 5 h duration	I^-/thiosulphate	137
Methylene blue	Neutral solution + bichromate	Unused determined in filtrate with I^-/thiosulphate	138
$—OC_2H_5$, $=CHCH_3$ and $—CH_2CH_2OH$ groups	Modified oxidation of method of refs 47 and 59. Temp. raised to 155°, giving acetic acid	Distillation begun at 135° and distillate titrated with NaOH to phenolphthalein	139
Lipids in blood	Reagent of method of ref. 75, + $AgNO_3$; 2 h/130°	I^-/thiosulphate	140
Biochemical oxygen demand values of sewage	+ bichromate/H_2SO_4/H_3PO_4; boiled and partly evaporated	I^-/thiosulphate	141
C-Methyl groups	Oxidation as in method of refs 47 and 59, giving acetic acid	Acetic acid distilled without preliminary reduction of unused bichromate with hydrazine	142
Ethanol in wine	Distilled into reagent; 15 min (modification of method of ref. 12)	+ excess Fe(II) and back titrated with bichromate to diphenylamine/H_2SO_4	143
Ethanol from alkali hydrolysis, in determination of diethyl phthalate	Distilled into reagent; 75 min/100°	I^-/thiosulphate	144
Protein in insulin	15 min/100°	I^-/thiosulphate	145

Materials titrated	Reagent and reaction conditions	Subsequent treatment and final titration stage	Ref.
Oxygen consumption of sewage	+ bichromate/H_2SO_4/ H_3PO_4 + selenium catalyst; 60 min/145°	I^-/thiosulphate	146
Lower alcohols, ether, acetaldehyde	Varied H_2SO_4 concentrations (binary mixtures thus analysed). Mostly oxidized to acetic acid	+ excess ferrous ammonium sulphate and back titrated with bichromate	147
Ethanol	5 min reflux, giving acetaldehyde	I^-/thiosulphate	148
Ethanol	15–30 min/100°	I^-/thiosulphate	149
Morphine	Oxidized to ψ-morphine	Unused titrated with Pb(II) amperometrically	150
Oxygen consumption of, e.g. industrial wastes or sewage (studied also many pure compounds, like sugars, phenols, amino acids, hydrocarbons)	2 h reflux	Unused titrated with Fe(II) to ferroin	151
Ethanol from alkali hydrolysis, in determination of ethyl urethane in body fluids	Aspirated into reagent	I^-/thiosulphate	152
Ethanol	Aspirated into reagent; 20 min	I^-/thiosulphate	153
Morphine in opium	15 min	Unused titrated with Fe(II) potentiometrically or to diphenylamine/H_2SO_4	154
4-Chloroacetanilide in phenacetin	Converted to $CrOCl$	Carried into $NaOH/H_2O_2$ and titrated with Hg(II) at pH 1·5–2 (citrate/HNO_3 buffer) to diphenylcarbazone indicator	155
Ethanol, ether	24–36 h/room temp. or 3–4 h/37°	Unused titrated with Fe(II) to diphenylanthranilic acid	156
Sugars	+ bichromate/Na_2CO_3; 5 min heating	+ H_2SO_4, then I^-/thiosulphate	157
Diethylene glycol in aqueous solutions	30 min reflux	I^-/thiosulphate	158

Materials titrated	Reagent and reaction conditions	Subsequent treatment and final titration stage	Ref.
Ethanol and ether in air or biological media	Passed through bichromate/HNO_3 (oxidized ethanol to acetic acid) and then bichromate/ H_2SO_4/HNO_3 (oxidized ether—30 min/room temp.)	I^-/thiosulphate	159
Reineckates of methonium compounds	+ excess bichromate, giving insoluble salts	Unused determined in filtrate	161
Lower alcohols, separated by partition chromatography	30 min/22–24°	I^-/thiosulphate	162
Methanol and ethanol in, e.g., tinctures	Two determinations with different reagents: one oxidized to CO_2 and acetic acid respectively; other, containing Ag_2SO_4, oxidized both to CO_2	Unused titrated with Fe(II) potentiometrically	163
Oxygen-consumption value of coke plant aqueous wastes	+ bichromate/H_2SO_4/ H_3PO_4; 5 min/100°	+ excess ferrous ammonium sulphate and back titrated with bichromate to barium diphenylamine sulphonate	164
Glucose	10–12 min heating	I^-/thiosulphate	165
Study of oxidation of *C*-methyl groups	Oxidation procedure of ref. 124, giving 62–99% yields of acetic acid	Distilled and titrated with alkali	166, 172
Blood ethanol	Oxidized to acetic acid	Unused titrated with Fe(II) to ferroin or barium diphenylamine sulphonate	167
C-Methyl groups joined to longer chains	Oxidation procedure of refs 47 and 59; temp up to 135°, giving 70–97% yields of acetic acid	Distilled and titrated with alkali to phenolphthalein	168
Hexadecyltrimethylammonium bromide	+ bichromate + a little HCl	Unused determined in filtrate with I^-/thiosulphate	169
Methanol	6 h/60°	I^-/thiosulphate	170
Plant sterols, precipitated as 'digitonides' in their determination	4 h/100°	Unused titrated with Fe(II) to ferroin	171

Materials titrated	Reagent and reaction conditions	Subsequent treatment and final titration stage	Ref.
Ethylene and diethylene glycols (study of oxidation)	Reagents with 12·5, 25 and 50% H_2SO_4; 2 h/100°	I^-/thiosulphate	173
Carbohydrates; many carboxylic acids and polyhydroxy compounds	10 min with reagent, hot from mixing	Unused titrated with ferrous ammonium sulphate potentiometrically	174
Celluloses	Method of ref. 174		175
Isoniazid	+ bichromate/H_2SO_4/KI (effectively iodine reagent). Slightly warmed	Unused iodine titrated with thiosulphate	176
Ethanol	Diffused into reagent; 12 h duration	I^-/thiosulphate	177
Starch and starch products; laurylamine acetate	30 min/120° or 2 h/100° for starch; 1 h/120° for the acetate	+ excess ferrous ammonium sulphate and back titrated with permanganate (also colorimetric determination of unused reagent)	178
C-Methyl groups	90 min/130°, giving acetic acid	+ $MgSO_4$, distilled and titrated with NaOH to phenolphthalein	179
Isopropanol in dextran and dextran solution	5 min/100°, giving acetone	Distilled and determined iodometrically (see Iodine reagents, ref. 316)	180
Barium acetate, formed from acetic acid, itself derived in determination of acetates by distillation with acid	+ excess bichromate, giving precipitate of barium chromate	Filtrate + acid/I^- and titrated with thiosulphate	181
C-Methyl groups	Oxidized to acetic acid	+ saturated Na_2SO_4, distilled and titrated with NaOH to phenolphthalein	182
Lignin in bleached pulp after treatment with H_2SO_4 to destroy other matter	Residue + reagent; 1 h/100°	Unused titrated with ferrous ammonium sulphate to ferroin	183
C-Methyl groups (micro)	60–90 min/165–175° giving acetic acid	Distilled and titrated with NaOH to phenolphthalein	184

Materials titrated	Reagent and reaction conditions	Subsequent treatment and final titration stage	Ref.
Hemicelluloses	Hot solution + reagent	+ excess ferrous ammonium sulphate and back titrated with permanganate	185
Indigo; indigo-sulphonic acid	Oxidized to isatin 1–30 min/room temp.; various H_2SO_4 concns. tried	I^-/thiosulphate, or unused determined with Fe(II)	186
Lower alcohols	5 min at temperature yielded by mixing sample and reagent components	Unused titrated with ferrous ammonium sulphate potentiometrically	187
Chemical oxygen demand of surface waters	Method of ref. 151		188
C-Methyl groups, e.g. in amines, ketones, acids, alcohols (study of oxidation)	15 min–4 h/120°, giving acetic acid	Distilled and titrated with NaOH to bromothymol blue	189
Gluconic acid		I^-/thiosulphate	190
Blood ethanol	Modification of method of ref. 88		191
Hydroquinone, derived from hydrolysis, in determination of arbutin	Oxidized to quinone	Steam distilled into I^-/acid and titrated with thiosulphate	192
2,2,6,6-Tetrabis-hydroxymethylcyclo-hexan-1-one and -cyclohexan-1-ol	4 h/95–100°, giving glutaric acid and CO_2	+ excess arsenite and back titrated with bromate or iodate	193
Acetone/butanol/ethanol	Two determinations with reagents of different H_2SO_4 concentration; 5 min/100° and 15 min/100°	I^-/thiosulphate	195, 205
Choline salts	3·5–4 h/*ca* 100°, oxidizing —CH_2OH group to —COOH	Unused titrated with ferrous ammonium sulphate to diphenylamine sulphonate	196
C-Methyl groups	Oxidized to acetic acid	Excess destroyed with H_2O_2, acid distilled and titrated	197
Oxidizability of sewage water	+ Ag_2SO_4/H_2SO_4; 1 h. Then + reagent and 15 min reflux	+ excess ferrous ammonium sulphate and back titrated with permanganate	198

Materials titrated	Reagent and reaction conditions	Subsequent treatment and final titration stage	Ref.
Chemical oxygen demand of petro-chemical wastes	1 h reflux. Then + Ag_2SO_4 and a further hour reflux	Unused titrated with ferrous ammonium sulphate to ferroin	199
Isopropanol/*sec*-butanol in wine and other fermented liquors	2 h, oxidizing to acetone and butanone respectively	Total ketones determined iodometrically (see Iodine reagents, ref. 361) (acetone alone determined colorimetrically)	200
Acetone/isopropanol	2 h/room temp., oxidizing isopropanol to acetone (combined with hypobromite oxidation to determine both)	Determined with alkali/excess iodine	201
Ethanol in pharma-ceutical products	15 min reflux	Unused titrated with ferrous ammonium sulphate to phenyl-anthranilic acid	202
Blood ethanol	Distilled into reagent; 25–30 min	I^-/thiosulphate	203
Tartrates, tartaric acid	45 min/100°	Unused titrated with hydro-quinone potentiometrically	204
Ethanol and acetalde-hyde in plant tissue	Diffused into reagent	I^-/thiosulphate (acetaldehyde determined colorimetrically)	206
Ethoxyl groups in some organic Si and Al compounds	30 min reflux	I^-/thiosulphate	207
Lactic, tartaric acids	At 100°	Unused titrated with Fe(II) to ferroin	208
Fatty, resin and naphthenic acids in fats and soaps (to charac-terize the acids)	Oxidation procedure of refs 47 and 59, giving acetic acid	Steam distilled and titrated with KOH	209
Blood ethanol	Diffused into reagent under *ca* 1 mm pressure. *Ca* 1 min duration	I^-/thiosulphate	210

Materials titrated	Reagent and reaction conditions	Subsequent treatment and final titration stage	Ref.
Lactic acid from hydrolysis of α-chloropropionic acid with $Hg(II)/HNO_3$	+ bichromate; 5 min	Excess reduced with Fe(II); 15 min reflux, oxidizing to pyruvic acid, which reacts with the Hg(II) forming O<(Hg)(Hg)>C<(CO.COOH)(Hg.NO$_3$) KI added, yielding KOH with this, titrated with HCl to phenolphthalein (see Mercury (II), ref. 145)	211
'Acaprin' (Bayer)—*N*,*N'*-bis-(*N*-methylquinolinylurea)methyl sulphate	+ excess bichromate; 15 min room/temp.	Unused determined in filtrate with I^-/thiosulphate	212
1-Phenyl-2,3-dimethyl-4-pyrrolidinyl-5-pyrazolone in medicines	1 h reflux	I^-/thiosulphate	213
Products from saponification of cellulose acetobutyrate	1 h reflux	I^-/thiosulphate; also acid formed distilled and titrated	214
1,4-Dihydrazinophthalazine	In dilute H_2SO_4, + bichromate, giving insoluble salt	Unused determined in filtrate with I^-/thiosulphate	215
Sugars, separated by paper chromatography	1 h/95°	I^-/thiosulphate	216
Surface-active polymers of ethylene oxide (determination of the number of epoxide units—in combination with spectrophotometric determination of the —OH groups with $(NH_4)_2Ce(NO_3)_6$)	60–90 sec boiling	I^-/thiosulphate	217
Trichlorobenzene in water, extracted with ether	Oxidized to chlorine	Carried with air into CdI_2 and titrated with thiosulphate (also determined colorimetrically)	219
Ethanol in body fluids	Diffused into reagent; 8 h duration	I^-/thiosulphate	220

Materials titrated	Reagent and reaction conditions	Subsequent treatment and final titration stage	Ref.
Ethanol in cellosolve, etc.	Carried with nitrogen into reagent; 30 min duration	I^-/thiosulphate	221
Hydroquinone from acid hydrolysis of arbutin in its determination	Oxidized to quinone	Steam distilled, reduced with Zn/H_2SO_4 and hydroquinone thus formed titrated with $Ce(SO_4)_2$ (see Metals, ref. 98 and Part I, Cerium (IV), ref. 80)	222
Benzene hexachloride	20 min/130–5°, giving chlorine	Chlorine carried out by air and determined iodometrically	223
Pentachlorophenol in commercial products	Heated with CrO_3, giving chlorine	Passed into CdI_2 and the iodine titrated with thiosulphate	224
Tartaric acid (study of oxidation)	28–29° (evidently initial fast reaction to tartronic acid, then slower change to mesoxalic acid)	I^-/thiosulphate	225
Chemical oxygen demand in waste waters	Reagent + Ag_2SO_4 catalyst; 1 min boiling	Unused titrated with ferrous ammonium sulphate to ferroin	226
Methyl groups in alkyl benzenes	3 h/130°, giving acetic acid	Distilled and titrated with NaOH to phenolphthalein	227
C-Methyl groups	Various procedures tried, from 125 to *ca* 170°, with preliminary reflux or with distillation from the beginning. Effect of factors on stability of the acetic acid also investigated	Distilled and titrated with NaOH to phenolphthalein	228
Ethylene and propylene oxide groups in polyalkylene glycols	Oxidation procedure of refs 47 and 59, giving 2 CO_2 and CO_2 + acetic acid respectively	Acetic acid distilled and titrated; (CO_2 determined with absorbtion tubes)	229
Tetraphenylborates	20 min/115°, giving CO_2	Unused titrated with Fe(II) to ferroin	230, 238
Di- and triethylene glycol in aqueous solution	Two determinations with different H_2SO_4 concentrations; 2 h/100°	I^-/thiosulphate	231
Alcohol in blood	Diffused into bichromate/HNO_3 (method of ref. 88)	I^-/thiosulphate	232

Materials titrated	Reagent and reaction conditions	Subsequent treatment and final titration stage	Ref.
Methanol	Not too concentrated H_2SO_4 (*ca* 50% better than conc.)	I^-/thiosulphate	233
Ethanol in mixtures containing aromatic solvents	Water extract + reagent, giving oxidation to acetic acid	I^-/thiosulphate on an aliquot	234
Various substances, e.g. ethylene glycol	90 min/100°	Unused titrated with ferrous ammonium sulphate amperometrically	235
Methanol	+ reagent in 2-fold excess; 10 min reflux	Unused titrated with ferrous ammonium sulphate to phenylanthranilic acid	236
Evaluation of volatile oils of spices	Distilled into reagent	I^-/thiosulphate	237
Organic substances in clay	+ CrO_3 + H_2SO_4; 5 min boiling	+ water and titrated amperometrically with Fe(II)	239
Indigo carmine	Left in the dark until disappearance of blue	I^-/thiosulphate	240
C-Methyl groups, e.g. in phenobarbital, pyramidone	Method of ref. 59, using modification of apparatus of refs. 142 and 189		241
Nitro, nitroso compounds	+ CrO_3 + H_2SO_4; 30 min/150°, giving HNO_3	Diluted, made alkaline and reduced with Devarda's alloy to ammonia; distilled in nitrogen current into HCl and back titrated to methyl red/methylene blue	242
Blood alcohol (after separation by distillation)	Distilled into bichromate/HNO_3	I^-/thiosulphate	243
Ethanol, propanols, n-butanol	Various reagents with varied acid and bichromate concs; 1 h/100° (30 min for isopropanol); studied oxidation and analysed reaction products in examination of analytical possibilities	+ excess ferrous ammonium sulphate and back titrated with bichromate to diphenylamine Ba sulphonate	245

Materials titrated	Reagent and reaction conditions	Subsequent treatment and final titration stage	Ref.
Cellulose in town refuse compost (previously treated to remove proteins and lignin)	90 min/*ca* 100°	+ excess ferrous sulphate and back titrated with MnO_4^-	246
Various organic compounds	Reagent with 50% H_2SO_4 or $HClO_4$, giving complete oxidation to CO_2	CO_2 passed into excess $Ba(OH)_2$, covered by a pentane layer to keep out atmospheric CO_2; back titrated with acid	247
Ethanol in injection solutions	2 h/55–60°	I^-/thiosulphate	248
2,2′-Sulphonyl- and 2,2′-sulphinyldiethanol from oxidation of 2,2′-thiodiethanol	15 min/*ca* 100°, giving sulphonyldiacetic acid	I^-/thiosulphate	249
Aldehydes, e.g. HCHO, CH_3CHO, paraldehyde, chloral	10 min/*ca* 100° (15 min for CH_3CHO)	Back titrated with Fe(II) to phenylanthranilic acid	251
Ethanol in various fermenting materials	Distillate, + CrO_3; 1–2 min	I^-/thiosulphate	252
Methanol in mixtures with HCHO (removed by oxidation to HCOOH and absorption in an ion-exchanger)	30 min/*ca* 100°	I^-/thiosulphate	253
Fatty acids (extracted with KOH)	1 h/*ca* 100°	I^-/thiosulphate	254
Hydroquinone		I^-/thiosulphate	255
HCHO/HCOOH/methanol mixtures	45–60 min reflux, oxidizing all to CO_2 (HCHO and HCOOH otherwise determined, giving methanol by difference)	I^-/thiosulphate	256
Quaternary ammonium salts	+ bichromate, giving precipitates	I^-/thiosulphate on filtrate	257
Ethanol in sour milk and urine (after separation by distillation)	20 min/*ca* 100°	I^-/thiosulphate	258
Citric + oxalic acids, precipitated as Ca salts in analysis of fermentation mixtures		I^-/thiosulphate	259

References

1. McNair, D. S., *Chem. News* **55**, 229 (1887).
2. Bourcart, E., *Bull. soc. ind. de Mulhouse* 558 (1889).
3. Hehner, O., *J. Soc. Chem. Ind.* (*London*) **8**, 4 (1889).
4. Blank, O, and Finkenbeiner, H., *Ber.* **39**, 1326 (1906).
5. Pässler, J., abstract in *Z. anal. Chem.* **47**, 321 (1908).
6. Steinfels, W., *Seifensieder-Ztg.* **37**, 793 (1910).
7. Hoepner, K., *Z. Nahr. Genussmittel* **41**, 193 (1921).
8. Lublin, A., *Klin. Wochschr.* **1**, 894 (1922).
9. Spatz, R., *Arch. Hyg.* **91**, 315 (1922).
10. Widmark, E. M. P., *Biochem. Z*, **131**, 473 (1922).
11. Bray, M. W. and Andrews, T. M., *Ind. Eng. Chem.* **15**, 377 (1923).
12. Fachini, S., *Chem. Trade J.* **73**, 127 (1923).
13. Shaffer, P. A. and Ronzoni, E., *J. Biol. Chem.* **57**, 741 (1923).
14. Vasilewska, J., *Trav. inst. M. Nencki* No. 28 (1923).
15. Bildsten, N. V., *Biochem. Z.* **146**, 361 (1924).
16. Fyleman, E., *J. Soc. Chem. Ind.* (*London*) **43**, 142T (1924).
17. Roos, L., *Ann. fals. et fraudes* **17**, 410 (1924).
18. Tervaert, D. G. C., *Arch. néerland. physiol.* **9**, 132 (1924).
19. Chabot, G., *Bull. soc. chim. Belg.* **34**, 328 (1925).
20. Hansen, K., *Tidsskr. Kjemi og Bergvesen* **5**, 172, 187 (1925).
21. Martini, M. and Nourisson, A., *Ann. fals. et fraudes* **18**, 235 (1925).
22. Täufel, K. and Wagner, C., *Z. anal. Chem.* **67**, 16 (1925).
23. Adeney, W. E. and Dawson, B. B., *Sci. Proc. Royal Dublin Soc.* **18**, 199 (1926).
24. v. Somogyi, E., *Z. angew. Chem.* **39**, 280 (1926).
25. Baum, F., *Chem.-Ztg.* **51**, 517, 538 (1927).
26. Cassar, H. A., *Ind. Eng. Chem.* **19**, 1061 (1927).
27. Gettler, A. O. and Tiber, A., *Arch. Path. Lab. Med.* **3**, 75 (1927).
28. Morvillez, F. and Défossez, M., *J. pharm. chim.* **6**, 204 (1927).
29. Noetzel, O., *Z. Untersuch. Lebensm.* **53**, 388 (1927).
30. Boivin, A., *Bull. soc. chim. biol.* **10**, 684 (1928).
31. Cordebard, H., *Bull. soc. chim. biol.* **10**, 461 (1928).
32. Ferré, L. and Bourges, J., *Chimie et industrie*, Special No. 775, April (1928).
33. Rae, J., *Pharm. J.* **120**, 71 (1928).
34. Rae, J., *Pharm. J.* **120**, 270 (1928).
35. Schwenk, E. and Wanko, L., *Z. anal. Chem.* **74**, 168 (1928).
36. Spencer, G. C., *J. Assoc. Offic. Agr. Chem.* **11**, 360 (1928).
37. Adams, C. A. and Nicholls, J. R., *Analyst* **54**, 2 (1929).
38. Evans, J. and Jones, A. O., *Analyst* **54**, 134 (1929).
39. Friedemann, F., *Z. ges. Schiess.-u. Sprengstoffw.* **24**, 208 (1929).
40. Kettle, S., *Chemist-Analyst* **18**, 7 (1929).

41. Semichon, L. and Flanzy, M., *Ann. fals. et fraudes* **22**, 139 (1929).
42. Okey, R., *J. Biol. Chem.* **88**, 367 (1930).
43. Semichon, L. and Flanzy, M., *Ann. fals. et fraudes* **23**, 583 (1930).
44. Jervell, O., *Biochem. Z.* **235**, 101 (1931).
45. Katsura, S. and Hatakeyama, T., *Biochem. Z.* **234**, 462 (1931).
46. Klauer, H., *Deut. Z. ges. gerichtl. Med.* **17**, 89 (1931).
47. Kuhn, R. and L'Orsa, F., *Z. angew. Chem.* **44**, 847 (1931).
48. Mohlman, F. W. and Edwards, G. P., *Ind. Eng. Chem., Anal. Ed.* **3**, 119 (1931).
49. Nicloux, M., *Compt. rend.* **192**, 985 (1931).
50. Smith, L., *Svensk Kem. Tidskr.* **43**, 83 (1931).
51. Werkman, C. H. and Osburn, O. L., *Ind. Eng. Chem., Anal. Ed.* **3**, 387 (1931).
52. Johnson, M. J., *Ind. Eng. Chem., Anal. Ed.* **4**, 20 (1932).
53. Labourasse, G., *Bull. assoc. chim. sucr. dist.* **49**, 56 (1932).
54. Lalande, A., *Bull. soc. chim. France* **51**, 916 (1932).
55. Lantz, R., *Chimie et industrie* **27**, 775 (1932).
56. Mayer, R. M., *Deut. Z. ges. gerichtl. Med.* **18**, 638 (1932).
57. Sato, M. and Murata, K., *J. Agr. Chem. Soc., Japan* **8**, 1303 (1932).
58. Semichon, L. and Flanzy, M., *Ann. fals. et fraudes* **25**, 414 (1932).
59. Kuhn, R. and Roth, H., *Ber.* **66**, 1274 (1933).
60. Kunke, W. F., *J. Assoc. Offic. Agr. Chem.* **16**, 348 (1933).
61. Alessandrini, E., *Ann. brasserie dist.* **32**, 104 (1934); *Analyst* **59**, 630 (1934).
62. Fabre, R. and Brard, D., *J. pharm. chim.* **19**, 5 (1934).
63. Kolthoff, I. M. and Lingane, J. J., *J. Am. Pharm. Assoc.* **23**, 404 (1934).
64. Procházka, R., *Plyn a Voda* **14**, 115, 302, 319, 342 (1934).
65. Christensen, L. M. and Fulmer, E. I., *Ind. Eng. Chem., Anal. Ed.* **7**, 180 (1935).
66. Harger, R. N., *J. Lab. Clin. Med.* **20**, 746 (1935).
67. Janke, A. and Kropacsy, S., *Biochem. Z.* **278**, 30 (1935).
68. Schmidt-Hebbel, H., *Rev. estud. farm. bioquím. (Buenos Aires)* **25**, 526 (1935).
69. Snethlago, H. C. S., *Z. anal. Chem.* **102**, 321 (1935).
70. Vucetich, D. C., *Rev. fac. cienc. quím. (La Plata)* **10**, 37 (1935).
71. Beletzkii, Yu. A. and Mil'cho, E. M., *Sintet. Kautschuk* No. 2, 27 (1936).
72. Deux, Y., *Petit. J. brass.* **44**, 790 (1936).
73. Kemal, H., *Z. anal. Chem.* **107**, 33 (1936).
74. Newman, H., *J. Pharmacol.* **56**, 278 (1936).
75. Nicloux, M., *Ann. fermentations* **1**, 449, 513, 596 (1936).
76. Snethlago, H. C. S., *Rec. trav. chim.* **55**, 58 (1936).
77. Shatalov, V. P. and Lapshinov, I. I., *Sintet. Kautschuk* No. 1, 38 (1936).
78. Trotzkii, Yu. and Mendelson, R., *Ukr. Biochem. J.* **9**, 157 (1936).

79. Auerbach, M. E., *J. Am. Pharm. Assoc.* **26**, 231 (1937).
80. Christensen, B. E., Williams, R. J. and King, A. E., *J. Am. Chem. Soc.* **59**, 293 (1937).
81. Goncharov, S. V. and Burvasser, F. G., *Org. Chem. Ind.* (*USSR*) **3**, 423 (1937).
82. Harris, E. J., *Analyst* **62**, 729 (1937).
83. Kheraskova, E. and Korsunskaya, E., *Caoutchouc & Rubber* (*USSR*) No. 7–8, 39 (July–August) (1937).
84. Proctor & Gamble Co., *Ind. Eng. Chem., Anal. Ed.* **9**, 514 (1937).
85. Randa, E., *Oil & Soap* **14**, 7 (1937).
86. Rappoport, F. and Engelberg, H., *Klin. Wochschr.* **16**, 610 (1937).
87. Boorman, E. J., *Analyst* **64**, 791 (1939).
88. Cordebard, H., *J. pharm. chim.* **30**, 263 (1939).
89. Goncharev, S. V. and Burvasser, F. G., *Bumazhnaya Prom.* **17**, No. 10. 27 (1939).
90. Hansen, K. and Dybing, O., *Biochem. Z.* **301**, 225 (1939).
91. Ostrovskaya, R. E., *Lab. Prakt.* (*USSR*), *Sammelband* 84 (1939).
92. Rapin, A., *Helv. Chim. Acta* **22**, 72 (1939).
93. Schulek, E. and Rózsa, P., *Z. anal. Chem.* **117**, 400 (1939).
94. Stanley, R. D., *J. Assoc. Offic. Agr. Chem.* **22**, 594 (1939).
95. Thivolle, L. and Sonntag, G., *Bull. soc. chim. biol.* **21**, 1369 (1939).
96. Allen, N., Charbonnier, H. Y. and Coleman, R. M., *Ind. Eng. Chem., Anal. Ed.* **12**, 384 (1940).
97. Andrews, E., Potter, R. M., Friedemann, T. E. and Livingston, H. M., *J. Lab. Clin. Med.* **25**, 966 (1940).
98. Bayly, W. A., *Soc. Chem. Ind. Victoria, Proc.* **40**, 267 (1940).
99. Johnson, G. W. and Gibson, R. E., *J. Lab. Clin. Med.* **26**, 399 (1940).
100. Levensen, J. J., *Ind. Eng. Chem., Anal. Ed.* **12**, 332 (1940).
101. Levine, H. and Bodansky, M., *J. Biol. Chem.* **133**, 193 (1940).
102. Stanley, R. D., *J. Assoc. Offic. Agr. Chem.* **23**, 576 (1940).
103. Dister, A., *J. pharm. Belg.* **23**, 25 (1941).
104. Ginzburg, S. L. and Bokova, G. B., *J. Chem. Ind* (*USSR*) **18**, No. 12, 33 (1941).
105. Kozelka, F. L. and Hine, C. H., *Ind. Eng. Chem., Anal. Ed.* **13**, 905 (1941).
106. Labourasse, G., *Bull. assoc. chim.* **58**, 161 (1941).
107. Orlovskii, S. T., *J. Appl. Chem. USSR.* **14**, 671 (1941).
108. Thivolle, L. and Sonntag, G., *Trav. memb. soc. chim. biol.* **23**, 1302 (1941).
109. Thivolle, L. and Raveux, R., *Trav. memb. soc. chim. biol.* **23**, 1445 (1941).
110. Caselli, P. and Cearanfi, E., *Biochem. Z.* **313**, 11 (1942).
111. Flotow, E., *Pharm. Zentralhalle* **83**, 181 (1942).
112. Kettering, J. H. and Conrad, C. M., *Ind. Eng. Chem., Anal. Ed.* **14**, 432 (1942).

113. Stanley, R. D., *J. Assoc. Offic. Agr. Chem.* **25**, 693 (1942).
114. Thivolle, L. and Raveux, R., *Trav. memb. soc. chim. biol.* **24**, 1066 (1942).
115. Tomaghelli, A. A., *Anales asoc. quím. arg.* **30**, 30 (1942).
116. Winnick, T., *Ind. Eng. Chem., Anal. Ed.* **14**, 523 (1942).
117. Burgess, V. L., Donaldson, W. E. and Batty, J. A., *ASTM Bulletin* **120**, 23 (1943); *Rubber Chem. Tech.* **19**, 792 (1943).
118. Griffon, H., *Compt. rend.* **217**, 404 (1943).
119. Malan, J. R., *Onderstepoort J. Vet. Sci Animal Ind.* **18**, 311 (1943).
120. Niculescu, M. and Cáplescu, N., *Z. anal. Chem.* **125**, 416 (1943).
121. Raveux, R., *Ann. chim. anal.* **25**, 70, 95 (1943).
122. Werner, H. W. and Mitchell, J. L., *Ind. Eng. Chem., Anal. Ed.* **15**, 375 (1943).
123. Barthel, W. F. and Laforge, F. B., *Ind. Eng. Chem., Anal. Ed.* **16**, 434 (1944).
124. Ginger, L. G., *J. Biol. Chem.* **156**, 453 (1944).
125. Heim, H. C., *J. Assoc. Offic. Agr. Chem.* **27**, 354 (1944).
126. Thouvenin, R., *Ann. chim. anal.* **26**, 72 (1944).
127. Jackerott, K. A., *Dansk Tids Farm.* **16**, 154 (1945).
128. Pucci, J. R. and Maffei, F. J., *Anais asoc. quím. Brasil* **4**, 65 (1945).
129. de Saint-Rat, L. and Hatey, J., *Ann. pharm. franç.* **3**, 166 (1945).
130. Wessel, C. J., Drigot, S. W. and Beach, G. W., *Ind. Eng. Chem., Anal. Ed.* **17**, 440 (1945).
131. Bizzozero, C. D., *Bol. inform. petrol.* (*Buenos Aires*) **23**, 451 (1946).
132. Blum, C. and Käsermann, H., *Pharm. Helv. Acta* **21**, 233 (1946).
133. Chaikelis, A. S. and Floersheim, R. D., *Am. J. Clin. Path. Tech. Sect.* **10**, 189 (1946).
134. Lindenberg, A. B., *Bull. soc. chim. biol.* **28**, 451 (1946).
135. Rochat, J., *Helv. Chim. Acta* **29**, 819 (1946).
136. Becker, H. E., *Pulp Paper Ind.* **21**, No. 1, 54, 56, 58 (1947).
137. Bonnor, T. G., *Analyst* **72**, 47 (1947).
138. Davidson, G. F., *Shirley Inst. Mem.* **21**, 29 (1947).
139. Lemieux, R. U. and Purves, C. B., *Can. J. Res.* **25B**, 485 (1947).
140. Monasterio, G. and Gigli, G., *Rass. fisiop. clin. e terap* (*Pisa*) **19**, 82 (1947).
141. Rhame, G. A., *Water & Sewage Works* **94**, 192 (1947).
142. Wiesenberger, E., *Mikrochemie ver. Mikrochim. Acta* **33**, 51 (1947).
143. Barini-Banchi, G., *Ann. chim. applicata* **38**, 423 (1948).
144. Butts, P. G., Prine, G. B., Kouka, D. L. and Becker, W. W., *Anal. Chem.* **20**, 1066 (1948).
145. Cordebard, H. and Schneider, J., *Ann. pharm. franç.* **6**, 542 (1948).
146. Ingols, R. S. and Murray, P. E., *Water & Sewage Works* **95**, 113 (1948).
147. Pudovik, A. N. and Sinaiskis, G. M., *Zhur. Prik. Khim.* **21**, 862 (1948).
148. Bacila, M. and Ferencz, G., *Arquiv. biol. e tecnol., inst. biol. e pesquisas tecnol.* **4**, 25 (1949).

149. Ferrari, P. V., *Ann. sper. agrar.* (*Rome*) (*N.S.*) **3**, 927 (1949).
150. Kalvoda, R. and Zýka, J., *Časopis českého Lékarnictvo.* **62**, 134 (1949).
151. Moore, W. A., Kroner, R. C. and Ruchhoft, C. C., *Anal. Chem.* **21**, 953 (1949).
152. Beickert, A., *Arch. exptl. Path. Pharmakol.* **210**, 479 (1950).
153. Bhattacharya, A. and Bose, I. B., *Indian Pharmacist* **5**, 263, 276 (1950).
154. Blažek, A., Kalvoda, R. and Zýka, J., *Časopis českého Lékarnictva* **63**, 69 (1950).
155. Hald, J., *Dansk Tids Farm.* **24**, 195 (1950).
156. Knox, K. D. and Pask, E. A., *Brit. J. Anaes*, **22**, 102 (1950).
157. Tul'chinskii, M. N., *Zhur. Prik. Khim.* **23**, 176 (1950).
158. Amlinskaya, M. A. and Erikh, Y. N., *Trudy Vsesoyuz. Nauch.—Issledovatel Inst. Khim. Pererabotki Gazov* **6**, 213 (1951).
159. Fabre, R., Truhaut, R. and Chéramy, P., *Ann. pharm. franç.* **9**, 408 (1951).
160. Fabre, R., Truhaut, R. and Chéramy, P., *Compt. rend.* **232**, 2266 (1951).
161. Heyrovský, A., *Sbornik Celostatní Pracovní Konf. Anal. Chemiků* **1**, 221 (1951).
162. Neish, A. C., *Can. J. Chem.* **29**, 552 (1951).
163. Šedivec, V., *Chem. Listy* **45**, 32 (1951).
164. Shaw, J. A., *Anal. Chem.* **23**, 1764 (1951).
165. Szeberényi, P., *Magyar Kem. Folyóirat* **57**, 47 (1951).
166. Campbell, A. D. and Morton, J. E., *J. Chem. Soc.* 1693 (1952).
167. Gottwald, E. and Voigt, G. E., *Deut. Z. ges. u gerichtl. Med.* **41**, 164 (1952).
168. Kirsten, W. and Stenhagen, E., *Acta Chem. Scand.* **6**, 682 (1952).
169. Renard, I., *J. pharm. Belg.* **7**, 403 (1952).
170. Seifert, P. and Leyers, H., *Arch. Exp. Path. Pharm.* **214**, 124 (1952).
171. Waghorne, D. and Ball, C. D., *Anal. Chem.* **24**, 560 (1952).
172. Campbell, A. D. and Chettleburgh, V. J., *J. Chem. Soc.* 1942 (1953).
173. Cardone, M. J. and Compton, J. W., *Anal. Chem.* **25**, 1869 (1953).
174. Launer, H. F. and Tomimatsu, Y., *Anal. Chem.* **25**, 1767 (1953).
175. Launer, H. F. and Tomimatsu, Y., *Anal. Chem.* **25**, 1769 (1953).
176. Montequi, F., *Farm. nueve* (*Madrid*) **18**, 10 (1953).
177. Newman, E. J. and Newman, H. W., *Stanford Med. Bull.* **11**, 96 (1953).
178. Schulz, N. F., *Anal. Chem.* **25**, 1762 (1953).
179. Eisenbraun, J., McElvain, S. M. and Aycock, B. F., *J. Am. Chem. Soc.* **76**, 607 (1954).
180. Frisone, G. J., *Anal. Chem.* **26**, 924 (1954).
181. Köszegi, D. and Simonyi, J., *Acta Chim. Acad. Sci. Hung.* **5**, 33 (1954).
182. Schöniger, W., Lieb, H. and El-Ibrahim, M. G., *Mikrochim. Acta* 96 (1954).
183. Troitsch, H., *Assoc. tech. ind. papetière, Bull.* 134 (1954).

184. Wiesenberger, E., *Mikrochim. Acta* 127 (1954).
185. Tomari, Y., *Sen-i-Gakkaishi* **11**, 727 (1955).
186. Gopala Rao, G. and Venkateswara Rao, N., *Z. anal. Chem.* **151**, 347 (1956).
187. Griffiths, V. S. and Stock, D. I., *J. Chem. Soc.* 1633 (1956).
188. Moore, W. A. and Walker, W. W., *Anal. Chem.* **28**, 164 (1956).
189. Tashinian, V. H., Baker, M. J. and Koch, C. W., *Anal. Chem.* **28**, 1304 (1956).
190. van den Buleke, I. A., *Pharm. Tijds Belg.* **34**, 126 (1957).
191. Cordebard, H., *Bull. soc. pharm. Nancy* No. 33, 14 (1957).
192. Fried, R., *Arch. Pharm.* **290**, 73 (1957).
193. Kamphenkel, L. and v. Hintzenstern, G., *Chem. Tech. (Berlin)* **9**, 704 (1957).
194. Melissinos, I. and Stylakakis, E., *Chim. Chronika (Athens)* **22A**, 83 (1957).
195. Nakhmanovich, B. M. and Pryanishnikova, N. A., *Zavodskaya Lab.* **23**, 165 (1957).
196. Saye, C., *Compt. rend.* **245**, 427 (1957).
197. Sudo, T., Shimoe, D. and Tsujii, Y., *Japan Analyst* **6**, 494, 498 (1957).
198. Bar, V. P., *Vestnik Tekh. i Ekon. Inform. Mezhotrasl. Lab. Tekh.-Ekon. Issledovan i Nauch.-Tekh. Inform. Nauch.-Issledovatel Fiz.-Khim. Inst. am L. Ya. Karpova* No. 6, 46 (1958).
199. Bertram, F. W., Carlisle, O. T., Murray, J. E., Warren, G. W. and Connell, C. H., *Anal. Chem.* **30**, 1482 (1958).
200. Génévois, L. and Lafon, M., *Chim. anal.* **40**, 156 (1958).
201. Grover, K. C. and Mehrotra, R. C., *Z. anal. Chem.* **160**, 274 (1958).
202. Karpov, O. N., *Aptechnoe Delo* **7**, 58 (1958).
203. Kirk, P. L., Gibor, A. and Parker, K. P., *Anal. Chem.* **30**, 1418 (1958).
204. Krejzová, E., Simon, V. and Zýka, J., *Českoslov. Farm.* **7**, 82 (1958).
205. Nakhmanovich, B. M. and Shcheblykina, N. A., *Trudy Vsesoyuz. Nauch.-Issl. Inst. Spirt. i Likero.-Vodoch. Prom.* No. 6, 58 (1958).
206. Wager, H. G., *Analyst* **83**, 291 (1958).
207. Bondarevskaya, E. A., Syavtsillo, S. V. and Potsepkina, B. N., *Zhur. Anal. Khim.* **14**, 501 (1959).
208. Courtoisier, A. J., *Ann. école natl. agr. Alger* **1**, 1 (1959).
209. Jureček, M. and Kazák, P., *Z. anal. Chem.* **167**, 32 (1959).
210. Mahal, H. S., *Anal. Chem.* **31**, 1908 (1959).
211. Marquardt, R. P. and Luce, E. N., *Anal. Chem.* **31**, 418 (1959).
212. Špinková, V. and Zýka, J., *Českoslov. Farm.* **8**, 551 (1959).
213. Strunz, W., *Sci. Pharm.* **27**, 145 (1959).
214. Bartels, U. and Hoyme, H., *Faserforsch. u. Textiltech.* **11**, 503 (1960).
215. Jančik, F., Buděšinský, B. and Körbl, J., *Českoslov. Farm.* **9** 304 (1960).
216. Jayme, G. and Hahn, G., *Angew. Chem.* **72**, 520 (1960).

217. Killheffer, J. V. and Jungermann, E., *Anal. Chem.* **32**, 1178 (1960).
218. Lafon, M. and Baraud, J., *Bull. soc. chim. France* 943 (1960).
219. Meleshchenko, K. F., *Gigiena i Sanit.* **25**, No. 5, 54 (1960).
220. Nickolls, L. C., *Analyst* **85**, 840 (1960).
221. Perepletchikova, I. M., Etlis, V. S. and Kalugin, A. A., *Zavodskaya Lab.* **26**, 154 (1960).
222. Rácz, G., Fuzi, J. and Fulop, L., *Acta Pharm. Hung.* **30**, 212 (1960); *Farmacia* (*Bucharest*) **8**, 377 (1960).
223. Szucki, B. and Soczewinska, Z., *Med. Pracy* **11**, 463 (1960).
224. Teplyakova, Z. M. and Timbekov, E. Kh., *Sbornik Nauch. Trudov Tashkentsk. Med. Inst.* **16**, 229 (1960).
225. Vaidya, L. S. and Datar, D. S., *J. Sci. Ind. Research* (*India*) **20B**, 35 (1961).
226. Zdybiewska, M., *Gaz, Woda i Tech. Sanit.* **34**, 254 (1960).
227. Brandenberger, S. G., Maas, L. W. and Dvoretzky, I., *Anal. Chem.* **33**, 453 (1961).
228. Gore, T. S. and Gupte, S. S., *Mikrochim. Acta* 654 (1961).
229. Kotschmar, A., *Z. anal. Chem.* **181**, 30 (1961).
230. Schneer, A. and Hartmann, H., *Acta Chim. Acad. Sci. Hung.* **28**, 271 (1961).
231. Whitman, C. L., Roecker, G. W. and McNerney, C. F., *Anal. Chem.* **33**, 781 (1961).
232. Boucherle, A., Serusclat, F. and Eynaud, M., *Rev. Alcoolisme* **7**, 87 (1961).
233. Dynakowski, R. and Kubalski, J., *Acta Polon. Pharm.* **18**, 21 (1961).
234. Gambardella, E. I., *Lako-Krasochyne Materialy i ikh Primenenie* No. 3, 60 (1961).
235. Ginzburg, V. I., *Zavodskaya Lab.* **27**, 1337 (1961).
236. Karpov, O. N., *Izv. Vysshikh Uchebn. Zavedenii, Khim. i Khim. Tekhnol.* **4**, 1039 (1961).
237. Misra, R. C. and Krishna Rao, G. S., *J. Sci. Ind. Research, India* **20D**, 331 (1961).
238. Schneer, A. and Hartmann, H., *Magyar Kem. Folyoirat* **67**, 309 (1961).
239. Kondrakhina, E. G., *Trudy Kazakh. Fil. Akad. Strod. i Arkhitekt, SSSR* 367 (1961).
240. Suzuki, M., Nakamura, E., Kanaya, Y. and Nagase, Y., *Tokyo Yakka Daigaku Kenkyu Nempo* No. **11**, 120 (1961).
241. Brancone, L. M., *Microchem. J. Symp. Sec.* **2**, 605 (1962).
242. Novák, V., Kozák, P., Matoušek, P. and Jureček, M., *Mikrochim. Acta* 1101 (1962).
243. Truhaut, R. and Boudene, U., *Ann. Med. Legale Criminol. Police Sci. et Toxicol.* **42**, 455 (1962).
244. Umeda, K. and Tarama, K., *Nippon Kagaku Zasshi* **83**, 1216 (1962).

245. Barnard, J. A. and Karayannis, N., *Anal. Chim. Acta* **26**, 253 (1962).
246. Mebius, L. J., *Analyst* **87**, 821 (1962).
247. Maros, L., Szakacs-Pinter, M. and Schulek, E., *Magyar Kem. Folyoirat* **68**, 213 (1962).
248. Paulssen, R. B. and Waaler, T., *Pharm. Acta Helv.* **37**, 125 (1962).
249. Stahl, C. R., *Anal. Chem.* **34**, 1001 (1962).
250. Chatterji, A. C., Shukla, S. N. and Lal, J., *Z. Physik. Chem.* (*Leipzig*) **222**, 305 (1963).
251. Karpov, O. N., *Tr. Komis. po Analit. Khim., Akad. Nauk SSSR, Inst. Geokhim. i Analit. Khim.* **13**, 132 (1963).
252. Kubiček, R., *Kvasný Průmsyl* **9**, 173 (1963).
253. Légrádi, L., *Magyar Kem. Folyoirat* **69**, 117 (1963).
254. Levitskii, A. P. and Bulatskii, M. P., *Ukr. Biokhim. Zhur.* **35**, 120 (1963).
255. Priestley, P. T., *Analyst* **88**, 194 (1963).
256. Szekeres, L. and Kardos, E., *Z. Anal. Chem.* **193**, 271 (1963).
257. Thoma, K., Ullmann, E. and Loos, P., *Pharmazie*, **18**, 414 (1963).
258. Andrews, R. E. S. and Cooper, P. J., *Analyst* **89**, 272 (1964).
259. Bártfay, J. and Varga, M., *Magyar Kem. Lapya* **17**, 430 (1962).

13. Bismuth (III)

Reagent. Both Bi^{3+} (as nitrate or occasionally chloride) and the iodobismuthate anion BiI_4^- (familiar as the Dragendorff reagent and usually prepared from $Bi(NO_3)_3 + HNO_3 + KI$) have been used. Recently a reagent containing equivalent amounts of $Bi(NO_3)_3$ and EDTA has been employed.

Reactions and materials titrated. All methods have depended on formation of precipitates usually via ion/ion combination with the Bi^{3+} or BiI_4^- ions. Simple reaction equations may be formulated:

$$3\,RCOO^- + Bi^{3+} \rightarrow Bi(RCOO)_3$$
$$Base + H^+ + BiI_4^- \rightarrow (Base.H^+)BiI_4$$
$$R_4N^+ + BiI_4^- \rightarrow R_4NBiI_4$$

The reaction is probably not always so simple and precipitated products with formulae like $(Base.H)_5^{n+}\ (BiI_4^-)_{4n}\ (I^-)_n$ or $(Base.H)_3^{n+}\ (BiI_4^-)_{2n}\ (I^-)_n$ are quoted. Complex formation may also occur, as for example with propyl gallate (ref. 12).

Bases and salts thus determined include many alkaloids, purines, isoniazid, oxine, caprolactam and quaternary ammonium and sulphonium salts; tartaric acid has been determined by precipitation as Bi(III) salt.

Subsequent treatment and final titration stage. (i) In about half the examples, unreacted Bi(III) was back titrated with EDTA to disappearance of the yellow of bismuth iodide or to indicators like xylenol orange or pyrocatechol violet.

(ii) The precipitate has been dissolved and determined by a titration procedure of, for example,

1. Bi(III) with EDTA,
2. I^- with iodate in HCl solution,
3. the organic moiety (tartaric acid) with excess MnO_4^- and back titration with oxalate.

(iii) Liberated EDTA from use of the reagent prepared from $Bi(NO_3)_3$ + equivalent amount of EDTA has been titrated with Zn(II) or Th(IV).

Examples

Materials titrated	Reagent and reaction conditions	Subsequent treatment and final titration stage	Ref.
Tartaric acid	Neutralized solution in water, at boiling point + $Bi(NO_3)_3$/acetic acid in *ca* 50% excess; 5 min stirring	Filtered, dissolved in hot H_2SO_4, titrated with MnO_4^- to slight excess and back titrated with oxalic acid	1
Nicotine	+ $HBiI_4$ reagent, giving precipitate of (nicotine.2H)$^{2+}(BiI_4^-)_2$	Precipitate dissolved in HCl and titrated with iodate	2
Alkaloids; oxine	In dil.H_2SO_4 + $KBiI_4$	Filtered and I^- of precipitate titrated with iodate	3
Organic bases and salts	+ $BiCl_3$/KI, giving precipitates of iodobismuthates	Filtered, filtrate + $Na_2S_2O_3$ + Na acetate and unreacted Bi(III) titrated with EDTA to disappearance of yellow-orange	4
Theophylline; theobromine; quinine; some imidazolines	+ $KBiI_4$ at pH 1·2–1·5	Filtered, filtrate + Na acetate, bringing to pH 4·5, + $Na_2S_2O_3$ and unreacted Bi(III) titrated with EDTA to end-point as in ref. 4	5
Alkaloids, e.g. narcotine, papaverine, strychnine, codeine, brucine	In HCl, + $BiCl_3$/ equivalent amount EDTA/KI/Na_2SO_3; 5 min/room temp., liberating EDTA	Centrifuged, aliquot of filtrate + borax and titrated with EDTA to eriochrome black T	6

Materials titrated	Reagent and reaction conditions	Subsequent treatment and final titration stage	Ref.
Vitamin B_2 (thiamine)	Hydrochloride in water, + HCl + KI + $KBiI_4$	Precipitate filtered, unused Bi(III) determined as in ref. 4	7
ε-Caprolactam	+ $KBiI_4$ + HCl; 3 h/20°, giving precipitate of $[(C_5H_{11}ON)\ H]_2\ BiI_4$	Filtered and unused Bi(III) determined as in ref. 4	8
Atropine	+ $KBiI_4$, giving precipitate	Precipitate dissolved in HCl, borate buffer + thiourea added and Bi(III) titrated with EDTA to methyl blue	9
Tertiary amines; quaternary ammonium bases and salts; sulphonium compounds	+ HCl + $Bi(NO_3)_3$ (or $BiCl_3$) + equivalent amount EDTA + NaOH + Na_2SO_3 + KI + KCl (all giving pH 4–5); 5 min/room temp.	Centrifuged, filtrate titrated at pH 2–3 with Th(IV) to methylthymol blue	10
Chelidonine hydrochloride and related alkaloids	In dilute acetic acid, + $KBiI_4$	Filtered, Na acetate and $Na_2S_2O_3$ added to filtrate and titrated with EDTA to xylenol orange	11
Propyl gallate	+ $Bi(NO_3)_3$, giving precipitate	Unused Bi(III) in filtrate back titrated with EDTA to xylenol orange or pyrocatechol violet	12
Alkaloids in *Chelidonium majus*	In dilute acetic acid + dilute H_2SO_4 + $KBiI_4$; 10 min/room temp.	Unused Bi(III) in filtrate titrated with EDTA to xylenol orange	13
EDTA in presence of complexing metals	+ 50% $HClO_4$ + excess $Bi(NO_3)_3$ + ascorbic[4] acid (to reduce Fe(III)); heated nearly to boiling, then 10 min standing	+ water and titrated with EDTA to xylenol orange	14
Some antihistamines, e.g. phenazoline, benzhydramine, pyribenzamine, Allergan S	+ water + HCl + $KBiI_4$	Filtered, aliquot + Na thiosulphate + acetate buffer, pH 4·5 and titrated with EDTA to disappearance of yellow	15
Piperazine salts	In citric acid solution, + KI + $KBiI_4$; 10 min	Filtered and filtrate titrated amperometrically with EDTA	16

References

1. Chapman, A. C. and Whitteridge, P., *Analyst* **32**, 163 (1907).
2. Mennelli, G., *Ann. chim. applicata* **31**, 68 (1941).
3. Poethke, W. and Trabert, H., *Pharm. Zentralhalle* **91**, 284 (1952).
4. Buděšinský, B., *Chem. Listy* **49**, 1524 (1955).
5. Buděšinský, B. and Vaníčková, E., *Chem. Listy* **50**, 1241 (1956).
6. Buděšinský, B., *Československ. Farm.* **5**, 579 (1956).
7. Buděšinský, B. and Vaníčková, E., *Českoslov. Farm.* **6**, 308 (1957).
8. Franc, J. and Knízek, J., *Chem. Listy* **51**, 72 (1957).
9. Krówczyński, L. and Weremczuk-Kroze, F., *Dissertationes Pharm.* **9**, 189 (1957).
10. Buděšinský, B. and Körbl, J., *Chem. Listy* **52**, 1513 (1958).
11. Ochyńska, J. and Krówczyński, L., *Chem. Anal.* (*Warsaw*) **4**, 309 (1959).
12. Malkus, Z. and Horáček, J., *Prům. Potravin* **11**, 43 (1960).
13. Ochyńska, J., *Chem. Anal.* (*Warsaw*) **6**, 261 (1961).
14. Starostin, V. V., *Zhur. Anal. Khim.* **16**, 620 (1961).
15. Ceglarski, R. and Roman, J., *Farm. Polska* **18**, No. 14, 327 (1962).
16. Weng, Y-K. and Lan, C-T., *Yao Hsueh Pao* **10**, 303 (1963).

14. Bisulphate

Two examples are given of the use of this reagent for the determination of hydroxyl compounds via dehydration:

Materials titrated	Reagent and reaction conditions	Subsequent treatment and final titration stage	Ref.
Glycerol; glycerides	+ 20-fold excess $KHSO_4$. Heated 30 min, giving acrolein	Distilled in CO_2 stream into alkaline Cu(II) reagent, giving Cu_2O; determined by solution in Fe(III) reagent and titration of the formed Fe(II) with MnO_4^- (see Copper (II), ref. 84)	1
Phenyl dimethyl carbinol	Refluxed in isopropylbenzene with $NaHSO_4$	Liberated water titrated with Karl Fischer reagent	2

References

1. Kataoka, E., *J. Biochem.* (*Japan*) **19**, 15 (1934).
2. Sokolov, A. V., Mikhailyan, N. K. and Korotaeva, G. F., *Zhur. Anal. Khim.* **13**, 369 (1958).

15. Bisulphite and sulphite

Reagent. Both the sodium and potassium salts have been used, at various pH values. Sulphite and bisulphite are related by the equilibrium:

$$SO_3^{2-} + H^+ \rightleftharpoons HSO_3^-$$

or, otherwise put,

$$SO_3^{2-} + H_2O \rightleftharpoons HSO_3^- + OH^-$$

An acidified solution of sulphite is thus effectively bisulphite and for this reason the two reagents have been grouped together.

Reactions and materials titrated. 1. Addition to: carbonyl groups (chiefly aldehydes); olefine groups in α,β-unsaturated carbonyl compounds and nitriles; and to α-epoxide rings. For example:

$$RCHO + HSO_3^- \rightarrow RCH\begin{cases}OH\\SO_3^-\end{cases} \quad \text{or}$$

$$RCHO + SO_3^{2-} + H_2O \rightarrow RCH\begin{cases}OH\\SO_3^-\end{cases} + OH^-$$

$$RCH{=}CH.CN + SO_3^{2-} + H_2O \rightarrow \underset{\displaystyle OH}{RCH}{-}\underset{\displaystyle SO_3^-}{CH.CN} + OH^-$$

$$\underset{\displaystyle \diagdown O \diagup}{CH_2{-}CH_2} + SO_3^{2-} + H_2O \rightarrow \underset{\displaystyle OH}{CH_2}{-}\underset{\displaystyle SO_3^-}{CH_2} + OH^-$$

Carbonyl compounds thus determined have been principally lower aldehydes like formaldehyde, acetaldehyde and furfuraldehyde. These determinations have frequently constituted the final stage of methods for lactic acid (oxidized with Ce(IV) or MnO_4^- to acetaldehyde); for pentoses and pentosans (hydrolysed with acids to furfuraldehyde): and for polyhydroxy compounds and amino acids (oxidized to aldehydes by periodate and also by ninhydrin in the latter case).

Acrylonitrile, maleic acid derivatives and ethylene oxide are typical examples of the other compound classes mentioned.

2. Fission of the disulphide link in determination of compounds like cysteine;

$$RS{-}SR' + SO_3^{2-} \rightarrow RS^- + R'SSO_3^-$$

3. Dehalogenation in a few cases like chloropicrin and pentabromoacetone:

$$R\text{—}Hal + SO_3^{2-} \rightarrow RSO_3^- + Hal^-$$

Reaction conditions. Most reactions have been carried out in aqueous solution or in mixtures of water with a miscible organic solvent like a lower alcohol.

Room temperature has been favoured, largely because of the moderate stability of the reagents.

Subsequent treatment and final titration stage. (i) In about one-fifth of the examples given below, unused reagent was back titrated. Iodine has been the principal titrant used, both directly and by using excess and concluding with a thiosulphate or, less often, with an arsenite or hydrazine titration. In two cases, chloramine T was used instead of iodine (refs 92, 130).

(ii) In the determination of aldehydes, the most used principle has been to destroy unused reagent first (usually by titration with iodine) and then decompose the addition compound into aldehyde and bisulphite by raising the pH of the solution to *ca* 8. This has been carried out by addition of carbonate, bicarbonate, borate or phosphate. Alternatively the addition product has been decomposed by addition of cyanide or hydroxylamine:

$$RCH(OH)SO_3^- \xrightarrow{\text{pH 8}} RCHO + HSO_3^-$$
$$RCH(OH)SO_3^- \xrightarrow{CN^-} RCH(OH)CN + SO_3^{2-}$$
$$RCH(OH)SO_3^- \xrightarrow{NH_2OH} RCH{=}NOH + H_2O + HSO_3^-$$

The sulphite or bisulphite thus set free have as a rule been titrated with iodine, but chloramine T has also occasionally been used.

In a determination of acetaldehyde in presence of crotonaldehyde (ref. 110), the bisulphite compound of the former was similarly decomposed but the liberated aldehyde was then distilled out and thus separated from the crotonaldehyde.

(iii) The OH^- formed during addition reactions with sulphite, has been titrated with acid, usually to phenolphthalein or other indicators with colour change in the pH 9 region. Reaction in the presence of measured excess of acid has also been used, with concluding back titration of the remaining acid.

(iv) Reactions of type 2 in the determination of disulphides have been followed by titration with Ag(I) or Hg(II) reagents of the mercaptan formed. End-point determination has been amperometric in the majority of cases (see Part 1 under the headings of these titrants).

(v) Titration with Ag(I) has been used also to conclude determinations of halides based on reactions of type 3.

(vi) Where the sulphite or bisulphite reagent has been used to remove a component or to eliminate its influence, the determination has been terminated by titration of another component. An example is the determination of certain amino acids by oxidation with periodate to aldehydes and ammonia. Bisulphite was added and the ammonia distilled out and titrated with acid.

Ref. 131 is to a review of indirect titration methods for carbonyl compounds, including bisulphite and sulphite methods.

Examples

Material titrated	Reagent and reaction conditions	Subsequent treatment and final titration stage	Ref.
Acetaldehyde	In 50% ethanol, + Na_2SO_3/H_2SO_4/50% ethanol. Overnight/50–60°	Unused titrated with iodine	1
Aldehydes; some ketones	Aqueous solution + $KHSO_3$; *ca* 15 min/room temp.	Unused titrated with iodine	2
HCHO	+ Na_2SO_3; neutralized to phenolphthalein with some drops $NaHSO_3$	Titrated with H_2SO_4 to the phenolphthalein	3
HCHO; polymers, e.g. trioxymethylene	+ Na_2SO_3, titrated to phenolphthalein with H_2SO_4	Titrated with acid (to same indicator)	4
Acetaldehyde	Method of ref. 4		5
Ketones	In *ca* 20% ethanol, + equivalent amount $NaHSO_3$. Various reaction times and temperatures (study of effect of groups on extent of reaction)	Unreacted titrated with iodine	6
Furfuraldehyde (from acid hydrolysis of pentoses)	+ $KHSO_3$; 2 h/room temp.	Unused titrated with iodine	7
Acetaldehyde from lactic acid in its determination by oxidation with permanganate/H_2SO_4	Distilled into HSO_3^-	Unused titrated with iodine	8

Materials titrated	Reagent and reaction conditions	Subsequent treatment and final titration stage	Ref.
Free acetaldehyde in paraldehyde	Neutral water solution + neutralized Na_2SO_3	Titrated with HCl to thymolphthalein	9
HCHO, benzaldehyde	Neutral water solution + neutralized Na_2SO_3; 30 min/room temp.	Titrated with H_2SO_4 to phenolphthalein	10
Acetaldehyde from acid hydrolysis in determination of acetal and paraldehyde	Method of ref. 2		11
Acetaldehyde from lactic acid in its determination by heating with H_2SO_4	Distilled into $NaHSO_3$	Unreacted destroyed with iodine; $NaHCO_3$ added and HSO_3^- from the bisulphite compound titrated with iodine	12
HCHO	+ Na_2SO_3 (compared with other methods)	Titrated with acid	13
HCHO, acetaldehyde	Method of ref. 2		14
HCHO in paraformaldehyde	+ Na_2SO_3, titrated with acid to rosolic acid	Titrated with acid (to same indicator)	15
HCHO	+ Na_2SO_3; 10 min/room temp.	Titrated with H_2SO_4 to rosolic acid	16
Acetaldehyde, from determination of blood lactic acid by heating with permanganate/H_2SO_4	Distilled into $KHSO_3$	Unused titrated with iodine	17
Acetaldehyde from determination of lactic acid in animal organs by heating with permanganate/H_2SO_4	Distilled into ice-cold $KHSO_3$	Unused titrated with iodine	18
Acetaldehyde from determination of lactic acid by heating with permanganate/H_2SO_4	Distilled into $KHSO_3$	Unused titrated with iodine	19
HCHO	+ $KHSO_3$ + Na_2SO_3 (catalyst); 15 min/room temp.	Titrated with NaOH to rosolic acid	20
Aldehydes, ketones, e.g. benzaldehyde, cinnamaldehyde	+ $KHSO_3/Na_2SO_3$; 45 min (aldehydes) to 4–5 h (ketones)/room temp.	Titrated with NaOH to rosolic acid	21

Materials titrated	Reagent and reaction conditions	Subsequent treatment and final titration stage	Ref.
Acetaldehyde from determination of lactic acid by heating with permanganate/H_2SO_4	Distilled into $KHSO_3$	Unused titrated with iodine	22
Acetaldehyde from determination of lactic acid by heating with H_2SO_4	Distilled into $NaHSO_3$	Unreacted HSO_3^- destroyed with iodine, $NaHCO_3$ added and HSO_3^- from the bisulphite compound titrated with iodine	23
HCHO	+ Na_2SO_3	Titrated with acid to phenolphthalein or thymolphthalein (addition of NaCl helps with former indicator)	24
Acetaldehyde from determination of lactic acid by heating with permanganate/$MnSO_4$/H_2SO_4	Distilled into $NaHSO_3$	Unreacted removed by titration with iodine, $NaHCO_3$ added and HSO_3^- from the bisulphite compound titrated with iodine	25
Acetaldehyde from determination of lactic acid by heating with permanganate/H_2SO_4	Distilled into $KHSO_3$	Unreacted removed by titration with iodine, $NaHCO_3$ or Na_2HPO_4 added and retitrated with iodine	26
Furfuraldehyde from heating glucuronic acid with HCl	Distilled into $NaHSO_3$	Unused titrated with iodine	27
Acetaldehyde from determination of lactic acid in tannin extracts by heating with permanganate/$MnSO_4$/H_2SO_4	Distilled into $NaHSO_3$	Unreacted removed by titration with iodine, $NaHCO_3$ added and retitrated with iodine	28
Acetaldehyde	+ Na or $KHSO_3$	Unreacted removed by titration with iodine, brought to pH 8 with $NaHCO_3$ and retitrated with iodine	29
Acetaldehyde from determination of lactic acid in milk and milk products by heating with permanganate/H_2SO_4	Distilled into $NaHSO_3$	Unused titrated with iodine	30
HCHO	Neutral solution in water (to thymolphthalein), + Na_2SO_3 also titrated to thymolphthalein	Titrated with HCl	31

Materials titrated	Reagent and reaction conditions	Subsequent treatment and final titration stage	Ref.
Acetaldehyde from determination of lactic acid in vegetable tan liquors by heating with permanganate/H_2SO_4	Distilled into $NaHSO_3$	Unreacted removed by titration with iodine, $NaHCO_3$ added and retitrated with iodine	32
Furfuraldehyde	+ HSO_3^-; 10–15 min in dark/room temp.	Unused titrated with iodine	33
HCHO	+ small excess $NaHSO_3$ + some $NaHCO_3$; 15 min/ room temp.	Acidified to methyl orange with acetic acid, unreacted HSO_3^- removed by titration with iodine, Na_2CO_3 added and retitrated	34
benzaldehyde	+ small excess $NaHSO_3$ + some $NaHCO_3$; 15 min/ room temp.	acidified with phosphoric acid, unreacted reagent titrated, $NaHCO_3$ added and retitrated with iodine	
Acetaldehyde from determination of lactic acid in blood by heating with permanganate/H_2SO_4	Distilled into HSO_3^-	+ Na_2HPO_4 + excess standard iodine and back titrated with arsenite	35
Ethylene oxide	Passed into Na_2SO_3 saturated with H_2S	Titrated with HCl	36
Aldehydes in rancid fats; heptaldehyde	In benzene, + $NaHSO_3$; 60–90 min/ room temp. (30 min for heptaldehyde)	Unreacted HSO_3^- removed by titration with iodine, $NaHCO_3$ added and retitrated with iodine	37
HCHO	Neutral solution, + neutralized Na_2SO_3 (both to thymolphthalein)	Titrated with acid	38
Aldehydes	+ $NaHSO_3$, some + ethanol. Mostly 30–60 min/room temp.	+ excess iodine, then quickly back titrated with thiosulphate. Some directly titrated with iodine but found less satisfactory	39
Acetaldehyde	+ HSO_3^-	+ excess iodine and back titrated with thiosulphate; also removed excess reagent with iodine, added $NaHCO_3$ and retitrated with iodine	40
Acetaldehyde in biological substrates	+ HSO_3^-; 20 min/ room temp.	Unreacted HSO_3^- removed by titration with iodine, $NaHCO_3$ added and retitrated with iodine	41

Materials titrated	Reagent and reaction conditions	Subsequent treatment and final titration stage	Ref.
Acetaldehyde in wines, etc.	+ HSO_3^-/phosphate buffer at pH 7; 20 min/room temp.	+ HCl and unreacted HSO_3^- removed by titration with iodine; $NaOH/H_3BO_3$ added and retitrated with iodine	42
Acetaldehyde from determination of lactic acid by heating with permanganate/$MnSO_4$/H_2SO_4	Distilled under reduced pressure into $NaHSO_3$. *Ca* 60 min duration	Titrated with iodine, $NaHCO_3$ added and retitrated	43
Furfuraldehyde from acid distillation of pentosans	Distilled into $NaHSO_3$	Titrated into standard iodine (claimed better than the usual titration direction)	44
Acetaldehyde from hydrolysis of acetals in determination of pH of wine	Distilled into $NaHSO_3$/ phosphate buffer, pH 7	Combined HSO_3^- determined by method of ref. 42	45
$CCl_3.NO_2$ in treated grain	Carried by air current into alkaline Na_2SO_3, giving $NO_2.CH(SO_3Na)_2$ + 2 NaCl	Cl^- determined by using excess Ag^+ reagent and back titrating with SCN^-	46
Isovaleraldehyde from determination of leucine by reaction with ninhydrin	Distilled into $NaHSO_3$	Unused HSO_3^- titrated with iodine	47
Acetaldehyde in wines	+ $NaHSO_3$/10% ethanol; 30 min/ room temp.	+ excess iodine and back titrated with thiosulphate	48
	also + $NaHSO_3$/ phosphate buffer, pH *ca* 7	unreacted titrated with iodine, NaOH/boric acid added and retitrated	
Acetaldehyde from determination of lactic acid by heating with permanganate/$MnSO_4$/H_2SO_4	Distilled into HSO_3^-	Unused titrated with iodine	49
Furfuraldehyde in mixtures with furfuryl alcohol	+ $NaHSO_3$; 15 min/ room temp.	Unused titrated with iodine	50
Acetaldehyde from determination of lactic acid by oxidation with $Ce(SO_4)_2$	Distilled into $NaHSO_3$	Titrated with iodine, $NaHCO_3$ added and retitrated with iodine	51

Materials titrated	Reagent and reaction conditions	Subsequent treatment and final titration stage	Ref.
Acetaldehyde from determination (sub-micro) of lactic acid by heating with permanganate/$MnSO_4$/H_2SO_4	Distilled into $NaHSO_3$	Titrated with iodine, $NaHCO_3$ added and retitrated with iodine	52
Pyruvic acid	+ $NaHSO_3$	Titrated with iodine, $NaHCO_3$ added and retitrated with iodine	53
Aldehydes from determination of amino acids like alanine, valine, leucine, isoleucine, by reaction with ninhydrin	Distilled into $NaHSO_3$	Unused HSO_3^- titrated with iodine	54, 78
Carbonyl compounds	+ $NaHSO_3$/HCl or NaOH; 1 h/room temp.	Unused titrated with iodine; also titrated with iodine, $NaHCO_3$ added and retitrated	55
Acetaldehyde from determination of methylpentoses by oxidation with periodate	Carried by CO_2 stream into $NaHSO_3$	Combined HSO_3^- determined by procedure like that of ref. 12	56
HCHO from resins	Distilled into $NaHSO_3$	Unused titrated with iodine, Na_2CO_3 added and retitrated	57
HCHO	+ Na_2SO_3	Titrated with HCl to phenolphthalein/α-naphtholphthalein	58
Acetaldehyde from determination of threonine by oxidation with periodate	Carried by CO_2 stream into $NaHSO_3$	Combined HSO_3^- determined as in method of ref. 56	59
Acetone	Diffused into $NaHSO_3$; 5–6 h/room temp. or 3 h/40–50°	Unused titrated with iodine, Na_2HPO_4 added and retitrated	60
HCHO + acetaldehyde from determination of glycerol/ethylene glycol/propylene glycol mixtures by oxidation with periodate	+ 12·5% Na_2SO_3 (in *ca* 200-fold excess)	Titrated with HCl to phenolphthalein	61
Aldehydes in synthetic acetic acid	Method of ref. 48		62

Materials titrated	Reagent and reaction conditions	Subsequent treatment and final titration stage	Ref.
HCHO from determination of hexamine by heating with tartaric acid	Distilled into $NaHSO_3$	Unused titrated with iodine, $NaHCO_3$ added and retitrated	63
Some compounds with the —C=C—CO group, e.g. salts of maleic acid	Neutral solution + Na_2SO_3; 8 h boiling	Titrated with HCl	64
Acetaldehyde from determination of lactic acid by reaction with Ce(IV)	Diffused into $NaHSO_3$	Combined HSO_3^- determined by method of ref. 60	65
Acetaldehyde from determination of threonine by reaction with periodate	Method of ref. 65		66
HCHO in air	Passed into 1% $NaHSO_3$	Titrated with iodine, CO_3^{2-}/acetate added and retitrated	67
HCHO + acetaldehyde from determination of glycerol/2,3-butylene glycol by periodate oxidation	Method of ref. 61		68
HCHO in milk	+ measured excess Na_2SO_3 + NaOH; 15 min/room temp.	+ acetic acid and titrated with chloramine T to I^- indicator	69
HCHO from determination of hexamine by heating with H_2SO_4	Distilled into neutral Na_2SO_3	Titrated with H_2SO_4 to rosolic acid	70
HCHO, acetaldehyde from determination of ethylene and propylene glycols and glycerol by periodate oxidation	+ $NaHSO_3$	Titrated with iodine, Na_2CO_3/borax added and retitrated	71
Pentabromoacetone from determination of citric acid by reaction with $MnO_4^-/Br^-/H_2SO_4$ or $MnO_2/BrO_3^-/Br^-/H_2SO_4$	+ $NaHSO_3$, giving 5 Br^-; 3 min/100°	Determined by titration with Ag^+	72
Acetaldehyde from determination of 2,3-butylene glycol by periodate oxidation	Distilled into $NaHSO_3$	Titrated with iodine, $NaHCO_3$ added and retitrated	73

Materials titrated	Reagent and reaction conditions	Subsequent treatment and final titration stage	Ref.
Acetaldehyde in mixtures with ethyl acetate	+ $NaHSO_3$; 30 min/room temp. with intermittent shaking	+ excess iodine and back titrated with thiosulphate	74
Furfuraldehyde from determination of pentoses by heating with phosphoric acid	Distilled into $NaHSO_3$	Titrated with iodine, $NaHCO_3$ added and retitrated with iodine	75
Furfuraldehyde from determination of pentoses by heating with 85% phosphoric acid	Distilled into $NaHSO_3$	Titrated with iodine, $NaHCO_3$ added and retitrated	76
Acetaldehyde from determination of propylene glycol by periodate oxidation	Carried by CO_2 stream into $NaHSO_3$	Titrated with iodine, $NaHCO_3$/Na_2CO_3/borax added and retitrated	77
Aldehydes from determination of certain amino acids (e.g. alanine, valine, leucine) by oxidation with hypochlorite	Passed into $NaHSO_3$	Unused titrated with iodine,	79, 86
Furfuraldehyde	+ $NaHSO_3$ at pH *ca* 4; 5 min/room temp.	+ HCl giving pH *ca* 1 and unused reagent titrated with chloramine T; + $MgCO_3$, and HSO_3^- from the bisulphite compound titrated with chloramine T	80
Acetaldehyde from determination of α-alanine by reaction with ninhydrin	Distilled into $NaHSO_3$	Titrated with iodine, $NaHCO_3$ added and retitrated	81
Ketal + acetal from acid hydrolysis of polyvinyl acetal ketal resins	+ $NaHSO_3$; 1 h/room temp.	+ excess iodine/acetic acid and back titrated immediately with thiosulphate	82
Aldehydes	+ Na_2SO_3 excess + excess standard H_2SO_4; 2–3 min shaking/room temp.	Titrated with alkali potentiometrically	83
Acetaldehyde, also from acetals, vinyl ethers (hydrolysed by the acid)	+ Na_2SO_3 + excess H_2SO_4. A few min shaking	Titrated with NaOH potentiometrically	84

Materials titrated	Reagent and reaction conditions	Subsequent treatment and final titration stage	Ref.
HCHO from determination of hexamine by heating with H_2SO_4	Distilled into neutral Na_2SO_3	Titrated with H_2SO_4 to phenolphthalein	85
HCHO from determination of glycerol in fermentation residues by periodate oxidation	At pH 9·3, + 12% Na_2SO_3	Titrated with HCl back to pH 9·3 potentiometrically	87
Acetaldehyde in industrial alcohols	In phosphate buffer, + Na_2SO_3/H_2SO_4; 20 min/room temp.	+ HCl and titrated with iodine; NaOH/boric acid added and retitrated with iodine	88
HCHO from determination of glycerol by periodate oxidation	Distilled into $NaHSO_3$ reagent (Method of ref. 42)		89
HCHO	+ Na_2SO_3. Best at 0°	Titrated with HCl or H_2SO_4 to thymolphthalein	90
Maleic acid in presence of other acids, e. g. benzoic, phthalic	Many procedures tested, e.g. (a) Neutralized, + excess $NaHSO_3$; 5 min boiling (b) neutralized, + Na_2SO_3, also neutralized (thymolphthalein). Brought to boiling, *ca* 1 h boiled (c) as in (b), but + excess H_2SO_4; 30 min boiling	Titrated with NaOH titrated continuously with H_2SO_4 titrated with NaOH	91
aldehydes	+ Na_2SO_3, neutralized; 5 min/room temp.	titrated with H_2SO_4	
Carbonyl compounds	+ $NaHSO_3$	Unused titrated with chloramine T	92, 130
HCHO in aqueous solutions in presence of its polymers	+ $NaHSO_3$/acetate buffer, pH 4–5 (no hydrolysis of polymers)	Unused determined iodometrically	93
Acetaldehyde from determination of lactic acid by oxidation with Ce(IV)	Diffused into $NaHSO_3$; 30 sec/100°	Titrated with iodine, phosphate added and retitrated	94

Materials titrated	Reagent and reaction conditions	Subsequent treatment and final titration stage	Ref.
Acetaldehyde from determination of lactic acid by oxidation with permanganate/H_2SO_4	Distilled into $NaHSO_3$; 30 min/room temp.	+ NaCl, titrated with iodine, $NaHCO_3$ added and retitrated	95
Acetaldehyde from hydrolysis of ethylene halohydrins; also HCHO from periodate oxidation of ethylene glycol	+ $NaHSO_3$; 30 min/room temp.	Titrated with iodine, Na_2CO_3/borax added and retitrated	96
HCHO from mono- and dimethylolurea after alkaline hydrolysis	+ $NaHSO_3$; 15 min/room temp.	Acidified, titrated with iodine, Na_2CO_3 added and retitrated	97
Acetone	+ $NaHSO_3$; pH 5 and 30 min/0° found best conditions after study	+ excess iodine and back titrated with thiosulphate	98
Cystine	In ammonia buffer + Na_2SO_3, giving cysteine. Nitrogen atmosphere —S—S— + SO_3^{2-} → —S + —SSO_3^-	Titrated with Ag^+ amperometrically (see Part I, Silver, ref. 47)	99
Acetaldehyde from determination of lactic acid in beverages by oxidation with MnO_4^-/$MnSO_4$/H_2SO_4	Distilled into HSO_3^- at pH 7	Combined HSO_3^- determined by method of ref. 42	100
HCHO	+ HSO_3^-/phosphate buffer, pH 7·3	+ HCl, bringing pH to 4, and unused titrated with iodine	101
Acetaldehyde from determination of lactic acid in wine, grape juice, etc., by oxidation with MnO_4^-/$MnSO_4$/phosphoric acid	Distilled into $NaHSO_3$/phosphate buffer	+ HCl, bringing pH to 2–3, titrated with iodine; $NaHCO_3$ added and retitrated	102
HCHO in a kinetic study of its reaction with aniline and substituted anilines in dilute HCl	+ Na_2SO_3 + measured excess NaOH	Titrated with HCl to rosolic acid	103
HCHO in study of reaction with urea	+ SO_3^{2-} at pH 8·5 (maintained by adding HCl during reaction); 7 min/room temp. also + excess SO_3^{2-}	Titrated with iodine, Na_2CO_3 added and retitrated; titrated with HCl	104

Materials titrated	Reagent and reaction conditions	Subsequent treatment and final titration stage	Ref.
Acetaldehyde in vinyl acetate	+ $NaHSO_3/NaCl$	Aqueous layer titrated with iodine, $NaHCO_3$ added and retitrated	105
π-Oxocamphor	+ $NaHSO_3$ (*ca* 10 × equivalent amount); 1 h/10°	+ excess iodine and back titrated with thiosulphate	106
Aldehyde groups in chromic acid oxy-starches	+ Na_2SO_3 + excess H_2SO_4; 3 h/room temp.	Titrated with NaOH potentiometrically to pH 9·5 (corrected for —COOH groups)	107
Acetaldehyde in spirits	+ $NaHSO_3$ in neutral medium	Acidified, titrated with iodine, $NaOH/H_3BO_3$ added to bring to pH 9·5 and retitrated	108, 113
Acetaldehyde from determination of lactic acid by oxidation with Ce(IV)	Distilled into $NaHSO_3$/ buffer of pH 7; 20 min/room temp.	+ HCl and unused titrated with iodine	109
Acetaldehyde in presence of crotonaldehyde	+ $NaHSO_3$. Overnight/70–80°	+ $NaHCO_3$, liberating the acetaldehyde from its bisulphite compound. Distilled into $NaHSO_3$ and determined by method of ref. 40	110
Acetaldehyde from determination of lactic acid by oxidation with $MnO_4^-/MnSO_4$/phosphoric acid	Distilled into $NaHSO_3$	Titrated with iodine at 0°, $NaHCO_3$ added and retitrated	111
Protein —S—S— groups	In NH_4OH/NH_4NO_3 buffer + Na_2SO_3, reacting —S—S— + $SO_3^{2-} \rightleftharpoons$ —S^- + —SSO_3^-	—S^- titrated with Ag^+, amperometrically (see Part I, Silver, refs 73 and 145)	112, 146
Acetaldehyde; also from determination of lactic acid by oxidation with Ce(IV)	Distilled into $NaHSO_3$ + ethanol, at pH 7 in phosphate buffer; 20 min/room temp.	+ HCl to bring to pH 0·7–3·0, excess iodine added and back titrated with thiosulphate; or + HCl to bring to pH *ca* 2·5, titrated with iodine, $NaHCO_3$ added and retitrated	114
Aldehydes in wines, fruit juices	Distilled into Na_2SO_3/H_2SO_4, at pH 7 with phosphate buffer; 10 min	+ HCl, titrated with iodine, borate buffer added and retitrated	115

Materials titrated	Reagent and reaction conditions	Subsequent treatment and final titration stage	Ref.
Aldehydes, e.g. HCHO, acetaldehyde, propionaldehyde, benzaldehyde	+ $NaHSO_3$/phosphate buffer + layer of toluene to prevent access of air oxygen	+ HCl and unused titrated with iodine	116
Cystine in protein hydrolysates	In ammonia or borax buffer, pH 9·2, + Na_2SO_3 Nitrogen atmosphere	Titrated with Hg(II) amperometrically (see Part I, Mercury (II), ref. 32)	117
a-Epoxides	+ Na_2SO_3; 30 min–3 h/room temp. with occasional shaking —C—C— + H_2O + SO_3^{2-} (with O bridging the two C atoms) → —C—C— (with OH on the first C and SO_3^- on the second) + OH^-	Titrated with HCl to alizarin yellow R/xylene cyanol FF, or potentiometrically to pH *ca* 9·5	118
HCHO in aqueous urea solution	Extract in isoamyl alcohol, + Na_2SO_3; 10–15 min/room temp.	Titrated with H_2SO_4 to thymolphthalein	119
Compounds containing —C=C—CO or —C=C—CN groups	+ isopropanol + Na_2SO_3 + measured excess H_2SO_4. Nitrogen atmosphere; 5–120 min/25–98°	Titrated with NaOH to alizarin yellow R/xylene cyanol FF	120
Free HCHO in resin solutions containing hydroxymethylurea or melamine	Solution + Na_2SO_3 + excess HCl	Titrated with NaOH to thymolphthalein/phenolphthalein	121
Acetaldehyde in vinyl acetate	+ $NaHSO_3$	+ excess iodine and back titrated with thiosulphate	122
Acetaldehyde in frozen vegetables	Steam distilled into $NaHSO_3$; 30 min/room temp.	+ excess iodine and back titrated with thiosulphate	123
Cystine in protein hydrolysates	In alkaline solution, + Na_2SO_3 (Method of ref. 117)	Titrated with Hg(II) amperometrically (see Part I, Mercury (II), ref. 36)	124
Small amounts acetaldehyde in aqueous solutions	+ $NaHSO_3$ at pH 2; 90 min/room temp.	Titrated with iodine, brought to pH 8 with HCO_3^- and retitrated with iodine	125

Materials titrated	Reagent and reaction conditions	Subsequent treatment and final titration stage	Ref.
Cystine	In NH_4OH/NH_4NO_3 buffer, + Na_2SO_3	Titrated with Ag^+ amperometrically (see Part I, Silver (I), ref. 105)	126
Glyoxal	+ $NaHSO_3$/phosphate buffer, pH 7·3; 3 min/room temp.	Brought to pH 4·5 with HCl and titrated with iodine	127
Acetaldehyde from determination of lactic acid in wine by oxidation with MnO_4^-/H_2SO_4	Distilled into $NaHSO_3$	Titrated with iodine, Na_2CO_3 added and retitrated	128
Acrylonitrile	In dioxan, +Na_2SO_3; 60–90 min/room temp.	Titrated with HCl to thymolphthalein/alizarin yellow	129
Disulphides	In alkaline solution + Na_2SO_3	Titrated with Hg(II) at pH 2 potentiometrically (see Part I, Mercury (II), ref. 40)	132
Disulphides	In alkaline solution + Na_2SO_3	Titrated with Hg(II) amperometrically (see Part I, Mercury (II), ref. 41)	133
Acetaldehyde from determination of lactic acid in blood by oxidation with $MnO_4^-/MnSO_4/H_2SO_4$	Distilled into $NaHSO_3$	Titrated with iodine, Na_2CO_3 added and retitrated	134
Aldehydes in wine and cognac	Distilled into $NaHSO_3$/phosphate buffer, pH 7; 1 h/room temp.	+ HCl and titrated with iodine; then + borate/alkali and retitrated	135
Acrylonitrile	+ Na_2SO_3; 15 min/100°	Titrated with acid to thymolphthalein	136
Acetaldehyde from determination of lactic acid in fish meat by oxidation with MnO_4^-/H_2SO_4	Distilled into $NaHSO_3$	+ excess iodine and back titrated with thiosulphate	137
Acetaldehyde in technical crotonaldehyde	+ $NaHSO_3$; 4 h/75°	+ $NaHCO_3$ and liberated acetaldehyde distilled into hydroxylamine hydrochloride solution and titrated with alkali	138
Disulphides	In alkaline solution + Na_2SO_3	Titrated with Hg(II) amperometrically (see Part I, Mercury (II), ref. 48)	139

Materials titrated	Reagent and reaction conditions	Subsequent treatment and final titration stage	Ref.
Aldehydes from determination of amino acids by oxidation with ninhydrin	Carried with nitrogen current into $NaHSO_3$	Unused reagent removed with iodine; aldehyde determined by adding Na_2CO_3/iodine and determining unused iodine	140
Free HCHO in urea and melamine resins	Resin in water, + Na_2SO_3 + HCl	Titrated with NaOH	141
HCHO, acetaldehyde	In water + Na_2SO_3 + acetic acid + pentane layer to prevent access of oxygen and loss of SO_2; 10, 20 min/room temp. resp.	Unused SO_3^{2-} removed by titration with iodine, NaOH/KCN added, yielding cyanohydrin of aldehyde and liberating equivalent of SO_3^{2-}; acidified and titrated with iodine (see Cyanide, refs 30, 31 and 44)	142, 143, 164
Acetaldehyde from determination of lactic acid in beer by oxidation with MnO_4^-/H_2SO_4	Distilled into $NaHSO_3$	Titrated with iodine, $NaHCO_3$ added and retitrated	144
Carbonyl compounds in the atmosphere	Passed into $NaHSO_3$ at 0°	Titrated with iodine, Na_2CO_3/acetic acid added and retitrated	145
Disulphides, e.g. cystine	In borax buffer, + KCl + Na_2SO_3	Titrated with Hg(II) amperometrically (see Part I, Mercury (II), ref. 61)	147
Disulphides	At pH 9, + Na_2SO_3	Titrated with Hg(II) amperometrically (see Part I, Mercury (II), ref. 62)	148
Glyoxal	As in method of refs 142, 143, but 30 min reaction time	Unused SO_3^{2-} removed by titration with iodine; NaOH/hydroxylamine hydrochloride added, yielding in 5 min the oxime and liberating equivalent of SO_3^{2-}; acidified and titrated with iodine (see Hydroxylamine, ref. 145)	149, 154, 164
HCHO from determination of 1,2-glycols (e.g. glycerol, mannitol) by periodate oxidation	As in method of refs 142, 143; the SO_3^{2-} also, removes IO_3^- and unused IO_4^-	(see Cyanide, refs 32 and 33)	150, 151
HCHO from determination of glucose by periodate oxidation	As in method of refs 150, 151	(see Cyanide, ref. 34)	152

Materials titrated	Reagent and reaction conditions	Subsequent treatment and final titration stage	Ref.
Glyoxalic acid from determination of tartaric acid by periodate oxidation	As in method of refs 150, 151; 30 min reaction time,	(see Cyanide, refs 35, 36 and 46)	153, 155, 166
Heptaldehyde and other aldehydes from oxidation of butter fat	Method of ref. 37		156
Glyoxalic acid or salts	+ Na_2SO_3	Titrated with H_2SO_4 to pH 9·5 potentiometrically	157
HCHO from determination of fructose by periodate oxidation	Method of refs 150, 151	(see Cyanide, refs 38 and 41)	158, 161
HCHO from determination of glyceraldehyde by periodate oxidation	Method of refs 150, 151	(see Cyanide, refs 39 and 42)	159, 162
HCHO or acetaldehyde from determination of serine or threonine respectively, by periodate oxidation	Method of refs 150, 151 also + $NaHSO_3$ to combine with the aldehyde	(see Cyanide, refs 40, 43 and 45) ammonia distilled and titrated	160, 163, 165
Acetaldehyde	+ $NaHSO_3$/phosphate buffer, pH 7; 20 min/room temp.	+ acid to bring to pH 1–2 and titrated with iodine; brought to pH 8 with borate/alkali and retitrated	167
Dithioglycollic acid; disulphide of 2-mercaptoethanol	In NH_4OH/NH_4NO_3 buffer, pH *ca* 9, + Na_2SO_3	Titrated with Ag^+ amperometrically (see Part I, Silver (I), ref. 183)	168
Some disulphides, e.g. cystine	In borax or ammonia buffer, + Na_2SO_3 + some Hg(II) nitrate or acetate	Brought to pH 2 with HNO_3 and completed titration with Hg(II) amperometrically (see Part I, Mercury (II), ref. 91)	169
HCHO from determination of ethanolamines and ethylenediamine by periodate oxidation	Method of refs 150, 151	(see Cyanide, refs 47 and 48)	170, 171
Cystamine isolated from biological materials via ion exchange	+ $NaHSO_3$; 5 min.	Titrated with Ag^+ amperometrically at pH 7·4 (see Part I, Silver (I), ref. 177)	172

Materials titrated	Reagent and reaction conditions	Subsequent treatment and final titration stage	Ref.
Acrylonitrile	+ Na_2SO_3	Titrated with HCl to thymol-phthalein/alizarin yellow	173
Aldehydes, e.g. HCHO, acetaldehyde, benzaldehyde	+ $NaHSO_3$/5% ethanol; 30 min/room temp.	+ excess iodine and back titrated with hydrazine to starch or biamperometrically (see Iodine reagents, ref. 417)	174
HCHO; also HCHO from phenol resins, alcohols, etc.	In water, + Na_2SO_3, titrated with H_2SO_4 to methyl red; 7–10 min/room temp.	+ acetic acid and titrated with iodine; NaOH or $NaHCO_3$ added and retitrated with iodine	175
Diethyldithiobis(thio-formate) ('Dixan-thogen')	In methanol or ethanol, + Na_2SO_3; 30 min/room temp.	Unused sulphite removed with HCHO/acetic acid; titrated with iodine	176
Cystine	In phosphate (pH 8), borate (pH 9·2) buffers or in NaOH (pH 12), + Na_2SO_3	Titrated with C_2H_5HgCl amperometrically (see Part I, Mercury (II), ref. 92)	177
Bisulphite binding ability of bread (mainly aldehydes)	+ $NaHSO_3$	Titrated with iodine, Na_2CO_3 added and retitrated	178
Acetaldehyde in wine, etc.	+ $K_2S_2O_5$ + HCl; 15 min/room temp.	+ KH_2PO_4/NaOH bringing to pH 7, left 15 min, then + HCl and titrated with iodine to starch; + borate/NaOH, making alkaline and SO_2 liberated from the aldehyde bisulphite compound titrated with iodine	179
Monomer in poly-acrylonitrile fibres	+ Na_2SO_3 + H_2SO_4; 10–90 min/35–98°	Unused acid titrated with NaOH to alizarin yellow R	180
Disulphides in rabbit serum, etc.	+ Na_2SO_3 + NH_4OH/ NH_4NO_3	Titrated with Ag^+ amperometrically (see Part I, Silver (I), ref. 180)	181
HCHO from deter-mination of ethanol-amine and ethylene diamine by oxidation with periodate	Method of refs 142 and 143	(see Cyanide, ref. 50)	182
Acetaldehyde from de-termination of lactic acid by oxidation with MnO_4^-/ $MnSo_4$/phosphoric acid	Distilled into $NaHSO_3$	Unused titrated with iodine	183

Materials titrated	Reagent and reaction conditions	Subsequent treatment and final titration stage	Ref.
Disulphides	+ Na_2SO_3	Mercaptan formed titrated in 'tris' buffer, pH 7·4 with $AgNO_3$ amperometrically	184
Disulphides in flour	+ Na_2SO_3 at pH 9 in NH_4OH/NH_4Cl buffer; 5 min/room temp.	Titrated with $AgNO_3$ potentiometrically	185

References

1. Rocques, X., *Compt. rend.* **127**, 524, 764 (1898).
2. Ripper, M., *Monatsh.* **21**, 1079 (1900).
3. Lemme, G., *Chem.-Ztg.* **27**, 896 (1903).
4. Seyewitz, A. and Gibello, *Bull. soc. chim. France* (3) **31**, 691 (1904).
5. Seyewitz, A. and Bardin, *Bull. soc. chim. France* **33**, 1000 (1905).
6. Stewart, A. W., *J. Chem. Soc.* **87**, 185 (1905).
7. Jolles, A., *Ber.* **39**, 96 (1906); *Z. anal. Chem.* **45**, 196 (1906).
8. v. Fürth, O. and Charnass, D., *Biochem. Z.* **26**, 199 (1910).
9. Richter, R., *Pharm.-Ztg.* **57**, 125 (1912).
10. Feinberg, B. G., *Am. Chem. J.* **49**, 87 (1913).
11. Orton, K. J. P. and McKie, P. V., *J. Chem. Soc.* **109**, 184 (1916).
12. Clausen, S. W., *J. Biol. Chem.* **52**, 263 (1922).
13. Kühl, F., *Collegium* 133 (1922).
14. Blair, E. W. and Wheeler, T. S., *Analyst* **48**, 110 (1923).
15. Borgstrom, P. and Horsch, W. G., *J. Am. Chem. Soc.* **45**, 1496 (1923).
16. Herrmann, R., *Z. anal. Chem.* **62**, 104 (1923).
17. Macleod, J. J. R. and Armour, M. E., *J. Lab. Clin. Med.* **7**, 635 (1923).
18. Hirsch-Kauffmann, H., *Z. physiol, Chem.* **140**, 25 (1924).
19. Collazo, J. and Supniewski, J., *Compt. rend. soc. biol.* **92**, 370 (1925).
20. Romeo, G., *Ann. chim. applicata* **15**, 300 (1925).
21. Romeo, G. and D'Amico, E., *Ann. chim. applicata* **15**, 320 (1925).
22. Tsukasaki, R., *Tohoku J. Exptl. Med.* **5**, 429 (1925).
23. The Brehme and Brahdy, B., *Biochem. Z.* **175**, 348 (1926).
24. Täufel, K. and Wagner, C., *Z. anal. Chem.* **68**, 25 (1926).
25. Friedemann, T. E., Cotonio, M. and Shaffer, P. A., *J. Biol. Chem.* **73**, 335 (1927).
26. Lehnartz, E., *Z. physiol. Chem.* **179**, 1 (1928).
27. Haendel, M., *Rev. asoc. med. Argentina* **42**, 215 (1929).
28. Simskaya, A., *Vestnik kozhevennoi Prom. Torgov* 700 (1929).
29. Tomada, Y., *J. Soc. Chem. Ind., London* **48**, 76 (1929).

30. Lampitt, L. H. and Bogod, M., *Chim. et ind.*, Special No. 510, March 1930.
31. Büchi, J., *Pharm. Helv. Acta* **6**, 1 (1931).
32. Highberger, J. H. and Youel, D. L., *J. Am. Leather Chem. Assoc.* **27**, 343 (1932).
33. Serchel, L., *Vestnik Kozhevennoi Prom. Torgov* 51 (1932).
34. Donnally, L. H., *Ind. Eng. Chem., Anal. Ed.* **5**, 91 (1933).
35. Müller-Parcham, W., *Z. physiol. Chem.* **218**, 209 (1933).
36. Kireev, V. A. and Popov, A. A., *J. Appl. Chem., USSR* **7**, 489 (1934).
37. Lea, C. H., *Ind. Eng. Chem., Anal. Ed.* **6**, 241 (1934).
38. Malaprade, L., *Compt. rend.* **198**, 1037 (1934).
39. Parkinson, A. E. and Wagner, E. C., *Ind. Eng. Chem., Anal. Ed.* **6**, 433 (1934).
40. Hähnel, S., *Svensk Kem. Tidskr.* **47**, 275 (1935).
41. Janke, A. and Kropacsy, S., *Biochem. Z.* **278**, 30 (1935).
42. Jaulmes, P. and Espezal, R., *Ann. fals.* **28**, 325 (1935).
43. Hinsberg, K. and Ammon, R., *Biochem. Z.* **284**, 343 (1936).
44. Gorokholinskaya, M. S., *Zavodskaya Lab.* **6**, 188 (1937).
45. Peynaud, E., *Ann. fals.* **30**, 390 (1937).
46. Grub, S., *Mukomol'e* **13**, No. 3, 15 (1938).
47. Laine, T., *Suomen Kemistilehti* **11B**, 28 (1938).
48. Joslyn, M. A. and Comar, C. L., *Ind. Eng. Chem., Anal. Ed.* **10**, 364 (1938).
49. Urinson, A. P., *J. Physiol. (USSR)* **25**, 748 (1938).
50. Dunlop, A. P. and Trimble, F., *Ind. Eng. Chem., Anal. Ed.* **11**, 602 (1939).
51. Gordon, J. J. and Quastel, J. H., *Biochem. J.* **33**, 1332 (1939).
52. McCready, R. M., Mitchell, H. K. and Kirk, P. L., *Mikrochemie* **28**, 23 (1939).
53. Schrader, G. A., *J. Lab. Clin. Med.* **25**, 520 (1940).
54. Virtanen, A. L., Laine, T. and Toivonen, T., *Z. physiol. Chem.* **266**, 193 (1940).
55. Hähnel, S. and Lennerstrand, M., *Svensk Kem. Tidskr.* **53**, 336 (1941).
56. Nicolet, B. H. and Shinn, L. A., *J. Am. Chem. Soc.* **63**, 1456 (1941).
57. Nitschmann, H. and Hadorn, H., *Helv. Chim. Acta* **24**, 237 (1941).
58. Poethke, W., *Pharm. Zentralhalle* **82**, 529 (1941).
59. Shinn, L. A. and Nicolet, B. H., *J. Biol. Chem.* **138**, 91 (1941).
60. Winnick, T., *J. Biol. Chem.* **141**, 115 (1941).
61. Hoepe, G. and Treadwell, W. D., *Helv. Chim. Acta* **25**, 353 (1942).
62. Lazzari, G., *Ann. chim. applicata* **32**, 78 (1942).
63. Paulais, R., *Bull. sci. pharm.* **49**, 191 (1942).
64. Rosenthaler, L., *Pharm. Acta Helv.* **17**, 196 (1942).
65. Winnick, T., *J. Biol. Chem.* **142**, 451 (1942).
66. Winnick, T., *J. Biol. Chem.* **142**, 461 (1942).

67. Goldman, F. H. and Yagoda, H., *Ind. Eng. Chem., Anal. Ed.* **15**, 378 (1943).
68. Hoepe, G., *Helv. Chim. Acta* **26**, 1931 (1943).
69. Macdonald, F. J., *Analyst* **68**, 171 (1943).
70. Rapine, M., *Ann. chim. anal* **25**, 113 (1943).
71. Shupe, I. S., *J. Assoc. Offic. Agr. Chem.* **26**, 249 (1943).
72. Goldberg, A. S. and Bernheim, A. R., *J. Biol. Chem.* **156**, 33 (1944).
73. Johnson, M. J., *Ind. Eng. Chem., Anal. Ed.* **16**, 626 (1944).
74. Lindeken, C. L., Clayton, J. O. and Skoog, D. A., *Ind. Eng. Chem., Anal. Ed.* **16**, 734 (1944).
75. Meissner, R., *Biochem. Z.* **317**, 17 (1944).
76. Heines, V., *Arch. Biochem.* **11**, 531 (1946).
77. Reincke, R. C. and Luce, E. N., *Ind. Eng. Chem., Anal. Ed.* **18**, 244 (1946).
78. Virtanen, A. I. and Rautanen, N., *Suomen Kemistilehti* **19B**, 50 (1946).
79. Aubel, E. and Asselineau, J., *Bull. soc. chim. France* 689 (1947).
80. Höpner, T., *Das Papier* **1**, 102 (1947).
81. Roine, P. and Rautanen, N., *Acta Chem. Scand.* **1**, 854 (1947).
82. Ryan, J. D. and Shaw, F. B., *US Patent No.* 2,425,568, Aug. 12, 1947.
83. Siggia, S. and Maxcy, W., *Anal. Chem.* **19**, 1023 (1947).
84. Siggia, S., *Anal. Chem.* **19**, 1025 (1947).
85. de Souze, A. H., *Pubs. farm.* (*Sao Paulo*) **12**, No. 48, 5, 9 (1947).
86. Aubel, E. and Asselineau, J., *Biochim. et. Biophys. Acta* **2**, 198 (1948).
87. Elving, P. J., Warshowsky, B., Shoemaker, E. and Margolit, J., *Anal. Chem.* **20**, 25 (1948).
88. Martraire, M., *Inds. agr. et aliment.* **65**, 123 (1948).
89. Peynaud, E., *Ann. fals. et fraudes* **41**, 384 (1948).
90. Reynolds, J. G. and Irwin, M., *Chem. & Ind.* (*London*) 419 (1948).
91. Wurtzschmitt, B., *Z. anal. Chem.* **128**, 549 (1948).
92. Afanas'ev, B. N., *Zavodskaya Lab.* **15**, 1271 (1949).
93. Iliceto, A., *Ann. chim.* (*Rome*) **39**, 703 (1949); **40**, 711 (1950).
94. McCarvill, M. and Conway, E. J., *Biochem. Abstracts of Comms., 1st Intern. Congress, Cambridge*, 301 (1949).
95. Arkawa, T., *Hirosaki Med. J.* **1**, 33 (1950).
96. Cowan, H. D., McCabe, C. L. and Warner, J. C., *J. Am. Chem. Soc.* **72**, 1194 (1950).
97. Donnally, L. H., *Anal. Chem.* **22**, 364 (1950).
98. Iliceto, A. and Malatesta, A., *Ann. chim.* (*Rome*) **40**, 494 (1950).
99. Kolthoff, I. M. and Stricks, W., *J. Am. Chem. Soc.* **72**, 1952 (1950).
100. Peynaud, A. and Charpentie, Y., *Ann. fals et fraudes* **43**, 246 (1950).
101. Salomaa, P., *Nord. Kemistmötet, Helsingfors* **7**, 20 (1950).
102. Koch, J. and Bretthauer, G., *Z. anal. Chem.* **132**, 346 (1951).
103. Ogata, Y., Okano, M. and Sugawara, M., *J. Am. Chem. Soc.* **73**, 1715 (1951).

104. de Jong, J. J. and de Jonge, J., *Rec. trav. chim.* **71**, 890 (1952).
105. Arikawa, Y., *Japan Analyst* **2**, 436 (1953).
106. Asahi, Y., *Ann. Repts. Takeda Research Lab.* **12**, 75 (1953).
107. Ellington, A. C. and Purves, C. B., *Can. J. Chem.* **31**, 801 (1953).
108. Jaulmes, P. and Dieuzède, J. C., *Trav. soc. pharm. Montpellier* **13**, 182 (1953).
109. Lucas, J. F. C., *Rev. cienc. apl.* (*Madrid*) **7**, 526 (1953).
110. Sjöström, E., *Acta Chem. Scand.* **7**, 1392 (1953).
111. Smith, R. J., *Anal. Chem.* **25**, 505 (1953).
112. Carter, J. R., *Science* **120**, 895 (1954).
113. Jaulmes, P. and Dieuzède, J. C., *Ann. fals. et fraudes* **47**, 9 (1954).
114. Lucas, J. F. C., *Rev. cienc. apl.* (*Madrid*) **8**, 103 (1954).
115. Paul, F., *Mitt. Klosterneuburg, Ser. A, Rebe u. Wein* **4**, 225 (1954).
116. Salomaa, P., *Suomen Kemistilehti* **27B**, No. 2, 12 (1954).
117. Stricks, W., Kolthoff, I. M. and Tanaka, N., *Anal. Chem.* **26**, 299 (1954).
118. Swan, J. D., *Anal. Chem.* **26**, 878 (1954).
119. Petz, A. and Cherubini, M., *Holz, Roh-u. Werkstoff* **13**, 70 (1955).
120. Critchfield, F. E. and Johnson, J. B., *Anal. Chem.* **28**, 73 (1956).
121. Endo, A., *Japanese Patent No.* 1750, March 10, 1956.
122. Frehden, O. and Ecsichof, T., *Rev. chim.* (*Bucharest*) **7**, 304 (1956).
123. Gutterman, B. M., *J. Assoc. Offic. Agr. Chem.* **39**, 282 (1956).
124. Human, J. P. E. and Leach, S. J., *Chem. & Ind.* (*London*) 149 (1956).
125. Impey, N. R. M. and Verdier, E. T., *J. S. African Chem. Inst.* **9**, 51 (1956).
126. Ray Sarkar, B. C. and Swaraman, R., *Analyst* **81**, 668 (1956).
127. Salomaa, P., *Acta Chem. Scand.* **10**, 306 (1956).
128. Sapondzhyan, S. O. and Gevorkyan, K. S., *Vinodelie i Vinogradarstvo SSSR* **16**, No. 8, 10 (1956).
129. Terent'ev, A. P. and Obtemperanskaya, S. I., *Zhur. Anal. Khim.* **11**, 638 (1956).
130. Afanas'ev, B. N., *Trudy Sverdlovsk. Sel'skokhoz. Inst.* **1**, 361 (1957).
131. Berka, A., *Chemie* (*Prague*) **9**, 528 (1957).
132. Cecil, R. and McPhee, J. R., *Biochem. J.* **66**, 538 (1957).
133. Csagoly, E., *Acta Pharm. Hung.* **27**, 267 (1957).
134. Drzhevetskaya, I. A., *Laboratornoe Delo* **3**, No. 4, 21 (1957).
135. Dukhovnyi, A. I., *Samovodstvo, Vinograd. i Vinodelie Moldavii* **12**, No. 3, 46 (1957).
136. Kostin, L. D. and Vidanova, V. A., *USSR Patent No.* 104,643 Jan. 25, 1957.
137. Trawińska, J., *Ann. Univ. Mariae Curie-Sklodowska, Lublin, Polonia*, Sect. DD **12**, 41 (1957).
138. Bellen, Z. and Bellen, N., *Chem. Anal.* (*Warsaw*) **4**, 19 (1958).
139. Human, J. P. S., *Textile Research J.* **28**, 647 (1958).
140. Hunter, I. R. and Potter, E. F., *Anal. Chem.* **30**, 293 (1958).

141. Kotrelev, V. and Zarubitskii, A., *Stroitel. Materialy* **4**, No. 7, 32 (1958).
142. Schulek, E. and Maros, L., *Magyar Kem. Folyoirat* **64**, 480 (1958).
143. Schulek, E. and Maros, L., *Acta Chim. Acad. Sci. Hung.* **17**, 369 (1958).
144. Silbereisen, K. and Kremkow, C., *Brauerei Wiss. Beil.* **11**, 128 (1958).
145. Wilson, K. W., *Anal. Chem.* **30**, 1127 (1958).
146. Carter, J. R., *J. Biol. Chem.* **234**, 1705 (1959).
147. Kapoor, R. C., *Z. anal. Chem.* **166**, 1 (1959).
148. Leach, S. J., *Biochim. et Biophys. Acta* **33**, 264 (1959).
149. Maros, L. and Schulek, E., *Magyar Kem. Folyoirat* **65**, 195 (1959).
150. Maros, L. and Schulek, E., *Magyar Kem. Folyoirat* **65**, 361 (1959).
151. Maros, L. and Schulek, E., *Acta. Chim. Acad. Sci. Hung.* **20**, 359 (1959).
152. Maros, L. and Schulek, E., *Acta. Chim. Acad. Sci. Hung.* **21**, 91 (1959).
153. Schulek, E., Molnar-Perl, I. and Maros, L., *Magyar Kem. Folyoirat* **65**, 363 (1959).
154. Schulek, E. and Maros, L., *Acta Chim. Acad. Sci. Hung.* **19**, 473 (1959).
155. Schulek, E. and Maros, L., *Acta. Chim. Acad. Sci. Hung.* **20**, 443 (1959).
156. Tamsona, A. and Powell, R. D., *J. Agr. Food Chem.* **7**, 643 (1959).
157. McFadden, B. A. and Howes, W. V., *Anal. Biochem.* **1**, 240 (1960).
158. Maros, L. and Schulek, E., *Magyar Kem. Folyoirat* **66**, 197 (1960).
159. Maros, L., Molnar-Perl, I. and Schulek, E., *Magyar Kem. Folyoirat* **66**, 319 (1960).
160. Maros, L., Molnar-Perl, I. and Schulek, E., *Magyar Kem. Folyoirat* **66**, 321 (1960).
161. Maros, L. and Schulek, E., *Acta Chim. Acad. Sci. Hung.* **22**, 359 (1960).
162. Maros, L., Molnar-Perl, I. and Schulek, E., *Acta Chim. Acad. Sci. Hung.* **24**, 67 (1960).
163. Maros, L., Molnar-Perl, I. and Schulek, E., *Acta Chim. Acad. Sci. Hung.* **24**, 213 (1960).
164. Maros, L. and Schulek, E., *Ann. Univ. Sci. Budapest Rolando Eötvös nominatae, Sect. Chim.* **2**, 227, 231 (1960).
165. Maros, L., Molnar-Perl, I. and Schulek, E., *Ann. Univ. Sci. Budapest Rolando Eötvös nominatae, Sect. Chim.* **2**, 237 (1960).
166. Schulek, E. and Maros, L., *Ann. Univ. Sci. Budapest Rolando Eötvös nominatae, Sect. Chim.* **2**, 243 (1960).
167. Burroughs, L. F. and Sparks, A. H., *Analyst* **86**, 381 (1961).
168. Kolthoff, I. M. and Eisenstädter, J., *Anal. Chim. Acta* **24**, 83 (1961).
169. Kolthoff, I. M. and Eisenstädter, J., *Anal. Chim. Acta* **24**, 280 (1961).
170. Maros, L., Molnar-Perl, I. and Schulek, E., *Magyar Kem. Folyoirat* **67**, 203 (1961).
171. Maros, L., Molnar-Perl, I. and Schulek, E., *Acta Chim. Acad. Sci. Hung.* **26**, 467 (1961).
172. Mondovi, B., Costa, M. T. and Ferro-Luzzi, G., *Ital. J. Biochem.* **10**, 42 (1961).

173. Obtemperanskaya, S. I., Terent'ev, A. P. and Buzlanova, M. M., *Zhur. Anal. Khim.* **16**, 372 (1961).
174. Panwar, K. S., Rao, S. P. and Gaur, J. N., *Anal. Chim. Acta* **25**, 218 (1961).
175. Probsthain, K., *Z. anal. Chem.* **182**, 409 (1961).
176. Satyanarayana Rao, V. R. and Vasudeva Murthy, A. R., *Chemist-Analyst* **50**, 30 (1961).
177. Stricks, W. and Chakravarti, S. K., *Anal. Chem.* **33**, 194 (1961).
178. Tokareva, R. R. and Kretovich, V. L., *Khlebopekar i Konditer. Prom.* **5**, No. 6, 11 (1961).
179. Jaulmes, P. and Hamelle, G., *Ann. fals.* **54**, 338 (1961).
180. Philipp, B., Bartels, U. and Hayme, H., *Faserforsch.*, *Textiltech.* **12**, 581 (1961).
181. Schwartz, A., Pora, E. A., Kis, Z., Madar, I. and Fabian, N., *Comun. acad. rep. populare Romîne* **11**, 45 (1961).
182. Maros, L., Molnar-Perl, I. and Schulek, E., *Acta Chem. Acad. Sci. Hung.* **30**, 119 (1962).
183. Šepitka, A. and Zradulová, E., *Listy Cukvovar* **77**, 16 (1961).
184. Nedić, M, and Berkeš, I., *Acta Pharm. Jugoslav*, **13**, 13 (1963).
185. Tsen, C. C. and Anderson, J. A., *Cereal Chem.* **40**, 314 (1963).

16. Bromine reagents

Reagents. Several reagents have been classified together under this heading:

(i) Bromine in various organic solvents like acetic acid, CCl_4, $CHCl_3$. It has been stated that hydrogen perbromides are formed in the $CHCl_3$ solution from the reaction:

$$5\ Br_2 + 2\ CHCl_3 \rightarrow HBr_3 + HBr_5 + 2\ CBrCl_3 \quad \text{(ref. 137)}$$

The odour of bromine is then no longer noticeable.

(ii) Bromine + Br^-, dissolved in water; the reagent is probably mainly in the form of the Br_3^- ion.

(iii) Bromine + Br^-, dissolved in methanol. In the so-called Kaufmann reagent, the solution is saturated with NaBr and its stability is claimed to exceed that of other reagents prepared from bromine.

(iv) Bromine in acetic acid/pyridine/H_2SO_4. The solution contains pyridine sulphate dibromide, formulated $C_5H_5N.H_2SO_4.Br_2$ and is claimed not to take part in other than addition reactions.

(v) Methylpyridinium tribromide, $(C_5H_5NCH_3)^+Br_3^-$, in acetic acid/anhydrous Na acetate.

(vi) Bromine in alkaline solution, functioning as hypobromite. The bromine may be used directly or formed from bromate/bromide/acid, followed by addition of alkali. In two examples in the tables below, the bromine was yielded from hypochlorite/bromide mixture.

(vii) Bromate, usually with Br^-, in aqueous solution. This reagent has the advantage of being stable for long periods—in contrast to all those mentioned above—but can only be used in acid solution necessary for bromine liberation:

$$BrO_3^- + 5\ Br^- + 6\ H^+ \rightarrow 3\ Br_2 + 3\ H_2O$$

The reagent may contain only bromate and sufficient bromide is then added to the reaction mixture. In some cases, bromate is used (as a oxidizing reagent) in absence of added bromide. This is not strictly a 'bromine reagent' but it is convenient to classify it here because the same oxidation reaction would have occurred in the presence of bromide. In any case, the oxidation yields bromide ($BrO_3^- \rightarrow Br^- + 3\ O$).

(viii) Electrolytically generated bromine. This is being increasingly used since it circumvents the difficulty of reagent instability and the reagent amount can be measured with high accuracy by the coulometric principle.

(ix) Bromine chloride, BrCl, prepared from bromate/bromide/conc. HCl.

Reactions and materials titrated. 1. Addition, principally to olefine groups but also in some cases to acetylenes:

$$\text{—C=C—} + Br_2 \rightarrow \text{—CBr—CBr—}$$

$$\text{or} \quad \text{—C=C— + BrCl} \rightarrow \text{—CBr—CCl—}$$

The olefines thus determined have included hydrocarbons like indene, styrene and terpenes; unsaturated barbiturates like allyl and cyclohexenyl derivatives; furfuraldehyde (especially derived from pentoses and pentosans); vinyl ethers and ketones; cinnamic and crotonic acids; allyl isothiocyanate. A most important example is the widespread determination of unsaturation, notably of petroleum fractions, fats and oils, often expressed as the 'bromine number' or 'iodine number' (in the tables, the former expression has been exclusively used, even where the authors used the latter).

In the determination of enols, addition is evidently followed by rapid elimination of HBr;

$$(\text{—CO—CH}_2\text{—}) \rightleftharpoons \text{—C(OH)=CH—} \xrightarrow{Br_2} \text{—C(OH)(Br)—CH(Br)—} \xrightarrow{-HBr}$$
$$\text{—C(OH)—CBr—} \rightleftharpoons (\text{—CO—CBrH—})$$

This probably occurs also with the *aci*-form of nitro compounds, e.g.

$$CH_3\text{—}CH\text{=}N(\text{→}O)(OH) \xrightarrow{Br_2} CH_3\text{—}CHBr\text{—}NBr(\text{→}O)(OH) \xrightarrow{-HBr}$$
$$CH_3\text{—}CHBr\text{—}NO_2$$

2. Substitution, nearly always of nuclear hydrogen atoms:

$$\text{—CH=} + Br_2(\text{or } BrCl) \rightarrow \text{—CBr=} + HBr\ (\text{or } HCl)$$

Phenols and aromatic amines are well represented on account of their ready reaction. Examples of the former, determined in this way, are phenol itself; cresols; naphthols and naphtholsulphonic acids; salicylic acid and salicylamide; phenolphthalein; *p*-hydroxybenzoic acid (from hydrolysis of its esters); oxine and diethylstilbestrol. Among aromatic amines can be mentioned: aminophenols and *p*-aminosalicylic acid (also phenols of course); sulphanilamides; *p*-aminobenzoic acid from hydrolysis of its esters; sulphanilic acid; diphenylamine and related compounds like 'centralite'; reduced chloramphenicol; *N*-methylaniline; and anils. Nuclear bromine substitution has been the basis of determination of also anthracene, phenothiazines, indole and derivatives, sulphonamides and carbazole.

Some equations are given here:

$$H_3C\text{—}C_6H_3(OH)_2 \xrightarrow{4\,Br} H_3C\text{—}C_6HBr_2(OH)_2$$

$$Cl\ (\text{or —}NO_2)\text{—}C_6H_4\text{—}OH \xrightarrow{4\,Br} Cl\ (\text{or —}NO_2)\text{—}C_6H_2Br_2\text{—}OH$$

$$NH_2\text{—}C_6H_4\text{—}SO_2NH_2 \xrightarrow{4\,Br} NH_2\text{—}C_6H_2Br_2\text{—}SO_2NH_2$$

$$COOH\text{—}C_6H_4\text{—}OH \xrightarrow{6\,Br} Br_3C_6H_2\text{—}OH + CO_2$$

OH COOH $\xrightarrow{6\,Br}$ Br, OH, Br, Br (2,4,6-tribromophenol) or $\xrightarrow{8\,Br}$ OBr, Br, Br, Br

NH_2 COOH, SO_3H $\xrightarrow{6\,Br}$ NH_2, Br, Br, Br $+ CO_2 + H_2SO_4$

$N{=}CH_2$ $\xrightarrow{6\,Br}$ $N{=}CH_2$, Br, Br, Br

3. Oxidation, in determination of a variety of compound classes. The chief examples are: hydrazines (e.g. isoniazid); sulphur-containing compounds (e.g. mercaptans like 6-mercaptopurine and glutathione, sulphides like methionine and thiophene, disulphides like cystine and further, thioureas, thiouracils and thiobarbiturates); polyhydroxy compounds (e.g. hydroquinone, glycerol and sugars); aldehydes (e.g. formaldehyde and also formates); and some amides and amino acids (e.g. urea and glycine).

The bromine oxidation of the alkyl iodides formed in the determination of lower alkoxyl groups by heating with hydriodic acid, is classified here and some 50 examples are given in the tables.

Some typical oxidation equations are given here:

$$C_5H_4N.CONHNH_2 + H_2O + 2\,Br_2 \rightarrow C_5H_4N.COOH + N_2 + 4\,HBr$$

$$R.S.R' + H_2O + Br_2 \rightarrow R.\underset{\substack{\downarrow\\ O}}{S}.R' + 2\,HBr$$

$$R.S.S.R + 4\,H_2O + 5\,Br_2 \rightarrow 2\,RSO_2Br + 8\,HBr$$

$$CS(NH_2)_2 + 7\,OBr^- + 2\,OH^- \rightarrow CO_2 + N_2 + SO_4^{2-} + 7\,Br^- + 3\,H_2O$$

$$CH_2OH.CHOH.CH_2OH + OBr^- \rightarrow CH_2OH.CO.CH_2OH + Br^- + H_2O$$

$$HO{-}C_6H_4{-}OH + Br_2 \rightarrow O{=}C_6H_4{=}O + 2\,HBr$$

$$CO(NH_2)_2 + 3\,OBr^- \rightarrow CO_2 + N_2 + 3\,Br^- + 2\,H_2O$$

$$-CO{-}CO- + H_2O + Br_2 \rightarrow -CO{-}O{-}CO- + 2\,HBr$$

$3\ HCHO + 2\ BrO_3^- \rightarrow 3\ CO_2 + 3\ H_2O + 2\ Br^-$

$5\ HCOOH + 2\ HBrO_3 \rightarrow 5\ CO_2 + 6\ H_2O + Br_2$ (ref. 16)

$CH_3I + Br_2 \rightarrow CH_3Br + IBr$, followed by $IBr + 2\ Br_2 + 3\ H_2O \rightarrow HIO_3 + 5\ HBr$

In a few cases, more than one of these reactions may occur. Thus diethylstilbestrol, containing an olefinic bond and hydroxyl-substituted aromatic nuclei, reacts with 10 atoms bromine, of which 2 add on and 2 enter each nucleus. The oxidation of isopropanol to acetone is usually followed by partial substitution of the methyl groups (see ref. 480 for example). The end-product from determination of cyclohexanone oxime was given as bromonitrocyclohexane, $C_5H_{10}C(NO_2)Br$, presumably as a result of oxidation and substitution (or addition, followed by elimination of HBr) (ref. 505).

4. Reactions which cannot be classified in the above three groups appear to be those on which the determination of lead tetraethyl and of silicon-phenyl groups depend:

$$Pb(C_2H_5)_4 \rightarrow PbBr_2$$

$$—Si—C_6H_5 \rightarrow —SiBr + C_6H_5Br$$

No examples of ion combination yielding perbromides of organic bases have been found, analogous to those formed with iodine/iodide reagents.

Reaction conditions. The pH of the reaction mixture has varied over a wide range, from comparatively strongly acid (especially with bromate/bromide reagent, so that bromine is liberated sufficiently fast) usually through addition of HCl or H_2SO_4 (often acetic acid may be there as solvent), to alkaline with hypobromite.

Frequently the excess of reagent has been kept at a minimum, to avoid undesirable side reactions. This has been done with the help of a preliminary determination, or by titrating to a pale yellow or brown colour and sometimes then adding a small further amount of reagent. On the other hand, large excesses have been used only rarely (to accelerate reaction) because of this danger of side reactions. This danger is particularly marked with addition reactions, where substitution may take place.

Reaction has nearly always been at or below room temperature. This is mainly to prevent loss of the volatile bromine reagent. A further reason is to suppress substitution reactions in determinations based on addition.

Catalysts have been used with addition reactions. Mercury (II) salts like the sulphate, and ammonium molybdate are the chief examples.

The reaction medium has mostly been homogeneous but there are examples, especially with the water-soluble bromate/bromide reagent, where two layers were present.

Even more frequently than with iodine reagent, reactions have been carried out in the dark.

Subsequent treatment and final titration stage. (i) In well over half of the examples tabulated below, the unreacted bromine reagent was determined as the final stage. This was done in a variety of ways:

1. Direct back titration, using, for example:
thiosulphate/NaOH to I^-/starch indicator, reacting

$$S_2O_3^{2-} + OH^- + Br_2 \rightarrow 2\,Br^- + SO_4^{2-} + H_2O \quad \text{(ref. 38)},$$

β-naphthol to decoloration,
Ti(III) to decoloration of methylene blue indicator,
anethole to decoloration,
electrolytically generated Cu(I) amperometrically,
hydrazine sulphate potentiometrically.

2. Indirect back titration, principally using arsenite excess. The unreacted arsenite was then back titrated with bromate or bromine to indicators like methyl red, methyl orange, *p*-ethoxychrysoidine, indigo carmine or brilliant carmoisine; with iodine to starch; or with hypohalite to yellow or to indigo carmine indicator.

Other indirect back titrations have been with excess Sn(II), followed by back titration with iodine; with excess SCN^-, followed by coulometric oxidation (to $CN^- + SO_4^{2-}$); and via reaction with phenol yielding Br^- which was converted to BrCN and iodometric titration of the last named (ref. 125).

Easily the most widely used indirect titrimetric determination of unreacted bromine reagent has been by addition of iodide and titration of the liberated iodine, almost always with thiosulphate to disappearance of the yellow iodine colour, using starch, or instrumentally, e.g. biamperometrically. Before addition of iodide, alkaline hypobromite solutions were neutralized or acidified and sodium chloride was added to mixtures containing mercury (II) catalyst to liberate bromine from the complex with mercury. Very occasionally, excess thiosulphate was added and the final titration operation carried out with iodine. There are two references to titration of the liberated iodine with sulphite instead of thiosulphate. Also in two articles the technique of aspirating out unreacted bromine into a potassium iodide solution is described, this latter solution then being titrated with thiosulphate.

(ii) Determination of a reaction product. Three principles have served as bases for most of these determinations, namely titrimetric measurement of the organically held bromine in a reaction product (usually from an addition or substitution reaction) or titration of hydrobromic acid or of bromide ion formed in substitution and sometimes in oxidation. In all cases, unreacted bromine must be removed and agents for this purpose include thiosulphate, phenol, β-naphthol, aniline (these foregoing four yield HBr and are not suitable if titration of this acid is the final stage), Hg(I), sulphite, I^-/thiosulphate, diisobutylene, organic solvents like CCl_4 or $CHCl_3$ and a current of air or boiling off.

1. The bromine in some organic compounds such as brominated enols (from determination of enols), tribromophenyl hypobromite (from determination for example, of phenol and *p*-hydroxybenzoic acid) or α,β-dibromocinnamic acid (from determination of cinnamic acid) is reactive and has been determined by allowing to react for up to 15 min with iodide and titrating the liberated iodine with thiosulphate:

$$C_6H_2Br_3OBr + H^+ + 2\,I^- \rightarrow C_6H_2Br_3OH + Br^- + I_2$$

$$C_6H_5CHBr.CHBr.COOH + 2\,I^- \rightarrow C_6H_5CH{=}CH.COOH + 2\,Br^- + I_2$$

$$\text{—CO.CHBr—} + H^+ + 2\,I^- \rightarrow \text{—CO—CH}_2\text{—} \rightleftharpoons (\text{—C(OH)=CH—}) + Br^- + I_2$$

Reaction products containing more firmly held bromine require more drastic treatment, e.g. with alkalies or oxidizing agents, to convert the covalent —Br into Br^- (see for example, refs 26, 63 and 525). The Br^- has been titrated with Ag^+ or Hg^{2+}.

2. Compounds determined via a final titration of the hydrobromic acid reaction product include: sulphides; phenol; oxine; piperazine; 4-methyluracil; formic and oxalic acids; and isoniazid (the isonicotinic acid is then titrated at the same time). Titration was usually carried out with NaOH or KOH, to indicators like methyl red, changing in the pH 3 to 6 range. In the last mentioned example, phenolphthalein was used because isonicotinic acid was present.

The HBr formed by substitution during addition has thus been determined and also by adding iodate and titrating the iodine yielded with thiosulphate. The value serves to correct for error due to substitution.

3. Determination (according to Volhard, with excess Ag(I) and back titration with SCN^-) of the bromide ion formed in the bromination reaction has been performed for phenol and formates.

Some final titrimetric determinations of reaction products other than the three just enumerated, are tabulated below.

Reaction product	From determination of:	Titration procedure
Tribromophenol	Phenol	Dissolved in excess alkali and back titrated with acid
Brominated phenols	Phenols	Titrated with alkali
Quinone	Hydroquinone	+ I^-/acid and titrated with thiosulphate
1,2-Dibromobutane	1-Butene	Converted with KOC_2H_5 to ethylacetylene, then determined with excess Ag(I) and back titration with SCN^-
Iodate	Iodide of an organic base	+ I^-/acid and titrated with thiosulphate
Pb(II)	Lead tetraethyl	Titrated with MoO_4^{2-}; determined with excess $Cr_2O_7^{2-}$ and iodometric back titration; titrated with EDTA
Ammonia	Aminophenols	Distilled and titrated with acid

(iii) In a single example, the bromine reagent was used to destroy the aldose part of a ketose/aldose mixture. The final stage was a Cu(II) titration of sugar before and after this treatment.

Examples

The expression 'I^-/thiosulphate' in the last column is used as a convenient abbreviation for the widely used determination of unused bromine by adding iodide and titrating with thiosulphate.

Material titrated	Reagent and reaction conditions	Subsequent treatment and final titration stage	Ref.
Bromine number of fats and oils	+ HBr + excess BrO_3^-; best + $CHCl_3$	Thiosulphate	1
Orcinol	Titrated with bromine water until yellow	I^-/thiosulphate	2

Materials titrated	Reagent and reaction conditions	Subsequent treatment and final titration stage	Ref.
Phenol	+ excess bromine water; or + $BrO_3^-/Br^-/H_2SO_4$; 10–15 min/room temp.	I^-/thiosulphate	3
Bromine number of hydrocarbons	+ OBr^-/Br^- + HCl. Shaken and left a few min	Hydrocarbon layer extracted with NaOH, non-aqueous layer acidified and determined via I^-/thiosulphate	4
Urea	+ excess OBr^-	+ excess arsenite and back titrated with OBr^- to indigo carmine	5
Bromine number of fats	In CCl_4, + bromine/CCl_4 (ref. 8) or CS_2 (ref. 6); 15 min/room temp.	Back titrated with β-naphthol (ref. 8) or with I^-/thiosulphate (ref. 6)	6, 8
Urea	+ excess OBr^-	+ excess arsenite and back titrated with iodine	7
Bromine number of oils, etc.	In CCl_4 + bromine/CCl_4; 18 h in dark	I^-/thiosulphate; then + IO_3^- and I^-/thiosulphate again	9
Salicylic acid	+ BrO_3^-/Br^- in at least 100% excess, + HCl. *Ca* 5 min/room temp.	I^-/thiosulphate	10
m-Cresol in mixtures with *o*- and *p*-cresol	In water, + BrO_3^-/Br^- + HCl; 1 min shaking/room temp.	I^-/thiosulphate	11
Thymol	+ BrO_3^-/Br^- + HCl; 5 min/room temp.	I^-/thiosulphate	12
Allyl alcohol	+ BrO_3^-/Br^- + dilute H_2SO_4	I^-/thiosulphate	13
Phenol	+ HCl; titrated with bromine/KOH until yellow and 10–20% excess added	I^-/thiosulphate	14
Formic acid	+ bromine/NaOH in *ca* 100% excess, then HCl added until permanent yellow colour	I^-/thiosulphate	15
Formic acid	+ BrO_3^-/Br^- + H_2SO_4; 1 h/100° until no more bromine evolved	I^-/thiosulphate	16

Materials titrated	Reagent and reaction conditions	Subsequent treatment and final titration stage	Ref.
Bromine numbers	In $CHCl_3$ or CCl_4, + HBr + OCl^-/water. *Ca* 20 min/room temp.	+ excess arsenite and back titrated with OCl^- to yellow	17
Bromine numbers of essential oils	In CCl_4, + BrO_3^-/Br^- + H_2SO_4; 6 h/room temp.	+ excess $SnCl_2$ and back titrated with iodine	18
Formates	+ bromine/water until permanently yellow	Excess bromine boiled off and Br^- determined with excess Ag(I) and back titration with SCN^-.	19
Unsaturation of fats and oils	In CCl_4, + Br^-/water + HCl + excess BrO_3^-; 1 min/room temp.	Unused titrated with sulphite to trace of iodine as indicator (formed by adding a KI crystal)	20
Cinnamic acid	Titrated with bromine water until yellow persistent for 5 min	I^-/thiosulphate	21
Terpenes	In $CHCl_3$, + BrO_3^-/ Br^- + H_2SO_4	I^-/thiosulphate	22
Enols	In methanol or without solvent, + bromine/ methanol at − 10°	+ β-naphthol immediately (to remove excess bromine), + I^- and titrated with thiosulphate after 10 min/35° (see Iodides and hydriodic acid, ref. 10)	23
Enols	In 96% ethanol at − 10°, + bromine/ alcohol until pale yellow	Unreacted bromine removed immediately with thiosulphate, I^- added and titrated with thiosulphate (see Iodides and hydriodic acid, ref. 9)	24
Resorcinol	In water, + bromine/ water + HCl; 1 min/ room temp.	I^-/thiosulphate	25
Salicylic acid	+ bromine/water, giving tribromophenol precipitate	Filtered, oxidized with MnO_4^- giving Br^- and determined with excess Ag(I) and back titration with SCN^- (see Permanganate, ref. 17)	26
Formic acid	+ excess BrO_3^-/Br^- + H_3PO_4; 12–15 h/room temp.	I^-/thiosulphate	27

Materials titrated	Reagent and reaction conditions	Subsequent treatment and final titration stage	Ref.
Phenol	Studied effect of acid concentration, excess Br^-, reaction time and temperature on method of ref. 3		28
Urea	+ excess OBr^-; 1 min/room temp.	+ acetic acid; I^-/thiosulphate	29, 43
Cresol	+ excess BrO_3^-/Br^- + HCl; 1 min shaking/ room temp.	I^-/thiosulphate (better end-point if CCl_4 added)	30
Salicylic acid	+ BrO_3^-/Br + HCl; 5–10 min/room temp.	I^-/thiosulphate	31
Enols	+ excess bromine/ alcohol Also tried method of ref. 22, removing excess bromine with β-naphthol or aniline but claimed that the further reaction with I^- is too slow; see Iodides and hydriodic acid, ref. 18)	I^-/thiosulphate	32
Bromine numbers of petroleum products	In CCl_4, + bromine/ CCl_4; 30 min/room temp. in dark	I^-/thiosulphate; then + IO_3^- and I^-/thiosulphate again	33
Enol content, e.g. of diacetylsuccinic acid or its diethyl ester	In alcohol, + bromine/ methanol until yellow and excess added	Unused immediately removed with β-naphthol; then I^-/thiosulphate (5 min/60° reaction) or + water + excess HCO_3^- and back titrated with HCl to methyl orange	34
m-Diphenols or amines (also from di-nitro compounds by reduction with Ti(III))	In water, ethanol or dilute H_2SO_4, + excess BrO_3^-/Br^-	I^-/thiosulphate	35
Unsaturation of vegetable oils	In $CHCl_3$, + bromine/ acetic acid or bromine/ 20% HCl	+ excess arsenite and back titrated with bromine/acetic acid to indigo carmine or trinitroresorcinol	36
Urea	+ OBr^-; warmed + OBr^-; 10 min/ room temp.	+ excess HCl, unreacted bromine driven off by heating; back titrated with NaOH; + acetic acid; I^-/thiosulphate	37

Materials titrated	Reagent and reaction conditions	Subsequent treatment and final titration stage	Ref.
Erythrene	In ethanol, + bromine/ CCl_4; 5 min/room temp., giving dibromo derivative; 12 h, giving tetrabromo derivative	Unused titrated with NaOH/ thiosulphate to I^-/starch	38
Furfuraldehyde	+ excess BrO_3^-/Br^- + HCl; 1 h/room temp. in dark	I^-/thiosulphate	39
Unsaturation of fats and oils; phenol	In $CHCl_3$ + bromine/ acetic acid/pyridine/ H_2SO_4 reagent. Not over 5 min/room temp.	I^-/thiosulphate	40
Erythrene	+ excess BrO_3^-/Br^- + H_2SO_4, giving dibromo derivative	I^-/thiosulphate	41
Proteins (e.g. gelatine, casein), hippuric acid, etc.	In water, + NaOH + bromine/NaOH. At 0°; samples removed at intervals in study of decomposition	+ acid; I^-/thiosulphate	42
Aniline, formed in determination of nitrobenzene by reduction with Ti(III)	+ excess BrO_3^-/Br^- + acid; 5 min/room temp.	I^-/thiosulphate	44
Unsaturation of petroleum products	+ slight excess BrO_3^-/ Br^- + H_2SO_4; 1 min shaking/room temp.	I^-/thiosulphate	45
Unsaturation of fats and oils	In $CHCl_3$, + bromine/ methanol, saturated with NaBr; 30 min–2 h/room temp.	I^-/thiosulphate	46
Diphenylamine; $Ar_2N.CONR_2$	+ excess BrO_3^-/Br^- + HCl, giving dibromo substitution products	I^-/thiosulphate	47
Phenols in raw ammonia water from coking and gas plants	+ excess BrO_3^-/Br^- + H_2SO_4; 1 h/room temp.	I^-/thiosulphate	48
Amino acid derivatives	In water, + bromine/ NaOH. At 0°. Samples removed at intervals in study of decomposition	+ acid; I^-/thiosulphate	49

Materials titrated	Reagent and reaction conditions	Subsequent treatment and final titration stage	Ref.
Phenols	+ excess BrO_3^-/Br^- + HCl; 30 min/room temp. to determine cresols in lysol	I^-/thiosulphate; $CHCl_3$ added near the end-point to free iodine occluded in the precipitate	50
Mixtures of isomeric unsaturated compounds, e.g. cyclohexenylacetic acids	In CCl_4 or $CHCl_3$, + bromine/same solvent. Various reaction times	I^-/thiosulphate	51
Itaconic + mesaconic acids	In water, + bromine/Br^-/water; 10 min/room temp. in dark	I^-/thiosulphate; interpolation gave composition of mixture	52
Phenol	+ excess BrO_3^-/Br^- + H_3PO_4	I^-/thiosulphate	53
Formic acid	+ $NaHCO_3$ or Na acetate + bromine/Br^- until deep yellow; 15 min/room temp.	+ excess arsenite and back titrated with bromine/Br^-/water to indigo carmine/trinitroresorcinol (2:1)	54
2,4-Dichloroaniline, unused after reaction with, in determination of acetic anhydride	In acetic acid (from previous reaction) + water + BrO_3^-/Br^- + HCl; 5 min/room temp.	I^-/thiosulphate	55
Phenol from study of alkaline fusion of Na benzene sulphonate	+ bromine, giving tribromophenol	Precipitate dissolved in excess NaOH and back titrated with HCl	56
Bromine-iodine numbers of oils and fats	+ BrO_3^-/Br^- + acid; 2 h/room temp. (giving 'secondary' number) or 2 days/room temp. (giving 'tertiary' number)	I^-/thiosulphate	57
Unsaturation of lubricating oils	In benzene or gasoline, + H_2SO_4, + BrO_3^-/Br^- till yellow	+ I^- + excess thiosulphate and aqueous layer back titrated with iodine	58
Brominated cresols	In acetic acid/water, + BrO_3^-/Br^- until slight excess (yellow); 1 min/room temp.	I^-/thiosulphate	59
Phenols; aromatic amines	+ excess BrO_3^-/Br^- + HCl; 5–30 min/room temp.	I^-/thiosulphate	60

Materials titrated	Reagent and reaction conditions	Subsequent treatment and final titration stage	Ref.
Bromine numbers of fatty substances	Method of ref. 40 found satisfactory		61
Unsaturation of oils, etc.	+ excess BrO_3^-/Br^- + water + CCl_4 + HCl. Up to 20 h/room temp.	I^-/thiosulphate	62
Oleic/linoleic acid mixture in an oil	In ether at − 10°, + bromine till brown; 2 h/− 10°	Unreacted bromine removed with thiosulphate, ether distilled off and brominated product refluxed with KOH; Br^- determined with Ag(I). Interpolation gave composition (see Alkalies, ref. 57)	63
Unsaturation	In CCl_4, + slight excess BrO_3^-/Br^- + H_2SO_4; 3 min shaking/ room temp.	I^-/thiosulphate	64
Thymol	+ excess BrO_3^-/Br^- + HCl. Warmed, giving dibromo derivative	I^-/thiosulphate	65, 85
Furfuraldehyde from acid distillation of pentoses and pentosans	+ excess BrO_3^-/Br^- + acid + ammonium molybdate; 4 min/room temp.	I^-/thiosulphate	66
Phenols in waste water	Extract in benzene/ quinoline, + excess BrO_3^-/Br^- + H_2SO_4; 2 h/room temp.	I^-/thiosulphate	67
Unsaturation of fats and oils	Method of ref. 40 but with slightly longer reaction time (10–15 min)		68
Bromine number of saponified oils, e.g. olive oil	Method of ref. 40		69
Unsaturated hydrocarbons, acids, esters, etc., e.g. crotonic and cinnamic acids	In CCl_4 + bromine/ CCl_4. Up to 18 h/0° to 75°	Unreacted bromine and HBr formed carried with nitrogen current into KI solution; titrated with thiosulphate, IO_3^- added and retitrated	70
Lead tetraethyl in gasoline	+ bromine/CCl_4; 5 min/room temp., giving $PbBr_2$	Filtered, dissolved in HNO_3, evaporated with H_2SO_4, giving $PbSO_4$; dissolved in ammonium acetate and titrated with ammonium molybdate to external tannin indicator	71

Materials titrated	Reagent and reaction conditions	Subsequent treatment and final titration stage	Ref.
1-Butene/2-butene mixtures	+ bromine, giving mixture of three dibromobutanes (1,2-, *meso*-2,3- and racemic 2,3-) (suggested possibility)	+ I^-/methanol, giving iodine at different rates; titrate with thiosulphate at intervals (see Iodides and hydriodic acid, ref. 27)	72
Zn or Na phenolsulphonates	+ excess BrO_3^-/Br^- + H_2SO_4; 2 h/room temp. in dark	I^-/thiosulphate	73
β,γ-Unsaturated nitriles	In $CHCl_3$, + *ca* 200% excess bromine/Br^-/water; 10 sec shaking/room temp.	I^-/thiosulphate	74
$(C_6H_5NC_2H_5)_2CO$ ('Centralite') in double-base smokeless powders	In ethanol, + excess BrO_3^-/Br^- + HCl; 30 sec/room temp.	I^-/thiosulphate	75
Urea; formates	+ borax or $KHCO_3$ + bromine; 30 min/room temp.	I^-/thiosulphate	76
Furfuraldehyde	+ HCl + excess BrO_3^-; 2 h/room temp.	I^-/thiosulphate	77
Phenols in coking-plant waters	+ H_2SO_4 + BrO_3^-/Br^- until odour of bromine detected	I^-/thiosulphate	78
Alkyl iodides from determination of lower alkoxyl groups by reaction with HI	Passed into bromine/acetic acid, giving IBr; + Na acetate, so that IBr is further oxidized to IO_3^-	Excess bromine removed with formic acid then + H_2SO_4; I^-/thiosulphate	79
Alkyl iodides from determination of lower alkoxyl groups by reaction with HI	Micro adaptation of method of ref. 79		80
Gaseous olefines and acetylenes	+ excess BrO_3^-/Br^- + H_2SO_4; 60–90 min shaking/room temp.	I^-/thiosulphate	81
Aromatic amines and derivatives, e.g. aniline, *p*-toluidine, diphenylamine, 'centralite'	Modification of method of ref. 75, using CCl_4 instead of the less inert ethanol as solvent		82
p-Chlorophenol	+ excess BrO_3^-/Br^- + HCl, giving dibromo derivative	I^-/thiosulphate	

Materials titrated	Reagent and reaction conditions	Subsequent treatment and final titration stage	Ref.
Phenolsulphonates	+ excess BrO_3^-/Br^- + $HgCl_2$ + HCl or H_2SO_4 (studied influence of Br^- concentration, bromine excess and reaction time; recommended 3 h/room temp. in the dark)	I^-/thiosulphate; a few drops $CHCl_3$ gave a more easily observable end-point	84
Salicylic acid	+ excess BrO_3^-/Br^- + HCl; 20 min/room temp.	I^-/thiosulphate	86
Salicylic acid	+ excess BrO_3^-/Br^- + HCl; 1 min/room temp.	I^-/thiosulphate	87
Bromine numbers of natural and petroleum asphalts	Method of ref. 70		88
Phenol	+ excess bromine/water, giving tribromophenol and HBr	Filtered, unreacted bromine removed in air current and titrated with NaOH to methyl red	89
Salicylic acid, *m*-cresol	Method of ref. 89		90
Phenol, cresols	+ Br^- + HCl + excess BrO_3^-; 1 h/room temp.	I^-/thiosulphate	91
Methyl iodide from determination of methoxyl groups by reaction with HI	Method of ref. 79		92
β,γ-Hexeno- and butenonitriles in presence of α,β-nitriles	Method of ref. 74		93
Bromine numbers of lubricating oils	Method of ref. 9, using 50-70% excess bromine and 15–30 min reaction time		94, 128
Methyl or ethyl iodides from determination of methoxyl or ethoxyl groups by reaction with HI	Method of ref. 79		95
Phenol in various medicaments, e.g. in lozenges	Method of ref. 3 (after preliminary separation)		96
Esters of *p*-aminobenzoic acid, e.g. novocaine, anesthesine	+ HCl + excess BrO_3^-/Br^-; 15 min/room temp.	+ excess arsenite and back titrated with BrO_3^- to methyl red	97

Materials titrated	Reagent and reaction conditions	Subsequent treatment and final titration stage	Ref.
Phenol	+ bromine/water, giving precipitate of tribromophenyl hypochlorite	Unreacted bromine removed with HgCl or by extraction with $CHCl_3$ or CCl_4 and HBr formed titrated to methyl red or bromocresol green, etc.; or precipitate treated with I^-, liberating iodine, titrated with thiosulphate (see Iodides and hydriodic acid, ref. 39)	98
Furfuraldehyde from determination of pentosans by heating with HCl	+ excess BrO_3^-/Br^- + acid; 1 h/room temp. in dark	I^-/thiosulphate	99
Hydroquinone	Method of ref. 89		100
Formic, oxalic acids	+ excess bromine water; 15–30 min and 1–2 h respectively/room temp.	Unreacted bromine removed in air current and HBr titrated	101
Sulphides	In benzene, + water + bromine/water until colour persisted. Not over 15 sec/room temp.	Unreacted bromine removed by adding I^- and titrating with thiosulphate; then HBr in aqueous layer titrated with NaOH to bromocresol purple or litmus	102
Methyl iodide from determination of methoxyl or *N*-methyl groups by reaction with HI	Method of ref. 79		103
Formic acid	+ NaCl + bromine/ acetic acid; 30 min/room temp.	I^-/thiosulphate	104
Tyrosine	+ HCl + BrO_3^-/Br^- until distinctly yellow; 2 h/room temp.	I^-/thiosulphate	105
Hexylresorcinol	+ excess BrO_3^-/Br^- + acid. Left overnight/70°	I^-/thiosulphate	106
Furfuraldehyde from treatment of hardwoods with HCl	+ excess BrO_3^-/Br^- + HCl; 1 h/room temp. in dark	I^-/thiosulphate	107
Sympathol	+ excess BrO_3^-/Br^- + HCl; 15 min/room temp. in dark	I^-/thiosulphate	108

Materials titrated	Reagent and reaction conditions	Subsequent treatment and final titration stage	Ref.
Phenol in presence of 2,4-dinitroresorcinol	+ excess BrO_3^-/Br^- + HCl; 15 min/0°	I^-/thiosulphate	109
Phenol in sulphonic acid/alkali melts	+ bromine/water at 0° (saturated with NaCl), giving precipitate of tribromophenol	Unreacted bromine removed with thiosulphate, precipitate dissolved in excess NaOH and back titrated with HCl to methyl orange	110
HCHO	+ reagent from excess BrO_3^-/Br^- + HCl, then made alkaline; 30 min/room temp.	+ acid; I^-/thiosulphate	111
Methanol; polyhydroxy compounds like glycerol, sugars	+ excess OBr^- + conc. alkali in light	+ acid; I^-/thiosulphate	112
Mono- and di-saccharides	In water, + excess OBr^- in light; 15 min (mono-) or 20 (di-)/ 16–17°, giving oxalic acid	+ HCl; I^-/thiosulphate	113
Apiole (4-allyl-3,6-dimethoxy-1,2-methylenedioxybenzene)	+ BrO_3^-/Br^- + acid; 5 min/room temp., then + borax and 15–20 min	I^-/thiosulphate	114
Methyl iodide from determination of methionine by reaction with HI	Method of ref. 79		115
Phenol, cresols, salicylic acid	Method of ref. 89		116
Oxine	+ HCl + BrO_3^-/Br^- until excess (tested with starch/I^- paper); 5 min/room temp.	+ CS_2; I^-/thiosulphate	117
Salicylic acid	+ excess BrO_3^-/Br^- + HCl; 30 min/room temp.	I^-/thiosulphate	118
Furfuraldehyde	+ excess BrO_3^-/Br^- + acid. Various reaction times/0° tried; recommended 5 min, giving reaction with 2 atoms bromine	I^-/thiosulphate	119, 187
5-Bromo-2-furoic acid	+ excess BrO_3^-/Br^- + HCl; 10 min/21°, giving addition of 4 atoms bromine	I^-/thiosulphate	120

Materials titrated	Reagent and reaction conditions	Subsequent treatment and final titration stage	Ref.
Furfuraldehyde from acid hydrolysis of pentosans	+ excess BrO_3^-/Br^- + HCl	I^-/thiosulphate	121
Methyl or ethyl iodides from determination of methoxyl or ethoxyl groups (e.g. in vanillin, pectin) by reaction with HI	Oxidized with bromine/ water to IO_3^-	Unused bromine removed with phenol; then + H_2SO_4 and I^-/thiosulphate	122
Phenol	+ excess BrO_3^-/Br^- + acid; 20–30 min/room temp.	I^-/thiosulphate	123
Aniline in amino-azobenzene	+ excess BrO_3^-/Br^- + HCl; 5–10 min/room temp.	I^-/thiosulphate	124
Unsaturated acids (e.g. oleic, cinnamic)	In CCl_4 + bromine/ CCl_4; 10–15 min/room temp.	+ water + phenol to convert unused bromine to Br^-; Br^- determined by treatment with chlorine giving BrCl, then with KCN, giving BrCN, then reacted with I^-, giving iodine, $BrCN + 2 I^- \rightarrow I_2 + Br^- + CN^-$; titrated with thiosulphate	125
Total sugar in honey	In water, + excess OBr^- in light	I^-/thiosulphate	126
Phenols from alkali melts	Method of ref. 3		127
Oxine	In HCl solution, + bromine/water, giving 5,7-dibromoquinolyl 8-hypobromite	Unreacted bromine removed with air current and HBr formed titrated with NaOH (allowed for original HCl)	129
Diphenylamine	+ nitrocellulose + ethanol, + excess BrO_3^-/Br^- + HCl; 2 min/0°	I^-/thiosulphate	130
Xylidines	+ excess BrO_3^-/Br^- + HCl; 5 min/room temp.	I^-/thiosulphate	131
Methyl iodide from determination of methoxyl groups by reaction with HI	Slight modification of method of ref. 79		132

Materials titrated	Reagent and reaction conditions	Subsequent treatment and final titration stage	Ref.
Phenol in official preparations	+ excess BrO_3^-/Br^- + H_2SO_4; 5–10 min shaking/room temp.	I^-/thiosulphate	133
Unsaturation in aliphatic hydrocarbons (especially mono-olefines)	+ excess BrO_3^-/Br^- + H_2SO_4 (giving yellow colour persisting 2 min)	I^-/thiosulphate	134
Allyl groups	Recommended method of ref. 40		135
Xylidines	Slight improvement of method of ref. 131		136
Unsaturation of olefines	+ bromine/$CHCl_3$ in 60–70% excess; 1–10 min/room temp., claiming no substitution	I^-/thiosulphate	137
Ag or Cd derivatives of glutathione, precipitated in its determination in biological material	+ excess BrO_3^-/Br^- + HCl; 8 min/room temp.	+ Na_2HPO_4; then I^-/ thiosulphate	138
Furfuraldehyde from determination of pentoses by heating with HCl	+ excess BrO_3^-/Br^- + HCl; 1 h/room temp.	I^-/thiosulphate	139
Toluidine from determination of nitrotoluene by reduction with Zn/HCl/acetic acid	Method of ref. 35		140
Nitroanilines	+ excess BrO_3^-/Br^- + acid; 30 min/0°	I^-/thiosulphate	141
Methyl iodide from determination of methoxyl groups by reaction with HI	Method of ref. 79		142
Anthracene and carbazole in crude anthracenes; also latter after reaction of former with maleic anhydride	In acetic acid, + HCl, titrated with BrO_3^-/Br^- until external starch/I^- indicator remained blue for 10 min	I^-/thiosulphate	143
Lead tetraethyl in gasoline	In kerosene, + bromine/CCl_4, giving $PbBr_2$ precipitate	Pb(II) ultimately determined by precipitating with excess $Cr_2O_7^{2-}$ and back titrating iodometrically	144

Materials titrated	Reagent and reaction conditions	Subsequent treatment and final titration stage	Ref.
Acetylene in aqueous solution in study of its hydration	Excess BrO_3^-/Br^- + H_2SO_4; left 2–3 min. Then + $HgSO_4$ + sample; left 5–7 min. All under reduced pressure	+ NaCl; I^-/thiosulphate	145
Unsaturation of hydrocarbons	+ bromine/methanol, saturated with NaBr, as in method of ref. 46. Stated that the methanol must be pure and recommended 10–15 min reaction time with *ca* 60% excess	I^-/thiosulphate	146
Indene	+ bromine/CCl_4, *ca* twice theoretical amount; not over 30 sec/room temp.	+ water; I^-/thiosulphate	147
cyclopentadiene	+ same amount bromine/CCl_4, then immediate back titration		
Mixtures of furfuraldehyde and methylfurfuraldehyde	+ excess BrO_3^-/Br^- + HCl; 5, 10 or 30 min/0°	I^-/thiosulphate, giving 2 equations	148
Micro bromine number of fats and oils	In $CHCl_3$, + bromine/methanol/NaBr as in method of ref. 45; 1–60 min/room temp.	I^-/thiosulphate	149
Aniline from determination of acetanilide by hydrolysis with HCl	+ excess BrO_3^-/Br^- + HCl; 20 min/room temp.	I^-/thiosulphate	150
Sulphanilamide	+ excess BrO_3^-/Br^- + HCl; 5 min/room temp. in dark	I^-/thiosulphate	151
Chloral	+ excess BrO_3^-/Br^- + acid; 5 min/room temp., then + borax and left 15–20 min	+ excess arsenite and back titrated with bromate	152
Unsaturation in benzene	+ BrO_3^-/Br^- + H_2SO_4; 7–30 sec/room temp.	I^-/thiosulphate	153
Fumaric acid	At pH 8·4, + bromine/Br^-/water; 2 h/room temp. in dark	I^-/thiosulphate	154

Materials titrated	Reagent and reaction conditions	Subsequent treatment and final titration stage	Ref.
Allyl compounds	+ HCl + BrO_3^-/Br^- until yellow	I^-/thiosulphate	155
Enol contents, e.g. of $(C_6H_5CO)_2CH_2$	In methanol, + bromine/dry methanol at − 5°	Unreacted bromine immediately removed with diisobutylene, I^- added and titrated with thiosulphate after 5–10 min (see Iodides and hydriodic acid, ref. 59)	156
Glycerol	+ OBr^-; 90 min boiling	I^-/thiosulphate	157
Methyl iodide from determination of methoxyl and *N*-methyl groups by reaction with HI	Method of ref. 79, compared with other methods, e.g. that of ref. 3 under 'Amines and heterocyclic bases' and the Zeisel gravimetric method		158
Aniline from determination of nitrobenzene by reduction with Zn amalgam/HCl	+ BrO_3^-/Br^- + HCl	I^-/thiosulphate	159
Glycerol in aqueous solutions	+ bromine/water; 15 min/room temp.	I^-/thiosulphate	160
p-Chlorophenol	In NaOH, + BrO_3^-/Br^- + HCl; 15 min/room temp., giving dibromo derivative	+ $CHCl_3$; I^-/thiosulphate	161
Alkyl iodides from determination of lower alkoxyl groups by reaction with HI	Note on the technique of method of ref. 79 (if insufficient bromine used)		162
Salicylic acid	+ BrO_3^-/Br^- + HCl, not over 0·4N. Not shaken	I^-/thiosulphate	163
Furfuraldehyde from determination of pentosans by distillation with HCl	Distillate + BrO_3^-/Br^- + acid	I^-/thiosulphate	164
Aromatic amines from determination of aromatic nitro compounds by reduction with Cd in the Jones reductor	Method of ref. 60		165

Materials titrated	Reagent and reaction conditions	Subsequent treatment and final titration stage	Ref.
Olefines and acetylenes	BrO_3^-/Br^- + H_2SO_4 + $HgSO_4$ + sample in CCl_4 + acetic acid with water-insoluble samples; 7 min shaking/room temp. in dark (other reaction times tested)	+ NaCl, then I^-/thiosulphate	166
Phenols in blood, after precipitation of proteins	+ BrO_3^-/Br^- + HCl; 15 min/room temp. in dark	I^-/thiosulphate	167
p-Hydroxybenzoic acid, from determination of esters by saponification	+ BrO_3^-/Br^- + HCl; 15 min/room temp., reacting with 6 bromine atoms	I^-/thiosulphate	168, 206
Procaine	+ BrO_3^-/Br^- + HCl; 10 min/room temp.	+ ethanol; I^-/thiosulphate	169
Olefines in gasoline	+ CCl_4/dilute H_2SO_4 at 0°; titrated with BrO_3^-/Br^- till CCl_4 layer permanently yellow	I^-/thiosulphate	170
Unsaturation of fats	Method of ref. 46, with 2–4 h reaction time in micro-adaptation		171
Aniline in food colours and kitchen tinctures	+ BrO_3^-/Br^- + HCl; 30 min/room temp.	I^-/thiosulphate	172
Allyl alcohol in air	Solution from absorption in water, + BrO_3^-/Br^- + H_2SO_4; 15 min/room temp.	I^-/thiosulphate	173
Salicylic acid from determination of salol (phenyl salicylate) by hydrolysis with NaOH	In ethanol/water +, BrO_3^-/Br^- + H_2SO_4; 15 min/room temp. in dark	I^-/thiosulphate	174
Ethylene in the internal atmosphere of plants	Evacuated into BrO_3^-/H_2SO_4, Br^- added; 15 min/room temp. with shaking	I^-/thiosulphate	175
Methyl or ethyl iodide from determination of methoxyl or ethoxyl groups by reaction with HI	Slight modification of method of ref. 79		176

Materials titrated	Reagent and reaction conditions	Subsequent treatment and final titration stage	Ref.
Alkyl iodides from determination of lower alkoxyl groups by reaction with HI	Modifications of apparatus of method of ref. 79 (concerned the reaction stage with HI)		177
Furfuraldehyde from determination of pentosans by heating with HCl	Method of ref. 39		178
Furfuraldehyde from study of determination of pentosans by heating with HCl	+ BrO_3^-/Br^- + acid; 1 h/room temp.	I^-/thiosulphate	179
Sulphanilamide	In water, + BrO_3^-/Br^- + HCl; 5 min/room temp in dark, giving dibromo derivative	I^-/thiosulphate	180
Aromatic amino acids and aldehydes from determination of nitro acids and aldehydes by reduction with Zn amalgam	+ BrO_3^-/Br^- + acid	I^-/thiosulphate	181
Camphene	In alcohol, + BrO_3^-/Br^- + HCl; 10 min/room temp. in dark	I^-/thiosulphate	182
Methyl iodide from determination of methoxyl groups in pulp and paper materials	Method of ref. 79		183
Crotonic acid in kinetic study of its hydration	+ 50–100% excess BrO_3^-/Br^- + H_2SO_4; 5 min/room temp.	I^-/thiosulphate	184
Anthranilic acid 5-sulphonic acid	+ BrO_3^-/Br^- + HCl, giving tribromoaniline + H_2SO_4	H_2SO_4 titrated with $BaCl_2$	185
Esters of *p*-aminobenzoic acid, e.g. benzocaine, procaine	+ bromine reagent; 1 h/*ca* 0°	I^-/thiosulphate	186
Ethyl iodide from determination of ethoxyl groups in ketene acetals	Method of ref. 79		188
Bromine number of fats	In $CHCl_3$, + bromine/methanol/NaBr; 30 min–2 h/room temp.	+ HCl and back titrated with arsenite to methyl red	189

Materials titrated	Reagent and reaction conditions	Subsequent treatment and final titration stage	Ref.
Unsaturation in mixtures of aliphatic hydrocarbons	Sample + H_2SO_4/ Br^-/n-heptane titrated with BrO_3^-/Br^- to pale yellow and slight excess added; 2 min/room temp.	+ water; I^-/thiosulphate	190
Furfuraldehyde	+ BrO_3^-/Br + HCl; 30 min/*ca* 0°	I^-/thiosulphate	191
Xylidines	In water/alcohol, + BrO_3^-/Br^- + HCl; 10 min/− 4 to − 8° (combined with nitrite titration to give amounts of each)	I^-/thiosulphate	192
Phenol in soap	+ BrO_3^-/Br^- + HCl; 15 min/room temp.	I^-/thiosulphate	193
Benzocaine	+ BrO_3^-/Br^- + HCl; 10–15 min/room temp. in dark	I^-/thiosulphate	194
Resorcinol	+ BrO_3^-/Br^- + HCl; 10–15 min/room temp.	I^-/thiosulphate	195
Sulphides	+ bromine/water; 10 min shaking/room temp., giving sulphoxides + HBr	Unreacted bromine removed by I^-/thiosulphate and HBr titrated with KOH to methyl red	196
Phenols, cresols, diphenols, phloroglucinol	+ BrO_3^-/Br^- + acid. Studied reaction times	I^-/thiosulphate or back titrated with arsenite	197
Alkyl iodides from determination of lower alkoxyl groups by reaction with HI		Slight modifications of method of ref. 79 (concerned with the apparatus and preparation of the HI)	198
o-Toluidine in leather dyes (separated by distillation)	+ BrO_3^-/Br^- + HCl, reacting with 4 bromine atoms	I^-/thiosulphate	199
HCHO or formic acid from determination of polyalcohols by periodate oxidation	+ bromine/water; 1 h/room temp., oxidizing to CO_2	+ excess arsenite and back titrated with iodine	200
Phenols	Comments on methods of refs 35 and 209		201

Materials titrated	Reagent and reaction conditions	Subsequent treatment and final titration stage	Ref.
Unsaturated compounds, mostly hydrocarbons	+ H_2SO_4 and titrated with BrO_3^-/Br^- until persistent yellow; slight excess added, left 3 min/room temp. with shaking	I^-/thiosulphate	202
Furfuraldehyde from determination of pentoses and pentosans by heating with 40% HBr	+ BrO_3^-/Br^- + HCl+ ammonium molybdate; 4 min/room temp. after appearance of yellow	I^-/thiosulphate	203
Styrene, indene	In $CHCl_3$ + bromine/CCl_4 or bromine/methanol/NaBr; 2 h/room temp. (studied reaction)	I^-/thiosulphate; then titrated with alkali or IO_3^- added and titrated with thiosulphate again	204
Formic acid in acetic acid	+ bromine/Na acetate; 30 min/room temp. in dark	I^-/thiosulphate	205
Aniline oxalate, precipitated in determination of aniline in diphenylamine	In warm water, titrated with BrO_3^-/Br^- to pale yellow; left 5–10 min/room temp.	I^-/thiosulphate	207
Formalaniline, $C_6H_5N{=}CH_2$	+ bromine/methanol/NaBr; 2 h/room temp., giving tribromo derivative	I^-/thiosulphate	208
Phenols	In alkali, + BrO_3^-/Br^-, then + HCl; 10 min/room temp.; some at − 5° with various reaction times	I^-/thiosulphate	209
Benzocaine	Slight modification of method of ref. 186		210
Methyl iodide from determination of methoxyl groups, e.g. in lignin preparations	Slight modifications of apparatus of method of ref. 79		211
Piperazine	Neutralized solution + bromine/water. A few min/room temp., giving precipitate of tetrabromo derivative	Filtered, unused bromine removed with air current and HBr formed titrated with NaOH to phenolphthalein	212

Materials titrated	Reagent and reaction conditions	Subsequent treatment and final titration stage	Ref.
Sulphathiazole	+ BrO_3^-/Br^- (10–20% excess) + HCl; 5 min/room temp.	I^-/thiosulphate	213
Ethyl iodide from determination of ethanol in blood, by heating with HI	Principle of method of ref. 79		214
p-Hydroxybenzoic acid from determination of its esters by hydrolysis with NaOH	+ BrO_3^-/Br^- + HCl, giving 2,4,6-tribromophenol	I^-/thiosulphate	215
Acrolein and acrylic acid, in study of their hydration	Method of ref. 184		216
1-Butene in presence of 2-butene	Bromine added at − 70° until solution red. Then 30 min/room temp.	Unused bromine removed with sulphite and the 1,2-dibromobutane converted with K ethoxide to ethylacetylene, then determined argentometrically (see Alkalies, ref. 145, and Silver (I), ref. 75)	217
Alkyl iodides from determination of lower alkoxyl groups by heating with HI	Slight modification of technique of method of ref. 79 (concerned the reaction with HI)		218
Lead tetraethyl	In CCl_4, + bromine/CCl_4; 30–60 min/room temp. in dark	I^-/thiosulphate	219
Diethylstilbestrol	+ NaOH + BrO_3^-/Br^- + HCl; 30 min/25–30°	I^-/thiosulphate	220
Olefines in gaseous hydrocarbons	In $CHCl_3$, + bromine/acetic acid until slight excess present; 30 sec or more/room temp.	I^-/thiosulphate	221
β-Naphthol in hair lotions	+ BrO_3^-/Br^- + HCl; *Ca* 15 min/room temp.	I^-/thiosulphate	222
Derivatives of *p*-aminobenzoic acid	Method of ref. 186		223
p-Aminobenzenesulphonic acid from determination of sulphanilamides by hydrolysis with HCl	+ BrO_3^-/Br^- + acid	I^-/thiosulphate	224

Materials titrated	Reagent and reaction conditions	Subsequent treatment and final titration stage	Ref.
Formic acid, also from determination of formyl groups by distillation with *p*-toluenesulphonic acid	+ bromine/water; 5 min/room temp.	I^-/thiosulphate	225
Benzocaine	Aliquot of extract in methanol, + bromine/HCl; 1 h/room temp. in dark	I^-/thiosulphate	226
Methyl + ethyl iodides from determination of methoxyl + ethoxyl groups by heating with HI	Method of ref. 79		227
tetramethylammonium iodide from reaction with trimethylamine of methyl iodide, formed in determination of methoxyl groups likewise by heating with HI	Method of ref. 79		
Cinnamic acid	+ bromine, giving $\alpha\beta$-dibromocinnamic acid	+ NaI/ethanol, boiled giving cinnamic acid, NaBr and iodine; titrated with thiosulphate (see Iodides and hydriodic acid, ref. 88)	228
Bromine numbers	In $CHBr_3$, + bromine/methanol/NaBr ($CHBr_3$ to give quicker layer separation in final stage, than with $CHCl_3$)	+ water/methanol and titrated with arsenite in water/methanol, to indigo carmine	229
Sulphathiazole	+ HCl and titrated with BrO_3^-/Br^- until in excess	I^-/thiosulphate	230
Alkyl iodides from determination of lower alkoxyl groups by reaction with HI	Method of ref. 79		231
Unsaturation (with study of substitution occurring concurrently during determination)	Technique of method of ref. 190, using measured amount of H_2SO_4	I^-/thiosulphate: IO_3^- added to aqueous layer and re-titrated with thiosulphate, giving HBr formed in substitution (allowed for original H_2SO_4)	232
Bromine numbers of human milk fat	In $CHCl_3$, + bromine/acetic acid/pyridine/H_2SO_4 reagent	I^-/thiosulphate	233

Materials titrated	Reagent and reaction conditions	Subsequent treatment and final titration stage	Ref.
Bromine number of oils	In $CHCl_3$, + bromine/methanol/NaBr; 2 h/room temp.	+ water, titrated with arsenite until colour almost disappeared, then I^-/thiosulphate	234
Bromine number of tall oil	In CCl_4, + bromine/acetic acid/pyridine/H_2SO_4 + Hg acetate (studied effect of excess reagent and reaction time, recommending *ca* 70% excess and 90 min/room temp.)	+ water; I^-/thiosulphate	235
Bromine numbers of fats (micro)	In cellosolve, + bromine/methanol/NaBr; 5 min/room temp.	I^-/thiosulphate	236
Phenol in urine in presence of hydroquinone	+ BrO_3^-/Br^- + H_2SO_4 (high conc., so that the hydroquinone was not attacked); 30 min/room temp.	+ I^- and titrated with sulphite to potentiometric end-point.	237
hydroquinone in same sample	then + $NaHCO_3$, reducing the acid conc., + pyridine + BrO_3^-/Br^- 1 h/room temp., reacting with 10 bromine atoms	+ I^- and similarly back titrated with sulphite	
Sulphonamides	In 50–70% acetic acid, + BrO_3^-/Br^- + HCl; 90 sec/room temp.	Back titrated with arsenite	238
Methyl iodide from determination of *N*-methyl groups by reaction with HI	Method of ref. 79		239
Itaconic acid in fermentation liquor	+ bromine/KBr/KCl/HCl/water, pH 1·2; 10 min/room temp., then 5 min/*ca* 0°	I^-/thiosulphate	240
p-Nitrophenol in full chrome leather	+ BrO_3^-/Br^- + acid, reacting with 4 bromine atoms	I^-/thiosulphate	241
Guaiacolsulphonic acid ('Thiocol') and quinosol ('Sunoxol'—oxine sulphate)	Method of ref. 3		242

Materials titrated	Reagent and reaction conditions	Subsequent treatment and final titration stage	Ref.
Phenols in soap	+ BrO_3^-/Br^- + HCl; 1 h/15–17°	I^-/thiosulphate	243
Ethylene formed with ethyl iodide in determination of ethylene glycol ethers or esters by reaction with HI; propylene (and isopropyl iodide) likewise formed from propylene glycol derivatives	Carried with CO_2 stream into bromine/ methanol or acetic acid (alkyl iodides determined with a Ag(I) reagent—see Silver (I), ref. 82)	I^-/thiosulphate	244
Phenol	+ BrO_3^-/Br^- + H_2SO_4	Excess bromine removed with sulphite and Br^- determined with excess Ag(I) and back titration with SCN^-	245
Many phenols	+ BrO_3^-/Br^- + HCl. Study of effect of many factors, e.g. excess of reagent, acid conc., time and temperature of reaction	I^-/thiosulphate	246
Allyl, cyclohexenyl and other unsaturated barbiturates	In $CHCl_3$ or $CHCl_3$/ methanol, + BrO_3^-/Br^- + H_2SO_4; 1 h shaking/ room temp.	I^-/thiosulphate	247
4-vinyl-1-cyclohexene in tetrahydrophthalic anhydride	Method of ref. 134		248
Diphenylamine and derivatives like $(C_6H_5)_2N.CONH_2$; also $(C_6H_5.N.C_2H_5)_2CO$	In CCl_4 or acetic acid, + BrO_3^-/Br^- + HCl; 15 sec–5 min/room temp.	I^-/thiosulphate	249
Unsaturated hydrocarbons in gasoline	Principle of method of ref. 40		250
Furan, sylvane, furfuryl alcohol	+ bromine/acetic acid/ pyridine/ H_2SO_4; 1 h/ room temp. in dark, adding 4 bromine atoms (claimed negligible substitution)	I^-/thiosulphate	251

Materials titrated	Reagent and reaction conditions	Subsequent treatment and final titration stage	Ref.
Allyl groups in ethers and esters	In $CHCl_3$, + bromine/ $CHCl_3$; 1, 2 or 3 h/4°. Also methods of refs 40 and 45 (last named stated to give results *ca* 10% low)	I^-/thiosulphate	252
Furfuraldehyde from determination of pentosans in plant pulp by heating with HCl	Partly neutralized, then + BrO_3^-/Br^- + ammonium molybdate; 5 min/room temp.	I^-/thiosulphate	253
Unsaturation, e.g. of allyl compounds	+ BrO_3^-/Br^- + pyridine + acetic acid	I^-/thiosulphate	254
Ethyl iodide from determination of phenetidine by heating with HI	Method of ref. 79		255
Ethyl centralite, $(C_6H_5.N.C_2H_5)_2CO$ in rocket propellant powder	Extract in acetic acid, + BrO_3^-/Br^- + HCl; 1 min/room temp.	I^-/thiosulphate	256
Phenols, extracted from aviation gasoline with NaOH	+ BrO_3^-/Br^- + HCl	I^-/thiosulphate	257
Bromine numbers of olefines	In CCl_4 + acetic acid + BrO_3^-/Br^- at 25° until yellow, stable for 5 sec. Slight excess added, then 40 sec	I^-/thiosulphate	258
Bromine number	Remarks on method of ref. 40		259
Micro bromine number of fatty acids	In $CHCl_3$, + bromine/ acetic acid/pyridine/ H_2SO_4 reagent; 15 min/ room temp.	I^-/thiosulphate	260
Oxine and its metal derivatives (e.g. Cu, Al)	In methanol + HCl + KBr, titrated with BrO_3^- to decoloration of methyl red; small excess added	I^-/thiosulphate or back titrated with arsenite to *p*-ethoxychrysoidine or brilliant carmoisine	261
Formates	+ BrO_3^-/Br^- + HCl; left 2 min for bromine development. Then + Na acetate; 30 min/room temp. in dark	+ HCl and I^-/thiosulphate	262

Materials titrated	Reagent and reaction conditions	Subsequent treatment and final titration stage	Ref.
Triphenylarsine, unchanged in analysis of a mixture with phenylchloroarsines after reaction with $NaOH/H_2O_2$	Extract in CCl_4, + excess BrO_3^-	Back titrated with arsenite	263
Aniline from determination of acetanilide by hydrolysis with H_2SO_4	+ BrO_3^-/Br^-	I^-thiosulphate	264
Furfuraldehyde from determination of pentosans by reaction with acid	+ BrO_3^-/Br^- + ammonium molybdate; 4 min/14–18°	I^-/thiosulphate	265
Oxine	In 20% HCl + excess electrolytically generated bromine	Back titrated with arsenite	266
Butyl iodide from determination of butoxyl groups in urea/HCHO resin films	Method of ref. 79		267
Aldoses	+ BrO_3^-/Br^- + H_2SO_4; 10 min/room temp., then + excess NaOH and 20 min/30°	+ H_2SO_4; I^-/thiosulphate	268
Micro bromine number	Study of method of ref. 149		269
Bromine number	In CCl_4, + BrO_3^-/Br^- + HCl; 5–15 min/room temp.	I^-/thiosulphate or + excess arsenite and back titrated with BrO_3^-	270
Unsaturated barbiturates, e.g. allylcyclopentenyl-, diallyl-	+ BrO_3^-/Br^- + HCl. A few min/room temp., adding 2 or 4 atoms bromine	I^-/thiosulphate	271
Allyl isothiocyanate	+ BrO_3^-/Br^- + HCl; 10–12 min/room temp.	+ excess arsenite and back titrated with BrO_3^-	272
Ammonium uranyl urate, precipitated in determination of uric acid	In hot H_2SO_4, + BrO_3^-/ Br^- + HCl; 2 h/room temp. in dark	I^-/thiosulphate or back titrated with arsenite	273
Caffein ein medicinale mixtures	+ BrO_3^-/Br^- + HCl; 2 h/room temp. in dark	I^-/thiosulphate or back titrated with arsenite	274

Materials titrated	Reagent and reaction conditions	Subsequent treatment and final titration stage	Ref.
Phenol from determination of diphenyl carbonate by hydrolysis with alkali	+ BrO_3^-/Br^- + HCl; 5 min shaking/room temp.	I^-/thiosulphate	275
Methyl iodide from determination of the insect repellent 'Dimalone' by reaction with HI	Method of ref. 79		276
'dimalone' on cloth	extract in CCl_4 or acetic acid, + BrO_3^-/Br^- + HCl; 10 min shaking/room temp.	I^-/thiosulphate	
Bromine numbers	+ bromine/methanol/NaBr; 20 min/room temp. in dark	Back titrated with Ti(III) to methylene blue or with arsenite to methyl red (after acidification)	277
Quinine	+ BrO_3^-/Br^- + acid	I^-/thiosulphate	278
Aromatic amines from determination of nitro compounds by reduction with Zn/Hg/HCl	+ BrO_3^-/Br^- + HCl; 10 min–1 h/room temp.	I^-/thiosulphate	279
Rubber in latex (solution in CCl_4)	Dispersion in water(+ bentonite as stabilizer), + BrO_3^-/Br^- + HCl; 15 min/room temp. in dark	I^-/thiosulphate	280
Phenol	+ BrO_3^-/Br^- + HCl; 5–10 min/room temp.	+ excess arsenite and back titrated with BrO_3^- to *p*-ethoxychrysoidine or brilliant carmoisine	281
Salicylic acid	+ BrO_3^-/Br^- + H_2SO_4; 10 min/*ca* 15°	+ $NaHCO_3$ + Na_2SO_3 to convert unreacted bromine to Br^-; + HNO_3 + excess $AgNO_3$ and back titrated with SCN^-.	282
Methallyl chloride, $CH_2{=}C(CH_3).CH_2Cl$	Methods of refs 40 and 46, with small modifications		283
Ethylene in gases	Transferred to evacuated flask containing $BrO_3^-/Br^-/H_2SO_4$; 5 min shaking/room temp.	+ NaOH; after 3–5 min, + I^-; then + H_2SO_4 and titrated with thiosulphate	284

Materials titrated	Reagent and reaction conditions	Subsequent treatment and final titration stage	Ref.
Olefines in C_4 hydrocarbon gases	Method of ref. 221		285
Sulphonamides	+ BrO_3^-/Br^- + acetic acid + HCl or H_2SO_4; 10 sec to 1 h/room temp.	I^-/thiosulphate	286
Pantocaine, panthesine	+ BrO_3^-/Br^- + acid, reacting with 2 and 4 atoms bromine respectively	I^-/thiosulphate	287
p-Aminosalicylic acid; *p*-aminophenol	+ BrO_3^-/Br^- + acetic acid + HCl; 5 min/ room temp.	I^-/thiosulphate	288
Dixanthydrylurea from determination of urea in urine by precipitation with xanthydrol	+ Ca hypobromite; 5 min. (Blank directly on urine without precipitation)	+ HCl; I^-/thiosulphate	289
Furfuraldehyde from determination of cellulosic materials by hydrolysis with H_2SO_4	Method of ref. 119		290
Caffeine in coffee, etc. (after preliminary extraction)	Method of ref. 274		291
4-Vinyl-1-cyclohexene ('Butadiene dimer')	Extract in $CHCl_3$, + acetic acid, titrated with BrO_3^-/Br^- until yellow, then slight excess added. Several min shaking/ room temp.	I^-/thiosulphate	292
Phenyl benzyl sulphide	+ bromine/water + tert-butanol; 5–10 min/ room temp.	I^-/thiosulphate	293
Methyl and ethyl iodides from determination of alkoxysilanes, $Si(OCH_3)_4$ and $Si(OC_2H_5)_4$ by reaction with HI	Principle of method of ref. 79		294
Some unsaturated carbonyl compounds like α- and ψ-ionones, cinnamaldehyde	+ bromine/dry methanol/NaBr. Various times/room temp., e.g. 10 min for ψ-ionone, 12 h for the α-ionone	Back titrated with anethole/ methanol to colour disappearance	295

Materials titrated	Reagent and reaction conditions	Subsequent treatment and final titration stage	Ref.
Phenacetin; benzocaine	In 80% acetic acid, + BrO_3^-/Br^- + HCl; 10–30 min/room temp.	I^-/thiosulphate	296
Phenolphthalein	In alkali solution, + BrO_3^-/Br^- + acetic acid + HCl; 1 min shaking/ room temp.	I^-/thiosulphate	297
Ethylene from determination of blood ethanol by passing over pumice/H_3PO_4 at *ca* 300°	Absorbed in bromine/ CCl_4	I^-/thiosulphate	298
Furfuraldehyde from determination of pentosans in cellulose by hydrolysis with HCl	+ BrO_3^-/Br^- + acid	I^-/thiosulphate	299
(compared with the barbiturate precipitation method)			
Phenols, olefines and other compounds (e.g. limonene, oleic acid, naphthalene, cholesterol)	+ bromine/acetic acid	Back titrated with arsenite	300
Some pharmaceuticals, etc., mostly phenols (e.g. salicylic acid, resorcinol, β-naphthol, thymol, vanillin, salol) and bases (e.g. quinine, strychnine, codeine, benzocaine)	In acetic acid or acetic acid/water, + bromine/ acetic acid; some + Na acetate; 10–30 min/room temp. in dark (studied reaction conditions)	I^-/thiosulphate	301
Procaine	+ BrO_3^-/Br^- + acid, giving dibromo derivative	I^-/thiosulphate; or back titrated with arsenite; or + excess arsenite and back titrated with BrO_3^- to indigo carmine	302
Urea	+ OBr^-	Back titrated with arsenite	303
phenol, aniline, thymol, sulphanilic acid	+ bromine/water	back titrated with nitrite	
Monomer in partly polymerized acrylic acid and allyl esters	Aliquot in pyridine + BrO_3^-/Br^- + H_2SO_4; 20 min/room temp. or 10–15 min/0° respectively	+ CCl_4; I^-/thiosulphate	304

Materials titrated	Reagent and reaction conditions	Subsequent treatment and final titration stage	Ref.
Bromine numbers of non-conjugated oils and fats	In CCl_4, + bromine/acetic acid/pyridine/H_2SO_4 + Hg acetate; 1 min/room temp.	I^-/thiosulphate	305
Ethylene, formed with ethyl iodide in determination of hydroxyethyl groups in cellulose by heating with HI	Method of ref. 244		306
p-Aminosalicylic acid in urine (extracted with ether)	+ BrO_3^-/Br^- + acetic acid + HCl, reacting with 6 bromine atoms	I^-/thiosulphate	307
Terpenes	+ H_2SO_4 + BrO_3^-/Br^- until colour persisted for 30 sec	I^-/thiosulphate	308
Methyl iodide from determination of dimethyl sulphate by reaction with I^-/water	Principle of method of ref. 79		309
Bromine numbers of conjugated systems (e.g. of tung oil, oil of oiticica)	Method of ref. 305 but with 30 min–2 h reaction time		310
Ethylene in gas mixtures	Shaken with bromine/acetic acid	I^-/thiosulphate	311
Indene in presence of hydrindene	Method of ref. 147		312
Aci-form of nitro-ethane + its anion	+ bromine/water	I^-/thiosulphate	313
Phenol in biological and other protein-containing solutions (isolated by distillation)	+ BrO_3^-/Br^- + HCl; 10 min/room temp.	I^-/thiosulphate	314
Cresol	+ BrO_3^-/Br^- + HCl; 1–2 h/room temp in dark	I^-/thiosulphate	315
Methyl or ethyl iodide from determination of *p*-nitrophenyl-diethyl (or methyl) monothio-phosphate by reaction with HI	Method of ref. 79		316
Allyl alcohol	+ BrO_3^-/Br^- + acid	I^-/thiosulphate	317

Materials titrated	Reagent and reaction conditions	Subsequent treatment and final titration stage	Ref.
Allyl alcohol	+ bromine/water (evidently bromine added and product hydrolysed to give $CH_2Br.CHOH.CH_2OH$ + HBr)	titrated HBr formed	317
Sulphanilic acid	+ BrO_3^-/Br^- + acid; 5 min/room temp. in dark.	I^-/thiosulphate	318
Unsaturation of motor fuels	Tried methods of refs 40 and 46		319
Sulphathiazole; succinyl- and phthalylsulphathiazole	+ BrO_3^-/Br^- + acid; studied effect of factors like excess of reagent, Br^- conc., acid conc., time and light. Proposed 2 min/room temp.	I^-/thiosulphate	320
Thiophene	+ BrO_3^-/Br^- + HCl; 5–30 min/room temp.	I^-/thiosulphate	321
Isopropyl iodide from determination of glycerol by heating with HI	Method of ref. 79		322
Bromine numbers	Method of ref. 310		323
Oxine	+ BrO_3^-	Back titrated with arsenite amperometrically	324
Thenyl alcohol + salicylic acid from determination of the miticide 2-thenyl salicylate by alkali hydrolysis	+ BrO_3^-/Br^- + HCl; 20 min/room temp. Components react with 6 and 8 bromine atoms respectively	I^-/thiosulphate	325
3,3-Diethyl-2,4-dioxo-tetrahydropyridine ('Persedon')	In water, + BrO_3^-/Br^- + HCl; Not over 30 sec/room temp.	I^-/thiosulphate	326
Acetylene in blood	+ bromine/water	I^-/thiosulphate	327
Acetylacetone in kinetic study of its alcoholysis	Added to dilute acid + bromine/water; 4 min/room temp.	Unused bromine removed with phenol; + I^- and titrated with thiosulphate after 5–10 min	328
Salicylamide	+ BrO_3^- + HCl; 10 min/room temp.	I^-/thiosulphate	329

Materials titrated	Reagent and reaction conditions	Subsequent treatment and final titration stage	Ref.
Allyl alcohol from determination of copolymers of methyl and allyl methacrylates by alkali hydrolysis	+ BrO_3^-/Br^- + acid; 1 min/room temp.	I^-/thiosulphate	330
Thiosemicarbazone of *p*-acetylamino-benzaldehyde	+ BrO_3^-/Br^- + HCl; 5–10 min heating	I^-/thiosulphate	331
Zn derivative of oxine in determination of latter by precipitation	Solution in HCl, + BrO_3^-/Br^-; 1 min/room temp.	I–/thiosulphate	332
Aniline	+ electrolytically generated bromine, from solution in HCl/NaBr/$CuSO_4$	Electrode polarity reversed and back titrated coulometrically with Cu(I)	333
aniline (standardization)	+ BrO_3^-/Br^- + HCl; 3 min/room temp.	I^-/thiosulphate	
Isoniazid	In water, + BrO_3^-/Br^- + HCl; 5 min/room temp.	I^-/thiosulphate	334
p-Aminosalicylic acid	Method of ref. 307 (288)		335
Bromine numbers	Method of ref. 310 with biamperometric final titration of iodine with thiosulphate		336
Volatile phenols in waste waters (micro)	Distillate + small excess bromine; 15–20 min/room temp.	I^-/thiosulphate	337
Isoniazid	In water, + BrO_3^-/Br^- + HCl; 10–15 min/room temp.	I^-/thiosulphate	338
Phenols from determination of aralkyl sulphonates by fusion with alkali	Neutralized solution in water, + bromine/CCl_4; 2 min shaking/room temp.	I^-/thiosulphate	339
Hexabarbital; its Na salt	+ BrO_3^-/Br^- + H_2SO_4; (modification of method of ref. 82 under 'Permanganate')	I^-/thiosulphate	340
2,3-Dihydropyran	In benzene at 0°, + $HgCl_2$ + HCl + *ca* 100% excess BrO_3^-/Br^-; 5 min/room temp.	I^-/thiosulphate	341

Materials titrated	Reagent and reaction conditions	Subsequent treatment and final titration stage	Ref.
Methantheline bromide	+ BrO_3^-/Br^- + HCl; 1 h/room temp.	I^-/thiosulphate	342
Resacetophenone	+ BrO_3^-/Br^- + acid, giving dibromo derivative. Various amounts in excess used and results extrapolated to excess = 0	I^-/thiosulphate	343
Phenols	In water, + BrO_3^-/Br^-, then + HCl, giving bromo-substituted phenols	Dissolved in ethanol and titrated with alkali thermometrically or conductometrically (see Part I, Alkali and alkaline earth hydroxides' ref. 84)	344
8-Hydroxyquinaldine	+ BrO_3^-/Br^- + HCl; 5 min/room temp.	I^-/thiosulphate	345
Vinyl- + ethylacetylene freed by reaction with saturated KBr from their Ag derivatives, isolated in their determination in gas mixtures	+ acetate buffer + bromine/water/KBr + $HgCl_2$; 10 min/room temp. with shaking	I^-/thiosulphate	346
Bromine numbers of paraffin oils	Method of ref. 40	Preferred I^-/thiosulphate to back titration with arsenite	347
Acrylic acid in β-propiolactone	+ BrO_3^-/Br^- + H_2SO_4; 5 min/room temp., then + $HgSO_4$ and 5 min/room temp.	+ NaCl; I^-/thiosulphate	348
Enol contents of formyl compounds	Critical study of method of refs 23 and 24 (see Iodides and hydriodic acid, ref. 457)		349
Quinine in tablets	+ bromine/acetic acid/pyridine/H_2SO_4; 15 min/room temp., reacting with 4 bromine atoms	I^-/thiosulphate	350
Isoniazid	+ BrO_3^- + HCl or H_2SO_4 (with or without Br^- made no difference)	I^-/thiosulphate	351
Aromatic or heterocyclic sulphides	In acetic acid + some water, + HCl + BrO_3^-/Br^-; 5 min/*ca* 45°	I^-/thiosulphate	352

Materials titrated	Reagent and reaction conditions	Subsequent treatment and final titration stage	Ref.
Unsaturation of fats	In CCl_4, $CHCl_3$ or methanol/NaBr, + bromine/CCl_4; 1 h/room temp. in dark	I^-/thiosulphate; + IO_3^- and aqueous layer retitrated with thiosulphate	353
Unsaturated fatty acids in faecal fat	+ BrO_3^-/Br^- + HCl + HgI_2 + CCl_4 + water. Unused bromine almost immediately determined	I^-/thiosulphate	354
Butyl iodide from determination of butoxyl groups in phenol/HCHO intermediates by heating with HI		Principle of method of ref. 79	355
Bromine numbers of polymerized oils, e.g. linseed oil		Criticized method of ref. 305, saying that values depended on the amount of reagent in excess	356
Formic acid	In pyridine/water, + bromine reagent; 3 min/room temp.	I^-/thiosulphate	357
Undecylenic acid and salts	+ BrO_3^-/Br^- + HCl; 5 min/room temp.	I^-/thiosulphate	358
Phenols in water or tar	+ bromine; studied factors such as pH, amount of excess reagent, time and temperature of reaction, recommending pH 6 to 9 and 1 h/*ca* 0°	I^-/thiosulphate	359
Camphoquinone	In methanol, ethanol or acetic acid, + BrO_3^-/Br^- + H_2SO_4 + $HgSO_4$; 7–10 min/room temp., giving camphoric anhydride + HBr	+ conc. NaCl, then I^-/thiosulphate	360
Bromine number of some conjugated materials, e.g. tung oil	+ Hg acetate, then + bromine/acetic acid/pyridine/H_2SO_4; 1 h/room temp. in dark	I^-/thiosulphate	361
Unsaturation, e.g. in essential oils	+ methylpyridinium tribromide/acetic acid + anhydrous Na acetate; 2–12 h/room temp.	I^-/thiosulphate	362

Materials titrated	Reagent and reaction conditions	Subsequent treatment and final titration stage	Ref.
Some thiobarbiturates	+ BrO_3^- + HCl; 10–15 min/room temp	+ Br^- and I^-/thiosulphate	363
Dimethyl sulphide	+ saturated bromine/water; 10 min/room temp.	+ I^-, iodine removed with thiosulphate and HBr formed titrated with KOH to methyl red	364
Vitamin B_6	In water, + BrO_3^-/Br^- + HCl; 45 min/room temp. in dark	I^-/thiosulphate	365
Methylenesalicylic acid	In alkali, + BrO_3^-/Br^- + H_2SO_4; 15 min/room temp. in dark	I^-/thiosulphate	366
Penicillin G (as Na salt) solutions	+ BrO_3^-/Br^- + H_2SO_4; 30 min/room temp. in dark	I^-/thiosulphate	367
Squalene in sebum and sebum-like materials	Extract in CCl_4, + bromine/acetic acid/pyridine/H_2SO_4; 15 min/room temp.	I^-/thiosulphate	368
Thiouracils	Solution in NaOH, + BrO_3^- + HCl; 30–60 min/room temp.	+ excess arsenite and back titrated with BrO_3^- to *p*-ethoxychrysoidine	369
Phenols, e.g. *o*-cresol, 4-chloro-2-methyl-phenol, 2-methyl-phenoxyacetic acid	Solution in NaOH, + HCl, titrated with BrO_3^-/Br^- to yellow, then slight excess added; 30 sec/room temp.	I^-/thiosulphate	370
Unsaturation of petroleum distillates, purified gasolines, etc.	In $CHCl_3$ + bromine/methanol/NaBr; 20 min/room temp.	I^-/thiosulphate	371
Vinyl chloride in air	Absorbed in $CHCl_3$, bromine added; 40 min/room temp.	I^-/thiosulphate	372
Atoxyl (Na *p*-amino-phenylarsonate, $H_2N.C_6H_4.AsO_3HNa$)	In water, + BrO_3^-/Br^- + HCl; 10 min/room temp in dark	+ excess arsenite and back titrated with BrO_3^- to methyl orange	373
Various medicinals, e.g. purines, sulphon-amides, terpenes, esters of *p*-aminobenzoic acid	+ bromine/methanol/NaBr. Various reaction times/room temp. in dark	I^-/thiosulphate	374

Materials titrated	Reagent and reaction conditions	Subsequent treatment and final titration stage	Ref.
Salicylic acid	+ electrolytically generated bromine from HCl/KBr/$CuSO_4$ solution; 2 min/room temp.	Electrode polarity reversed and back titrated coulometrically with Cu(I) to amperometric end-point	375
α- and β-Diketones	BrO_3^-/Br^- + H_2SO_4 + $HgSO_4$ + sample	+ NaCl; I^-/thiosulphate	376
Precipitate with digitonin from determination of cholesterol	In methanol, + bromine/methanol/ NaBr	I^-/thiosulphate	377
Mixtures of aldoses and ketoses	+ bromine/water + acid at 100°, destroying the aldoses	Total sugars determined before and after bromine treatment, by titration with Cu(II) reagent	378
Olefine impurities in organic solvents (such as allyl alcohol, crotonaldehyde)	+ bromine/acetic acid; 3 min/0°	I^-/thiosulphate	379
p-Hydroxyhydrocinnamic acid	In water, + BrO_3^-/Br^- + H_2SO_4; 3 min/*ca* 0°	I^-/thiosulphate	380
Methyl and ethyl iodide from study of determination of methoxyl and ethoxyl groups by reaction with HI	Method of ref. 79		381, 399
2-Butyne-1,4-diol and other alkynols	Method of ref. 46		382
Many phenols (e.g. salicylic acid, β-naphthol, resorcinol) alkaloids and other bases (e.g. strychnine, quinine, codeine, novocaine, benzocaine, phenacetin), barbiturates and ascorbic acid	In acetic acid, + bromine/acetic acid; some + water; 10–80 min/room temp.	I^-/thiosulphate	383
Alkyl iodides from determination of lower alkoxyl groups by reaction with HI (semimicro and micro)	Method of ref. 79		384
Butyl iodide from determination of butoxyl groups by heating with HI	Method of ref. 79		385

Materials titrated	Reagent and reaction conditions	Subsequent treatment and final titration stage	Ref.
Phenols and their mixtures in aqueous solution	+ BrO_3^-/Br^- + H_2SO_4	I^-/thiosulphate	386
Monophenols	+ BrO_3^-/Br^- + HCl or H_2SO_4; 45 min/room temp.	I^-/thiosulphate	387
Urea	+ BrO_3^-/Br^- + HCl; 10 min/room temp., then + NaOH and 15 min/100°	+ acid; I^-/thiosulphate	388
Chloroprocaine	+ BrO_3^-/Br^- + HCl; 5 min/room temp.	I^-/thiosulphate	389
N-Methylaniline, in study of reaction with 2,4-dinitrofluorobenzene in 99·9% ethanol	Sample + benzene/conc. HCl; aqueous layer + small excess BrO_3^-/Br^-; 12 min/room temp.	I^-/thiosulphate	390
2,4-Dinitrophenol in presence of picric acid	+ *ca* 100% excess BrO_3^-/Br^- + HCl; 30 min/20–25° in dark	I^-/thiosulphate	391
Residual unsaturation in synthetic resins from allyl esters; also furfuryl alcohol	In CCl_4 + bromine/acetic acid/pyridine/H_2SO_4 + Hg acetate	I^-/thiosulphate	392
Isoniazid	+ BrO_3^-/Br^- + HCl (best 0·7–0·86N); 30 min/room temp.	I^-/thiosulphate	393
Some unsaturated hydrocarbons in air	Bubbled through ethanol + bromine/NaBr; 30 min/room temp. in dark	I^-/thiosulphate	394
Isoniazid	+ bromine/water, giving isonicotinic acid + HBr	Acid titrated with alkali to phenolphthalein	395
Phenothiazine derivatives	+ BrO_3^-/Br^- + HCl	I^-/thiosulphate	396
Phenol in presence of reducing substances	+ bromine water until solution red-brown, giving tribromophenyl hypobromite	Unreacted bromine removed with SO_3^{2-}, then phenol; + HCl + I^-, and after 10–15 min titrated with thiosulphate (see Iodides and hydriodic acid, ref. 175)	397

Materials titrated	Reagent and reaction conditions	Subsequent treatment and final titration stage	Ref.
Mixtures of alkylated phenols	+ BrO_3^-/Br^- + HCl; 5 sec–4 min, giving differing stoichiometric relations	I^-/thiosulphate	398
Phenols, cresols	+ BO_3^-/Br^- + 4–5M HCl; 4–5 min/room temp.	Unreacted bromine removed with excess SCN^- and unused SCN^- titrated coulometrically (oxidized to CN^- + SO_4^{2-})	400
Indole; indole-3-acetic acid; indole 3- α-butyric acid	Method of ref. 400		401
1-Methyl-2-mercaptoimidazole ('Methimazole', 'Tapazole' or 'Metothyrine')	In water, + BrO_3^-/Br^- + HCl; 15 min/room temp.	I^-/thiosulphate	402
Cu oxinate	+ H_2SO_4 + BrO_3^-/Br^-; 10 min/room temp.	+ tartrate, bringing to pH 6·2; then I^-/thiosulphate	403
Methyl iodide from determination of methoxyl groups by reaction with HI	Method of ref. 79		404
Urea	+ KBr + boric acid; at 50–60°, + OCl^- 2 min/50–60°	+ NaOH + thiosulphate equivalent to original OCl^- + drop KI and titrated with OCl^- to brasilin indicator (red changing to yellow-green)	405
Olefines	NaBr + BrO_3^-/Br^-/HCl/methanol/water + sample (also in water, methanol or other solvent); 1 min–3 h/room temp.	+ methanol; I^-/thiosulphate	406
Decamethylenebis (trimethylammonium iodide)	+ bromine/water/H_2SO_4; 10 min boiling, oxidizing I^- to IO_3^-	Unreacted bromine removed with phenol, then + I^- and titrated with thiosulphate	407
Diethyl stilbestrol	+ BrO_3^-/Br^- + HCl; 25 min/25–30° in dark	I^-/thiosulphate	408
its dipropionate ester	in acetic acid, + BrO_3^-/Br^- + H_2SO_4; 80–83 min/25–35°	I^-/thiosulphate	
Phenol	Method of ref. 3 (compared with gravimetric and a colorimetric method)		409

Materials titrated	Reagent and reaction conditions	Subsequent treatment and final titration stage	Ref.
Phenol in phenolates	$+ H_2SO_4 + BrO_3^-/Br^-$; 15–20 min/room temp. in dark	I^-/thiosulphate	410
Trifluoroethyl vinyl ether ('Fluoromar') in blood	Aspirated into bromine/methanol	I^-/thiosulphate	411
Ethylene, formed with ethyl iodide in determination of hydroxyethyl groups in low substituted starch ethers, by heating with HI	Passed through bromine/acetic acid/KBr	I^-/thiosulphate	412
Amines	$+ OBr^-$, giving bromoamines	Aspirated through KI/water/H_2SO_4, giving iodine; titrated with thiosulphate (see Iodides and hydriodic acid, ref. 183)	413
Methyl iodide from determination of methoxyl groups in essential oils by heating with HI	Method of ref. 79		414
Unsaturation, e.g. of cracked petroleum distillates	In CCl_4, + *ca* 60–70% excess bromine/CCl_4; 10, 20 and 30 min/0°	I^-/thiosulphate. Extrapolated to reaction time = 0	415
Bromine numbers of fats	In $CHCl_3$, + bromine/methanol/NaBr; 30 min up to 2 h/room temp. in dark (preferred to ICl method)	I^-/thiosulphate	416
Synestrol (diethylstilbestrol dipropionate)	In alcohol, $+ BrO_3^-/Br^-$ + acid; 15 min/8–10°	I^-/thiosulphate	417
Many phenols	In acetic acid with slight or 100% excess BrO_3^-/Br^-; 3 min/room temp.	I^-/thiosulphate	418
Nitrodichlorobenzene	$+ BrO_3^-/Br^-$ + acid	I^-/thiosulphate	419
Ethyl and butyl iodides from determination of ethoxyl and butoxyl groups in silicon organic compounds by heating with HI	Modification of method of ref. 294		420

Materials titrated	Reagent and reaction conditions	Subsequent treatment and final titration stage	Ref.
p-Coumaric acid	+ *ca* 3 times equational amount BrO_3^-/Br^- + HCl, 0·5–0·6N; 30 min/*ca* 40°, reacting with 12 atoms bromine	I^-/thiosulphate	421
Sugar	+ conc. NaOH + OBr^-. At least 4 min/room temp. or boiling (reacting with 2 or 6 equivalents respectively)	+ HCl; I^-/thiosulphate	422
Amine formed in determination of chloramphenicol by reduction with Zn/HCl	+ BrO_3^-/Br^- + acid; 2 min	I^-/thiosulphate	423
Alkyl iodides from submicro determination of lower alkoxyl groups by heating with HI	Principle of method of ref. 79		424
Vinyl methyl ketone	In water, + BrO_3^-/Br^- + HCl; 5 min/room temp.	I^-/thiosulphate	425
cis-β-Methoxy-α-ethoxymethyl-acrylonitrile	In acetic acid, + some pyridine + Hg acetate + bromine/acetic acid; 2 min/room temp.	I^-/thiosulphate	426
Furfuraldehyde in air	Passed into BrO_3^-/Br^- + HCl; 1 h/room temp.	I^-/thiosulphate	427, 450
p-Hydroxybenzoic acid from determination of its esters by hydrolysis with alkali	+ BrO_3^-/Br^- + acid	I^-/thiosulphate	428
p-Chlorophenyl-*p*-chlorobenzyl sulphide	In acetic acid, + bromine/acetic acid; 10 min/10°, oxidizing to sulphoxide	+ H_2SO_4; I^-/thiosulphate	429
Unsaturated barbiturates, e.g. ethyl crotonyl	In $CHCl_3$, + BrO_3^-/Br^- + HCl. Shaken, then 30 min/room temp. in dark	I^-/thiosulphate	430
4-Butyl-1,2-diphenyl-pyrazolidine-3,5-dione	In acetic acid, + BrO_3^-/Br^-	Unused bromine removed with aniline, I^- added and iodine formed titrated after 5 min with thiosulphate	431

Materials titrated	Reagent and reaction conditions	Subsequent treatment and final titration stage	Ref.
6-Mercaptopurine	In H_2SO_4 solution, + BrO_3^-; 15 min/room temp. in dark	I^-/thiosulphate	432
Phenol in pharmaceutical products	In water, + bromine/water + HCl; 30 min shaking, then 15 min standing, all at room temp.	+ $CHCl_3$; I^-/thiosulphate	433
2-Nitrodiphenylamine	In acetic acid/CCl_4, + BrO_3^-/Br^-	I^-/thiosulphate	434
Thiophosphoric acid from determination of its esters by alkali hydrolysis	+ BrO_3^-/Br^- + HCl; 15 min/room temp.	I^-/thiosulphate	435
Aldrin, isodrin	In acetic acid, + BrO_3^-/Br^- + HCl; 45 min/room temp. in dark	I^-/thiosulphate	436
Hydroquinone; quinhydrone	+ bromine/water until yellow; 30 sec/room temp.	Unreacted bromine removed with phenol, I^-/HCl added and titrated with thiosulphate after 15–20 min (see Iodides and hydriodic acid, ref. 193)	437
Aryloxysilanes; also phenols from acid hydrolysis of aryloxysilanes containing *tert*-butoxy groups	In acetic acid, + BrO_3^-/Br^- + HCl	I^-/thiosulphate	438
Free *o*- and *p*-positions in phenols	In acetic acid, + HCl, titrated with BrO_3^-/Br^- to yellow, then not over 10% excess added	I^-/thiosulphate	439
Higher alkyl ketene dimers	In CCl_4, + bromine/CCl_4; 30 sec/under 20°	I^-/thiosulphate	440
Some C_5 and C_6 olefines and dienes	In $CHCl_3$, + bromine/methanol/NaBr; 20 min/room temp.	I^-/thiosulphate	441
Salicylic acid from determination of the methyl ester by hydrolysis with NaOH	+ BrO_3^-/Br^- + HCl; 15 min/room temp. in dark	I^-/thiosulphate	442

Materials titrated	Reagent and reaction conditions	Subsequent treatment and final titration stage	Ref.
p-Hydroxyphenylalkylamines, e.g. Veritol, Paredrine (Pilsoton)	$+ BrO_3^- + H_2SO_4$	I^-/thiosulphate	443
Cystine, methionine	$+ BrO_3^-/Br^- + HCl$; 10 min/room temp.	I^-/thiosulphate	444
Cinnamic, *m*-coumaric acids	Method of ref. 421		445
Methyl iodide from submicro determination of methoxyl or *N*-methyl groups by heating with HI	Principle of method of ref. 79		446
Furfuraldehyde from determination of pentosans by heating with HCl	$+ BrO_3^-/Br^-$ + acid; 2 min/15–30°	+ Na acetate; I^-/thiosulphate	447
Furfuraldehyde and 5-hydroxymethylfurfuraldehyde from treatment of pentosans with acid (separated by partition between $CHCl_3$ and dilute HCl)	Method of ref. 447		448
1-(4-Hydroxyphenyl)-2-butylaminoethanol sulphate ('Vasculat')	$+ BrO_3^-/Br^- + HCl$; 2 min/room temp.	I^-/thiosulphate	449
Urea, thiourea	$+ BrO_3^-/Br^- + HCl$; 10 min/room temp., then + NaOH and 20 min boiling, giving CO_2, N_2 and SO_4^{2-}(with latter)	+ acid; I^-/thiosulphate	451
Phenols	+ bromine/acetic acid + pyridine catalyst; 2–20 min/room temp. (study of the number of atoms reacting)	I^-/thiosulphate (visual or biamperometric)	452
Bromine numbers of petroleum samples	+ n-heptane + dilute H_2SO_4, titrated with BrO_3^-/Br^- until upper layer distinctly yellow	I^-/thiosulphate	453
Salol; Nipagin A	+ electrolytically generated bromine from $HCl/KBr/CuSO_4$ solution	Electrode polarity reversed and back titrated coulometrically with Cu(I)	454

Materials titrated	Reagent and reaction conditions	Subsequent treatment and final titration stage	Ref.
HCHO, hexamine	+ BrO_3^- + HCl; 20 min/*ca* 100°	I^-/thiosulphate	455
β-Naphtholsulphonic acids, e.g. R-acid, Schäfer's acid	+ BrO_3^-/Br^- + acid. Not over 1–2 min/room temp.	I^-/thiosulphate	456
Dichlorodiethyl sulphide	+ BrO_3^-/Br^- + acid	I^-/thiosulphate	457
Alkyl iodides from determination of lower alkoxyl groups in silicon organic compounds	Method of ref. 79		458
Disulphides, sulphides (micro)	In acetic acid/water/HCl, + BrO_3^-/Br^-; 5 min/room temp., reacting with 10 and 4 bromine atoms respectively	I^-/thiosulphate	459
2,4-Dichloroaniline, unused from reaction with, in micro determination of anhydrides	In acetic acid, + BrO_3^-/Br^- + HCl; 5 min/room temp.	I^-/thiosulphate	459
Phenol in presence of reducing substances	+ large excess bromine/water; 20–30 min/room temp., giving tribromophenyl hypobromite	Unused bromine removed with SO_3^{2-}, then phenol; + HCl + I^- and after 15–20 min, titrated with thiosulphate (see Iodides and hydriodic acid, ref. 203)	460
Salicylic, acetylsalicylic acids	+ excess BrCl (from BrO_3^-/Br^- + conc. HCl) + HCl; 2 min/room temp.	I^-/thiosulphate	461
p-Hydroxybenzoic acid; also from determination of methyl ester by hydrolysis with alkali	+ bromine/water until brown	Unused bromine removed with SO_3^{2-} and phenol; + HCl + I^- and titrated with thiosulphate after *ca* 20 min	462
Antipyrine; phenol	+ BrCl (from BrO_3^-/Br^-/conc. HCl), yielding 4-bromoantipyrine and tribromophenol or tribromophenyl hypochlorite	(suggested analytical possibilities)	463
Oxalate	BrO_3^-/Br^- + acid, then + Na acetate and + sample	+ HCl and titrated with arsenite to I^-/starch	464

Materials titrated	Reagent and reaction conditions	Subsequent treatment and final titration stage	Ref.
Product from determination of Diamox by alkali hydrolysis	+ BrO_3^-/Br^- + HCl; 5 min/room temp.	I^-/thiosulphate	465
Crotonaldehyde	In water + BrO_3^-/Br^- + HCl; 3 min/0°	I^-/thiosulphate	466
Eg., Na salicylate	In water + BrO_3^-/Br^- + HCl; 10 min in dark	Titrated potentiometrically with hydrazine sulphate	467
Hexabarbital	+ BrCl (from BrO_3^-/Br^- + conc. HCl) + HCl; 5 min/room temp., adding to olefine linkage	I^-/thiosulphate	468
α,*β*-Unsaturated acids and salts (also from determination of esters by alkali hydrolysis)	Neutralized aliquot, + NaBr + bromine/methanol/NaBr in large excess; 5–60 min/room temp.	+ methanol; I^-/thiosulphate	469
Unsaturation in polypropylene glycol	+ bromine/CCl_4; 1 min/*ca* 0°	I^-/thiosulphate; + IO_3^- and retitrated with thiosulphate	470
Alkyl iodides from determination of methoxyl, ethoxyl and isopropoxyl groups in esters, ketals and silicon organic compounds by heating with HI	Principle of method of ref. 79		471
Cyanoacethydrazide	+ HCl + Br^- and titrated with BrO_3^- to first yellow; 20% excess added	I^-/thiosulphate	472
Diethylstilbestrol	In acetic acid, + BrO_3^-/Br^- + HCl; 20 ± 1 min/room temp. in dark	I^-/thiosulphate	473
Methyl + ethyl iodide from determination of methoxyl + ethoxyl groups by reaction with HI	Method of ref. 79		474
Phenol, cresols	+ HCl and titrated with BrO_3^-/Br^- until yellow; *ca* 20–25% extra added; 2 min/room temp.	I^-/thiosulphate	475
4-Methyluracil	In water, + bromine/water; 15 min/room temp.	Unused bromine boiled out, excess KOH added and back titrated with HCl	476

Materials titrated	Reagent and reaction conditions	Subsequent treatment and final titration stage	Ref.
Solasodine	In $CHCl_3$, + bromine/ acetic acid/pyridine/ $H_2SO_4/CHCl_3$	I^-/thiosulphate	477
Methyl iodide from determination of methoxyl groups in humic acid and its oxidation products, by heating with HI	Method of ref. 79		478
Vinyl acetate monomer	In dilute acetic acid, titrated with bromine/ acetic acid until yellow; slight excess added	I^-/thiosulphate	479
Isopropanol in mixtures with methanol, ethanol, acetone and n-propanol	+ BrO_3^-/Br^- + H_3PO_4; 1 h/40°, giving brominated acetone	+ I^-, left 15 min/90° (for complete reaction with the bromoacetone) and titrated with thiosulphate	480
Olefines from determination of diphenylethanol and 1-phenyl-1-(*p*-bromophenyl) ethanol by dehydration with acetic anhydride	+ bromine/acetic acid; 5 min/room temp. in the dark	I^-/thiosulphate	481
Unsaturated aldehydes, e.g. acrolein, crotonaldehyde, cinnamaldehyde	In ethanol, + BrCl (from BrO_3^-/Br^- + conc. HCl) until just yellow; 5 min/room temp.	I^-/thiosulphate	482
Maleic, fumaric acids (also latter after precipitation of former with Hg(II))	+ BrCl in at least 20% excess, + $HgSO_4$; 15 min/room temp. (2 or 6h respectively in absence of $HgSO_4$)	I^-/thiosulphate	483, 484, 498
Degree of unsaturation of saponified unsaturated polyesters	+ BrCl; 6 h	I^-/thiosulphate	485
Hexamine	+ BrO_3^- + HCl; 20–35 min/*ca* 100°, giving CO_2,H_2O and N_2	I^-/thiosulphate	486
Isoprene in the air of industrial areas	Absorbed in alcohol and small excess BrO_3^-/ Br^-/HCl added	I^-/thiosulphate	487

Materials titrated	Reagent and reaction conditions	Subsequent treatment and final titration stage	Ref.
Purines, like caffeine, 1-dihydroxypropyl-theobromine and 7-dihydroxypropyl-theophylline	+ BrO_3^-/Br^- + H_2SO_4; 30 min, 30 min and 5 h in dark respectively	I^-/thiosulphate	488
Phenols, aromatic amines	+ BrO_3^-/Br^- + acid	I^-/thiosulphate potentiometrically	489
Phenol in water in presence of reducing substances	Solution neutralized to methyl red, + bromine water; 20 min	+ Na_2SO_3 until yellow, then + phenol to remove excess bromine; + I^-/HCl and titrated after 15 min with thiosulphate	490
Lead tetraethyl in benzene	+ bromine/CCl_4 until solution brown for 5 min; + methanol until precipitate dissolved; boiled, KOH added to remove bromine, slight excess water added and boiled 5 min	+ excess EDTA + NH_4OH/NH_4Cl buffer and back titrated with $ZnSO_4$ to eriochrome black T	491
Anthracene	In acetic acid, + bromine/acetic acid; 30 min/room temp. in dark, giving 9,10-dibromoanthracene	I^-/thiosulphate	492
Pyrrole	In acetic acid/water, 1:1, + bromine/acetic acid; 40–60 min/room temp.	I^-/thiosulphate	493
Urea, biuret	BrO_3^-/Br^- + HCl; after 5 min, K_2HPO_4 and sample added; 30 min/room temp., giving CO_2,H_2O and N_2	I^-/thiosulphate	494
Diethylstilbestrol; dienestrol	Solution in alkali, + BrO_3^-/Br^- + H_2SO_4; 25 ± 2 min or 15 ± 1 min/room temp. in the dark respectively	I^-/thiosulphate	495
Diethylstilbestrol propionate	In acetic acid, + BrO_3^-/Br^- + H_2SO_4; 80–83 min in the dark, giving the dibromo derivative	I^-/thiosulphate	496

Materials titrated	Reagent and reaction conditions	Subsequent treatment and final titration stage	Ref.
Hydroquinine in presence of quinine	In HCl, + methanol + bromine solution; 10 min/20° in the dark	+ methanol; I^-/thiosulphate	497
Thiourea	+ excess OBr^- + NaOH; 1 h/room temp.	+ H_2SO_4; I^-/thiosulphate	499
Thioacetamide	Method of ref. 499		500
($CH_3CSNH_2 + 4\ OBr^- + 2\ OH^- \rightarrow CH_3COO^- + SO_4^{2-} + 4\ Br^- + NH_4^+$)			
1-Naphthylamine-5-sulphonic acid	+ BrO_3^-/Br^- + HCl; 15–20 min	I^-/thiosulphate	501
Esculoside	+ BrO_3^-/Br^- + acid, giving the dibromide	I^-/thiosulphate	502
Unsaturated hydrocarbons, aldehydes, ketones, acids, alcohols, etc.; iodine numbers of oils and fats; ascorbic acid	+ BrO_3^-/Br^- + HCl + CCl_4; some + ammonium molybdate or Hg acetate catalysts; up to 20 h/room temp.	I^-/thiosulphate	503
Enol contents of acetoacetic esters	Added to 5% bromine/methanol at − 50° (also added after standing in various solvents)	Immediately + 10% β-naphthol/methanol; then I^-/thiosulphate (see Iodides and hydriodic acid, ref. 238)	504
Cyclohexanone oxime	Phosphoric acid/H_2SO_4 + BrO_3^- + sample in acetic acid; 5 min, converting via bromonitroso- to the bromonitrocyclohexane	I^-/thiosulphate biamperometrically	505
Condensation products of phenols with HCHO (determination of bromine uptake giving a measure of the degree of polymerization)	+ BrO_3^-/Br^- + HCl; 40 min	I^-/thiosulphate	506
Formate	+ BrCl/HCl (from BrO_3^-/Br^-/conc. HCl); 1 min, then + NaOH/acetate buffer; (optimum pH 4·2–6); 5 min/room temp.	I^-/thiosulphate	507
($HCOO^- + BrCl + OH^- \rightarrow H_2O + CO_2 + Br^- + Cl^-$; undissociated HCOOH reacts only slowly)			

Materials titrated	Reagent and reaction conditions	Subsequent treatment and final titration stage	Ref.
Urea	+ BrO_3^-/Br^- + H_2SO_4 + molybdate; 5 min/room temp.	I^-/thiosulphate	508
Procaine in partly hydrolysed form	+ H_2SO_4 + BrO_3^-/Br^-; 5 min/room temp.	I^-/thiosulphate	509
Phenols, e.g. sulphosalicylic acid	+ electrolytically generated bromine in presence of Cu(II)	Back titrated with Cu(I) by reversing polarity	510
Si–H and –Si–C_6H_5 groups	+ bromine/acetic acid; at room temp. for the former, with heating for the latter $-Si-C_6H_5 + Br_2 \rightarrow -SiBr + C_6H_5Br$	I^-/thiosulphate	511
Acenaphthylene in presence of styrene and acenaphthene	In chloroform, + bromine/methanol/NaBr; 10 min in dark	I^-/thiosulphate	512
Olefines from determination of tertiary alcohols by reaction with acetic acid/H_2SO_4	+ BrO_3^-/Br^-; 5 min	I^-/thiosulphate	513
Olefines from determination of ethers of 1, 1-diphenylethanol and its derivatives, by reaction with acetic acid/H_2SO_4	+ BrO_3^-/Br^-; 5 min	I^-/thiosulphate	514
Methyl iodide from determination of methoxyl groups in polymers and copolymers	Method of ref. 79		515
Reineckates, precipitated in determination of reserpine and kamamycin	+ hot Fehlings B solution + Br^- + conc. HCl and titrated with BrO_3^- until yellow; 15 sec	I^-/thiosulphate	516
Total unsaturation of oils and fatty acids	Method of ref. 40 with reagent in 2–2·5-fold excess		517
Urea	In water, + bromine + saturated borax solution; 1 h	+ I^- + HCl; thiosulphate	518

Materials titrated	Reagent and reaction conditions	Subsequent treatment and final titration stage	Ref.
2-Ethyl-3-methylbut-2-en-1-al in presence of 2-methylvaleraldehyde	In methanol or ethanol, + BrCl (from $BrO_3^-/Br^-/$ conc. HCl) until yellow; 5 min	I^-/thiosulphate	519
Formates	Neutral solution + excess BrO_3^-, boiled, bromine/KBr added until yellow, then excess added; boiled 3–5 min (evidently to expel unreacted bromine)	$+ I^- + H_2SO_4$; thiosulphate	520
Mercuriacetic acid + mercuric acetate	+ HCl + bromine/water	Excess bromine removed by heating, cooled, $NH_4OH + SO_3^{2-}$ added and titrated with Na mercaptoacetate to thiofluorescein	521
1-(5-Tetrazolyl)-4-guanyltetrazene hydrate ($C_2H_8N_{10}O$)	$+ BrO_3^- + H_2SO_4 +$ water; 30 min/room temp, then 15 min boiling	Cooled and titration completed with BrO_3^-	522
Ethyl formate from determination of ethyl orthoformate by reaction with acetic acid	Method of ref. 507		523
p-Hydroxypropiophenone in Frenantol H-305 tablets	In dilute HCl, $+ BrO_3^-/Br^-$; 10 min, giving dibromo derivative	I^-/thiosulphate	524
Unsaturation of rubber	In CCl_4, $CHCl_3$ or benzene, + liquid bromine; 2 h in dark	+ NaOH until bromine colour gone, dibromide precipitated with hexane, ignited and Br^- determined by titration with $Hg(NO_3)_2$ solution	525
Aromatic thioureas	In water or acetic acid/water, + HCl + BrO_3^-/Br; 20-30 min, oxidizing to ureas + H_2SO_4 (results not always theoretical)	I^-/thiosulphate	526
Dihydrochlorothiazide	In NaOH, $+ BrO_3^-/Br^-$ + HCl; 10 min	I^-/thiosulphate	527
Alkyl iodides from determination of alkoxyl groups by reaction with HI	Method of ref. 79		528

Materials titrated	Reagent and reaction conditions	Subsequent treatment and final titration stage	Ref.
Lead tetraethyl in gasoline	+ bromine/CCl_4 until bromine colour persisted over 2 min	+ HNO_3, aqueous layer freed from excess bromine and Pb^{2+} ultimately titrated with EDTA to eriochrome black T	529
Methyl iodide from determination of methoxyl groups in certain poly-functional derivatives of xylitol and sorbitol	Method of ref. 79		530
Mono- and disubstituted hydrazines	In HCl/water + Br^-/BrO_3^-; 10 min, 1 mole hydrazine reacting with 4Br	I^-·thiosulphate	531
Rubber hydrocarbons	In benzene + Na_2MoO_4/HCl/acetic acid + BrO_3^-/Br^-; 100 min in dark	+ I^- + borax; excess thiosulphate added after 5 min, then back titrated with iodine after further 5 min	532
Rubber in vegetative parts of hevea brasiliensis	Method of ref. 532		533
Monomer residue in copolymers of vinyl acetate with 2-ethyl hexylacrylate	In 70% acetic acid, + Na acetate + bromine/acetic acid; 40–48 h/room temp.	I^-/thiosulphate	534
(gave total monomers; vinyl acetate alone determined by direct titration with bromine)			
Cholesterol; β-sitosterol	In $CHCl_3$ + bromine/acetic acid; 30 min	I^-/thiosulphate	535
Sorbic acid	Neutralized solution + bromine/CCl_4	I^-/thiosulphate	536
Theophylline, caffeine, theobromine	+ Br^-/BrO_3^-/H_2SO_4; 30 min in dark (empirical factor gave total)	I^-/thiosulphate	537
m-Aminophenol from *p*-aminosalicylic acid by decarboxylation in dilute H_2SO_4	Aliquot of solution + Br^-/BrO_3^-/H_2SO_4; 20 min	I^-/thiosulphate; also removed excess bromine with SO_3^{2-}, distilled NH_3 into excess HCl and back titrated with NaOH to methyl red	538
Phenol, after separation from resorcinol by steam distillation	+ BrO_3^-/Br^- + HCl; 15 min in dark	+ I^- and titrated with thiosulphate after 5 min	539

Materials titrated	Reagent and reaction conditions	Subsequent treatment and final titration stage	Ref.
Phenol + resorcinol	In water, + BrO_3^-/Br^- + HCl; 15 min/0° (resorcinol alone determined with excess iodine)	I^-/thiosulphate	540
HCHO + HCOOH in presence of methanol	$BrO_3^-/Br^-/H_2SO_4$ mixture left 30 min, then + NaOH + sample; 15 min	+ water + I^- + H_2SO_4 and titrated with thiosulphate	541
Cholesterol	In $CHCl_3$ + BrO_3^-/Br^- + 20%HCl; 3–5 min	I^-/thiosulphate	542
Unreacted *m*-toluidine, steam distilled from reaction mixture in determination of diazonium salts	+ $BrO_3^-/Br^-/HCl$	I^-/thiosulphate	543
Aromatic or heterocyclic sulphides	In acetic acid + HCl, + BrO_3^-/Br^-	I^-/thiosulphate	544
p-Aminophenol; metol	In dilute H_2SO_4, + bromine/water until yellow; 10–20 min (reacted to yield quinone + NH_3)	Unreacted bromine removed with phenol, then + I^- and titrated with thiosulphate after 15 min; also + excess SO_3^{2-}, SO_2 boiled out, made alkaline, NH_3 distilled into excess HCl and back titrated with NaOH to methyl red	545

References

1. Knop, W., *Zentralblatt* 321, 403, 499 (1854).
2. Reymann, S., *Ber.* **8**, 790 (1875).
3. Koppeschaar, W. F., *Z. anal. Chem.* **15**, 233 (1876).
4. Allen, A. H., *Analyst* **6**, 177 (1881).
5. Quinquand, E., *Moniteur scientifique* **23**, 641, abstracted in *Z. anal. Chem.* **21**, 607 (1882).
6. Mills, E. and Snodgrass, *J. Soc. Chem. Ind.* (*London*) **2**, 435 (1883).
7. Hamburger, H. T., *Rec. trav. chim.* **2**, 181 (1883).
8. Mills, E. and Akitt, *J. Soc. Chem. Ind.* (*London*) **3**, 366 (1884).
9. McIlhiney, P. C., *J. Am. Chem. Soc.* **16**, 275 (1894).
10. Freyer, F., *Chem.-Ztg.* **20**, 820 (1896).
11. Ditz, H., *Z. angew. Chem.* **13**, 1051 (1900).
12. Zdarek, E., *Z. anal. Chem.* **41**, 228 (1902).

13. Stritar, M. J. and Zeidler, H., *Z. anal. Chem.* **43**, 396 (1904).
14. Lloyd, S. J., *J. Am. Chem. Soc.* **27**, 16 (1905).
15. Rupp, E., *Arch. Pharm.* **243**, 69 (1905).
16. Rupp, E., *Arch. Pharm.* **243**, 98 (1905).
17. Telle, F., *J. pharm. chim.* **21**, 111 (1905).
18. Mossler, *Z. allgem. österr. Apoth.-Verein* **45**, 223, 235, 251, 267, 283, 299 (1907).
19. Joseph, A. F., *J. Soc. Chem. Ind.* (*London*) **29**, 1189 (1910).
20. Vaubel, W., *Z. angew. Chem.* **23**, 2078 (1910).
21. de Jong, A. W. K., *Rec. trav. chim.* **30**, 223 (1911).
22. Klimont, I. J. and Neumann, W., *Pharm. Post* **44**, 587 (1911).
23. Meyer, K. H. and Kappelmeier, P., *Ber.* **44**, 2718 (1911).
24. Meyer, K. H., *Ann.* **380**, 212 (1911).
25. Pence, C. M., *J. Ind. Eng. Chem.* **3**, 820 (1911).
26. Lagrange, A., abstract in *Z. anal. Chem.* **51**, 264 (1912).
27. Mäder, H., *Deut. Apotheker-Ztg.* **27**, 746 (1912).
28. Redman, L. V., Werth, A. J. and Buck, F. P., *Ind. Eng. Chem.* **5**, 389 (1913).
29. Golse, J., *Bull. soc. pharm., Bordeaux* **56**, 186 (1919); *J. pharm. chim.* (7) **19**, 20 (1919).
30. Fox, J. J. and Barker, M. F., *J. Soc. Chem. Ind.* (*London*) **39**, 169T (1920).
31. Kolthoff, I. M., *Pharm. Weekblad* **58**, 699 (1921).
32. Dieckmann, W., *Ber.* **55**, 2470 (1922).
33. Johansen, E. M., *Ind. Eng. Chem.* **14**, 288 (1922).
34. Kaufmann, H. P., *Ann.* **429**, 247 (1922).
35. Francis, A. W. and Hill, A. J., *J. Am. Chem. Soc.* **46**, 2498 (1924).
36. Manchot, W. and Oberhauser, F., *Z. Untersuch. Nahr. u. Genussm.* **47**, 261 (1924).
37. Pohorecka-Lelesz, B., *Bull. soc. chim. biol.* **6**, 773 (1924).
38. Povarnin, G. G. and Belikova, A. V., *J. Russ. Phys.-Chem. Soc.* **55**, 226 (1924).
39. Powell, W. J. and Whittaker, H., *J. Soc. Chem. Ind.* (*London*) **43**, 35T (1924).
40. Rosenmund, K. W., *Z. angew. Chem.* **37**, 58 (1924).
41. Dobryanski, A. F., *Petroleum Domain* 574 (1925).
42. Goldschmidt, S. and Steigenwald, C., *Ber.* **58**, 1350 (1925).
43. Golse, J., *Bull. soc. chim. biol.* **7**, 167 (1925).
44. Kolthoff, I. M., *Chem. Weekblad* **22**, 558 (1925).
45. Francis, A. W., *Ind. Eng. Chem.* **18**, 821, 1095 (1926).
46. Kaufmann, H. P., *Z. Untersuch. Lebensm.* **51**, 3 (1926).
47. Turek, O., *Chem. Obzor* **1**, 295 (1926).
48. Ulrich, F. and Kather, K., *Z. angew. Chem.* **39**, 229 (1926).
49. Gränacher, C. and Wolf, G., *Helv. Chim. Acta* **10**, 815 (1927).

50. Järvinen, K. K., *Z. anal. Chem.* **71**, 108 (1927); **73**, 446 (1928).
51. Linstead, R. P., *J. Chem. Soc.* 355 (1927).
52. Linstead, R. P. and Mann, J. T. W., *J. Chem. Soc.* 723 (1927).
53. del Mundo, S., *Phillipine J. Sci.* **33**, 363 (1927).
54. Oberhauser, F. and Heusinger, W., *Z. anorg. u. allgem. Chem.* **160**, 366 (1927).
55. Orton, K. J. P. and Bradfield, A. E., *J. Chem. Soc.* 983 (1927).
56. Rhodes, F. H., Jayme, D. W. and Bivins, F. H., *Ind. Eng. Chem.* **19**, 804 (1927).
57. Vaubel, W., *Z. angew. Chem.* **40**, 1143 (1927).
58. Bacon, F. S., *Ind. Eng. Chem.* **20**, 970 (1928).
59. Buxton, J. and Lucas, H. J., *J. Am. Chem. Soc.* **50**, 249 (1928).
60. Day, A. R. and Taggart, W. T., *Ind. Eng. Chem.* **20**, 545 (1928).
61. Furia, A., *Boll. soc. chim., Sao Paulo* **1**, 15 (1928).
62. Hansen, A., *Dansk Tids. Farm.* **12**, 89, 112 (1928).
63. Volmar, Y. and Samdahl, B., *J. pharm. chim.* **7**, 106 (1928).
64. Cortese, F., *Rec. trav. chim.* **48**, 564 (1929).
65. Hart, L., *J. Assoc. Offic. Agr. Chem.* **12**, 296 (1929).
66. Kullgren, C. and Tydén, H., *Ing. Vetenskaps Akad. Handl.* No. 94, 3 (1929).
67. Rosin, P. and Just, H., *Z. angew. Chem.* **42**, 965, 984, 1002 (1929).
68. Yushkevish, S., *Masloboino-Zhirovoe Delo* **45**, 39 (1929).
69. Bolton, E. R. and Williams, K. A., *Analyst* **55**, 5 (1930).
70. Buckwalter, H. M. and Wagner, E. C., *J. Am. Chem. Soc.* **52**, 5241 (1930).
71. Catlin, L. J. and Starrett, J. E., *Refiner Natural Gasoline Mfr.* **9**, No. 7, 155 (1930).
72. Dillon, R. T., Young, W. G. and Lucas, H. J., *J. Am. Chem. Soc.* **52**, 1953 (1930).
73. Harris, M., *J. Assoc. Offic. Agr. Chem.* **13**, 364 (1930).
74. Heim, G., *Bull. soc. chim. Belg.* **39**, 458 (1930).
75. Levenson, H., *Ind. Eng. Chem., Anal. Ed.* **2**, 246 (1930).
76. van der Meulen, J. H., *Chem. Weekblad* **27**, 550 (1930).
77. Sasaki, K., *J. Agr. Chem. Soc., Japan* **6**, 538 (1930).
78. Travers, A. and Avenet, *Compt. rend.* **190**, 875 (1930).
79. Vieböck, F. and Schwappach, A., *Ber.* **63**, 2818 (1930).
80. Vieböck, F. and Brecher, C., *Ber.* **63**, 3207 (1930).
81. Davis, H. S., Crandall, G. S. and Higbee, W. E., *Ind. Eng. Chem., Anal. Ed.* **3**, 108 (1931).
82. Ellington, O. C. and Beard, H. G., *J. Soc. Chem. Ind. (London)* **50**, 151T (1931).
83. Feist, K. and Klatt, F., *Pharm. Ztg.* **76**, 112 (1931).
84. Grant, E. H., *J. Assoc. Offic. Agr. Chem.* **14**, 351 (1931).
85. Hart, L., *J. Assoc. Offic. Agr. Chem.* **14**, 330 (1931).

86. Kulskaya, O. A., *Ukrain. Khim. Zhur.* **6**, Sci. pt. 1 (1931).
87. Myung, C.-W., *Folio Pharm. Jap.* **12**, No. 3, 417 (1931).
88. Pöll, H., *Petroleum Z.*, **27**, 817 (1931).
89. Rosenthaler, L., *Pharm. Acta Helv.* **6**, 179 (1931).
90. Rosenthaler, L., *Pharm. Acta Helv.* **6**, 209 (1931).
91. Scott, R. D., *Ind. Eng. Chem., Anal. Ed.* **3**, 67 (1931).
92. Bruckner, V., *Mikrochemie* **12**, 153 (1932).
93. Bruylants, P., *Bull. soc. chim. Belg.* **41**, 309 (1932).
94. Casimir, E. E. and Dimitriu, M., *Inst. Géol. Roumanie, Compt. rend.* **21**, 241 (1932-3).
95. Clark, E. P., *J. Assoc. Offic. Agr. Chem.* **15**, 136 (1932).
96. Corfield, C. E. and Mundy, C. M., *Quart. J. Pharm. and Pharmacol.* **5**, 504 (1932).
97. Fiyalkov, Ya. and Yampolskaya, M., *Farm. Zhur.* 13 (1932).
98. Kolthoff, I. M. and Lingane, J. J., *Pharm. Weekblad* **69**, 1147 (1932).
99. Rosenberger, N. A., Rebinovich, R. V. and Frenkel, K. Ya., *Trans. All-Union Sci. Research Inst. Paper Cellulose No. 1* 109 (1932).
100. Rosenthaler, L., *Pharm. Acta Helv.* **7**, 45 (1932).
101. Rosenthaler, L., *Pharm. Acta Helv.* **7**, 223 (1932).
102. Sampey, J. R., Slagle, K. H. and Reid, E. E., *J. Am. Chem. Soc.* **54**, 3401 (1932).
103. Slotta, K. H. and Haberland, G., *Ber.* **65**, 127 (1932).
104. v. Szelényi, G., *Z. Untersuch. Lebensm.* **63**, 534 (1932).
105. Bonicatti, M., *Boll. ufficiale. staz. sper. seta* **3**, 66 (1933).
106. Carol, J., *J. Assoc. Offic. Agr. Chem.* **16**, 384 (1933).
107. Iddles, H. A. and Robbins, P. J., *Ind. Eng. Chem., Anal. Ed.* **5**, 55 (1933).
108. Källström, E., *Pharm. Zentralhalle* **74**, 269 (1933).
109. Rostovtzeva, E. and Gofman, E., *Anilinokrasochnaya Prom.* **3**, 457 (1933).
110. Shemyakin, M. M., *Anilinokrasochnaya Prom.* **3**, 403 (1933).
111. Spitzer, L., *Chem.-Ztg.* **57**, 224 (1933).
112. Száhlender, K., *Magyar Gyógyszerésztud. Társaság Értesitöje* **9**, 135 (1933).
113. Száhlender, K., *Pharm. Monatsh.* **14**, 281 (1933).
114. Vignoli, L., *Bull. soc. pharmacol.* **40**, 344 (1933).
115. Baernstein, H. D., *J. Biol. Chem.* **106**, 451 (1934).
116. Beukema-Goudsmit, M., *Pharm. Weekblad* **71**, 380 (1934).
117. Fleck, H. R., Greenane, F. J. and Ward, A. M., *Analyst* **59**, 325 (1934).
118. Hoshall, E. M., Grove, D. C. and Jenkins, G. L., *J. Am. Pharm. Assoc.* **23**, 118 (1934).
119. Hughes, E. E. and Acree, S. F., *Ind. Eng. Chem., Anal. Ed.* **6**, 123 (1934).
120. Hughes, E. E. and Acree, S. F., *Ind. Eng. Chem., Anal. Ed.* **6**, 292 (1934).
121. Krishnan, T. S., *J. Indian Chem. Soc.* **11**, 651 (1934).
122. Nanji, H. R., *Analyst* **59**, 96 (1934).

123. Shcherbachev, K. D., *Khim. Farm. Prom.* **5**, 37 (1934).
124. Shcherbachev, K. D., *Anilinokrasnochaya Prom.* **4**, 562 (1934).
125. Skhodtzev, S. T., *Zhur. Priklad Khim.* (*J. Appl. Chem. USSR*) **7**, 605 (1934).
126. Száhlender, K., *Magyar Gyógyszerésztud. Társaság Értesitöje* **10**, 52 (1934).
127. Vorozhtzov, N. N., *Anilinokrasochnaya Prom.* **4**, 166 (1934).
128. Casimir, E. E. and Dimitriu, M., *Petroleum Z.* **31**, No. 33, 1 (1935).
129. Castiglioni, A., *Ann. chim. applicata.* **25**, 236 (1935).
130. Cook, S. G., *Ind. Eng. Chem., Anal Ed..* **7**, 250 (1935).
131. Fedorov, B. P. and Spryskov, A. A., *Anilinokrasochnaya Prom.* **5**, 143 (1935).
132. Gibson, D. T. and Caulfield, T. H., *J. Chem. Soc.* 1419 (1935).
133. Jenkins, G. L. and Dunker, M. F. W., *J. Am. Pharm. Assoc.* **24**, 840 (1935).
134. Mulliken, S. P. and Wakeman, R. L., *Ind. Eng. Chem., Anal. Ed.* **7**, 59 (1935).
135. Berezova, M. K., *Hig. Truda* **14**, No. 3, 72 (1936).
136. Fedorov, B. P. and Spryskov, A. A., *Org. Chem. Ind.* (*USSR*) **2**, 101 (1936).
137. Gal'pern, G. D. and Vinogradova, J. V., *Neftyanoe Khoz.* **1**, 59 (1936).
138. Hartner, F. and Schleiss, E., *Mikrochemie* **20**, 163 (1936).
139. Litvak, I. M., *Sovet Sakhar* **14**, No. 11, 40 (1936).
140. Melamed, F. and Gofman E., *Org. Chem. Ind* (*USSR*) **1**, 616 (1936).
141. Skvirskaya, V. M., *Org. Chem. Ind.* (*USSR*) **1**, 163 (1936).
142. White, E. V. and Wright, G. F., *Can. J. Research* **14**, 427 (1936).
143. Ardashev, B. I., *Zhur. Priklad Khim.* (*J. Appl. Chem., USSR*) **10**, 1032 (1937); *Trudy Ural Ind. Inst. im S. M. Kirova* No. 6, 70 (1938).
144. Epler, W. N., *Refiner Natural Gasoline Mfr.* **16**, 83 (1937).
145. Frieman, R. H., Kennedy, E. R. and Lucas, H. J., *J. Am. Chem. Soc.* **59**, 723 (1937).
146. Gal'pern, G. D. and Vinogradova, E. V., *Khim. Tverdovo Topliva* **8**, 384 (1937).
147. Hammick, D. Ll. and Langrish, D., *J. Chem. Soc.* 797 (1937).
148. Hughes, E. E. and Acree, S. F., *Ind. Eng. Chem., Anal. Ed.* **9**, 318 (1937).
149. Kaufmann, H. P. and Hartweg, L., *Ber.* **70**, 2554 (1937).
150. Khaletskii, A. M. and Mikryukova, N. S., *Farmatsiya i Farmakol* (*SSSR*) No. 8, 21 (1937).
151. Schulek, E. and Boldizár, I., *Z. anal. Chem.* **108**, 396 (1937).
152. Schwicker, A., *Z. anal. Chem.* **110**, 161 (1937).
153. Sliva, V., *Plyn, Voda, zdravotní tech.* **17**, 9 (1937).
154. Szegedy, E., *Z. anal. Chem.* **109**, 95, 316 (1937).
155. Wessel, F. W. and Keszler, M. R., *Ber. ungar. pharm. Ges.* **13**, 161 (1937).

156. Cooper, S. R. and Barnes, R. P., *Ind. Eng. Chem., Anal. Ed.* **10**, 379 (1938).
157. Cuthill, R. and Atkins, C., *J. Soc. Chem. Ind. (London)* **57**, 89 (1938).
158. Furter, M., *Helv. Chim. Acta* **21**, 1144, 1151 (1938).
159. Gordon, B. and Dakhnov, V., *Neftyanoe Khoz.* **19**, No. 9, 53 (1938).
160. Juhlin, O., *Z. anal. Chem.* **113**, 339 (1938).
161. Khaletskii, A. M. and Yanovitskaya, A. M., *Farmatsiya i Farmakol. (SSSR)* No. 1, 17 (1938).
162. Kinsman, S. and Noller, C. R., *Ind. Eng. Chem., Anal. Ed.* **10**, 424 (1938).
163. Kälin, A., *Pharm. Acta Helv.* **13**, 488 (1938).
164. Litvak, I., *Spirto-Vodochn. Prom.* **15**, No. 2, 7 (1938).
165. Lobunets, N. N., *Zavodskaya Lab.* **7**, 872 (1938).
166. Lucas, H. J. and Pressman, D., *Ind. Eng. Chem., Anal. Ed.* **10**, 140 (1938).
167. Nassi, L., *Diagnostica tec. lab. (Napoli), Riv. mens.* **9**, 161 (1938).
168. Reimers, F., *Dansk Tids. Farm.* **12**, 203 (1938).
169. Rossi, O. A., *Rev. centro estud. farm. bioquím.* **28**, 60 (1938).
170. Thomas, C. L., Black, H. S. and Hoekstra, J., *Ind. Eng. Chem., Anal. Ed.* **10**, 153 (1938).
171. Trappe, W., *Biochem. Z.* **296**, 174, 180 (1938).
172. Valencien, C. and Deshusses, J., *Mitt. Lebensm. Hyg.* **29**, 119 (1938).
173. Baranov, N. B., *Zavodskaya Lab.* **8**, 931 (1939).
174. Belenit'ska, D. S., *Ukrain. Gosudarst. Inst. Eksptl. Farm. (Kharkov), Konsul'attsionye Materialy* No. 2, 44 (1939).
175. Christensen, B. E., Hansen, E. and Cheldelin, J. H., *Ind. Eng. Chem., Anal. Ed.* **11**, 114 (1939).
176. Clark, E. P., *J. Assoc. Offic. Agr. Chem.* **22**, 109, 622 (1939).
177. Elek, A., *Ind. Eng. Chem., Anal. Ed.* **11**, 174 (1939).
178. Fertman, G. and Rodzevich, V., *Spirto-Vodochnaya Prom.* **16**, No. 7, 40 (1939).
179. Hallsworth, E. G., *J. Soc. Chem. Ind. (London)* **58**, 357 (1939).
180. Hoshall, E. M., *J. Assoc. Offic. Agr. Chem.* **22**, 748 (1939).
181. Lobunets, M. M., *Univ. état. Kiev, Bull. sci., Recueil chim.* No. 4, 23, 41 (1939).
182. Osanov, B. P. and Zarakovskaya, I., *Lesokhimicheskaya Prom.* No. 12, 27 (1939).
183. Peniston, Q. P. and Hibbert, H., *Paper Trade J.* **109**, No. 17, 46 (1939).
184. Pressman, D. and Lucas, H. J., *J. Am. Chem. Soc.* **61**, 2271 (1939).
185. Reznitskaya, T. V., *Org. Chem. Ind. (USSR)* **6**, 666 (1939).
186. Valencien, C. and Deshusses, J., *Mitt. Lebensm. Hyg.* **30**, 246 (1939).
187. Hughes, E. E. and Acree, S. F., *J. Research Natl. Bur. Standards* **24**, 175 (1940).
188. Johnson, P. R., Barnes, H. M. and McElvain, S. M., *J. Am. Chem. Soc.* **62**, 969 (1940).

189. Kaufmann, H. P., *Fette u. Seifen* **47**, 4 (1940).
190. Lewis, J. B. and Bradstreet, R. B., *Ind. Eng. Chem., Anal. Ed.* **12**, 387 (1940).
191. Pedinelli, M. and Pessarelli, V., *Boll. sci. fac. chim. ind., Bologna* 99 (1940).
192. Seaman, J. W., Norton, A. R. and Mason, R. W., *Ind. Eng. Chem., Anal. Ed.* **12**, 345 (1940).
193. Semenov, S. N. and Zaliopa, M., *Masloboino-Zhirovskoe Delo* **16**, No. 3, 20 (1940).
194. Sol'ts, L. M. and Kolik, E. M., *Ukrain. Gosudarst. Inst. Eksptl. Farm. (Kharkov), Konsul'tatsionye Materialy* No. 5, 162 (1940).
195. Songina, A. O., *Nauch.-Information Byull. Tsentral. Nauch.-Issledovatel. Aptechnovo Inst. GAPU, Norkamzdrava RSFSR* **4**, No. 12. 10 (1940).
196. Bell, R. T. and Agruss, M. S., *Ind. Eng. Chem., Anal. Ed.* **13**, 297 (1941).
197. Bielenberg, W., Goldhahn, H. and Zoff, A., *Öl u. Kohle* **37**, 496 (1941).
198. Christensen, B. E., Friedman, L. and Sato, Y., *Ind. Eng. Chem., Anal. Ed.* **13**, 276 (1941).
199. Deshusses, J., *Mitt. Lebensm. Hyg.* **32**, 176 (1941).
200. Fleury, P. and Courtois, J., *Ann. chim. anal. chim. appl.* **23**, 117 (1941).
201. Francis, A. W. and Hill, A. J., *Ind. Eng. Chem., Anal. Ed.* **13**, 357 (1941).
202. Green, S. J., *J. Inst. Petroleum* **27**, 66 (1941).
203. Jayme, G. and Sarten, P., *Biochem. Z.* **308**, 109 (1941).
204. Jordan, C. W., *J. Am. Chem. Soc.* **63**, 2687 (1941).
205. Lazzari, G., *Ann. chim. applicata* **31**, 266 (1941).
206. Reimers, F., *Z. anal. Chem.* **122**, 404 (1941).
207. Schretter, O., *Z. anal. Chem.* **122**, 24 (1941).
208. Soloveichik, L. and Alekseev, P., *J. Chem. Ind. (USSR)* **18**, No. 21, 26 (1941).
209. Sprung, M. M., *Ind. Eng. Chem., Anal. Ed.* **13**, 35 (1941).
210. Wells, E. H., *J. Assoc. Offic. Agr. Chem.* **24**, 736 (1941).
211. Bailey, A. J., *Ind. Eng. Chem., Anal. Ed.* **14**, 181 (1942).
212. Castiglioni, A., *Z. anal. Chem.* **123**, 405 (1942).
213. Conway, H. S., *J. Assoc. Offic. Agr. Chem.* **25**, 791 (1942).
214. Gettler, A. O. and Umberger, C. J., *J. Biol. Chem.* **143**, 633 (1942).
215. Poethke, W., *Pharm. Zentralhalle* **83**, 1, 13 (1942).
216. Pressman, D. and Lucas, H. J., *J. Am. Chem. Soc.* **64**, 1953 (1942).
217. Russo, F., *Ann. chim. applicata* **32**, 216 (1942).
218. Samsel, E. P. and McHard, J. A., *Ind. Eng. Chem., Anal. Ed.* **14**, 750 (1942).
219. Sánchez, J. V., *Ciencia* **3**, 18 (1942).
220. Sondern, C. W. and Barson, C., *Ind. Eng. Chem., Anal. Ed.* **14**, 358 (1942).

221. Stanerson, B. R. and Levin, H., *Ind. Eng. Chem., Anal. Ed.* **14**, 782 (1942).
222. Weiss, L. C., *J. Assoc. Offic. Agr. Chem.* **25**, 896 (1942).
223. Wells, E. H., *J. Assoc. Offic. Agr. Chem.* **25**, 537 (1942).
224. Wells, E. H., *J. Assoc. Offic. Agr. Chem.* **25**, 747 (1942).
225. Alicino, J. F., *Ind. Eng. Chem., Anal. Ed.* **15**, 764 (1943).
226. Burson, C. and Sondern, C. W., *Pharm. Arch.* **14**, 17 (1943).
227. Cooke, L. M. and Hibbert, H., *Ind. Eng. Chem., Anal. Ed.* **15**, 24 (1943).
228. Lespagnol, A. and Merville, R., *Ann. chim. anal.* **25**, 53 (1943).
229. Korpáczy, I., *Kem. Lapya* **4**, 106 (1943).
230. Wojahn, H., *Arch. Pharm.* **281**, 289 (1943).
231. Houghton, A. A. and Wilson, H., *Analyst* **69**, 363 (1944).
232. Lewis, J. B. and Bradstreet, R. B., *Ind. Eng. Chem., Anal. Ed.* **16**, 617 (1944).
233. Moriwaki, Y., *Tohoku J. Exptl. Med.* **47**, 34 (1944).
234. Müller, A. and Fehér, L., *Fette u. Seifen* **51**, 171 (1944).
235. Rowe, R. G., Furnas, C. C. and Bliss, H., *Ind. Eng. Chem., Anal. Ed.* **16**, 371 (1944).
236. Schmidt-Nielsen, K., *Compt. rend. trav. lab. Carlsberg, Sér. chim.* **25**, 87 (1944).
237. Baernstein, H. D., *J. Biol. Chem.* **161**, 685 (1945).
238. Conway, H. S., *J. Am. Pharm. Assoc.* **34**, 236 (1945).
239. Fierz-David, H. E., Pfanner, E. and Oppliger, F., *Helv. Chim. Acta* **28**, 1463 (1945).
240. Friedkin, M., *Ind. Eng. Chem., Anal. Ed.* **17**, 637 (1945).
241. Ganday, R., *J. Intern. Soc. Leather Trades' Chem.* **29**, 143 (1945).
242. Chambon, M. and Rochebillard, R., *Lyon pharm.* **5/6**, 2 (1946).
243. Cox, H. E., *Analyst* **71**, 301 (1946).
244. Morgan, P. W., *Ind. Eng. Chem., Anal. Ed.* **18**, 500 (1946).
245. Riemschneider, R., *Pharmazie* **1**, 161 (1946).
246. Ruderman, I. W., *Ind. Eng. Chem., Anal. Ed.* **18**, 753 (1946).
247. Schill, G., *Svensk Farm. Tid.* **50**, 385 (1946).
248. Warshowsky, B. and Elving, P. J., *Ind. Eng. Chem., Anal. Ed.* **18**, 276 (1946).
249. Waugh, T. D., Harbottle, G. and Noyes, R. M., *Ind. Eng. Chem., Anal. Ed.* **18**, 636 (1946).
250. Wilson, G. E. and Nisbet, H. B., *Analyst* **71**, 183 (1946).
251. Angell, F. G., *Analyst* **72**, 178 (1947).
252. Boyd, H. M. and Roach, J. R., *Anal. Chem.* **19**, 158 (1947).
253. Brissaud, L., *Mém. services chim. état. (Paris)* **33**, 75 (1947).
254. Caccia-Bava, A. M., *Ateneo parmense* **18**, 467, 477 (1947).
255. Green, N. and Green, M. W., *J. Am. Pharm. Assoc.* **36**, 235 (1947).
256. Hirschhorn, I. S., *Anal. Chem.* **19**, 880 (1947).

257. Jirsa, F., *Chemie (Prague)* **3**, 130 (1947).
258. Johnson, H. L. and Clark, R. A., *Anal. Chem.* **19**, 861 (1947); correction ibid. **20**, 490 (1948).
259. Montequi, R. and Alvarez, A., *Anales fis. y quím. (Madrid)* **43**, 1159 (1947).
260. Niemierko, W., *Acta Biol. Exptl. (Warsaw)* **14**, 199 (1947).
261. Poethke, W., *Pharm. Zentralhalle* **86**, 2 (1947).
262. Poethke, W., *Pharm. Zentralhalle* **86**, 357 (1947).
263. Prat, J. and Vaganay, J., *Mém. services chim. état. (Paris)* **33**, 391 (1947).
264. Robinson, E. D. and Werch, S. C., *J. Am. Pharm. Assoc., Sci. Ed.* **36**, 185 (1947).
265. Savard, J., Leclercq, A. and Reygrobellet, J., *Agron. trop.* **2**, 170 (1947).
266. Savioli, F., *Chimica e industria (Milan)* **29**, 206 (1947).
267. Shaw, B. M., *J. Soc. Chem. Ind. (London)* **66**, 147 (1947).
268. Shrikhande, J. G. and Dev, R., *J. Indian Chem. Soc., Ind. & News Ed.* **10**, 125 (1947).
269. Thayer, L. and Glase, B., *Proc. Louisiana Acad. Sci.* **10**, 213 (1947).
270. Awe, W., Skroch, B. and Derelius, F., *Süddeutsch. Apotheker-Ztg.* **88**, 155 (1948).
271. Bar, D., *Bull. soc. pharm., Lille* No. 2, 16 (1948).
272. Cavicchi, G., *Riv. ital. essenze profumi, piante offic. olii vegetali, saponi* **30**, 473 (1948).
273. Fungairiño, L. V. and Puertas, P. G., *Anales real soc. espan., fis. y quím.* **44**, 459 (1948).
274. Fungairiño, L. V., *Anales real acad. farm.* **14**, 707 (1948).
275. Goldenson, J. and Sass, S., *Anal. Chem.* **20**, 730 (1948).
276. Goldenson, J. and Sass, S., *Anal. Chem.* **20**, 1118 (1948).
277. Kaller, A., *Angew. Chem.* **60**, 334 (1948).
278. Lespagnol, A. and Bar, D., *Ann. pharm. franç.* **6**, 515 (1948).
279. Lobunets, N., *Z. anal. Chem.* **128**, 279 (1948).
280. Maffei, F. J. and Outa, M., *Anais asoc. quím. Brasil* **7**, 195 (1948).
281. Poethke, W., *Pharmazie* **3**, 69 (1948).
282. Riemschneider, R., *Pharmazie* **3**, 207 (1948).
283. Shafik Ali El Khishen, *Anal. Chem.* **20**, 1078 (1948).
284. Soos, I., *Z. anal. Chem.* **128**, 110 (1948).
285. Thomas, P. R., Donn, L. and Becker, H. C., *Anal. Chem.* **20**, 209 (1948).
286. Wojahn, H., *Süddeutsch. Apotheker-Ztg.* **88**, 395 (1948).
287. Zanetti, G. C., *Atti accad. sci. Ferrara* **26**, No. 1 (1948–9).
288. Coppini, D., *Farm. sci. e tec. (Pavia)* **4**, 526 (1949).
289. Dán, S. and Braun, M., *Orvosi Hetilap* **90**, 283 (1949).
290. Dunning, J. W. and Dallas, D. E., *Anal., Chem.* **21**, 727 (1949).
291. Fungairiño, L. V. and García-Puertas, P., *Anales bromatol (Madrid)* **1**, 219 (1949).
292. Hablitzel, C. P. and Jezl, J. L., *Anal. Chem.* **21**, 1049 (1949).

293. Harnish, D. P. and Tarbell, D. S., *Anal. Chem.* **21**, 968 (1949).
294. Kreshkov, A. P. and Nessonova, G. D., *Zhur. Anal. Khim.* **4**, 220 (1949).
295. Petrova, L. N., *Zhur. Priklad Khim.* (*J. Appl. Chem. USSR*) **22**, 122 (1949).
296. Popov, S. F., *Med. Prom. SSSR* No. 3, 31 (1949).
297. Popov, S. F., *Med. Prom. SSSR* No. 6, 25 (1949).
298. Schifferli, E., *Folia Med.* (*Naples*) **32**, 562 (1949).
299. Teinissen, P. H., *Anal. Chem.* **21**, 620 (1949).
300. Tomíček, O. and Dolězal, J., *Chem. Listy* **43**, 193 (1949).
301. Tomíček, O. and Zýka, J., *Časopis českého Lékarnictva* **62**, 49 (1949).
302. Wankmüller, A., *Pharmazie* **4**, 510 (1949).
303. Zethelius, P. S., *Rev. colomb. quím.* **3**, No. 1, 5 (1949).
304. Albertson, C. E. and MacGregor, I. R., *Anal. Chem.* **22**, 806 (1950).
305. Benham, G. H. and Klee, L., *J. Am. Oil Chemists' Soc.* **27**, 127 (1950).
306. Cohen, S. G. and Haas, H. C., *J. Am. Chem. Soc.* **72**, 3954 (1950).
307. Coppini, D. and Costa, E., *Farm. sci. e tec.* (*Pavia*) **5**, 411 (1950).
308. Eschinazi, H. E. and Bergmann, E. D., *J. Am. Chem. Soc.* **72**, 5651 (1950).
309. Jureček, M., *Chem. Listy* **44**, 134 (1950).
310. Klee, L. and Benham, G. H., *J. Am. Oil Chemists' Soc.* **27**, 130 (1950).
311. Miller, S. A. and Pearman, F. H., *Analyst* **75**, 492 (1950).
312. Naidus, E. S. and Meuller, M. B., *J. Am. Chem. Soc.* **72**, 1829 (1950).
313. Pearson, R. G. and Dillon, R. L., *J. Am. Chem. Soc.* **72**, 3574 (1950).
314. Portner, P. C., *Anal. Chem.* **22**, 570 (1950).
315. Ray, N., *Indian Pharm.* **5**, 148 (1950).
316. Reckendorfer, P., *Pflanzenschutzber.* **5**, 287 (1950).
317. Schulek, E. and Bayer, I., *Acta. Pharm. Intern.* **1**, 177 (1950).
318. Schulek, E. and Rózsa, P., *Acta Pharm. Intern.* **1**, 127 (1950).
319. Wilson, G. E., *J. Inst. Petroleum* **36**, 25 (1950).
320. Aasness, H., *Medd. Norsk Farm. Selskap* **12**, 115, 125, 139 (1951); **13**, 2 (1951).
321. Bar, D., *Bull. soc. pharm., Lille* No. 1, 29 (1951).
322. Bradbury, R. B., *Mikrochemie ver. Mikrochim. Acta* **38**, 114 (1951).
323. Dupin, S., *Bull. mens ITERG* **5**, 469 (1951).
324. Duyckaerts, G. and Pitance, T., *Sbornik Mezinárod. Polorograf. Sjezdu v Praze*, 1st Congress Pt. 1, 51 (1951).
325. Goldenson, J. and Sass, S., *Anal. Chem.* **23**, 1170 (1951).
326. Jaminet, F., *Compt. rend.* 1. *Symposium intern. contrôle spécialités pharm., Brussels* 325 (1951).
327. Ludes, H., *Z. ges. exptl. Med.* **118**, 1 (1951).
328. Pearson, R. G. and Sandy, A. C., *J. Am. Chem. Soc.* **73**, 931 (1951).
329. Pulido-Cuchi, F. and Hernández-Gutiérrez, F., *Anales real soc. espan., fis. y quím.* **47B**, 351 (1951).

330. Rutovskii, B. N. and Shur, A. M., *Zhur. Priklad Khim.* (*J. Appl. Chem. USSR*) **24**, 1074 (1951).
331. Sandri, G., *Ann. chim.* (*Rome*) **41**, 135 (1951).
332. Bontemps, R., *J. pharm. Belg.* **7**, 553 (1952).
333. Buck, R. P. and Swift, E. H., *Anal. Chem.* **24**, 499 (1952).
334. Coppini, D., Cameroni, R. and Monzani, A., *Ricerca sci.* **22**, 1783 (1952).
335. Costa, E. and Grassi, G., *Boll. chim. farm.* **91**, 227 (1952).
336. Duke, J. A. and Maselli, J. A., *J. Am. Oil Chemists' Soc.* **29**, 126 (1952).
337. Gorbach, G. and Rohner, K., *Mikrochemie ver. Microchim. Acta* **39**, 299 (1952).
338. Haugas, E. A. and Mitchell, B. W., *J. Pharm. Pharmacol.* **4**, 687 (1952).
339. Jouslin, D., *Chim. anal.* **34**, 34 (1952).
340. Kalinowski, K., *Farm. Polska* **8**, 408 (1952).
341. McCullough, R. L. and Stone, K. G., *Anal. Chem.* **24**, 1206 (1952).
342. Matta, G. and Nunes, M. L., *Anais azevedos* (*Lisbon*) **4**, 161 (1952).
343. Neelakantam, K. and Viswanath, G., *Proc. Indian Acad. Sci.* **35A**, 72 (1952).
344. Paris, R. A. and Vial, J., *Chim. anal.* **34**, 3 (1952).
345. Phillips, J. P., Emery, J. F. and Price, H. P., *Anal. Chem.* **24**, 1033 (1952).
346. Robey, R. F., Hudson, B. E. and Wiese, H. K., *Anal. Chem.* **24**, 1080 (1952).
347. Rosenmund, K. W. and Grandjean, H. H., *Erdöl u Kohle* **5**, 348 (1952).
348. Tyler, W. P. and Beesing, D. W., *Anal. Chem.* **24**, 1511 (1952).
349. Bokadia, M. M., *Agra Univ. J. Research* **2**, Pt. 1, 9 (1953).
350. Fenech, G. and Tommasine, A., *Boll. chim. farm.* **92**, 327 (1953).
351. Horn, D., *Pharmazie* **8**, 646 (1953).
352. Houff, W. H. and Schuetz, R. D., *Anal. Chem.* **25**, 1258 (1953).
353. Kamath, N. R., *Oils and Oilseeds J.* (India) **5**, No. 10/12, 82 (1953).
354. Kamer, J. H. van de, *Scand. J. Clin. and Lab. Invest.* **5**, 30 (1953).
355. Kantorovich, S. A. and Alegina, O. N., *Byull. Obmenu Opyt. v Lakokrasoch. Prom.* No. 4, 70 (1953).
356. Lips, H. J., *J. Am. Oil Chemists' Soc.* **30**, 399 (1953).
357. Longstaff, J. V. L. and Singer, K., *Analyst* **78**, 491 (1953).
358. Masotti, M., *Atti accad. sci., Ferrara* **30**, 23 (1953).
359. Meissner, B., *Chem. Tech.* (*Berlin*) **5**, 381 (1953).
360. Modiano, J. and Pariaud, J.-C., *Compt. rend.* **236**, 1897 (1953).
361. Planck, R. W., Park, F. C. and Goldblatt, L. A., *J. Am. Oil Chemists' Soc.* **30**, 417 (1953).
362. Rosenmund, K. W. and Grandjean, H. H., *Arch. Pharm.* **286**, 531 (1953).
363. Sandri, G. and Lambardi, F., *Atti. accad. sci., Ferrara* **30**, 27 (1953).
364. Segal, W. and Starkey, R. L., *Anal. Chem.* **25**, 1645 (1953).

365. Szabolcs, L., *Magyar Kem. Folyoirat* **59**, 218 (1953).
366. Vaisman, G. A., *Aptechnoe Delo* **2**, No. 6, 25 (1953).
367. Vogt, H., *Arch. Pharm.* **286**, 389 (1953).
368. Wheatley, V. R., *Biochem. J.* **55**, 637 (1953).
369. Wojahn, H. and Wempe, E., *Pharm. Zentralhalle* **92**, 124 (1953).
370. Aichenegg, P. and Haynes, H. G., *J. Appl. Chem.* **4**, 137 (1954).
371. Gal'pern, G. D., *Trudy Inst. Nefti., Akad. Nauk SSSR*, **4**, 116 (1954).
372. Gronsberg, E. S. L., *Gigiena i Sanit.* No. 11, 43 (1954).
373. Gvozdik, V. A., Trotsenko, M. A. and Potapova, V. P., *Aptechnoe Delo* **3**, No. 3, 33 (1954).
374. Kaufmann, H. P. and Arends, W., *Arch. Pharm.* **287**, 590 (1954).
375. Kawamura, F., Momoki, K. and Suzuki, S., *Bunseki Kagaku* (*Japan Analyst*) **3**, 29 (1954).
376. Modiano, J. and Pariaud, J-C., *Bull. soc. chim. France* 189 (1954).
377. Orlowski, M. and Simon, J., *Acta Biochim. Polon.* **1**, 231 (1954).
378. Rastelli, A., *Chimica* (*Milan*) **9**, 75 (1954).
379. Reid, V. W. and Beddard, J. D., *Analyst* **79**, 456 (1954).
380. Ruzhentseva, A. K. and Goryacheva, N. S., *Aptechnoe Delo* **3**, No. 5, 7 (1954).
381. Steyermark, A. and Loeschauer, E. E., *J. Assoc. Offic. Agr. Chem.* **37**, 433 (1954).
382. Tamate, E. and Kinoshita, S., *J. Chem. Soc., Japan, Ind. Chem. Sect.* **57**, 322, 922 (1954).
383. Zýka, J., *Pharmazie* **9**, 812 (1954).
384. Belcher, R., Fildes, J. E. and Nutten, A. J., *Anal. Chim. Acta* **13**, 16 (1955).
385. Ditrych, Z., Rejková, H. and Ulbrich, V., *Chem. Listy* **49**, 869 (1955).
386. v. Erichsen, L. and Rudolphi, N., *Erdöl u. Kohle* **8**, 16 (1955).
387. Ettre, L., Herédy, L. and Kovács, M., *Magyar Kem. Lapya* **10**, 23 (1955).
388. Grover, K. C., *Agra Univ. J. Research* **4**, 627 (1955).
389. Hädicke, M., *Pharm. Zentralhalle* **94**, 384 (1955).
390. Hammond, G. S. and Parks, L. R., *J. Am. Chem. Soc.* **77**, 340 (1955).
391. Johnson, L. D., McNabb, W. M. and Wagner, E. C., *Anal. Chem.* **27**, 1494 (1955).
392. Kasterina, T. N., Fedotova, E. N. and Shevchenko, O. S., *Zavodskaya Lab.* **21**, 408 (1955).
393. Kochi, Z., *Yakugaku Zasshi* (*J. Pharm. Soc. Japan*) **75**, 748 (1955).
394. Morozov, V. A., *Gigiena i Sanit.* No. 7, 47 (1955).
395. Rosenthaler, L., *Pharm. Acta Helv.* **30**, 69 (1955).
396. Sandri, G., *Il Farmaco* (*Pavia*) *Ed. Sci.* **10**, 444 (1955).
397. Schulek, E. and Burger, K., *Magyar Kem. Folyoirat* **61**, 359 (1955).
398. Spliethoff, W. L. and Hart, H., *Anal. Chem.* **27**, 1492 (1955).
399. Steyermark, A., *J. Assoc. Offic. Agr. Chem.* **38**, 367 (1955).

400. Sykut, K., *Ann. Univ. Marie Curie-Sklodowska, Lublin, Polonia.* Sect. AA 10, No. 3, 25 (1955).
401. Sykut, K., *Ann. Univ. Marie Curie-Sklodowska, Lublin, Polonia,* Sect. AA 10, No. 6, 53 (1955).
402. Varga E. and Zöllner, E., *Acta Pharm. Hung.* **25**, 150 (1955).
403. Verma, M. R. and Bhuchar, V. M., *J. Sci. Ind. Research (India)* **14B**, 419 (1955).
404. Bethge, P. O. and Carlson, O. T., *Anal. Chim. Acta* **15**, 279 (1956).
405. Bitskei, J., *Magyar Kem. Folyoirat* **62**, 71 (1956).
406. Byrne, R. E. and Johnson, J. B., *Anal. Chem.* **28**, 126 (1956).
407. Dmowska, W. and Pech, M., *Acta Polon. Pharm.* **13**, 219 (1956).
408. Gyenes, I., *Magyar Kem. Folyoirat* **62**, 242 (1956).
409. Ioanid, N., Bors, G., Popa, I. and Lorent, L., *Farmacia (Bucharest)* **4**, 303 (1956).
410. Kotlik, B. E. and Smyslova, A. I., *Koks i Khim.* No. 7, 41 (1956).
411. Linde, H. W., *Anesthesiology* **17**, 777 (1956).
412. Lortz, H. J., *Anal. Chem.* **28**, 892 (1956).
413. Reis, N. V., *Sbornik Nauch.-Trudov, Samarkand, Med. Inst.* **11**, 117 (1956).
414. v. Schantz, M., *Farm. Aikakauslehti* **65**, 265 (1956).
415. Shell Method Series, Designation 221/50, from '*Organic Analysis*', Vol. 3, Interscience, New York, 1956.
416. Shteinde, H., *Biul. Inst. Roslin Leczniczych* **2**, 160 (1956).
417. Shub, M. E. and Vasilenko, A. S., *Aptechnoe Delo* **5**, No. 3, 25 (1956).
418. Smith, B., *Acta Chem. Scand.* **10**, 1589 (1956).
419. Spryskov, A. A. and Erykalov, Yu. G., *Zhur. Anal. Khim.* **11**, 492 (1956).
420. Syavtsillo, S. V. and Bondarevskaya, E. A., *Zhur. Anal. Khim.* **11**, 613 (1956).
421. Verma, M. R., Agrawal, K. C. and Paul, S. D., *J. Sci. Ind. Research (India)* **15B**, 589 (1956).
422. Yoshimura, C. and Kiboku, M., *Nippon Kagaku Zasshi (J. Chem. Soc., Japan, Pure Chem. Sect.)* **77**, 1547 (1956).
423. Awe, M. and Stohlmann, H., *Arzneimittelforschung* **7**, 495 (1957).
424. Belcher, R., Bhatty, M. K. and West, T. S., *J. Chem. Soc.* 4480 (1957).
425. Buděšinský, B., Mňouček, K., Jančík, F. and Kraus, E., *Chem. Listy* **51**, 1819 (1957).
426. Buděšinský, B. and Vaníčková, E., *Československ. Farm.* **6**, 305 (1957).
427. Dyachkov, G. S., *Gidroliz. i Lesokhim. Prom.* **10**, No. 5, 16 (1957).
428. Helou, J. H., *Anais farm. e quím., Sao Paulo* **8**, 7 (1957).
429. Higgins, D. J. and Stephenson, W. H., *Analyst* **82**, 435 (1957).
430. Horsch, W., *Pharmazie* **12**, 124 (1957).
431. Jančík, F., Kraus, E., Buděšinský, B. and Činková, O., *Československ. Farm.* **6**, 105 (1957).

432. Jančík, F., Buděšinský, B. and Činková, O., *Českoslov. Farm.* **6**, 108 (1957).
433. Kokoski, R. J. and Allen, B. F., *Drug Standards* **25**, 17 (1957).
434. Marvillet, L. and Tranchant, J., *Mém. poudres* **39**, 329 (1957).
435. Meltzer, H., *Nachbrl. deut. Pflanzenschutzdienst* (*Berlin*) **11**, 178 (1957).
436. Prat, J. and Colas, A., *Chim. anal.* **39**, 298 (1957).
437. Schulek, E. and Burger, K., *Acta Pharm. Hung.* **27**, 51 (1957).
438. Smith, B., *Acta Chem. Scand.* **11**, 558 (1957).
439. Smith, B., *Acta Chem. Scand.* **11**, 839 (1957).
440. Takei, F., Murai, K. and Akazame, G., *Kôgyô Kagaku Zasshi* **60**, 1271 (1957).
441. Timofeeva, E. A., Kleimanova, V. M. and Dobrynina, T. P., *Izvest. Akad. Nauk SSSR, Otdel Khim. Nauk* 122 (1957).
442. Vaisman, G. A. and Benderskaya, S. N., *Aptechnoe Delo* **6**, No. 2, 32 (1957).
443. Varga, E. and Vastagh, G., *Pharm. Zentralhalle* **96**, 149 (1957).
444. Vastagh, G. and Varga, E., *Pharm. Zentralhalle* **96**, 99 (1957).
445. Verma, M. R., Agrawal, K. C. and Paul, S. D., *J. Sci. Ind. Research* (*India*) **16B**, 213 (1957).
446. Belcher, R., Bhatty, M. K. and West, T. S., *J. Chem. Soc.* 2393 (1958).
447. Bethge, P. O., *Svensk Papperstidn.* **61**, 267 (1958).
448. Bethge, P. O., *Svensk Papperstidn.* **61**, 565, 856 (1958).
449. Blažek, J., *Českoslov. Farm.* **7**, 25 (1958).
450. Dyachkov, G. S., *Gidroliz. i Lesokhim. Prom.* **11**, No. 2, 19 (1958).
451. Grover, K. C. and Mehotra, R. C., *Z. anal. Chem.* **166**, 267 (1958).
452. Ingberman, A. K., *Anal. Chem.* **30**, 1003 (1958).
453. Javes, A. R. and Liddell, C., *Anal. Chem.* **30**, 1570 (1958).
454. Kalinowski, K. and Piotrowska, A., *Acta Polon. Pharm.* **15**, 321 (1958).
455. Köszegi, D. and Salgó, E., *Z. anal. Chem.* **164**, 320 (1958).
456. Laszlovsky, J., *Magyar Kem. Folyoirat* **64**, 5 (1958).
457. Malatesta, P. and Lorenzini, A., *Ricerca sci.* **28**, 1874 (1958).
458. Nessonova, G. D. and Pogosyants, E. K., *Zavodskaya Lab.* **24**, 953 (1958).
459. Roth, H., *Mikrochim. Acta* 766 (1958).
460. Schulek, E. and Burger, K., *Z. anal. Chem.* **161**, 184 (1958).
461. Schulek, E. and Burger, K., *Acta Pharm. Hung.* **28**, 96 (1958).
462. Schulek, E. and Burger, K., *Acta Pharm. Hung.* **28**, 100 (1958).
463. Schulek, E. and Burger, K., *Talanta* **1**, 147 (1958).
464. Szekeres, L., Zergényi-Balazsfalvy, M. and Molnár, L. G., *Magyar Kem. Folyoirat* **64**, 96 (1958).
465. Varga, E. and Vastagh, G., *Acta Pharm. Hung.* **28**, 44 (1958).
466. Bellen, Z. and Bellen, N., *Chem. Anal.* (*Warsaw*) **4**, 19 (1959).
467. Berka, A. and Zýka, J., *Českoslov. Farm.* **8**, 17 (1959).

468. Burger, K., Schulek, E. and Ladányi, L., *Acta Pharm. Hung.* **29**, 241 (1959).
469. Critchfield, F. E., *Anal. Chem.* **31**, 1406 (1959).
470. Dege, G. J., Harris, R. L. and Mackenzie, J. S., *J. Am. Chem. Soc.* **81**, 3374 (1959).
471. Favorskaya, I. A. and Auvinen, E. M., *Vestnik Leningrad Univ.* **14**, Ser. Fiz. i Khim. No. 3, 119 (1959).
472. Jančík, F., Činková, O. and Körbl, J., *Collection Czechoslov. Chem. Communs.* **24**, 2695 (1959).
473. Kraft, I., *Arch. Pharm.* **292/64**, 306 (1959).
474. Makens, R. F., Lothringer, R. L. and Donia, R. A., *Anal. Chem.* **31**, 265 (1959).
475. Młodecka, J., *Rev. chim.* (*Bucharest*) **10**, 343 (1959).
476. Perel'man, Ya. M. and Krasulina, V. N., *Trudy Leningrad Khim.-Farm. Inst.* No. 6, 69 (1959).
477. Ruzhentseva, A. K. and Tubina, I. S., *Med. Prom. SSSR* **13**, No. 1, 40 (1959).
478. Sági, M., *Veszprémi Vegyipari Egyetem Közleményei* **3**, 47 (1959).
479. Sodomka, J., *Chem. Průmysl* **9**, 363 (1959).
480. Wehle, H., *Z. anal. Chem.* **169**, 241 (1959).
481. Buděšinský, B. and Aixnerová, M., *Českoslov. Farm.* **9**, 312 (1960).
482. Burger, K. and Schulek, E., *Talanta* **7**, 46 (1960).
483. Burger, E. and Schulek, E., *Z. anal. Chem.* **172**, 98 (1960).
484. Schulek, E. and Burger, K., *Ann. Univ. Sci. Budapest Rolando Eötvös nominatae, Sect. Chim.* **2**, 145 (1960).
485. Greger, K. M., Szmrecsanyi, I. V. and Bödi, E. M., *Magyar Kem. Lapya* **15**, 72 (1960).
486. Köszegi, D. and Salgó, E., *Magyar Kem. Folyoirat* **66**, 142 (1960).
487. Nemirovskii, N. L. and Meerovich, G. I., *Tr. Leningr. Sanit. Gigien. Med. Inst.* **62**, 66 (1960).
488. Ott, R. and Raber, H., *Sci. Pharm.* **28**, 206 (1960).
489. Prasad, B. B. and Das, B., *J. Sci. Research Banares Hindu Univ.* **11**, 22 (1960–1).
490. Schulek, E. and Burger, K., *Ann. Univ. Sci. Budapest Rolando Eötvös nominatae, Sect. Chim.* **2**, 537 (1960).
491. Uvarova, E. I. and Vanyarkina, N. M., *Zavodskaya Lab.* **26**, 1097 (1960).
492. 'Die Organische Analyse'—Bauer-Moll, 4th Edition, Leipzig, 1960, p. 38.
493. 'Die Organische Analyse'—Bauer-Moll, 4th Edition, Leipzig, 1960, p. 203.
494. 'Die Organische Analyse'—Bauer-Moll, 4th Edition, Leipzig, 1960, p. 446.
495. 'Die Organische Analyse'—Bauer-Moll, 4th Edition, Leipzig, 1960, p. 571.

496. 'Die Organische Analyse'—Bauer-Moll, 4th Edition, Leipzig, 1960, p. 573.
497. Böhme, H., Neidlein, R. and Tauber, E., *Arch. Pharm.* **294**, 315 (1961).
498. Burger, K. and Schulek, E., *Magyar Kem. Folyoirat* **67**, 33 (1961).
499. Claeys, A., Sion, H. and Campe, A., *Bull. soc. chim. Belges* **70**, 455 (1961),
500. Claeys, A., Sion, H., Campe, A. and Thun, H., *Bull. soc. chim. Belges* **70**. 576 (1961).
501. Dranitskaya, R. M., *Nauch. Ezhegodnik, Odessk, Gosudarst. Univ., Khim. Fak.* No. 2, 70 (1961).
502. Faure, M. and Peyrieux, R., *Bull. trav. soc. pharm., Lyon* **5**, 53 (1961).
503. Hamann, V. and Herrmann, A., *Mikrochim. Acta* 105 (1961).
504. Korte, F. and Wüsten, F., *Ann.* **647** ,18 (1961).
505. Podurovskaya, O. M., Kutulina, R. A. and Efimova, N. I., *Zavodskaya Lab.* **27**, 403 (1961).
506. Probsthain, K., *Z. anal. Chem.* **182**, 409 (1961).
507. Schulek, E., Burger, K. and Gaizer, F., *Acta Pharm. Hung.* **31**, 241 (1961).
508. Tanay, I., *Acta Pharm. Hung.* **31**, 247 (1961).
509. Wisniewski, W. and Furmanczyk, Z., *Acta Polon. Pharm.* **18**, 415 (1961).
510. Delgado, O. A., *Rev. fac. ing. quim., Argentina* **30**, 85 (1961).
511. Fritz, G. and Burdt, H., *Z. anorg. u. allgem. Chem.* **317**, 35 (1962).
512. Bezugli, V. D., Dmitrieva, V. N. and Batovskaya, T. A., *Zhur. Anal. Khim.* **17**, 109 (1962).
513. Körbl, J. and Jančik, F., *Czechoslovak Patent No.* 105, 606, Nov 15, 1962.
514. Körbl, J. and Jančik, F., *Czechoslovak Patent No.* 105, 608, Nov 15, 1962.
515. Lebedeva, A. I. and Pisarenko, E. S., *Zhur. Anal Khim.* **17**, 636 (1962).
516. Montequi, R. and de Valderrama, F., *Anales Real Acad. Farm.* **28**, 133 (1962).
517. Spagnolo, F., *Mater. Res. & Stand.* **2**, 899 (1962).
518. Studený, J. and Uhrová, D., *Chem. Průmysl* **12**, 553 (1962).
519. Tokár, G. and Simonyi, I., *Magyar, Kem. Folyoirat* **68**, 338 (1962).
520. Verma, R. M. and Bose, S., *J. Indian Chem. Soc.* **39**, 329 (1962).
521. Wronski, M., *Chem. Anal.* (*Warsaw*) **7**, 1011 (1962).
522. Ballreich, K., *Z. anal. Chem.* **195**, 274 (1963).
523. Barcza, L. and Burger, K., *Magyar Kem. Folyoirat* **69**, 178 (1963)
524. Beral, H. and Constantinescu, T., *Rev. Chim.* (*Bucharest*) **14**, 235 (1963).
525. Darovskikh, G. T. and Trofimov, G. A., *Kauchuk i Rezina* **22**, 49 (1963).
526. Gupta, P. C., *Analyst*, **88** 896 (1963).
527. Kertesz, P., *Acta Pharm. Hung.* **33**, 150 (1963).
528. Klimova, V. A. and Zabrodina, K. S., *Zhur. Anal. Khim.* **18**, 109 (1963).
529. Koyama, K., Taguchi, Y. and Eguchi, S., *Bunseki Kagaku* **12** 435 (1963).

530. Lebedeva, A. I. and Pisarenko, E. S., *Zhur. Anal. Khim.* **18**, 892 (1963).
531. Marzadro, M. and De Carolis, A., *Mikrochim. Acta* 726 (1963).
532. Middleton, K. R., *Analyst* **88**, 368 (1963).
533. Middleton, K. R. and Westgarth, D. R., *Analyst* **88**, 544 (1963).
534. Mintzer, I. and Montzoi, I., *Z. anal. Chem.* **196**, 27 (1963).
535. Perel'man, Ya. A. and Gavrilin, G. F., *Zhur. Anal. Khim.* **18**, 529 (1963).
536. Polyanskii, N. G. and Tsekhmister, E. F., *Zhur. Anal. Khim.* **18**, 888 (1963).
537. Raber, H. and Ott, R., *Sci. Pharm.* **31**, 10 (1963).
538. Schulek, E., Maros, L. and Molnár-Perl, I., *Talanta* **10**, 561 (1963).
539. Sobczak, N., *Chem. Anal.* (*Warsaw*) **8**, 801 (1963).
540. Sobczak, N., *Chem. Anal.* (*Warsaw*) **8**, 613 (1963).
541. Szekeres, L. and Kardos, E., *Z. anal. Chem.* **193**, 271 (1963).
542. Tanay, I., *Magyar Kem. Folyoirat* **69**, 226 (1963).
543. Terent'ev, A. P. and Tubina, I. S., *Zhur. Anal. Khim.* **18**, 113 (1963).
544. Zabrodina, K. S., *Izv. Akad. Nauk SSSR, Otd. Khim. Nauk* 941 (1963).
545. Schulek, E., Maros, L. and Molnár-Perl, I., *Mikrochim. Acta* 336 (1964).

17. Cadmium (II)

Reagent. Various cadmium salts have been used—halides, sulphate, acetate, thiocyanate. The cadmium derivative of EDTA has also been used and complex anions containing cadmium, such as the cadmi-iodides CdI_4^{2-}.

Reactions and materials titrated. 1. Ion/ion combination of Cd^{2+} with mercaptides such as from glutathione; and of CdI_4^{2-} with organic cations like certain quaternary ammonium cations, and those derived from mepacrine, quinine, rivanol, etc.

$$2\,RS^- + Cd^{2+} \rightarrow (RS)_2Cd$$

$$2\,NR_4^+ + CdI_4^{2-} \rightarrow (NR_4)_2CdI_4$$

$$2\,\text{Base} + 2\,H^+ + CdI_4^{2-} \rightarrow (\text{Base.H})_2\,CdI_4$$

These reaction products are poorly soluble in water and are precipitated.

2. Complex formation with certain bases, e.g. pyramidone, isoniazid, pyridine, piperazine and metrazole. The most usual reaction is:

$$2\,\text{Base} + Cd^{2+} + 2\,\text{Anion}^- \rightarrow Cd(\text{Base})_2(\text{Anion})_2$$

where the anion may be a halide or SCN^-. As under reaction type 1, the products are precipitated.

3. Fission of C—S links with certain sulphur-containing molecules which are broken down to yield CdS precipitate. Thiourea and some thiosemicarbazones have been determined in this way.

Subsequent treatment and final titration stage. (i) Mostly by determination of unused Cd(II) in the filtrate from the precipitated derivative, by titration with EDTA. In one example, unused SCN^- from precipitation with a combined Cd(II)/SCN^- reagent, was back titrated with Ag(I).

(ii) The reaction product has been determined in one of several ways:

1. Precipitate dissolved and Cd(II) titrated with EDTA.
2. CdS precipitate treated with acid/excess iodine and back titrated with thiosulphate.
3. The original organic compound, effectively isolated by means of the Cd(II) reagent, has been titrated; e.g. glutathione (as Cd derivative) with excess bromine reagent and iodometric back titration, and other mercaptans by reaction with excess iodine and back titration with thiosulphate.
4. The EDTA liberated from use of a Cd(II)/EDTA reagent, was titrated with Ca(II).

Examples

Materials titrated	Reagent and reaction conditions	Subsequent treatment and final titration stage	Ref.
Glutathione	+ $CdSO_4$ + NaOH, giving Cd derivative of the mercaptan	Reaction product + BrO_3^-/Br^-/acid and excess determined via I^-/thiosulphate (see Bromine reagents, ref. 138)	1
Mercaptans in gases	Passed through $CdCl_2$/Na_2CO_3	+ HCl + excess iodine and back titrated with thiosulphate	2
Thiourea in mixtures	+ acetic acid + Cd acetate + NaOH. Heated to 80° and left 1 h	+ acetic acid and filtered; then + HCl + excess iodine and back titrated with thiosulphate	3
Cysteine in protein hydrolysates	+ $CdSO_4$ + alkali, giving Cd derivative of the mercaptan	Treated with alkali, ultimately converting to CdS; dissolved in H_2SO_4, excess iodine added and back titrated with thiosulphate after 20 min	4

Materials titrated	Reagent and reaction conditions	Subsequent treatment and final titration stage	Ref.
Pyramidone; isoniazid	In water, + CdI_2 or $Cd(SCN)_2$, giving precipitate of complex $Cd(Base)_2^{2+}I_2$ (or $(SCN)_2$)	Filtered and unreacted Cd(II) in filtrate determined by adding NH_4 buffer, (pH 10) and titrating with EDTA to eriochrome black T	5
Pyramidone	In water, + buffer pH 10 + $Cd(SCN)_2$, giving complex	Filtered and unused Cd(II) in filtrate titrated with EDTA	6
Isoniazid; hexamine	In water + $Cd(SCN)_2$; 10 min or 2 h respectively	Filtered and unused Cd(II) titrated with EDTA	7
Pyramidone in pharmaceuticals	Boiling solution in water + $Cd(SCN)_2$ (from $CdCl_2$ + NH_4SCN); neutralized to methyl red with NaOH and left 90–120 min	Filtered, precipitate dissolved in NH_4OH/NH_4Cl and Cd(II) titrated with EDTA to eriochrome black T	8
Quaternary ammonium salts	+ K_2CdI_4, giving precipitate of cadmiiodide	Unused Cd(II) in filtrate titrated with EDTA; or Cd(II) in precipitate likewise titrated	9
Pyridine in ethanol	+ $CdCl_2$/90% ethanol. A few min standing, giving $Cd(C_5H_5N)^{2+}Cl_2$ precipitate	Filtrated and unreacted Cd(II) in filtrate determined by adding NH_4OH/NH_4Cl buffer, pH 10 and titrating with EDTA to eriochrome black T	10
Quinine hydrochloride	In water, + CdI_2/KI, giving precipitate of complex; 15 min	Filtered and unused Cd(II) in filtrate determined by adding NH_4OH/NH_4Cl buffer, pH 10 and titrating with EDTA to acid chrome dark blue	11
Nicotinaldehyde thiosemicarbazone in presence of isoniazid	In water, + Cd acetate + NaOH; 10 min boiling, giving CdS	Filtered and CdS determined by adding HCl + excess iodine and back titrating with thiosulphate after 5 min	12
Quinine	+ excess K_2CdI_4, giving precipitate of complex	Filtered and unreacted Cd(II) titrated with EDTA	13
Pachycarpine	+ KI/CdI_2; 15 min, giving precipitate	Filtered, ammonia buffer added to filtrate and unused Cd(II) titrated with EDTA to acid chrome dark blue	14
Rivanol	In water, + CdI_2/KI, giving precipitate of complex	Filtered and Cd(II) in filtrate titrated with EDTA to xylenol orange/hexamine	15

Materials titrated	Reagent and reaction conditions	Subsequent treatment and final titration stage	Ref.
Chloropromazine	Method of ref. 15		16
Metrazole (cardazole, leptazole) $C_6H_{10}N_4$	In water/isopropanol, 2:3, + $CdCl_2$/water/isopropanol; 10 min, giving precipitate of $C_6H_{10}N_4.CdCl_2.3H_2O$	Filtered, precipitate dissolved in hot water, ammonia buffer added and titrated Cd(II) with EDTA to eriochrome black T	17
Organic bases, e.g. quinine, chloropromazine, piperidine bromide, gallamine triethiodide	In H_2SO_4, + $CdSO_4$/Na_2CO_3/EDTA/KI reagent; 5 min, giving precipitate of Cd complex, setting free EDTA	Filtered and titrated the EDTA with $CaCl_2$ to methylthymol blue	18
Thiourea and some derivatives like acetylthiourea; thiosemicarbazones of nicotinaldehyde or *p*-acetamidobenzaldehyde	In dilute NaOH + hydrazine, + $CdSO_4$/Na_2CO_3/EDTA. Heated 30 min–3 h, giving CdS and liberating EDTA	Filtered, NH_4OH/NH_4Cl buffer, pH 10 added and titrated with EDTA as in ref. 18	19
Mepacrine(atebrine), $C_{23}H_{30}ON_2Cl$	In water, + K_2CdI_4, giving precipitate of cadmiiodide salt	Filtered and unused Cd(II) titrated in ammonia buffer with EDTA to eriochrome black T	20
Piperazine	In water, + NH_4SCN + $CdCl_2$ or $CdSO_4$; 10–15 min, giving precipitate of $[Cd(C_4H_{10}N_2)](SCN)_2$	Filtered and SCN^- in filtrate titrated with Ag(I)	21
2-(Furfurylidene-1-methylethylidene) hydrazide ('Larusan')	In acetone/water, + Cd acetate, giving precipitate of complex	Filtered, hexamine added and titrated with EDTA to xylenol orange	22
Tofranil (Imipramine), *N*-(3-Dimethylamino-propyl)-iminodibenzyl hydrochloride	In water, + CdI_2/KI, giving precipitate of derivative	+ hexamine and titrated unused Cd(II) in filtrate with EDTA to xylenol orange	23
Pyramidone	+ $(NH_4)_2Cd(SCN)_4$/water; 10 min	Filtered, precipitate dissolved in NH_4OH, brought to pH 10 and titrated with EDTA to eriochrome black T	24

References

1. Hartner, F. and Schleiss, E., *Mikrochemie* **20**, 163 (1936).
2. Hakewill, H. and Rueck, E. M., *Proc. Am. Gas Assoc.* **28**, 529 (1946).

3. Korinfskii, A. A., *Zavodskaya Lab.* **12**, 418 (1946).
4. Ghiglione, C. and Bozzi-Tichadou, M., *Bull. soc. chim. biol.* **36**, 659 (1954).
5. Buděšinský, B., *Pharmazie* **10**, 597 (1955).
6. Buděšinský, B., *Českoslov. Farm.* **4**, 71 (1955).
7. Buděšinský, B., *Českoslov. Farm.* **4**, 181 (1955).
8. Groebel, W. and Schneider, E., *Z. anal. Chem.* **146**, 191 (1955).
9. Buděšinský, B. and Vaníčková, E., *Chem. Listy* **50**, 1241 (1956).
10. Castiglioni, A., *Z. anal. Chem.* **156**, 426 (1957).
11. Zaitsev, V. A., *Aptechnoe Delo* **6**, No. 4, 48 (1957).
12. Buděšinský, B. and Vachek, J., *Českoslov. Farm.* **7**, 241 (1958).
13. Chou, Y.-Y. and Hsu, J.-Ch., *Yao Hsueh Hsueh Pao* (*Acta Pharm. Sinica*) **6**, 7 (1958).
14. Zaitsev, V. A., *Aptechnoe Delo* **7**, No. 5, 78 (1958).
15. Przyborowski, L., *Acta Polon. Pharm.* **16**, 31 (1959).
16. Przyborowski, L. and Krowczyński, L., *Chem. Anal.* (*Warsaw*) **4**, 59 (1959).
17. Andersson, E., Fors, M. and Lindgren, J.-E., *Acta Chem. Scand.* **14**, 1957 (1960).
18. Buděšinský, B. and Körbl, J., *Collection Czechoslov. Chem. Communs.* **25**, 76 (1960).
19. Buděšinský, B., Vaníčková, E. and Körbl, J., *Collection Czechoslov. Chem. Communs.* **25**, 456 (1960).
20. Chou, Y.-Y., Ch'eng Ch.-L. and Hsu J.-Ch., *Yao Hsueh Hsueh Pao* (*Acta Pharm. Sinica*) **8**, 61 (1960).
21. Grecu, I., *Farmacia* (*Bucharest*) **8**, 261 (1960); *Rev. chim.* (*Bucharest*) **11**, 714 (1960).
22. Komaritsya, I. D., *Farm. Zhur.* (*Kiev*) **16**, No. 6, 31 (1961).
23. Domagalina, E. and Przyborowski, L., *Chem. Anal.* (*Warsaw*) **7**, 1153 (1962).
24. Vasiliev, R., Scintee, V., Chialda, I., Sisman, E., Fruchter, J. and Jecu, M., *Rev. Chim.* (*Bucharest*) **13**, 759 (1962).

18. Calcium (II)

Reagent. Nearly always acetate or chloride; an insoluble reagent (carbonate, hydroxide) has been used also (see below).

Reaction and materials titrated. All the determinations depend on ion/ion combination or hydrogen replacement with formation of Ca salts or derivatives. The carboxyl group has been determined in all the examples except one; in this instance, cresols were determined.

$$2\,RCOO^- + Ca^{2+} \rightarrow (RCOO)_2Ca$$

$$2\ RCOOH + Ca^{2+} \rightarrow (RCOO)_2Ca + 2\ H^+$$

$$2\ ArOH + Ca^{2+} \rightarrow (ArO)_2Ca + 2\ H^+$$

The two most frequently occurring applications are the determination of oxalate by precipitation as calcium oxalate; and that of carboxylic acid groups in treated (oxidized) celluloses by formation of calcium salts and liberation of H^+. The medical and technical (paper industry, etc.) literature respectively contains many references to these two chief applications and a selection is given in the tables.

Other acids or anions determined include tartaric, lactic, laevulinic, oleic and other fatty acids, amino acids and cresols. The determination of an optically active tartaric acid has been mentioned here; it depends on addition of the antimer + Ca(II) reagent, precipitating Ca racemate.

Reaction conditions. Mostly in aqueous, near-neutral solution and sometimes with longer periods of standing to ensure complete precipitation.

Subsequent treatment and final titration stage. (i) Titration (direct or indirect) of unreacted Ca^{2+} with EDTA (after filtration of the Ca salt).

(ii) Titration with acid of unchanged basic groups in amino acids after conversion of the latter to the Ca salts.

(iii) Determination of a reaction product, such as:

1. acid liberated from —COOH groups of treated celluloses, using alkali reagent,
2. precipitated Ca salts of polycarboxylic and hydroxy acids, especially oxalate (also tartrate, citrate and lactate). This has nearly always been carried out by adding or dissolving in H_2SO_4 and titrating directly or indirectly (excess and iodometric back titration) with MnO_4^-. In one case, periodate was used instead of MnO_4^-, and also laevulinate was determined with alkali/iodine reagent and citrate + oxalate with bichromate. In the determination of cresols, the soluble Ca cresolates were precipitated as Ca oxalate and likewise titrated with MnO_4^-.

Examples

Materials titrated	Reagent and reaction conditions	Subsequent treatment and final titration stage	Ref.
Oxalate, from determination of lactate by heating with MnO_4^-/KOH	Excess MnO_4^- destroyed with H_2O_2, acetic acid + Ca acetate added, giving precipitate of Ca oxalate	Filtered, added to H_2SO_4 and titrated with MnO_4^-	1

Materials titrated	Reagent and reaction conditions	Subsequent treatment and final titration stage	Ref.
Laevulinic acid	+ $CaCO_3$ to prepare the Ca salt	Determined with alkali/ excess iodine (see Iodine reagents, ref. 27)	2
d-Tartaric acid	+ excess *l*-tartrate + Ca acetate, giving precipitate of Ca racemate	Precipitate titrated with MnO_4^-	3, 5
d-Tartaric acid	Criticism of method of ref. 3		4
Oxalic acid from determination of propionic acid by oxidation with MnO_4^-/alkali	+ Ca(II) reagent, giving Ca oxalate	Titrated precipitate with MnO_4^- (see Permanganate, ref. 42)	6
Lactic acid	+ acetic acid/Ca acetate, giving precipitate of Ca lactate	Titrated with MnO_4^-	7
Oxalic acid in blood (deproteinized)	+ $CaCl_2$; 30–60 min	Centrifuged, Ca oxalate precipitate dissolved in H_2SO_4 and titrated with MnO_4^-	8
Oxalate in urine (deproteinized)	+ Na acetate + $CaCl_2$; 12 h/0°	Precipitate ultimately dissolved in H_2SO_4, $MnSO_4$ + excess MnO_4^- added and after 3 min, I^- added and titrated with thiosulphate (see Permanganate, ref. 50)	9
Oxalate in plant tissue	Extract, + dil. acetic acid + $CaCl_2$; 3 min boiling, then 12–16 h at room temp.	Precipitate dissolved in H_2SO_4 and titrated with MnO_4^-	10
—COOH groups in polysaccharides, artificial silks, etc.	+ Ca acetate; 30 min	Filtered and filtrate titrated with NaOH to phenolphthalein	11
Cresols	+ $Ca(OH)_2/CaCO_3$; 1 h shaking, then left overnight	Filtrate + NH_4Cl + oxalate, giving Ca oxalate; precipitate dissolved in H_2SO_4 and titrated with MnO_4^- (see Carboxylic acids, ref. 13)	12
Oxalic acid in urine	+ measured amount oxalic acid + Na acetate + Ca acetate. Left overnight	Precipitate + H_2SO_4 + excess MnO_4^-; then + I^- and back titrated with thiosulphate	13

Materials titrated	Reagent and reaction conditions	Subsequent treatment and final titration stage	Ref.
Oxalate in urine	+ dilute NaOH + $CaCl_2$; 1 h/room temp.	Centrifuged, precipitate + H_2SO_4 + $MnSO_4$ + excess MnO_4^-; after 3 min, I^- added and titrated with thiosulphate	14
Oxalate	+ acetate buffer (pH 5·6) + Ca acetate. Not less than 2 h	Filtered, Ca oxalate dissolved in H_2SO_4 and titrated with MnO_4^-	15
—COOH groups in cellulose oxidized with NO_2	+ Ca acetate; 2 h/25°	Liberated acetic acid titrated with NaOH	16
	(modification of method of ref. 11)		
Oxalic acid in urine	Extract with ether, + acetic acid + ethanol; ether evaporated, then + $CaCl_2$ and left overnight	Centrifuged precipitate + acid + excess MnO_4^-; unused determined after 8–10 min via addition of I^- and titration with thiosulphate	17
Tartrate	+ Ca(II), giving Ca tartrate precipitate; 10 h	Filtered, dissolved in H_2SO_4 and titrated with MnO_4^-	18
—COOH groups in cellulose oxidized with CrO_3 or hypochlorite	At pH not below 6·3, + Ca acetate; 24 h/25°	Titrated with alkali	19
(compared with Ag(I) method and preferred if negative groups present)			
—COOH groups in cotton celluloses and oxycelluloses	At pH 6·5–6·7, + Ca acetate; 17 h	Titrated with NaOH to pH 8·4–8·6 (to cresol red/thymol blue)	20
Basic groups in amino acids and proteins	+ $Ca(NO_3)_2/Ca(OH)_2$. Shaken 2 h	Filtered and filtrate titrated with HCl	21
—COOH groups in cellulose oxidized with NO_2; also celluronic and alginic acids		Method of ref. 16, but with potentiometric titration with NaOH	22
Oxalate from determination of lactic acid by heating with MnO_4^-/alkali	+ Ca(II) reagent	Ca oxalate precipitate dissolved in H_2SO_4 and titrated with MnO_4^- (see Permanganate, ref. 87)	23
d-Tartrate in wine must	+ NH_4 *l*-tartrate + Ca acetate, giving precipitate of Ca racemate	Precipitate filtered, dissolved in H_2SO_4 and determined with IO_4^- (see Periodates and periodic acid, ref. 50)	24

Materials titrated	Reagent and reaction conditions	Subsequent treatment and final titration stage	Ref.
Oxalate in fermentation media (micro)	At pH 4–5·6, + Ca acetate	Ca oxalate precipitate + H_2SO_4 + $MnSO_4$ and titrated with MnO_4^-	25
Oxalate in fresh plant material	Extract with HCl, + NH_4OH + $CaCl_2$. Left overnight/5–7°	Centrifuged, precipitate dissolved in H_2SO_4 and titrated with MnO_4^-	26
—COOH in oxidized starches (giving a measure of the degree of oxidation)	+ Ca acetate; 30 min shaking	Liberated acetic acid titrated with NaOH to pH 8·3 (potentiometrically)	27
—COOH groups in CrO_3 oxystarches	At pH 8·2, + Ca acetate; 24 h/room temp.	Acetic acid titrated with NaOH to pH of blanks	28
Pectin	Alkaline extract, + acetic acid + $CaCl_2$; 10 min, giving precipitate of Ca pectate	Filtered, borax/NaOH/Na_2S buffer added, + excess EDTA and back titrated with $CaCl_2$ to eriochrome black T	29
Oxalic acid in blood plasma, serum and red cells	+ Ca(II) reagent, giving Ca oxalate precipitate	Titrated with MnO_4^-	30
Fatty acid in unbuilt soap products	In water, + excess $CaCl_2$. Heated to boiling	Cooled, filtered, NaOH added to filtrate and unused Ca(II) titrated with EDTA to murexide	31
—COOH groups in cellulosic materials	At pH 6·5–7, + Ca acetate	Filtered and unused Ca(II) in filtrate titrated with EDTA to eriochrome black T	32
Saponified (with NaOH) monoesters and -chlorides of oxalic acid in their determination	+ Na acetate and $CaCl_2$ added to boiling solution	Filtered and unused Ca(II) titrated with EDTA to eriochrome black	33
Oleate and oleic acid in fats, soaps	+ $CaCl_2$/KOH, with shaking	Unused Ca(II) titrated with EDTA to murexide	34
Small amounts of oxalic acid in glucoheptonic acid lactone	Boiling solution, + $CaCl_2$. Left overnight	Filtered, precipitate + H_2SO_4 and titrated with MnO_4^-	35
—COOH in celluloses	Method of ref. 32		36
Fatty acids in toilet soap	In water, + excess $CaCl_2$; heated until coagulation occurred	Filtered and unused Ca(II) titrated with EDTA to chromogen black	37

Materials titrated	Reagent and reaction conditions	Subsequent treatment and final titration stage	Ref.
Citric and oxalic acids in fermantation mixtures	+ $Ca(OH)_2$ + $CaCO_3$ giving pH 8	Precipitate dissolved in H_2SO_4 and acids determined by oxidation with excess $Cr_2O_7^{2-}$ and iodometric back titration; oxalic acid alone determined by reprecipitation with $CaCl_2$ and titration with MnO_4^- (see Bichromate and chromic oxide, ref. 259)	38
Oxalic acid in spinach (water extract)	Solution containing CCl_3COOH, + borax/ NH_4Cl, boiled, Ca acetate added; 2 min stirring at boiling point	Centrifuged, precipitate dissolved in H_2SO_4 and titrated with MnO_4^- at 80°	39
–COOH groups in insoluble carbonaceous materials	+ water + Ca acetate/ water; heated	Acetic acid set free continuously distilled and titrated with NaOH to *o*-cresolphthalein	40

References

1. Ulzer, F. and Seidel, H., *Monatsh.* **18**, 138 (1897).
2. Savaré, B., *Gazz. Chim. Ital.* **36**, II 344 (1906).
3. Kling, A., *Ann. fals.* **4**, 186 (1911).
4. François, M. and Lormand, C., *Ann. fals.* **16**, 602 (1923); *Ann. chim. anal. chim. appl.* **5**, 33 (1924).
5. Kling, A. and Lassieur, A., *Ann. fals.* **17**, 162 (1924); *Ann. chim. anal. chim. appl.* **6**, 103 (1924).
6. McNair, J. B., *J. Am. Chem. Soc.* **54**, 3249 (1932).
7. Hartmann, B. G. and Hillig, F., *J. Assoc. Off. Agr. Chem.* **16**, 435 (1933).
8. Izumi, S., *Japan J. Med. Sci. II, Biochem.* **2**, 195 (1933).
9. Maugeri, S., *Z. physiol. Chem.* **217**, 138 (1933).
10. Sotnikov, E. I., *Compt. rend. acad. sci. URSS* No. 6, 83 (1933A).
11. Lüdtke, M., *Biochem. Z.* **268**, 372 (1933); *Angew. Chem.* **48**, 650 (1935).
12. Münch, W., *Z. anal. Chem.* **98**, 107 (1934).
13. Koch, K., *Biochem. Z.* **283**, 422 (1936).
14. Oikawa, S., *Japan J. Med. Sci. II Biochem.* **3**, 211 (1937).
15. Pucher, G. W., Wakeman, A. J. and Vickery, H. B., *Ind. Eng. Chem., Anal. Ed.* **13**, 244 (1941).
16. Yackel, E. C. and Kenyon, W. O., *J. Am. Chem. Soc.* **64**, 121 (1942).
17. Powers, H. H. and Levatin, P., *J. Biol. Chem.* **154**, 207 (1944).

18. Touratier, M., *Ann. chim. anal.* **27**, 112 (1945).
19. Meesook, B. and Purves, C. B., *Paper Trade J.* **123**, No. 18, 35 (1946); *Tech. Assoc. Papers Ser.* **29**, 508 (1946).
20. Davidson, G. F. and Nevell, T. P., *Shirley Inst. Mem.* **21**, 85 (1947).
21. Grettie, D. P., *Science* **106**, 277 (1947).
22. McGee, D. A., Fowler, W. F. and Kenyon, W. O., *J. Am. Chem. Soc.* **69**, 347 (1947).
23. Hummel, V., *Listy Cukrovar* **64**, 229 (1948); *Chem. Obzor* **23**, 42 (1948).
24. Poux, C., *Ann. fals.* **42**, 439 (1949).
25. Halliwell, G., *Anal. Chem.* **22**, 1184 (1950).
26. Baker, C. J. L., *Analyst* **77**, 340 (1952).
27. Mattisson, M. F. and Legendre, K. A., *Anal. Chem.* **24**, 1942 (1952).
28. Ellington, A. C. and Purves, C. B., *Can. J. Chem.* **31**, 801 (1953).
29. Holt, R., *Analyst* **79**, 623 (1954).
30. Grott, J. V., *Acta Gastro-Enterol. Belg.* **18**, 772 (1955).
31. Webster, H. L. and Robinson, A., *Analyst* **80**, 616 (1955).
32. Sobue, H. and Okubo, M., *Tappi* **39**, 415 (1956).
33. Hennart, C. and Merlin, E., *Anal. Chim. Acta* **17**, 534 (1957).
34. Antonacci, M., *Chim. e ind.* (*Milan*) **42**, 375 (1960).
35. Traiter, M., *Chem. Zvesti* **14**, 623 (1960).
36. Samuelson, O. and Törneli, B., *Svensk Papperstidn.* **64**, 198 (1961).
37. Bartashevich, E. I. and Kopysev, V. A., *Maslob.-Zhir. Prom.* **28**, No. 9 34 (1962).
38. Bártfay, J. and Varga, M., *Magyar Kem. Lapya* **17**, 430 (1962).
39. Kovacs, A. S. and Denker, P., *Ind. Obst-Gemüseverwert.* **47**, 250 (1962).
40. Fester, J. I. and Robinson, W. E., *Anal. Chem.* **36**, 1392 (1964).

19. Carbon disulphide

Reagent and reaction conditions. Mostly in alkaline solution (with alkali hydroxide, ammonium hydroxide).

Sometimes in presence of a Ni(II) compound (although this may be added later) where a Ni(II) derivative is ultimately precipitated (see below).

Reactions, materials titrated and subsequent procedure. CS_2 evidently enters into 3 types of reaction:

1. Dithiocarbamate formation in determination of —NH_2 and —NH— groups,

$$RNH_2 + CS_2 \rightarrow RNH\text{—}CS\text{—}SH$$

$$R_2NH + CS_2 \rightarrow R_2N\text{—}CS\text{—}SH$$

Several titration methods have been proposed for determination of the dithiocarbamates:

(i) titration with NaOH to phenol- or thymolphthalein,

(ii) via formation of insoluble salts with metals, e.g.

(a) titration with Cu(II),

(b) coulometric titration with Hg(I) or Hg(II),

(c) precipitation as Ni(II) salt. This has then been determined by decomposition with HNO_3 and ultimately titrating with EDTA; by treating with excess EDTA and back titrating with Ni(II); or by converting to Ag dithiocarbamate and titration of the liberated Ni(II) with EDTA. As mentioned above, the Ni(II) may be present in the reagent or may be added in a second stage of the determination.

(iii) titration of the dithiocarbamate with $HClO_4$ in non-aqueous solution.

2. Xanthate formation, in determination of primary or secondary alcohols. The reaction is analogous to that with amines above:

$$ROH + CS_2 + OH^- \rightarrow RO{-}CS{-}S^- + H_2O$$

(the reaction is carried out in alkaline solution because the free acids RO—CS—SH are unstable and decompose into the starting materials). The xanthates have been determined like the dithiocarbamates by precipitation as Ni salts, which were then titrated with EDTA. In addition, iodometric titration has also been used, based on the oxidation reaction:

$$2\ RO{-}CS{-}S^- + I_2 \rightarrow (RO{-}CS{-}S{-})_2 + 2\ I^-$$

(see in this part and in Part I, under 'Iodine').

3. A single example has been found of determination of a guanidine derivative (diphenyl guanidine) via replacement of the =NH group with =S:

$$C_6H_5NH{-}\underset{\underset{NH}{\|}}{C}{-}NHC_6H_5 + CS_2 \rightarrow C_6H_5NH{-}\underset{\underset{S}{\|}}{C}{-}NHC_6H_5 + HSCN$$

(as salt of diphenyl guanidine)

The determination was concluded by titration of the SCN^- with Ag(I) to Fe(III) indicator.

Examples

Materials titrated	Reagent and reaction conditions	Subsequent treatment and final titration state	Ref.
Dimethylamine	In water, + NH_4OH + CS_2; 15 min/25°	Titrated with $CuSO_4$ until spot test with dithiocarbamate (evidently for Cu(II)) was negative	1
Diphenyl guanidine	Refluxed with CS_2/ethanol/a little CaO	Evaporated to dryness and SCN^- titrated with $AgNO_3$ to Fe(III) indicator	2
Primary and secondary alcohols (determination of molecular weight)	Alcohol + solid KOH (heated until dissolved) + ether + CS_2	K xanthate filtered and titrated with iodine (see Part I, Iodine, ref. 40)	3
Secondary amines in presence of primary and tertiary	In benzene or isopentanol, + CS_2 + $NiSO_4$	Ni salt from the primary amine extracted with NaOH/NH_4OH; that from the secondary amine decomposed with HNO_3 or, with small samples, treated with $AgNO_3$; liberated Ni(II) then titrated with EDTA to murexide	4
Ethanol in dilute aqueous solution	+ CS_2 + KOH + dioxan; 80–90 min/40–45° (giving 73% conversion to xanthate—this empirical factor used in the determination)	+ some acetic acid and CO_2 passed through for 40 min; then + Ni(II) acetate, giving Ni xanthate; after 10–15 min, filtered, dissolved in NH_4OH and Ni(II) titrated with EDTA to murexide (see Nickel(II), ref. 2)	5
Monomethylamine in presence of other methylamines	+ CS_2 + NaOH, giving dithiocarbamates	Dithiocarbamate from the primary amine precipitated from neutral solution with Ni(II) and determined with excess EDTA, back titrating with $NiSO_4$ to murexide (see Nickel(II), ref. 3)	6
Primary and secondary amines; latter after removal of former with 2-ethylhexaldehyde; also morpholine, unused from determination of acetic anhydride	In an appropriate mixture of pyridine, isopropanol, and water (depending on the amine) + CS_2	Titrated with NaOH to phenol- or thymolphthalein (below 0° in presence of more NH_4OH)	7

Materials titrated	Reagent and reaction conditions	Subsequent treatment and final titration stage	Ref.
Hexamethylenimine in presence of hexamethylenediamine	In water, + CS_2/benzene + Ni(II) salt	Benzene layer shaken with $AgNO_3/NH_4OH$ and the liberated Ni(II) titrated with EDTA to murexide (see Silver(I), ref. 152)	8
Secondary amines, e.g. diethyl-, dipropyl-, dibutylamines, morpholine; also in presence of primary amines after removal of these with salicylaldehyde	+ acetone/CS_2,3:1 + $NaClO_4.H_2O$; 10 min in N_2 current	Dithiocarbamate titrated coulometrically with Hg(II) (Hg anode) (see Part I, Mercury(II), ref. 52)	9
Primary and secondary amines	Filtrate from ammonia determination, + n-butanol/pyridine, neutralized with NaOH, then + CS_2	Titrated with NaOH potentiometrically	10
Piperazine, *N*-hydroxyethyl- and *N*-dihydroxyethylpiperidine	In $CHCl_3$ + CS_2; 40–80 min reflux, giving reaction of the first two	Dithiocarbamates dissolved in acetonitrile and titrated with $HClO_4$ to crystal violet; third base (not reacting with CS_2) titrated in filtrate	11
Higher aliphatic amines (primary & secondary)	+ $CS_2/CHCl_3$/isopropanol	Titrated with NaOH to phenolphthalein	12

References

1. Katcher, E. F. and Voroshilova, N., *Anilinokrasochnaya Prom.* **4**, 39 (1934).
2. Minatoya, S., Kojima, K., Aoe, I., Ebe, T. and Nagai, I., *Researches Electrotech. Lab.* (*Tokyo*) No. 385; see also *J. Soc. Rubber Ind.* (*Japan*) **8**, 328 (1935).
3. Whitmore, W. F. and Lieber, E., *Ind. Eng. Chem., Anal. Ed.* **7**, 127 (1935).
4. Nebbia, L. and Guerrieri, F., *Chim. e Ind.* (*Milan*) **35**, 896 (1953).
5. Arikawa, Y. and Kato, T., *Tech. Reports Tohoku Univ.* **19**, 104 (1954); also Arikawa, Y., *Bunseki Kagaku* (*Japan Analyst*) **4**, 94 (1955).
6. Nebbia, L. and Guerrieri, F., *Chim. e Ind.* (*Milan*) **37**, 198 (1955).
7. Critchfield, F. E. and Johnson, J. B., *Anal. Chem.* **28**, 430 (1956).
8. Nebbia, L. and Guerrieri, F., *Chim. e Ind.* (*Milan*) **39**, 672 (1957).

9. Przybylowicz, E. P. and Rogers, L. B., *Anal. Chim. Acta* **18**, 596 (1958).
10. Bellen, N. and Bellen, Z., *Chem. Anal.* (*Warsaw*) **6**, 63 (1961).
11. Toldy, E., Csillag, F., Bobák, T. and Gyenes, I., *Magyar Kem. Folyoirat* **67**, 180 (1961).
12. Oktawiec, C., *Prace Inst. Hutn.* **14**, 203 (1962).

20. Carbonyl compounds

Reagent. Principally formaldehyde, with occasional use of other aldehydes like benzaldehyde and salicylaldehyde. Dimedone and 2,4-pentanedione are also classified here.

Reactions and materials titrated. All methods depend on a condensation reaction. One of two types may occur, depending on the reagent:

1. Condensation of the reagent carbonyl group with an $—NH_2$ group in primary amines, amino acids and related compounds, or in hydrazines. In the case of carbazole, condensation with a nuclear $=CH—$ group evidently takes place, or possibly addition introducing a hydroxymethyl group.

$$RNH_2 + ArCHO \rightarrow ArCH{=}NR + H_2O$$

$$RNH_2 + CH_3COCH_2COCH_3 \rightarrow CH_3C({=}NR)CH_2COCH_3 \rightleftharpoons CH_3C({=}NR)CH{=}\underset{\displaystyle OH}{\underset{|}{C}}.CH_3 + H_2O$$

$$HOOC—X—NH_2 + HCHO \rightarrow HOOC—X—N{=}CH_2 + H_2O$$

This last quoted equation is the basis of the so-called 'Sörensen' titration of amino acids and many examples are to be found in the medical, biochemical, agricultural and other specialist literature; only a small number of examples has been given here.

2. Condensation of the active $—CH_2—$ group of the reagent (dimedone) with aldehydes, giving poorly soluble products

$$2\,(CH_3)_2C\begin{matrix}\diagup CH_2—CO \diagdown \\ \diagdown CH_2—CO \diagup\end{matrix}CH_2 + RCHO$$

$$\rightarrow \left((CH_3)_2C\begin{matrix}\diagup CH_2—CO \diagdown \\ \diagdown CH_2—CO \diagup\end{matrix}CH—\right)_2 CHR + H_2O$$

Formaldehyde and acetaldehyde have been determined in this way.

Reaction conditions. As a rule, amino acids have been determined in aqueous solution and primary amines reacted in organic solvents. Most of the reactions are fairly fast.

Subsequent treatment and final titration stage. Three distinct techniques may be distinguished:

(i) Back titration of unused reagent has been carried out with dimedone, 2,4-pentanedione and salicylaldehyde, using an alkali or alkoxide titrant.

(ii) Determination of an unchanged functional group or compound class. This is the most usual final stage and there are two types, namely:

1. Titration with alkali of the —COOH groups in amino acids after condensation with HCHO of the $—NH_2$ group to the azomethine group $—N{=}CH_2$. The latter group is much more weakly basic than the original $—NH_2$ group and does not interfere in the alkali titration.

2. Titration of unused secondary and/or tertiary amines after conversion of the primary amines to Schiff's bases. This has usually been with HCl or $HClO_4$ in non-aqueous solution but in one instance the unchanged secondary amines were determined by reaction with CS_2 to give dithiocarbamic acids which were then titrated with alkali.

(iii) Determination of various reaction products, which includes:
titration of water with the Karl Fischer reagent
titration using alkali of the precipitates with dimedone
titration with acid of anils and hydrazones
splitting of combined HCHO from the reaction product with carbazole and determination of it with alkali/H_2O_2.

Examples

Materials titrated	Reagent and reaction conditions	Subsequent treatment and final titration stage	Ref.
Amino acids	+ HCHO/50% ethanol at pH 9–9·5 + excess $Ba(OH)_2$	+ HCl and finally titrated with $Ba(OH)_2$ to phenol- or thymolphthalein	1
Amino acids	Solution neutralized to litmus, + neutral HCHO	Titrated with NaOH to comparison colour of a blank	2
Amino acids, e.g. cysteine or hippuric acid	+ excess NaOH + HCHO	Titrated with HCl	3
Amino acids	Solution neutralized to neutral red, + HCHO	Titrated with NaOH to pH 8·5 (phenolphthalein)	4

Materials titrated	Reagent and reaction conditions	Subsequent treatment and final titration stage	Ref.
Amino acids in protein hydrolysates	Neutral alcoholic solution + HCHO	Titrated with NaOH to phenolphthalein	5
HCHO, acetaldehyde	+ excess dimedone; 12 h/50° then 12–16 h/ room temp., giving precipitate of condensation product	1. Filtered and unused dimedone titrated with alkali 2. precipitate dissolved in ethanol and titrated with NaOH to phenolphthalein 3. with HCHO, unused reagent directly titrated with alkali	6
Amino acids in products of the sugar industry	Neutral solution + HCHO	Titrated with NaOH to pH 9	7
Amino acids, e.g. glycine, *dl*-alanine	In water, + HCHO (pretreated with $MgCO_3$ to remove formic acid)	Titrated with NaOH potentiometrically	8
Carbazole	Refluxed 20 min with $HCHO/K_2CO_3$, giving *N*-hydroxymethyl derivative as precipitate	Filtered, product heated with water, setting HCHO free, determined with H_2O_2/alkali (see Hydrogen peroxide, ref. 11)	9
Amino acids	Method of ref. 1		10
Amino acids; peptones	Neutralized to bromothymol blue, then + HCHO neutralized to phenolphthalein	Titrated with alkali to phenolphthalein	11
Primary amines	In dry pyridine + benzaldehyde; 30 min/60°	+ NaCN/HCN/pyridine to decompose unreacted aldehyde and after 45 min titrated with Karl Fischer reagent	12
Primary amines in mixture with secondary and tertiary	+ salicylaldehyde/ methanol; 30 min/room temp.	Secondary and tertiary amines titrated with HCl/isopropanol potentiometrically	13
Some synthetic amine salts, e.g. ephedrine hydrochloride, synephrine tartrate	Principle of method of ref. 1		14
Primary amines in mixture with secondary and tertiary	In isopropanol/ethylene glycol, + salicylaldehyde; 30 min/room temp.	Unreacted secondary and tertiary amines titrated with HCl/isopropanol/ethylene glycol potentiometrically (see Part I, Hydrochloric acid, ref. 25)	15

Materials titrated	Reagent and reaction conditions	Subsequent treatment and final titration stage	Ref.
Amine nitrogen in protein hydrolysates	At pH 6, + HCHO at pH 7·5	Titrated with NaOH to pH 9	16
Glycine; histidine hydrochloride	+ neutral HCHO	Titrated with NaOH to pH 9·4 potentiometrically	17
Ethylenediamine	Solution neutralized to methyl orange, + HCHO; 10 min/room temp.	Titrated with NaOH	18
Mixtures of primary, secondary and tertiary amines	+ 2-ethylhexaldehyde (+ isopropanol in some cases); 5 min/ room temp., converting primary amine to Schiff's base	+ pyridine/water/isopropanol + CS_2 at − 10°, converting the secondary amines into dithiocarbamic acids; titrated with NaOH to phenolphthalein (see Carbon disulphide, ref. 7)	19
Aliphatic primary amines	+ salicylaldehyde/ pyridine; 15 min/ room temp.	Unused aldehyde back titrated with $NaOCH_3$/methanol–pyridine to phenol- or thymol-phthalein (see Part I, Alkoxides, ref. 66)	20
Histidine hydro-chloride	In water, + HCHO	Titrated with NaOH to phenolphthalein	21
Mixtures of primary, secondary and tertiary amines	In $CHCl_3$, + salicyl-aldehyde; 15 min/ room temp.	Secondary and tertiary amines titrated with $HClO_4$/ dioxan to bromocresol green; congo red added and Schiff's base from the primary amine titrated with the $HClO_4$ (see Part I, Perchloric acid, ref. 167)	22
Primary aliphatic amines (including amino acids, alcohol-amines and alkyleneamines)	+ 2,4-pentanedione/ pyridine; 15 min–2 h/ room temp. to 98°	Unreacted dione titrated with $NaOCH_3$/methanol/pyridine to thymolphthalein (see Part I, Alkoxides, ref. 78)	23
HCHO in presence of polymer	+ acetate buffer, pH 4·6 + dimedone/ water; 3 h/room temp., giving precipitate of condensation product	Precipitate dissolved in ethanol and titrated with NaOH to phenolphthalein or potentiometrically	24, 26
Amino acids from acid hydrolysis of poly-amides, e.g. polyamino-undecanoic acid	Neutralized solution + HCHO	Titrated with KOH	25

Materials titrated	Reagent and reaction conditions	Subsequent treatment and final titration stage	Ref.
Amino acid from acid hydrolysis of *D*-pantothenol	Neutralized solution + HCHO	Titrated with NaOH	27
'Formaldehyde number' of orange juice	At pH 8 + HCHO at pH 8	Titrated with NaOH back to pH 8	28
Mixtures of hexamethylenediamine and hexamethyleneimine	In aqueous alcohol, + salicylaldehyde	Unreacted imine titrated with HCl	29
Proteins in cheese, after heating with NaOH	At pH 8–8·5, + HCHO at the same pH	Titrated with NaOH electrometrically	30
Mixtures of hydrazine, 1,1-dimethylhydrazine and diethylenetriamine	In methanol, + salicylaldehyde, yielding azine, dimethylhydrazone and anil;	Secondary —NH groups in the anil titrated with acid;	31
	in acetic acid, + salicylaldehyde, yielding same products	hydrazone and all nitrogen in the anil titrated with acid	
	(also titrated total in acetic acid)		
Amino acids in wine, e.g. alanines, phenylalanine, lysine, proline, tyrosine	+ $BaCl_2$ + NaOH to pH 9 (phenolphthalein) + HCHO	Immediately titrated with NaOH to bright red, then with HCl to colourless	32
ε-Aminocaproic acid in its lactam	In water, neutralized to phenolphthalein, + HCHO; 10 min	+ NaOH and titrated with HCl to phenolphthalein	33
Mixtures of primary, secondary and tertiary amines	Aliquot in acetic acid, + Hg acetate + salicylaldehyde; 1h/80–90°	+ acetone and secondary + tertiary amines titrated with $HClO_4$/acetic acid potentiometrically	34
	(combined with titration of total with acid and of tertiary after acetylation with acetic anhydride)		
ε-Aminocaproic acid from determination of caprolactam by hydrolysis with alkali and precipitation as Ba salt	Neutralized solution (Ba salt + HCl) + 30% HCHO; 10 min	Titrated with NaOH potentiometrically or to phenolphthalein	35

References

1. Sörensen, S. P. L., *Biochem. Z.* **7**, 45 (1908); *Z. physiol. Chem.* **63**, 27 (1909); **64**, 120 (1910). (with Henriques, V.)

2. König, J. and Grossfeld, J., *Z. Untersuch. Nahr. u. Genussm.* **27**, 508 (1914).
3. Iodidi, S. L., *J. Am. Chem. Soc.* **48**, 751 (1926).
4. Northrop, J. H., *J. Gen. Physiol.* **9**, 767 (1926).
5. Davies, W. L., *Biochem. J.* **21**, 815 (1927).
6. Vorländer, D., Ihle, C. and Volkholz, H., *Z. anal. Chem.* **77**, 321 (1929).
7. Riehm, H., *Z. Wirtschaftsgruppe Zuckerind.* **85**, 381 (1935).
8. Dunn, M. S. and Loshakoff, A., *J. Biol. Chem.* **113**, 359 (1936).
9. Il'inski, M. and Roshal, R. B., *Compt. rend. acad. sci. URSS* **17**, 117 (1937).
10. Al'per-Yul'chevskaya, B. Ya. and Nemova, S. V., *Lab. Prakt.* (*USSR*) **16**, No. 2, 61 (1941).
11. Auronsseau, L., *J. pharm. chim.* (9) **1**, 329 (1941).
12. Hawkins, W., Smith, D. M. and Mitchell, J., *J. Am. Chem. Soc.* **66**, 1662 (1944).
13. Wagner, C. D., Brown, R. H. and Peters, E. D., *J. Am. Chem. Soc.* **69**, 2611 (1947).
14. Stempel, B., *Ber.* **81**, 80 (1948).
15. Siggia, S., Hanna, J. G. and Kervenski, I. R., *Anal. Chem.* **22**, 1295 (1950).
16. Ganguly, S. K., *J. Proc. Inst. Chemists* (*India*) **24**, 48 (1952).
17. Golstein, S. W., *Drug Standards* **20**, 223 (1952).
18. De Lorenzi, F., *Boll. chim. farm.* **94**, 343 (1955).
19. Critchfield, F. E. and Johnson, J. B., *Anal. Chem.* **28**, 430 (1956).
20. Johnson, J. B. and Funk, G. L., *Anal. Chem.* **28**, 1977 (1956).
21. Khait, G. Ya., *Aptechnoe Delo* **5**, No. 5, 59 (1956).
22. Critchfield, F. E. and Johnson, J. B., *Anal. Chem.* **29**, 957 (1957).
23. Critchfield, F. E. and Johnson, J. B., *Anal. Chem.* **29**, 1174 (1957).
24. Bellen, Z., *Chim. anal.* **40**, 250 (1958).
25. Schröder, E., *Plaste u. Kautschuk* **5**, 103 (1958).
26. Bellen, Z., *Chem. Anal.* (*Warsaw*) **4**, 13 (1959).
27. Helou, J. H., *Anais farm. e quím.*, *Sao Paulo* **10**, 73 (1959).
28. Intouli, R., Ramuzino, F. C. and Stacchini, A., *Ind. conserve* (*Parma*) **34**, 222 (1959).
29. Khudyakova, T. A., Nemtseva, L. I. and Belousova, Z. S., *Tr. po Khim. i Khim. Tekhnol.* **4**, 772 (1961).
30. Armandola, P., *Latte* **36**, 709 (1962).
31. Malone, H. E. and Barron, R. E., *US Dept. Com. Office Tech. Serv.* AD 278, 499 (1962).
32. Politova-Souzenko, T. K., *Vinodelie i Vinogradarstvo SSSR* **22**, No. 8 18 (1962).
33. Majewska, J., *Chem. Anal.* (*Warsaw*) **8**, 589 (1963)
34. Strepikheev, Yu. A., Zalikin, A. A. and Chimishkyan, A. L., *Zhur. Anal. Khim.* **18**, 1262 (1963).
35. Ziotkowski, Z., Respondek, J. and Przondo, J., *Chem. Anal.* (*Warsaw*) **8**, 273 (1963).

21. Carboxylic acids and carboxylates

Reagent. Eight different reagents are given in the tables below, and include aliphatic and aromatic acids, mono- and dicarboxylic acids. Formic, acetic and oxalic acids have been the most used. (Salicylic acid is classified under 'Phenols', since its use depends on the phenolic group.)

Reactions and materials titrated. As expected from the variety of reagents (and reaction conditions) many different reactions have been exploited:

1. Ion/ion combination, yielding water-insoluble products. Aniline, substituted anilines, melamine and ephedrine have been thus determined by precipitation as oxalates. The same reagent has served to determine some calcium salts by precipitation (although this is the determination of Ca^{2+}, some examples are included of calcium salts of organic compounds). Alkyl thiouronium salts have also been determined by precipitation with 3,5-dinitrobenzoate.

2. Ester-formation, for determination of hydroxy compounds, notably of lower alcohols and those in essential oils. Apart from one example of the use of lauric acid, only formic and acetic acids have been used. Catalysts for the esterification have been BF_3,H_2SO_4 and *p*-toluenesulphonic acid. Formic acid alone and together with acetic anhydride has been used without added catalyst.

3. Addition, usually to olefines like camphene with ester formation:

$$-\underset{|}{C}=\underset{|}{C}- + RCOOH \rightarrow -\underset{|}{CH}-\overset{|}{\underset{|}{C}}-OCOR$$

Formic and acetic acids have been used; camphene thus yields isobornyl formate or acetate; dicyclopentadiene yields dicyclopentenyl formate.

The determination of diazomethane by addition of benzoic acid to give the methyl ester (and nitrogen) can be classified here.

4. Hydration, as in the determination of acetic anhydride and carbodiimide with oxalic acid:

$$(CH_3CO)_2O + (COOH)_2 \rightarrow 2\ CH_3COOH + CO + CO_2$$

5. Reduction, as in the determination of *tert*-butyl hypochlorite with oxalate:

$$C_4H_9OCl + (COOH)_2 \rightarrow C_4H_9OH + HCl + 2\ CO_2$$

6. Racemate formation, used in the determination of one tartaric acid optical isomer by addition of the other and precipitation of the calcium racemate.

7. As mild catalysts (compared to mineral acids) for hydrolysis (e.g. of hexamine to $HCHO + NH_3$; dithiocarbamates to CS_2; novobiocin to *O*-carbamoylnoviose) or decarboxylation, e.g. of aconitic acid.

Reaction conditions. Few general remarks can be made. As already mentioned above, reactions of type 2 (and 3) need usually a strong acid catalyst. Conditions of time and temperature have varied widely from a few minutes at room temperature for precipitations to an hour or more at higher temperature for esterification or decarboxylation.

Subsequent treatment and final titration stage. (i) Unreacted reagent has been back titrated in about half a dozen cases. This has been via acid/base titration (unused acid with alkali or unused acid anion with acid titrant) or, in two examples of the use of oxalic acid reagent, by an oxidimetric procedure with MnO_4^- or Ce(IV).

(ii) The reaction product determined in the other cases is one of 2 types, which can be distinguished by the equations:

1. A	+	X	→	A.X
(Component determined)		(Reagent)		(Salt or racemate or type of loose addition product)

The conclusion has then been in one of 3 ways, namely:

(a) determination of the reagent moiety X, e.g. with alkali, with an oxidizing titrant such as MnO_4^- for oxalates, or with Ti(III) for 3,5-dinitrobenzoates,

(b) determination of the component moiety A, e.g. aniline or *p*-chloroaniline with bromate titrant; the method then consists effectively of isolation of the component by means of the reagent,

(c) Ca racemate from 'reaction' of type 6 above, has been determined by titration with MnO_4^- or periodate.

2. $A + X \rightarrow B + C + D$, etc. . . .

The reaction product most usually encountered here, where covalent bonds are formed and/or broken during reaction, is an ester (reactions 2 and 3 above) and has been determined by a saponification procedure after previous isolation. Two examples are given of the final stage of titration with Karl Fischer reagent of water formed during esterification.

Examples

Materials titrated	Reagent and reaction conditions	Subsequent treatment and final titration stage	Ref.
p-Toluidine from reduction of *p*-nitrotoluene in its determination in a mixture of nitrotoleuenes	In ether, + oxalic acid/ether, giving precipitate of the amine salt	Dissolved in water and titrated with NaOH to phenolphthalein	1
Diazomethane in ether solution	+ benzoic acid (or *m*- or *p*-nitrobenzoic acid)/ether. Cooled, then warmed	Unused acid back titrated with Ba(OH) to phenolphthalein	2
d-Tartaric acid	+ excess *l*-tartrate + Ca acetate, giving precipitate of Ca racemate	Precipitate dissolved in hot H_2SO_4 and titrated with permanganate	3, 6, 8
d-Tartaric acid	Criticism of method of ref. 3		4
—OH groups in essential oils	+ formic acid/acetic anhydride, *ca* 1:2; 3–4 days/room temp.	Ester oil separated and determined by hydrolysis with excess KOH (see Alkalies, ref. 36)	5
Methanol, ethanol	+ large excess formic acid (400–800%) + H_2SO_4	Formate ester distilled and swept out into excess standard alkali; back titrated with acid (see Alkalies, ref. 43)	7
Acetic anhydride	+ excess anhydrous oxalic acid + dry pyridine; 10 min/50°, giving $CO + CO_2$	+ water and unused acid titrated with permanganate	9
Camphene in pine oil	+ acetic acid/water/H_2SO_4. Heated, giving isobornyl acetate	Unreacted acid titrated with KOH to phenolphthalein and then with acid to tetrabromosulphonephthalein	10
Citronellol in otto of roses	+ 90% formic acid; 1 h/100°	Unused acid back titrated with alkali	11
p-Chloroaniline in mixtures of chloroanilines; also from determination of *p*-nitrochlorobenzene after reduction with Zn dust/HCl	In ether, + oxalic acid/ether, giving precipitate of the amine salt	Filtered, dissolved in hot water and titrated with bromate	12

Materials titrated	Reagent and reaction conditions	Subsequent treatment and final titration stage	Ref.
Ca cresolates from determination of cresols by reaction with $CaCO_3/Ca(OH)_2$	+ oxalate, giving precipitate of Ca oxalate	Dissolved in H_2SO_4 and titrated with MnO_4^-	13
Camphene	+ formic acid/H_2SO_4; 2·5–3·5 h/room temp., giving isobornyl formate	+ saturated NaCl to salt out the ester and unused acid titrated with NaOH saturated with NaCl. Control	14
—OH groups	In dioxan, + acetic acid/BF_3; 2 h/67 ± 2°	+ pyridine and water formed titrated with Karl Fischer reagent	15
Aniline in diphenylamine	In absolute ether, + oxalic acid/ether, giving precipitate of aniline oxalate	Dissolved in water and determined with excess bromate/bromide and iodometric back titration of the unused part (see Bromine reagents, ref. 207)	16
Hexamine	Distilled with aqueous solution of tartaric acid, hydrolysing to HCHO	Distilled into $NaHSO_3$ and combined part titrated with iodine	17
Aconitic acid in sugar-house products	Method of ref. 20, absorbing any SO_2 first in bichromate solution		18
Aconitic acid in mixes with citric acid	Method of ref. 20, with boric acid added to reagent to prevent decarboxylation of the citric acid		19
Aconitic acid; aconitates	+ acetic acid/K acetate, with minimum amount water. Heated *ca* 1 h, giving CO_2	Absorbed in excess NaOH, $BaCl_2$ added and back titrated with HCl to phenolphthalein	20
Dicyclopentadiene	+ excess HCOOH. Refluxed 5 h/135–140°, giving dicyclopentenyl formate	Ester product determined by hydrolysis with excess alkali and back titration with acid (see Alkalies, ref. 208)	21
d-Tartaric acid in wine must	+ NH_4 *l*-tartrate + Ca acetate, giving precipitate of Ca racemate	Filtered, dissolved in H_2SO_4 and determined with excess periodate (see Periodates and periodic acid, ref. 50)	22
Pinene/camphor mixtures	+ acetic acid/H_2SO_4; 10 min/50°	Unused acid titrated with NaOH to phenolphthalein. Results evaluated from data with known mixtures	23

Materials titrated	Reagent and reaction conditions	Subsequent treatment and final titration stage	Ref.
Alcohols	+ formic acid/acetic anhydride, *ca* 1:2	+ water + pyridine and titrated with NaOH/alcohol. Control	24
Alcohols	+ excess lauric acid + *p*-toluenesulphonic acid catalyst; 20 min/80° (up to C_4) or 100°	Dissolved in ethanol, titrated to phenolphthalein with NaOH; the Na laurate then titrated with acid to methyl red	25
Melamine	In water, + oxalic acid/ethanol, giving hemioxalate precipitate; 30 min/below 4°	Precipitate + H_2SO_4 and titrated at 70° with MnO_4^-	26
Hydroxyl groups	+ acetic acid/H_2SO_4; 1 h/60°	Water formed titrated with Karl Fischer reagent	27
Ca pantothenate	Hot aqueous solution + NH_4OH + ammonium oxalate. Heated and left 2 h, giving Ca oxalate	Precipitate dissolved in H_2SO_4 and titrated with MnO_4^-	28
Alkyl thiouronium iodides from determination of secondary or tertiary alcohols by conversion to halides with $HCl/ZnCl_2$ and then treatment with thiourea/KI	At pH 5–6 in acetate buffer, + Na 3,5-dinitrobenzoate/water; 2 h heating in sealed ampoule, giving precipitate of dinitrobenzoate	Precipitate + ethanol + Na citrate + excess Ti(III) and back titrated with Fe(III) (see 'Titanium (III)', ref. 51)	29
tert-Butyl hypochlorite (standardization of solution in acetic acid)	Excess Na oxalate + acetic acid + sample; 1 h shaking/room temp., reacting to give CO_2 and *tert*-butyl alcohol	+ water + HCl + a little ICl and unused oxalate titrated with Ce(IV) at 50° to ferroin	30
Camphene	+ $HCOOH/H_2SO_4$; 3 min/room temp., giving isobornyl formate	+ saturated NaCl, ester layer separated and determined by hydrolysis with excess KOH and back titration with H_2SO_4 (see Alkalies, ref. 379)	31
isoborneol	also + HCOOH/H_2SO_4; 15 min/room temp., giving ester	ester layer similarly separated and titrated directly with NaOH. Control	

Materials titrated	Reagent and reaction conditions	Subsequent treatment and final titration stage	Ref.
Novobiocin in presence of isonovobiocin	+ anhydrous trifluoro-acetic acid; 2 h/room temp. in dark, giving 3-*O*-carbamylnoviose	Determined by oxidation with excess periodic acid and back titration with arsenite (see Periodates and periodic acid, ref. 97)	32
Citronellol	+ acetic anhydride/formic acid; 72 h/0°	+ water + NaCl, ester separated and determined by hydrolysis with excess KOH	33
Ascorbigen in brassica	+ 2% acetic acid; 10 min/100° in CO_2 atmosphere, giving ascorbic acid	Titrated with Tillmans' reagent	34
Carbodiimide	+ oxalic acid/dioxan; 45 min reflux in absence of air and water; $RN{=}C{=}NR' + (COOH)_2 \rightarrow RNH{-}CO{-}NHR' + CO + CO_2$	Titrated with $NaOCH_3$/benzene/methanol to thymol blue	35
Ethyl orthoformate	+ acetic acid, giving ethyl formate	Determined with excess BrCl and iodometric back titration (see Bromine reagents, ref. 523)	36

References

1. Glasman, B., *Ber.* **36**, 4260 (1903).
2. Marshall, E. K. and Acree, S. F., *Ber.* **43**, 2323 (1910).
3. Kling, A., *Ann. fals.* **4**, 186 (1911).
4. François, M. and Lormand, C., *Ann. fals.* **16**, 602 (1923); *Ann. chim. anal. chim. appl.* **6**, 33 (1924).
5. Glichitch, L. S., *Bull. soc. chim. France* (4) **33**, 1284 (1923); *Compt. rend.* **177**, 268 (1923).
6. Kling, A. and Lassieur, A., *Ann. fals.* **17**, 162 (1924); *Ann. chim. anal. chim. appl.* **6**, 103 (1924).
7. Wimmer, J., *Z. angew. Chem.* **38**, 721 (1925).
8. Kling, A. and Lassieur, A., *Z. anal. Chem.* **68**, 471 (1926).
9. Rosenbaum, C. K. and Walton, J. K., *J. Am. Chem. Soc.* **52**, 3366 (1930).
10. Ezrielev, I. M. and Magidova, S. S., *Plasticheskie Massui* No. 2–4, 11 (1932).
11. Glichitch, L. S. and Naves, Y.-R., *Parfums de France* **11**, 154 (1933).
12. Mizuch, K. G. and Savchenko, A. Ya., *Anilinokrasochnaya Prom.* **4**, 204 (1934).

13. Münch, W., *Z. anal. Chem.* **98**, 107 (1934).
14. Lyubomilov, V. I., *Org. Chem. Ind. USSR* **6**, 167 (1939).
15. Bryant, W. M. D., Mitchell, J. and Smith, D. M., *J. Am. Chem. Soc.* **62**, 1 (1940).
16. Schretter, O., *Z. anal. Chem.* **122**, 24 (1941).
17. Paulais, R., *Bull. sci. pharm.* **49**, 191 (1942).
18. Ambler, J. A. and Roberts, E. J., *Anal. Chem.* **19**, 877 (1947).
19. Ambler, J. A. and Roberts, E. J., *Anal. Chem.* **19**, 879 (1947).
20. Roberts, E. J. and Ambler, J. A., *Anal. Chem.* **19**, 118 (1947).
21. Bergmann, F. and Japhe, H., *Anal. Chem.* **20**, 146 (1948).
22. Poux, C., *Ann. fals.* **42**, 439 (1949).
23. Fortunato, A. D. and Hourquebie, H., *Rep. Argentina Ministerio ind. y com. nacion, Direc. gen. ind. manuf., Inst. tecnol., Ser. A*, No. 4, **3** (1950).
24. Sabetay, S., *Intern. Perfumer* **1**, No. 2, 11 (1951).
25. Perron, R. and Petit, J., *Bull. soc. chim. France* 1072 (1952).
26. Steel, J. R., Glover, J. H. and Hodgson, H. W., *J. Appl. Chem. (London)* **2**, 296 (1952).
27. Mlejnek, O., *Chem. Zvesti* **9**, 27 (1955).
28. Greulich, J. and Meiner, K., *Pharmazie* **12**, 643 (1957).
29. Jureček, M., Chládek, O., Chládková, R., Souček, M. and Srpová, B., *Chem. Listy* **51**, 448 (1957).
30. Van Hall, C. E. and Stone, K. G., *Anal. Chem.* **30**, 1416 (1958).
31. Blaskowicz, J., Roczniakowa, K., Wantuch, S. and Bukala, M., *Chem. Anal. (Warsaw)* **4**, 719, 725 (1959).
32. Forist, A. A., Theal, S. and Struck, W. A., *Anal. Chem.* **31**, 100 (1959).
33. van Os, F. H. L. and de Boer, G. D., *Pharm. Weekblad* **95**, 735 (1960).
34. Bogdański, K. and Czajka, G., *Chem. Anal. (Warsaw)* **7**, 1149 (1962).
35. Zarembo, J. E. and Watts, M. M., *Microchem. J. Symp. Ser.* **2**, 591 (1962).
36. Barcza, L. and Burger, K., *Magyar Kem. Folyoirat* **69**, 178 (1963).

22. Cerium (IV)

Reagent. Principally ceric sulphate; other reagents include the perchlorate, ammonium (and diethylene tetraammonium) sulphatocerate and ammonium hexanitratocerate. The reagents are always acid, often strongly acid.

Reaction and materials titrated. Oxidation, mostly to carbon dioxide and water

$$Ce^{4+} + \epsilon \rightarrow Ce^{3+}$$

Occasionally the oxidation is halted at an intermediate stage (see below).

Oxidized have been:

(i) Poly- and hydroxycarboxylic acids (e.g. oxalic, malonic, glycollic, tartaric, malic, citric). Formic acid is a stable end-product under certain conditions. Lactic acid has been oxidized to acetaldehyde.

(ii) Mono- and polyhydroxy compounds (alcohols, glycols, phenols, sugars, etc.), yielding CO_2 or formic acid.

(iii) A miscellaneous group, including ketones and ketoacids (e.g. pyruvic), aldehydes (e.g. formaldehyde), aromatic amines and determinations of total organic matter of soils, sewage wastes, etc. (only a single example is given of this latter analysis).

Reaction conditions. In acid, frequently hot, aqueous solution. Catalysts have sometimes been used, such as ICl, OsO_4, Cr(III), Ag(I)/Mn(II), Br^- and I^-; radiation in the visible and ultraviolet region has been used also to accelerate the oxidation.

Some binary mixtures have been analysed by oxidation under two sets of conditions (usually with and without a particular catalyst).

Subsequent treatment and final titration stage. (i) In almost all cases, unused reagent has been determined, using one of the following methods:

1. Titration with Fe(II) (usually the sulphate or ammonium sulphate; there is an example of coulometric back titration with Fe(II)).

2. Titration with oxalate. This has been direct and also indirect by using excess oxalate and following with a back titration by permanganate or Ce(IV).

3. Titration with arsenite in presence of OsO_4 catalyst. As with oxalate, this titration has been both direct and indirect (then using back titration with Ce(IV)).

4. Addition of iodide and titration of the iodine formed with thiosulphate.

5. Titration with hydroquinone.

End-point determination in these titrations has been instrumental (potentiometric chiefly) or with the usual indicators for Ce(IV) and other oxidizing reagents (e.g. ferroin, nitroferroin, *N*-phenylanthranilic acid).

(ii) Determination of a reaction product namely the acetaldehyde derived from lactic acid determination. This was absorbed in bisulphite and the unused bisulphite or the bisulphite/aldehyde addition compound determined iodometrically.

Ref. 17 is to a review of the use of Ce(IV) in analysis. Refs. 57 and 58 are to kinetic studies of oxidation with Ce(IV) of lactic acid and glycerol respectively. Ref. 61 to an article on oxalate interference in Ce (IV) oxidations.

Examples

Materials titrated	Reagent and reaction conditions	Subsequent treatment and final titration stage	Ref.
Some organic acids, e.g. tartaric, malic, malonic, citric, glycollic	+ $Ce(SO_4)_2$; 10–120 min/90–95°, giving CO_2 + formic acid	Unused titrated with Fe(II) potentiometrically	1
Citric acid	+ $Ce(SO_4)_2/H_2SO_4$; 1 h/90–95°, giving CO_2	Unused titrated in hot solution with oxalic acid potentiometrically	2
Pyruvic acid	+ $Ce(SO_4)_2/H_2SO_4$; 5 min, giving CO_2 + acetic acid	Unused titrated with Fe(II)	3
Glycerol	+ $Ce(SO_4)_2$; 1 h reflux, giving tartronic acid	Unused titrated with Fe(II) to xylene cyanol FF	4
Lactic acid in biological material	+ $Ce(SO_4)_2$; 50°, giving CH_3CHO	Aldehyde determined with bisulphite (see Bisulphite and sulphite, ref. 51)	5
Glycerol + dextrose	+ $Ce(SO_4)_2/H_2SO_4$; 1 h/100°	Unused titrated with Fe(II) to ferroin or erioglaucin	6
Oxalate (submicro)	+ $Ce(SO_4)_2/H_2SO_4$ + ICl or OsO_4 catalyst; 30 min/100° in absence of catalyst	Unused titrated with Fe(II) to setopaline C	7
Glycerol	+ $(NH_4)_4Ce(SO_4)_4/H_2SO_4$; 90 min/90–100°; or + $(NH_4)_2Ce(NO_3)_6/HClO_4$ and 15 min/50° (oxidized to formic acid)	Unused titrated with oxalic acid to nitroferroin	8
Lactic acid	+ $Ce(SO_4)_2$; 5 h/25° or 2 h/50°, giving acetaldehyde	Diffused into bisulphite and determined iodometrically (see Bisulphite and sulphite, ref. 65)	9

Materials titrated	Reagent and reaction conditions	Subsequent treatment and final titration stage	Ref.
Polyhydroxy compounds, diketones, some carboxylic acids (compared with periodate oxidation in study of reaction mechanisms)	+ $H_2Ce(ClO_4)_6$/$HClO_4$; 10–120 min/10–45°	Unused titrated with oxalate to nitroferroin	10
Citric acid in milk products (isolated as Pb salt)	+ $Ce(ClO_4)_4/HClO_4$	Unused titrated with oxalate to nitroferroin	11
Glycerol in soap	+ $Ce(ClO_4)_4/HClO_4$; 12–13 min/50°	Unused titrated with oxalate to nitroferroin	12
Pentaerythritol	+ $Ce(ClO_4)_4$	Unused titrated with oxalate	13
Tetrahydrofurfuryl alcohol	+ $Ce(SO_4)_2/H_2SO_4$; 1 h reflux	Unused titrated with Fe(II)	14
Lactic acid	+ $Ce(SO_4)_2$, giving CH_3CHO; 90 min	Aldehyde diffused into bisulphite and determined iodometrically (see Bisulphite and sulphite, ref. 94)	15
Sodium alginate	+ $Ce(SO_4)_2$ + Ag and K sulphates; 2 min boiling	Filtered and unused titrated with Fe(II) to ferroin	16
Total soil organic matter	Short preliminary heating with H_2SO_4/HNO_3, then + $(NH_4)_4Ce(SO_4)_4$ (60 min boiling) or $(NH_4)_2Ce(NO_3)_6$ (5–10 min boiling)	+ water + KI and titrated with thiosulphate	18
α-Tocopherol (from alkali hydrolysis of acetate in serum)	+ $Ce(SO_4)_2/HCl/H_2SO_4$	Unused determined by adding excess oxalic acid and back titrating with permanganate	19
Mono- and polyalcohols; mono-, di- and triphenols; arylamines	+ $Ce(SO_4)_2$. Various reaction conditions	Unused titrated with Fe(II)	20
Polyhydroxy compounds, e.g. mannitol, sorbitol, pentaerythritol, inositol, alginic acid	+ $Ce(SO_4)_2$. Heated	Unused titrated with Fe(II) potentiometrically	21
Monohydric alcohols, e.g. methanol, ethanol, butanol	+ $Ce(SO_4)_2/H_2SO_4$; 2–3 h/100°	Unused titrated with Fe(II) potentiometrically	22

Materials titrated	Reagent and reaction conditions	Subsequent treatment and final titration stage	Ref.
Dihydric phenols	+ $Ce(SO_4)_2$. Heated	As in refs 21, 22	23
Oxalic acid, formed in determination of glutamic acid by reaction with nitrite	+ $Ce(SO_4)_2$; 15 min heating	As in refs 21, 22	24
Lactic acid in wine	+ $Ce(SO_4)_2$, giving CH_3CHO	Distilled into bisulphite and determined iodometrically (see Bisulphite and sulphite, ref. 109)	25
Methanol in water	+ dilute HNO_3 + $(NH_4)_2Ce(NO_3)_6$; 10 min/100°, giving formic acid	+ dilute H_2SO_4 + OsO_4 and unused titrated with arsenite to ferroin	26
Carboxylic acids, formed in determination of amino acids by reaction with nitrite	+ $Ce(SO_4)_2$; 15 min heating	As in refs 21, 22	27
Phenol, pyrogallol, phloroglucinol	+ $Ce(SO_4)_2$. Boiled 50, 5 and 5 min respectively	As in refs 21, 22	28
Aromatic amines, *o*- and *p*-aminophenols, sodium *p*-phenylenediaminesulphonate	+ $Ce(SO_4)_2$; 5 min/*ca* 20° (1 h/100° for last)	As in refs 21, 22	29
Lactic acid in wines, etc.	Boiling solution + $Ce(SO_4)_2/H_2SO_4$ dropwise, giving CH_3CHO; 12 min distillation	Aldehyde distilled into bisulphite and determined iodometrically (see Bisulphite and sulphite, ref. 114)	30
Phenols	In H_2SO_4(pH *ca* 1) + $Ce(SO_4)_2$; 1–3 min/room temp.	Unused titrated with Fe(II) biamperometrically	31
Formic, tartaric, malic, glycollic, maleic, fumaric, benzoic, phthalic, salicylic and other acids	+ $Ce(SO_4)_2/H_2SO_4$; 15 min reflux: acid concentration then raised to 66% and refluxed 1–3 h further. Oxidized to CO_2	Unused titrated with Fe(II) to *N*-phenylanthranilic acid	32, 33
Mandelic acid	+ $Ce(SO_4)_2/H_2SO_4$; 20 min boiling	Unused titrated with Fe(II) to ferroin	34

Materials titrated	Reagent and reaction conditions	Subsequent treatment and final titration stage	Ref.
Dicalcium salt of 2-methyl-1,4-naphthaquinone diphosphate	In water + $Ce(SO_4)_2$ + H_2SO_4; 10 min/room temp.	Unused titrated with hydroquinone to ferroin	35
Methanol, formed by HNO_3 hydrolysis in determination of methoxy groups in methoxyborohydrides	+ $(NH_4)_2Ce(NO_3)_6$; 10 min/100°	+ H_2SO_4 + OsO_4 catalyst and titrated with arsenite to ferroin	36
Sugars	+ $Ce(ClO_4)_4/HClO_4$; 1 h/25°	Unused determined by adding excess oxalate and back titrating with Ce(IV) to nitroferroin; or by adding OsO_4 catalyst and excess arsenite and similarly back titrating with Ce(IV)	37
Oxalic acid	+ $Ce(SO_4)_2/H_2SO_4$; 5–15 min in strong light	Unused titrated with Fe(II) to ferroin	38
Glycerol + glycol	+ $Ce(SO_4)_2$; 30 min reflux, giving formic acid; then Cr(III) catalyst added and further heated giving CO_2	Unused titrated with Fe(II) to *N*-phenylanthranilic acid	39
Oxalic acid	+ $Ce(SO_4)_2$; 80 min/100°	Unused titrated coulometrically with Fe(II)	40
Oxalic acid, hydroquinone	+ diethylene tetraammonium sulphatocerate/H_2SO_4. Hydroquinone oxidized at room temp., oxalic acid on heating	Unused titrated with Fe(II) potentiometrically or to ferroin	41
p-Coumaric acid	+ $Ce(SO_4)_2$/50% H_2SO_4; 2 h heating	Unused titrated with Fe(II) to ferroin	42
Many reducing agents, e.g. oxalate, hydroquinone, pyruvic acid	+ $Ce(SO_4)_2/H_2SO_4$. Heated to 60°	Unused titrated with Fe(II) potentiometrically	43
Formic + acetic acids	+ $Ce(SO_4)_2$; 5 min reflux, oxidizing only oxalic acid; then Cr(III) catalyst added and refluxed 50–80 min, giving CO_2	Unused titrated with Fe(II) to *N*-phenylanthranilic acid	44

Materials titrated	Reagent and reaction conditions	Subsequent treatment and final titration stage	Ref.
Formaldehyde + formic acid	+ $Ce(SO_4)_2$; 5 min boiling, oxidizing aldehyde to acid; then Cr(III) catalyst and H_2SO_4 added, and boiled 75–90 min, giving CO_2	Unused titrated with Fe(II) to *N*-phenylanthranilic acid	45
Antabuse	In acetic acid, + $Ce(SO_4)_2$ + KI catalyst; 5 min/21–3°	Unused titrated with Fe(II) to ferroin	46
Mandelic acid in pharmaceutical preparations	In water, + $Ce(SO_4)_2/H_2SO_4$; 20 min reflux	Back titrated with Fe (II) to ferroin	47
Tartrate, citrate	+ $Ce(ClO_4)_4/HClO_4$; 10 min	Unused titrated with oxalate amperometrically	48
Lactic acid in wine (after preliminary partial separation)	+ $Ce(SO_4)_2$, giving CH_3CHO; 15 min distillation	Distilled into bisulphite and determined unused iodometrically	49
Tartaric acid	+ $Ce(SO_4)_2/H_2SO_4$; refluxed 15 min	Back titrated with Fe (II) to ferroin	50
(study of reaction; 1 mole tartaric acid → $3CO_2$ + HCOOH, via intermediate formation of tartronic acid)			
Hydroxy acids, e.g. malic, lactic, citric, tartaric, mandelic, glycollic	+ $Ce(SO_4)_2/H_2SO_4$; 15–30 min in radiation of 575 mμ	Unused titrated with Fe(II) to ferroin	51
Glucose, fructose, sucrose	+ $Ce(ClO_4)_4/HClO_4$; 35–50 min/60°, giving formic acid + CO_2	Unused titrated with oxalate amperometrically	52
Polyhydric alcohols, e.g. glycerol, erythritol, pentaerythritol; oxine and oxinates	+ $Ce(SO_4)_2/HClO_4$ + Ag(I)/Mn(II) catalyst; heated at 95° till permanganate pink visible (3–5 min)	Unused titrated with Fe(II) to ferroin	53
Formic acid and other acids which yield it during non-catalysed Ce(IV) oxidation (e.g. tartaric, citric)	+ $Ce(SO_4)_2/H_2SO_4$ + Br^- catalyst (evidently yielding bromine); 45–100 min	Unused determined by adding I^- and titrating with thiosulphate	54
Aniline, phenol, β-naphthylamine	In dilute H_2SO_4 + electrolytically generated Ce(IV); room temp.	Back titrated with electrolytically generated Fe(II)	55

Materials titrated	Reagent and reaction conditions	Subsequent treatment and final titration stage	Ref.
oxalic acid, sorbitol, mannitol; hydroxyglutaric acid from determination of glutamic acid by reaction with HNO_2	+ electrolytically generated Ce(IV); 3 min/80–100°	back titrated with electrolytically generated Fe(II)	
Lactic, mandelic, DL-malic acids	+ excess $Ce(SO_4)_2$; several days/25° (kinetic study of oxidation reaction)	Back titrated with ferrous ammonium sulphate to *N*-phenylanthranilic acid	56
Iodine numbers of fatty oils	Oil + ethanol + $Ce(SO_4)_2$ + KI + water (effectively iodine reagent); 5 min/room temp in the dark	Back titrated with thiosulphate	59
Oxalic acid	In acetic acid + $(NH_4)_2Ce(NO_3)_6$/acetonitrile; 5–10 min/room temp. (study of the oxidation, stated to be evidently via the intermediate Ce (IV) oxalate)	Back titrated with hydroquinone/acetic acid or acetonitrile to diphenylamine	60
Oxalic + maleic acids	Refluxed with $Ce(SO_4)_2$ (oxalic acid determined by separate, direct titration)	Back titrated with Fe (II)	62

References

1. Willard, H. H. and Young, P., *J. Am. Chem. Soc.* **52**, 132 (1930).
2. Wilkinson, J. A., Sipherd, I. R., Fulmer, E. I. and Christensen, L. M., *Ind. Eng. Chem., Anal. Ed.* **6**, 161 (1934).
3. Fromageot, C. and Desnuelle, P., *Biochem. Z.* **279**, 174 (1935).
4. Cuthill, R. and Atkins, C., *J. Soc. Chem. Ind. (London)* **57**, 89 (1938).
5. Gordon, J. J. and Quastel, J. H., *Biochem. J.* **33**, 1332 (1939).
6. Fulmer, E. I., Hickey, R. J. and Underkofler, L. A., *Ind. Eng. Chem., Anal. Ed.* **12**, 729 (1940).
7. Kirk, P. L. and Tompkins, P. C., *Ind. Eng. Chem., Anal. Ed.* **13**, 277 (1941).
8. Smith, G. F. and Duke, F. R., *Ind. Eng. Chem., Anal. Ed.* **13**, 558 (1941).
9. Winnick, T., *J. Biol. Chem.* **142**, 451 (1942).
10. Smith, G. F. and Duke, F. R., *Ind. Eng. Chem., Anal. Ed.* **15**, 120 (1943).

11. Heinemann, B., *J. Dairy Science* **27**, 377 (1944).
12. Silverman, L., *J. Am. Oil Chemists' Soc.* **24**, 410 (1947).
13. Silverman, L., *J. Am. Oil Chemists' Soc.* **25**, 359 (1948).
14. Haslam, J. and Ruddle, L. H., *Analyst* **74**, 559 (1949).
15. McCarvill, M. and Conway, E. J., *Intern. Congr. Biochem., Abstracts of Comms., 1st Congress, Cambridge* 301 (1949).
16. Gädeke, A., *Z. anal. Chem.* **131**, 428 (1950).
17. Guardia, C. C., *Afinidad* **27**, 289, 454 (1950).
18. Pacheco, J. de la R. and López-Rubio, F. B., *Trans.* 44 *Intern. Congr. Soil Sci., Amsterdam* **2**, 101; **4**, 79 (1950).
19. Schulz, H. G., *Z. physiol. Chem.* **288**, 31 (1951).
20. Kimoto, K., *Repts. Inst. Ind. Sci. Tokyo Univ.* **3**, 20 (1952).
21. Takahashi, T., Kimoto, K. and Minami, S., *J. Chem. Soc. Japan, Ind. Chem. Sect.* **55**, 115, 168 (1952).
22. Takahashi, T. and Hayase, C., *J. Chem. Soc. Japan, Ind. Chem. Sect.* **55**, 205 (1952).
23. Takahashi, T., Kimoto, K. and Kimoto, M., *J. Chem. Soc. Japan, Ind. Chem. Sect.* **55**, 283 (1952).
24. Takahashi, T., Kimoto, K. and Minami, S., *J. Chem. Soc. Japan, Ind. Chem. Sect.* **55**, 805 (1952).
25. Lucas, J. F. C., *Rev. cienc. apl.* (*Madrid*) **7**, 526 (1953).
26. Skoog, D. A. and Budde, M. M., *Anal. Chem.* **25**, 822 (1953).
27. Takahashi, T., Kimoto, K. and Minami, S., *J. Chem. Soc. Japan, Ind. Chem. Sect.* **56**, 417 (1953).
28. Takahashi, T., Kimoto, K. and Minami, S., *J. Chem. Soc. Japan, Ind. Chem. Sect.* **56**, 491 (1953).
29. Takahashi, T., Kimoto, K. and Takano, Y., *J. Chem. Soc. Japan, Ind. Chem. Sect.* **56**, 591 (1953).
30. Lucas, J. F. C., *Anales real soc. espan. fis. y quím.* (*Madrid*) **50B**, 535 (1954).
31. Spencer, W. R. and Duke, F. R., *Anal. Chem.* **26**, 919 (1954).
32. Sharma, N. N. and Mehotra, R. C., *Anal. Chim. Acta* **11**, 417 (1954).
33. Sharma, N. N. and Mehotra, R. C., *Anal. Chem. Acta* **11**, 507 (1954).
34. Verma, M. R. and Paul, S. D., *J. Sci. Ind. Research, India* **13B**, 346 (1954).
35. Yamagishi, M., Fujiwara, H. and Shiraki, S., *Ann. Repts. Takamine Research Lab.* **13**, 25 (1954).
36. Alexander, A. P., Bourne, P. G. and Littlehale, D. S., *Anal. Chem.* **27**, 105 (1955).
37. Forist, A. A. and Speck, J. C., *Anal. Chem.* **27**, 1166 (1955).
38. Gopala Rao, G. and Aravamudan, G., *Z. anal. Chem.* **145**, 426 (1955).
39. Sharma, N. N. and Mehotra, R. C., *Anal. Chim. Acta* **13**, 419 (1955).
40. Takahashi, T., Kimoto, K. and Sakurai, H., *Rept. of Inst. of Ind. Sci., Univ. Tokyo* No. 6, Nov. (1955).

41. Balwant Singh, Surjit Singh and Harbans Singh, *Anal. Chim. Acta* **15**, 320 (1956).
42. Verma, M. R., Agrawal, K. C. and Paul, S. D., *J. Sci. Ind. Research, India* **15B**, 636 (1956).
43. Balwant Singh, Sarwan Singh and Harbans Singh, *J. Sci. Ind. Research, India* **16B**, 173 (1957).
44. Sharma, N. N., *Z. anal. Chem.* **157**, 110 (1957).
45. Sharma, N. N., *Z. anal. Chem.* **162**, 321 (1958).
46. Varga, E., *Acta Pharm. Hung.* **28**, 38 (1958).
47. Helmstaedter, G., *Deut. Apotheker-Ztg.* **99**, 589 (1959).
48. Michalski, E. and Czarnecki, K., *Chem. Anal. (Warsaw)* **4**, 83 (1959).
49. Dimotaki-Kourakou, V., *Ann. fals. et expert. chim.* **53**, 569 (1960).
50. Hsu, L-S. and Chou, T-H., *Yao Hsueh Hsueh Pao* **8**, 141 (1960).
51. Mathur, N. K. and Rao, S. P., *Current Sci. (India)* **29**, 92 (1960).
52. Michalski, E., Czarnecki, K. and Ignaczak, M., *Talanta* **5**, 137 (1960).
53. Guilbault, G. G. and McCurdy, W. H., *Anal. Chem.* **33**, 580 (1961).
54. Mathur, N. K., Rao, S. P. and Chowdhary, D. R., *Anal. Chim. Acta* **24**, 533 (1961).
55. Takahashi, T. and Sakurai, H., *J. Chem. Soc. Japan, Ind. Chem. Sect.* **63**, 608 (1960).
56. Krishna, B. and Tewari, K. C., *J. Chem. Soc.* 3097 (1961).
57. Bhargava, K. P., Shanker, R. and Joshi, S. N., *J. Sci. Ind. Res. (India)* **21B**, 573 (1962).
58. Guilbault, G. G. and McCurdy jr., W. H., *J. Phys. Chem.* **67**, 283 (1963)
59. Jungnickel, H. E. and Klinger, W., *Pharmazie* **18**, 130 (1963).
60. Prabhakar Rao, G. and Vasudeva Murthy, A. R., *Z. anal. Chem.* **195**, 406 (1963).
61. Rechnitz, G. A. and El-Tantawy, Y., *Z. anal. Chem.* **193**, 434 (1963).
62. Sumathi, S. C., *Leather Sci. (Madras)* **10**, 351 (1963).

23. Chlorate

Chlorate (as the potassium salt) has been used in acid solution (nitric or hydrochloric acid) as an oxidizing agent, reacting:

$$ClO_3^- + 6\,H^+ + 6\,\epsilon \rightarrow Cl^- + 3\,H_2O$$

The determinations have been concluded by argentometric titration of the Cl^- thus formed, or, in the case of lead tetraethyl, by titration of the Pb(II).

Examples

Materials titrated	Reagent and reaction conditions	Subsequent treatment and final titration stage	Ref.
HCHO	Heated with $KClO_3$/HNO_3/excess $AgNO_3$, giving formic acid + AgCl	Unused Ag(I) back titrated with SCN^- or Cl^-	1
Amyl nitrite	+ $KClO_3$ + HNO_3; 1 h shaking with warming	+ $AgNO_3$, filtered and unused Ag(I) in filtrate titrated with SCN^-	2
Amyl nitrite	+ $KClO_3$ + HNO_3; 15 min	+ $AgNO_3$, filtered, and Ag(I) in filtrate titrated with SCN^-	3
Lead tetraethyl in gasoline	+ 40% HNO_3 + 6% $KClO_3$ in water; 3 min shaking	Pb(II) in acid-aqueous layer precipitated as chromate, dissolved in HCl,I^- added and titrated with thiosulphate	4
Lead tetraethyl in gasoline	+ conc. HCl + $KClO_3$	+ water; NH_4OH/NH_4Cl added to the aqueous layer and titrated with EDTA to eriochrome black T	5

References

1. Grützner, B., *Arch. Pharm.* **234**, 634 (1896).
2. Andrews, M. J., *J. Am. Pharm. Assoc.* **21**, 799, 886 (1932).
3. Krantz, J. C. and Carr, C. J., *Pharm. Weekblad* **69**, 101 (1932).
4. Schwartz, L., *Ind. Eng. Chem., Anal. Ed.* **15**, 499 (1943).
5. Blumenthal, A., *Mitt. Lebensm. Hyg.* **51**, 159 (1960).

24. Chlorine reagents

Reagents. The reagents which are classified here are free chlorine (as gas or in solution); $C_6H_5ICl_2$ which behaves as a mixture of iodobenzene and chlorine; and, principally, hypochlorite, usually as sodium or calcium salts.

Reactions and materials titrated. 1. Addition to olefines, usually in determination of unsaturation of oils, fats and other naturally occurring materials.

$$\text{—}\overset{|}{C}\text{=}\overset{|}{C}\text{—} + Cl_2 \rightarrow \text{—}\overset{|}{C}Cl\text{—}\overset{|}{C}Cl\text{—}$$

$$\text{—}\underset{|}{C}\text{=}\underset{|}{C}\text{—} + HOCl \rightarrow \text{—}\underset{|}{C}(OH)\text{—}\underset{|}{C}Cl\text{—}$$

2. Oxidation, e.g. of aldehydes, urea, amino acids and hydrazines, and using hypochlorite. The oxidation may be written:

$$OCl^- + H_2O + 2\,\epsilon \rightarrow Cl^- + 2\,OH^- \quad \text{or, effectively,}$$

$$OCl^- \rightarrow Cl^- + O$$

Some typical oxidation equations are:

$$HCHO + 2\,OCl^- \rightarrow CO_2 + 2\,Cl^- + H_2O$$

$$CO(NH_2)_2 + 3\,OCl^- \rightarrow CO_2 + N_2 + 2\,H_2O + 3\,Cl^-$$

$$RCH(NH_2)COOH + OCl^- \rightarrow RCHO + CO_2 + NH_3 + Cl^-$$

$$NH_2.NH_2 + 2\,OCl^- \rightarrow N_2 + 2\,H_2O + 2\,Cl^-$$

$$CH_3NH.NH_2 + 4\,OCl^- \rightarrow CO + N_2 + 3\,H_2O + 4\,Cl^-$$

3. Substitution by chlorine of hydrogen, usually joined to nitrogen (this could of course be regarded as oxidation but it is convenient to classify it separately). For example:

$$H_2N\text{—}C_6H_4\text{—}NH_2 \rightarrow ClN\text{=}C_6H_4\text{=}NCl$$

$$\underbrace{NH\text{—}CO\text{—}NH\text{—}CO}_{C(C_6H_5)_2} \rightarrow \underbrace{NCl\text{—}CO\text{—}NCl\text{—}CO}_{C(C_6H_5)_2}$$

$$ArSO_2NH_2 \rightarrow ArSO_2NCl_2$$

$$RCH_2NO_2 \rightarrow RCCl_2NO_2$$

$$R_2CHNO_2 \rightarrow R_2CClNO_2$$

Reaction conditions. Addition reactions have mostly been carried out in organic solvents, as in other halogenation methods of addition. For the other reactions of oxidation and substitution, alkaline aqueous solution has generally been employed.

Subsequent treatment and final titration stage. (i) Unused reactant has been determined in several ways, e.g.

1. Addition of iodide (+ acid) and titration of the iodine formed with thiosulphate.
2. Back titration with arsenite, or via addition of excess arsenite and final titration with iodine.
3. Addition of excess thiosulphate, followed by titration with hypochlorite.

(methods 2 and 3 apply to back titration of only hypochlorite.)

4. Addition of excess thiocyanate and back titration with Ag^+.

(ii) Conclusion via a reaction product has been about equally used. For example:

1. *N*-Chlorides by addition of iodide and titration of the liberated iodine with thiosulphate:

$$=NCl + 2\,I^- + H^+ \rightarrow =NH + Cl^- + I_2$$

2. Aldehydes from amino acids by reaction with excess bisulphite and back titration with iodine.
3. Ammonia from amino acids by absorption in excess acid and alkali back titration.
4. CO_2 from urea by reaction with $Ba(OH)_2$ and acid titration of the precipitate.

Examples

Materials titrated	Reagent and reaction conditions	Subsequent treatment and final titration stage	Ref.
Acetone	+ KI/alkali + excess NaOCl; 1 min shaking	+ HCl + excess thiosulphate; back titrated with NaOCl after a few min	1
Amines, nitriles, imides	+ Ca(OCl)Cl + NaOH 12–15 h in dark	+ excess arsenite + H_2SO_4, then + $NaHCO_3$ and unused arsenite titrated with iodine	2
Unsaturation, e.g. of triolein	+ $C_6H_5ICl_2/CCl_4$; 4 h/room temp.	+ excess SCN^- and back titrated with $AgNO_3$ to Fe(III) indicator	3
p-Phenylenediamine	+ NaOCl, oxidizing to *N*,*N'*-dichloroquinonediimine	Back titrated with arsenite to external I^-/starch	4
HCHO	In water, + NaOCl. Shaken	+ I^- + HCl and titrated with thiosulphate	5

Materials titrated	Reagent and reaction conditions	Subsequent treatment and final titration stage	Ref.
Unsaturation of oils	+ saturated $C_6H_5ICl_2/CCl_4$	Cl^- titrated with $AgNO_3$	6
Unsaturation of oils and fats (after saponification)	Neutralized solution, + NaOCl + H_2SO_4	+ KI, then + H_2SO_4 after 5–15 min and titrated with thiosulphate	7
Unsaturation, e.g. of oleic acid	Sample + chlorine/ CCl_4; 30 min in dark	+ I^- and titrated with thiosulphate	8
p-Phenylene and *p*-toluylenediamines	In water, + NaOCl, giving *N,N'*-dichloroquinonediimines	Unused reagent destroyed with arsenite, diimine extracted with $CHCl_3$ and determined by reaction with I^-/HCl and titration with thiosulphate (see Iodides and hydriodic acid, ref. 68)	9
5,5-Diphenylhydantoin in biological material	In dilute NaOH + chlorine reagent, giving 1,3-dichloro derivative	Dissolved in acetic acid, I^- added and titrated with thiosulphate	10
Amino acids, e.g. alanine, valine and leucine	+ NaOCl at 0°, oxidizing to aldehydes; 12 min	Excess reagent removed with urea, phosphate buffer pH 8·5 added and aldehydes distilled into bisulphite; unused titrated with iodine (see Bisulphite and sulphite, refs 79 and 86)	11, 12
Sulphonamides in nickel plating baths	Chlorine bubbled through for 10–15 min	Product extracted with $CHCl_3$, solvent evaporated off, I^-/acetic acid added and titrated with thiosulphate	13
Amino acids	Boiling alkaline solution + NaOCl + NaOH added in 1 min giving ammonia	Absorbed in excess HCl and back titrated to methyl red/ methylene blue	14
Unsaturation of fatty acids	+ hypochlorous acid in 3-fold excess; 15 min/37°	+ I^-/acid and titrated with thiosulphate	15
Iodine numbers of oils (even with conjugated double bonds)	+ 0·3N hypochlorous acid in 3- to 4-fold excess + Hg acetate; 1 h	+ I^- and back titrated with thiosulphate	16

Materials titrated	Reagent and reaction conditions	Subsequent treatment and final titration stage	Ref.
Unsaturation of fats and oils	Solution or suspension in acetic acid, + NaOCl reagent; 4–5 min in dark	+ I^- and titrated with thiosulphate	17
Unsaturation in cyclized rubber	In CCl_4 + $C_6H_5ICl_2$; 2 h reflux	Reaction product precipitated with ethanol and successively dissolved in benzene and precipitated with methanol; Cl^- determined on finally obtained product by combustion and titration with Ag^+	18
Urea	+ KBr + boric acid, heated to 50–60° and NaOCl at 50–60° added; 2 min	+ NaOH + thiosulphate equivalent to the original NaOCl and titrated with NaOCl to indicator of brasilin + drop KI solution	19
Primary and secondary nitroparaffins	+ NaOCl + NaOH; 15 min/room temp., giving chloronitro-paraffins	+ acetic acid + KI solution and titrated with thiosulphate	20
Unsaturation of fats and oils	+ acetic acid + commercial bleaching powder solution; 10 min	+ I^- and titrated with thiosulphate	21
Urea in swimming-bath water (solution concentrated and extra urea added)	+ $Ba(OCl)_2$ + HCl; 10 min, giving CO_2	+ $Ba(OH)_2$, giving $BaCO_3$; filtered, dissolved in excess HCl and back titrated with NaOH to phenolphthalein (corrected for added urea)	22
p-Phenylenediamine in hair dyes	Added to NaOCl/$NaHCO_3$, giving the dichlorodiimine	Extracted with $CHCl_3$, I^-/HCl added, shaken 1 min and titrated with thiosulphate (see Iodides and hydriodic acid, ref. 226)	23
Methylhydrazine + hydrazine	In Na_2HPO_4/Na_3PO_4 buffer + KBr + NaOCl; 15 min/*ca* 60°, oxidizing with 4 and 2 moles reagent respectively (in combination with titration with chloramine T)	+ I^- + acetic acid and titrated with thiosulphate	24
HCHO, benzaldehyde	+ excess NaOCl, then + alkali + OsO_4 catalyst	Back titrated with arsenite potentiometrically	25

References

1. Kebler, L. F., *J. Am. Chem. Soc.* **19**, 316 (1897).
2. Effront, J., *Ber.* **37**, 4290 (1904).
3. Zlatarow, A., *Z. Untersuch. Nahr. u Genussm.* **26**, 348 (1913).
4. Callan, T. and Henderson, J. A. R., *J. Soc. Chem. Ind. (London)* **38**. 408T (1919).
5. Bicskei, J., *Z. anorg. u. allgem. Chem.* **161**, 309 (1927).
6. Kettle, S., *Chemist-Analyst* **18**, 7 (1929).
7. Goswami, M. and Basu, K. L., *Analyst* **59**, 533 (1934).
8. Palfray, L. and Sabetay, S., *Ann. chim. anal. chim. appl.* **20**, 288 (1938).
9. Herd, R. L., *J. Assoc. Off. Agr. Chem.* **22**, 158 (1939).
10. Kozelka, F. L. and Hine, C. H., *J. Pharmacol.* **72**, 276 (1941).
11. Aubel, E. and Asselineau, J., *Bull. soc. chim. France* 689 (1947).
12. Aubel, E. and Asselineau, J., *Biochim. et. Biophys. Acta* **2**, 198 (1948).
13. Sirota, J., *Metal Finishing* **46**, No. 9, 68 (1948).
14. Wieland, T., Vogelbach, C. and Bielig, H.-J., *Ann.* **561**, 116 (1948).
15. Mukherjee, S., *J. Am. Oil Chemists' Soc.* **29**, 97 (1952).
16. Chowdhury, R. B. and Mukherjee, S., *J. Am. Oil Chemists' Soc.* **32**, 484 (1955).
17. Mukherjee, S., *J. Am. Oil Chemists' Soc.* **32**, 351 (1955).
18. Rao, N. V. C., *Makromol. Chem.* **16**, 198 (1955).
19. Bitskei, J., *Magyar Kem. Folyoirat* **62**, 71 (1956).
20. Jones, L. R. and Riddick, J. A., *Anal. Chem.* **28**, 1137 (1956).
21. Chowdhury, R. B. R., *J. Am. Oil Chemists' Soc.* **37**, 198 (1960).
22. Fuchs, J., *Chem.-Ztg.* **84**, 805 (1960).
23. van de Pol, A., *Chem. Weekblad* **56**, 21 (1960).
24. Clark, J. D. and Smith, J. R., *Anal. Chem.* **33**, 1186 (1961).
25. Norkus, P., *Zhur. Anal. Khim*, **18**, 650 (1963).

25. Chlorite

Chlorite in weakly acid solution (pH *ca* 3) has been used to determine aldehydes, especially aldoses, by oxidation according to the equation:

$$RCHO + 3\,HClO_2 \rightarrow RCOOH + H_2O + HCl + 2\,ClO_2$$

More recently, some nitrogen-containing compounds like isoniazid, oxine and anilines have been similarly determined.

Unused reagent has been determined by reaction with I^-/ acid and titrating with thiosulphate.

Some of the examples below are studies of the reaction with the possibility of a quantitative determination kept in mind.

Examples

Materials titrated	Reagent and reaction conditions	Subsequent treatment and final titration stage	Ref.
Glucose	In acetate buffer, pH 3·5; 20 h/40°	$+ I^- +$ acid and titrated with thiosulphate	1
Glucose	In phosphate buffer, pH 2·4–3·4. In nitrogen current (evidently to sweep out ClO_2) in the dark at *ca* 50°; studied effect of concentrations, excess and time and found stoichiometric reaction at the pH mentioned	$+ I^- + H_2SO_4$ and titrated with thiosulphate photometrically	2
Glucose	In phosphate buffer, pH 2·4–3·4 at 50° in a study of the kinetics	Method of ref. 2	3
Aldoses other than glucose, e.g. xylose, arabinose, lyxose, ribose, rhamnose	Study of reaction at pH 3·5 and 40°		4
– CHO groups in oxidized cellulose	At pH 3·5 (acetate/oxalate buffer) + $NaClO_2$. Left overnight	ClO_2 aerated out with nitrogen, $I^- +$ acid added and titrated with thiosulphate	5
Aldehydes (e.g. benzaldehyde); sugars	In phosphate buffers of different concentration and pH 2 to 4. Nitrogen current to remove ClO_2. Studied the stoichiometry	$+ I^- +$ acid and titrated with thiosulphate	6
– CHO groups in polysaccharides	In phosphate buffers of various concentrations and pH from 2·4 to 3·2; 25–50°. Study of the kinetics of the reaction	Method of ref. 2	7
Isoniazid	In dilute HCl, + excess $NaClO_2$; 5 min	$+ I^-$ and titrated with thiosulphate	8
– CHO groups in polysaccharides	Compared the chlorite method with the usual alkaline reagent methods, e.g. with hypoiodite, alkaline Cu(II) and alkaline $Fe(CN)_6^{3-}$		9

Materials titrated	Reagent and reaction conditions	Subsequent treatment and final titration stage	Ref.
Aniline, *N*-methyl- and *N*-ethylaniline	In dilute HCl, + excess $NaClO_2$ + further HCl; not less than 5 min	+ I^- and titrated with thiosulphate	10
Oxine, metal oxinates	+ $NaClO_2$/HCl, giving the 5,7-dichlorooxine	+ I^- and titrated potentiometrically or visually with thiosulphate	11

References

1. Launer, H. F., Wilson, W. K. and Flynn, J. H., *J. Research Nat. Bur. Standards* **51,** 237 (1953).
2. Launer, H. F. and Tomimatsu, Y., *Anal. Chem.* **26,** 382 (1954).
3. Launer, H. F. and Tomimatsu, Y., *J. Am. Chem. Soc.* **76,** 2591 (1954).
4. Wilson, W. K. and Padgett, A. A., *Tappi* **38,** 292 (1955).
5. Ströle, U., *Das Leder* **11,** 453 (1957).
6. Launer, H. F. and Tomimatsu, Y., *Anal. Chem.* **31,** 1385 (1959).
7. Launer, H. F. and Tomimatsu, Y., *Anal. Chem.* **31,** 1569 (1959).
8. Spacu, P. and Dumitrescu, H., *Analele Univ. 'C. I. Parhon', Ser. Stiint. Nat.* **9,** 79 (1960).
9. Launer, H. F. and Tomimatsu, Y., *Anal. Chem.* **33,** 79 (1961).
10. Popa, G., Albert, F. M. and Grigore, E., *Z. Anal. Chem.* **199,** 210 (1963).
11. Spacu, P., Gheorghiu, C. and Paralescu, I., *Z. Anal. Chem.* **195,** 321 (1963).

26. Chromium (II)

Reagent. Chloride or sulphate, in acid solution.

Reaction and materials titrated. All methods depend on reduction, in the determination predominantly of nitro, nitroso and azo compounds. Other functional groups or compound classes determined have been: diazonium salts, oximes, diketones and quinones, acetylenes, halides and dyes

$$Cr^{2+} \rightarrow Cr^{3+} + e$$

e.g. $RNO_2 + 6\,Cr^{2+} + 6\,H^+ \rightarrow RNH_2 + 2\,H_2O + 6\,Cr^{3+}$

$RNO + 4\,Cr^{2+} + 4\,H^+ \rightarrow RNH_2 + H_2O + 4\,Cr^{3+}$

$C_6H_5N(NO)ONH_4$ evidently reduced first to $C_6H_5N(NH_2)ONH_4$, splitting into $C_6H_5ONH_4 + NH_3$

$$(ArN{\equiv}N)^+ + 3\,Cr^{2+} + 3\,H^+ \rightarrow (ArNH.NH_3)^+ + 3\,Cr^{3+}$$

Reaction conditions. Most reactions have proceeded fairly fast in a few minutes at room temperature. They have been carried out in an atmosphere of inert gas to prevent the ready oxidation of the reagent with atmospheric oxygen.

Final titration stage. In all cases, unreacted Cr(II) has been titrated with an oxidizing agent. Fe(III) is evidently the usual agent employed, but an example is given of the use of bichromate.

Examples

Materials titrated	Reagent and reaction conditions	Subsequent treatment and final titration stage	Ref.
p-Nitroaniline, picric acid, *p*-nitrophenol	+ $CrCl_2$; 2–5 min	Back titrated with Fe(III) alum	1
Methylene blue	+ $CrSO_4/H_2SO_4$ at 50° in CO_2 atmosphere	Back titrated with $Cr_2O_7^{2-}$ potentiometrically	2
Acetoxime; dimethyl glyoxime	+ Cr(II) reagent at suitable pH (7 to 12·4 and 0·8 to 11·7 respectively)	+ HCl and titrated with Fe(III) alum to SCN^-	3
$CHCl_3$; CCl_4	+ $CrCl_2/HCl$; 20 min/80° or room temp. respectively	Titrated with Fe(III) alum to SCN^-	4
Nitro, nitroso, azo compounds, anthraquinones and acetylenic compounds like HOOC.C≡C.COOH	+ $CrCl_2$ + HCl; 1–2 min	Titrated potentiometrically with Fe(III) alum	5
Diazonium salts	In water or dil. HCl, + $CrCl_2/HCl$; in CO_2 atmosphere. At least 1 min	Titrated with Fe(III) alum potentiometrically	6
Some nitroso compounds, e.g. *p*-nitrosodimethylaniline, ammonium cupferron: *N*-nitrosophenylbenzylamine	In dil HCl, ethanol/HCl or acetic acid/HCl, + $CrCl_2$; 1 min standing	Titrated with Fe(III) alum potentiometrically	7

Materials titrated	Reagent and reaction conditions	Subsequent treatment and final titration stage	Ref.
Nitro, nitroso compounds; quinones, quinhydrone; benzil	In some cases in conc. HCl, + $CrSO_4$. In CO_2 atmosphere	Titrated with Fe(III) to SCN^-	8
Aromatic nitro compounds; cellulose nitrate; cyclic nitroamines	In dimethylformamide, + HCl + $CrCl_2$/HCl (last named at 70°)	Back titrated with Fe(III) alum to phenosafranine	9
Picrolonic acid and picrolonates	In dilute H_2SO_4, + $CrSO_4$ in *ca* 10% excess; 2 min/55–60°	Back titrated with $FeCl_3$ to safranine T or neutral red	10
E.g., dyes (such as Orange II, tartrazine), azoxybenzene, propiolic acid, diacetyl, benzil	Usually solution in water, acetic acid or 95% ethanol, free from dissolved oxygen, + HCl + excess $CrCl_2$; 1–2 min	Back titrated with Fe (III)	11

References

1. Someya, K., *Z. anorg. u. allgem. Chem.* **161,** 293 (1928).
2. Davidson, G. F., *Shirley Inst. Mem.* **21,** 29 (1947).
3. Kiba, T. and Yamazaki, Y., *J. Chem. Soc. Japan, Pure Chem. Sect.* **74,** 808 (1953).
4. Kiba, T. and Terada, K., *J. Chem. Soc. Japan, Pure Chem. Sect.* **75,** 196 (1954).
5. Bottei, R. S. and Furman, N. H., *Anal. Chem.* **27,** 1182 (1955).
6. Bottei, R. S. and Furman, N. H., *Anal. Chem.* **29,** 119 (1957).
7. Bottei, R. S. and Furman, N. H., *Anal. Chem.* **29,** 121 (1957).
8. Tandon, J. P., *Z. anal. Chem.* **167,** 184 (1959).
9. Selig, W., *U.S. At. Energy Comm., UCRL* **6639**, 20, (1961).
10. Dworzak, R., Krause, H. and Friedrich, P., *Ann.* **653,** 12 (1962).
11. Bottei, R. S., *Anal. Chim. Acta* **30**, 6 (1964).

27. Copper (I)

Reagent. Both CuCl and a Cu(I) reagent prepared in situ from Cu(II) and a reducing agent have been used. Sulphite and hydroxylamine have been used as reducing agents and the Cu(II)/NH_2OH/

NH_4OH mixture is the well-known Ilosvay reagent (for detection of acetylenic hydrogen).

Reactions and material titrated. 1. Hydrogen substitution in determination of acetylenes and uric acid (this could equally well be considered as ion/ion combination):

$$RC{\equiv}CH + Cu^+ \rightarrow RC{\equiv}CCu + H^+$$

$$C_5H_4O_3N_4 + Cu^+ \rightarrow C_5H_3O_3N_4Cu + H^+$$

These derivatives separate as precipitates.

2. Bromine replacement in a determination of bromoacetylenes:

$$RC{\equiv}CBr + 3\,Cu^+ \rightarrow RC{\equiv}CCu + 2\,Cu^{2+} + Br^-,$$

followed by:

$$RC{\equiv}CCu + RC{\equiv}CBr \rightarrow (RC{\equiv}C{-})_2 + Cu^+ + Br^-$$

3. Complex formation, e.g. with metrazole, which yields an insoluble product of the formula $C_6H_{10}N_4.2\,CuCl$.

Subsequent treatment and final titration stage. (i) In most cases this has involved dissolving the Cu(I) precipitate and oxidizing it to Cu(II), e.g.

1. Using Fe(III) and then titrating the Fe(II) formed with permanganate (the usual technique for acetylides).

2. Using agents like HNO_3 or H_2O_2 and determining the Cu(II) by titration with EDTA or by adding I^- (or I^-/SCN^-) and titrating the liberated iodine with thiosulphate.

(ii) In the example of reaction 2 above, conclusion was by titration of the Br^- with $AgNO_3$.

(iii) Unused Cu(I) in the filtrate has been determined by the methods of (i) 2.

Examples

Materials titrated	Reagent and reaction conditions	Subsequent treatment and final titration stage	Ref.
Uric acid in urine	+ acetic acid + Cu(II)/$(NH_4)_2SO_3$ reagent, yielding Cu(I) urate; 30 min standing	Filtered, aliquot of filtrate heated with H_2SO_4 and the Cu(II) determined with I^-/acetic acid and titration with thiosulphate	1

Materials titrated	Reagent and reaction conditions	Subsequent treatment and final titration stage	Ref.
Uric acid	+ $CuSO_4$/alkali/tartrate/ $NaHSO_3$; 5 min standing, giving Cu(I) urate	Filtered, dissolved in H_2SO_4 and titrated with MnO_4^-	2
Acetylene	+ $CuCl/NH_4Cl/NH_2OH$ A few min shaking	Filtered, precipitate added to $Fe(III)/H_2SO_4$ and the Fe(II) titrated with MnO_4^- (see Iron (III), ref. 1)	3
Phenylacetylene	In alcohol, + CuCl/ NH_4OH/NH_2OH. Shaken a few min	Precipitate dissolved in Fe(III) reagent and titrated with MnO_4^-	4
Acetylene	In water, + $CuSO_4$/ NH_4OH/NH_2OH; 2–3 min shaking	Filtered, Cu_2C_2 decomposed with HNO_3 and Cu(II) determined by adding I^-/SCN^- and titrating with thiosulphate	5
Metrazole ('Cardazole', 'Leptazole')	In water, + CuCl; 3 h shaking, giving precipitate of complex	Filtered, H_2O_2 added to filtrate, boiled 10 min and Cu(II) determined by adding I^- and titrating with thiosulphate	6
Acetylene from treatment of Cu_2C_2 with KCN	Carried with nitrogen into $Cu(NO_3)_2$/ NH_4OH/NH_2OH	Filtered, precipitate dissolved in HCl and ultimately Cu(II) determined by adding I^- and titrating with thiosulphate	7
Metrazole	In water, + CuCl; 1 h/room temp., giving precipitate of complex	Filtered, precipitate dissolved in HCl, oxidized with H_2O_2 and Cu(II) ultimately titrated with EDTA to murexide	8
Bromoacetylenes, RC≡CBr	+ $CuSO_4/NH_2OH$/ ethylamine/methanol/ water reagent; 5 min	+ HNO_3 and titrated Br^- with $AgNO_3$	9

References

1. Repiton, F., *Revue generale de chim. pure et appl.* **11**, 285 (1908).
2. Pégurier, G., *Répert. pharm.* **32**, 65 (1920).
3. Willstätter, R. and Maschmann, E., *Ber.* **53**, 939 (1920).
4. Hein, F. and Meyer, A., *Z. anal. Chem.* **72**, 30 (1927).
5. Voronkov, M. G., *Zhur. Anal. Khim.* **1**, 285 (1946).
6. Sharp, L. K., *J. Pharm. Pharmacol.* **4**, 52 (1952).

7. Polyakov, N. N., *Zhur. Anal. Khim.* **8**, 302 (1953).
8. Paulsen, A., *Medd. Norsk Farm. Selskap* **18**, 139 (1956).
9. Chodkiewicz, W. and Cadiot, P., *Bull. soc. chim. France* 298 (1959).

28. Copper (II)

Reagent. Most copper (II) reagents are based on the sulphate, with the chloride and acetate also finding occasional use.

Oxidizing Cu(II) reagents, especially for determination of reducing sugars, are mostly alkaline. The alkali hydroxides or carbonates have been principally used for this purpose. In some methods and studies, alkaline buffers have been used in order to operate at definite pH values; CO_3^{2-}, HCO_3^- and phosphates have been the most frequently used buffer components. The Cu(II) must then be maintained in solution by addition of polyhydroxy compounds, hydroxy acids or other complexing agents; those used include glycerol, mannitol, tartrate, citrate, lactate, trihydroxyglutarate, salicylate, sulphosalicylate, triethanolamine and EDTA (high alkali concentration has also served). In the interests of stability, these reagents usually consist of 2 or 3 separate solutions which are mixed just before use.

Other additions may be made to the reagent, of substances which play a part in the subsequent stages of the determination (e.g. iodide; iodate; alkali sulphates to reduce solubility of air oxygen in the solution; thiocyanate or ferrocyanide to prevent formation of the red Cu_2O precipitate). These additions may be made after the oxidation stage, however.

For some oxidations and most precipitation reactions, a neutral to weakly acid reagent has been preferred.

Where the component to be determined reacts to yield a water-soluble copper derivative, a suspension of cupric hydroxide, or, more usually, phosphate, has been used as reagent.

Reactions and materials titrated. 1. Oxidation, with formation of Cu(I), usually as Cu_2O under the conditions employed. Well over one half of the total list of examples quoted are determinations of hexoses; the reaction products from this oxidation depend on the reaction conditions and although the principal reaction can be formulated as oxidation of aldehyde group to carboxylic acid, the stoichiometry is usually more complex. The determinations have therefore been carried out under standardized conditions of pH, temperature and time of reaction, etc., and compared to a control titration carried out under the same conditions.

The other larger group of oxidation determinations is that of aldehydes such as HCHO, acrolein, chloral and furfuraldehyde;

$$RCHO + 2\,Cu^{2+} + H_2O \rightarrow RCOOH + 2\,Cu^{+} + 2\,H^{+}$$

A few miscellaneous compounds have been determined also via oxidation (e.g. certain amino ketones, ascorbic acid, uric acid, acetate and penicillin) and some titrimetric measurements of 'reducing power' or 'reducing value' of solutions (principally of polysaccharide origin) have been made.

2. Ion/ion combination, yielding either insoluble Cu(II) derivatives from a soluble reagent or soluble derivatives from an insoluble reagent. Examples are given of combination with the following ions:

$RCOO^-$: as with mandelate, *p*-aminobenzoate, gluconate, citrate, carboxymethylcellulose, oxidized starch, anthranilate (all yielding insoluble Cu(II) salts)
with α-amino acids, where chelation with the $-NH_2$ group takes place (giving soluble Cu(II) salts):

$$2\,RCH\begin{matrix}\diagup COO^- \\ \\ \diagdown NH_2\end{matrix} + Cu^{2+} \rightarrow RCH\begin{matrix}\diagup COO\diagdown \\ \\ \diagdown NH_2\nearrow\end{matrix} Cu \begin{matrix}\swarrow H_2N\diagdown \\ \\ \diagdown OOC\diagup\end{matrix} CHR$$

RSO_3^-: with certain sulphonic acids

ArO^-: with picric acid (in presence of ammonia) yielding the insoluble cuprammonium salt $Cu(NH_3)_4(OC_6H_2(NO_2)_3)$

RS^-: with xanthates and mercaptans (with the latter, oxidation takes place also: $4\,RSH + 2\,Cu^{2+} \rightarrow RSSR + 2\,RSCu + 4\,H^{+}$)

$RR'N^-$: e.g. with barbital

3. Hydrogen replacement, yielding water-soluble or insoluble Cu derivatives as under reaction type 2. The distinction from these type 2 reactions is vague and the separate category is included here for polyhydroxy compounds like mannitol, glycerol, sorbitol, etc., where the organic compound can hardly be considered to exist as an anion. The determination of enols, such as β-dicarbonyl compounds, and of tartrates can be classified here also:

$$2\,CH\begin{matrix}\diagup \overset{R}{C}\!\!=\!O \\ \\ \diagdown\!\!\underset{R}{C}\!-\!OH\end{matrix} + Cu^{2+} \rightarrow CH\begin{matrix}\diagup \overset{R}{C}\!\!=\!O\searrow \\ \\ \diagdown\!\!\underset{R}{C}\!-\!O\diagup\end{matrix} Cu \begin{matrix}\diagup O\!-\!\overset{R}{C}\!\!\diagdown \\ \\ \nwarrow O\!=\!\underset{R}{C}\diagup\end{matrix} CH + 2\,H^{+}$$

4. Complex formation as with a number of bases, mostly heterocyclic. Pyridine, isoniazid and aniline have been determined in the presence of SCN^- ions, yielding water-insoluble complexes usually accorded the structure $(Cu(Base)_2)^{2+}(SCN^-)_2$. Quinine and piperazine have been precipitated in the presence of other anions, but the cation is again a Cu^{2+}/base complex.

Reaction conditions. Determinations of reducing sugars and some other reducing substances have in general been carried out at higher temperature. Conditions of time and temperature have ranged from 2 to 30 min boiling to *ca* 2·5 h at *ca* 50°.

As a rule, reactions of types 2, 3 and 4 have been carried out at room temperature and occasionally in the presence of organic solvents.

Specimen references are given to studies of the kinetics of alkaline cupric oxidation of sugars (188) and to the effect of concentration of Cu (II) and of Rochelle salt on the determination of reducing sugars (189).

Subsequent treatment and final titration stage. In nearly all analyses, the concluding stage has been a titration of Cu(I) or Cu(II).

(i) Determination of unreacted Cu(II), usually after filtration of a precipitated derivative. Two general procedures have been used:

1. Direct titration of the Cu(II), using reagents like:

   Sn(II) (to disappearance of blue)
   Cr(II) (to neutral red or phenosafranine)
   CN^- (to disappearance of blue)
   NH_2OH (to disappearance of blue)
   EDTA (to murexide or 1-(2-pyridylazo)-naphthol)
   Hydroquinone (potentiometrically)

2. Indirect titration, in most instances by addition of I^-/acid and titrating the iodine with thiosulphate

$$2\,Cu^{2+} + 4\,I^- \rightarrow 2\,CuI \downarrow + I_2$$

This is the most frequently used method for determination of Cu(II) In one example given, the iodine was titrated with Sn(II).

SCN^- has been used as a partial replacement for I^- and has the advantage of being cheaper and that the CuSCN is *ca* 10 times more insoluble than CuI (see ref. 31 for example).

In one example, I^-/SCN^-/excess thiosulphate was added and the unreacted thiosulphate back titrated with iodine.

(ii) Determination of a copper-containing reaction product. This may be either a derivative of the organic compound (i.e. usually a soluble or insoluble salt or chelate compound); or Cu_2O:

1. Determination of a Cu(II) organic derivative has generally been by the methods used and quoted under (i) above. Most used appear to be direct titration with EDTA and indirect with I^-/acid.

2. Determination of Cu(I) formed (from reactions of type 1). Four main procedures may be distinguished:

(a) Direct titration in a limited number of cases, e.g. with iodine or with $Cr_2O_7^{2-}$.

(b) Addition of a measured excess of oxidizing agent and back titration of the unused part. The following oxidizing reagents have been used (with the back titration agent mentioned):

Ce(IV)	Fe(II) to ferroin	
Iodine	Thiosulphate	
IO_3^-/I^-	Thiosulphate	(in some cases the IO_3^- and/or I^- were in the original reagent)
$AgNO_3$	SCN^-.	

(c) Oxidation of the Cu(I) to Cu(II), followed by determination of the Cu(II) formed. As oxidation agents have been employed: bromine, hypochlorite, permanganate and nitric acid. The concluding titration of the Cu(II) has used some of the methods already outlined under (i), namely, directly with CN^- or EDTA and indirectly with I^-/acid and thiosulphate titration.

(d) Oxidation of Cu(I) to Cu(II) and subsequent determination of the reduced part of the agent. Some examples are tabulated below:

Oxidizing agent	Reaction product from oxidation of the Cu(I)	
Fe(III)	Fe(II)	Back titrated with standard reagents like MnO_4^-, $Cr_2O_7^{2-}$, BrO_3^- or Ce(IV)
Ce(IV)	Ce(III)	
V (V) (vanadate)	V (IV)	
Cr(VI) (bichromate)	Cr(III)	
Mo(VI) (molybdo-phosphate or -arsenate)	Mo(III)	

(e) An example which is not classifiable above is the solution of Cu_2O in H_2SO_4/H_2O_2 and back titration of the unused acid:

$$Cu_2O + H_2O_2 + 2\,H_2SO_4 \rightarrow 2\,CuSO_4 + 3\,H_2O$$

In the above determinations, the Cu(I) has nearly always existed as Cu_2O. In rather more than half the examples, the Cu_2O has been separated by filtration or centrifuging and then determined; this has not always been necessary. Considerable precautions are necessary to prevent air oxidation of the Cu(I) to Cu(II), achieved by devices such as working in an inert gas (CO_2 or hydrogen) or under a layer of an immiscible organic solvent (e.g. toluene).

(iii) In a small number of cases, a reaction product other than one containing copper has been determined as the final stage. A few of these examples are tabulated here:

Oxalate (from determination of acetate by oxidation with CuO), titrated with MnO_4^-
Amines (from determination of certain amino ketones) distilled into acid and back titrated with alkali
Ammonia (from determination of penicillin) likewise distilled into acid and back titrated

(iv) Other reagents present have been back titrated, the principal example being SCN^- from the precipitations based on reactions of type 4; unused SCN^- was titrated with Ag(I). In one oxidative determination of reducing sugars, the unused alkali was back titrated instead of proceeding via a Cu determination.

Examples

Materials titrated	Reagent and reaction conditions	Subsequent treatment and final titration stage	Ref.
Sugar	+ $CuSO_4$/alkali/tartrate. Heated	Cu_2O dissolved in $FeCl_3$ and Fe(II) formed titrated with permanganate	1
Uric acid	+ $CuSO_4$/alkali. Boiled	Unused Cu(II) determined by adding I^-/HCl and titrating the iodine formed with $SnCl_2$	2
Sugar	+ $CuSO_4$/alkali/tartrate. Heated	Cu_2O dissolved in $Fe_2(SO_4)_3$ and Fe(II) formed titrated with permanganate	3
Sugars	+ alkali Cu(II) reagent. Heated	Cu_2O dissolved in HNO_3 and Cu(II) formed titrated with CN^- to disappearance of blue (suggestion made)	4

Materials titrated	Reagent and reaction conditions	Subsequent treatment and final titration stage	Ref.
Glucose and other sugars	+ alkali Cu(II) reagent. Heated	Cu_2O boiled with HCl/NaCl and titrated with permanganate	5
Sugars	Method suggested in ref. 4 tried		6
Sugars	+ $CuSO_4$/alkali/tartrate. Heated	Cu_2O dissolved in HNO_3 and Cu(II) formed determined by reduction to Cu(I) with SO_2, precipitation of CuSCN with excess NH_4SCN and back titration of unused SCN^- with Ag^+; unused Cu(II) in filtrate from Cu_2O also similarly determined	7
Uric acid	+ $CuSO_4$/alkali/tartrate; 5 min boiling	Cu_2O dissolved in HNO_3, partly neutralized with Na_2CO_3, then Cu(II) determined with I^-/H_2SO_4 and titration with thiosulphate	8
Sugars in sweet wines	+ alkali Cu(II) reagent	Cu_2O dissolved in HNO_3, NH_4OH added and titrated with CN^- to disappearance of blue	9
Sugars	+ $CuSO_4$/alkali/tartrate	Cu_2O dissolved in HNO_3, Cu(II) formed subsequently reduced with SO_3^{2-} to Cu(I), then determined with excess SCN^- and back titration with Ag^+	10
Sugars	+ $CuSO_4$/alkali/tartrate; 2 min boiling	Filtrate + I^-/H_2SO_4 and titrated with thiosulphate to starch	11
Invert sugar	+ $CuSO_4$/alkali/tartrate. Boiled	Unused Cu(II) titrated with $SnCl_2$ to disappearance of blue	12
Dextrose, fructose	+ $CuSO_4$/glycerol/citrate/measured excess alkali; 5 min boiling	Filtered and unused alkali titrated with HCl or H_2SO_4 to phenolphthalein	13
Sugars	+ $CuSO_4/KHCO_3/K_2CO_3$/KSCN; 3 min boiling	Unused Cu(II) titrated with hydroxylamine to disappearance of blue	14
Sugars	+ $CuSO_4$/NaOH/tartrate; 3 min boiling	Filtered, Cu_2O dissolved in Fe(III) and Fe(II) formed titrated with MnO_4^-	15

Materials titrated	Reagent and reaction conditions	Subsequent treatment and final titration stage	Ref.
Xanthate, formed in CS_2 determination with alkali/alcohol	+ excess cupric acetate + acetic acid; 15 min/room temp.	Unused Cu(II) determined by adding I^- and titrating with thiosulphate	16
Furfuraldehyde, from acid hydrolysis, in determination of pentoses	Distillate + $CuSO_4$/alkali/tartrate; 35 min boiling	Unused Cu(II) determined iodometrically	17
Glycerol	+ $CuSO_4$/NaOH; 12 h standing, giving soluble Cu derivative	Aliquot of clear liquid, + I^-/H_2SO_4 and titrated with thiosulphate	18
Glucose, lactose, maltose, invert sugar	+ $CuSO_4/K_2CO_3$/salicylic acid; 20 min/100°	Cu_2O dissolved in HNO_3, nitrite oxidized with NaOCl, excess reagent destroyed with phenol, I^- added and titrated with thiosulphate	19
Furfuraldehyde	Comments on method of ref. 17, saying that reducing power depends on concentration		20
Sugars	+ $CuSO_4$/NaOH/tartrate; 10 min boiling	Unused Cu(II) determined by adding I^-/H_2SO_4 and titrating with thiosulphate	21, 25
Sugars, e.g. in blood	+ $CuSO_4/KHCO_3/K_2CO_3$/KCl; 3 min boiling	Cu(I) (kept in solution as CuCl) titrated with iodine to starch	22
Amino acids in blood, urine, protein hydrolysates	Neutral solution, + borate buffer, pH 7–9 + $Cu(OH)_2$; 2–3 min shaking	Cu(II) in filtrate determined by adding I^-/acetic acid and titrating with thiosulphate to starch	23, 26
Mannitol	Method of ref. 18		24
Reducing sugars	+ $CuSO_4$/NaOH/tartrate; 2 min boiling	Cu_2O dissolved in Fe(III) reagent and Fe(II) formed titrated with permanganate; or filtrate + I^-/H_2SO_4 and titrated with thiosulphate to starch	27
Sugars in blood, urine	+ $CuSO_4$/alkali/tartrate. Heated	Cu_2O dissolved in Fe(III) reagent and titrated with permanganate	28
Sugars	+ $CuSO_4/NaHCO_3/Na_2CO_3$/citrate; 3 min boiling	+ HCl + acetic acid + excess iodine and back titrated with thiosulphate	29

Materials titrated	Reagent and reaction conditions	Subsequent treatment and final titration stage	Ref.
Sugars in blood	+ $CuSO_4/KHCO_3/K_2CO_3/KCl$; 3 min boiling	Cu(I) formed titrated with iodine in CO_2 atmosphere to starch	30
Sugars	+ $CuSO_4$/alkali/tartrate; 2 min boiling	+ I^-/SCN^- + HCl or H_2SO_4 and titrated with thiosulphate to starch	31, 32
Enols	Stated that method of ref. 35 applies only to *cis*-enols		33
Glucose	+ $CuSO_4/Na_2CO_3$/tartrate; 6 min/100°, then + $MgSO_4/Na_2CO_3$ and 1 min/100°	+ molybdophosphoric acid, giving blue Mo(III); titrated with permanganate	34
Enols, e.g. benzoylacetone, acetoacetic ester	In alcohol at *ca* −10°, + Cu acetate/ethanol/$CHCl_3$ at −10°	+ water, Cu enol chelate separated in non-aqueous layer, I^-/H_2SO_4 added and titrated with thiosulphate	35
Invert sugar	Solution at boiling point + boiling $CuSO_4/Na_2CO_3$/tartrate reagent; 10 min boiling	+ HCl + excess iodine to dissolve the Cu_2O; back titrated with thiosulphate	36
Maltose, lactose, in presence other sugars	+ Cu acetate/Na acetate/NaOH: and + $CuSO_4$/NaOH/tartrate reagents (different oxidizing powers)	Cu_2O dissolved in Fe(III) and titrated with permanganate	37
Reducing sugars	+ $CuSO_4$/NaOH/tartrate; 30 min/80°	Cu_2O determined as in method of ref. 19	38
Sugars in blood, urine, etc.	+ $CuSO_4$/NaOH/tartrate (and other reagents)	Cu_2O determined by adding $IO_3^-/I^-/H_2SO_4$/oxalate and back titrating with thiosulphate; or unused Cu(II) determined by adding I^-/H_2SO_4 and titrating with thiosulphate	39
Lactose in milk	Method of ref. 34		40
Pyridine	+ excess Cu(II) + SCN^-, giving precipitate of $Cu(C_5H_5N)_2^{2+}(SCN^-)_2$	Unused Cu(II) in filtrate determined iodometrically	41
Sugars	+ $CuSO_4$/NaOH/tartrate; 5 min heating	+ oxalic acid/excess iodine and back titrated with thiosulphate	42

Materials titrated	Reagent and reaction conditions	Subsequent treatment and final titration stage	Ref.
Blood sugar	+ $CuSO_4/HCO_3^-/CO_3^{2-}/$ tartrate/I^-/IO_3^-; 90 sec boiling	+ HCl and titrated with thiosulphate	43
Glucose	+ $CuSO_4$/NaOH/ tartrate; 6 min/100°	Cu_2O dissolved in molybdo-phosphoric acid giving Mo(III) and titrated with permanganate	44
Sugars in biological fluids	+ $CuSO_4$/alkali/tartrate	Cu_2O dissolved in $Fe_2(SO_4)_3$ and titrated with permanganate	45
Invert sugar in presence of sucrose	+ $CuSO_4$/NaOH/ tartrate; 2 min boiling	Unused Cu(II) determined by adding I^-/H_2SO_4 and titrating with thiosulphate	46
Fructose (in presence of aldoses)	+ $CuSO_4/K_2CO_3/$ $KHCO_3$; $2\frac{1}{2}$ h/48·5–49° or 20 min/100° or 5 min boiling	Cu_2O dissolved in Fe(III) and titrated with permanganate	47
Invert sugar	+ $CuSO_4/Na_2CO_3/$ tartrate	+ oxalic acid + excess iodine and titrated with thiosulphate	48
Invert sugar in presence of sucrose	+ $CuSO_4/Na_2CO_3/$ citrate; 5 min boiling	Unused Cu(II) determined by adding I^-/H_2SO_4 and titrating with thiosulphate	49
Sugars in blood	+ $CuSO_4/Na_2CO_3/$ tartrate/I^-/IO_3^-; 15 min/100°	+ H_2SO_4 and titrated with thiosulphate	50
Sugars	+ $CuSO_4$/NaOH/ tartrate	Cu_2O dissolved in $IO_3^-/CO_3^{2-}/$ HCl (→ CO_2 atmosphere) then + oxalate/I^- and titrated with thiosulphate	51
Sugar, e.g. in blood	+ $CuSO_4$/NaOH/ citrate	Cu_2O dissolved in Fe(III) reagent and Fe(II) formed titrated with bromate potentiometrically	52
Glucose, e.g. in blood	+ $CuSO_4/CO_3^{2-}/$ tartrate/oxalate $HCO_3^-/I^-/IO_3^-$ of pH 9·4–9·55; 15 min/100°	+ H_2SO_4 and titrated with thiosulphate	53

Materials titrated	Reagent and reaction conditions	Subsequent treatment and final titration stage	Ref.
Sugar in urine	+ $CuSO_4$/NaOH/ tartrate; 2 min boiling	+ I^-/SCN^-/HCl and iodine titrated with thiosulphate	54
Blood sugar	Method of ref. 34		55
Lactose	+ $CuSO_4$/alkali/tartrate. Heated	Cu_2O dissolved in molybdo-phosphoric acid and the Mo(III) formed titrated with permanganate	56
Glucose	+ $CuSO_4$/conc. NaOH; 15 min/100°	Cu_2O dissolved in molybdo-phosphoric acid and titrated with permanganate	57
Sugar in dilute solutions	+ $CuSO_4$/NaOH/ tartrate; 2 min boiling	Cu_2O dissolved in Na_2SO_4/ NH_4OH, excess $AgNO_3$ added, giving Cu(I) and Ag^+; back titrated with SCN^-	58
Glucose	+ $CuSO_4$/NaOH/ tartrate. Heated	Cu_2O dissolved in H_2O_2/ excess H_2SO_4 ($Cu_2O + H_2O_2 + 2\,H_2SO_4 \rightarrow 2\,CuSO_4 + 3\,H_2O$) and unused acid titrated with $NaHCO_3$ to methyl orange	59
Glucose	+ alkali Cu(II) reagent. Heated	Unused Cu(II) in filtrate titrated with CN^- to disappearance of blue	60
Reducing sugars	+ $CuSO_4$/NaOH/ tartrate. Heated	Cu_2O dissolved in HCl/ NaCl/$MnSO_4$ and oxidized with permanganate to Cu(II); determined iodometrically	61
Sugars	+ $CuSO_4$/Na_2CO_3/ Na_2HPO_4/tartrate. Heated	+ I^-/SCN^-/HCl and iodine titrated with thiosulphate	62, 66
HCHO from acid hydrolysis of hexamine in its determination	+ $CuSO_4$/NaOH/ tartrate. Heated	Cu_2O dissolved in $Fe_2(SO_4)_3$ and Fe(II) titrated with permanganate	63
Reducing sugars	+ $CuSO_4$/NaOH/ tartrate. Heated	Cu_2O dissolved in molybdo-phosphoric acid and the Mo(III) titrated with permanganate	64

Materials titrated	Reagent and reaction conditions	Subsequent treatment and final titration stage	Ref.
Sugars	+ $CuSO_4/Na_2CO_3$/ citrate; 10 min boiling	Unused Cu(II) determined by adding I^-/H_2SO_4 and titrating with thiosulphate	65
Monosaccharides (e.g. glucose, galactose) in presence of lactose	+ $CuSO_4$/Na acetate/ acetic acid; 6·5 min/100°	Cu_2O dissolved in $Fe_2(SO_4)_3$ and Fe(II) titrated with permanganate	67
Blood sugar, etc.	+ $CuSO_4/Na_2CO_3$/ tartrate; 15 min/100°	Cu_2O dissolved in I^-/IO_3^-/ oxalate/H_2SO_4 and titrated with thiosulphate	68
Lactose in milk	+ $CuSO_4$/NaOH/ tartrate; 6 min boiling	Cu_2O dissolved in HNO_3, nitrite oxidized with bromate/ bromide, ammonia added, boiled and Cu(II) determined with I^-/H_2SO_4 and titration with thiosulphate	69
Lactose in milk chocolate; acid hydrolysed sucrose	+ $CuSO_4$/NaOH/ tartrate; 5 min boiling	+ HCl/NaCl to dissolve Cu_2O; + $NaHCO_3$ + excess iodine and back titrated with thiosulphate	70
Fructose	+ $CuSO_4/Na_2CO_3$/ citrate; 10 min boiling	+ $I^-/IO_3^-/H_2SO_4$ and titrated with thiosulphate	71
Glucose	+ $CuSO_4$/KOH/tartrate (studied effect of different alkali concentrations)	Cu_2O dissolved in Fe(III) alum and titrated with permanganate	72
Sugars	+ $CuSO_4/Na_2CO_3$/ Na_2HPO_4/tartrate; 5 min boiling	+ HCl + excess iodine and back titrated with thiosulphate	73, 78, 79
Glucose	+ $CuSO_4$/NaOH/ tartrate/$K_4Fe(CN)_6$; 2 min boiling (claimed 1 glucose equivalent to 4 oxygen atoms)	Titrated with hydroxylamine sulphate to disappearance of blue or to Nessler reagent as external indicator	74
Fructose	+ $CuSO_4/K_2CO_3$/ $KHCO_3$; 75 min/55°	Cu_2O dissolved in HCl and Cu(I) determined by titration with bichromate	75
Lactose in milk and milk products	+ $CuSO_4$/NaOH/ tartrate; 6 min boiling	+ oxalic acid + excess iodine and back titrated with thiosulphate	76

Materials titrated	Reagent and reaction conditions	Subsequent treatment and final titration stage	Ref.
Reducing sugars	Study of method of ref. 39 (effect of time to reach boiling, temperature changes in solution, etc.)		77
Reducing sugars	+ $CuSO_4$/NaOH/ tartrate; 20 min/62–3°	Unused Cu(II) determined iodometrically in solution decanted from the Cu_2O	80
Acetate	+ KOH/CuO; 10–15 min/220–240°, giving oxalate ($CH_3COO^- + 6\,CuO + OH^- \rightarrow C_2O_4^{2-} + 3\,Cu_2O + 2\,H_2O$)	Dissolved in water, acidified and titrated with permanganate	81
Sugars in blood, etc.	+ $CuSO_4/Na_2CO_3$/ tartrate/IO_3^-. Some + $NaHCO_3 + I^-$; 15 min/100° (study of factors)	+ H_2SO_4 or H_2SO_4/oxalate and titrated with thiosulphate	82
Monosaccharides in presence of di-saccharides	+ $CuSO_4$/acetate; 20 min/100°	Hot solution + H_2SO_4 + excess iodine; back titrated with thiosulphate	83
Acrolein, from glycerol in its determination by heating with large excess $NaHSO_4$	Carried by CO_2 current into $CuSO_4$/NaOH/ tartrate	Cu_2O dissolved in Fe(III) reagent and Fe(II) formed titrated with permanganate	84
Furfuraldehyde from acid hydrolysis of pentosans	+ $CuSO_4$/NaOH/ tartrate	Cu_2O dissolved in Fe(III) reagent and Fe(II) titrated with permanganate	85
Sugars	+ $CuSO_4$/NaOH/ tartrate	Cu_2O dissolved in excess $Ce(SO_4)_2$ and unused titrated with $FeSO_4$ to ferroin	86
Glucose	+ $CuSO_4$/NaOH/ tartrate	Cu_2O dissolved in Fe(III) reagent and Fe(II) formed titrated with bichromate to diphenylamine/H_2SO_4	87
Glucose	+ $CuSO_4$/acetate/acetic acid/tartrate; 5 min boiling (study of factors—effect of time, Cu concentration, etc.)	Cu_2O dissolved in NaCl/ acid/tartrate, neutralized with $NaHCO_3$ and titrated with iodine	88
Mannitol	Method of ref. 24		89

Materials titrated	Reagent and reaction conditions	Subsequent treatment and final titration stage	Ref.
Sugars	+ $CuSO_4$/NaOH/ tartrate	+ large excess KI + HCl giving pH 2–3·2 and titrated with thiosulphate	90
Picric acid	+ $CuSO_4$/NH_4OH, giving insoluble cuprammonium picrate	Unused Cu(II) determined in filtrate by adding KI/ H_2SO_4 and titrating with thiosulphate	91
Sugars	+ alkaline Cu(II) reagent	Unused Cu(II) determined by adding acetate/acetic acid/ excess thiosulphate/I^-/SCN^- ($2\,Cu^{2+} + 2\,SCN^- + 2\,S_2O_3^{2-} \rightarrow 2\,CuSCN + S_4O_6^{2-}$). Unused thiosulphate titrated with iodine	92
δ-sulphonic acids from fat splitting	In water + excess $CuSO_4$, giving insoluble Cu salts (γ-acids give soluble salts)	Unused Cu(II) in filtrate determined iodometrically	93
Sugars	+ $CuSO_4$/NaOH/ tartrate	Cu_2O dissolved in HNO_3, + excess $AgNO_3$ and unused titrated with SCN^-	94
Sugars in body fluids	+ $CuSO_4$/CO_3^{2-}/ tartrate/K_2SO_4; 20 min/100°	Cu_2O dissolved in molybdo-phosphoric acid and Mo(III) titrated with permanganate	95
Reducing sugars	+ $CuSO_4$/KOH/ glycerol or mannitol; 2 min boiling	Unused Cu(II) determined by adding I^-/H_2SO_4 and titrating with thiosulphate	96
Dextrose; dextrose + maltose after acid hydrolysis	+ $CuSO_4$/NaOH/ tartrate/acetate; 20 min/100°	Cu_2O dissolved in Fe(III) alum and Fe(II) formed titrated with permanganate	97
Invert sugar, sucrose	+ $CuSO_4$/Na_2CO_3/ Na_2HPO_4/tartrate. Study of reaction and effect of pH, Cu concentration, time and temperature	Cu_2O determined by adding excess iodine, acidifying and back titrating with thiosulphate	98
Sugars	+ $CuSO_4$/NaOH/ tartrate	Cu_2O dissolved in various oxidizing agents (e.g. Fe(III)) and Fe(II) titrated with permanganate, Ce(IV) or bichromate	99

Materials titrated	Reagent and reaction conditions	Subsequent treatment and final titration stage	Ref.
Fructose	+ $CuSO_4/K_2CO_3/KHCO_3$; 2·5 h/48·5–49°	Unused Cu(II) determined in filtrate by adding I^-/H_2SO_4 and titrating with thiosulphate	100
Furfuraldehyde from HCl hydrolysis of pentosans	+ $CuSO_4$/NaOH/ tartrate	Cu_2O dissolved in Fe(III) reagent and titrated with permanganate	101
Sugars	+ alkali Cu(II) reagent	Cu_2O oxidized to Cu(II) with bromine/acetic acid, and determined iodometrically by adding I^- and titrating with thiosulphate	102
Reducing sugars	+ $CuSO_4$/KOH/ salicylic acid; 2 min boiling	Unused Cu(II) determined by adding I^-/H_2SO_4 and titrating with thiosulphate	103
Sugars	+ $CuSO_4/CO_3^{2-}/HCO_3^-/I^-/IO_3^-$/alkali SO_4^{2-} (last named to reduce oxygen solubility and thus oxidation of Cu_2O)	Acidified and titrated with thiosulphate	104
Aniline	+ $CuSO_4$ + measured excess SCN^-, giving insoluble $Cu(C_6H_5NH_2)_2^{2+}(SCN^-)_2$	Unused SCN^- in filtrate titrated with $AgNO_3$	105
Sugars	+ $CuSO_4$/NaOH/ tartrate; 20 min/100°	+ I^-/SCN^-/acid and titrated with thiosulphate	106
Glycerol, mannitol, sorbitol, tartaric acid	+ $CuCl_2$/NaOH/ ethanol, giving soluble Cu derivatives (first and last react with one Cu, the other two with 2)	Cu(II) in filtrate determined by adding I^-/H_2SO_4 and titrating with thiosulphate	107
Sugars	+ $CuSO_4$/NaOH/ glycerol	+ I^-/SCN^-/acid and titrated with thiosulphate	108
Sugars	+ $CuSO_4$/NaOH/ tartrate; 3 min boiling	Cu_2O dissolved in Fe(III) reagent and titrated with permanganate	109
Sugar mixtures	Used several methods, mostly with alkali Cu(II) reagents		110

Materials titrated	Reagent and reaction conditions	Subsequent treatment and final titration stage	Ref.
Amino acids	+ Cu(II) in phosphate/borate buffer, giving soluble Cu salts	Cu(II) in filtrate determined by adding I^-/acid and titrating with thiosulphate	111
Glycerol	+ $CuCl_2$/NaOH/methanol, giving soluble Cu derivative	Cu(II) in clear liquid from centrifuging determined by adding I^-/H_2SO_4 and titrating with thiosulphate	112
$HOCH_2$—SO_2Na	+ $CuSO_4$/H_2SO_4 oxidizing to $HOCH_2.SO_3Na$. Short reaction time	Unused Cu(II) determined by adding I^- and titrating with thiosulphate	113
Sugars in cane juice	+ $CuSO_4$/Na_2CO_3/Na_2HPO_4/tartrate; 3 min boiling	+ HCl + excess iodine and back titrated with thiosulphate	114
Invert sugar in food products	+ $CuSO_4$/NaOH/tartrate; 5 min/100°	Cu_2O dissolved in Fe(III) reagent and titrated with permanganate	115
Dextrose in presence of glycol	+ $CuSO_4$/CO_3^{2-}/HCO_3^-/I^-/IO_3^-/alkali SO_4^{2-}; 35 min/100°	Acidified and titrated with thiosulphate	116
Reducing sugars	+ $CuSO_4$/NaOH/tartrate. Heated to 80°	Cu_2O dissolved in Fe(III) reagent and titrated with bichromate to diphenylamine/H_2SO_4	117
Glycerol	+ In water, + NaOH + ethanol + $CuCl_2$, giving soluble derivative	Cu(II) determined in clear liquid after centrifuging, by adding acetic acid/I^- and titrating with thiosulphate	118
Reducing sugars	+ $CuSO_4$/HCO_3^-/CO_3^{2-}/tartrate; 15 min/100°	Cu_2O dissolved in Fe(III) alum and titrated with permanganate to ferroin	119
Reducing sugars	+ $CuSO_4$/NaOH/tartrate	Cu_2O dissolved in Fe(III) alum and titrated with bichromate to diphenylamine/H_2SO_4	120
Amino acids	+ Cu(II) phosphate/NaOH suspension; 10 min/room temp., giving soluble salts	Cu(II) in filtrate determined by adding I^-/acetic acid and titrating with thiosulphate	121

Materials titrated	Reagent and reaction conditions	Subsequent treatment and final titration stage	Ref.
Reducing sugars in the tung tree	+ $CuSO_4$/NaOH/ tartrate; 2 min boiling	Cu_2O dissolved in Fe(III) alum and titrated at 50–60° with $Ce(SO_4)_2$ to ferroin	122
–COOH groups in commercial starches, modified by oxidation	+ Cu acetate; 18 h/room temp., giving insoluble Cu salt	Unused Cu(II) determined in supernatant liquid by adding I^-/acetic acid and titrating with thiosulphate	123
Many reducing compounds, e.g. HCHO, chloral, hexamine	+ alkali Cu(II) reagent	Cu_2O dissolved in molybdophosphoric acid and the Mo(III) titrated with permanganate	124
Sugars in apple tissue	+ alkali Cu(II) reagents, e.g. with NaOH/tartrate or CO_3^{2-}/HCO_3^-	Cu_2O dissolved in $Fe_2(SO_4)_3$ and titrated with bichromate to diphenylamine/H_2SO_4	125
Reducing sugars	+ $CuSO_4$/NaOH/ tartrate + layer of petroleum ether; 3 min boiling	Cooled under hydrogen, Cu_2O dissolved in acetic acid/ excess iodine and back titrated with thiosulphate	126
Reducing sugars in fermentation media	+ $CuSO_4$/Na_2CO_3/ tartrate/(pH 9·48) + I^-/ IO_3^-/Na_2SO_4; 30 min/100°	+ oxalate/I^-/H_2SO_4 and titrated with thiosulphate	127
Amino acids in urine	+ $CuCl_2$/Na_3PO_4/borax; 5 min/room temp., giving soluble Cu salts	Cu(II) in filtrate determined by adding I^-/acetic acid and titrating with thiosulphate	128
Laevulinic acid	+ boiling $CuSO_4$/ NaOH/tartrate reagent	Cu_2O dissolved in Fe(III) reagent and titrated with permanganate	129
Sugars	+ $CuSO_4$/NaOH/ tartrate; 7 min/100°	Cu_2O in CO_2 atmosphere dissolved in HCl/NaCl, $NaHCO_3$ + tartrate added, + excess iodine and back titrated with thiosulphate	130
Reducing sugars from acid hydrolysis of woods	Method of ref. 82		131
Sugars	+ $CuSO_4$/NaOH/ Na_2HPO_4/Na_2SO_4/ tartrate (pH 10·2); 10 min/100°	+ IO_3^-/I^-/H_2SO_4 and titrated with thiosulphate	132

Materials titrated	Reagent and reaction conditions	Subsequent treatment and final titration stage	Ref.
Methylated glucoses	+ $CuSO_4$/NaOH/ tartrate; 3, 5, 10 and 15 min boiling	Cu_2O dissolved in Fe(III) reagent and titrated with permanganate	133
Invert sugar	+ $CuSO_4$/Na_2CO_3/ Na_2HPO_4/tartrate; 5 min boiling	+ HCl + acetic acid + I^- + excess iodine and back titrated with thiosulphate	134, 137
Sugars, e.g. in urea	+ $CuSO_4$/NaOH/ triethanolamine	+ I^-/SCN^-/acid and titrated with thiosulphate	135
Reducing sugars	+ $CuSO_4$/K_2CO_3/ $KHCO_3$; 45 min/100°	+ I^-/CO_3^{2-} + HCl/acetic acid/ Pb acetate; shaken, KSCN added and titrated with thiosulphate	136
	[compared with Ferricyanide (ref. 77), and Iodine methods (ref. 249)]		
β-Dicarbonyl compounds	+ Cu acetate/Na acetate; 5 min shaking, giving insoluble chelate derivative	Unused Cu(II) determined in aqueous layer after filtration and extraction with $CHCl_3$, by adding I^-/HCl and titrating with thiosulphate	138
Reducing sugars from acid hydrolysis of hemicelluloses	Method of ref. 132, but with 15 min/100° to ensure reaction of arabinose		139
Reducing sugars after paper chromatographic separation	+ reagent of ref. 132; 25 min/100°, then 10 min/35°	+ I^-/H_2SO_4 and titrated with thiosulphate	140
Amino acids after paper chromatographic separation	In phosphate/borate + Cu phosphate suspension giving soluble Cu salts	Cu(II) in filtrate determined with I^-/acid and titration with thiosulphate	141
Theophylline in blood, urine	In dry methanol, + Cu acetate/methanol, giving insoluble Cu derivative	Precipitate dissolved in H_2SO_4, I^- added and titrated with thiosulphate	142
Glucose from acid hydrolysis of starch	+ $CuSO_4$/NaOH/ Na_2HPO_4/tartrate/IO_3^-; 15 min/100°	+ I^-/H_2SO_4 and titrated with thiosulphate	143
Fructose in presence of glucose	+ $CuSO_4$/K_2CO_3/ $KHCO_3$; 2·5 h/48–48·5°. Also with $CuSO_4$/NaOH/ tartrate, reacting with both sugars	Cu_2O dissolved in Fe(III) and titrated with permanganate	144

Materials titrated	Reagent and reaction conditions	Subsequent treatment and final titration stage	Ref.
Enol content of hydroxymethylene ketones	+ Cu(II) reagent, giving $CHCl_3$-soluble derivative	Cu(II) in $CHCl_3$ extract determined iodometrically	145
Reducing powers of sugars	+ $CuSO_4/Na_2CO_3$/ tartrate/I^-/IO_3^-/ $NaHCO_3$ giving pH values between 8·9 and 9·4. Studied effect of pH, time of reaction, concentrations, type of sugar	+ oxalate/I^-/H_2SO_4 and titrated with thiosulphate	146
Amino acids in beets and sugar factory products	In alkaline solution, + Cu phosphate suspension at pH 10, giving soluble derivatives	Cu(II) in filtrate determined by adding I^-/acetic acid and titrating with thiosulphate	147
Sugar in forage plants (after acid hydrolysis)	+ $CuSO_4$/alkali/tartrate	Cu_2O dissolved in Fe(III) reagent and titrated with bichromate to diphenylamine/ H_2SO_4	148
Blood glucose	+ $CuSO_4/CO_3^{2-}/HCO_3^-$; 6 min/100°	+ molybdoarsenate/H_2SO_4 reagent and Mo(III) titrated with permanganate	149
Reducing sugars	+ $CuSO_4$/NaOH/ tartrate	Cu_2O dissolved in vanadate/ H_2SO_4, bichromate/H_2SO_4 or molybdoarsenic acid and titrated with permanganate or ferric alum	150
Glycerol in soap	+ $CuCl_2$/methanol/ ethanol/NaOH, giving soluble derivative	Cu(II) in filtrate determined by adding I^-/H_2SO_4 and titrating with thiosulphate	151
Carboxymethyl-cellulose	+ $CuSO_4$ at pH 4, giving insoluble derivative	Precipitate dissolved in HNO_3/H_2SO_4 and Cu(II) ultimately determined by adding I^- and titrating with thiosulphate	152
Reducing sugars	+ $CuSO_4/Na_2CO_3$/ $NaHCO_3/I^-/IO_3^-$/ tartrate, pH 8·6–9·3. Study of method	+ oxalate/I^-/H_2SO_4 and titrated with thiosulphate	153
Plant sugars	+ $CuSO_4$/NaOH/ tartrate; 2 min boiling	Cu_2O dissolved in Fe(III) reagent and titrated with permanganate	154

Materials titrated	Reagent and reaction conditions	Subsequent treatment and final titration stage	Ref.
Amino acids	+ Cu phosphate/borate buffer, pH 9·1; 5 min with occasional shaking, giving soluble Cu derivative	Cu(II) in clear solution after centrifuging determined by adding I^-/acetic acid and titrating with thiosulphate biamperometrically	155
Invert sugar	+ $CuSO_4/Na_2CO_3$/ citrate; 10 min boiling	+ $I^-/SCN^-/H_2SO_4$ and titrated with thiosulphate	156
Mercaptans in hydrocarbon gases (RSH)	Passed into Cu acetate/ acetic acid, giving RSCu and RSSR	+ I^- and titrated with thiosulphate	157
Glucose in presence of maltose	+ $CuSO_4$/Na acetate; 20 min/100°	+ I^-/IO_3^-/oxalate/H_2SO_4 and titrated with thiosulphate after 30 min	158
Reducing sugars	+ $CuSO_4$/alkali/tartrate, pH 10·4; 10 min/100°	+ excess iodine + acetic acid and back titrated with thiosulphate	159
Fructose	+ $CuSO_4/Na_2CO_3$/ $NaHCO_3$/tartrate; 2 h/50°	+ NaCl, neutralized, then + I^-/H_2SO_4 and titrated with thiosulphate to starch	160
Mannitol in seaweeds	+ $CuSO_4$/NaOH; 5 min shaking	Cu(II) in filtrate determined by adding I^-/acetic acid and titrating with thiosulphate	161
Sugars	+ $CuSO_4$/NaOH/ tartrate; 20 min/100°	Cu_2O dissolved in molybdophosphoric acid and titrated with permanganate	162
Glucose in biological materials	+ $CuSO_4/Na_2CO_3$/ tartrate; 20 min/100°	Cu_2O dissolved in HNO_3, NH_4OH added and titrated with EDTA to murexide	163
Certain amino ketones (X, Y-substituted phenyl —$COCH_2NRR'$)	+ $CuSO_4$/NaOH/ tartrate; boiling, yielding amine RR'NH	Distilled into standard acid and back titrated	164
Pectins in cotton, flax	Solution in alkali, + acetic acid + $CuSO_4$, giving insoluble Cu pectate	Precipitate dissolved in NH_4OH and Cu(II) determined by adding I^-/H_2SO_4 and titrating with thiosulphate	165

Materials titrated	Reagent and reaction conditions	Subsequent treatment and final titration stage	Ref.
Sodium *p*-amino-salicylate	In water, + excess $CuSO_4$ giving insoluble Cu salt	Unused Cu(II) in filtrate determined iodometrically	166
Sugars in dietetic foods	+ alkali Cu(II) reagent	Cu_2O dissolved in HNO_3 and ultimately titrated with EDTA to murexide	167
Sugars	+ $CuSO_4$/NaOH/ tartrate	Review of methods; proposed dissolving the Cu_2O in Fe(III) and titrating with permanganate	168
Pyridine or its perchlorate	+ $Cu(NO_3)_2$ + excess SCN^-, giving insoluble $Cu(C_5H_5N)_2^{2+}(SCN^-)_2$ pH 5·2–5·7; 1 h/room temp.	Unused SCN^- determined in the filtrate by adding excess Ag(I) and back titrating with SCN^-	169
Fatty acids in a soap mother liquor	+ excess Cu(II) + measured amount of Na carboxymethylcellulose, giving precipitate of Cu carboxymethylcellulose, which entrains the Cu salts of the fatty acids	Cu(II) in filtrate determined by adding I^-/acetic acid and titrating with thiosulphate (added Na carboxymethylcellulose allowed for)	170
Sugars	+ $CuSO_4$/NaOH/ lactate	Cu_2O dissolved in Fe(III) reagent and titrated with permanganate	171
Lactose in chocolate	+ alkali Cu(II) reagent	Cu_2O dissolved in HNO_3 and ultimately titrated in ammoniacal solution with EDTA to murexide	172
Penicillin	+ $CuSO_4$/NaOH/ tartrate. Heated giving NH_3	Distilled into standard acid and back titrated	173
Amino acids, peptides	+ Cu phosphate/borate buffer, pH 9·1	Cu(II) determined in filtrate by adding HCl and titrating with EDTA to 1-(2-pyridylazo)-naphthol	174
Quinine hydrochloride	In acetone/benzene or toluene, + $CuCl_2$/ acetone, giving insoluble $Cu(C_{20}H_{25}N_2O_2)Cl_2.(CH_3COCH_3)x$	Precipitate dissolved in NH_4OH and titrated with EDTA to murexide	175

Materials titrated	Reagent and reaction conditions	Subsequent treatment and final titration stage	Ref.
Reducing sugars	+ $CuSO_4/Na_2CO_3$/ EDTA; 10 min boiling	Cu_2O dissolved in HNO_3 and titrated with EDTA to murexide	176
Reducing sugars	+ $CuSO_4$/NaOH/ tartrate	Discussed methods for determination of the Cu_2O	177
Glucose	+ Cu(II)/NaOH/ sulphosalicylic acid	Unused Cu(II) determined iodometrically	178
Other sugars	Method of ref. 178		179
Isoniazid	+ excess $CuSO_4$; 30 min reaction, giving insoluble Cu derivative	Cu(II) in filtrate determined iodometrically	180
Theophylline	+ excess Cu acetate; 30 min/room temp., giving insoluble Cu derivative	Unused Cu(II) in clear liquid after centrifuging determined by adding I^- and titrating with thiosulphate	181
Amino acids	+ Cu phosphate suspension giving soluble Cu salts (criticized method of ref. 147)	Cu(II) in filtrate determined by adding I^-/HCl and titrating with thiosulphate	182
Glucose	+ $CuSO_4$/NaOH/ tartrate	Cu_2O dissolved in HNO_3 and titrated with EDTA	183
Sugars in medicinal syrups	+ $CuSO_4$/alkali/EDTA	Cu_2O dissolved in HNO_3, NH_4OH added and titrated with EDTA to murexide	184
Reducing substances in wool, cotton, cotton-wool, etc. ('copper number')	+ $CuSO_4$/NaOH/ tartrate; 3 min boiling	Cu_2O dissolved in Fe(III) alum and titrated with permanganate	185
Ascorbic acid	Method of ref. 178		186
Fructose	Method of ref. 178		187
Glucose in presence of much lactose	+ Cu acetate/Na acetate/ lactic acid; 5 min boiling	Cu_2O dissolved in Fe(III) reagent and titrated with permanganate	190
Na carboxymethyl-cellulose	In water/ethanol/H_2SO_4, + $CuSO_4$ (pH 3·35). Warmed to 50–55°, giving insoluble Cu salt	Unused Cu(II) determined in filtrate by adding I^-/acetic acid and titrating with thiosulphate	191

Materials titrated	Reagent and reaction conditions	Subsequent treatment and final titration stage	Ref.
Gluconate	+ Cu phosphate suspension giving soluble salt	Cu(II) in filtrate determined by adding $I^-/SCN^-/HCl$ and titrating with thiosulphate	192, 200
Citric acid	Method of ref. 192		193, 200
Mercaptans (micro-)	+ Cu butylphthalate/hydrocarbon, methanol or amyl alcohol mixture, + *ca* 5% acetic acid; 5 min shaking	+ I^- and titrated with thiosulphate	194
Glucose in biological fluids	+ $CuSO_4$/alkali/tartrate; 2 min/100°	Unused Cu(II) titrated with EDTA to murexide	195
Reducing sugars	+ $CuSO_4$/NaOH/tartrate; 2 min boiling	Filtrate, + H_2SO_4 + Na acetate + NH_4Cl + NH_4SCN and titrated with hydroquinone potentiometrically	196
Reducing sugars in tanning extracts	+ $CuSO_4$/NaOH/tartrate; 2 min boiling	Cu_2O dissolved in HCl, pH brought to 8 with NH_4OH and titrated with EDTA to murexide	197
α-Amino nitrogen in urine	Method of ref. 111; studied composition of the Cu derivatives		198
Mandelic acid and its compounds used in medicine	+ Cu(II) reagent, giving insoluble salt	Cu(II) in precipitate determined by titration with EDTA	199
Piperazine in ethylenediamine	In water, + $CuSO_4$, giving insoluble Cu derivative	Precipitate dissolved in HCl or H_2SO_4, NH_4OH added and titrated with EDTA to murexide	201
Glycine in glycine/potassium trioxalatochromate	+ Cu phosphate suspension/borate buffer, pH 9·1; 5 min shaking, giving soluble salt	Centrifuged, potassium salt removed in ion-exchange column and Cu(II) determined by adding I^-/acetic acid and titrating with thiosulphate biamperometrically	202
Carbohydrates	+ $CuSO_4$/NaOH/tartrate. Sample added to boiling reagent	Filtered and Cu(II) determined in filtrate by acidification with HCl and titrating with Cr(II) in CO_2 atmosphere to neutral red or phenosafranine	203

Materials titrated	Reagent and reaction conditions	Subsequent treatment and final titration stage	Ref.
Barbital	In pyridine/water/ KH_2PO_4, pH 8·5, + $CuSO_4$/25% pyridine; 1–2 h/room temp., giving insoluble derivative	Unused Cu(II) in filtrate determined by bringing pH to 8 with NH_4Cl and titrating with EDTA to murexide	204
Fructose	+ $CuSO_4$/K_2CO_3/ $KHCO_3$; 135 min/50°	Cu_2O dissolved in Fe(III) reagent and titrated with permanganate	205
Sugars	+ $CuSO_4$/NaOH/tri-hydroxyglutaric acid; 6 min/100°	Cu_2O dissolved in Fe(III) and titrated with permanganate	206
Theophylline	In methanol, + Cu acetate/methanol; 3 h/room temp., giving insoluble derivative	Precipitate dissolved in acetic acid/acetate and Cu(II) titrated with EDTA to 1-(2-pyridylazo)- β-naphthol	207
Isoniazid	In water, + measured excess SCN^- + slight excess $CuSO_4$; 30 min/ room temp., giving insoluble derivative	Unused SCN^- determined in filtrate by titration with Ag^+ to Fe^{3+} indicator	208
Piperazine	Method of ref. 208		209
Invert sugar in refined white sugars	+ $CuSO_4$/NaOH/ Na_2CO_3/tartrate; 5 min/100°	Unused Cu(II) titrated with EDTA to murexide	210
Glucose from acid hydrolysis of starch in bandages	Neutralized solution + $CuSO_4$/NaOH/tartrate; 2 min boiling	+ I^-/H_2SO_4 and titrated with thiosulphate	211
Sugar in silages and forages (after preliminary isolation and inversion)	+ $CuSO_4$/NaOH/ Na_2HPO_4/IO_3^-; 15 min boiling	+ I^-/H_2SO_4 and titrated with thiosulphate	212
Reducing value of high molecular weight polysaccharides (after acid hydrolysis)	(Method of ref. 132 and extrapolated values to reaction time = zero)		213
Proteins	+ NaOH/H_2O/Cu acetate; 1–2 h	Centrifuged; clear liquid + excess EDTA; boiled, acetate buffer added and titrated with Zn acetate to α-pyridylazo-β-naphthol	214

Materials titrated	Reagent and reaction conditions	Subsequent treatment and final titration stage	Ref.
Invert sugar	+ $CuSO_4/Na_2CO_3/$ citric acid; 10 min boiling	+ I^-/H_2SO_4 and titrated with thiosulphate	215
Tannins	+ Cu acetate; 15 min/100°	Centrifuged and determined unreacted Cu(II) iodometrically	216
Amino acids	+ Cu phosphate suspension; 1 min shaking	Filtered, filtrate titrated with EDTA to murexide (in ammoniacal solution) or to 1-(2-pyridylazo)- β-naphthol (in HCl solution)	217
Sulphonamides	In NaOH + borate solution, + $CuSO_4$, giving precipitate of Cu derivative	Filtered and unused Cu(II) in filtrate titrated with EDTA to 1-(2-pyridylazo)-2-naphthol ('PAN')	218
Barbiturates, e.g. veronal	+ $CuSO_4/NH_4OH/$ pyridine; 10–15 min, giving precipitate of cupropyridinium derivative, $Cu(C_5H_5N)_2^{2+}$ $(Barbiturate)^{2-}$	Filtered, filtrate brought to pH 8 and titrated with EDTA to murexide	219, 224
Glucose	+ $CuSO_4/NaOH/$ tartrate; 2 min boiling	Cu_2O filtered and unused Cu(II) in filtrate titrated with KCN at the boiling point to decoloration	220
Theophyllin	In water, + NH_4OH + $CuSO_4$; 5 min	Filtered, aliquot of filtrate + acetic acid + KI and titrated with thiosulphate	221
Reducing sugars in sucrose products	+ $CuSO_4/NaOH/Na_2CO_3$/tartrate; 5 min/100°	Unused Cu(II) titrated with EDTA to murexide	222
Isoniazid	+ NH_4SCN + $CuSO_4/$ NH_4OH/NH_4Cl reagent, giving precipitate of Cu derivative	Centrifuged and unused Cu(II) in supernatant liquid titrated with EDTA to murexide	223
Reducing sugars in sugar industrial products	+ $CuSO_4/Na_2CO_3/$ Na_2HPO_4/Na tartrate; heated 4–5 min	Brought to pH 8 (acetic acid) excess iodine added and back titrated with thiosulphate	225
Sorbose in mixtures with acetone, mono- and diisopropylidene-sorbose	Heated with $CuSO_4/$ NaOH/tartrate	Unused Cu(II) determined iodometrically	226

Materials titrated	Reagent and reaction conditions	Subsequent treatment and final titration stage	Ref.
'Captax' (principally 2-mercaptobenzthiazole)	In ethanol + $CuSO_4$ and heated, giving precipitate of Cu derivative	Filtered, filtrate brought to pH 8 with NH_4OH and unreacted Cu(II) titrated with EDTA to murexide	227
D-Glucosamine hydrochloride and related compounds	+ $CuSO_4$/NaOH/ tartrate; 10 min/ca 100°	Precipitated Cu_2O dissolved in HNO_3,NH_4OH added and titrated with EDTA to murexide	228
Cellulose carboxymethyl ethers	In ethanol/dilute H_2SO_4 (pH 2·2–2·5) + $CuSO_4$/ NH_4OH, giving pH 4–4·1 and precipitate of Cu derivative	Filtrate + acetic acid + I^- and iodine titrated with thiosulphate; also precipitate + water/ethanol/NH_4OH, then + acetic acid/I^- and likewise titrated	229

References

1. Schwarz, H., *Ann.* **84**, 84 (1853).
2. v. Babo, C. H. L., *J. prakt. Chem.* **74**, 120 (1858).
3. Mohr, F., *Z. anal. Chem.* **12**, 296 (1873).
4. Perrot, F., *Ber.* **9**, 1939 (1876).
5. Pillitz, W., *Z. anal. Chem.* **15**, 262 (1876).
6. Ullbricht, R., *Ber.* **10**, 128 (1877).
7. Arnold, C., *Z. anal. Chem.* **20**, 331 (1881).
8. Riegler, E., *Z. anal. Chem.* **35**, 31 (1896).
9. Pinette, J., *Chem.-Ztg.* **21**, 395 (1897).
10. Pflüger, *Archiv für physiol. Chem.* **69**, 409 (1898).
11. Schoorl, N., *Z. angew. Chem.* **12**, 633 (1899).
12. Weil, F., *Compt. rend.* **134**, 115 (1902).
13. Rosenthaler, L., *Z. anal. Chem.* **43**, 282 (1904).
14. Bang, I., *Biochem. Z.* **2**, 271 (1906); **11**, 538 (1908).
15. Bertrand, G., *Bull. soc. chim. France* **35**, 1285 (1906).
16. Harding, E. P. and Doran, J., *J. Am. Chem. Soc.* **29**, 1476 (1907).
17. Flohil, J. T., *Chem. Weekblad* **7**, 1057 (1910).
18. Wagenaar, M., *Pharm. Weekblad* **48**, 947 (1911).
19. Kendall, E. C., *J. Am. Chem. Soc.* **34**, 317 (1912).
20. Eynon, L. and Lane, J. H., *Analyst* **37**, 41 (1912).
21. Schoorl, N., *Chem. Weekblad* **9**, 678 (1912).
22. Bang, I., *Biochem. Z.* **49**, 1 (1913).
23. Kober, P. A. and Sugiura, K., *J. Am. Chem. Soc.* **35**, 1546 (1913).
24. Smit, J., *Chem. Weekblad* **10**, 894 (1913).

25. Schoorl, N., *Chem. Weekblad* **12**, 481 (1915).
26. Kober, P. A., *J. Ind. Eng. Chem.* **9**, 501 (1917).
27. Schoorl, N. and Regenbogen, A., *Z. anal. Chem.* **56**, 191 (1917).
28. Kowarsky, A., *Deut. med. Wochschr.* **45**, 188 (1919).
29. Scales, F., *J. Ind. Eng. Chem.* **11**, 747 (1919).
30. Vigevani, G., *Boll. chim. farm.* **58**, 436 (1919).
31. Bruhns, G., *Z. anal. Chem.* **59**, 337 (1920).
32. Bruhns, G., *Chemiker-Ztg.* **45**, 486 (1921).
33. Dieckmann, A., *Ber.* **54**, 2251 (1921).
34. Fontes, G. and Thivolle, L., *Bull. soc. chim. biol.* **3**, 226 (1921).
35. Hieber, W., *Ber.* **54**, 902 (1921).
36. Kreisy, A., *Z. Verein Deut. Zuckerind.* **71**, 123 (1921).
37. Legrand, *Compt. rend.* **172**, 600 (1921).
38. Quisumbing, F. A. and Thomas, A. W., *J. Am. Chem. Soc.* **43**, 1503 (1921).
39. Shaffer, P. A. and Hartmann, A. F., *J. Biol. Chem.* **45**, 365 (1921).
40. Fontes, G. and Thivolle, L., *Bull. soc. chim. biol.* **4**, 23 (1922).
41. Spacu, G. and Creangà, C., *Bull. soc. Stiinte, Cluj* **2**, 105 (1923).
42. Blanchetière, A., *Bull. soc. chim. biol.* **6**, 509 (1924).
43. Coppens, P. A., *Nederland. Tydschr. Geneeskunde* **68**, I, 153 (1924).
44. Spehl, P., *Compt. rend. soc. biol.* **90**, 638 (1924).
45. Csapó, J., *Biochem. Z.* **157**, 350 (1925).
46. van den Hout, M. A. H., Neeteson, P. A. and van Scherpenberg, A. L., *Chem. Weekblad* **22**, 126 (1925).
47. Nijns, L., *Bull. assoc. école sup. brasserie Louvain* **25**, 36 (1925).
48. Pick, L., *Listy Cukrovar.* **43**, 185 (1925).
49. Schoorl, N., *Chem. Weekblad* **22**, 132 (1925).
50. Tervaert, D. G. C., *Biochem. J.* **19**, 541 (1925).
51. Kolthoff, I. M., *Chem. Weekblad* **23**, 61 (1926).
52. Mislowitzer, E. and Schaefer, W., *Biochem. Z.* **168**, 217 (1926).
53. Somogyi, M., *J. Biol. Chem.* **70**, 599 (1926).
54. Stoffella, C. G., *Boll. chim. farm.* **65**, 225 (1926).
55. Fontes, G. and Thivolle, L., *Bull. soc. chim. biol.* **9**, 353 (1927).
56. Fontes, G. and Thivolle, L., *Lait* **7**, 547 (1927).
57. Amick, C. A., *Chemist-Analyst* **17**, 10 (1928).
58. Biazzo, R., *Ann. chim. applicata* **18**, 447 (1928).
59. Hadjeff, M. D., *Z. Untersuch. Lebensm.* **55**, 615 (1928).
60. Horne, W. D., *Planter Sugar Mfr.* **81**, 1 (1928).
61. Semiganovski, N., *Trans. Sci. Chem.-Pharm. Inst.* (*Moscow*) 33 (1926), in *Z. anal. Chem.* **74**, 400 (1928).
62. Ofner, R., *Listy Cukrovar.* **47**, 737 (1929).
63. Rebagliatti, E. E., *Rev. farm.* (*Buenos Aires*) **2**, 340 (1929).
64. Ross, J. H., *Research Notes* **2**, 11 (1929).
65. Schoorl, N., *Chem. Weekblad* **26**, 130 (1929).

66. Ofner, R., *Z. Zuckerind. Czech. Rep.* **53**, 733 (1930).
67. Svanberg, O., *Z. physiol. Chem.* **188**, 219 (1930).
68. Tompsett, S. L., *Biochem. J.* **24**, 1148 (1930).
69. Demont, P., *Mitt. Lebensm. Hyg.* **22**, 48 (1931).
70. v. Fellenberg, T., *Mitt. Lebensm. Hyg.* **22**, 9 (1931).
71. Hinton, C. L. and Macara, T., *Analyst* **56**, 286 (1931).
72. Khadzhiev, M. D., *Ann. univ. Sofia* **9**, 163 (1931).
73. Ofner, R., *Z. Zuckerind. Czech. Rep.* **56**, 249 (1931–2).
74. Heiduschka, A. and Bietham, W., *J. prakt. Chem.* **133**, 273 (1932).
75. Jackson, R. F. and Matthews, J. A., *Bur. Stds. J. Research* **8**, 403 (1932); *J. Assoc. Offic Agr. Chemists* **15**, 198 (1932).
76. Kometiani, P. A., *Z. Untersuch. Lebensm.* **63**, 194 (1932).
77. Marsh, G. L. and Joslyn, M. A., *Ind. Eng. Chem., Anal. Ed.* **4**, 368 (1932).
78. Ofner, R., and Gracko, I., *Listy Cukrovar.* **50**, 148 (1932); *Z. Zuckerind. Czech. Rep.* **57**, 125 (1932–3).
79. Ofner, R., *Listy Cukrovar.* **50**, 270, 278 (1932).
80. Labourasse, G., *Bull. assoc. chim. sucr. dist.* **50**, 447 (1933).
81. Mugdan, M. and Wimmer, J., *Angew. Chem.* **46**, 117 (1933).
82. Shaffer, P. A. and Somogyi, M., *J. Biol. Chem.* **100**, 695 (1933).
83. Steinhoff, G., *Z. Spiritusind.* **56**, 64 (1933).
84. Kataoka, E., *J. Biochem. (Japan)* **19**, 15 (1934).
85. Oshmyan, G., *Brodiln. Prom.* **11**, No. 5, 26 (1934).
86. Stegeman, R. A. and Englis, D. T., *Trans. Illinois State Acad. Sci.* **27**, 75 (1934).
87. Taran, E. N., *J. Appl. Chem. USSR* **7**, 213 (1934).
88. v. Fellenberg, T., *Mitt. Lebensm. Hyg.* **26**, 182 (1935).
89. Kizevetter, I. V., *Ruibnoe Khoz. Dal'nege Vostoka* **13**, No. 1, 123 (1935).
90. Rosenblüh, E. and Vavrinecz, G., *Listy Cukrovar.* **53**, 157 (1935).
91. Ugnyachev, N. Ya. and Rikhter, D. A., *Zavodskaya Lab.* **4**, 1062 (1935).
92. Bitskei, J., *Angew. Chem.* **49**, 310 (1936).
93. Eisenstein, P., *Przemysl Naftowy* **11**, 322 (1936).
94. Harlay, V., *J. pharm. chim.* **23**, 589 (1936).
95. Le Berre, M., *Bull. sci. pharmacol.* **43**, 507 (1936).
96. Platkovskaya, V. M. and Vekhotko, T. I., *Zhur. Priklad Khim.* **9**, 177 (1936).
97. Sichert, K. and Bleyer, B., *Z. anal. Chem.* **107**, 328 (1936).
98. Spengler, O., Tödt, F. and Scheuerer, M., *Z. Wirtschaftsgruppe Zuckerind.* **86**, 130, 322 (1936).
99. Stegeman, R. A. and Englis, D. T., *J. Assoc. Offic. Agr. Chemists* **19**, 480 (1936).
100. Strepkov, S. M., *Ann. chim. anal. chim. appl.* **18**, 231 (1936).
101. Khristich, K. I., *Zavodskaya Lab.* **6**, 558 (1937).
102. Pall, D. B., *Intern. Sugar J.* **39**, 153 (1937).

103. Platkovskaya, V. M. and Vekhotko, T. I., *J. Appl. Chem. USSR* **10**, 212 (1937).
104. Somogyi, M., *J. Biol. Chem.* **117**, 771 (1937).
105. Spacu, G. and Dima, L., *Z. anal. Chem.* **110**, 25 (1937).
106. Sotonin, K., *Spirito-vodoch. Prom.* **14**, No. 6, 30 (1937).
107. Bertram, S. H. and Rutgers, R., *Rec. trav. chim.* **57**, 681 (1938).
108. Sotonin, K. and Evdokimova, V., *Spirito-vodoch. Prom.* No. 1, 27 (1938).
109. Szakács, Ö., *Kisérletügyi Közlemények* **41**, 143 (1938).
110. Zerban, F. W. and Sattler, L., *Ind. Eng. Chem., Anal. Ed.* **10**, 669 (1938).
111. Pope, C. G. and Stevens, M. F., *Biochem. J.* **33**, 1070 (1939).
112. Schoorl, N., *Pharm. Weekblad* **76**, 777 (1939).
113. Spitzer, L., *Ann. chim. applicata* **29**, 184 (1939).
114. Yosida, T., Tanabe, T. and Yamahuzi, K., *Bull. Agr. Chem. Soc. Japan* **15**, 49 (1939).
115. Arutyunyan, L. A. and Akopdzhanyan, V. I., *Voprosy Pitaniya* **9**, No. 4, 44 (1940).
116. Fulmer, E. I., Hickey, R. J. and Underkofler, L. A., *Ind. Eng. Chem., Anal. Ed.* **12**, 729 (1940).
117. Wildman, S. G. and Hansen, E., *Plant Physiology* **15**, 719 (1940).
118. Andrews, J. T. R., *Oil & Soap* **18**, 14 (1941).
119. Phillips, T. G., *J. Assoc. Offic. Agr. Chemists* **24**, 181 (1941).
120. Svershkov, I. V., *Lab. Prakt. USSR* **16**, No. 6, 27 (1941).
121. Abelin, I., *Verhandl. Verein schweiz. Physiol.* 7 (1942).
122. Best, A. H., Peterson, A. H. and Sell, H. M., *Ind. Eng. Chem., Anal. Ed.* **14**, 145 (1942).
123. Elizer, L. H., *Ind. Eng. Chem., Anal. Ed.* **14**, 635 (1942).
124. Ionescu-Matiu, A., Popescu, A. and Petrescu, E., *Bull. acad. med. Roumanie* **14**, 598 (1943).
125. Leonard, R. H., Meade, R. C. and Dustman, R. B., *Ind. Eng. Chem., Anal. Ed.* **15**, 579 (1943).
126. Phillipson, T., *Arkiv Kemi Min. Geol. Ser. A* **16**, No. 22, 1 (1943).
127. Underkofler, L. A., Guyman, J. F., Rayman, M. M. and Fulmer, E. I., *Iowa State College J. Sci.* **17**, 251 (1943).
128. Albanese, A. A. and Irby, V., *J. Biol. Chem.* **153**, 583 (1944).
129. Boinon, R., *Ing. chim.* **27**, No. 161, 8 (1945).
130. Hadorn, H. and v. Fellenberg, T., *Mitt. Lebensm. Hyg.* **36**, 359 (1945).
131. Saeman, J. F., Bubl, J. L. and Hanna, E. G., *Ind. Eng. Chem., Anal. Ed.* **17**, 35, 95 (1945).
132. Somogyi, M., *J. Biol. Chem.* **160**, 61, 69 (1945).
133. Jeanloz, R., *Helv. Chim. Acta* **29**, 57 (1946).
134. McDonald, E. J. and Turrotte, A. L., *J. Research Natl. Bur. Standards* **37**, 429 (1946).

135. Tschirch, E., *Pharmazie* **1**, 230 (1946).
136. Blom, J. and Rosted, C. O., *Acta Chem. Scand.* **1**, 32 (1947).
137. McDonald, E. J. and Turrotte, A. L., *J. Assoc. Offic. Agr. Chemists* **30**, 124 (1947).
138. Seaman, W., Woods, J. T. and Massad, E. A., *Anal. Chem.* **19**, 250 (1947).
139. Auernheimer, A. H., Wickerham, L. J. and Schniepp, L. E., *Anal. Chem.* **20**, 876 (1948).
140. Flood, A. E., Hirst, E. L. and Jones, J. K. N., *J. Chem. Soc.* 1679 (1948).
141. Martin, A. J. P. and Mittelman, R., *Biochem. J.* **43**, 353 (1948).
142. Plummer, A. J., *J. Pharm. Exp. Therap.* **93**, 142 (1948).
143. Pucher, G. W., Leavenworth, C. S. and Vickery, H. B., *Anal. Chem.* **20**, 850 (1948).
144. Besson, S. and Petot, M., *Bull. soc. sci. Nancy* **8**, 36 (1949–50).
145. Bokadia, M. M. and Seshapande, S. S., *J. Indian Chem. Soc.* **26**, 455 (1949).
146. Heidt, L. J., Southam, F. W., Benedict, J. D. and Smith, M. E., *J. Am. Chem. Soc.* **71**, 2190 (1949).
147. Slavíčková, A., *Listy Cukrovar.* **66**, 185 (1949–50).
148. Thomas, J. W., Melin, C. G. and Moore, L. A., *Anal. Chem.* **21**, 1363 (1949).
149. (Anonymous), *Ann. biol. chim.* **8**, 516 (1950).
150. Bevillard, P., *Bull. soc. chim. France* 1298 (1950).
151. Bore, P., *Bull. mens. ITERG* **4**, 168 (1950).
152. Conner, A. Z. and Eyler, R. W., *Anal. Chem.* **22**, 1129 (1950).
153. Heidt, L. J. and Southam, F. W., *J. Am. Chem. Soc.* **72**, 589 (1950).
154. Lisitsyn, D. I., *Biokhimiya* **15**, 165 (1950).
155. Schroeder, W. A., Kay, L. M. and Mills, R. S., *Anal. Chem.* **22**, 760 (1950).
156. Borghi, M. and Maurandi, V., *Ind. sacc. ital.* **44**, 158 (1951).
157. Ellis, E. W. and Barker, T., *Anal. Chem.* **23**, 1777 (1951).
158. Phillips, L. L. and Caldwell, M. L., *Anal. Chem.* **23**, 1172 (1951).
159. Schneider, F. and Emmerich, A., *Zucker-Beihefte* No. 2, 17 (1951).
160. Prillinger, F., *Mitt. Höherer Bundeslehr- u. Versuchsanstalt, Wein u. Obstbau, Klosterneuburg; höherer Bundeslehr- u. Versuchsanstalt Bienenkunde, Wien-Grinzing* **2**, 20 (1952).
161. Suzuki, N. *Bull. Fac. Fisheries Hokkaido Univ.* **3**, 59 (1952).
162. Carles, J., *Bull. soc. chim. biol.* **35**, 365 (1953).
163. Bultasová, H. and Horáková, E., *Chem. Listy* **48**, 1698 (1954).
164. Simonyi, I., Gál, G. and Tokár, G., *Magyar Kem. Folyoirat* **60**, 289 (1954).
165. Sobolev, M. A. and Krasivskaya, A. A., *Tekstil Prom.* **14**, No. 7, 39 (1954).
166. Baron, M. S., *Aptechnoe Delo* **4**, No. 5, 17 (1955).

167. Hadorn, H. and Suter, H., *Mitt. Lebensm. Hyg.* **46**, 341 (1955).
168. Marotta, C. R. C. and Pena, C., *pR* (*Montevideo*) **5**, Nos. 1–3 D9 (1955).
169. Musha, S. and Munemori, M., *J. Chem. Soc. Japan, Ind. Chem. Sect.* **58**, 393 (1955).
170. Pavlovich, V. A. and Abuladze, L. M., *Tekstil. Prom.* **15**, No. 10, 56 (1955).
171. Pijanowski, E. and Žebrowska, M., *Przem. Spozywczy* **9**, 282 (1955).
172. Raymond, P., *Mitt. Lebensm. Hyg.* **46**, 246 (1955).
173. Tokár, G., Simonyi, I. and Gál, G., *Magyar Kem. Folyoirat* **61**, 148 (1955).
174. Buděšinský, B., *Chem. Listy* **50**, 1236 (1956).
175. Buděšinský, B. and Vaničková, E., *Československ. Farm.* **5**, 277 (1956).
176. Eschmann, H., *Chemist-Analyst* **45**, 5 (1956).
177. Klautschnigg, P., *Ann. sper. agrar.* (*Rome*) **10**, 1405 (1956).
178. Rabega, C., *Analele Univ. 'C. I. Parhon', Bucuresti, Ser. stiinte nat.* No. 12, 57 (1956).
179. Rabega, C., Stanescu, R., Rabega, M. and Osorhan, T., *Analele Univ. 'C. I. Parhon', Bucuresti, Ser. stiinte nat.* No. 12, 65 (1956).
180. Ruggieri, R., *Boll. chim. farm.* **95**, 467 (1956).
181. Runti, C., *Il Farmaco* (*Pavia*), *Ed. prat.* **11**, 218 (1956).
182. Vavrinecz, G., *Cukroripar.* **9**, 49 (1956).
183. Hayakawa, H., *Kôbe Daigaku Kyôikugakubu Kenkyu Shûroku* No. 15, 7 (1957).
184. Kleflin, Z. and Šumanović, K., *Farm. Glasnik* **13**, 95 (1957).
185. Paape, W. and Gebert, P., *Pharmazie* **12**, 475 (1957).
186. Rabega, C., Stanescu, R. and Rabega, M., *Analele Univ. 'C. I. Parhon', Bucuresti, Ser. stiinte nat.* No. 16, 107 (1957).
187. Rabega, C., Rabega, M., and Stanescu, R., *Analele Univ. 'C. I. Parhon', Bucuresti, Ser. stiinte nat.* No. 16, 111 (1957).
188. Singh, M. P. and Ghosh, S., *Z. physik. Chemie* (*Leipzig*) **207**, 187 (1957).
189. Arnoux, M. J., Pastor, J. and Morel, B., *Bull. soc. pharm. Marseille* **7**, 231 (1958).
190. Evstratova, K. I., *Biokhimiyia* **23**, 181 (1958).
191. Finkel'shtein, M. Z., Timokhin, I. M. and Mukhamedov, Kh.U., *Izvest. Vyssikh. Ucheb. Zavedenii Naft. i. Gaz* No. 12, 45 (1958).
192. Leopold, H. and Valtr, Z., *Nahrung* **2**, 464 (1958).
193. Leopold, H. and Valtr, Z., *Nahrung* **2**, 532 (1958).
194. Roth, H., *Mikrochim. Acta* 767 (1958).
195. Street, H. V., *Analyst* **83**, 628 (1958).
196. Berka, A. and Zýka, J., *Československ. Farm.* **8**, 576 (1959).
197. Blažej, A. and Mládek, M., *Kožařstvi* **9**, 131 (1959).
198. Bottini, E., Strigini, P. and Antognoni, G., *Boll. soc. ital. biol. sper.* **35**, 772 (1959).
199. Helmstaedter, G., *Deut. Apotheker-Ztg.* **99**, 589 (1959).
200. Leopold, H. and Valtr, Z., *Československ. Farm.* **8**, 486 (1959).

201. Nebbia, L. and Pagani, B., *Chim. e ind.* (*Milan*) **41**, 870 (1959).
202. Spaulding, G. H., *Anal. Chem.* **31**, 1109 (1959).
203. Tandon, J. P., *Z. anal. Chem.* **167**, 184 (1959).
204. Tatsuzawa, M., *Eisie Shikenjo Hokoku* **77**, 109 (1959).
205. Wu, C. C., *Formosan Sci.* **13**, 37, 45 (1959).
206. Ablov, A. V. and Batyr, D. G., *Zhur. Anal. Khim.* **15**, 112 (1960).
207. Blagajević, Z., Bradić, P. and Bunović, M., *Schweiz. Apotheker-Ztg.* **98**, 654 (1960).
208. Grecu, I. and Curea, E., *Farmacia* (*Bucharest*) **8**, 503 (1960).
209. Grecu, I. and Curea, E., *Farmacia* (*Bucharest*) **8**, 625 (1960).
210. Knight, J. and Allen, C. H., *Intern. Sugar J.* **16**, 344 (1960).
211. Šimková, A. and Haller, A., *Pharm. Zentralhalle* **99**, 113 (1960).
212. Wiseman, H. G., Mallack, J. C. and Jacobson, W. C., *J. Agr. Food Chem.* **8**, 78 (1960).
213. Casier, J. P. J. and Hendrix, R., *Agricultura* (*Louvain*) (2) **8**, 741 (1960).
214. Holasek, A. and Dugandzic, M., *Arztl. Lab.* **6**, 1 (1960).
215. Tanner, H., *Fruchtsaft. Ind.*, **5**, No. 1, 13 (1960).
216. Stanciu, N. and Ionica, V., *Farmacia* (*Bucharest*) **9**, 49 (1961).
217. Gauthier, B. and Maréchal, M.-C., *Ann. pharm. franc.* **20**, 156 (1962).
218. Abdine, H., and Abdel Sayad, W. S., *J. Pharm. Pharmacol.* **14**, 761 (1962).
219. Ciogolea, G., Morait, G., Baloescu, C., Teodorescu, N., Creanga, S., Tudor, M., Petroniu, L. and Ionescu, G., *Farmacia* (*Bucharest*) **10**, 257 (1962).
220. Manolov, K. R., *Zhur. Anal. Khim.* **17**, 898 (1962).
221. Plumel, M., *Ann. Pharm. Franç.* **20**, 34 (1962).
222. Roche, M., *Ind. Aliment. Agr.* (*Paris*) **79**, 647 (1962).
223. Tatsuzawa, M., *Bunseki Kagaku* **11**, 1055 (1962).
224. Ciogolea, C., Creanga, S., Mihai, T. and Petroniu, L., *Ann. Pharm. Franç.* **21**, 681 (1963).
225. Friml, M. and Včeláková, D., *Listy Cukrovar* **79**, 241 (1963).
226. Kvapil, J., Konupčik, M. and Liška, M., *Tech. Publ. Středisko Tech. Inform Potravinar Průmyslu* No. 139 334 (1963).
227. Parushev, M., *Khim. Ind.* (*Sofia*) **35**, 49 (1963).
228. Tamura, Z. and Miyazaki, M., *Bunseki Kagaku* **12**, 470 (1963).
229. Timokhin, I. M. and Finkel'shtein, M. Z., *Zhur. Priklad Khim.* **36**, 415 (1963)

29. Copper (III)

('Percuprate')

Most examples of use of this oxidizing agent are direct titration. A single instance is given below of an indirect titration:

Material titrated	Reagent and reaction conditions	Subsequent treatment and final titration stage
Tartaric acid	+ $K_7Cu(IO_6)_2$ + KOH; 5–10 min/room temp.	Unused reagent back titrated with arsenite to the colour change blue to green

Reference

Velikonja, N., *Arkiv. Kem.* **27**, 161 (1955).

30. Cyanide

Reagent. An alkali cyanide, nearly always the potassium salt, appears to be the only reagent. It has been used in aqueous solution in most cases.

Reactions and materials titrated. 1. Addition to carbonyl compounds, principally aldehydes:

$$RCHO + CN^- + H_2O \rightarrow RCH\begin{cases}OH \\ CN\end{cases} + OH^-$$

Most examples of this type of reaction are of the determination of formaldehyde, with the determination of sugars next. The HCHO determination has sometimes been the concluding stage of an analysis method for its condensation products or polymers, such as hexamine, phenol resins, paraformaldehyde or trioxymethylene (with or without separation of the aldehyde by distillation).

The kinetics of this cyanhydrin formation have been studied by some authors. Ref. 25 is an example, according to which acetaldehyde and propionaldehyde react quantitatively and the ketone, acetone, does not.

2. Cyanohydrin formation with displacement of sulphite, in determination of bisulphite compounds of aldehydes:

$$RCH\begin{cases}OH \\ SO_3Na\end{cases} + CN^- \rightarrow RCH\begin{cases}OH \\ CN\end{cases} + SO_3^{2-} + Na^+$$

This has been employed mainly to determine HCHO and CH_3CHO, derived from periodate oxidations; these were first converted into the bisulphite compounds (see Bisulphite and sulphite) and then treated with cyanide.

Essentially the same in principle is the determination of some methanesulphonic acid derivatives like novalgin and melubrin. The overall reaction may be written:

$$X—CH_2SO_3^- + CN^- + H_2O \rightarrow X—H + CH_2(OH)CN + SO_3^{2-}$$

The formaldehyde cyanohydrin is hydrolysed to glycollate under the conditions used. In the examples mentioned, X is a —NH— group, evidently yielding $-NH_2$.

3. Fission of S—S links with formation of SCN^-, used in the determination of compounds like thiosulphonates, thiuram disulphides and dibutyl xanthogen:

$$RSO_2S^- + CN^- \rightarrow RSO_2^- + SCN^-$$

$$R_2N—CS—S—S—CS—NR_2 + CN^- \rightarrow R_2N—CS—S—CS—NR_2 + SCN^-$$

$$C_4H_9O—CS—S—S—CS—OC_4H_9 + CN^- \rightarrow C_4H_9O—CS—S—CS—OC_4H_9 + SCN^-$$

Reaction conditions. Organic solvents have been only rarely added, and then mainly for determinations based on reaction type 3.

Reaction has usually been in weakly alkaline solution (pH 8 to 9) for sugars and other carbonyl compounds.

Reactions of type 2 have been carried out under a pentane layer to minimize air oxidation of the sulphite set free.

Subsequent treatment and final titration stage. (i) Unreacted CN^- has been determined in one of three ways:

1. Titration with Ag(I); this has been performed directly in the presence of I^- as indicator (end-point of turbidity) or indirectly by adding excess and back titrating with SCN^-. Normally the titration has been carried out on the reaction mixture but in one instance the excess CN^- was distilled out as HCN and titrated.

2. Titration with Hg(II); as with silver, this has been direct (with $Hg(NO_3)_2$ to diphenylcarbazone) or indirect (excess and back titration with SCN^- or excess, then addition of excess Cl^- and final titration with Hg(II) to nitroprusside).

3. Conversion to BrCN with excess bromine, removal of excess reagent with phenol and addition of I^-, reacting

$$BrCN + 2\,I^- \rightarrow Br^- + CN^- + I_2$$

The iodine was titrated with thiosulphate.

(ii) Techniques depending on titration of a reaction product have also been used and some examples are:

1. The cyanohydrin from type 1 reaction has been hydrolysed to NH_3 in alkaline solution (with or without removal of excess CN^-), the NH_3 distilled and determined by acid titration.

2. SO_3^{2-} from type 2 reactions has been titrated with iodine.

3. SCN^- from type 3 reactions has been titrated with Ag(I) or determined by oxidation with bromine to CNBr, then reacted with I^- to yield iodine and concluding with thiosulphate titration (cf. (i)3 above).

Examples

Materials titrated	Reagent and reaction conditions	Subsequent treatment and final titration stage	Ref.
HCHO	+ excess KCN/water	Added to HNO_3/excess $AgNO_3$, filtered and unused Ag(I) titrated with SCN^- to Fe(III)	1
Thiosulphonates, RSO_2S^-	+ excess KCN + alkali hydroxide; 30 min/*ca* 100°	Unused CN^- titrated with $AgNO_3$ to turbidity with Cl^- (Liebig), then + excess $AgNO_3$ + HNO_3 and unused Ag(I) back titrated with SCN^-	2
HCHO	+ KCN + $MgSO_4$ catalyst; 1–2 min/room temp.	+ NH_4OH/NH_4Cl + a little I^- and unused CN^- titrated with $AgNO_3$ to turbidity	3
HCHO (micro)	+ KCN; 3 min	+ HCl + bromine water until yellow; unused bromine removed with phenol, I^- added and titrated with thiosulphate	
Trioxymethylene	Excess KCN + solution in KOH/ethanol	+ $MgSO_4$, dissolved precipitate in NH_4Cl, a little I^- added and titrated with $AgNO_3$ to turbidity	4
HCHO	+ KCN; 5 min/room temp.	+ tartaric acid; HCN from unused CN^- distilled out and titrated with $AgNO_3$ to turbidity with Cl^- indicator	5
Sugars, e.g. lactose, glucose,	In water, + KCN; 10 min/room temp.	As in method of ref. 5, each sugar giving its characteristic 'HCN number'	6

Materials titrated	Reagent and reaction conditions	Subsequent treatment and final titration stage	Ref.
HCHO from determination of paraformaldehyde by adding H_2SO_4 and steam distilling	+ KCN, stirred. Control without sample	+ excess $AgNO_3$ + HNO_3, filtered and back titrated with SCN^- to Fe(III)	7
HCHO from determination of hexamine by distillation with H_2SO_4	+ KCN; 30 min	+ phosphoric acid + bromine/water until yellow; unused bromine removed with phenol, I^- added and titrated with thiosulphate after 30 min	8
HCHO	Method of ref. 3		9
HCHO	+ aqueous KCN	+ excess $AgNO_3$ + drops HNO_3 and titrated with SCN^- to Fe(III)	10
HCHO from determination of glycerol + glycols by oxidation with periodate	+ KCN	+ excess $AgNO_3$ and back titrated with SCN^- (control to allow for $AgIO_3$ and $AgIO_4$ formed)	11
HCHO from determination of glycerol and butane-2,3-diol by oxidation with periodate	Method of ref. 11		12
HCHO	+ KCN	Unused CN^- determined by adding excess $Hg(NO_3)_2$ (giving unionized $Hg(CN)_2$), then excess NaCl, giving $HgCl_2$ with excess Hg(II) and finally titrating unreacted Cl^- with $Hg(NO_3)_2$ to Na nitroprusside indicator (turbidity)	13
Aldehydes, ketones, hemiacetals, hemiketals	In dilute acetic acid, + KCN; 24 h/room temp.	+ NH_4OH + I^- and titrated unreacted CN^- to turbidity with $AgNO_3$	14
Sugars	Procedure of method of ref. 14, working at pH 9·1		15
HCHO	+ KCN	Unused CN^- determined with excess $Hg(NO_3)_2$ and back titration with SCN^-	16
Glucose	+ KCN + acetic acid, pH 8·5; 3 h/39°	Acidified to methyl red, unreacted CN^- driven off as HCN; + NaOH, NH_3 distilled into excess HCl and back titrated with alkali to methyl purple	17

Materials titrated	Reagent and reaction conditions	Subsequent treatment and final titration stage	Ref.
Aldose end-groups	+ KCN + NH_4NO_3, pH 8·3	Unused CN^- titrated with $Hg(NO_3)_2$	18
HCHO	+ KCN	+ phosphoric acid + bromine water; excess bromine removed with phenol, I^- added and titrated with thiosulphate	19
HCHO	+ KCN + diphenylcarbazone + HNO_3 until colour just disappeared	Immediately back titrated with $Hg(NO_3)_2$ to violet persisting for 1 min	20
Fructose	+ KCN at pH 8 (acetic acid added); 48 h/45°	pH brought to 11·5 with NaOH and NH_3 from hydrolysed cyanohydrin distilled into excess H_2SO_4; back titrated with alkali to methyl red or purple	21
Carbonyl groups in chromic acid oxy-starches	+ $NaCN$ + acetic acid, giving pH 9·5; 24 h/room temp.	+ NaOH and NH_3 distilled into boric acid; titrated with HCl to methyl red/bromocresol green	22
HCHO in presence of phenols and phenol alcohols	+ KCN at pH 7 or above	Unreacted CN^- titrated with $Hg(NO_3)_2$ to diphenylcarbazone	23
Methylol groups in urea/HCHO condensates	+ KCN/alkali	Unused CN^- titrated with $Hg(NO_3)_2$ to diphenylcarbazone	24
Thiuram disulphides	+ KCN/acetone, giving monosulphide + $KSCN$	SCN^- titrated with $AgNO_3$	26
Derivatives of methanesulphonic acid like melubrin C_6H_5—N(—CO—C(—$NHCH_2SO_3Na$)=C(CH_3)—N(CH_3)—) or novalgin (methylmelubrin)	+ KCN + NaOH under pentane layer, giving sulphite + glycollic acid in 2–3 min reaction	Acidified to methyl red with H_2SO_4 and titrated with iodine to starch	27, 29
HCHO bisulphite, $CH_2OH—SO_3Na$	+ KCN + NaOH under pentane, liberating sulphite	Iodometrically titrated as in method of ref. 27	28

Materials titrated	Reagent and reaction conditions	Subsequent treatment and final titration stage	Ref.
HCHO, acetaldehyde bisulphite compounds from determination of the aldehydes by reaction with Na_2SO_3 + acetic acid under pentane	Excess sulphite removed with iodine, then technique of ref. 28 carried out	As in method of ref. 28	30, 31, 44
HCHO bisulphite compound from determination of HCHO yielded from determination of 1,2-glycols (e.g. glycerol, mannitol) by periodate oxidation	Method of refs 30/31		32, 33
HCHO bisulphite compound, derived from HCHO from determination of glucose by periodate oxidation	Method of refs 30/31		34
Glyoxylic acid bisulphite compound from glyoxylic acid from determination of tartaric acid by periodate oxidation	Method of refs 30/31		35, 36, 46
Thiuram disulphides	In acetone, + KCN/ NH_4NO_3; 30 min shaking	Reaction product extracted with benzene, aqueous layer + acetic acid and HCN distilled out; SCN^- titrated with $AgNO_3$ amperometrically	37
HCHO bisulphite compound, derived from HCHO from determination of fructose by periodate oxidation	Method of refs 30/31		38, 41
HCHO bisulphite compound from HCHO from determination of glycerinaldehyde by periodate oxidation	Method of refs 30/31		39, 42
Bisulphite compounds of HCHO or acetaldehyde from determination of serine or threonine respectively by periodate oxidation	Method of refs 30/31		40, 43, 45

Materials titrated	Reagent and reaction conditions	Subsequent treatment and final titration stage	Ref.
HCHO bisulphite compound from HCHO, formed in determination of ethylenediamine and ethanolamines by oxidation with periodate	Method of refs 30/31		47, 48, 50
Carbonyl groups in starch	+ CO_3^{2-}/HCO_3^- buffer (pH 9·5) + NaCN (at least twice the theoretical amount); 2–24 days	Filtered and filtrate titrated with $AgNO_3$ to first turbidity with KI indicator	49
Free HCHO in HCHO/thiourea resins	+ KCN, titrated with H_2SO_4 at 0–4° to thymolphthalein; 5 min/room temp.	+ HCl + bromine water; excess bromine destroyed with phenol; + I^- and titrated with thiosulphate after 30 min	51
—CH_2OH groups in HCHO/thiourea resins	+ KCN + NaOH; 30 min/room temp.	+ HCl and concluded as for free HCHO	
HCHO bound in insoluble hide proteins	Distillate from phosphoric acid, + KCN; 3 min/room temp.	+ conc. HCl + bromine water; excess bromine removed with phenol, KI added and titrated with thiosulphate after 30 min in the dark	52
Dibutyl dixanthogen, $(C_4H_9O—CS—S—)_2$	+ KCN/NH_4NO_3/acetone; *ca* 25 min/40–50°, giving KSCN + $C_4H_9O—CS—S—CS—OC_4H_9$	Xanthogen monosulphide extracted with benzene, SCN^- in aqueous layer determined by adding H_3PO_4, boiling to expel HCN from unreacted CN^- then oxidizing with bromine to BrCN and SO_4^{2-}; + I^- + $NaHCO_3$ and titrated iodine after 10 min with thiosulphate	53

References

1. Romijn, G., *Z. anal. Chem.* **36**, 18 (1897).
2. Gutmann, A., *Z. anal. Chem.* **47**, 294 (1908).
3. Schulek, E., *Ber.* **58**, 732 (1925).
4. Alessandrini, M. E., *Atti II congresso naz. chim. pura applicata* 1356 (1926).
5. Lippich. F., *Z. anal. Chem.* **76**, 241, 255 (1929).
6. Lippich, F., *Z. anal. Chem.* **76**, 401 (1929).
7. Weinberger, W., *Ind. Eng. Chem., Anal. Ed.* **3**, 357 (1931).
8. Schulek, E. and Gervay, V., *Magyar Gyógyszerésztud. Társaság Ertesitöje* **9**, 26 (1933); *Z. anal. Chem.* **92**, 406 (1933).

9. Mutschin, A., *Z. anal. Chem.* **99**, 335 (1934).
10. Thompson, F., *Chemist & Druggist* **121**, 523 (1934).
11. Hoepe, G. and Treadwell, W. D., *Helv. Chim. Acta* **25**, 353 (1942).
12. Hoepe, G., *Helv. Chim. Acta* **26**, 1931 (1943).
13. Láska, F. and Protiva, M., *Chem. Listy* **37**, 76 (1943).
14. Militzer, W. E., *Arch. Biochem.* **9**, 91 (1946).
15. Militzer, W. E., *Arch. Biochem.* **21**, 143 (1949).
16. Bring, A., *Chem. Prŭmysl* **1** (26), 272 (1951).
17. Frampton, V. L., Foley, L. P., Smith, L. L. and Malone, J. G., *Anal. Chem.* **23**, 1244 (1951).
18. Yundt, A., *TAPPI* **34**, 95 (1951).
19. Konno, K., Kageyama, M. and Ueda, T., *J. Pharm. Soc. Japan* **72**, 1153 (1952).
20. Pfeil, E. and Schroth, G., *Z. anal. Chem.* **134**, 333 (1952).
21. Coombs, R. D., Reid, A. R. and Purves, C. B., *Anal. Chem.* **25**, 511 (1953).
22. Ellington, A. C. and Purves, C. B., *Can. J. Chem.* **31**, 801 (1953).
23. de Jong, J. I., *Rec. trav. chim.* **72**, 356 (1953).
24. de Jong, J. I., *Rec. trav. chim.* **72**, 653 (1953).
25. Svirbely, W. J. and Roth, J. F., *J. Am. Chem. Soc.* **75**, 3106 (1953).
26. Scheele, W. and Gensch, C., *Kautschuk u. Gummi* **7**, WT 122 (1954).
27. Schulek, E. and Maros, L., *Acta Pharm. Hung.* **27**, 237 (1957).
28. Maros, L., *Magyar Kem. Folyoirat* **64**, 41 (1958).
29. Schulek, E. and Maros, L., *Anal. Chim. Acta* **19**, 4 (1958).
30. Schulek, E. and Maros, L., *Magyar Kem. Folyoirat* **64**, 480 (1958).
31. Schulek, E. and Maros, L., *Acta Chim. Acad. Sci. Hung.* **17**, 369 (1958).
32. Maros, L. and Schulek, E., *Magyar Kem. Folyoirat* **65**, 361 (1959).
33. Maros, L. and Schulek, E., *Acta Chim. Acad. Sci. Hung.* **20**, 359 (1959).
34. Maros, L. and Schulek, E., *Acta Chim. Acad. Sci. Hung.* **21**, 91 (1959).
35. Schulek, E., Molnar-Perl, I. and Maros, L., *Magyar Kem. Folyoirat* **65**, 363 (1959).
36. Schulek, E., Molnar-Perl, I. and Maros, L., *Acta Chim. Acad. Sci. Hung.* **20**, 443 (1959).
37. Chatterjee, P. K., Banerjee, D. and Sircar, A. K., *J. Sci. Ind. Research* (*India*) **19B**, 1 = C, 118 (1960).
38. Maros, L. and Schulek, E., *Magyar Kem. Folyoirat* **66**, 197 (1960).
39. Maros, L., Molnar-Perl, I. and Schulek, E., *Magyar Kem. Folyoirat* **66**, 319 (1960).
40. Maros, L., Molnar-Perl, I. and Schulek, E., *Magyar Kem. Folyoirat* **66**, 321 (1960).
41. Maros, L. and Schulek, E., *Acta Chim. Acad. Sci. Hung.* **22**, 359 (1960).
42. Maros, L., Molnar-Perl, I. and Schulek, E., *Acta Chim. Acad. Sci. Hung.* **24**, 67 (1960).

43. Maros, L., Molnar-Perl, I. and Schulek, E., *Acta Chim. Acad. Sci. Hung.* **24**, 213 (1960).
44. Maros, L. and Schulek, E., *Ann. Univ. Sci. Budapest Rolando Eötvös nominatae, Sect. Chim.* **2**, 227, also 231 (1960).
45. Maros, L., Molnar-Perl, I. and Schulek, E., *Ann. Univ. Sci. Budapest Rolando Eötvös nominatae, Sect. Chim.* **2**, 237 (1960).
46. Schulek, E. and Maros, L., *Ann. Univ. Sci. Budapest Rolando Eötvös nominatae Sect. Chim.* **2**, 243 (1960).
47. Maros, L., Molnar-Perl, I. and Schulek, E., *Magyar Kem. Folyoirat* **67**, 203 (1961).
48. Maros, L., Molnar-Perl, I. and Schulek, E., *Acta Chim. Acad. Sci. Hung.* **26**, 467 (1961).
49. Schmorak, J. and Lewin, M., *Anal. Chem.* **33**, 1403 (1961).
50. Maros, L., Molnar-Perl, I. and Schulek, E., *Acta Chim. Acad. Sci. Hung.* **30**, 119 (1962).
51. Probsthain, K., *Z. anal. Chem.* **187**, 104 (1962).
52. Rosmus, J. and Deyl, Z., *Kožařstvi* **11**, 111 (1961).
53. Shankaranarayana, M. L. and Patel, C. C., *Analyst* **86**, 98 (1961).

31. Diazonium Salts

There appear to be fewer examples of the use of diazonium salts in indirect than in direct titration, which is no doubt to be ascribed to the comparatively low stability of the reagent.

The examples given here are based on coupling reactions and have been used for the determination of phenols in all but one case. The determinations were concluded by back titration of unused reagent with β–naphthol or of the reaction product with Ti(III); or by adding excess of an amine and determining the unreacted part.

Colorimetric evaluation of the azo coupling product has been the most usual conclusion of analyses with diazonium salt reagents.

Examples

Materials titrated	Reagent and reaction conditions	Subsequent treatment and final titration stage	Ref.
Tannides	+ Na acetate + *p*-nitrobenzenediazonium salt; 40–45 min	Back titrated with β-naphthol to external indicator of R salt	1
Tannides in willow, pine bark, oak pulp, etc.	Method of ref. 1		2

Materials titrated	Reagent and reaction conditions	Subsequent treatment and final titration stage	Ref.
β-Naphthol in the dye D & C Red No. 35	+ diazotized sulphanilic acid	Azo reaction product titrated with $TiCl_3$ (see Part 1, Titanium (III) ref. 37)	3
β-Naphthol in dyes	Method of ref. 3		4
Cis-1-cyano-1,3-butadiene in crude acrylonitrile	In acetic acid/Na acetate + *p*-nitrobenzenediazonium salt; 15–30 h in darkness	Back titrated with β-naphthol	5
Phenolic compounds in coals and humic acids	In NaOH + Na acetate + diazonium salt; 1 h with cooling	Back titrated with β-naphthol to external indicator of 5% resorcinol solution	6
Phenols	+ excess *p*-toluenediazonium chloride + Na_2CO_3	+ hexamethyleneimine: 5 min; then + NaOH, unused imine distilled out into boric acid and titrated with HCl (see Amines and heterocyclic bases, ref. 112)	7

References

1. Maslov, I. G. and Pakhomova, O. I., *Izvestiya Tsentral. Nauch.-Issledovatel. Inst. Kozhevennoi Prom.* No. 5, 18 (1932).
2. Mendlina, N. G., *Izvestiya Tsentral. Nauch.-Issledovatel. Inst. Kozhevennoi Prom.* No. 8, 41; No. 9, 28 (1932).
3. Holtzman, H. and Graham, H., *J. Assoc. Off. Agr. Chem.* **32**, 617 (1949).
4. Holtzman, H. and Graham, H., *J. Assoc. Off. Agr. Chem.* **34**, 393 (1951).
5. de Malde, M., *Ann. chim. (Rome)* **42**, 431 (1952).
6. Kukharenko, T. A. and Ekaterina, L. N., *Trudy Inst. Goryuchikh Iskopaemykh, Akad. Nauk SSSR* **8**, 142 (1959).
7. Terent'ev, A. P. and Tubina, I. S., *Zhur. Anal. Khim.* **18**, 880 (1963).

32. Digitonin

Precipitation of a complex with the reagent digitonin is a standard method for cholesterol. The determination has been concluded gravimetrically as a rule, but in some cases, quoted below, the precipitate of complex has been determined volumetrically.

Examples

Reagent and reaction conditions	Subsequent treatment and final titration stage	Ref.
In ether/alcohol extract, + 1% digitonin in 50% ethanol. Evaporated to dryness	Unreacted digitonin extracted with ether and the residue of complex determined by oxidation with excess $Cr_2O_7^{2-}$ and iodometric back titration (see Bichromate, ref. 42)	1
Slight modification of method of ref. 1		2
Extract in ether/alcohol, + digitonin/alcohol. Evaporated to dryness	+ water and heated to dissolve out unused reagent; + acetone and reaction product determined by oxidation with excess $Cr_2O_7^{2-}$	3
In ethanol (plant sterols), + digitonin/80% ethanol. Left overnight	Centrifuged and precipitate determined by oxidation with excess $Cr_2O_7^{2-}$ and back titration with Fe(II) (see Bichromate, ref. 171)	4
	Precipitate dissolved in methanol and determined with excess bromine/NaBr/methanol reagent (see Bromine reagents, ref. 377)	5

References

1. Okey, R., *J. Biol. Chem.* **88**, 367 (1930).
2. Turner, M. E., *J. Biol. Chem.* **92**, 495 (1931).
3. Yasuda, M., *J. Biol. Chem.* **92**, 303 (1931).
4. Waghorne, D. and Ball, C. D., *Anal. Chem.* **24**, 560 (1952).
5. Orlowski, M. and Simon, J., *Acta Biochim. Polon.* **1**, 231 (1954).

33. Dimethyl sulphate

Three examples are given of determinations based on alkylation with this reagent:

Materials titrated	Reagent and reaction conditions	Subsequent treatment and final titration stage	Ref.
Certain heterocyclic compounds (β- or γ-substituted pyridines; some alkaloids)	+ alkali + $(CH_3)_2SO_4$ (or C_2H_5I). Heated in a sealed tube at 120° for different periods, breaking the heterocyclic ring	+ MnO_4^- and methylamine reaction product distilled out and titrated with H_2SO_4	1, 2

Materials titrated	Reagent and reaction conditions	Subsequent treatment and final titration stage	Ref.
—OH groups in alkali lignin	In NaOH, + $(CH_3)_2SO_4$; 6 h/60°, methylating the groups (treatment repeated twice more)	+ a little H_2SO_4, filtered, washed and dried; retreated twice with the reagent and the methoxyl groups determined by reaction with HI, converting to CH_3I and ultimately to iodate, then determined iodometrically	3

References

1. Sackur, O., *Bull. soc. chim. France* **16**, 270 (1949).
2. Kahane, E. and Sackur, O., *Ann. pharm. franç.* **11**, 175 (1953).
3. Farkas, J., *Chem. zvesti* **13**, 536 (1959).

34. Dithionite

Four examples are given below of analyses based on reduction with dithionite. In three of these, back titration of unused reagent concluded the determination.

Materials titrated	Reagent and reaction conditions	Subsequent treatment and final titration stage	Ref.
Benzenediazonium chloride	In HCl at 0°, + $S_2O_4^{2-}$, giving phenylhydrazine	Back titrated with the dye acid green	1
Azo compounds, e.g. the dyes methyl and congo red	+ $NaHSO_3$ + Zn (evidently reacting to give $S_2O_4^{2-}$: $4\,NaHSO_3 + Zn \rightarrow ZnSO_3 + Na_2SO_3 + 2\,H_2O + Na_2S_2O_4$) 5 min reaction: $3\,RN = NR' + 2\,S_2O_4^{2-} + 8\,H_2O \rightarrow 3\,RNH_2 + 3\,R'NH_2 + 4\,HSO_4^-$	+ acetic acid; after 10 min, + $NaHCO_3$ and back titrated with iodine	2
Nitro and azo compounds	Reduced with $S_2O_4^{2-}$ to amines	Nitrogen determined by the Kjeldahl method	3
Chloropicrin in fumigated grain products	Absorbed in ethanol and $S_2O_4^{2-}$ added	Back titrated with iodine	4

References

1. Knecht, E. and Thompson, L., *J. Soc. Dyers Colourists* **36**, 215 (1920).
2. Zaraus, V. I., *Boll. soc. quim. Peru* **5**, 124 (1939).
3. Shaefer, W. E. and Becker, W. W., *Anal. Chem.* **19**, 307 (1947).
4. Demyanenko, M. P., *USSR Patent No.* 107, 182, Sept. 25 (1957).

35. Dyes

There are a few examples of the use of dyes, principally methylene blue, as oxidizing agents. The determinations have been generally concluded by back titration with Ti(III) of unreacted dye.

In contrast to direct titration, there appear to be no examples of determinations based on ion/ion combination yielding water-insoluble products.

Examples

Materials titrated	Reagent and reaction conditions	Subsequent treatment and final titration stage	Ref.
Phenylhydrazine	In dilute HCl, + methylene blue; boiled in CO_2 atmosphere *ca* 1 min	Back titrated with $TiCl_3$	1
Glucose	In water, + methylene blue + NaOH. Heated to boiling and boiled 5 sec in CO_2 atmosphere	Back titrated with $TiCl_3$ (see Part 1, Titanium (III), ref. 13)	2
Ascorbic acid	+ methylene blue; 30–50 sec in sunlight	Back titrated in CO_2 atmosphere with $TiCl_3$ (see Part I, Titanium (III), ref. 24)	3
Hydrazo compounds (from study of benzidine rearrangement)	Sample + Bindschedler's green	Back titrated with $Ti_2(SO_4)_3$ (see Part I, Titanium (III), ref. 36)	4
Hydrazobenzene (study of benzidine rearrangement)	Sample in ethanol/water, + Bindschedler's green	Back titrated in nitrogen atmosphere with $TiCl_3$ (see Part I, Titanium (III), ref. 38)	5

References

1. Knecht, E. and Hibbert, E., *J. Chem. Soc.* 1537 (1924).
2. Knecht, E. and Hibbert, E., *J. Soc. Dyers Colourists* **41**, 94 (1925).
3. Gál, T., *Nature* **138**, 791 (1936).
4. Dewar, M. J. S., *J. Chem. Soc.* 777 (1946).
5. Hammond, G. S. and Shine, H. J., *J. Am. Chem. Soc.* **72**, 220 (1950).

36. Electrolytic reduction

Three examples are given:

Materials titrated	Reagent and reaction conditions	Subsequent treatment and final titration stage	Ref.
Cystine	Reduced to cysteine	Titrated iodometrically	1
Ethyl bromide	In ethanol, + KOH/alcohol: Pt or Ni electrodes	Titrated argentometrically	2
Disulphide groups in beer	Reduced to mercaptans	Mercaptans determined by reaction with iodoacetamide + alkali and back titration of the unneutralized alkali (see Halides (active), ref. 64)	3

References

1. Hata, T., *Bull. Research Inst. Food Sci., Kyoto Univ.*, No. 3, 63 (1950).
2. Maleeva, E. G., *Nauch. Doklady Vysshei Shkoly, Khim. i Khim. Tekhnol.* No. 3, 505 (1958).
3. Brenner, M. W., Owades, J. L., Schapiro, G. J. and Laufer, S., *Am. Brewer* **93**, 28, 38 (1960).

37. Ferricyanide

Reagent. Nearly always the potassium salt has been used, in aqueous solution, frequently alkaline and containing zinc sulphate (see below under Reaction conditions).

Reactions and materials titrated. 1. Oxidation, in almost all the examples given, based on the equation:

$$Fe(CN)_6^{3-} + \epsilon \rightarrow Fe(CN)_6^{4-},$$

or, in the usually obtaining alkaline solution:

$$2\,Fe(CN)_6^{3-} + 2\,OH^- \rightarrow 2\,Fe(CN)_6^{4-} + H_2O + O$$

Sugars comprise over 80% of the oxidation examples. Other materials to the determination of which there are at least two references below are: tannin, glucuronic acid, ascorbic acid, morphine and thiamine (vitamin B_1).

As in the oxidation of sugars with alkaline copper (II) reagents, the reaction is not stoichiometric but reproducible under constantly-held conditions which are used also for the standardization of the reagent.

2. Ion/ion combination in the determination of some higher molecular weight bases such as acridine and phenanthridine derivatives and certain quaternary ammonium compounds. A varied stoichiometry is possible:

$$\left.\begin{array}{l}(Base.H)^+ + H_2Fe(CN)_6^- \rightarrow \\ 2\,(Base.H)^+ + HFe(CN)_6^{2-} \rightarrow \\ 3\,(Base.H)^+ + Fe(CN)_6^{3-} \rightarrow \end{array}\right\}\ \text{Precipitated product}$$

Reaction conditions. Most oxidations have been conducted in alkaline solution, using added alkali hydroxide, carbonate, phosphate or borate.

Zinc sulphate has often been added in order to precipitate ferrocyanide formed in the oxidation reactions.

Oxidations have been carried out under widely varying conditions of time and temperature. For example in the determination of sugars, temperature has ranged from the boiling point (*ca* 100°) to about 40°, with corresponding reaction times from 1 to 20 min.

The precipitations of reaction type 2 have usually been in acetate buffer.

Subsequent treatment and final titration stage. (i) Back titration of unused reagent. Both direct and indirect procedures have been used:

1. Direct titration with reducing agents e.g., ascorbic acid, Ce(III), arsenite, alkaline *p*-nitroethylisoquinolinium iodide or indigosulphonic acid; also precipitation titration with Ag^+.
2. Indirect titration, easily the most often used, by addition of iodide and acid and titration of the liberated iodine with thiosulphate.

(ii) About equally frequently, the ferrocyanide formed from oxidation reactions, has been titrated:

1. With oxidizing titrants like cerium (IV), bichromate, permanganate and Tillmans' reagent.
2. With the precipitating agent, zinc (II), biamperometrically or potentiometrically.

(iii) Only two examples are given in well over one hundred, in which an organic reaction product was determined. In one (ref. 100) quinone from oxidation of diphenols was reacted with I^-/acid and the iodine equivalent to the quinone titrated with thiosulphate; in the other (ref. 111) CS_2 from determination of dithiocarbamates (really hydrolysis with acid in presence of ferricyanide) was converted to xanthate, then iodometrically titrated.

Examples

Materials titrated	Reagent and reaction conditions	Subsequent treatment and final titration stage	Ref.
Glucose in blood, etc.	+ ferricyanide/alkali; 1 min boiling	+ H_2SO_4 and titrated with permanganate to colour change from green to pink	1
Blood sugar	+ ferricyanide/Na_2CO_3; 3 min/75–85°	+ KI/$ZnSO_4$/NaCl/acetic acid and titrated with thiosulphate to starch	2
Blood sugar	+ ferricyanide/Na_2CO_3; 15 min/100°	+ KI/$ZnSO_4$/NaCl/acetic acid and titrated with thiosulphate to starch	3
Micro blood sugar	Method of ref. 3		4
Glucose	+ ferricyanide/alkali; 1 min boiling	+ acid and titrated with permanganate as in ref. 1	5
Micro blood sugar	Method of ref. 3 improved		6
Blood sugar	+ ferricyanide/Na_2CO_3/ $ZnSO_4$; 5 min/100°	+ KI/acetic acid and titrated with thiosulphate	7
Glucose	Method of ref. 3		8
Blood sugar	Method of ref. 3 compared with Copper (II) oxidation method of Shaffer/Hartmann (see Copper (II), ref. 39)		9
Urine sugar	Study of method of ref. 3		10

Materials titrated	Reagent and reaction conditions	Subsequent treatment and final titration stage	Ref.
Blood glucose	+ ferricyanide/Na_2CO_3; 15 min/100°	+ excess bichromate + HCl + excess arsenite + KBr and titrated unused arsenite with bromate to methyl orange	11
Micro sugar	+ ferricyanide/Na_2CO_3; 20 min/100°	+ KI/$ZnSO_4$/NaCl/acetic acid and titrated with thiosulphate to starch	12
Blood sugar, uric acid	+ ferricyanide/Na_2CO_3; 15 min/100°	Unused titrated with indigo-sulphonic acid	13
glutathione, thiazine	+ ferricyanide/KOH	unused titrated with indigo-sulphonic acid	
Micro reducing sugars	+ ferricyanide/KOH	+ acid and titrated with permanganate as in ref. 1	14
Sugars	Method of ref. 3 compared with other methods for carbohydrate determination		15
Dihydroxyacetone in blood	+ ferricyanide/Na_2CO_3. In cold (then no interference from glucose)	As in method of ref. 3	16
Reducing sugars in blood	+ ferricyanide/alkali	+ KI/$ZnSO_4$/NaCl/acid and titrated with thiosulphate	17
Reducing sugars in blood	+ ferricyanide/Na_2CO_3	+ $ZnSO_4$, then + KI/acid and titrated with thiosulphate	18
Reducing sugars	Modification of method of ref. 3		19
Lactose in milk	+ ferricyanide/Na_2CO_3; 20 min/100°	As in method of ref. 3	20
Blood sugar	+ ferricyanide/K_2HPO_4/ K_3PO_4	+ KI/$ZnSO_4$/NaCl/acid and titrated with thiosulphate	21
Glucose	Modification of method of ref. 19		22
Sugars	+ ferricyanide/NaOH; 15 min/100°	As in method of ref. 3	23
Micro glucose	Modification of method of ref. 3 (double amount of ferricyanide)		24
Maltose in flour and related cereal products	Adaptation of method of ref. 3		25
Lactose	Method of ref. 3		26

Materials titrated	Reagent and reaction conditions	Subsequent treatment and final titration stage	Ref.
Glucuronic acid in blood	+ ferricyanide/NaOH; 15 min/100°	+ $KI/ZnSO_4/NaCl$, then + HCl and titrated with thiosulphate	27
Flavine dyes, e.g. acriflavine	In water + excess ferricyanide + acetate/HCl; 10 min/room temp.	Unused determined in filtrate with I^-/acid and titration of the iodine formed with thiosulphate	28
Lactose in milk	+ ferricyanide/Na_2CO_3; 15 min/100°	+ $KI/ZnSO_4/NaCl$/acetic acid and titrated with thiosulphate to starch	29
Blood sugar	Method of ref. 3		30
Reducing sugars, e.g. glucose, fructose, cane sugar	+ ferricyanide/Na_2CO_3; *ca* 30 min/80°	+ H_2SO_4 and titrated with Ce(IV) to alphazurine G to colour change from yellow-green to green	31
Blood sugar	+ ferricyanide/alkali; 5 min/100°	+ KI/citric acid/$ZnSO_4$ and titrated with thiosulphate	32
Glucose	+ ferricyanide/Na_2CO_3; 10 min/100°	+ H_2SO_4 and titrated with Ce(IV) to methyl violet	33
Blood sugar	+ ferricyanide/Na_2CO_3; 5 min/100°	+ H_2SO_4 and titrated with Ce(IV) to ferroin or Alphazurin GG	34
Reducing sugars (micro, in plants)	Extract + ferricyanide/ Na_2CO_3; 10 min/100°	+ H_2SO_4 and titrated with Ce(IV) to ferroin	35
Lactose in milk	+ ferricyanide/K_2HPO_4/ K_3PO_4; 15 min/100°	+ $KI/ZnSO_4/NaCl$, then HCl and titrated with thiosulphate	36
Blood sugar	+ ferricyanide/Na_2CO_3; 15 min/100°	+ H_2SO_4 and titrated with Ce(IV) to Setopaline C to colour change from golden yellow to golden brown	37
Fructose in presence of glucose	+ ferricyanide/ Na_2HPO_4; 2·5 h/60°	+ acetic acid and excess standard iodine and back titrated with thiosulphate	38
Glucose (from maltose by oxidation with iodine and treatment with HCl)	+ ferricyanide/Na_2CO_3; 15 min/100°	+ $KI/ZnSO_4$/acetic acid and titrated with thiosulphate	39

Materials titrated	Reagent and reaction conditions	Subsequent treatment and final titration stage	Ref.
Micro blood glucose	+ ferricyanide/Na_2CO_3; 5 min/100°	+ H_2SO_4 and titrated with Ce(IV) to methyl violet	40
Sugar in plants	Extract + ferricyanide/ Na_2CO_3; 15 min/100°	+ H_2SO_4 and titrated with Ce(IV) to Setopaline C	41
Submicro blood glucose	+ ferricyanide/Na_2CO_3; 5 min/100°	+ H_2SO_4 and titrated with Ce(IV) to ferroin	42
Tannins	+ ferricyanide/KOH; 5 min boiling	+ H_2SO_4 and titrated with permanganate	43
Invert sugar	+ ferricyanide/Na_2CO_3; 20 min/100°	+ KI/$ZnSO_4$/NaCl, then acetic acid and titrated with thiosulphate	44
Blood sugar	+ ferricyanide/NaOH; 6 min/100°	+ H_2SO_4 and titrated with indigo carmine	45
Sucrose in flour (after acid hydrolysis)	+ ferricyanide/Na_2CO_3; 20 min/100°	+ KCl/$ZnSO_4$/acetic acid, then KI and titrated with thiosulphate to starch	46
Glucose (semimicro)	Method of ref. 3		47
Reducing sugars from acid hydrolysis of hexosans	+ ferricyanide/ferrocyanide/Na_2CO_3; 15 min/100°	+ KI/$ZnSO_4$, then acetic acid and titrated with thiosulphate	48
Sugars	+ ferricyanide/Na_2CO_3; 15 min/100°	Titrated with bichromate to diphenylamine/H_2SO_4	49, 50
Sugars	+ ferricyanide/Na_2CO_3; 20 min/100°	+ H_2SO_4 and titrated with Ce(IV) to Setopaline C	51
Micro glucose	Modification of method of ref. 21 (15 min/100°)		52
Blood glucose	+ ferricyanide/CO_3^{2-}; 15 min/100°	+ acetic acid and titrated with Tillmans' reagent to pink	53
Carbohydrates in root extracts	Method of ref. 41.		54
Reducing sugars from plant extracts	Method of ref. 21		55
Fructose in presence of dextrose	+ ferricyanide/Na_2CO_3/ Na_2HPO_4. Various reaction times and temperatures studied (mostly at 50°)	+ H_2SO_4 and titrated with Ce(IV) to ferroin	56

Materials titrated	Reagent and reaction conditions	Subsequent treatment and final titration stage	Ref.
Blood galactose	Method of ref. 3		57
Inositol, sorbitol, mannitol	Method of ref. 3		58
Glucose from acid hydrolysis of sucrose in its determination	Method of ref. 3		59
Reducing sugars from hydrolysis of starch with saliva	Method of ref. 41		60
Glucose in biological fluids and tissues	Study of method of ref. 3		61
Fructose in presence of dextrose and sucrose	+ ferricyanide/Na_2CO_3/ Na_2HPO_4; 1 h/50°	+ H_2SO_4 and titrated with Ce(IV) to diphenylamine/ H_2SO_4	62
Sorbose	Method of ref. 51		63
Reducing power of starches and dextrins	+ ferricyanide/Na_2CO_3 + measured amount glucose (allowed for); 15 min/100° (materials of low reducing power gave inaccurate results unless glucose added)	+ H_2SO_4 and titrated with Ce(IV) to Setopaline C	64
Blood sugar	+ ferricyanide/Na_2CO_3; 15 min/100°	+ H_2SO_4 and titrated with permanganate to Setopaline, Eriogrün or Erioglaucin	65, 70
Reducing sugars	+ ferricyanide/Na_2CO_3/ Na_2HPO_4; 1 h/100°	Made slightly acid, excess iodine added (in *ca* 60–70% excess) and back titrated with thiosulphate after 15 min	66
Blood sugar	Method of ref. 37		67
Glucuronic acid from acid hydrolysis of mentholglucuronic acid in its determination	+ ferricyanide/alkali; 15 min/100°	+ KI/$ZnSO_4$/acetic acid and titrated with thiosulphate	68
5-Aminoacridine	+ sodium acetate/ferricyanide giving insoluble salt; 5 min/room temp.	Unused determined in filtrate by adding KI/HCl/$ZnSO_4$ and titrating with thiosulphate	69

Materials titrated	Reagent and reaction conditions	Subsequent treatment and final titration stage	Ref.
Some phenanthridinium salts	+ sodium acetate/ferricyanide giving insoluble salt; 5 min/room temp.	Unused determined in filtrate as in ref. 69	71
Quaternary ammonium compounds in foods	Method of ref. 75 after different preliminary extraction		72
Glucuronic acid	+ ferricyanide/Na_2CO_3; 15 min/100°	+ H_2SO_4 and titrated with Ce(IV) to Setopaline C	73
Blood glucose	+ ferricyanide/Na_2CO_3; 15 min/100°	+ H_2SO_4 and titrated with Ce(IV) to Setopaline C	74
Quaternary ammonium compounds in foods, drinks, etc.	+ acetate buffer + ferricyanide, giving insoluble salt	Unused determined in filtrate by adding KI/HCl/$ZnSO_4$ and titrating with thiosulphate	75, 81
Blood glucose	Method of ref. 3		76
Reducing sugars	Comparison of the ferricyanide method of ref. 3 with Cu(II) and iodometric methods (see also Copper (II), ref. 136 and Iodine, ref. 249)		77
Vitamin B_1	In water + ferricyanide/ Na_2CO_3; 2 min	Ferrocyanide formed or unused ferricyanide determined by: 1. titration with indigo-carmine to light green 2. + $ZnSO_4$/KI/NaCl/ acetic acid and titrated with thiosulphate 3. + H_2SO_4 and titrated with Ce(IV) to ferroin	78
Reducing sugars	Method of ref. 3. Study of reaction time and temperature. 40 min/85° recommended		79
Morphine	+ ferricyanide/alkali	+ KI/$ZnSO_4$/NaCl/acid and titrated with thiosulphate	80
Reducing sugars in plant materials	Method of ref. 41		82
Glucose in tears	Method of ref. 3		83
Crystalline penicillins, e.g. procaine penicillin	+ ferricyanide/NaOH; 15–20 min/100°	+ H_2SO_4 and titrated with Ce(IV) to Setopaline. (Blank with neutral ferricyanide under the same conditions)	84

Materials titrated	Reagent and reaction conditions	Subsequent treatment and final titration stage	Ref.
Lactose; acid hydrolysed sucrose in milk products	+ ferricyanide/Na_2CO_3; 20 min/100°	+ acetic acid/$ZnSO_4$/KCl, then + KI and titrated with thiosulphate	85
Blood glucose	Modification of method of ref. 3		86
Submicro glucose	Modification of method of ref. 42 (e.g. different ferricyanide concentration)		87
Blood sugar	+ ferricyanide/Na_2CO_3; 10 min/100°	Titrated with indigo to blue	88
Glucose in plant materials	Method of ref. 19 (for comparison with a glucose determination using cyanide—see Cyanide, ref. 17)		89
Blood sugar	Method of ref. 3		90
Blood sugar	Method of ref. 3		91
Vitamin B_1	+ ferricyanide/phosphate buffer at pH 10; 5 min/100°	+ H_2SO_4 and titrated with Ce(IV) to ferroin	92
Lactose in milk	Modification of method of refs 35/41		93
Quinidine diethyl iodide	Added to ferricyanide/KOH at 50–55°	Titrated with *p*-nitroethyl-isoquinolinium iodide/KOH at 50–60°, visually or potentiometrically (see Part I, Ferricyanide, ref. 34)	94
Reducing sugars in citrus wastes	Method of ref. 25		95
Gallotannins	+ ferricyanide/Na_2CO_3; 20 min/40°	+ $ZnSO_4$/NaCl, then + acetic acid/KI and titrated with thiosulphate	96
Some thiobarbituric acid derivatives	+ ferricyanide/alkali; 15–20 min	Titrated with permanganate/H_2SO_4	97
Blood glucose	+ ferricyanide at pH 10; 5 min/100°	+ H_2SO_4 and titrated with Ce(IV) to ferroin	98
Methantheline bromide	In water/acetate buffer + excess ferricyanide giving insoluble salt; 1 h/room temp.	Unused determined in filtrate by adding KI/$ZnSO_4$/HCl and titrating with thiosulphate	99

Materials titrated	Reagent and reaction conditions	Subsequent treatment and final titration stage	Ref.
o-Diphenols	+ ferricyanide/$ZnSO_4$/ acetate buffer; 5 min/room temp.	+ KI, iodine formed titrated, then acidified with H_2SO_4 and iodine equivalent to the quinone titrated	100
Ascorbic acid	+ ferricyanide/$ZnSO_4$; 3–5 min/room temp.	+ H_2SO_4/KI and titrated with thiosulphate	101
Blood glucose	Method of ref. 3—discussion of possible errors (recommended fast final titration to minimize loss of iodine)		102
Thiourea	+ ferricyanide/OsO_4 catalyst	Unused titrated with arsenite or ferrocyanide formed with Ce(IV)	103
Glucose from acid hydrolysed dextrin	+ ferricyanide/NaOH/ $ZnSO_4$; 20 min/100°	+ KI/acetic acid and titrated with thiosulphate	104
Isoniazid	+ ferricyanide/NaOH. Short reaction time	+ HCl/KI/$ZnSO_4$ and titrated after 5 min with thiosulphate	105
Reducing sugars	Compared with other sugar methods (cf. refs 1, 5, 14 and 20)	Titrated with permanganate	106
Thiourea	+ ferricyanide/alkali; 20–30 min/100°, or 30 min/room temp. in presence OsO_4 catalyst	+ KI/$ZnSO_4$/HCl or H_2SO_4 and titrated with thiosulphate; or titrated with Ce(IV) to ferroin	107
Mono- and dihydrazino-phthalazines	+ ferricyanide/NaOH	+ H_2SO_4 and titrated with permanganate	108
Blood reducing sugars	Method of ref. 3		109
Blood sugar	+ ferricyanide/NaOH/ $ZnSO_4$	+ acetic acid/I^- and titrated with thiosulphate	110
Dithiocarbamates	+ ferricyanide/H_2SO_4 giving CS_2	Absorbed in KOH/alcohol and the xanthate formed titrated with iodine (see Alcohols, ref. 52)	111
Glucose	+ ferricyanide/KOH/ HPO_4^{2-}; 10 min/100°	+ H_2SO_4 and titrated with $ZnSO_4$ biamperometrically	112
Ascorbic acid	+ $NaHCO_3$ and slightly over titrated (biamperometrically) with ferricyanide	+ H_2SO_4 and titrated with $ZnSO_4$	113

Materials titrated	Reagent and reaction conditions	Subsequent treatment and final titration stage	Ref.
Reducing sugars, separated by paper chromatography	Adaptation of method of ref. 37		114
Adrenaline, after 10 min heating with H_2SO_4	Neutralized solution + ferricyanide/borax; 5 min	+ H_2SO_4 and titrated with Zn^{2+} biamperometrically	115
Morphine in poppy capsules	Extract + ferricyanide/ phosphate-carbonate buffer; 5 min	+ HCl and titrated with Ce(IV) to ferroin	116
Glucose	+ ferricyanide/K_2CO_3; 15 min/100°, then 3 min/23–24°	Unused titrated in CO_2 with Ce(III) with potentiometric, amperometric or biampero-metric end-point	117
Carbohydrates in technical penta-erythritol	+ ferricyanide/Na_2CO_3; 15 min/100°	+ KI/$ZnSO_4$/NaCl/acetic acid and titrated with thio-sulphate	118
Ascorbic acid, cysteine, reducing sugars, etc.	(review of uses of ferricyanide reagent)	Unused determined iodo-metrically or ferrocyanide formed by Ce(IV) titration	119
Morphine	+ equivalent amounts ferri- and ferrocyanide at pH 9 (borate buffer); 12–15 min, oxidizing to pseudo-morphine	+ drops tungstosilicic acid and titrated with $ZnSO_4$ potentio-metrically or biampero-metrically	120
Quaternary ammonium compounds	In acetate buffer, + ferricyanide; 1 h shaking	Filtered and unreacted reagent titrated with $AgNO_3$ potentiometrically	121
Morphine	Method of ref. 120, claimed applicable in presence of lactose, atropine, hyoscine, phenacetin and aspirin		122
Tannins and dyestuffs in dry wines	+ $Fe(CN)_6^{3-}$/Na_2CO_3/ $ZnSO_4$; heated; also control after removal of tannins and dyestuffs with active carbon	Unused reagent determined by adding I^-/acetic acid and titrating with thiosulphate	123
Hydroquinone	+ H_2SO_4 + $Fe(CN)_6^{3-}$ in large excess	Ferrocyanide titrated with Zn^{2+} to diphenylamine/H_2SO_4	124

Materials titrated	Reagent and reaction conditions	Subsequent treatment and final titration stage	Ref.
Formate	+ excess ferricyanide + KOH + OsO_4 catalyst; 30–40 min/room temp., oxidizing to CO_2	Unreacted titrated biamperometrically with arsenite	125
Reducing sugars	+ ferricyanide/Na_2CO_3; 30 min/80°	+ I^-/$ZnSO_4$/acetic acid and titrated with thiosulphate	126
Semicarbazide	+ ferricyanide/Na_2CO_3 or borax/carbonate; 25–30 min	+ HCl and unreacted titrated with ascorbic acid to disappearance of colour with 2-oxyvariamine blue	127
Xanthate from determination of CS_2 by reaction with KOH/alcohol	Aliquot + KOH (giving 2N conc.) + excess ferricyanide + OsO_4; 15 min/20°	+ H_2SO_4, bringing to pH 7–10; + dimethylglyoxime and titrated with $FeSO_4$ to red	128
Quaternary ammonium compounds	+ ferricyanide, giving precipitate of quaternary ammonium salts	Unused reagent determined by adding I^- and titrating with thiosulphate	129

References

1. Ionescu, A. and Vargolici, V., *Bull. soc. chim. Romania* **2**, 102 (1921).
2. Rosenthal, A., *Biochem. Z.* **133**, 469 (1922).
3. Hagedorn, H. C. and Jensen, B. N., *Biochem. Z.* **135**, 46 (1923).
4. Dingemanse, E., *Biochem. Z.* **154**, 483 (1924).
5. Ionescu, A. and Spirescu, E., *Bull. soc. chim. Romania* **6**, 101 (1924).
6. Kaufmann, E., *Biochem. Z.* **166**, 207 (1925).
7. von Fazekas, E., *Biochem. Z.* **168**, 175 (1926).
8. Holden, H. F., *Biochem. J.* **20**, 263 (1926).
9. Jonsell, S., Jorpes, E. and Sikström, N., *Acta Med. Scand.* **63**, 446 (1926).
10. Power, M. H. and Wilder, R. M., *J. Pharmacol.* **27**, *Proc.* 255 (1926).
11. Hansen, A., *Dansk Tids. Farm.* **1**, 195 (1927).
12. v. Issekutz, B. and v. Roth, J., *Biochem. Z.* **183**, 298 (1927).
13. Flatow, L., *Biochem. Z.* **194**, 132 (1928).
14. Ionescu-Matiu, A., *Bull. soc. chim. biol.* **10**, 252 (1928).
15. Pucher, G. W. and Finch, M. W., *J. Biol. Chem.* **76**, 331 (1928).
16. Silberstein, F. and Rappaport, F., *Biochem. Z.* **194**, 105 (1928).
17. Toscani, V. A., *Chemist-Analyst* **18**, 7 (1929).
18. Bryant, H. L., *J. Lab. Clin. Med.* **14**, 1082 (1929).

19. Hanes, C. S., *Biochem. J.*, **23**, 99 (1929).
20. Gohr, H., *Z. Untersuch. Lebensm.* **59**, 90 (1930).
21. Fujita, A. and Iwatake, D., *Biochem. Z.* **242**, 43 (1931).
22. Hulme, A. C. and Narain, R., *Biochem. J.* **25**, 1051 (1931).
23. Mosonyi, L., *Biochem. Z.* **238**, 95 (1931).
24. Carrasco-Farmiguera, R., *Compt. rend. soc. biol.* **110**, 730 (1932).
25. Blish, M. J. and Sandstedt, R. M., *Cereal Chem.* **10**, 189 (1933).
26. Fromageot, C. and Moulin, M., *Bull. soc. chim.* **53**, 266 (1933).
27. Masamune, H., *J. Biochem. (Japan)* **18**, 259 (1933).
28. Powell, A. D. and Hall, G. F., *Quart. J. Pharm. Pharmacol.* **6**, 389 (1933).
29. Blackwood, J. H., *J. Dairy Research* **5**, 245 (1934).
30. Macco, G. D., *Boll. soc. ital. biol. sper.* **9**, 1008 (1934).
31. Whitmoyer, R. B., *Ind. Eng. Chem., Anal. Ed.* **6**, 268 (1934).
32. Hagedorn, H. C., Halstrøm, F. and Jensen, B. N., *Hospitalstidende* **78**, 1193 (1935).
33. Vanossi, R. and Ferramola, R., *Anales asoc. quim. arg.* **23**, 162 (1935).
34. Giragossintz, G., Davidson, C. and Kirk, P. L., *Mikrochemie* **21**, 21 (1936).
35. Hassid, W. Z., *Ind. Eng. Chem., Anal. Ed.* **8**, 138 (1936).
36. Kern, A., *Biochem. Z.* **288**, 375 (1936).
37. Miller, B. F. and v. Slyke, D. D., *J. Biol. Chem.* **114**, 583 (1936).
38. Strepkov, S. M., *Biochem. Z.* **287**, 33 (1936).
39. Strepkov, S. M., *Biochem. Z.* **289**, 38 (1936).
40. Vanossi, R. and Ferranola, R., *Biochem. Z.* **288**, 369 (1936).
41. Hassid, W. Z., *Ind. Eng. Chem., Anal. Ed.* **9**, 228 (1937).
42. Heck, K., Brown, W. H. and Kirk, P. L., *Mikrochem.* **22**, 306 (1937).
43. Ionescu-Matiu, A. and Popescu, C., *Bull. soc. Stiinte Farm. Romania* **2**, No. 3–4, 38 (1937).
44. Lynovskii, O. P. and Srogis, A. A., *Voprosy Pitaniya* **6**, No. 5, 140 (1937).
45. Patterson, J., *Biochem. J.* **31**, 244 (1937).
46. Sandstedt, R. M., *Cereal Chem.* **14**, 767 (1937).
47. Schrader, G. A., *Chemist-Analyst* **26**, 52 (1937).
48. Strepkov, S. M., *Biochem. Z.* **289**, 295 (1937).
49. Strepkov, S. M., *Biochem. Z.* **290**, 91 (1937).
50. Strepkov, S. M., *Ukrain. Khim. Zhur.* **12**, 105 (1937).
51. Hildebrand, F. C. and McClellan, B. A., *Cereal Chem.* **15**, 107 (1938).
52. Niemierko, W., *Acta Biol. Expt. (Warsaw)* **12**, 178 (1938).
53. Abrahamson, E. M., *Am. J. Clin. Path. Tech. Suppl.* **3**, 60 (1939).
54. Barr, C. G., *Plant Physiology* **14**, 285 (1939).
55. Doak, B. W., *New Zealand J. Sci. Tech.* **218**, 90 (1939).
56. Englis, D. T. and Becker, H. C., *Ind. Eng. Chem., Anal. Ed.* **11**, 145 (1939).

57. Larsson, P. A. and Sveinsson, S. L., *Skand. Arch. Physiol.* **83**, 58 (1939).
58. Todd, W. R., Vreeland, J., Myers, J. and West, E. S., *J. Biol. Chem.* **127**, 269 (1939).
59. Zeller, A., *Biochem. Z.* **303**, 92 (1939).
60. Hassid, W. Z., McCready, R. M. and Rosenfels, R. S., *Ind. Eng. Chem., Anal. Ed.* **12**, 142 (1940).
61. Shergin, N. P., *Lab. Prakt. USSR* **15**, No. 12, 17 (1940).
62. Becker, H. C. and Englis, D. T., *Ind. Eng. Chem., Anal. Ed.* **13**, 15 (1941).
63. Broome, F. K. and Sandstrom, W. M., *Ind. Eng. Chem., Anal. Ed.* **13**, 142 (1941).
64. Farley, F. F. and Hixon, R. M., *Ind. Eng. Chem., Anal. Ed.* **13**, 616 (1941).
65. Fiorentino, M. and Boni, P., *Biochem. Z.* **307**, 245 (1941).
66. Englis, D. T. and Becker, H. C., *Ind. Eng. Chem., Anal. Ed.* **15**, 262 (1943).
67. MacFadyen, D. A. and v. Slyke, D. D., *J. Biol. Chem.* **149**, 527 (1943).
68. Shimosawa, T., *J. Pharm. Soc. Japan* **63**, 462 (1943).
69. Amor, G. and Foster, G. E., *Analyst* **70**, 174 (1945).
70. Fiorentino, M. and Boni, P., *Diagn. tec. lab. (Napoli), Riv. mens.* **11**, 449 (1945).
71. Foster, G. E. and Grove, W. F., *Analyst* **71**, 287 (1946).
72. Harris, T. H., *J. Assoc. Offic. Agr. Chem.* **29**, 310 (1946).
73. Levvy, G. A., *Biochem. J.* **40**, 396 (1946).
74. Nimmo-Smith, R. H., *Biochem. J.* **40**, 414 (1946).
75. Wilson, J. B., *J. Assoc. Offic. Agr. Chem.* **29**, 311 (1946).
76. Accoyer, P., Camelin, A., Garnung, H. and Bernard, M., *J. Med., Lyon* **28**, 301 (1947).
77. Blom, J. and Rosted, C. O., *Acta Chem. Scand.* **1**, 32 (1947).
78. Wachsmuth, H., *Bull. soc. chim. Belges* **56**, 261 (1947).
79. Schäffeler, K., *Helv. Physiol. et Pharm. Acta* **6**, 584 (1948).
80. Wachsmuth, H. and Meyten, E., *J. pharm. Belge (N.S.)* **3**, 163 (1948).
81. Wilson, J. B., *J. Assoc. Offic. Agr. Chem.* **31**, 480 (1948).
82. Bevenue, A., *Anal. Chem.* **21**, 586 (1949).
83. Giardini, A., *Atti* 37 *Cong. sez. regionali soc. oftalmol. ital.* **10**, 392 (1949).
84. Hiscox, D. J., *Anal. Chem.* **21**, 658 (1949).
85. Hites, B. D., Ackerson, C. W. and Volkmer, G. H., *Anal. Chem.* **21**, 993 (1949).
86. Pruner, G., *Ann. chim. applicata* **39**, 181 (1949).
87. Stern, H. and Kirk, P. L., *J. Biol. Chem.* **177**, 37 (1949).
88. Rappaport, F. and Eichhorn, E., *Am. J. Clin. Path.* **20**, 834 (1950).
89. Frampton, V. L., Foley, L. P., Smith, L. L. and Malone, J. G., *Anal. Chem.* **23**, 1244 (1951).

90. Kirberger, E. and Frank, H., *Klin. Wochschr.* **29**, 297 (1951).
91. Merkel, H. and Ausbüttel, F., *Deut. Z. ges. u. gerichtl. Med.* **40**, 485 (1951).
92. Pruner, G., *Rend. ist. super sanità* (*Rome*) **14**, 222 (1951).
93. Francis, F. J. and Smith, M. D., *J. Dairy Research* **19**, 83 (1952).
94. Tomíček, O. and Simon, J., *Českoslov. Farm.* **1**, 25 (1952).
95. Wells, W. N., Rohrbaugh, P. W. and Doty, G. A., *Sewage & Ind. Wastes* **24**, 212 (1952).
96. Kimura, K., Kuwano, S., Hikino, H., Iida, S., Ueda, M., Manabe, T. and Ida, Y., *J. Pharm. Soc. Japan.* **73**, 1200 (1953).
97. Sandri, G. and Lambardi, F., *Atti accad. sci. Ferrara* **30**, 27 (1953).
98. Pruner, G., *Rend. ist. super sanità* **17**, 123 (1954).
99. Sangra, C. S. and Parreño, R., *Rev. asoc. bioquím. arg.* **19**, 87 (1954).
100. Mikhel'son, V. Ya., *Trudy Tallinsk. Politekh. Inst.* A No. 63, 127 (1955).
101. Abramov, M. K. and Kadyrov, Ya. K., *Aptechnoe Delo* **5**, No. 2, 28 (1956).
102. D'Arcangelo, P., *Giorn. Biochim.* **5**, 465 (1956).
103. Bapat, M. G. and Sharma, B., *J. Sci. Research Banaras Hindu Univ.* **7**, 262 (1956–7).
104. Soladovnikov, P., *Trudy Kazan. Aviatsion. Inst.* **31**, 127 (1956).
105. Akiyama, T., Fujiwara, M. and Ichida, H., *Kyoto Yakka Daigaku Gakuho* **5**, 42 (1957).
106. Ionescu-Matiu, A., *Produits Pharm.* **12**, 247 (1957).
107. Joshi, M. K., *Naturwissenschaften* **44**, 537 (1957).
108. Sandri, G. C., *Boll. chim. farm.* **96**, 431 (1957).
109. D'Arcangelo, P., *Arch. sci. biol.* (*Bologna*) **42**, 459 (1958).
110. Brahmachari, H. D. and Kumar, M., *Current Sci.* (*India*) **27**, 486 (1958).
111. Cartoni, L., *Ricerca sci.* **28**, 1639 (1958).
112. v. Pinxteren, J. A. C., *Pharm. Weekblad* **93**, 753 (1958).
113. v. Pinxteren, J. A. C. and Verloop, E., *Pharm. Weekblad* **93**, 982 (1958).
114. Thaler, H., *Nahrung* **2**, 111 (1958).
115. v. Pinxteren, J. A. C. and Verloop, M. E., *Pharm. Weekblad* **94**, 169 (1959).
116. Pruner, G., *Rend. ist. super. sanità* **22**, 710 (1959).
117. Furman, N. H. and Fenton, A. J., *Anal. Chem.* **32**, 745 (1960).
118. Salova, A. S. and Antonova-Antipova, I. P., *Lakokrasochnye Materialy i ikh Primenenie* No. 6, 55 (1960).
119. Sant, B. R. and Sant, S. B., *Talanta* **3**, 261 (1960).
120. v. Pinxteren, J. A. C. and Verloop, M. E., *Pharm. Weekblad* **96**, 545 (1961).
121. Hefferren, J. J. and Dietz, C., *J. Pharm. Sci.* **50**, 535 (1961).
122. v. Pinxteren, J. A. C. and Verloop, M. E., *Pharm. Weekblad* **97**, 1 (1962).
123. Korablev, A. I. and Trofimenko, B. S., *Sadovodstvo, Vinogradarstvo i Vinodelie Moldavii* **37**, No. 1 (1962).

124. Brinkman, U. A. T. and Snelders, H. A. M., *Z. Anal. Chem.* **199**, 432 (1963).
125. Desmukh, G. S. and Rao, A. L. J., *Z. Anal. Chem.* **194**, 110 (1963).
126. Friedemann, T. E., Weber, C. W. and Witt, N. F., *Anal. Biochem.* **4**, 358 (1963).
127. Kasa, I. and Erdey, L., *Acta Chim. Acad. Sci. Hung.* **39**, 21 (1963).
128. Kiboku, M., *Bunseki Kagaku* **12**, 797 (1963).
129. Thoma, K., Ullmann, E. and Loos, P., *Pharmazie* **18**, 414 (1963).

38. Ferrocyanide

Potassium ferrocyanide has been used to precipitate certain bases or polymers based on ethylene oxide in reactions of ion/ion combination or complex formation respectively.

Examples

Materials titrated	Reagent and reaction conditions	Subsequent treatment and final titration stage	Ref.
Antipyrine in presence of pyramidone	In dilute HCl + $K_4Fe(CN)_6$; 30 min, giving precipitate of $(C_{11}H_{12}N_2O)_2H_4Fe(CN)_6$	Filtered, precipitate suspended in water and titrated with NaOH to phenolphthalein	1
Ethylene oxide adducts, e.g. non-ionic detergents	+ HCl + NaCl + excess $K_4Fe(CN)_6$/water	Filtered and unused reagent back titrated with $ZnSO_4$ to diphenylamine	2,3
Non-ionic surface-active materials from ethylene oxide	+ excess $K_4Fe(CN)_6$	Unused reagent back titrated with $ZnSO_4$ potentiometrically	4
Non-ionic surface-active agents (polyoxyethylene nonyl phenol ether) after separation of cationic and amphoteric agents	Method of refs 2/3		5
A polyethylene glycol ('Oxydwachs AN') in viscose	Material in aqueous solution, + HCl + $Fe(CN)_6^{4-}$; 5 min stirring	Filtered, filtrate + $(NH_4)_2SO_4$ + some drops $Fe(CN)_6^{3-}$ and titrated with $ZnSO_4$ to diphenylamine	6

References

1. Kolthoff, I. M., *J. Am. Pharm. Assoc.* **22**, 947 (1933).
2. Schönfeldt, N., *Nature* **172**, 820 (1953).
3. Schönfeldt, N., *J. Am. Oil Chemists' Assoc.* **32**, 77 (1955).
4. Roussos, M., Passedouet, H. and Cariou, J., *Rev. franc. corps gras* **5**, 13 (1958).
5. Izawa, Y., Nakogawa, O. and Kimura, W., *J. Jap. Oil Chem. Soc.* **11**, 174 (1961).
6. Zimmermann, K., *Faserforsch. u. Textiltech.* **14**, 180 (1963).

39. Gelatine

One example is given of the use of gelatine to precipitate tannin from a mixture with gallic acid.

Material titrated	Reagent and reaction conditions	Subsequent treatment and final titration stage
Tannin + gallic acid in tannin and other materials	Aqueous solution, + gelatine/NaCl solution	Filtered; aliquot + iodine excess + alkali; after 15 min in the dark, H_2SO_4 added and unused iodine titrated with thiosulphate (see Iodine reagents, ref. 400) (in conjunction with a parallel iodometric determination without precipitation, giving the sum of tannin + gallic acid)

Reference

Mudzhiri, K. S. and Zhuk, I. M., *Sb. Tr. Tbilissk. Nauchn.-Issled. Khim.-Farmatsev. Inst.* **9**, 29 (1960).

40. Halides (active)

Reagents. All contain comparatively active halogen atoms linked to C, N or S. (No cases appear to be known of the use of O-Hal in organic compounds, such as organic hypochlorites, although there is in fact an example in Part I of direct titration with *tert*-butyl hypochlorite.) The activation is in almost all cases due to $-CO$ or $-SO_2$ groups or to aromatic nuclei, sometimes containing *o*- and *p*-nitro groups. Reagents thus include:

C-Hal: e.g. acyl halides, especially acetyl chloride; some alkyl (including benzyl and trityl) halides; and nitrochloro- and nitrofluorobenzenes

N-Hal: e.g. chloramines and *N*-bromosuccinimide

S-Hal: e.g. sulphonyl halides; chlorosulphonic acid (this is of course an inorganic reagent but it is convenient to group it here)

Reactions and reaction conditions. In all cases, the reaction depends on the ready splitting of the halogen atom from the rest of the reagent molecule.

1. Elimination of hydrohalic acids in determination of some types of active hydrogen such as $-OH$ groups in alcohols and phenols; $-NH_2$ and $-NH-$ groups in aniline, morphine and other amines; $-SH$ groups in thiophenol and xanthates. Principally used as reagent have been the acyl and sulphonyl halides. Trityl and nitrochlorobenzenes such as picryl chloride, chlorosulphonic acid and iodoacetamide have also been used.

$$ROH + R'COCl \rightarrow R'COOR + HCl$$

$$RNH_2 + ArSO_2Cl \rightarrow ArSO_2NHR + HCl$$

$$RSH + ICH_2CONH_2 \rightarrow RSCH_2CONH_2 + HI$$

The products thus formed have often been insoluble in the medium used, or could be extracted from it.

2. Addition or ion/molecule combination in which the active halogen atom appears as an anion of quaternary ammonium or sulphonium in the determination of, respectively, tertiary amines or sulphides:

$$R_3N + R'I \rightarrow (R_4N)^+ I^-$$

$$R_2S + R'COBr \rightarrow (R_2S.COR')^+ Br^-$$

3. Dehydration, as in a determination of acid amides, based on the reaction:

$$RCONH_2 + R'COCl \rightarrow RCN + R'COOH + HCl$$

4. Formation of metal halides in determination of metal organic compounds such as lithium or potassium alkyls:

$$3\ RK + 3\ R'Hal \rightarrow 3\ KHal + R{-}R + R'{-}R' + R{-}R'$$

(This may not necessarily be the exact stoichiometry, but all three hydrocarbons are usually formed; in any case, each metal atom is equivalent to one halogen atom.)

In the other reactions given below, the reagents used have been the chloramines or *N*-bromosuccinimide. These function effectively as hypochlorite or hypobromite in the aqueous solution generally used:

$$ArSO_2\overset{(-)}{N}Cl + H_2O \rightarrow ArSO_2NH_2 + OCl^-$$

$$\begin{array}{l} CH_2{-}CO \\ | \\ CH_2{-}CO \end{array}\!\!\!>\!NBr + H_2O \rightarrow \begin{array}{l} CH_2{-}CO \\ | \\ CH_2{-}CO \end{array}\!\!\!>\!NH + HOBr$$

5. Oxidation of a variety of compounds, including: aldehydes (HCHO, furfuraldehyde, benzaldehyde, also aldoses); hydrazine derivatives like isoniazid and methylhydrazine; sulphur-containing compounds such as thiourea, mustard gas, xanthates and dixanthogen; polyhydroxy compounds like glycol, glycerol and aldoses (mentioned above); amino acids; quaternary ammonium nitrites, and ascorbic acid. E.g.

$$RCHO + O \rightarrow RCOOH$$

$$HOCH_2.CH_2OH + 5\,O \rightarrow 2\,CO_2 + 3\,H_2O$$

$$C_2H_5O{-}CS{-}S{-}S{-}CS{-}OC_2H_5 + 13\,O + 7\,H_2O \rightarrow 2\,C_2H_5OH + 4\,H_2SO_4 + 2\,HCOOH$$

6. Substitution, carried out in presence of acid/I^- or Br^-, in the determination of phenols (such as phenol itself, *m*-cresol or salicylic acid) or aromatic amines (like aniline or anthranilic acid).

7. Addition, in determination of iodine numbers or unsaturation, e.g. of fats. As with substitution, the reaction is carried out in the presence of Br^- or I^-, so that in effect, bromine or iodine are added to the organic molecule.

Reaction conditions. No comprehensive generalization can be made. Reactions 1 to 4 have been usually carried out in non-aqueous and 5 to 7 in aqueous solution. Reaction times and temperatures have varied too widely between the various reactions to permit more to be said.

As has already been mentioned, bromide or iodide has been present in reactions of substitution and addition and often in oxidation also.

Bases have usually been required for reactions of type 1, especially acylations; pyridine, *N*-dimethylaniline and $NaHCO_3$ have been most used.

Subsequent treatment and final titration stage. (i) Determination of excess reagent, as in reactions of type 5, 6 and 7, by adding iodide (and acid if necessary) and titrating with thiosulphate.

(ii) Determination of unused reagent + acid reaction products, used in the acylation reactions of type 1 and also in the example of type 3. A control reaction is carried out using the reagent alone;

$$X\text{—}H + RCOCl \rightarrow RCO\text{—}X + HCl$$
$$H_2O \quad + RCOCl \rightarrow RCOOH \quad + HCl$$

The difference between the two titrations with alkali corresponds to the X-H compound (generally a hydroxy-compound).

(iii) Reaction products whose determination has concluded the procedure, include:

1. Hydrohalic acids or halide ions, from the participation of the active halogen atoms in reactions of types 1, 2 and 4. The final stage has then been:

   (a) titration of the acid with alkali (often after separation in a gas stream); addition of excess alkali and back titration with acid has been used also,

   (b) argentometric by direct titration with Ag(I) or by using excess and back titrating with SCN^-,

   (c) in one case by conversion to OH^- in an ion-exchanger and titration with acid.

2. Esters from acylation (type 1), isolated and determined by saponification with excess alkali and back titration with acid; or, in one case of esters of dinitrobenzoic acid reagent, by reduction with excess V(II). Sulphonamide reaction products from determination of primary and secondary amines by reaction with a sulphonyl chloride, have been similarly determined in one instance, namely by hydrolysis (this time with acid) and ultimate titration of the recovered amines.

3. CO_2 from oxidations of some polyhydroxy compounds or amino acids, by absorption in $Ba(OH)_2$ and back titration with HCl, or by absorption in benzylamine/dioxan/ethanol and direct titration with $NaOCH_3$.

4. The sulphonium cation from a determination via type 2 reaction was precipitated as picrate and ultimately titrated with $HClO_4$; a quaternary ammonium cation from a similar determination was broken down to methylamine, subsequently titrated with acid.

5. The ethers of morphine from its determination by reaction with dinitrochlorobenzene, have been treated with excess HCl and back titrated with alkali.

6. Some conclusions with only single examples in the tables are: Kjeldahl determination of the nitrogen content (after using $ClCH_2CON(C_2H_5)_2$ reagent); titration with cetyl trimethyl ammonium bromide of the alkyl sulphates derived from higher alcohols by reaction with $ClSO_3H$; and isolation of the original mercaptans, then titrated with Ag^+.

Examples

Materials titrated	Reagent and reaction conditions	Subsequent treatment and final titration stage	Ref.
—OH groups, e.g. in fusel oil	+ acetyl chloride/ $CHCl_3$; 5–10 min. Control	+ water and titrated with NaOH to phenolphthalein	1
Phenol; salicylic acid	In water, + KI + excess 'Halamine' T (p-CH_3—$C_6H_4SO_2N$<X, Met) Met = K or Na; X = Cl, Br or I; 5 min/60°	+ H_2SO_4, filtered and filtrate titrated with thiosulphate	2
Aldose sugars, especially in milk	Deproteinized solution + NaOH + KI + chloramine T; 90 min/17·5°	+ HCl and titrated with thiosulphate	3
Potassium phenyl isopropyl, C_6H_5—$C(CH_3)_2$—K	In dry ether, + butyl bromide (does not react with alkoxides or KOH) $3 RK + 3 BuBr \rightarrow 3 KBr + Bu_2 + R_2 + RBu$	Br^- formed determined with excess Ag(I) and back titration with SCN^-	4
Lithium alkyls	+ excess butyl bromide as in method of ref. 4; then + Hg dibenzyl, which reacts giving lithium benzyl, capable of faster reaction with butyl bromide than was the lithium alkyl	As in method of ref. 4	5
—OH groups, e.g. in phenols	+ acetyl or benzoyl chlorides (or acetic anhydride). Control without sample	+ water and titrated with alkali	6

Materials titrated	Reagent and reaction conditions	Subsequent treatment and final titration stage	Ref.
Aniline	In ethyl acetate, + picryl chloride/ethyl acetate + solid $NaHCO_3$; 15 min/room temp., then 15 min reflux. Allowed to stand 3 h	NaCl filtered and titrated with Ag(I) (or gravimetrically)	7
Iodine values	+ dichloramine T/acetic acid/KI reagent	Titrated with thiosulphate	8
Aniline in presence of *N*-methyl- and *N*-dimethylanilines	Method of ref. 7		9
Cellulose xanthate in viscose	Neutralized solution, + chloroacetyldiethylamide, $ClCH_2CON(C_2H_5)_2$; 1 h, giving insoluble product	Filtered and determined by Kjeldahl digestion and distillation	10
—OH groups in alcohols and phenols	+ benzoyl or *p*-nitrobenzoyl chloride in boiling tetralin	HCl carried by air, nitrogen or hydrogen into water and titrated with NaOH to methyl red	11
Morphine in opium	In methanol/alkali, + 2,4-dinitrochlorobenzene, giving precipitate of dinitrochlorophenyl ether. Left overnight	Filtered, treated with excess HCl/NaCl, giving hydrochloride, and unused HCl in filtrate titrated with NaOH to methyl red	12
—OH groups in alcohols	In toluene, + 1·5-fold excess of acetyl chloride/pyridine at 0°. Then 20 min/60°. Control	+ water and titrated with alkali to phenolphthalein	13
Primary alcohols in presence of secondary and tertiary	+ trityl chloride/toluene; 40–60 min boiling	HCl passed into alcoholic $AgNO_3$ and back titrated with SCN^- to Fe(III)	14
HCHO; benzaldehyde	+ chloramine T + NaOH + KI; 30 min/room temp.	+ HCl and titrated with thiosulphate	15
Morphine	Stated that the method of ref. 12 is unsuitable		16
—OH groups in fats and oils	In pyridine, + at least 2-fold excess of acetyl chloride/toluene; 5 min/65–70°. Control	+ water, heated and titrated with KOH to phenolphthalein	17

Materials titrated	Reagent and reaction conditions	Subsequent treatment and final titration stage	Ref.
Thiophenol	Method of ref. 13 (not found too satisfactory for amines, especially aliphatic amines)		18
amines	+ acetyl chloride/dibutyl ether; 20 min/70°. Control	+ water and titrated with alkali to phenolphthalein	
—OH groups	In benzene or CCl_4, + stearoyl chloride. Boiled in a current of dry air	HCl carried out and titrated with NaOH	19
Amyl alcohol (in fusel oil, separated previously by CCl_4 extraction)	+ acetyl chloride/ toluene/pyridine; 30 min/60°. Control	+ water + excess NaOH and back titrated with H_2SO_4 to phenolphthalein	20
Furfuraldehyde	+ chloramine T + NaOH + KI; 90 min/room temp.	+ HCl and titrated with thiosulphate	21
—OH groups	+ acetyl chloride (no solvent); 20 min/40°. Control	+ water and titrated with NaOH to phenolphthalein	22
l-Ascorbic acid	+ chloramine T + KI + HCl	Back titrated with thiosulphate	23
—OH groups in peppermint oil	+ acetyl chloride (no solvent); 20–30 min/50°. Control	+ water and titrated with NaOH to phenolphthalein (allowed for any HCl reacted with the pinene present, by titration with $AgNO_3$ to chromate)	24
Morphine in opium	Extract + 2,4-dinitrochlorobenzene in acetone/NH_4OH; 24 h/room temp., yielding precipitate of the ether	Dissolved in HCl/NaCl and back titrated with KOH to methyl red	25
Alcohols; —OH groups in ether alcohols	+ acetyl chloride without solvent; 10–15 min for primary alcohols, 20 min for secondary 30 min for glycols	+ water and titrated with alkali	26
Lithium alkyls, e.g. n-butyl	In ether, + benzyl chloride, (reaction as in ref. 4) Control without reagent	+ water and titrated with acid to phenolphthalein	27
—OH groups in fats	+ acetyl chloride/ toluene/pyridine; 15 min/65°. Control	+ water/ethanol and titrated with alcoholic KOH	28

Materials titrated	Reagent and reaction conditions	Subsequent treatment and final titration stage	Ref.
Cellulose xanthate in viscose	Compared method of ref. 10 with an iodometric method		29
Aniline in presence of *N*-methyl and *N*-dimethylanilines	+ picryl chloride/ethyl acetate + $NaHCO_3$; 15 min (based on method of ref. 7)	NaCl extracted with water and titrated with Ag(I) potentiometrically	30
Amides	+ 2,4-dinitrobenzoyl chloride/dioxan + pyridine; 30 min/60°; 1 h/70° for amides of dibasic acids. Control	Excess reagent decomposed with methanol and acid titrated with $NaOCH_3$/methanol to phenolphthalein or ethyl bis-2,4-dinitrophenylacetate	31
Mixtures of primary, secondary and tertiary amines	In benzene at 0°, + *p*-toluenesulphonyl chloride/dry pyridine; 30 min/0°	Sulphonamides of *sec*-amines separated; made acid and sulphonamides of primary amines separated; amines recovered by hydrolysis with conc. HCl, making alkaline, extracting into benzene and from benzene into excess aqueous acid and back titrating the acid (see Hydrochloric acid, ref. 63)	32
Aniline in *N*-alkylanilines	+ benzene + picryl chloride/benzene; 20 min/room temp.	HCl extracted with water and titrated with NaOH	33
Trimethylamine	Passed into methyl iodide/ethanol, giving insoluble tetramethylammonium iodide	Excess methyl iodide distilled off and I^- titrated with Ag(I)	34
Mustard gas	In kerosene or cyclohexane, + dichloramine T/CCl_4; 20 min/27°	+ KI + acetic acid and titrated with thiosulphate	35
Linalool	+ acetyl chloride/acetic anhydride/*N*-dimethylaniline; 30 min room temp., then 3 h/*ca* 40°	Ester separated and determined by saponification with excess KOH (see Alkalies, ref. 197)	36
Iodine number of fats	In $CHCl_3$ or CCl_4, + chloramine T/ acetic acid + equivalent I^- or Br^-; 1 h/room temp.	+ I^- and titrated with thiosulphate	37
Aminothiazole	+ picryl chloride/ethanol	NaCl determined argentometrically	38

Materials titrated	Reagent and reaction conditions	Subsequent treatment and final titration stage	Ref.
—OH groups in fats, oils, lower aliphatic alcohols and polyalcohols	+ acetyl chloride/ toluene; 2 h reflux. Control	+ water and titrated with NaOH to phenolphthalein	39
Certain β- and γ-substituted pyridine derivatives and alkaloids	+ ethyl iodide/alkali (also with dimethyl sulphate). Various reflux times, yielding alkyl pyridinium iodides	Steam distilled in presence of MnO_4^- giving methylamine; titrated with H_2SO_4	40
Morphine in opium	Extract + 2,4-dinitro-chlorobenzene/acetone; 3 h, yielding insoluble ether	Precipitate dissolved in excess HCl/NaCl and back titrated with NaOH to methyl red	41
Unsaturation in fat acids	+ chloramine T + H_2SO_4 (+ Na acetate to reduce substitution). Various reaction times	+ HCl/I^- and titrated with thiosulphate	42
Furfuraldehyde	Method of ref. 21		43
Phenols (e.g. *m*-cresol); aromatic amines (e.g. aniline, anthranilic acid)	In water, + chlor-amine B + KBr + HCl; 1 min shaking, then 20–30 min/0°	+ I^- and titrated with thio-sulphate	44
Long chain alcohols	+ chlorosulphonic acid/ dry ether	+ NaOH, evaporated off ether, leaving the Na alkyl sulphates; pH brought to 8 and titrated with cetyl trimethylammonium bromide in $CHCl_3$/water to methylene blue (same colour intensity in each layer) (see Part I, Surface-active materials, ref. 26)	45
'Acetylation equivalent' of alcohols and phenols	+ acetyl chloride/ toluene; 30–40 min reflux for alcohols; 90–120 for phenols. Control	+ water and titrated with NaOH to phenolphthalein	46
—OH groups, e.g. in methanol, ethanol, benzyl alcohol, phenol	+ 3,5-dinitrobenzoyl chloride, giving esters	Esters determined with excess VSO_4 and back titration with $Cr_2O_7^{2-}$ (see Vanadium (II), ref. 3)	47

Materials titrated	Reagent and reaction conditions	Subsequent treatment and final titration stage	Ref.
glycine	+ 2,4-dinitrochlorobenzene, giving HOOC.$CH_2NH.C_6H_3(NO_2)_2$	nitro compound determined with V(II) as in ref. 47	
Isoniazid	+ chloramine T + KI + alkali	+ H_2SO_4 and titrated with thiosulphate	48
Dialkyl sulphides (identification)	+ *p*-bromophenacyl bromide in methanol; 10 min reflux, giving precipitate of sulphonium salt after addition of ether	Dissolved in water, precipitated as picrate and titrated with $HClO_4$ (see Nitrophenols, ref. 60; and Part I, Perchloric acid, ref. 161)	49
Glycerol; ethylene glycol	+ solid *N*-bromosuccinimide; 15 min/*ca* 100°, oxidizing to CO_2	Passed into excess $Ba(OH)_2$ and back titrated with HCl to phenolphthalein	50
Mercapto groups	+ iodoacetamide in 2- to 5-fold excess at pH 5·5; brought to pH 9 with alkali 2 min/room temp.	Titrated with acid to pH 5·5	51
Linalool (semimicro)	+ acetyl chloride/acetic anhydride/dimethylaniline; 4 h/55°	Ester determined by saponification with excess alkali (see Alkalies, ref. 344)	52
Phenolic —OH groups	+ *m*-nitrobenzenesulphonyl chloride/acetone, + NaOH; 5 min/room temp. Control	+ excess NaOH and back titrated with acid	53
Organic sulphides	+ methyl iodide/methanol; 2–3 h/100° in a sealed tube, giving sulphonium iodides	Unreacted methyl iodide distilled off and the sulphonium iodide determined with HNO_3/excess $AgNO_3$ and back titration with SCN^- (see Silver (I), ref. 154)	54
Aldehydes, e.g. vanillin, salicylaldehyde, furfuraldehyde; also thiopentabarbital	+ NaOH/50% ethanol + chloramine T. Up to 10 min (1 h for the last-named)	+ HCl + KI and titrated with thiosulphate	55
—OH groups in epoxy resins	+ stearoyl chloride/$CHCl_3$	HCl carried out by a nitrogen stream and titrated with NaOH	56
—OH groups in alkyd resins	In toluene/pyridine, + acetyl chloride/toluene; 30 min/100°. Control	+ water/ethanol and titrated with KOH to phenolphthalein	57

Materials titrated	Reagent and reaction conditions	Subsequent treatment and final titration stage	Ref.
Iodine number of fatty acids	+ *N*-bromosuccinimide/acetic acid; 1 h in the dark	+ water/KI and titrated with thiosulphate	58
Quaternary ammonium nitrites with a long chain group	In dimethylformamide (+ ether in some cases) + a little acetic acid + chloramine T/dimethylformamide; 15 min in dark	+ I^- and titrated with thiosulphate	59
End —OH groups in polyethylene terephthalate	In nitrobenzene, + bromoacetyl bromide; 1 h/80°	Polymer precipitated with acetone, treated with KOH; then + HNO_3 + excess $AgNO_3$ and back titrated with SCN^- to Fe(III)	60
Menthol in peppermint oil	+ $ClCH_2COCl$/toluene at *ca* 100°	HCl carried by dry nitrogen into excess $AgNO_3$; back titrated with SCN^-	61
'Chloramine value' of fruit juices and preparations like syrups and drinks	+ chloramine T; 15 min in dark	+ I^- + H_2SO_4 and titrated with thiosulphate	62
Phenolic —OH groups in presence of alcohols	+ *m*-nitrobenzenesulphonyl chloride/acetone/water/alkali, giving precipitate of sulphonate ester	+ excess base, left 20–30 min, then back titrated with acid to methyl red	63
Mercaptans, from determination of disulphides in beer by electrolytic reduction	Method of ref. 51		64
Xanthate from determination of CS_2 by reaction with KOH/alcohol	+ chloramine T/HCl + ethanol; 30 min/room temp.	+ I^- and titrated with thiosulphate	65
—SH groups in reduced hair keratin	+ iodoacetamide + borate buffer, pH 10; 45 min/room temp.	Aliquot + HNO_3 bringing to pH 7 and titrated with $AgNO_3$ potentiometrically	66
Aldrin	In acetic acid, + chloramine T + KBr + conc. HCl; 45 min/room temp.	+ I^- and titrated with thiosulphate	67

Materials titrated	Reagent and reaction conditions	Subsequent treatment and final titration stage	Ref.
Morphine in opium	Extract + NH_4OH + 2,4-dinitrofluorobenzene/acetone; 1 min shaking, then 30 min/room temp. and 15 min/5°, giving precipitate of derivative	Precipitate dissolved in acetic acid, acetic anhydride added and titrated with $HClO_4$ to crystal violet	68
Methylhydrazine (+ hydrazine)	+ water + chloramine T; 10 min/room temp. (in combination with titration with hypochlorite—see Chlorine reagents, ref. 24)	+ I^- + acetic acid and titrated with thiosulphate	69
Organosilyl metallic compounds, e.g. triphenyl lithium silane; diphenyl methyl lithium silane; phenyl dimethyl lithium silane	In tetrahydrofuran, + butyl bromide; in nitrogen atmosphere; 2 min/room temp., giving LiBr	+ dilute H_2SO_4 and neutralized to phenolphthalein; Br^- determined with Ag^+ excess and back titration with SCN^-	70
Amino acids, e.g. alanine, glycine, asparagine	At pH 4·7, + $PdCl_2$ + *N*-bromosuccinimide, oxidizing to CO_2	CO_2 passed into benzylamine/dioxan/ethanol and titrated with $NaOCH_3$ to thymol blue	71
Dixanthogens	+ chloramine T/HCl; 1 h/room temp.	+ I^- and titrated with thiosulphate	72
Hydroxyl groups in primary, secondary, some tertiary alcohols, polyalcohols, phenols and acetonoxime; benzylamine	+ 3,5-dinitrobenzoyl chloride/pyridine; mostly 5–15 min/room temp., but some up to 96 h	+ drops water + pyridine and titrated with tetrabutylammonium hydroxide in benzene/methanol, 7:1 potentiometrically or to yellow →red in solution	73
Oxine and metal oxinates	+ HCl + KBr + chloramine T in 15% excess; 5 min/room temp.	+ I^- and titrated with thiosulphate; or + excess As(III) + HCl and back titrated with the chloramine T to α-naphthoflavone or *p*-ethoxychrysoidine	74
Hydroxyl groups in mono- and diglycerides	Method of ref. 73		75
Hydroxyl number of free fatty acids, fats, glycerides, higher alcohols	In pyridine, + acetyl chloride/toluene in up to 2-fold excess; 20 min/60°. Control	+ water, warmed 15 min/60° and titrated with KOH/alcohol to phenolphthalein	76

Materials titrated	Reagent and reaction conditions	Subsequent treatment and final titration stage	Ref.
Long-chain amine oxides in presence of long-chain tertiary amines	In isopropanol, + methyl iodide; 15 min/50°, giving quaternary salts with the amines	Oxides titrated with HCl/alcohol potentiometrically	77
Hydroxyl groups in lignin	Tested various methods, e.g. that of ref. 73 and also methods using 2,4-dinitrochloro- and fluorobenzene reagents. Low values found		78
Phenols	In *N*-dimethylaniline, + chlorosulphonic acid; 1 h/room temp.	+ excess NaOH and back titrated with acid	79
Hydroxyl groups in polymers	In benzene, dichloroethane, ethylene glycol dimethyl ether or other solvent, + $COCl_2$; *ca* 1 h/ca −80°	Unreacted $COCl_2$ allowed to evaporate, chloroformate hydrolysed with alkali and Cl^- titrated with $AgNO_3$ after adding acetic acid	80
Mercaptans in petroleum products	+ 2,4-dinitrochlorobenzene/ethanol + KOH/alcohol, converting to thioethers	Isolated thioether + isopropanol, setting the mercaptans free; titrated with Ag^+ in ammoniacal solution	81
Iodine number of eleostearic acid and wood oil	+ *N*-bromosuccinimide/acetic acid (wood oil in $CHCl_3$); 24 h/room temp.	+ I^- and titrated with thiosulphate	82
Alcohols and phenols	+ *p*-toluenesulphonyl chloride/pyridine; various times tried (5, 30, 60, 90, 120 and 180 min) in study of extent of reaction	+ pyridine/water and titrated with NaOH	83, 84
ε-Caprolactam	+ acetyl chloride/toluene/pyridine; 30 min/60°	+ water and titrated with NaOH to phenolphthalein	85
Thiourea	At pH 10, + excess chloramine T; 2 min	+ I^- + HCl and titrated with thiosulphate	86
	$(NH_2CSNH_2 + 10\,OH^- \rightarrow NH_2CONH_2 + SO_4^{2-} + 5\,H_2O + 8\epsilon)$		

References

1. Adam, F., *Österr. Chem.-Ztg.* **2**, 241 (1899).
2. Roberts, E., *J. Chem. Soc.* 2707 (1923).

3. Hinton, C. L. and Macara, T., *Analyst* **52**, 668 (1927).
4. Ziegler, K., Crössmann, F., Kleiner, H. and Schäfer, O., *Ann.* **473**, 21 (1929).
5. Ziegler, K., Crössmann, F., Kleiner, H. and Schäfer, O., *Ann.* **473**, 31 (1929).
6. Huppmann, *Pharm. Ztg.* **76**, 113, 329 (1931).
7. Linke, B., Preissecker, H. and Stadler, J., *Ber.* **65**, 1280 (1932).
8. Hunter, L. and Hyde, F. F., *Analyst* **58**, 523 (1933).
9. Nelyubina, A., *Anilinokrasochnaya Prom.* **3**, 355 (1933).
10. Fink, H., Stahn, R. and Matthes, A., *Angew. Chem.* **47**, 429, 602 (1934).
11. Meyer, T. M., *Rec. trav. chim.* **53**, 387 (1934).
12. Mannich, C., *Arch. Pharm.* **273**, 97 (1935).
13. Smith, D. M. and Bryant, W. M. D., *J. Am. Chem. Soc.* **57**, 61 (1935).
14. Sabetay, S., *Compt. rend.* **203**, 1164 (1936).
15. Carli, B. and Airoldi, R., *Ann. chim. applicata* **27**, 56 (1937).
16. Eder, R. and Wäckerlin, *Quart. J. Pharm. Pharmacol.* **10**, 680 (1937).
17. Kaufmann, H. P. and Funke, S., *Ber.* **70**, 2549 (1937).
18. Olson, V. R. and Feldman, H. B., *J. Am. Chem. Soc.* **59**, 2003 (1937).
19. Raymond, E. and Bouvetier, E., *Compt. rend.* **209**, 439 (1939).
20. Schicktanz, S. T. and Etienne, A. D., *Ind. Eng. Chem., Anal. Ed.* **11**, 390 (1939).
21. Bionda, G., *Ann. chim. applicata* **31**, 31 (1941).
22. Christensen, B. E., Pennington, L. and Dimick, K. P., *Ind. Eng. Chem., Anal. Ed.* **13**, 821 (1941).
23. Leonhardt, H. and Moeser, W., *Z. anal. Chem.* **122**, 3 (1941).
24. Christensen, B. E. and Pennington, L., *Ind. Eng. Chem., Anal. Ed.* **14**, 54 (1942).
25. Mannich, C., *Arch. Pharm.* **280**, 386 (1942).
26. Montes, A. L., *Anales asoc. quím. argentina* **31**, 109 (1943).
27. Gilman, H. and Haubein, A. H., *J. Am. Chem. Soc.* **66**, 1515 (1944).
28. Houget, J., *Bull. soc. chim.* **11**, 139 (1944).
29. Jung, K. P., *Kolloid-Z.* **108**, 120 (1944).
30. Haslam, J. and Sweeney, F., *Analyst* **70**, 413 (1945).
31. Mitchell, J. and Ashby, C. E., *J. Am. Chem. Soc.* **67**, 161 (1945).
32. Seaman, W., Norton, A. R., Woods, J. T. and Bank, H. N., *J. Am. Chem. Soc.* **67**, 1571 (1945).
33. Spencer, G. and Brimley, J. E., *J. Soc. Chem. Ind. (London)* **64**, 53 (1945).
34. Wilson, H. N. and Heron, A. E., *Analyst* **70**, 38 (1945).
35. Kinsey, V. E. and Grant, W. M., *Ind. Eng. Chem., Anal Ed.* **18**, 794 (1946).
36. Hoffmann, A. and Maffei, F. J., *Inst. pesq. tecnol. (Sao Paulo)*, separate No. 196, 93 (1947).
37. Kácl, K. and Fink, F., *Chem. Listy* **41**, 34 (1947).
38. Aubry, G., *Bull. soc. pharm. Lille* No. 2, 22 (1948).

39. Johnson, B. L., *Anal. Chem.* **20**, 777 (1948).
40. Sackur, O., *Bull. soc. chim. France* **16**, 270 (1949).
41. van Pinxteren, J. A. C. and Smeets, M. A. G., *Pharm. Weekblad* **85**, 1, 48 (1950).
42. Basu, K. L., *Indian Soap J.* **18**, 259 (1953).
43. Bionda, G., *Atti accad. sci. Torino, Classe sci. fis. mat. e nat.* **88**, 3 (1953–4).
44. Apar Singh, *J. Indian Chem. Soc.* **31**, 605 (1954).
45. Blickenstaff, R. T., Schaeffer, J. R. and Kathman, G. G., *Anal. Chem.* **26**, 746 (1954).
46. Kepner, R. E. and Webb, A. D., *Anal. Chem.* **26**, 925 (1954).
47. Witry-Schwachtgen, G., *Inst. Grand-Ducal Luxembourg, Sect. Sci. nat. phys. et. math., Arch.* **22**, 87 (1955).
48. Spacu, P., Teodorescu, G. and Gavanescu, D., *Bul. inst. politeh., Bucuresti* **18**, 51 (1956).
49. Veibel, S. and Nielsen, B. J., *Acta Chem. Scand.* **10**, 1488 (1956).
50. Abdel-Wahab, M. F. and Barakat, M. Z., *Monatsh.* **88**, 692 (1957).
51. Benesch, R. and Benesch, R., *Biochim. et Biophys. Acta* **23**, 643 (1957).
52. Fujita, Y., Ueda, T. and Kusumoto, N., *Koryo (Aromatics)* No. 47, 42 (1957).
53. Shuter, L. M. and Berkman, Ya. P., *Ukrain. Khim. Zhur.* **23**, 669 (1957).
54. Aarna, A. Ya. and Silland, Kh. A., *Zhur. Anal. Khim.* **13**, 473 (1958).
55. Berka, A. and Zýka, J., *Pharmazie* **13**, 90 (1958).
56. Bring, A. and Kadlacek, F., *Plaste u. Kautschuk* **5**, 43 (1958).
57. Kappelmeier, C. P. A. and Mostert, J., *Verfkroniek* **31**, 61 (1958).
58. Jovtscheff, A., *Nahrung* **3**, 153 (1959).
59. Kilheffer, J. V. and Jungermann, E., *Anal. Chem.* **31**, 581 (1959).
60. Matveeva, S. P. and Myagkov, V. A., *Khim. Volokna* No. 5, 8 (1959).
61. Blake, M. I., *J. Am. Pharm. Assoc., Sci. Ed.*, **49**, 175 (1960).
62. Benk, E., *Riechstoffe u. Aromen* **10**, 122 (1960).
63. Berkman, Ya. P. and Shuter, L. M., *Doklady L'vov Politekh. Inst.* **4**, No. 1, 2, 33 (1960).
64. Brenner, M. W., Owades, J. L., Schapiro, G. J. and Laufer, S., *Am. Brewer* **93**, 28,38, (1960).
65. Satyanarayana Rao, V. R. and Vasudeva Murthy, A. R., *Talanta* **4**, 206 (1960).
66. Stein, H. H. and Guarnaccio, J., *Anal. Chim. Acta* **23**, 89 (1960).
67. Velniceriu, A. and Ionescu, E., *Rev. chim. (Bucharest)* **11**, 533 (1960).
68. Büchi, J. and Huber, R., *Pharm. Acta Helv.* **36**, 313 (1961).
69. Clark, J. D. and Smith, J. R., *Anal. Chem.* **33**, 1186 (1961).
70. Gilman, H., Klein, R. A. and Winkler, H. J. S., *J. Org. Chem.* **26**, 2474 (1961).

71. Patchornik, A. and Shalitin, Y., *Anal. Chem.* **33**, 1887 (1961).
72. Ramachandra Rao, S., *Talanta* **8**, 747 (1961).
73. Robinson, W. T., Cundiff, R. H. and Markunas, P. C., *Anal. Chem.* **33**, 1030 (1961).
74. Bishop, E. and Jennings, V. J., *Talanta* **9**, 679 (1962).
75. Jensen, R. G. and Sampugna, J., *J. Am. Oil Chemists' Soc.* **39**, 309 (1962).
76. Kaufmann, H. P. and Schmuelling, E., *Fette u. Seifen, Anstrichmittel* **64**, 319 (1962).
77. Metcalfe, L. D., *Anal. Chem.* **34**, 1849 (1962).
78. Wildenhain, W., Heinichen, G. and Henseke, G., *J. prakt. Chem.* **20**, 35 (1963).
79. Randsepp, H. and Mikkal, M., *Tr. Tallinsk. Politekhn. Inst., Ser.* A No. 198, 101 (1962).
80. Bush, D. G., Kunzelsauer, L. J. and Merrill, S. H., *Anal. Chem.* **35**, 1250 (1963).
81. Dahmen, E. A. M. F., Dijkstra, R. and Verjaal, A. J., *Erdöl, Kohle* **16**, 768 (1963).
82. Jovtscheff, A., Bontscheff, N. and Jonkow, D., *Nahrung* **7**, 375 (1963).
83. Mesnard, P., Gibirila, B. and Bertucat, M., *Compt. Rend.* **257**, 2999 (1963).
84. Mesnard, P., Gibirila, B. and Bertucat, M., *Chim. Anal.* **45**, 491 (1963).
85. Polaczek, L. and Grzezkiewicz, A., *Chem. Anal. (Warsaw)* **8**, 961 (1963).
86. Aravamudan, G. and Satyanarayana Rao, V. R., *Talanta* **11**, 55 (1964).

41. Halogen reagents in determination of unsaturation

The most extensively used principle of determination of unsaturation is based on addition of halogen or *ψ*-halogens. These include: chlorine; bromine; iodine; thiocyanogen; bromine chloride; iodine chloride; iodine bromide; iodine thiocyanate; and halogen oxyacids/halide reagents, yielding the halogens in situ. While direct titration methods, particularly with bromine reagents, have been moderately widely used, the majority of determinations has been based on indirect (back) titration. Under these conditions, different reagents, especially in determinations on complex mixtures such as oils and fats, frequently furnish different data. Numerous authors have undertaken comparisons of the most used reagents and a selection of references to such work is given below. One plus sign in the column signifies that one method based on the relevant reagent was studied; two plus signs means more than one method.

Reagents Compared						Ref.
Br_2	I_2	$(SCN)_2$	ICl	IBr	ISCN	
++	+		++	+		1
			++	+		2
	+		++	+		3
+			+			4
+			+			5
++	+	+	+	+	+	6
++			+	+		7
++			++	+		8
		+	+	+		9
		+	+	+		10
'Various procedures'						11
++			+	+		12
++		+	+	+		13
++			++			14
+				+		15
++			+	+		16
'Various procedures'						17
+			+	+		18
+			+			19
+			+	+		20
+			+			21
+			+			22
		+			+	23

References

1. Yushkevich, S., *Masloboino-Zhirovoe Delo* No. 2, 9 (1930).
2. Settimj, M., *Ann. chim. applicata* **21**, 507 (1931).
3. Yushkevich, S., *Trudui VNIIZh.* No. 2, 9 (1934).
4. Casimir, E. E. and Dimitriu, M., *Petroleum Z.* **31**, No. 33, 1 (1935).
5. Casimir, E. E. and Dimitriu, M., *Inst. Géol. Roumanie, Compt. rend.* **21**, 241 (1932–3), published 1937.
6. Grosse-Oetringhaus, H., *Brennstoff-Chemie* **19**, 417 (1938).
7. Earle, F. R. and Milner, R. T., *Oil & Soap* **16**, 69 (1939).
8. Richter, M., *Öl, Kohle, Erdöl, Teer* **15**, 69 (1939).
9. Riemenschneider, R. W. and Wheeler, D. H., *Oil & Soap* **16**, 219 (1939).
10. Schloemer, A. L. and Eckardt, H. H., *Vorratspflege u. Lebensmittelforsch.* **2**, 710 (1939).
11. Schoorl, N., *Pharm. Weekblad* **76**, 1295 (1939).
12. Senderikhina, D. P., *Trudy Moskov. Sanit. Inst. im Erismana* 86 (1939).
13. Koch, H. and Hilberath, F., *Brennstoffchemie* **21**, 185 (1940).
14. Boyd, H. M. and Roach, J. R., *Anal. Chem.* **19**, 158 (1947).
15. Thayer, L. and Glass, B., *Proc. Louisiana Acad. Sci.* **10**, 213 (1947).
16. Savary, P., *Bull. soc. chim. France* 635 (1949).

17. Cerdeiras Alonso, J. J., *pR (Montevideo)* **1**, No. 2, 39 (1951).
18. Duke, J. A. and Maselli, J. A., *J. Am. Oil Chemists' Soc.* **29**, 126 (1952).
19. Bodley, D. S., *J. Am. Oil Chemists' Soc.* **32**, 235 (1955).
20. Stähli, H., *Mitt. Lebensm. Hyg.* **46**, 121 (1955).
21. Shteindel, H., *Biul. Inst. Roslin Leczniczych* **2**, 160 (1956).
22. Seher, A. and Arends, W., *Mitt. Gebiete Lebensm. u. Hyg.* **48**, 1 (1957).
23. Mesnard, P. and Raby, C., *Chim. anal.* **44**, 463 (1962).

42. Hydrazines

Reagent. Principally phenylhydrazine and its nitro-substituted derivatives.

Reactions and materials titrated. 1. Condensation in determination of aldehydes and ketones, which yield insoluble products

$$RR'CO + H_2N.NH.R'' \rightarrow RR'C{=}N.NH.R' + H_2O$$

2. Ion/ion/molecule combination in determination of sulphonic acids which form water-insoluble salts.

$$H^+ + RSO_3^- + R'NH.NH_2 \rightarrow (R'NH.NH_3)^+(RSO_3)^-$$

Reaction conditions. Up to 24 hours reaction time for complete formation of condensation products in some cases. Salt formation in type 2 reactions is usually fast.

Subsequent treatment and final titration stage. Back titration of unused reagent and determination of a reaction product appear to have been about equally used.

(i) Unused hydrazine reagent has been titrated by:
(a) acid,
(b) oxidizing agents like iodine, chloramine T, iodate and Cu(II),
(c) reducing agents like Ti(III) for nitro-substituted phenylhydrazines.

(ii) Precipitated and separated reaction products have been determined via their functional groups as follows:
(a) as in (i)(c) with reducing agents such as Ti(III), Sn(II) or V(II) for nitro-substituted products,
(b) titration with alkali of sulphonates from reaction type 2 above and of condensation products of keto acids and with *p*-carboxyphenylhydrazine,
(c) hydrolysis of semicarbazones to titratable NH_3.

(iii) acid liberated in the reaction:

Carbonyl compound	+	(Substituted) Hydrazine hydrochloride or sulphate	→	(Substituted) Hydrazone	+	H_2O + HCl or H_2SO_4

has been titrated with alkali.

Examples

Materials titrated	Reagent and reaction conditions	Subsequent treatment and final titration stage	Ref.
Carbonyl compounds	+ excess phenylhydrazine in alcohol; 15 h in the dark	+ water, filtered and unused determined with excess iodine, followed by back titration with thiosulphate (see Iodine reagents, ref. 3)	1
α-Diketones	In 80% ethanol + equivalent amount of phenylhydrazine; 1 h/15–17° (study of extent of reaction with different ketones)	Unused titrated with iodine	2
Ketones and cyclic ketones	Method and study of ref. 2		3
Formaldehyde	+ excess hydrazine hydrate; 1 h digestion in a closed vessel	Unused titrated with H_2SO_4 to methyl orange	4
Carbonyl compounds	+ excess phenylhydrazine	Unused titrated with acid	5
Aromatic aldehydes; also from acid hydrolysis in determination of oximes, azines, hydrazones, etc.	+ excess hydrazine sulphate. A few hours shaking	Filtered, aliquot of filtrate + excess iodine + NaOH; after evolution of nitrogen ceased, + H_2SO_4 and titrated with thiosulphate	6
Furfuraldehyde from hydrolysis of pentoses and pentosans	+ excess phenylhydrazine	Unused determined with excess iodine as in method of ref. 1 (see Iodine reagents, ref. 53)	7
Glucose, lactose, fructose and other sugars	+ phenylhydrazine/acetic acid + sodium tartrate; 10 min/*ca* 100°	Osazone determined with excess $TiCl_3$ and back titration with Fe(III) (see Titanium (III), ref. 18)	8

Materials titrated	Reagent and reaction conditions	Subsequent treatment and final titration stage	Ref.
Pyruvic acid	+ phenylhydrazine or *p*-bromophenylhydrazine hydrochloride; 3–4 h	Filtered and titrated with NaOH to phenolphthalein	9
Carbonyl compounds	+ phenylhydrazine hydrochloride + disodium phosphate; mostly 30 min/100°	Phenylhydrazone extracted with petroleum ether and unused reagent determined with excess iodine, followed by back titration with thiosulphate	10
Citral	+ phenylhydrazine hydrochloride; 30 min/room temp.	Titrated with Na_2CO_3	11
Ketones	+ semicarbazide	Semicarbazones hydrolysed with $HCl/HgCl_2$ giving ammonia. Distilled out and titrated (see Hydrochloric acid, ref. 11)	12
Naphthalene-2-sulphonic acid	+ phenylhydrazine hydrochloride; 1 h/0°	Precipitate boiled with water and titrated with NaOH to phenolphthalein	13
Dehydroascorbic acid	+ 2,4-dinitrophenyl-hydrazine/HCl; (24 h reaction time if ascorbic acid present, which must be oxidized by the reagent)	Precipitate + methanol + excess $TiCl_3$/HCl. Back titrated with Fe(III) (see Titanium (III), ref. 30)	14, 15
Carbonyl compounds (determination of equivalent weight)	In ethanol if necessary, + *p*-carboxyphenyl-hydrazine/water/HCl. A few min reaction	Precipitate + ethanol and titrated with NaOH or $Ba(OH)_2$ to phenolphthalein or potentiometrically (see Part I, Alkali and alkaline earth hydroxides, refs 31 and 51)	16, 20
Cinnamic aldehyde in oil of cinnamon	+ hydrazine sulphate	Titrated with NaOH to methyl red	17
Laevulinic acid	+ phenylhydrazine	Precipitate dissolved in excess HCl and titrated with NaOH to methyl red, then phenolphthalein. Difference equivalent to the laevulinic acid	18
Aldehydes, e.g. furfuraldehyde	+ hydrazine sulphate	Titrated with NaOH to methyl red; or added excess and back titrated with acid	19

Materials titrated	Reagent and reaction conditions	Subsequent treatment and final titration stage	Ref.
Cinnamic aldehyde in oil of cinnamon	In water/methanol or ethanol, + hydrazine sulphate neutralized with NaOH; 6 h/room temp.	Filtered and filtrate titrated with NaOH to methyl red	21
Carbonyl compounds	In water or water/ethanol, + *p*-nitrophenylhydrazine/acetic acid	Precipitate dissolved in 50% H_2SO_4 and determined with excess Sn(II), back titrating with iodine; or dissolved in alkali and determined with excess stannite (see Tin (II), ref. 20)	22
Aromatic aldehydes, e.g. benzaldehyde, piperonal	+ neutralized hydrazine sulphate. Up to 6 h/room temp.	Filtered and filtrate titrated with iodine	23
Methyl glyoxal	+ 20-fold excess hot 20% *m*-nitrobenzhydrazide/10% acetic acid	Precipitate + excess $TiCl_3$, back titrated with Fe(III) (see Titanium (III), ref. 40)	24
Carbonyl compounds	In water, + excess 2,4-dinitrophenylhydrazine/HCl. Various reaction times	Filtered and unused determined with excess $TiCl_3$ and back titration with Fe(III) (see Titanium (III), refs 41 and 42)	25, 26
Carbonyl compounds	+ hydrochlorides of phenylhydrazine, semicarbazide or thiosemicarbazide	Titrated with alkali potentiometrically to original pH values of 4·2, 3·15 and 2·6 respectively	27
Carbonyl compounds	+ *p*-nitro-, 2,4-dinitro- or 2,4,6-trinitrophenylhydrazine	Unused determined with excess Ti(III) (see Titanium (III), ref. 45)	28
Carbonyl compounds	+ excess phenylhydrazine hydrochloride in pyridine/water	Unused titrated with cupric acetate to colour change from yellow brown to green brown (see Part I, Copper (II), ref. 107)	29
Carbonyl compounds	+ 2,4-dinitrophenylhydrazine/HCl; 1 h/0° or 2–24 h/room temp.	Filtered and unused titrated with iodate or determined with excess iodate and back titration with iodine (see Iodate in this volume, ref. 60 and in Part I, ref. 43)	30

Materials titrated	Reagent and reaction conditions	Subsequent treatment and final titration stage	Ref.
Glyoxal, glyoxylic acid	+ excess semicarbazide hydrochloride/water; 4 h/*ca* 60°	+ acetic acid + excess IO_3^-; unused and iodine formed titrated with thiosulphate (see Iodate, ref. 62)	31
Aldehydes	+ 1,1-dimethylhydrazine in methanol or ethylene glycol; 15 min–2 h/room temp.	+ methanol and titrated unused with HCl/methanol potentiometrically (see Part I, Hydrochloric acid, ref. 44)	32
Carbonyl compounds, e.g. HCHO, glucose, anthraquinone	+ 2,4-dinitrophenylhydrazine	Precipitates determined with excess VSO_4 and back titration with bichromate (see Vanadium (II), ref. 3)	33
Carbonyl compounds	+ excess phenylhydrazine	Unused titrated with copper acetate potentiometrically (see Part I, Copper II, ref. 118)	34
Carbonyl compounds	In 96% ethanol, + 2,4-dinitrophenylhydrazine; 12 h/room temp.	Filtered and titrated unused potentiometrically with chloramine T in presence of KBr (see Part I, Chloramine B and T, refs 15, 16 and 20)	35, 36, 41
Mesoxalic acid	+ excess phenylhydrazine hydrochloride; 15 min/95°	Unused determined with excess iodine and back titration with thiosulphate (see Iodine reagents, ref. 334)	37
Carbonyl compounds	+ excess *p*-nitrophenylhydrazine in dioxan/acetic acid; 10 min/below 20°	Unused titrated with $HClO_4$/acetic acid potentiometrically. Control titration without sample (see Part I, Perchloric acid, ref. 152)	38
Benzene *o*-disulphonic acid	+ phenylhydrazine hydrochloride	Precipitate titrated in boiling solution with NaOH to phenolphthalein (see Part I, Alkali and alkaline earth hydroxides, ref. 127)	39
Carbonyl compounds	In pyridine + excess phenylhydrazine hydrochloride; 15 min/*ca* 100°	Unused titrated potentiometrically with copper acetate in ethanol/pyridine, 1:1 (see Part I, Copper (II), ref. 128)	42

Materials titrated	Reagent and reaction conditions	Subsequent treatment and final titration stage	Ref.
Benzaldehyde from acid hydrolysis of, in determination of benzal groups	Distilled into 2,4-dinitrophenylhydrazine in HCl solution; 1 h standing. Or into *p*-nitrophenylhydrazine in HCl; 6–8 h standing	Unused determined with excess $TiCl_3$ and back titration with Fe(III) (see Titanium (III), ref. 56)	43
Carbonyl compounds	+ 2,4-dinitrophenylhydrazine	Separated by paper chromatography, extracted with acetate buffer and determined with excess $TiCl_3$, back titrating with Fe(III) (see Titanium (III), ref. 59)	44
Carbonyl compounds in foods	In ethanol or ethanol/water, + 2,4-dinitrophenylhydrazine in HCl; 1 h/room temp., then 1 h reflux	Filtered and determined unused with excess iodine and back titration with thiosulphate (see Iodine reagents, ref. 395)	45
Monochloroacetaldehyde	In water, + excess hydrazine sulphate; 10 min	+ HNO_3 and determined with excess $AgNO_3$ and back titration with SCN^-	46
3-Methyl-chromone	+ hydrazine hydrate; 3 h	Unused titrated with HCl to methyl red/methylene blue	47
Cyclic ketones; substituted benzaldehydes	+ Girard T reagent (hydrazide of carboxymethyl-trimethylammonium chloride) (study of reaction rates)	Unused reagent determined with excess iodine	48
Carbonyl compounds	In ethanol, + 2,4-dinitrophenylhydrazine/HCl; *ca* 10 min – 2 h	+ excess iodine, left 20 min and back titrated with thiosulphate (see Iodine reagents, ref. 442)	49

References

1. v. Meyer, E., *J. prakt. Chem.* (2) **36**, 115 (1887).
2. Petrenko-Kritschenko, P. and Eltschaninoff, E., *Ber.* **34**, 1699 (1901).
3. Petrenko-Kritschenko, P., and Lordkipanidze, S., *Ber.* **34** 1702 (1901).
4. Pfaff, A., *Chem.-Ztg.* **26**, 701 (1902).
5. Kleber, C., *Am. Perfumer* **6**, 284 (1912).
6. Lautenschläger, L., *Arch. Pharm.* **256**, 81 (1918).

7. Ling, A. R. and Nanji, D. R., *Biochem. J.* **15**, 466 (1921).
8. Knecht, E. and Hibbert, E., *J. Chem. Soc.* 2009 (1924).
9. Simon, L. J. and Piaux, L., *Bull. soc. chim. biol.* **6**, 477 (1924).
10. Ardagh, E. G. R. and Williams, J. G., *J. Am. Chem. Soc.* **47**, 2983 (1925).
11. Fernández, O. and Mosardó, A., *Anales soc. espan. fis. y quim.* **27**, 265 (1929).
12. Hobson, R. P., *J. Chem. Soc.* 1384 (1929).
13. Zin'kov, E., Danyushevskii, Ya. L., Reinshtein, V. and Khomyakovskii, G. M., *J. Appl. Chem. U.S.S.R.* **9**, 1997 (1936).
14. Espil, L. and Génévois, L., *Bull. soc. chim. France* (5) **5**, 1532 (1938).
15. Espil, L. and Mandillon, G., *Compt. rend. soc. biol.* **129**, 1187 (1938).
16. Veibel, S. and Hauge, N., *Bull. soc. chim. France* **5**, 1506 (1938).
17. Stempel, B., *Fette u. Seifen* **49**, 42 (1942).
18. Boinon, R., *Ing. Chim.* **27**, No 161, 8 (1945).
19. Monti, L. and Masserizi, M. T., *Ann. chim. applicata* **37**, 101 (1947).
20. Veibel, S., *Acta Chem. Scand.* **1**, 54 (1947).
21. Fuchs, L., *Scientiae Pharm.* **16**, 50 (1948).
22. Petit, G., *Bull. soc. chim. France* **15**, 141 (1948).
23. Fuchs, L. and Matzke, O., *Scientiae Pharm.* **17**, 1 (1949).
24. Prey, V., Waldmann, E. and Ludwig, F., *Monatsh.* **82**, 1022 (1951).
25. Schöniger, W. and Lieb, H., *Mikrochemie ver. Mikrochim. Acta* **38**, 165 (1951).
26. Schöniger, W., Lieb, H. and Gassner, K., *Z. anal. Chem.* **134**, 188 (1951).
27. Dvořák, K., Trekoval, J., Buzková, V. and Treybal, K., *Sborník Celostatní Pracovní Konf. Anal. Chemiků* **1**, 313 (1952).
28. Schöniger, W., *Mikrochim. Acta* 434 (1953).
29. Terent'ev, A. P. and Zabrodina, K. S., *Doklady Akad. Nauk SSSR* **95**, 85 (1954).
30. Barke, D. J. and Cole, E. P., *J. Appl. Chem. (London)* **5**, 477 (1955).
31. Salzer, F., *Z. anal. Chem.* **146**, 260 (1955).
32. Siggia, S. and Stahl, C. R., *Anal. Chem.* **27**, 1975 (1955).
33. Witry-Schwachtgen, G., *Inst. Grand-Ducal, Luxembourg, Sect. Sci. nat. phys. et meth. Arch.* **22**, 87 (1955).
34. Barro-Raffel, M. and Jacini, G., *Olii minerali, grassi e saponi, colori e vernici* **33**, 381 (1956).
35. Berka, A. and Zýka, J., *Chem. Listy* **50**, 831 (1956).
36. Berka, A. and Zýka, J., *Československ. Farm.* **5**, 30 (1956).
37. Hirayama, H. and Amano, T., *Ann. Rept. Shionagi Research Lab.* **6**, 55 (1956).
38. Nakamura, N., *Bunseki Kagaku* **5**, 459 (1956).
39. Spryskov, A. A. and Starkov, S. A., *Zhur. Obshchei Khim.* **26**, 2607 (1956).
40. Berka, A., *Chemie (Prague)* **9**, 528 (1957).
41. Berka, A. and Zýka, J., *Pharmazie* **13**, 89 (1958).

42. Buděšinský, B., *Chem. Listy* **52**, 2292 (1958).
43. Jureček, M. and Obruba, K., *Chem. Listy* **52**, 2066 (1958).
44. Blom, L. and Caris, J., *Nature* **184**, Suppl. No. 17, 1313 (1959).
45. Hamann, V. and Herrman, A., *Deut. Lebensm. Rundschau* **56**, 95, 133 (1960).
46. Yasnitskii, B. G. and Satanovskaya, T., *Med. Prom. SSSR* **14**, 36 (1960).
47. DeLorenzi, F. and DaRe, P., *Boll. chim. farm.* **100**, 23 (1961).
48. Wheeler, O. H., Gaind, V. S. and Rosado, O., *J. Org. Chem.* **26**, 3537 (1961).
49. Hozumi, K. and Hazama, K., *Bunseki Kagaku* **10**, 1240 (1961).

43. Hydrobromic acid

Reagent. Usually as a solution in water or in acetic acid, and often of high concentration. In some cases, a mixture of a bromide ($MgBr_2$) and sulphuric acid has been used (this has been classified also under Sulphuric acid).

Reactions and materials titrated. 1. Addition to epoxides and to olefines. Probably the reactions in determination of ascaridole and of eucalyptol (cineol) also involve addition of HBr after ring breaking.

$$\text{—}\underset{|}{\overset{|}{C}}\text{—O—}\underset{|}{\overset{|}{C}}\text{—}\ (\text{epoxide}) + HBr \rightarrow \text{—}\underset{OH}{\overset{|}{C}}\text{—}\underset{Br}{\overset{|}{C}}\text{—}$$

$$\text{—}\overset{|}{C}=\overset{|}{C}\text{—} + HBr \rightarrow \text{—}\overset{|}{C}H\text{—}\overset{|}{C}Br\text{—}$$

2. Ester formation with tertiary alcohols

$$R_3COH + HBr \rightarrow R_3CBr + H_2O$$

3. Fission of C—O bonds with formation of benzyl or substituted benzyl bromides. Benzyloxy groups in benzyl esters have been thus determined:

$$RCOOCH_2C_6H_5 + HBr \rightarrow RCOOH + C_6H_5CH_2Br$$

Benzyl and substituted benzyl ether groups have been determined according to the reaction:

$$(C_6H_5CH_2)_2O + 2\ HBr \rightarrow 2\ C_6H_5CH_2Br + H_2O$$

4. Acid catalyst in some hydrolysis reactions (e.g. of acetals, ketals or vinyl ethers) or in dehydration of pentoses to give furfuraldehyde. The greater cost of hydrobromic acid compared to hydrochloric or sulphuric acids has militated against a more extensive use as a catalyst unless it shows some marked advantage over these other acids. For example, the use of hydrobromic acid (or bromide in acid solution) is an especially effective catalyst in diazotization and other reactions of nitrosation. (No examples are given here, but this is mentioned in Part I under Nitrite.)

Reaction conditions. Most reactions have been at room temperature while reaction times have ranged from a few minutes to 48 h.

Subsequent treatment and final titration stage. (a) In about half the examples given, the conclusion has been by back titration of unused acid or bromide. This has been done by alkali hydroxide (where the reaction was in aqueous solution); by sodium acetate (reaction in acetic acid); or with silver reagent.

(b) Most frequently occurring of conclusions based on determination of a reaction product has been via the bromine atom introduced into the molecule. In two cases, this was liberated to yield hydrobromic acid, then titrated with an alkali; in a third case, which can be conveniently classified here, tertiary bromides were converted to thiouronium picrates which were titrated with perchloric acid:

$$R_3CBr + CS(NH_2)_2 \rightarrow (R_3C.S.\underset{\displaystyle NH_2}{\underset{|}{C}}{=}NH_2)^+Br^- \rightarrow \text{insoluble picrate}$$

(c) Furfuraldehyde from pentose and pentosan analysis has been bromometrically determined.

Examples

Materials titrated	Reagent and reaction conditions	Subsequent treatment and final titration stage	Ref.
Ethylene oxide	+ 50% $MgBr_2$ + H_2SO_4	Unused acid titrated with NaOH to methyl orange	1
Olefines in C_4, C_5 and C_7 mixtures	+ conc. HBr	Unused acid back titrated	2

Materials titrated	Reagent and reaction conditions	Subsequent treatment and final titration stage	Ref.
Pentoses; pentosans	Distilled with 40% HBr	Furfuraldehyde in distillate determined with bromine reagent	3
a,*p*-Dimethylstyrene in presence of *p*-methylstyrene, styrene and *p*-cymene	In CCl_4 + HBr. Bubbled in for 30 min	Unused HBr removed with nitrogen current; + 90% ethanol at 0° and HBr set free titrated with KOH to methyl red	4
Dibenzyl ether; hydroxybenzyl ethers; ether groups in phenolic resins	In $CHCl_3$ + HBr; 12–24 h	Water formed titrated with Karl Fischer reagent	5
Tertiary alcohols	+ conc. HBr; 5 min shaking, giving tertiary bromides	Converted to thiouronium picrate and titrated with $HClO_4$ (see Thiourea, ref. 1; Nitrophenols, ref. 55; and Part I, Perchloric acid, ref. 62)	6
Salts of epoxy acids	In acetic acid, + excess HBr/acetic acid	+ Na acetate and unused Br^- titrated to eosin Y with $AgNO_3$	7
Ethylene oxide in fumigation mixtures with CF_2Cl_2	Passed into saturated $MgCl_2$ + H_2SO_4; 15 min/room temp.	Unused acid titrated with NaOH	8
Ascaridole in chenopodium oil	+ acetic acid + excess HBr/acetic acid; 24 h/room temp.	Unused HBr titrated with Na acetate/acetic acid potentiometrically	9
Eucalyptol in mixtures with thymol, menthol or camphor	+ acetic acid + excess HBr/acetic acid; 48 h/room temp.	Unused HBr titrated with Na acetate/acetic acid rapidly to methyl violet	10
Acetals, ketals, vinyl ethers	+ HBr; 30 min/100°	+ measured amount hydroxylamine hydrochloride + HBr and after 30 min/100°, KOH added and titrated potentiometrically with $Fe(CN)_6^{3-}$	11
Pentosans in wood pulps	Distilled with 20% HBr	Furfuraldehyde in distillate determined bromometrically	12
Benzyloxy groups in benzyl esters and carbobenzyloxy derivatives	+ 30% HBr/acetic acid; 5–15 min/80–100° $RCOOC_7H_7 + HBr \rightarrow RCOOH + C_7H_7Br$	+ benzene, neutralized, benzene layer treated with aniline, reacting with the extracted benzyl bromide, giving HBr; titrated with $NaOCH_3$ to thymol blue (see Amines and heterocyclic bases, ref. 91)	13

Materials titrated	Reagent and reaction conditions	Subsequent treatment and final titration stage	Ref.
Ethylene oxide in low concentrations	Absorbed in 50% $MgBr_2$ + H_2SO_4	Back titrated with NaOH to bromocresol green	14
Tributyl phosphate	Hydrolysed with HBr/acetic acid	HBr and acetic acid evaporated off and the residual phosphoric acid titrated	15
3,3-Bis(chloromethyl)-oxacyclobutane	In an organic solvent, + HBr/acetone	Unreacted acid titrated with alkali	16
Carbobenzyloxy groups in high molecular weight peptides	+ HBr/acetic acid reagent + dichloroacetic acid; 15–45 min/room temp., then warmed to 80° $RNH—COOCH_2C_6H_5 + 2\ HBr \rightarrow RNH_3Br + C_6H_5CH_2Br + CO_2$	CO_2 absorbed in benzylamine/dioxan/ethanol and titrated with $NaOCH_3$ to thymol blue	17

References

1. Lubatti, O. F., *J. Soc. Chem. Ind. (London)* **54**, 424T (1935).
2. Stern, G., *Reichsamt. Wirtschaftsausbau Prüf. Nr.* **43** (PB 52003) 15 (1940).
3. Jayme, G. and Sarten, P., *Biochem. Z.* **308**, 109 (1941).
4. Elliott, J. H. and Cook, E. V., *Ind. Eng. Chem., Anal. Ed.* **16**, 20 (1944).
5. Lilley, H. S. and Osmond, D. W. J., *J. Soc. Chem. Ind. (London)* **66**, 425 (1947).
6. Schotte, L. and Veibel, S., *Acta Chem. Scand.* **7**, 1357 (1953).
7. Durbetaki, A. J., *Anal. Chem.* **30**, 2024 (1958).
8. Affens, W. A., Haenni, E. V. and Fulton, R. A., *Anal. Chem.* **31**, 1565 (1959).
9. Blake, M. and O'Neill, R. E., *Anal. Chem.* **32**, 1370 (1960).
10. Blake, M. I. and Rabjohn, E., *J. Am. Pharm. Assoc., Sci. Ed.* **49**, 650 (1960).
11. Buděšinský, B. and Körbl, J., *Mikrochim. Acta* 697 (1960).
12. Grobelny, I. and Illukowicz, W., *TAPPI* **43**, 244A (1960).
13. Patchornik, A. and Ehrlich-Rogazinsky, S., *Anal. Chem.* **33**, 803 (1961).
14. Saltzman, B. E., *Anal. Chem.* **33**, 1100 (1961).
15. U.K.A.E.A., *Report* PG 255(S), 1962.
16. Balandina, V. A. and Zinchenko, V. A., *USSR Patent* No. 154, 430, July 24, 1963.
17. Yaron, A., Ehrlich-Rogozinski, S. and Berger, A., *Anal. Chem.* **36**, 1387 (1964).

44. Hydrocarbons

Three examples of the use of comparatively reactive unsaturated hydrocarbons are given below, all of which depend on an addition reaction:

Materials titrated	Reagent and reaction conditions	Subsequent treatment and final titration stage	Ref.
Maleic anhydride	In benzene, + cyclo-pentadiene/benzene; 10 min/35°, giving the Diels–Alder addition product	Addition product extracted with KOH and determined by titration with bromate/bromide (see Part I, Bromate, ref. 112)	1
Maleic acid or anhydride in presence of many other acids and anhy-drides, e.g. tartaric, succinic, fumaric and phthalic	In chlorobenzene, + anthracene: refluxed 45 min, giving the Diels–Alder addition product	+ hot water and titrated with NaOH (evidently difference from a control NaOH titration without reaction with anthra-cene, gave the maleic acid or anhydride)	2
Binary metal acetate mixtures, of which one component was Hg acetate	In propylene glycol/ methanol, + some drops styrene (reacts with the Hg acetate)	Titrated other acetate with HCl/butanol to thymol blue; also titrated total acetate on a sample without treatment with styrene (see Part I, Hydro-chloric acid, refs 60 and 71)	3

References

1. Unger, P., *Analyst* **80**, 820 (1955).
2. Nebbia, L. and Guerrieri, F., *Chim. e ind.* (*Milan*) **39**, 17 (1957).
3. Kundu, K. K. and Das, M. N., *Science and Culture* **23**, 660 (1958); *Anal. Chem.* **31**, 1358 (1959).

45. Hydrochloric acid

(See general remarks under Acids)

Reagent. Usually in aqueous solution, in concentrations ranging from very low to 20% and over. Occasionally organic solvents have been used and here ethers have predominated (see below under Reaction conditions).

In five quoted cases, the hydrochloric acid has been used in the form of its salt with a weak tertiary base such as pyridine, collidine or trimethylamine.

Reactions and materials titrated. 1. Addition, in determination of α-epoxides, oxetanes and some olefines; in the former two, ring opening occurs.

$$\text{—C — C— (epoxide, bridged by O)} + HCl \rightarrow \text{—C(OH) — C(Cl)—}$$

$$-\overset{|}{C} = \overset{|}{C}- + HCl \rightarrow -\overset{|}{C}H - \overset{|}{C}Cl-$$

The determination of ethylene oxide (a standard method) is the most often encountered example.

2. Ester formation, exemplified in two specialized determinations, namely of secondary or tertiary alcohols and of methyl or ethyl ethers of certain aromatic compounds (the latter can be regarded also as dealkylation):

$$R_3COH + HCl \rightarrow R_3CCl + H_2O$$

$$ArOCH_3 + HCl \rightarrow ArOH + CH_3Cl$$

3. Ion/ion combination, yielding weak organic acids which are usually separable by filtration or other means. Examples include xanthates, mercury mercaptides, naphthenates of many metals like cobalt, and zinc mercaptobenzothiazole.

$$RO.\underset{\underset{S}{\|}}{C}.S^- + H^+ \rightarrow ROH + CS_2$$

$$RS^- + H^+ \rightarrow RSH$$

$$RCOO^- + H^+ \rightarrow RCOOH$$

4. Ion/molecule combination in determination of certain bases:

$$\text{Base} + H^+ \rightarrow (\text{Base.H})^+ \quad \text{(frequently precipitate)}$$

Some aromatic bases, the 2,4-dinitrophenyl ether of morphine, the end groups of polycaprolactam and some unsaturated amines have been determined through an initial stage of this sort.

Under this heading may be mentioned the determination of amines, formed from hydrolysis or other reaction using the hydrochloric acid reagent. The ensuing salt formation is a stage in the analytical determination. Amides and isocyanates have been determined in this way.

5. As an acid catalyst in 5 types of reaction:

(a) Hydrolysis of a wide variety of bonds:

C—O e.g. esters, acetals and polysaccharides ('inversion' of disaccharides like sucrose, and hydrolysis of hemicelluloses have been extensively used in food and agriculture methods; in order to limit the examples in the tables to reasonable dimensions, only one or two of these types have been quoted)

C—N e.g. amides and polyamides; hydrazides like isoniazid; hexamine; semicarbazide and hydroxamic acids:

$$RCONH_2 + H_2O \rightarrow RCOOH + NH_3$$
$$(CH_2)_6N_4 + 6\,H_2O \rightarrow 6\,HCHO + 4\,NH_3$$
$$RCONHNH_2 + H_2O \rightarrow RCOOH + NH_2NH_2$$
$$RCO(NHOH) + H_2O \rightarrow RCOOH + NH_3OH$$

The amides of aromatic amines predominate in this sub-group

C=N condensation products of carbonyl compounds such as oximes, osazones, hydrazones, phenylhydrazones and semicarbazones

$$R_2C{=}N.X + H_2O \rightarrow R_2CO + X.NH_2$$

C≡N Nitriles

C—C An example here is the determination of the $-CH_2OH$ groups in formaldehyde resins:

$$Ar.CH_2OH + H_2O \rightarrow ArH + CH_2(OH)_2$$
$$\downarrow$$
$$HCHO + H_2O$$

C—I e.g. iodoform and also tetraiodopyrrole, yielding iodine or iodide

C—Metal Principal example here is lead tetraethyl, converted to $PbCl_2$; some mercurials have also been determined via their decomposition into $HgCl_2$ with hydrochloric acid; and Grignard reagents by conversion into Mg^{2+}.

S—N Sulphonamides have been determined via hydrolysis:

$$ArSO_2NH_2 + H_2O \rightarrow ArSO_3H + NH_3$$

Si—O Some arylalkoxy silanes have been hydrolysed as the first stage in quantitative determination, with fission of the Si—O link

(b) Dehydration of pentoses giving furfuraldehyde is the standard method for their determination and also that of pentosans. Methylpentoses likewise yield methylfurfuraldehyde and hexoses, hydroxymethylfurfuraldehyde but there are few examples of the use of this reaction.

$$\begin{array}{l} \text{HOCH} - \text{CHOH} \\ \quad | \qquad\qquad | \\ \text{H}_2\text{C}\diagdown_{\text{OH HO}}\diagup\text{CH.CHO} \end{array} \xrightarrow{-3\,H_2O} \begin{array}{l} \text{CH} - \text{CH} \\ \| \qquad \| \\ \text{CH} \quad \text{C.CHO} \\ \quad \diagdown_{\text{O}}\diagup \end{array}$$

(c) Decarboxylation in determination of uronic acids and anhydrides and also, recently, of *N*-carboxyamino acid anhydrides:

$$\text{RCOOH} \rightarrow \text{RH} + CO_2$$

$$\text{RCH}\begin{array}{l}\diagup \text{CO—O} \\ \qquad\quad | \\ \diagdown \text{NH—CO}\end{array} (+ H_2O) \rightarrow \text{RCH}\begin{array}{l}\diagup \text{COOH} \\ \diagdown NH_2\end{array} + CO_2$$

(d) Depolymerization, e.g. of paraldehyde to give acetaldehyde.

(e) Addition (of water), e.g. in determination of isocyanates. The initial stage is effectively an addition, followed by decarboxylation.

$$\text{RN=C=O} + H_2O \rightarrow \text{RNH.COOH}$$

(The reaction of nitriles is considered as hydrolysis, although the initial stage is probably addition.)

Reaction conditions. The reaction has been carried out in the sensible absence of water in cases where the insolubility of the reaction product (salt) is thereby enhanced; and in the determination of epoxides (reaction 1, of addition above) in order to suppress the competition reaction with water:

$$\begin{array}{c} | \quad | \\ -\text{C} - \text{C}- \\ \diagdown \diagup \\ \text{O} \end{array} + H_2O \rightarrow \begin{array}{c} | \quad | \\ -\text{C} - \text{C}- \\ | \quad | \\ \text{OH OH} \end{array}$$

An organic solvent like glacial acetic acid has been used also in order to facilitate the ultimate back titration.

Metal chlorides, often in high concentration, have often been used for several reasons:

to favour the chlorohydrin formation in the epoxide determination (the highest possible chloride concentration has been attained by using the very soluble calcium or magnesium chlorides in saturated solution);

to oxidize an unwanted reaction product (using $HgCl_2$ to decompose hydrazine; this is really an influence of the Hg(II));

to catalyse various reactions like ester formation with secondary alcohols ($ZnCl_2$); olefine addition of HCl($BaCl_2$); decarboxylation (NaCl or $ZnCl_2$); dehydration of pentoses (NaCl); and decomposition of cellulose ($FeCl_3$) evidently to reduce solubility of salts.

Reaction conditions of time and temperature have naturally covered a wide range—from a few minutes at *ca* room temperature up to several days reflux for difficulty hydrolysable materials such as certain sulphonamides.

Subsequent treatment and final titration stage. Three broad types of procedure can be distinguished:

(i) Back titration of unused acid. This can clearly apply only to methods based on one of the first 4 reaction types, where acid is consumed. In fact it is the usual principle of conclusion after reactions of types 1 and 4; in a determination of tertiary butanol and in the determination of aromatic methyl or ethyl ethers mentioned under reaction type 2; and in a determination of xanthates classified under type 3 reactions.

Usually the back titration has been carried out with an alkali hydroxide in aqueous solution. Other titrants used include sodium acetate (in acetic acid as reaction medium), silver nitrate and mercuric nitrate.

(ii) Titration of unused reagent + acid produced (in a hydrolysis reaction). The chief examples here are sulphate and sulphonate esters:

$$(RO)_2SO_2 + 2\,H_2O \rightarrow H_2SO_4 + 2\,ROH$$

Examples are given also of determination of sulphonamides and of polyamides by the same principle (refs 61 and 121); this is practicable only when the amines, simultaneously formed, can be removed (e.g. in an ion exchange column) or when at least their effect is eliminated by selection of a suitable indicator.

In the examples quoted, alkali hydroxide was used as titrant.

(iii) In most cases, by titration of a reaction product. Some of the more frequently occurring are tabulated below:

1. Furfuraldehyde from reactions of type 5(c), by procedures with bisulphite, bromine, copper (II), hydroxylamine, iodine/alkali or silver (I) reagents.

2. Other carbonyl compounds from hydrolysis of acetals or the $-CH_2OH$ group of formaldehyde resins or from depolymerizations as

in reactions of type 5(d), using similar procedures to those for furfuraldehyde (bisulphite, hydroxylamine, iodine/alkali or mercury (II)).

3. Carbon dioxide from the decarboxylation reactions type 5(c), by absorption in alkali and determination of the unused. Barium hydroxide has been mostly used but sometimes sodium hydroxide which was then treated with $BaCl_2$ before acid titration.

4. Amines, usually aromatic, from hydrolytic determination of amides and sulphonamides, using methods based on titration with acid ($HCl, HClO_4$); diazotization with nitrite; or substitution with bromine or ICl reagents. The last two apply of course only to aromatic amines.

5. Other nitrogen-containing products derived from hydrolysis of C—N, S—N, C=N or C≡N links, e.g. ammonia, usually distilled into excess standard acid and back titrated; hydrazines, determined by oxidative titration with iodine, iodate or chloramine T or by titration with nitrite; and hydroxylamine, titrated with excess Fe(III).

6. Acid derived from hydrolysis of esters, amides or sulphonamides, using alkali titration.

7. Hexoses from determination of cellulose, hemi-celluloses, etc., by methods based on their reducing properties. Alkaline Cu(II) reagents have mostly been used, and also alkaline ferrocyanide.

8. Sulphur-containing compounds such as mercaptans from acid treatment of their metal derivatives (determined by titration with iodine or Ag(I)); or carbon disulphide from xanthate hydrolysis (determined by conversion back to xanthate with KOH/alcohol).

9. Metal cations like Hg(II), Pb(II), etc., derived from metal-containing organic compounds usually by hydrolysis, have been determined by standard inorganic procedures like EDTA titration.

10. Halide esters from a reaction of type 2, were converted to thiouronium picrates or to thiouronium 3,5-dinitrobenzoates and these determined respectively by titration with $HClO_4$ or by reduction of the nitro groups with Ti(III) reagent.

Examples

Materials titrated	Reagent and reaction conditions	Subsequent treatment and final titration stage	Ref.
Benzoyl groups, e.g. in esters of glycerol and dextrose or glucosamine	+ HCl/saturated benzoic acid (in cold); 1–2 days standing	Benzoic acid filtered and ultimately titrated with NaOH to phenolphthalein	1

Materials titrated	Reagent and reaction conditions	Subsequent treatment and final titration stage	Ref.
Pentoses; pentosans	Distilled with 10% HCl, giving furfuraldehyde	Distillate neutralized, concentrated and aldehyde determined with excess Ag(I) reagent (see Silver (I), ref. 9)	2
Pentoses; pentosans	Distilled with conc. HCl	Furfuraldehyde in distillate determined with excess bisulphite, back titrating with iodine (see Bisulphite and Sulphite, ref. 7)	3
Acetal in presence of paraldehyde	+ very dilute HCl (*ca* N/1000), giving acetaldehyde	Aldehyde distilled out and determined with excess bisulphite or with sulphite	4
paraldehyde	+ more conc. HCl	aldehyde distilled out and determined with excess bisulphite or with sulphite (see Bisulphite and sulphite, ref. 11)	
Osazones	+ HCl; 1 h/*ca* 100°, giving phenylhydrazine	Neutralized with NaOH, $NaHCO_3$ added and determined with excess iodine (see Iodine reagents, ref. 69)	5
Lead tetraethyl in gasoline	Refluxed with conc. HCl, giving $PbCl_2$	Evaporated to dryness, organic matter oxidized with HNO_3 and Pb(II) titrated with ammonium molybdate to external indicator of tannin	6
Xanthates	Neutral solution + excess HCl; 10 min/room temp.	Unused acid titrated with alkali to methyl red	7
Acetone derivatives of polyhydroxy compounds like glycerol or glycerides	+ HCl; 15 min–1 h	Acetone determined with alkali/excess iodine (see Iodine reagents, ref. 83)	8
Saccharine	+ HCl; 2 h reflux	+ excess NaOH, ammonia distilled into excess acid and back titrated with alkali	9
Lead glucuronate, from determination of glucuronic acid in urine by precipitation with Pb(II)	Distilled with conc. HCl, giving furfuraldehyde	Distillate + excess bisulphite and back titrated with iodine (see Bisulphite and sulphite, ref. 27)	10

Materials titrated	Reagent and reaction conditions	Subsequent treatment and final titration stage	Ref.
Semicarbazide; semicarbazones	+ 15% HCl + $HgCl_2$; 7–8 h reflux, giving ammonia (Hg(II) oxidizes hydrazine formed to nitrogen)	Made alkaline and NH_3 distilled and titrated	11
Pentoses; pentosans; methylpentoses and -pentosans	Distilled with conc. HCl + NaCl, giving furfuraldehyde or methylfurfuraldehyde	Aldehyde in distillate determined with excess bromate (see Bromine reagents, ref. 66)	12
Ethylene oxide	Passed through HCl/ 25% NaCl. Heated to 70°	Unused acid titrated with NaOH to methyl orange	13, 40
Pentoses; pentosans	Distilled with 12% HCl	Furfuraldehyde determined with excess bromine	14
Uronic acids	Heated with *ca* 12% HCl, decarboxylating	CO_2 passed into excess $Ba(OH)_2$ and back titrated with HCl to phenol- or thymolphthalein	15
α-Epoxides, e.g. 9,10-epoxystearic acid	+ HCl/dry ether in at least 200% excess; 2 h/room temp.	+ ethanol and unused acid titrated to phenolphthalein	16
Organic sulphates	+ HCl; 2 h reflux	Titrated with NaOH to methyl orange	17
Pentosans	Distilled with conc. HCl (not over 11% strength)	Furfuraldehyde in distillate titrated potentiometrically with bromate after adding bromide/acid	18
Hemicelluloses	+ 2·5% HCl; 4 h reflux, giving reducing sugars	Determined with Cu(II) reagent, dissolving Cu_2O in Fe(III), and finally titrating the Fe(II) formed with MnO_4^-	19
Pentosans	Distilled with 13% HCl	Distillate neutralized and furfuraldehyde content determined with hydroxylamine (see Hydroxylamine, ref. 21)	20
Uronic anhydride groups in pectic substances	Heated with 12% HCl, giving CO_2	Passed into $Ba(OH)_2$ and back titrated with oxalic acid to phenolphthalein	21
Ethylene oxide in air and food	Passed into HCl/nearly saturated $MgCl_2$ solution	Unused acid titrated with NaOH to methyl orange	22

Materials titrated	Reagent and reaction conditions	Subsequent treatment and final titration stage	Ref.
Pentosans	Distilled with 12% HCl	Furfuraldehyde determined in distillate with excess bromate/bromide and iodometric back titration (see Bromine reagents, ref. 99)	23
Acetyl groups in cellulose acetates	+ conc. HCl; left until no further change in viscosity	+ water, left overnight and titrated with NaOH potentiometrically (two inflections, corresponding to unused HCl and to acetic acid liberated)	24
Pentosans in hardwoods	Distilled with 12% HCl	Furfuraldehyde in distillate determined with excess bromate/bromide (see Bromine reagents, ref. 107)	25
Uronic acids	Method of ref. 15		26
Pentoses; pentosans	Method of ref. 12		27
Phenacetin; aspirin; acetanilide	+ excess HCl; 1 h hydrolysis	Unused titrated with NaOH to phenolphthalein	28
Uronic acids	+ 12% HCl/saturated NaCl. At least 2 h/133–6°	CO_2 carried into $Ba(OH)_2$ and back titrated with H_2SO_4 to phenolphthalein	29
Pentosans	Distilled with conc. HCl	Furfuraldehyde in distillate determined with excess bromate/bromide and iodometric back titration (see Bromine reagents, ref. 121)	30
Pentoses	Distilled with 12% HCl	Furfuraldehyde in distillate determined with Cu(II) reagent (Cu_2O formed dissolved in Fe(III) and Fe(II) titrated with MnO_4^-) (see Copper (II), ref. 85)	31
Hexamine	+ dilute HCl; 15 min reflux, giving HCHO	Determined with Hg(II) and iodometric determination of the Hg(I) formed (see Mercury (II), ref. 57)	32
Organic sulphate in commercial sulphated alcohols	+ HCl; 2 h reflux	+ ether to dissolve liberated alcohol; total acid then titrated with NaOH to methyl orange	33

Materials titrated	Reagent and reaction conditions	Subsequent treatment and final titration stage	Ref.
Cellulose xanthate	+ dilute HCl, giving CS_2	Aspirated into KOH/ethanol and xanthate formed titrated iodometrically	34
Ethylene oxide in commercial fumigants	+ $HCl/MgCl_2$ solution	Unused acid titrated with NaOH to methyl orange	35
Weak aromatic bases	In ether, + HCl/ether	Evaporated to dryness, salt dissolved in water and titrated with NaOH to phenolphthalein	36
Semicarbazone; semicarbazides	Heated with HCl in sealed tube, giving NH_3, CO_2 and hydrazine	+ Na acetate and hydrazine determined with excess iodine	37
Pentoses	Distilled with conc. HCl	Furfuraldehyde determined with excess bromine reagent and iodometric back titration (see Bromine reagents, refs 139 and 164)	38, 43
Maltobionic acid, from determination of maltose by reaction with iodine/alkali	Heated with HCl, giving glucose	Glucose determined with excess ferricyanide and iodometric titration of unused (see Ferricyanide, ref. 39)	39
Ethylene oxide	+ $HCl/CaCl_2$; 3 min shaking in closed vessel	Diluted and unused acid titrated with NaOH to phenolphthalein	41
Acetanilide	Boiled with HCl	Aniline determined with bromate/bromide/HCl excess (see Bromine reagents, ref. 150)	42
Lead tetraethyl in gasoline	Refluxed with conc. HCl	Evaporated to dryness, organic matter oxidized with HNO_3 and Pb(II) ultimately titrated with ammonium molybdate to tannin external indicator	44
Iodoform from determination of acetone by reaction with iodine/alkali	Heated with conc. HCl, giving iodine	Titrated with thiosulphate	45
C_4 olefines, e.g. isobutylene	+ HCl + $BaCl_2$	Unused acid back titrated with alkali	46
Dinitrosopentamethylene tetramine in cyclotrimethylene trinitroamine	Boiled with dilute HCl, giving HCHO + NH_3	HCHO oxidized with H_2O_2 and NH_3 distilled into excess acid; back titrated with alkali	47

Materials titrated	Reagent and reaction conditions	Subsequent treatment and final titration stage	Ref.
Glucose; cellulose and other materials yielding glucose with acid	Boiled with 9% HCl + $FeCl_3$ (catalyst), giving CO_2	Absorbed in excess $Ba(OH)_2$ and back titrated with acid	48
—CH_2OH groups in formaldehyde resins	Distilled with HCl (also H_2SO_4 or H_3PO_4)	Distilled into $NaHSO_3$ and combined part determined iodometrically (see Bisulphite and sulphite, ref. 57)	49
Precipitate from determination of morphine by reaction with 2,4-dinitrochlorobenzene	+ excess HCl + NaCl, giving precipitate of morphine ether hydrochloride	Back titrated HCl in filtrate, using KOH, to methyl red	50
Methoxyl and ethoxyl groups in aromatic compounds	+ pyridine hydrochloride; 3–4 h/220° (more heating for ethoxyl)	Unused HCl titrated with NaOH to phenolphthalein or potentiometrically	51
Sulphanilamides	Refluxed with HCl	Aromatic aminosulphonic acid determined with excess bromine reagent (see Bromine reagents, ref. 224)	52
HCHO from fibres	+ HCl; 15 min/55–60°, then 1 h/110° in pressure bottle	HCHO determined with hydroxylamine (see Hydroxylamine, ref. 58)	53
Pentoses; pentosans	Distilled with 12, 18·5 or 24% HCl (tested the different reagents)	Furfuraldehyde determined with excess bromine	54
Mentholglucuronic acid	+ HCl; 50 min/*ca* 100°, giving glucuronic acid	Acid determined with excess ferricyanide and iodometric titration of the unused	55
Acetal; methylal	+ HCl; 1 h reflux	Aldehydes determined with alkali/excess iodine and titration of the unused (see Iodine reagents, ref. 225)	56
Iodoform; tetraiodopyrrole	+ HCl/HNO_3, 2:1. Boiled 3 min, giving I^-	AgI precipitated with $AgNO_3$/NH_4OH; precipitate dissolved in excess KCN and titrated with $AgNO_3$ to opalescence	57
a,*p*-Dimethylstyrene in presence of *p*-methylstyrene, styrene and *p*-cymene	In benzene; gaseous HCl passed in for 30 min, giving tertiary chloride	Excess HCl removed by air current, halide hydrolysed by adding 80% ethanol and HCl titrated with KOH/ethanol to methyl red	58

Materials titrated	Reagent and reaction conditions	Subsequent treatment and final titration stage	Ref.
Atropine alkaloids	+ HCl. Heated and partly evaporated, giving tropic acid	Acid extracted with $CHCl_3$/isopropanol, 3:1, extract evaporated and residue titrated with NaOH to phenolphthalein	59
Xylose	Refluxed with 12% HCl	Furfuraldehyde distilled and determined with alkali/iodine (see Iodine reagents, ref. 231)	60
Sulphapyridine	+ HCl; 30 min reflux, giving sulphanilic acid + α-aminopyridine hydrochloride	Evaporated to dryness and titrated with NaOH to phenolphthalein	61
Lead tetraethyl in gasoline	Shaken with cold HCl	Evaporated to dryness, organic matter oxidized with HNO_3 or $HClO_4$ and Pb(II) determined by precipitation with excess $Cr_2O_7^{2-}$ and iodometric titration of unused part in the filtrate	62
Sulphonamides of primary and secondary amines, from separation via Hinsberg (reaction with aromatic sulphonyl chlorides)	+ HCl; 75–100 h boiling, giving original amines	Made alkaline, amines extracted with benzene; benzene layer extracted with excess HCl and unused acid titrated potentiometrically with NaOH	63
Uronic acids	+ 19% HCl; 1·5–2 h/145°	CO_2 carried into excess NaOH, $BaCl_2$ added and back titrated with HCl to phenolphthalein	64
Colchicine	+ HCl; 50 min/*ca* 100°	+ excess alkali + iodine and unused iodine titrated with thiosulphate (see Iodine reagents, ref. 247)	65
Sucrose in chocolate	+ HCl; 30 min reflux, 'inverting' to glucose + fructose	Monosaccharides, determined with alkali/excess iodine (see Iodine reagents, ref. 248)	66
Pentosans in plant pulp	Distilled with 13·2% HCl	Furfuraldehyde determined with excess bromine and iodometric back titration (see Bromine reagents, ref. 253)	67

Materials titrated	Reagent and reaction conditions	Subsequent treatment and final titration stage	Ref.
Sulphasolucin (disodium salt of 1-phenyl-3-*p*-sulphamoylanilino-1,3-propanedisulphonic acid)	+ HCl in CO_2 atmosphere; 45 min boiling	Amine titrated with $NaNO_2$ to starch/I^- external indicator (see Part I, Nitrite, ref. 46)	68
Pentosans	+ *ca* 13% HCl + NaCl. Distilled *ca* 140 min	Furfuraldehyde determined with excess bromine (see Bromine reagents, ref. 265)	69
Epoxides	+ HCl/ether; 3 h/room temp.	+ ethanol and unused acid titrated with NaOH to phenolphthalein	70
Starch, isolated as iodine complex	+ dilute HCl; 2·5 h/*ca* 100°, giving glucose	Glucose determined with Cu(II) and iodometric titration of unused (see Copper (II), ref. 143)	71
Epoxides	+ HCl/dioxan (not entirely anhydrous); 10 min/room temp.	+ ethanol and unused HCl titrated with NaOH to phenolphthalein	72
Sucrose (submicro)	+ HCl; 10 min/69°, giving glucose + fructose	Monosaccharides determined with ferricyanide and iodometric titration of unused (see Ferricyanide, ref. 87)	73
Pentosans in cellulose	+ 12% HCl. *Ca* 75 min distillation	Furfuraldehyde determined bromometrically (see Bromine reagents, ref. 299)	74
α-Epoxides in poly-epoxides and -resins	+ pyridinium chloride/ pyridine; 20 min reflux	Unreacted HCl titrated with NaOH to phenolphthalein	75
Ethylene oxide	Passed into HCl/ saturated $MgCl_2$	Unused acid titrated with NaOH	76
Sulphonamides	Heated to 100–120° with HCl in a sealed tube, giving sulphanilic acid + amine hydrochloride	Reaction products separated on Amberlite IR-100, sulphanilic acid eluted and titrated with KOH potentiometrically	77
Long chain hydroxamic acids	+ ethanol + excess HCl; 2–4 h reflux	Back titrated with NaOH to pH 4	78
(in presence of hydroxamic acids of less than 10 carbon atoms)	+ ethanol + excess HCl; 2–4 h reflux	Titrated also to pH 8; difference equivalent to $NH_2OH.HCl$ formed	

Materials titrated	Reagent and reaction conditions	Subsequent treatment and final titration stage	Ref.
α-Epoxides in study of autoxidation	+ HCl/dioxan; 10–15 min/room temp.	+ ethanol and unused acid titrated with alkali	79
Ethylene oxide	+ $HCl/CaCl_2$ or $MgCl_2$	Back titrated with NaOH to methyl red	80
Uronic acids	+ 3·3N HCl; 5 h/110° in sealed tube	CO_2 diffused into $Ba(OH)_2$ and back titrated with HCl to phenolphthalein	81
Ethylene oxide in tetrachloroethane	+ dry HCl/dry ether; 3 h/room temp.	+ water/benzene or toluene and titrated with NaOH to phenolphthalein	82
Alkyl sulphates; aralkyl sulphonates	+ HCl, giving acids	Extracted with ether and titrated with NaOH to methyl red (corrected for HCl with $AgNO_3$)	83
Acetanilide	+ HCl(4N); 30 min reflux	+ ICl/HCl, giving triiodo-aniline; unused determined by adding I^- and titrating with thiosulphate (see Iodine chlorides, etc., ref. 73)	84
Isopropyl phenyl-carbamate	+ acid, e.g. conc. HCl, giving aniline	Titrated with nitrite to external starch/I^- (see Part I, Nitrite, ref. 73)	85
Isoniazid in presence of Ca *p*-aminosalicylate	+ HCl; 10–12 min reflux, giving hydrazine	+ $CHCl_3$ or CCl_4 and titrated with iodate to disappearance of iodine colour from organic layer	86
Thioethoxy group in a sugar diethyl mercaptal	Heated with HCl, giving ethyl mercaptan; 2 h in CO_2 stream	Passed into iodine/I^-/ ethanol and unused back titrated with thiosulphate	87
Tertiary alcohols	+ conc. HCl; 5 min shaking, giving tertiary chloride	Converted to thiouronium picrate and titrated with $HClO_4$ (see Thiourea, ref. 1; Nitro-phenols, ref. 55; and Part I, Perchloric acid, ref. 62)	88
Hg dimethyl mercaptide, from determination of methyl mercaptan by reaction with Hg(II)	+ HCl; 30 min/room temp.	Passed into excess iodine and back titrated with thiosulphate (see Iodine reagents, ref. 313)	89

Materials titrated	Reagent and reaction conditions	Subsequent treatment and final titration stage	Ref.
Dextrans	+ HCl (or H_2SO_4) N–4N acid; 50 min–3 h reflux in study of hydrolysis conditions	Glucose determined with Cu(II) reagent	90
Epoxides in fats	+ dry HCl/ether; 3 h/room temp.	+ 96% ethanol and unused acid titrated with NaOH to phenolphthalein	91
Lead tetraethyl in gasoline	+ conc. HCl; 30 min reflux; then + water and refluxed 5 min	Water layer eventually + $MgCl_2$ + NH_4OH and Pb^{2+} + Mg^{2+} titrated with EDTA to eriochrome black T	92
Phenacetin	+ dil. HCl; 90 min reflux	Made alkaline, amine extracted with $CHCl_3$ and titrated with $HClO_4$/dioxan potentiometrically (see Part I, Perchloric acid, ref. 97)	93
Alginic acid	+ 19% HCl in sealed tube; 10 h/110°	CO_2 passed into $Ba(OH)_2$ and back titrated with acid potentiometrically	94
Naphthenates of Ca, Pb, Zn and Co	+ HCl, giving precipitate of organic acid	Filtered and metal cation titrated with EDTA to eriochrome black T or murexide	95
Epoxides in superheated fats	+ trimethylamine hydrochloride/acetic acid; 36 h/room temp.	Unused HCl determined with excess Ag(I) and back titration with SCN^-	96
Unsaturated amines	+ HCl/ethanol/$CHCl_3$, yielding salts	Iodine number then determined by halogen addition (the amine group is substituted by halogen but H atoms on the substituted ammonium cations are not)	97
Polysaccharides in woody tissues	+ HCl; 3 h reflux	Reducing sugars determined with Cu(II) reagent, the Cu_2O dissolved in Fe(III) and the Fe(II) formed titrated with MnO_4^-	98
Nitriles; amides	+ 50% HCl; 1 h reflux	Made alkaline and the NH_3 distilled into excess acid; final back titration with NaOH to methyl red	99

Materials titrated	Reagent and reaction conditions	Subsequent treatment and final titration stage	Ref.
Di- + trialkyl phosphites	In ethanol, + excess HCl; 10 min/room temp., hydrolysing tri- to diester	+ excess NaOH (hydrolysing di- to monoester) and back titrated with HCl to phenolphthalein (sum of both esters is equivalent to alkali used)	100
Ethyl *p*-aminobenzoate	+ conc. HCl at 0°, giving the aminobenzoic acid	Titrated with nitrite at 0° to external I^-/starch (see Part I, Nitrite, ref. 90)	101
Zn derivative of mercaptobenzothiazole	+ HCl, giving the free mercaptan	Titrated with $AgNO_3$ conductometrically, or with iodine to a visual end-point (see Part I, Silver (I), ref. 101)	102
End —NH_2 groups of polycaprolactam (precipitated from solution in phenol by 96% ethanol)	+ excess HCl/KCl; 10–20 min/room temp.	Filtered and unused acid titrated with NaOH	103
Unreacted —NCO groups in polyurethane resins and coatings	In cyclohexanone, + excess HCl + some quinhydrone	Unused acid titrated potentiometrically with HCl	104
Epoxides	+ HCl/dimethylformamide; 30 min/98°. Control	+ water/acetone + HNO_3 and titrated with $AgNO_3$ potentiometrically	105
Epoxides, e.g. epichlorohydrin or phenylglycidol	+ HCl/CCl_4/isopropyl ether; 6 h/room temp.	Unused acid titrated with Na acetate/acetic acid to methyl violet	106
Some organic mercury compounds, e.g. phenyl mercuric acetate, Na ethylmercurithiosalicylate, Hg salicylate	Heated with HCl or HCl/HNO_3	Hg(II) titrated with EDTA	107
Secondary, tertiary alcohols (principally for identification)	+ conc. $HCl/ZnCl_2$, giving chlorides	Dissolved in ethanol, + thiourea/I^-, giving alkylthiouronium iodides; + 3·5-dinitrobenzoate, giving precipitate of alkylthiouronium dinitrobenzoates, determined by titration with excess Ti(III) (see Thiourea, ref. 2; Carboxylic acid and carboxylates, ref. 29; Titanium (III), ref. 51)	108

Materials titrated	Reagent and reaction conditions	Subsequent treatment and final titration stage	Ref.
Oxetanes $>C<^{CH_2}_{CH_2}>O$	+ HCl/dry pyridine; 3 h reflux or 30 min/ 170° in sealed vessel	Unused acid titrated with aqueous alkali to phenolphthalein	109
Methoxyethyl mercuric chloride	Refluxed with HCl/ HNO_3	+ NH_4OH + excess KCN + I^- indicator and titrated with $AgNO_3$ to opalescence	110
Lead tetraethyl in gasoline	+ conc. HCl; 30 min reflux	Pb(II) precipitated as sulphate, dissolved in tartrate and after addition of Mg(II), titrated with EDTA (cf. ref. 92)	111
Aryloxysilanes with *tert*-butoxy groups	+ HCl; 30 min reflux	Phenol determined with excess bromate/bromide and iodometric back titration of unused (see Bromine reagents, ref. 438)	112
α-Epoxides	+ HCl/dioxan; 15 min/room temp.	+ dil. HNO_3 and unused HCl determined with excess $AgNO_3$ with final back titration with SCN^-	113
Ethylene oxide	Methods of refs 13 and 22		114
Uronic acids	+ 19% HCl; at least 2·5 h boiling	CO_2 absorbed in alkali and back titrated with acid	115
Tertiary butanol	+ conc. HCl; 2·5 min/50°	Cooled, + CCl_4, shaken and back titrated with NaOH to methyl orange	116
4-Hydroxy-3-acetamidophenylarsinate	+ HCl; 30 min reflux	Amine titrated with $NaNO_2$ potentiometrically (see Part I, Nitrite, ref. 108)	117
1-Propyl-*N*-(3-chlorophenyl) carbamate	Boiled with HCl, yielding *p*-chloroaniline	+ KBr and titrated with nitrite (see Part I, Nitrite, ref. 106)	118
Cyclohexanone oxime	Refluxed with HCl, giving hydroxylamine	Cyclohexanone distilled out with steam and hydroxylamine in residue determined by reaction with excess Fe(III) and back titration with MnO_4^-	119

Materials titrated	Reagent and reaction conditions	Subsequent treatment and final titration stage	Ref.
Chloramphenicol and its palmitate	Amide link hydrolysed by heating with HCl	Evaporated to dryness, amine hydrochloride dissolved in acetic acid, Hg acetate added and titrated with $HClO_4$ to crystal violet (see Part I, Perchloric acid, ref. 221)	120
Polyamides	+ conc. HCl. Heated, hydrolysing to carboxylic acid and amine hydrochloride	Passed through Wofatite ion exchanger and total acid eluted titrated with KOH to phenolphthalein; or + HCHO and titrated with alkali	121
Phenacetin	+ HCl; 60–90 min reflux	Titrated with nitrite potentiometrically (see Part I, Nitrite, ref. 120)	122
α-Epoxides in oils and fats	In isopropanol or chlorobenzene, + collidine hydrochloride/isopropanol; 1 h reflux	+ water + HNO_3 to give pH 3 to 5; unused HCl titrated with $AgNO_3$ to congo red/dextrine (rose → blue grey)	123
Uronic acids	+ $HCl/ZnCl_2$. Heated to 160° in nitrogen current	CO_2 passed into $Ba(OH)_2$ and unused titrated with HCl to high frequency end-point	124
Meprobamate	+ conc. HCl; 45 min reflux, then evaporated nearly to dryness, giving ammonium chloride	+ acetic acid + Hg acetate and titrated with $HClO_4$/acetic acid to crystal violet	125
N,*N'*-Bis-(*N*-methylquinolinylurea)methyl sulphate ('Acaprin')	+ 25% HCl; 6 h reflux	Titrated potentiometrically with $NaNO_2$ (see Part I, Nitrite, ref. 127)	126
Some sulphonamides	+ ethylene glycol + conc. HCl; 30 min/120–130°	+ NaOH, NH_3 distilled into excess HCl and back titrated with NaOH to methyl red	127
Saccharose	+ 10% HCl; 30 min/*ca* 100°	Glucose determined with Cu(II) reagent (Cu_2O formed added to Fe(III) reagent and the Fe(II) titrated with MnO_4^-) (see Copper (II), ref. 206)	128
p-Hydroxyacetanilide	In aqueous solution + HCl; 90 min reflux	+ more HCl + KBr and titrated with nitrite potentiometrically (see Part I, Nitrite, ref. 143)	129

Materials titrated	Reagent and reaction conditions	Subsequent treatment and final titration stage	Ref.
Lead tetraethyl in gasoline	+ conc. HCl + $KClO_3$, giving inorganic Pb(II)	+ water; aqueous layer + NH_4OH/NH_4Cl buffer and titrated with EDTA to eriochrome black T	130
1-Imino-2-cyano-cyclopentane in adiponitrile	In isopropanol/water, + excess HCl	Back titrated with NaOH to bromothymol blue	131
ε-Caprolactam	+ excess HCl; 4 h reflux, giving hexanoic acid	Back titrated with NaOH potentiometrically; 2 inflections, the interval between which gave the hexanoic acid	132
Starch in bandages	+ dilute HCl; 90 min reflux, giving glucose	Neutralized and glucose determined with Cu(II) excess, titrating the unused reagent iodometrically (see Copper (II), ref. 211)	133
5-Nitro-2-furfuraldehyde semicarbazone ('Nitrofurazone')	+ HCl/acetic acid/water, *ca* 1:1:1; heated to 70–80°, giving furfuraldehyde, CO_2, NH_4Cl and hydrazine hydrochloride	Hydrazine titrated with chloramine T to methyl red/methylene blue	134
Sugar in silages and forages	+ dilute HCl; left overnight, giving reducing monosaccharides	Determined with excess Cu(II) reagent and iodometric titration of the unused (see Copper (II), ref. 212)	135
Ethylene oxide in gas mixtures	+ HCl + saturated $MgCl_2$ + wetting agent (nonylphenolpolyethyleneglycol); several minutes shaking	Back titrated with alkali	136
Amide content of gelatine	+ 2N HCl; 1 h boiling giving ammonia	+ NaOH to bring to pH 5·2; NH_3 distilled into boric acid and titrated with HCl	137
Al alkoxides, $Al(OR)_3$	In absolute ethanol, + dilute HCl and brought to boil, giving Al(III)	+ excess EDTA + pyridine and back titrated with Cu(II) to pyrocatechol violet	138
Epoxide groups in epoxide resins	In butanone + HCl/butanone; 5–30 min/room temp.	+ water and back titrated with NaOH to cresol red	139

Materials titrated	Reagent and reaction conditions	Subsequent treatment and final titration stage	Ref.
N-Carboxyamino acid anhydrides	+ HCl or H_2SO_4, breaking the ring with CO_2 evolution	CO_2 carried with nitrogen into benzylamine/dioxan/ethanol; titrated with $NaOCH_3$ to thymol blue	140
Alkyl magnesium halides	In ether, + dilute HCl	Ether evaporated, brought to pH 10 with NH_4OH/NH_4Cl and titrated Mg(II) with EDTA to eriochrome black T	141
Tertiary amylenes (2-methyl-1-butene and 2-methyl-2-butene) in mixtures of amylenes	+ conc. HCl; 6 h/room temp., giving tertiary chlorides	Reaction product + excess KOH/alcohol; heated *ca* 90 min/100° and back titrated with HCl to phenolphthalein	142
Ethylene oxide in presence of Fe(III) salts and methacrylic acid	+ HCl/ethanol/water; 45 min/room temp.	Back titrated with Na acetate	143
Organic mercury compounds	Heated with conc. HCl giving inorganic Hg(II)	Brought to pH 6 with acetate and Hg(II) coulometrically titrated with thioglycollate	144
Isonicotinoyl hydrazones	+ conc. HCl/acetic acid; 15 min heating, giving carbonyl compound + isonicotinic acid hydrazide	Hydrazide titrated with nitrite potentiometrically or to starch/iodide	145
Acetanilide, phenacetin	Hydrolysed with HCl; 30–40 min	+ Br^- and liberated amine titrated potentiometrically with nitrite	146
Disodium alkenylsuccinates (surface active agents)	In acetone + excess HCl	Back titrated with alkali/alcohol potentiometrically, giving inflections first for unreacted HCl then for the organic acid	147
Epichlorohydrin	In dioxan, + HCl; 1 h/room temp.	Titrated unused with NaOH to phenolphthalein	148
Epoxy groups in modified resins	+ HCl/dioxan; 15 min/room temp.	Excess Cl^- titrated with $Hg(NO_3)_2$/methanol to diphenylcarbazone	149
Aminoalkyl esters, e.g. $(C_6H_5)_2CHCOOCH_2$-$CH_2N(C_6H_5)_2$ (as hydrochloride)	+ HCl; 30 min up to 2 h reflux	Amino alcohol product ultimately distilled out and titrated	150

References

1. Pum, G., *Monatsh.* **12**, 438 (1891).
2. Cormack, W., *J. Chem. Soc.* **77**, 990 (1900).
3. Jolles, A., *Ber.* **39**, 96 (1906); *Z. anal. Chem.* **45**, 196 (1906).
4. Orton, K. J. P. and McKie, P. V., *J. Chem. Soc.* **109**, 184 (1916).
5. Nanji, D. R., *Biochem. J.* **17**, 761 (1923).
6. Ferreri, G., *Giorn. chim. ind. applicata* **7**, 625 (1925).
7. Hirschkind, W., *Eng. Mining J-Press* **119**, 908 (1925).
8. Grün, A. and Limpacher, R., *Ber.* **59**, 695 (1926).
9. Lerrigo, A. F. and Williams, A. L., *Analyst* **52**, 377 (1927).
10. Haendel, M., *Rev. asoc. med. Argent.* **42**, 215 (1929).
11. Hobson, R. P., *J. Chem. Soc.* 1384 (1929).
12. Kullgren, C. and Tydén, H., *Ing. Vetenskaps Akad. Handl.* No. 94, 3 (1929).
13. Deckert, W., *Z. anal. Chem.* **82**, 297 (1930).
14. Deshpande, D. D., *J. Indian Inst. Sci.* **13A**, 110 (1930).
15. Dickson, A. D., Otterson, H. and Link, K. P., *J. Am. Chem. Soc.* **52**, 775 (1930).
16. Nicolet, B. H. and Poulter, T. C., *J. Am. Chem. Soc.* **52**, 1186 (1930).
17. Grimshaw, A. H., *Textile World* **79**, 1212, 1245 (1931).
18. Malhotra, R. C., *J. Indian Chem. Soc.* **8**, 51 (1931).
19. Malhotra, R. C., *Ind. Eng. Chem., Anal. Ed.* **3**, 161 (1931).
20. Noll, A. and Belz, W., *Papier-Fabr.* **29**, Tech. Wiss. Teil 33 (1931).
21. Buston, H. W., *Analyst* **57**, 220 (1932).
22. Lubatti, O. F., *J. Soc. Chem. Ind.* (*London*) **51**, 361T (1932).
23. Rozenberger, N. A., Rebinovich, R. V. and Frenkel, K. Ya., *Trans. All-Union Sci. Research Inst. Paper Cellulose* No. 1, 109 (1932).
24. Abribat, *Ann. chim. anal. chim. appl.* **15**, 147 (1933).
25. Iddles, H. A. and Robbins, P. J., *Ind. Eng. Chem., Anal. Ed.* **5**, 55 (1933).
26. Phillips, M., Goss, M. J. and Browne, C. A., *J. Assoc. Off. Agr. Chem.* **16**, 289 (1933).
27. Sadikov, V. S. and Belikova, K. S., *Schriften zentral biochem. Forsch.-Inst. Nahr.-Genussm. Ind.* (*USSR*) **3**, 299 (1933).
28. Vaisman, G., *Farm. Zhur.* **3**, 109 (1933).
29. Burkhart, B., Baur, L. and Link, K. P., *J. Biol. Chem.* **104**, 171 (1934).
30. Krishnan, T. S., *J. Indian Chem. Soc.* **11**, 651 (1934).
31. Oshmyan, G., *Brodilnaya Prom.* **11**, No. 5, 26 (1934).
32. Minatoya, S. and Nagai, I., *J. Soc. Rubber Ind., Japan* **7**, 337 (1934).
33. Biffen, F. M. and Snell, F. D., *Ind. Eng. Chem., Anal. Ed.* **7**, 234 (1935).
34. Fock, W. H., *Kunstseide* **17**, 117 (1935).
35. Brown, W. B., *J. Soc. Chem. Ind.* (*London*) **55**, 321T (1936).
36. Fedorov, B. P. and Spryskov, A. A., *Org. Chem. Ind.* (*USSR*) **1**, 620, (1936).

37. Harlay, V., *J. pharm. chim.* **23**, 199 (1936).
38. Litvak, I. M., *Sovet Sakhor* **14**, No. 11, 40 (1936).
39. Strepkov, S. M., *Biochem. Z.* **289**, 38 (1936).
40. Deckert, W., *Z. anal. Chem.* **109**, 166 (1937).
41. Kerckow, F. W., *Z. anal. Chem.* **108**, 249 (1937).
42. Khaletskii, A. M. and Mikryukova, N. S., *Farmatsiya i Farmakol., SSSR*, No. 8, 21 (1937).
43. Litvak, I., *Spirto-Vodochn. Prom.* **15**, No. 2, 7 (1938).
44. Calingaert, G. and Gambrill, C. M., *Ind. Eng. Chem., Anal. Ed.* **11**, 324 (1939).
45. Dulian, F., *Klin. Wochschr.* **18**, 1224 (1939).
46. Stern, G., *Reichsamt. Wirtschaftsausbau Prüf*, Nr. 43 (PB 52003) 15 (1940).
47. Bellini, L., *Ann. chim. applicata* **31**, 125 (1941).
48. Nickerson, R. F., *Ind. Eng. Chem., Anal. Ed.* **13**, 423 (1941).
49. Nitschmann, H. and Hadorn, H., *Helv. Chim. Acta* **24**, 237 (1941).
50. Mannich, C., *Arch. Pharm.* **280**, 386 (1942).
51. Prey, V., *Ber.* **75**, 350, 445 (1942).
52. Wells, E. H., *J. Assoc. Off. Agr. Chem.* **25**, 747 (1942).
53. Weltzien, W., *Zellwolle, Kunstseide, Seide* **47**, 197 (1942).
54. Duncan, F. J., *Ind. Eng. Chem., Anal. Ed.* **15**, 162 (1943).
55. Shimosawa, T., *J. Pharm. Soc. Japan* **63**, 462 (1943).
56. Zeidler, G. and Pogranitzky, N., *Lack- u. Farbenztg.* 140 (1943).
57. Douris, R. G., *Ann. pharm. franc.* **2**, 56 (1944).
58. Elliott, J. H. and Cook, E. V., *Ind. Eng. Chem., Anal. Ed.* **16**, 20 (1944).
59. Reimers, F., *Dansk Tids Farm.* **18**, 217 (1944).
60. Rogers, H. R., *Ind. Eng. Chem., Anal. Ed.* **16**, 319 (1944).
61. Khromov-Borisov, N. V., *Farmatsiya* **8**, No. 6, 31 (1945).
62. Lykken, L., Treseder, R. S., Tuemmler, F. D. and Zahn, V., *Ind. Eng. Chem., Anal. Ed.* **17**, 353 (1945).
63. Seaman, W., Norton, A. R., Woods, J. T. and Bank, H. N., *J. Am. Chem. Soc.* **67**, 1571 (1945).
64. McCready, R. M., Swenson, H. A. and Maclay, W. D., *Ind. Eng. Chem., Anal. Ed.* **18**, 290 (1946).
65. Uffelie, O. E., *Pharm. Weekblad* **81**, 426 (1946).
66. Vaeck, S. V., *Mededeel Vlaam. Chem. Ver.* **8**, 179 (1946).
67. Brissaud, L., *Mém. services chim. état (Paris)* **33**, 75 (1947).
68. Chapman, A. M. and Pierce, J. S., *Pharm. J.* **159**, 47 (1947).
69. Savard, J., Leclercq, A. and Reygrobellet, J., *Agron. trop.* **2**, 170 (1947).
70. Swern, D., Findley, T. W., Billen, G. N. and Scanlan, J. T., *Anal. Chem.* **19**, 414 (1947).
71. Pucher, G. W., Leavenworth, C. S. and Vickery, H. B., *Anal. Chem.* **20**, 850 (1948).
72. King, G., *Nature* **164**, 706 (1949).

73. Stern, H. and Kirk, P. L., *J. Biol. Chem.* **177**, 37 (1949).
74. Teunissen, P. H., *Anal. Chem.* **21**, 620 (1949).
75. Bradley, T. F., *U.S. Patent No.* 2,500,600, March 14, 1950.
76. El Khishen, S. A., *J. Sci. Food Agr.* **1**, 71 (1950).
77. Jindra, A. and Šipoš, F., *Chem. Listy* **44**, 235 (1950).
78. Roe, E. T. and Swern, D., *Anal. Chem.* **22**, 1160 (1950).
79. King, G., *J. Chem. Soc.* 1980 (1951).
80. Miller, S. A. and Williams, N. E., *Analyst* **76**, 224 (1951).
81. Ogston, A. G. and Stanier, J. E., *Biochem. J.* **49**, 591 (1951).
82. Tomisek, A. J. and Mahler, H. R., *J. Am. Chem. Soc.* **73**, 4685 (1951).
83. Etienne, H., *Ind. chim. belge* **17**, 373 (1952).
84. Gengrinovich, A. I. and Kadyrov, Ya. K., *Aptechnoe Delo* **1**, 46 (1952).
85. Baskakov, Yu. A. and Mel'nikov, N. N., *Zhur. Anal. Khim.* **8**, 119 (1953).
86. Biffoli, R., *Boll. lab. chim. prov.* (*Bologna*) **4**, 83 (1953).
87. Hirase, S. and Araki, C., *Bull. Chem. Soc. Japan* **28**, 481 (1953).
88. Schotte, L. and Veibel, S., *Acta Chem. Scand.* **7**, 1357 (1953).
89. Segal, W. and Starkey, R. L., *Anal. Chem.* **25**, 1645 (1953).
90. Dimler, R. J., Davis, H. A., Gill, G. J. and Rist, C. E., *Anal. Chem.* **26**, 1142 (1954).
91. Drozdov, N. S. and Materanskaya, N. P., *Myasnaya Ind. SSSR* **25**, No. 3, 50 (1954).
92. Milner, O. I. and Shipman, G. F., *Anal. Chem.* **26**, 1222 (1954).
93. Wollish, E. G., Colarusso, R. J., Pifer, C. W. and Schmall, M., *Anal. Chem.* **26**, 1753 (1954).
94. Jensen, A. and Sunde, I., *2nd Intern. Seaweed Symposium*, Trondheim 125 (1955).
95. Leggieri, G., *Chimica* (*Milan*) **10**, 287 (1955).
96. Seelkopf, C., *Fette, Seife, Anstrichsmittel* **57**, 111 (1955).
97. Smirnov, O. K. and Bezhentseva, V. M., *Zavodskaya Lab.* **21**, 414 (1955).
98. Treccani, C. P. and Tentorio, G., *Ann. sper. agrar.* (*Roma*) **9**, No. 6, Suppl. 27 (1955).
99. Andrade, J. L., et al., *Rev. sanidad y asistencia social* (*Venezuela*), **21**, 231 (1956).
100. Bernhart, D. N. and Rattenbury, K. H., *Anal. Chem.* **28**, 1765 (1956).
101. Kleflin, Z. and Šumanović, K., *Acta Pharm. Jugoslav.* **6**, 191 (1956).
102. Lorenz, O. and Echte, E., *Kautschuk u. Gummi* **9**, WT 300 (1956).
103. Myagkov, V. A. and Pakshver, A. B., *Zhur. Priklad Khim.* (*J. Appl. Chem. USSR*) **29**, 1703 (1956).
104. Navyazhskaya, F. A., *Khim. Prom.* 432 (1956).
105. Shechter, L., Wynstra, J. and Kurkjy, R. P., *Ind. Eng. Chem.* **48**, 94 (1956).
106. Hennart, C. and Merlin, E., *Chim. anal.* **39**, 269 (1957).
107. Iritani, N. and Tanaka, T., *J. Pharm, Soc. Japan* **77**, 106 (1957).

108. Jureček, M., Chládek, O., Chládková, R., Souček, M. and Srpová, B., *Chem. Listy* **51**, 448 (1957).
109. Keen, R. T., *Anal. Chem.* **29**, 1041 (1957).
110. Laubie, H., *Bull. soc. pharm. Bordeaux* **96**, 65 (1957).
111. Russ, J. J. and Reeder, W., *Anal. Chem.* **29**, 1331 (1957).
112. Smith, B., *Acta Chem. Scand.* **11**, 558 (1957).
113. Stenmark, G. A., *Anal. Chem.* **29**, 1367 (1957).
114. Afanas'eva, L. G., Rabovskaya, N. S. and Etlis, V. S., *Trudy Khim. i Khim Tekhnol.* **1**, 611 (1958).
115. Anderson, D. M. W., *Talanta* **1**, 283 (1958).
116. Ashworth, M. R. F., *Ann. Univ. Saraviensis, Nat. Sci.* **7** (2) 98 (1958).
117. Blažek, J., *Pharmazie* **13**, 529 (1958).
118. Baskakov, Yu. A. and Mel'nikov, N. N., *Org. Insektofungitsidy i Gerbitsidy* 279 (1958).
119. Goszczyński, S., *Chem. Anal.* (*Warsaw*) **3**, 117 (1958).
120. Salvesen, B., *Medd. Norsk Farm. Selskap* **20**, 65 (1958).
121. Schröder, E., *Plaste u. Kautschuk* **5**, 49, 101 (1958).
122. Baldinus, J. G. and Rothberg, I., *J. Am. Pharm. Assoc., Sci. Ed.* **48**, 318 (1959).
123. Krull, L., *Farben-Chemiker* **61**, 23 (1959).
124. Mozheiko, L. N. and Yaunzems, V., *Gidrolizi Lesokhim. Prom.* **12**, No. 3, 7 (1959).
125. Salvesen, B. and Solli, O., *Medd. Norsk Farm. Selskap* **21**, 85 (1959).
126. Špinková, V. and Zýka, J., *Českoslov. Farm.* **8**, 551 (1959).
127. Simionovici, R. and Conu, I., *Rev. chim.* (*Bucharest*) **10**, 107 (1959).
128. Ablov, A. V. and Batyr, D. G., *Zhur. Anal. Khim.* **15**, 112 (1960).
129. Aftalion, H., Keim, N. and Sterescu, M., *Rev. chim.* (*Bucharest*) **11**, 49 (1960).
130. Blumenthal, A., *Mitt. Geb. Lebensm. u. Hyg.* **51**, 159 (1960).
131. Kalugin, A. A., Perepletchikova, E. M., Zil'berman, E. N., Vodzinskii, Yu. V. and Kulikov, A. E., *Zhur. Anal. Khim.* **15**, 739 (1960).
132. Márkus, L. and Kayser, A., *Magyar Kem. Lapya* **15**, 86 (1960).
133. Šimková, A. and Haller, A., *Pharm. Zentralhalle* **99**, 113 (1960).
134. Spacu, P. and Teodorescu, G., *Z. anal. Chem.* **174**, 321 (1960).
135. Wiseman, H. G., Mallack, J. C. and Jacobson, W. C., *J. Agr. Food Chem.* **8**, 78 (1960).
136. Blouri, B. and Rafi, M., *Bull. soc. chim. France* 1170 (1961).
137. Eastoe, J. E., Long, J. E. and Willan, A. L. D., *Biochem. J.* **78**, 51 (1961).
138. Hennart, C., *Chim. anal.* **43**, 283 (1961).
139. Jung, G. and Kleeberg, W., *Kunststoffe* **51**, 714 (1961).
140. Patchornik, A. and Shalitin, Y., *Anal. Chem.* **33**, 1887 (1961).
141. Hennart, C., *Chim. anal.* **44**, 7 (1962).
142. Karpov, O. N., *Zhur. Anal. Khim.* **17**, 1029 (1962).

143. Khudyakova, T. A., Nemtseva, L. I. and Balandina, M. A., *Zhur. Priklad Khim.* **35**, 824 (1962).
144. Merkle, A. A. and Discher, C. A., *J. Pharm. Sci.* **51**, 117 (1962).
145. Nin'o, N., *Farmatsiya (Sofia)* **12**, No. 2, 27 (1962).
146. Dzottsoti, S. Kh., *Azerb. Khim. Zh.* No. 1, 143 (1962).
147. Malyshev, A. I. and Smirnov, O. K., *Zavodskaya Lab.* **29**, 1173 (1963).
148. Nikitin, V. M. and Skachkov, V. M., *Zavodskaya Lab.* **29**, 1309 (1963).
149. Vorobjov, V., *Chem. Pr˚mysl* **13**, 381 (1963).
150. Mikhailova, T. A. and Khromov-Borisova, N. V., *Zhur. Anal. Khim.* **19**, 648 (1964).

46. Hydrofluoric acid

This reagent has been used to convert organophosphorus chloridates into the corresponding fluoridates, which can then be determined with alkaline hydrogen peroxide:

$$R{-}\overset{\overset{\displaystyle O}{\|}}{\underset{\underset{\displaystyle OR'}{|}}{P}}{-}Cl + HF \rightarrow R{-}\overset{\overset{\displaystyle O}{\|}}{\underset{\underset{\displaystyle OR'}{|}}{P}}{-}F + HCl$$

Example

Material titrated	Reagent and reaction conditions	Subsequent treatment and final filtration stage
Organophosphorus chloridates	+ 5% HF/ethyl acetate; 30 min/room temp.	Added to isopropanol and the fluoridate determined by oxidation with H_2O_2/alkali (see Hydrogen peroxide, ref. 44)

Reference

Sass, S., Master, I., Davis, P. M. and Beitsch, N., *Anal. Chem.* **32**, 285 (1960).

47. Hydrogen gas

This reagent has been applied principally to determine unsaturated compounds (olefines, acetylenes) or certain reducible compounds (e.g.

nitro, nitroso or azo compounds). The procedure adopted has almost always been gas-volumetric, in which the consumption of hydrogen gas was measured by the change of its volume at constant pressure or of its pressure at constant volume.

In Part I of this book, examples have been given of direct, coulometric titration with hydrogen gas. There appear to be few methods of indirect titration and only six examples are given below. In five of these, a titratable product was formed by reaction with hydrogen of the component to be determined in the sample. In the remaining example (ref. 2), a potentially interfering component was removed by hydrogenation, so that the unattacked component in the sample could be subsequently titrated.

Examples

Materials titrated	Reagent and reaction conditions	Subsequent treatment and final titration stage	Ref.
DDT spray deposits (extracted with acetone or benzene)	Burnt in hydrogen or coal gas, giving HCl + chlorine	Reaction products absorbed in alkali/arsenite mixture, converting all halogen to Cl^-; + HNO_3 + excess $AgNO_3$ and back titrated with SCN^-	1
Mixtures of acetals and vinyl ethers	Latter reduced to ethyl ethers with hydrogen in presence of PtO (Adams catalyst); 30 min to 2 h	Unreacted acetal then determined by hydrolysis with H_2SO_4 to aldehyde, then in turn determined with sulphite/excess acid (see Sulphuric acid, ref. 64; and Bisulphite and sulphite, ref. 84)	2
Chloropicrin in gassed grain	Passed with hydrogen over Ni, giving NH_3	NH_3 absorbed in excess acid and back titrated with Na_2CO_3	3
Phenazine; benzophenazine	Reduced to the dihydroderivatives with hydrogen in presence of Pd/carbon	Filtered in nitrogen atmosphere into a conductivity cell and titrated with $Cr_2O_7^{2-}$/acetic acid to a 'high frequency' end-point (see Part I, Bichromate and chromic oxide, ref. 23)	4
Carbobenzyloxy groups, ($C_6H_5CH_2O.CO-$) in amino acids	Hydrogenated in ethanol in presence of 5% Pd/carbon, giving CO_2	CO_2 carried by hydrogen current into solvent mixture of benzylamine/dioxan/ethanol and titrated with $NaOCH_3$ to thymol blue	5

Materials titrated	Reagent and reaction conditions	Subsequent treatment and final titration stage	Ref.
Nitriles, e.g. acetonitrile, benzonitrile, adiponitrile, succinonitrile	In acetic acid + Pd or Pt catalyst + sample; 1–2 h, giving primary amine	Titrated with $HClO_4$/acetic acid or dioxan to crystal violet, α-naphtholbenzein or quinaldine red	6

References

1. Fahey, J. E., *J. Assoc. Off. Agr. Chem.* **28**, 152 (1945).
2. Siggia, S., *Anal. Chem.* **19**, 1025 (1947).
3. Zakharenko, G. A. and Vodaturskii, G. A., *Trudy Odessk. Tekhnol. Inst.* No. 5, 46 (1955).
4. Riolo, C. B. and Marcon, E., *Ann. chim. (Rome)* **46**, 1121 (1956).
5. Patchornik, A. and Shalitin, Y., *Anal. Chem.* **33**, 1887 (1961).
6. Huber, W., *Z. Anal. Chem.* **197**, 236 (1963).

48. Hydrogen peroxide

Reagent. Aqueous solutions, mostly of fairly high concentration, have been used.

Reactions and materials titrated. 1. Oxidation, according to the equation,

$$H_2O_2 \rightarrow H_2O + O$$

is the reaction on which most determinations have been based. The principal substance classes thus determined are: aldehydes, especially HCHO; dicarbonyl compounds; sulphur-containing compounds like methionine, thiourea and mercaptans; fatty acids; some organic arsenic-containing compounds; and certain halides. (H_2O_2 has then been a component of the reaction mixture and it is sometimes not clear if it has functioned as an oxidizing agent to destroy organic matter or hydrohalic acids, or as a reducing agent to convert hypohalites to halides.)

$$RCHO + H_2O_2 \rightarrow RCOOH + H_2O$$

$$RCO.COR' + H_2O_2 \rightarrow RCOOH + R'COOH$$

$$RS.CH_3 + H_2O_2 \rightarrow \underset{\displaystyle \overset{\downarrow}{O}}{RS.CH_3} + H_2O$$

$$CS(NH_2)_2 + 4\,H_2O_2 \rightarrow CO(NH_2)_2 + SO_3 + 4\,H_2O$$

$$\overset{|}{\underset{|}{RP}}\text{—}F \xrightarrow{H_2O_2} \overset{|}{\underset{|}{RP}}\text{—}OOH \xrightarrow{H_2O_2} \overset{|}{\underset{|}{RP}}\text{—}O^- + O_2 + H_2O + H^+$$

2. Hydrolysis, effectively, in determination of nitriles. The overall equation may be written:

$$RCN + 2\,H_2O_2 + OH^- \rightarrow RCOO^- + NH_3 + O_2 + H_2O$$

Reaction conditions. Many reactions, notably those involving carbonyl compounds and nitriles, have been carried out in alkaline aqueous medium.

Subsequent treatment and final titration stage. (i) In a limited number of cases (three are given) unused reagent has been determined by adding I^- (and acid if necessary) and titrating the liberated iodine with thiosulphate. Recently (ref. 51), unused H_2O_2 was directly titrated with Ce(IV).

(ii) The acid formed from reaction of carbonyl compounds and nitriles has been determined with alkali. In practice, as already mentioned, reaction has been carried out in alkaline solution. The unused alkali was then back titrated with acid in almost all instances. (In one example quoted, the solution was acidified and the acid—benzoic acid—distilled out and titrated with alkali.)

(iii) Halide ion from determination of halides, has generally been titrated with a silver (I) reagent, but in one case given here, Br^- was oxidized with OCl^- to bromate, then determined iodometrically.

(iv) Acetone from determination of some fatty acids, has been determined after distillation out of the reaction mixture, by the usual method with alkali/excess iodine.

(v) NH_3 from acrylonitrile and urea, derived from determination of thiourea, has been titrated as the final stage by distillation into excess acid and back titration with alkali.

(vi) Sulphate from oxidation of sulphur-containing compounds has been titrated with Ba(II).

(vii) There are several examples in which unreacted components of the original sample, after removal of potentially interfering compounds with the H_2O_2 reagent, have been determined by some titrimetric procedure.

Examples

Materials titrated	Reagent and reaction conditions	Subsequent treatment and final titration stage	Ref.
HCHO	+ excess alkali; H_2O_2 added slowly. Usually 2–3 min/room temp., but up to 10 min with dilute solutions	Titrated with H_2SO_4 to litmus	1
HCHO	As in method of ref. 1, but H_2O_2 added immediately after the addition of alkali		2
HCHO	Method of ref. 1		3
Solutions of HCHO	+ $NaOH/H_2O_2$. Several hours (overnight)/room temp.	Titrated with acid to litmus	4
HCHO	Alkali/H_2O_2 method compared with other methods		5
HCHO in paraformaldehyde	+ NaOH + H_2O_2 (neutralized to litmus); 5 min/*ca* 85°	Titrated with acid to the litmus	6
HCHO	+ NaOH + H_2O_2; 1 h/room temp.	Titrated with acid to litmus	7
Glyoxal; methylglyoxal	+ slight excess NaOH + H_2O_2; A few min/room temp.	Titrated with acid to phenolphthalein	8
Pyramidone/antipyrine mixtures	Aqueous solution, + H_2O_2. Heated, converting pyramidone to products which yield no picrate	Antipyrine determined by precipitation with excess picric acid (see Nitrophenols, ref. 19)	9
Butyric acid	+ H_2O_2/H_2SO_4/Fe(III) catalyst, giving acetone	Acetone determined with alkali/excess iodine (see Iodine reagents, ref. 140)	10
HCHO from *N*-hydroxymethylcarbazole, formed in determination of carbazole by reaction with HCHO	+ NaOH + H_2O_2	Titrated with H_2SO_4	11
Isobutyric acid	Distilled with H_2O_2, giving acetone	Acetone determined iodometrically (see Iodine reagents, ref. 185)	12

Materials titrated	Reagent and reaction conditions	Subsequent treatment and final titration stage	Ref.
Calcium acetate, formed in determination of acetic acid	+ H_2O_2, giving acetone	Determined with alkali/excess iodine (see Iodine reagents, ref. 194)	13
HCHO	+ NaOH + H_2O_2	Back titrated with H_2SO_4	14
HCHO from pyrolysis of wood	+ NaOH + H_2O_2	Titrated with acid to methyl red	15
Methionine	In water, + H_2O_2/$HClO_4$, giving the sulphoxide; 4–5 h	+ I^- + ammonium molybdate and titrated with thiosulphate. Control	16
HCHO from determination of the resin acid *d*-pimaric acid by treatment with ozone and decomposition of the ozonide	+ NaOH + H_2O_2	Titrated with acid	17
HCHO from urea/HCHO resins by distillation with phosphoric acid	Distilled into moderate excess NaOH, + H_2O_2; 30 min reflux	Titrated with HCl to methyl red	18
Lower aldehydes formed in flame studies on ether/oxygen mixtures	Neutralized sample (to phenolphthalein) + NaOH + H_2O_2; 10 min/100° in closed bottles	Titrated with H_2SO_4 to the indicator	19
HCHO from determination of ethylene glycol by oxidation with periodate	+ NaOH + H_2O_2; 1 h/room temp.	+ excess H_2SO_4 and back titrated with NaOH to cresol red	20
HCHO in formalin	+ NaOH + H_2O_2; 10 min/100° (high methanol concentrations give low results)	Titrated with H_2SO_4 to 2,4-dinitrophenol	21
Acetaldehyde + ethyl acetate	+ NaOH + H_2O_2; 15 min/*ca* 80°, then 1 h/room temp.	Titrated with HCl to phenolphthalein (aldehyde separately determined with HSO_3^- and allowed for)	22
Methyl bromide; trichloroacetonitrile	+ air/H_2O_2 and passed through silica tubes with hot platinum filaments, converting to inorganic halide (see also Pyrolysis, ref. 12)	Determined by titration with $AgNO_3$	23

Materials titrated	Reagent and reaction conditions	Subsequent treatment and final titration stage	Ref.
Acrylonitrile in air	Absorbed in conc. H_2SO_4, made alkaline and H_2O_2 added; 30 min reflux, yielding ammonia	Distilled into excess H_2SO_4 and back titrated with NaOH to methyl red	24
Acetaldehyde in presence of acetone	$+ H_2O_2 + V_2O_5$ or MoO_3 catalyst. At 55–60°, giving acetic acid	Titrated with NaOH at intervals	25
HCHO in urea/HCHO resins	$+ NaOH + H_2O_2$; 15 min/room temp., then 1 h heating	Acidified with slight excess H_2SO_4, formic acid distilled out and titrated with alkali to phenolphthalein	26
$(C_6H_5)_3$ As in presence of $(C_6H_5)_2AsCl$, $C_6H_5AsCl_2$ and $AsCl_3$	$+ NaOH + H_2O_2$, oxidizing all except the first	Unreacted compound extracted with CCl_4 and determined with excess bromate (see Bromine reagents, ref. 262)	27
Methyl bromide	Combustion procedure of ref. 23 (see also Pyrolysis, ref. 19)	Br^- determined by titration with $AgNO_3$ or by oxidation to BrO_3^- with hypochlorite, addition of I^- and titration with thiosulphate	28
HCHO in urea/HCHO resins	$+ NaOH + H_2O_2$; 15 min/room temp., then 1 h/100°	Slightly acidified, formic acid distilled and titrated with NaOH	29
Penicillin	Solution neutralized to phenolphthalein or phenol red, $+ NaOH + H_2O_2$	Titrated with HCl	30
HCHO	$+ NaOH + H_2O_2$ (comments on inaccuracy of the method, as used in the US and Italian Pharmacopoeia)	Titrated with acid	31
R_3As in presence of R_2AsCl, $RAsCl_2$, $AsCl_3$, RAsO, $R_2As.O.AsR_2$	$+ NaOH + H_2O_2$, oxidizing all except the first (*cf* method of ref. 27)	Unreacted compound extracted with CCl_4 and determined with excess bromate	32
Thiourea in blood, serum	$+$ alkali $+ H_2O_2$, oxidizing to urea	$+$ urease, giving NH_3; diffused into excess acid and back titrated with alkali to bromothymol blue	33
Benzil	In pyridine, $+ NaOH + H_2O_2$; 15 min reflux, giving sodium benzoate	Pyridine distilled off, acidified, benzoic acid distilled and titrated with NaOH	34

Materials titrated	Reagent and reaction conditions	Subsequent treatment and final titration stage	Ref.
π-Apocamphor 1-aldehyde	Aqueous solution + H_2O_2; 5 min shaking, giving pinophanic acid	Titrated with NaOH to neutral red	35
HCHO, acetaldehyde in presence of ethyl acetate	Modification of method of ref. 22 (larger excess H_2O_2, giving faster reaction)		36
Vanillin	+ NaOH + H_2O_2. Heated on water bath until gas evolution ceased	Titrated with HCl to phenolphthalein	37
Methionine in protein hydrolysates	+ $H_2O_2/HClO_4$/water; 6 h/room temp., giving the sulphoxide	+ I^- + H_2SO_4 + ammonium molybdate and titrated with thiosulphate. Control	38
Aldehydes in mixtures with H_2O_2	+ KOH + H_2O_2; 1 h/60°	Titrated with HCl to phenolphthalein	39
Higher aliphatic aldehydes in presence of ketones and fatty acids	+ NaOH + H_2O_2; 30–60 min/100°	+ ethanol and titrated with HCl to phenolphthalein (any free acid titrated separately)	40
Mersalyl (o-($NaOOC-CH_2-O$)$C_6H_4$$-CONH-CH_2-CH(OCH_3)-CH_2-HgOH$)	+ H_2SO_4 + H_2O_2 until decolorized; then 5 min boiling, converting to inorganic mercury	Unreacted H_2O_2 destroyed with MnO_4^-, decolorized with Fe(II) and titrated with SCN^- to Fe(III) indicator	41
Nitriles	+ KOH + H_2O_2; 5 min/room temp., then warmed, concentrating the solution	Titrated with H_2SO_4 to phenolphthalein	42
Bromine-containing barbiturates like bromural, carbromal	Refluxed with NaOH, then heated with H_2O_2, giving Br^-	Slightly acidified with acetic acid and titrated with Ag^+ coulometrically	43
Some organophosphorus fluoridates and pyrophosphonates	In isopropanol, + $Na_4P_2O_7$/borax/NaOH/H_2O_2 (pH 10); 2–4 min, giving peracids	+ H_2SO_4/I^- and titrated with thiosulphate. Control	44

Materials titrated	Reagent and reaction conditions	Subsequent treatment and final titration stage	Ref.
Biacetyl	+ KOH + H_2O_2; 5 min/*ca* 40°; or + H_2O_2; 10–15 min/*ca* room temp.	Titrated with H_2SO_4 to thymol blue; or titrated with KOH to phenolphthalein	45
Mercaptans + aryl trityl sulphides	In ethanol, + NaOH + H_2O_2; 20 min/65°	+ HNO_3 and sulphide titrated with Hg(II) to diphenylcarbazone	46
Na 1-phenyl-2, 3-dimethylpyrazol-5-one-4-methylamino-methane sulphonate ('Novalgin')	+ H_2O_2 + drops NH_4OH; 1 h/room temp., then evaporated on steam bath to low volume	Diluted and SO_4^{2-} formed titrated conductometrically with Ba acetate	47
'Novalgin'	In water, + 30% H_2O_2; 15 min, oxidizing to sulphate	Ultimately titrated with $BaCl_2$	48
HCHO/methanol mixtures	+ H_2O_2/NaOH; heated 1 h/*ca* 100° in a sealed tube	Unreacted NaOH and Na formate removed with a cation exchanger, then excess H_2O_2 in an anion exchanger and residual methanol determined with excess bichromate (see Bichromate and chromic oxide, ref. 253)	49
Benzoylacetyl	+ H_2O_2/NaOH; 2 h/*ca* 20°	Unused alkali titrated with HCl to phenolphthalein	50
Unreacted tri-phenylphosphine from determination of hydro-peroxides and dialkyl peroxides	+ H_2O_2/isopropanol; 30 min	Back titrated unused hydrogen peroxide with Ce (IV) to ferroin	51

References

1. Blank, O. and Finkenbeiner, H., *Ber.* **31**, 2979 (1898).
2. Fresenius, W. and Grünhut, L., *Z. anal. Chem.* **44**, 18 (1905).
3. Rabin, L., *Ann. chim. anal.* **13**, 53 (1908).
4. Robinson, R. H., *Chemist-Analyst* **29**, 21 (1920).
5. Kühl, F., *Collegium* 133 (1922).
6. Borgstrom, P. and Horsch, W. G., *J. Am. Chem. Soc.* **45**, 1493 (1923).
7. Mach, F. and Herrmann, R., *Z. anal. Chem.* **62**, 104 (1923).

8. Friedemann, T. E., *J. Biol. Chem.* **73**, 331 (1927).
9. Erikson, S., *Svensk Farm Tidskr.* **34**, 1 (1930).
10. Klinc, L., *Biochem. Z.* **273**, 1 (1934).
11. Il'inski, M. and Roshal, R. B., *Compt. rend. acad. sci. URSS* **17**, 117 (1937).
12. Klinc, L., *Biochem. Z.* **296**, 202 (1938).
13. Dulian, F., *Klin. Wochschr.* **18**, 1224 (1939).
14. Foschini, A. and Talenti, M., *Z. anal. Chem.* **117**, 94 (1939).
15. Sukhanovskii, S. I., *Lesokhim. Prom.* **2**, 37 (1939).
16. Kolb, J. J. and Toennies, G., *Ind. Eng. Chem., Anal. Ed.* **12**, 723 (1940).
17. Komshilov, N. P., *Lesokhim. Prom.* **3**, No. 6, 25 (1940).
18. Levenson, J. J., *Ind. Eng. Chem., Anal. Ed.* **12**, 332 (1940).
19. MacCormac, M. and Townend, D. T. A., *J. Chem. Soc.* 151 (1940).
20. Tappi, G. and Bertolina, G., *Ricerca sci.* **11**, 1001 (1940).
21. Homer, H. W., *J. Soc. Chem. Ind. (London)* **60**, 213T (1941).
22. Lindeken, C. L., Clayton, J. O. and Skoog, D. A., *Ind. Eng. Chem., Anal. Ed.* **16**, 734 (1944).
23. Lubatti, O. F. and Harrison, A., *J. Soc. Chem. Ind. (London)* **63**, 140 (1944).
24. Petersen, G. W. and Radke, H. H., *Ind. Eng. Chem., Anal. Ed.* **16**, 63 (1944).
25. Takigawa, T., *J. Soc. Chem. Ind. (Japan)* **47**, 262 (1944).
26. Picozzi, A., *Proc. XIth Intern. Congr. Pure & Appl. Chem., (London)* **5**, 627 (1947).
27. Prat, J. and Vaganay, J., *Mém. services chim. état (Paris)* **33**, 391 (1947).
28. Russell, J., *J. Soc. Chem. Ind. (London)* **66**, 22 (1947).
29. Coppa-Zuccari, G., *Inds. plastiques* **4**, 183 (1948).
30. Wise, W. S. and Twigg, G. H., *Analyst* **73**, 393 (1948).
31. Fiore, L., *Ann. chim. applicata* **39**, 604 (1949).
32. Prat, J., *Chim. anal.* **31**, 111 (1949).
33. Haurowitz, F. and Lisie, S. G., *Anal. Chim. Acta* **4**, 43 (1950).
34. Ruzhentseva, A. K. and Metsler, A. A., *Zhur. Anal. Khim.* **5**, 160 (1950).
35. Tanake, Y., *J. Agr. Chem. Soc. (Japan)* **24**, 27 (1950).
36. Kirjakka, P. and Piha, P., *Suomen Kemistilehti* **24B**, 1 (1951).
37. Sharp, L. K., *Analyst* **76**, 215 (1951).
38. Korpàczy, I., *Magyar Kem. Folyoirat* **60**, 241 (1954).
39. Satterfield, C. N., Wilson, R. E., LeClair, R. M. and Reid, R. C., *Anal. Chem.* **26**, 1792 (1954).
40. Metcalfe, L. D. and Schmitz, A. A., *Anal. Chem.* **29**, 1676 (1957).
41. Poethke, W. and Wigert, R., *Pharmazie* **13**, 389 (1958).
42. Whitehurst, D. H. and Johnson, J. B., *Anal. Chem.* **30**, 1332 (1958).
43. Kalinowski, K., *Acta Pharm. Polon.* **16**, 225 (1959).
44. Sass, S., Master, I., Davis, P. M. and Beitsch, N., *Anal. Chem.* **32**, 285 (1960).

45. Wolf, F., *Z. anal. Chem.* **172**, 413 (1960).
46. Gregg, D. C., Bouffard, P. E. and Barton, R., *Anal. Chem.* **33**, 269 (1961).
47. Alessandro, G., Dal Brollo, F. and Mecarelli, E., *Boll. Chim. Farm.* **101**, 34 (1962).
48. Fecko, J., *Acta Polon. Pharm.* **20**, 225 (1963).
49. Légradi, L., *Magyar Kém. Folyoirat* **69**, 117 (1963).
50. Ruzhentseva, A. K. and Larina, P. N., *Med. Prom. SSSR* **17**, No. 1, 42 (1963).
51. Dulog, L. and Burg, K. H., *Z. Anal. Chem.* **203**, 184 (1964).

49. Hydroxylamine

Reagent and reaction conditions. As salt of a strong acid, nearly always hydrochloride but occasionally sulphate. The formate and acetate have also been used.

The salt has been used directly and also in the presence of a base as strong as or stronger than the acid component of the hydroxylamine salt. Both organic bases (ethanolamines, higher aliphatic amines) and inorganic (alkali hydroxides, $CaCO_3$, $NaHCO_3$) have been employed. These bases may be used in amounts equivalent to the hydroxylamine salt (so that the effective reagent is free hydroxylamine) or in sub-equivalent or excess quantities. Sometimes they have been added to the reaction mixture, but often have formed part of the reagent itself.

The indicator used for the final titration stage is often present in the reagent, especially where it serves to indicate the end-point of a titration of the reagent with the base.

Organic solvents have been used for materials poorly soluble in water. The lower alcohols and dioxan with varying proportions of water have found most application.

Reaction temperature and time depend on the material determined. The condensation reactions of lower ketones and aldehydes are complete in 5–10 min at room temperature. Others of higher molecular weight or with sterically hindered carbonyl groups require several hours reflux.

Reactions and materials titrated. 1. In almost every case, condensation for determination of carbonyl compounds:

$$RR'CO + NH_2OH(.HCl) \rightarrow RR'C{=}NOH + H_2O\ (+ HCl)$$

The carbonyl compounds include lower aldehydes and ketones (form-

and acetaldehydes, acetone in particular), components of essential oils (notably citral, citronellal, menthone and carvone), aromatic aldehydes benz- and cinnamaldehydes), camphor, sugars, carbonyl groups in oxidized celluloses, α,β-unsaturated carbonyl compounds, quinones and diketones.

With certain types of ethers such as vinyl ethers and acetals, an acid reagent has sometimes been used so as first to convert the ether to the corresponding carbonyl compound which then reacts with the hydroxylamine reagent.

$$RCOCH{=}CH_2 + H_2O \rightarrow ROH + CH_3CHO$$

$$RCH(OR')_2 + H_2O \rightarrow RCHO + 2\ R'OH$$

α-Dicarbonyl compounds and their monoximes have been determined by oximation condensation in the presence of Ni(II), so that the nickel chelate complexes were precipitated.

2. The rarely encountered other types of reaction with hydroxylamine are:

Addition, e.g. to acrylonitrile in its determinaiton:

$$CH_2 = CH.CN + NH_2OH \rightarrow HOHN.CH_2.CH_2.CN$$

Displacement with oxime formation from bisulphite compounds as a final stage in the determination of aldehydes;

$$\underset{\displaystyle OH}{\overset{\displaystyle RCH.SO_3^-}{|}} + NH_2OH \rightarrow RCH{=}NOH + HSO_3^- + H_2O$$

Subsequent treatment and final titration stage. (i) Titration with standard alkali of the acid liberated from condensation with the hydroxylamine salt. This has been carried out potentiometrically or with indicators which change colour in the pH 3 to 4 region, such as bromophenol blue, methyl orange and dimethyl yellow.

(ii) Titration with standard acid of the unused base in the reaction mixture, where the reagent contained excess base. The same end-point determinations have been used as in (i).

(iii) Titration with Karl Fischer reagent of the water formed in the condensation.

(iv) Titration with oxidizing agents of the unreacted hydroxylamine. Iodine, ferricyanide and cupric reagents have been used, with potentiometric end-point indication.

(v) Titration of unreacted hydroxylamine with perchloric acid in non-aqueous medium; the hydroxylamine salt of a weak acid like the formate or acetate was then used as reagent.

(vi) Two special cases are the titration of freed bisulphite from the displacement reaction mentioned under reaction 2; and titration with EDTA of unused Ni(II) from the determination of α-dicarbonyl compounds with a hydroxylamine/Ni(II) reagent.

Control titrations have very often been performed in the absence of the sample, titrating to the same end-point pH or colour as in the determination. This is, incidentally, not mentioned in the individual ent ies in the tables below.

Examples

Materials titrated	Reagent and reaction conditions	Subsequent treatment and final titration stage	Ref.
Formaldehyde	+ hydrochloride	Titrated with alkali to methyl orange	1
Linear and cyclic ketones	+ sulphate + equivalent of $Ba(OH)_2$; in 50% ethanol (study of extent of reaction)	Titrated with HCl to methyl orange	2
Aldehydes in lemon oil	+ hydrochloride/ethanol + KOH/ethanol; 30 min reflux	Titrated with H_2SO_4 to methyl orange	3
Acetone	+ hydrochloride/some KOH/ethanol; 2 h/room temp., or reflux	Titrated with alkali to methyl orange or bromophenol blue	4
Pyruvic acid	+ hydrochloride	Titrated with alkali to methyl orange	5
Acetaldehyde, from determination of lactic acid by distillation with H_2SO_4	+ hydrochloride/90% ethanol, neutralized to phenolphthalein with KOH; 20 min/room temp.	Titrated with H_2SO_4 to methyl orange	6
Acetone	+ hydrochloride	Titrated with alkali to methyl orange	7
Ketones in hydrogenated phenols, etc.	+ hydrochloride	Titrated with NaOH to methyl orange	8

Materials titrated	Reagent and reaction conditions	Subsequent treatment and final titration stage	Ref.
Aldehydes in essential oils, e.g. citronellal in oil of citronella or citral in lemon oil	+ hydrochloride/ ethanol	Titrated with KOH to bromophenol blue	9
Acetone from determination of isopropanol by oxidation with bichromate	+ hydrochloride	Titrated with alkali	10
Acetone in isopropanol	+ hydrochloride/80% ethanol, + some KOH; 2 h/room temp.	Titrated with KOH to phenolphthalein, then with HCl to methyl orange	11
Citronellal in oil of citronella	+ hydrochloride + excess KOH + ethanol; 15 min/room temp.	Titrated with HCl to bromophenol blue	12
Citronellal in oil of citronella	+ hydrochloride, neutralized with KOH to methyl orange	Titrated with KOH (to the methyl orange)	13
Citronellal	Sample cooled below 0°, + hydrochloride/ ethanol, + excess KOH; 1 h/room temp.	Titrated with HCl to methyl orange	14
Citronellal	Modification of method of ref. 12		15
Acetaldehyde in wines	Distilled into neutralized hydrochloride	Titrated with NaOH to methyl orange	16
Furfuraldehyde	+ hydrochloride; 30 min/room temp.	Titrated with NaOH to methyl orange	17
Ketones in essential oils, e.g. carvone in oils of dill and caraway	+ hydrochloride/ ethanol + some KOH; 75°	Aliquots titrated at intervals with KOH to dimethyl yellow	18
Furfuraldehyde from determination of pentosans by distillation with conc. HCl	Distilled into hydrochloride	Titrated with alkali to methyl orange	19
Acetone	+ hydrochloride; 15 min/room temp.	Titrated with NaOH to methyl orange	20
Furfuraldehyde from determination of pentosans by distillation with conc. HCl	+ hydrochloride	Titrated with NaOH to methyl orange	21

Materials titrated	Reagent and reaction conditions	Subsequent treatment and final titration stage	Ref.
Cinnamaldehyde in cinnamon bark	In ethanol/ether, + hydrochloride/some NaOH; 30 min reflux	Titrated with alkali to phenolphthalein, then with H_2SO_4 to methyl orange	22
Citronellal in oil of citronella	+ hydrochloride/ alcohol, + excess KOH; 1 h/room temp.	Titrated with HCl to bromophenol blue	23
Aldehydes and ketones in essential oils	+ hydrochloride/ alcohol, + excess KOH; 1 h reflux	Titrated with HCl to bromophenol blue	24
Acetaldehyde from determination of 2,3-butylene glycol by periodate oxidation	Distilled into hydro-chloride, neutralized with NaOH to methyl orange	Titrated with NaOH (to methyl orange)	25
Carbonyl compounds	+ hydrochloride/ ethanol. Not over 1 h/room temp.	Titrated with alkali to bromophenol blue	26
Acetone, from determination of isopropanol by oxidation with bichromate	+ hydrochloride; 1 h/room temp.	Titrated with Na_2CO_3 to methyl orange	27
Acetone, acetaldehyde	+ hydrochloride; 30–40 min/room temp.	Titrated with NaOH to methyl orange	28
Carbonyl compounds	+ sulphate, neutralized to bromophenol blue. Various reaction times	Titrated with NaOH to same indicator (claimed better than methyl orange)	29
Citronellal in citronella oil	In ethanol, + hydro-chloride/ethanol + excess KOH; 1 h/room temp. (15 min in tropics)	Titrated with HCl to bromo-phenol blue	30
Menthone in pepper-mint essence	+ hydrochloride/ ethanol	Titrated with KOH/ethanol to methyl orange (heated to 100° at the end)	31
Carbonyl compounds	+ hydrochloride/80% ethanol + pyridine. Various reaction times at room temp. or *ca* 100°	Titrated with NaOH/methanol to bromophenol blue	32
Acetaldehyde in gas	Passed into hydro-chloride/saturated NaCl	Titrated with NaOH	33

Materials titrated	Reagent and reaction conditions	Subsequent treatment and final titration stage	Ref.
Camphor and related ketones like menthone, carvone	+ hydrochloride/80% ethanol + NaOH, $CaCO_3$ or Na_2CO_3; 1 h boiling	+ excess HCl and back titrated with NaOH	34
Camphor, hexetone	+ hydrochloride + $NaHCO_3$; 4 h reflux	Titrated with HCl to bromophenol blue, then with NaOH to phenolphthalein	35
Camphor, hexetone in medicinals	+ hydrochloride/ ethanol; + $NaHCO_3$	Titrated with HCl to bromophenol blue, then with alkali to phenolphthalein/Tropaelin	36
Camphor	+ hydrochloride + $NaHCO_3$; 2 h/75°	Titrated with HCl to methyl orange	37
Citronellal in oil of citronella	Studied methods of refs 9, 12, 13, 14, 15, 23, 24 and 30		38
Acetone	Method of ref. 7 but with methyl orange/Xylene cyanol as indicator		39
Cholesterone, formed in study of the velocity of dehydrogenation of cholesterol	+ hydrochloride/a little ethanol; 45°	Titrated with HCl to bromophenol blue	40
Menthone	Method of ref. 9		41
Carbonyl compounds	+ hydrochloride + varied amounts of NaOH, in 50–70% ethanol (study of speed of oximation as a function of pH and the structure of the carbonyl compound)	Acid formed or base disappeared titrated to bromophenol blue	42
Acetaldehyde in wines	Wine + hydrochloride, both neutralized to bromophenol blue; 30 min/room temp.	Titrated with NaOH (to bromophenol blue)	43
Carbonyl compounds in fats	+ hydrochloride/80% ethanol/pyridine; 30 min/room temp. to 3 h reflux	Titrated with NaOH to bromophenol blue	44
Carbonyl compounds in fats, oils	+ hydrochloride/ ethanol, + excess KOH; 2–3 min boiling	Titrated with HCl to methyl orange	45

Materials titrated	Reagent and reaction conditions	Subsequent treatment and final titration stage	Ref.
Carbonyl compounds	+ hydrochloride/*ca* 90% ethanol; 10 min/room temp.	Titrated with KOH to bromophenol blue	46
Carbonyl compounds in essential oils	+ hydrochloride/*ca* 90% ethanol, + $CaCO_3$ excess; 3 h	Excess HCl added and back titrated with KOH to bromophenol blue	47
Acetaldehyde, from determination of paraldehyde by distillation with H_2SO_4	Distilled into neutralized hydrochloride/50% ethanol	Titrated with NaOH to bromophenol blue	48
Camphor in smokeless powder	Method of ref. 34		49
Ketones from wood pyrolysis	+ hydrochloride	Titrated with alkali to methyl orange or bromophenol blue	50
Camphor in pharmaceutical preparations and medicinal mixtures	+ hydrochloride + $NaHCO_3$; 4 h reflux	Titrated with NaOH to bromophenol blue, then to phenolphthalein	51
p-Methylacetophenone, formed in study of Friedel–Crafts reaction between acetyl chloride and toluene	+ *ca* neutralized hydrochloride/methanol. Left overnight/room temp.	Titrated with NaOH/methanol to dimethyl yellow	52
E.g. acetaldehyde, crotonaldehyde, acetone aldol, acetal	+ hydrochloride; 15 or 30 min/room temp.	Titrated with NaOH to dimethyl yellow/methylene blue	53
Carbonyl compounds	+ hydrochloride/ethanol/pyridine; 2 h/60°	Titrated with Karl Fischer reagent	54
Carbonyl compounds	+ hydrochloride/water or ethanol. At room temp. or *ca* 100°	Titrated with NaOH potentiometrically to pH 4·1	55
Carbonyl groups in bile preparations	Method of ref. 32 with potentiometric titration		56
Benzaldehyde	+ sulphate/50% methanol, neutralized to tetrabromophenol blue	Titrated with NaOH (to same indicator)	57
HCHO from fibres, after hydrolysis with HCl	+ hydrochloride/ethanol; 10 min/room temp.	Titrated with NaOH	58

Materials titrated	Reagent and reaction conditions	Subsequent treatment and final titration stage	Ref.
Aldehydes in spirits	+ hydrochloride + extra HCl (to accelerate the reaction); 5 min/room temp.	Titrated with NaOH to methyl orange	59
Carbonyl groups in oxy-starches, oxycelluloses and sugars	+ hydrochloride, brought to pH 5 with NaOH; 1·5 or 14–18 h/room temp.	Titrated with NaOH to bromophenol blue	60
Acetone	+ hydrochloride/water	Titrated with NaOH to bromophenol blue	61
Camphor	+ hydrochloride/*N*-diethylethanolamine, triethanolamine or *N*-ethyldiethanolamine; 2 h/100°	Titrated with HCl or H_2SO_4 to bromophenol blue	62
Aldehydes in sewage	Method of ref. 1		63
Carbonyl groups in oxycellulose	+ hydrochloride + excess NaOH; 20 min/room temp.	Titrated with HCl to methyl orange	64
Carbonyl groups in oxidized cellulose	+ H_2NOCH_3 hydrochloride + some alkali; 1 day/room temp.	Titrated with alkali	65
Carbonyl compounds	+ hydrochloride/ethanol + excess $CaCO_3$; 1 h reflux	Titrated with HCl to bromophenol blue	66
Vinyl ethers	+ hydrochloride; 2 h/room temp., then 7–10 min/80–90°	Titrated with NaOH to bromophenol blue	67
Furfuraldehyde	+ hydrochloride + NaOH; 1 h/room temp.	Titrated with NaOH to dimethyl yellow	68
Aldehydes in orange oil	+ hydrochloride, neutralized to bromophenol blue. Short reaction time. also + excess KOH; 1 h reflux (compared the two techniques)	Titrated with KOH to same end-point; Titrated with HCl	69
Acetone in liquefied gases	Passed into hydrochloride, brought to pH 3·88	Titrated with KOH to this pH	70

Materials titrated	Reagent and reaction conditions	Subsequent treatment and final titration stage	Ref.
Vinyl ethers in presence of alcohols	+ hydrochloride + excess acid	Titrated with alkali	71
Butyral groups in polyvinyl butyral	In ethanol, + hydrochloride/ethanol; 90 min reflux	Titrated with NaOH to methyl orange	72
Ketones $RCOCH_2R'$, formed in determination of acetylenes $RC\equiv CR'$ by addition reaction with methanol and hydrolysis with bicarbonate	Distilled into hydrochloride; 10 min/room temp.	Titrated with NaOH to methyl orange/xylene cyanol	73
Vanillin, benzaldehyde, cinnamaldehyde	In ethanol, + hydrochloride/ethanol + excess KOH; 10 min	Titrated with HCl to naphthyl red	74
Menthone in garden mint oils	Methods of ref. 69		75
Acetaldehyde in industrial alcohols	+ hydrochloride	Titrated with NaOH to bromophenol blue	76
Vinyl ethers	+ hydrochloride + excess alkali	Titrated with acid	77
Aldehydes in essential oils	Modification of method of ref. 18		78
Carbonyl groups in gasoline oxidation products	+ hydrochloride/ ethanol. Room temp.	Titrated with alkali to methyl orange	79
Diacetone alcohol	+ hydrochloride, neutralized with NaOH to bromophenol blue. A few min/room temp.	Titrated with NaOH (to same indicator)	80
Acetaldehyde + acetone (from study of reaction between former and water)	+ hydrochloride (modification of method of ref. 28)	Titrated with NaOH to methyl orange	81
Carbonyl groups in fatty materials; also acetophenone, mesityl oxide, methyl isobutyl ketone	+ hydrochloride + some alkali; 10–30 min reflux	Titrated with HCl to pH 3 potentiometrically	82

Materials titrated	Reagent and reaction conditions	Subsequent treatment and final titration stage	Ref.
Carbonyl compounds and acetals	+ hydrochloride/ ethanol; 5 min/room temp.	Titrated with NaOH to bromophenol blue	83
HCHO from acid hydrolysis of polyvinylformal	Distilled into hydrochloride	Titrated with NaOH	84
Carbonyl compounds	+ hydrochloride; or + hydrochloride/alkali	Titrated with alkali or acid potentiometrically	85
Acetone, formed during decomposition of di-*tert*-butyl peroxide	Method of ref. 7		86
Furfuraldehyde, also from acid hydrolysis of pentoses and pentosans	+ hydrochloride/ ethanol	Titrated with NaOH to bromophenol blue	87
Aldehyde in a study of crotonaldehyde condensations	In methanol, + hydrochloride, neutralized to bromophenol blue, in 50% methanol. Short reaction time (to prevent acetal formation)	Titrated with alkali	88
Carbonyl compounds, including —CO—C=C— and —CO—CH_2— groups	+ hydrochloride or hydrochloride + excess KOH. Various conditions, from short time up to 1 h/100°	Titrated with alkali or H_2SO_4 to bromophenol blue	89
Acetone from study of decomposition of α-diethylamino-isobutyronitrile	+ hydrochloride at pH 3·5 (methyl orange)	Titrated with alkali to same pH	90
Carbonyl compounds in presence of organic acids; acetals, ketals	+ hydrochloride/80% ethanol at pH 2·5; 15 min/room temp. or 2 h/*ca* 100°	Titrated with NaOH to pH 2·5 (to thymol blue or potentiometrically)	91
Ketones (determination of equivalent weight or 'hydroxylamine number')	+ hydrochloride/excess KOH/ethanol; 1 h reflux	Titrated with HCl to bromophenol blue	92
Butanone + isobutyraldehyde formed in study of pinacol rearrangement	Method of ref. 32		93

Materials titrated	Reagent and reaction conditions	Subsequent treatment and final titration stage	Ref.
Citral in oil of lemon	+ hydrochloride/60% methanol, neutralized with KOH to methyl orange; 15 min/room temp.	Titrated with KOH/60% methanol	94
Mixtures of aldehydes, ketones and 'combined carbonyl compounds' (i.e. acetals, polymers, etc.)	+ hydrochloride, *ca* 70% neutralized with NaOH; 15 min/room temp. 'Combined carbonyl' at pH 1–3 and higher temp. Ketones alone after oxidation of aldehydes with Ag_2O	Titrated with alkali to methyl orange	95
Acetone; also from alkaline decomposition of diacetone alcohol	+ hydrochloride/ ethanol, neutralized to methyl orange	Titrated with alkali	96
Acetone in photo-chemical decomposition products of *tert*-butyl peroxide	+ hydrochloride (slight modification of method of ref. 83)	Titrated with NaOH potentiometrically	97
HCHO	+ hydrochloride, neutralized with KOH to dimethyl yellow/ methylene blue; 1 h/room temp.	Titrated with KOH	98
Many carbonyl compounds	Method of ref. 32 tested		99
Carbonyl compounds	Discussion of hydroxylamine methods; claimed that excess acid leads to acetal formation or polymerization		100
HCHO + acetone from oxidation of methyl radicals	Method of ref. 54		101
Vinyl propyl and iso-propyl ethers	Methods of refs 67, 71 and 77 tried (also iodometric method under Iodine, ref. 293)		102
Vanillin; irone	+ hydrochloride/90% ethanol, + some alkali; 15 min or 1 h respectively	Titrated with alkali to original pH	103
Carbonyl compounds in fat	+ hydrochloride/ ethanol + excess KOH; 30 min/100°	Titrated with HCl	104

Materials titrated	Reagent and reaction conditions	Subsequent treatment and final titration stage	Ref.
Carbonyl compounds	+ hydrochloride or hydrochloride + excess NaOH	Titrated with alkali or acid potentiometrically to pH 3·65	105
Aldehydes	+ hydrochloride; also with alternative additions of hydrochloride and NaOH; 10–60 min	Titrated with NaOH to pH 3·5 potentiometrically	106
Aldehydes	+ hydrochloride	Titrated with alkali to dimethyl yellow/methylene blue (claimed that free acid does not then interfere)	107
Carbonyl compounds in fatty acid oxidation products	In water or ethanol, + hydrochloride/ethanol; 30 min heating	Titrated with NaOH to bromophenol blue	108
Free HCHO in phenol/HCHO syrups	In ethanol, + hydrochloride. At least 30 min/room temp.	Titrated with NaOH to pH 3·4 potentiometrically	109
Carbonyl groups in oxycellulose	+ hydrochloride/90% ethanol + NaOH, giving pH 3·2–3·4 (bromophenol blue). 2 h heating	Filtrate titrated with NaOH to same pH	110
Aldehydes	+ hydrochloride/*tert*-butanol (to prevent acetal formation). Mostly 30 min/room temp.	Titrated with alkali potentiometrically to original pH	111
1,2,5-Trimethyl-4-piperidone	+ hydrochloride; 2 h reflux	Titrated with NaOH	112
Aldehydes in mixtures with H_2O_2	+ hydrochloride/80% ethanol; 10 min/60°, then 20 min/room temp.	Titrated with NaOH to thymol blue	113
Vanillin in presence of acetovanillone	In alcohol, + hydrochloride + excess KOH; 5 min	Titrated with HCl/ethanol to bromophenol blue	114
both	1 h reflux		
Higher ketones (e.g. stearone, palmitone)	+ hydrochloride/methanol/isopropanol, 1:2 + excess octadecenylamine/isopropanol; 30 min/70°	Titrated with HCl/isopropanol to bromophenol blue	115

Materials titrated	Reagent and reaction conditions	Subsequent treatment and final titration stage	Ref.
Aldehydes	+ hydrochloride/water-methanol, 1:1; 1 h reflux	Titrated with NaOH potentiometrically	116
Carbonyl compounds	+ acetate/acetic acid; 20 min/room temp. for aldehydes and simple aliphatic ketones	Titrated with $HClO_4$/acetic acid potentiometrically	117
Carbonyl compounds (acetaldehyde) in acrylonitrile	+ hydrochloride/methanol; 1 min/room temp. (for acetaldehyde) 5 min/room temp. (total carbonyl)	Titrated with NaOH/methanol to thymol blue	118
Camphor in pharmaceutical preparations	+ hydrochloride/ethanol + $NaHCO_3$	Titrated with HCl to dimethyl yellow, then with KOH to phenolphthalein	119
α, β-Unsaturated carbonyl compounds	+ hydrochloride/60% ethanol; 2 h/100°	Titrated with NaOH/ethanol to bromophenol blue	120
Acetone, free in its cyanohydrin	+ hydrochloride	Titrated with Na_2CO_3 to pH 3·5 or to dimethyl yellow/methylene blue	121
$RCOCH_2R'$, formed in determination of acetylenes, $RC{\equiv}CR'$, by catalytic addition of water	+ hydrochloride; 1 h reflux	Titrated with NaOH potentiometrically	122
Carbonyl groups in oxycellulose	In vacuum, + free NH_2OH; 2 h/50°	Titrated with HCl to pH 3·2	123
Pentoxyl (2,6-dihydroxy 4-methyl-5-hydroxy-methylpyrimidine)	+ hydrochloride; 30 min/100°	Titrated with NaOH to dimethyl yellow	124
Vinyl methyl ketone	+ hydrochloride; 15 min/room temp.	Titrated with KOH/alcohol to bromophenol blue	126
Camphor	+ hydrochloride/pyridine; 4 h boiling	Back titrated to bromophenol blue	127
Carbonyl compounds (determination of 'hydroxylamine number')	In methanol, + formate/methanol. Variable reaction time (usually 15 min but up to 48 h for camphor)	Titrated with $HClO_4$/ dioxan to thymol blue	128

Materials titrated	Reagent and reaction conditions	Subsequent treatment and final titration stage	Ref.
Carbonyl compounds, e.g. acetone, butanone, methyl isopropyl ketone, benzaldehyde	In pyridine, + hydrochloride; 15 min/*ca* 100°	Titrated with cupric acetate/ethanol/pyridine potentiometrically	129
Ketones in lacquer solvents or vehicles	In ethanol or ethanol/dioxan/water, + solid or aqueous hydrochloride; *ca* 1 h/room temp.	Titrated with KOH/methanol to thymol blue	130
Aldehydes	+ hydrochloride/60% alcohol	Titrated with NaOH to methyl orange	131
Carbonyl compounds —C=C—CO—C=C—	+ hydrochloride/60% alcohol; 2 h heating	Titrated with KOH/alcohol to bromophenol blue	132
Acrylonitrile	+ hydroxylamine/dioxan + excess alkali, giving *β*-hydroxylaminopropionitrile	Titrated with acid potentiometrically, giving jump first for excess alkali, then for the derivative	133
Carbonyl compounds	+ hydrochloride + KOH; 15–60 min	+ KOH and titrated with iodine or ferricyanide potentiometrically	134
Carbonyl compounds	+ hydrochloride/*N*-dimethylethanolamine/methanol/isopropanol; 5 min–3 h/room temp.	Titrated with $HClO_4$/methyl cellosolve to martius yellow	135
Diacetyl	+ hydrochloride + nickel acetate; 4 h reflux, giving nickel dimethylglyoxime (see also Nickel (II), ref. 9)	Ammonia added and unused nickel titrated with EDTA to murexide	136
Chloroacetyl pyrocatechol	In ethanol, + hydrochloride; 15 min/100°	Titrated with NaOH to bromophenol blue	137
Carbonyl compounds	+ hydrochloride/excess triethanolamine/ethanol; 30 min/room temp.	Saturated NaCl added and titrated with HCl to bromophenol blue	138
Carbonyl compounds	Method of ref. 138, but with 1–3 h/70—75°	As in method of ref. 138 and also with potentiometric titration	139
4′-Nitro-2-acetamidoacetophenone	+ hydrochloride; 1 h/room temp.	Titrated with NaOH conductometrically	140

Materials titrated	Reagent and reaction conditions	Subsequent treatment and final titration stage	Ref.
Laevulinic acid	+ hydrochloride, brought to pH 4·1; 45 min boiling	Titrated with alkali to pH 4·1 again (methyl orange or potentiometric)	141
Carbonyl groups in dark oils like Indian vetiver oil	+ hydrochloride; 24 h/room temp.	Titrated to pH 3·5 potentiometrically	142
Camphor in dilute solution	In methanol, + hydrochloride + excess KOH; 4 h reflux	Titrated with HCl photometrically with bromophenol blue (587 mμ)	143
Acetone	+ hydrochloride/ethanol	Titrated with KOH/alcohol to bromophenol blue	144
Aldehyde bisulphites, e.g. glyoxal bisulphite, from glyoxal in its determination by reaction with sulphite/acetic acid and after destruction of excess sulphite with iodine	+ hydrochloride + NaOH; 5 min/room temp., giving dioxime and HSO_3^-	Slightly acidified with HCl and titrated with iodine to starch	145
Acetals, ketals, vinyl ethers after hydrolysis with HBr	+ hydrochloride + HBr; 30 min/100°	KOH added, left 30 min and titrated with ferricyanide potentiometrically	146
1-Piperidino-2-methyl-3-*p*-tolylpropanone	+ hydrochloride + tri-*n*-butylamine excess/methanol/isopropanol; *ca* 1 h/70°	Titrated with HCl/propylene glycol-$CHCl_3$, 1:1 to dimethyl yellow/methylene blue	147
Carbonyl compounds, including aldoses, keto acids, quinones, diketones	+ hydrochloride/triethanolamine/96% ethanol; 30 min–2 h/room temp. or 1–4 h/70–75°	Titrated with HCl to bromophenol blue or potentiometrically	148
Camphor	Slight modification of method of ref. 135 (3 h reaction/85°)		149
HCHO + acetaldehyde, formed during pentaerythritol production	+ hydrochloride, neutralized to bromophenol blue; 30 min/room temp.	Titrated with NaOH	150
Free HCHO; paraformaldehyde after depolymerization with 1:1 H_2SO_4	+ hydrochloride, neutralized to bromophenol blue; 15 min/room temp.	Titrated with NaOH	151

Materials titrated	Reagent and reaction conditions	Subsequent treatment and final titration stage	Ref.
Diacetyl monoxime	+ hydrochloride + Na acetate + Ni acetate; 4 h boiling, giving Ni dimethylglyoxime (see also Nickel, ref. 12)	Ammonia added, filtered and unused Ni titrated with EDTA to murexide	152
α-Diketones, other than diacetyl	+ hydrochloride + Na acetate; some + alcohol; 3 h boiling	+ excess Ni acetate, left 1 h, filtered and unused Ni in filtrate titrated with EDTA to murexide (see Nickel (II), ref. 14)	153
Aldehydes, ketones, in presence of acids, acetals, etc.	+ formate/methyl cellosolve + excess KOH; 15–120 min/room temp.	Methanol/methyl cellosolve added and titrated with HNO_3/ methyl cellosolve to thymol blue	154
Mixtures of aldehydes and ketones, e.g. HCHO, acetaldehyde, acetone, butanone	In 80% methanol, + hydrochloride/80% methanol, brought to pH 3·5. At 4° (aliphatic) or room temp. (aromatic)	Titrated at intervals with NaOH to pH 3·5 (different rates of oximation; kinetic plot allows determination of both components)	155
Acetaldehyde + acetone	+ hydrochloride; 15 min/room temp.	Titrated with NaOH potentiometrically or to methyl orange	156
'Carbonyl value' of thermally oxidized fats	In pyridine/octanol, + hydrochloride/ethanol/ water; 24 h/room temp., in dark	Titrated potentiometrically with NaOH/methanol to pH of a control	157
'Carbonyl number' of oxidation products of paraffins	+ hydrochloride/ ethylene glycol/butanol/ water/excess KOH; 2–3 min boiling	Titrated with HCl to methyl red	158
Furfuraldehyde in mixtures with hexamine	In water, + hydrochloride; 10 min/room temp.	Titrated with Na_2CO_3 to 'high frequency' end-point	159
Acetone in oils	+ hydrochloride	Titrated with NaOH to bromophenol blue	160
Carbonyl groups in coal	+ hydrochloride/60% alcohol; 20–24 h simmering (one of many methods tested)	Titrated with NaOH to bromophenol blue	161
Carbonyl groups in peat wax	In 50% ethanol, + hydrochloride; 2 h reflux	+ petroleum ether, hexane or heptane + water and titrated with NaOH to bromophenol blue	162

Materials titrated	Reagent and reaction conditions	Subsequent treatment and final titration stage	Ref.
Benzaldehyde in mixtures with benzoic acid, maleic anhydride and benzoquinone	Method of ref. 32		163
HCHO in presence of dihydric phenols	+ hydrochloride; 30–45 min/room temp.	Titrated potentiometrically with NaOH to pH 4	164
Dihydroxyacetone in cosmetic products	In 50% ethanol + hydrochloride/water; 1 h/room temp.	Titrated with NaOH to bromophenol blue	165
HCHO + CH_3CHO in presence of ethylene oxide	+ hydrochloride	Titrated with NaOH to bromophenol blue	166
Aldehydes + acetals	+ hydrochloride/ ethanol	Immediately titrated with alkali to methyl orange	167
(aldehydes separately determined by reaction with aniline— see Amines and heterocyclic bases, ref. 104)			
Many carbonyl compounds, e.g. benzaldehyde and nitro-, hydroxy- and methoxy-substituted derivatives; benzoin, dibenzylketone (submicro scale)	2-dimethylamino-ethanol/ isopropanol + hydrochloride/iso-propanol/methanol + sample; up to 24 h in nitrogen atmosphere	+ 2-methoxyethanol and titrated with $HClO_4$ in same solvent to Martius Yellow/ methyl violet	168
Unreacted acetone from determination of Grignard reagents	+ formate; 15 min	Back titrated with $HClO_4$/ dioxan	169
Carbonyl compounds, e.g. acetophenone	+ hydrochloride at pH 6·2; 15 min reflux	+ water + $CHCl_3$ and titrated with HCl to methyl orange	170
Benzoylacetyl	+ hydrochloride; 10 min	Titrated with NaOH to bromophenol blue	171
Carbonyl groups in oxycelluloses	+ hydrochloride (study of rates of reaction)	Continuously titrated with NaOH	172
HCHO in para-formaldehyde	+ hydrochloride + NaOH; 5 min/room temp.	Titrated with HCl to bromothymol blue	173

References

1. Brochet, A. and Cambier, R., *Compt. rend.* **120**, 449 (1893).
2. Petrenko-Kritschenko, P. and Lordkipanidze, S., *Ber.* **34**, 1702 (1901).
3. Bennett, A. H., *Analyst* **34**, 14 (1909).
4. Bennett, A. H. and Donovan, F. K., *Analyst* **47**, 146 (1922).
5. Kayser, T., *Bull. soc. chim. biol.* **6**, 345 (1924).
6. Leone, P. and Tafuri, G. B., *Ann. chim. applicata* **15**, 206 (1925).
7. Marasco, M., *Ind. Eng. Chem.* **18**, 701 (1926).
8. Tilsit, A. N., *Z. Deut. Öl-Fett Ind.* **46**, 689 (1926).
9. Bennett, C. T. and Salamon, M. S., *Analyst* **52**, 693 (1927).
10. Noetzel, O., *Z. Untersuch. Lebensm.* **53**, 388 (1927).
11. Simmons, W. H., *Perfumery Essent. Oil Record* **18**, 168 (1927).
12. Holtappel, K. J., *Parfums de France* **6**, 5 (1928).
13. Laboratoires 'Dauphin', *Parfums de France* **6**, 77 (1928).
14. Meyer, R. F., *Parfums de France* **6**, 280 (1928).
15. Penfold, A. R. and Arneman, W. G., *Perfumery Essent. Oil Record* **20**, 392 (1929).
16. Charles, E., *Ann. fals.* **23**, 153 (1930).
17. Noll, A., Bolz, F. and Belz, W., *Papier-Fabr.* **28**, Tech.-Wiss. Teil 565 (1930).
18. Bennett, C. T. and Cocking, T. T., *Analyst* **56**, 79 (1931).
19. Klingstedt, F. W., *Pappers-Trävarntidskr., Finland* 950 (1931).
20. Krajčinovic, M., *Chem.-Ztg.* **55**, 894 (1931).
21. Noll, A. and Belz, W., *Papier-Fabr.* **29**, Tech.-Wiss. Teil 33 (1931).
22. Goday, S. R., *Bol. farm. militar* **10**, 18 (1932).
23. Rowaan, P. A., *Chem. Weekblad* **29**, 603 (1932).
24. Stillman, R. C. and Reed, A. M., *Perfumery Essent. Oil Record* **23**, 278 (1932).
25. Brockmann, M. C. and Werkmann, C. H., *Ind. Eng. Chem., Anal. Ed.* **5**, 206 (1933).
26. Meyer, R. E., *Deut. Parf.-Ztg.* **19**, 3 (1933).
27. Alessandrini, E., *Ann. brasserie dist.* **32**, 104 (1934).
28. Platonov, M. S. and Plakidina, V. A., *J. Gen. Chem. USSR* **4**, 472 (1934).
29. Schultes, H., *Angew. Chem.* **47**, 258 (1934).
30. Koolhaas, D. R., *Indische Mercuur* **58**, 429 (1935).
31. Parraud, G., *Bull. sci. pharmacol.* **42**, 337 (1935).
32. Smith, W. M. D. and Bryant, D. M., *J. Am. Chem. Soc.* **57**, 57 (1935).
33. Sulima, L., *Sintet. Kautschuk* **4**, 35 (1935).
34. Vandoni, R. and Desseigne, G., *Bull. soc. chim. France* (5) **2**, 1685 (1935).
35. Wolstadt, R., *Magyar Gyógyszerésztud. Társaság Ertesitöje* **11**, 257 (1935).

36. Schulek, E. and Wolstadt, R., *Z. anal. Chem.* **104**, 183 (1936).
37. Tishchenko, V. E. and Grekhnev, M. A., *J. Appl. Chem. USSR* **9**, 1700 (1936).
38. Etablissements Roure-Bertrand Fils et Justin Dupont, *Recherches* **1**, 132 (1937).
39. Haughton, C. O., *Ind. Eng. Chem., Anal. Ed.* **9**, 167 (1937).
40. Oppenauer, R. V., *Rec. trav. chim.* **56**, 142 (1937).
41. Ullrich, H. and Schneider, M., *Z. physiol. Chem.* **245**, 181 (1937).
42. Vavon, G. and Anziani, P., *Bull. soc. chim. France* (5) **4**, 2026 (1937).
43. Joslyn, M. A. and Comar, C. L., *Ind. Eng. Chem., Anal. Ed.* **10**, 364 (1938).
44. Kaufmann, H. P., Funke, S. and Fu Yung Liu, *Fette u. Seifen* **45**, 616 (1938).
45. Leithe, W., *Fette u. Seifen* **45**, 615 (1938).
46. Reclaire, A. and Frank, R., *Perfumery Essent. Oil Record* **29**, 212 (1938).
47. Sabetay, S., *Bull. soc. chim. France* (5) **5**, 1419 (1938).
48. Bagnall, D. J. T., Smith, A. and Tankard, A. R., *Analyst* **64**, 857 (1939).
49. Hunold, G. A., *Z. ges. Schiess. u. Sprengstoffe* **34**, 129 (1939).
50. Sukhanovskii, S. I., *Lesokhim. Prom.* **2**, 37 (1939).
51. Yampol'skaya, M. M., *Ukr. Gosud. Inst. Eksptl. Farm.* (*Kharkov*), *Konsul. Materialy* No. 1, 10 (1939).
52. Dermer, O. C., Wilson, D. M., Johnson, F. M. and Dermer, V. H., *J. Am. Chem. Soc.* **63**, 2881 (1941).
53. Hähnel, S. and Lennerstrand, M., *Svensk Kem. Tidskr.* **53**, 336 (1941).
54. Mitchell, J., Smith, D. M. and Bryant, W. M. D., *J. Am. Chem. Soc.* **63**, 573 (1941).
55. Eitel, A., *J. prakt. Chem.* **159**, 292 (1942).
56. Light, A. E., *Ind. Eng. Chem., Anal. Ed.* **14**, 42 (1942).
57. Schubert, M. and Dinkelspiel, J. G., *Ind. Eng. Chem., Anal. Ed.* **14**, 154 (1942).
58. Weltzien, W., *Zellwolle, Kunstseide, Seide* **47**, 197 (1942).
59. Doering, H., *Z. Spiritusind.* **65**, 63 (1943).
60. Gladding, E. K. and Purves, C. B., *Paper Trade J.* **116**, No. 14, 26 (1943).
61. Pevtsov, G. A., *J. Appl. Chem., USSR* **16**, No. 11/12, 363 (1943).
62. Desseigne, G., *Bull. soc. chim. France* **12**, 967 (1945).
63. Bandt, H. J., *Beit. Wasser-, Abwasser- u. Fischereichem., Magdeburg* 34 (1946).
64. Kraichinovich, M. and Kraichinovich, M., *J. Appl. Chem., USSR* **19**, 424 (1946).
65. Meesook, B. and Purves, C. B., *Paper Trade J.* **123**, No. 18, 35 (1946).
66. Mousseron, M. and Combes, G., *Trav. soc. pharm. Montpellier* **5**, 25 (1946).
67. Voronkov, M. G., *Zhur. Anal. Khim.* **1**, 218 (1946).

68. Angell, F. G., *Analyst* **72**, 178 (1947).
69. Hoffmann, A., *Inst. pesquisas tech. Sao Paulo*, Separata No. 198, 6 (1947).
70. Huckabay, W. B., Newton, C. J. and Mettler, A. V., *Anal. Chem.* **19**, 838 (1947).
71. Shostakovskii, M. F. and Prilezhaeva, E. N., *J. Gen. Chem., USSR* **17**, 1129 (1947).
72. Soloveichik, L. S. and Balandina, V. A., *Zavodskaya Lab.* **13**, 1051 (1947).
73. Wagner, C. D., Goldstein, T. and Peters, E. D., *Anal. Chem.* **19**, 103 (1947).
74. Diding, E. and Hellberg, H., *Farm. Revy* **47**, 109 (1948).
75. Hoffmann, A. M., *Anais asoc. quím. Brasil* **7**, 200 (1948).
76. Martraire, M., *Inds. agr. et aliment.* **65**, 123 (1948).
77. Prilezhaeva, E. N., Shapiro, E. S. and Shostakovskii, M. F., *J. Gen. Chem., USSR* **18**, 1663 (1948).
78. Rao, P. C., *J. Sci. Ind. Research, India* **7B**, 166 (1948).
79. Widmaier, O. and Mauss, F., *Rev. inst. franç. petrole* **3**, 183 (1948).
80. Frere, F. J. and Beisz, J. J., *Anal. Chem.* **21**, 616 (1949).
81. Isojima, T., *Repts. Inst. Chem. Research, Kyoto Univ.* **17**, 113 (1949).
82. Knight, H. B. and Swern, D., *J. Am. Oil Chemists' Soc.* **26**, 366 (1949).
83. Maltby, J. G. and Primavesi, G. R., *Analyst* **74**, 498 (1949).
84. Soloveichik, L. S. and Novikova, E. M., *Zavodskaya Lab.* **15**, 418 (1949).
85. Wanka, J., Jureček, M. and Holánek, F., *Collection Czechoslov. Chem. Communs.* **14**, 162 (1949).
86. Bell, E. R., Rust, F. F. and Vaughan, W. E., *J. Am. Chem. Soc.* **72**, 337 (1950).
87. Brissaud, L. and Perriot, G., *Chim. anal.* **32**, 241 (1950).
88. Hünig, S., *Ann.* **569**, 224 (1950).
89. Novikova, E. N. and Petrova, L. N., *Zhur. Priklad. Khim.* **23**, 1336 (1950).
90. Reiber, H. G. and Erway, J., *J. Am. Chem. Soc.* **72**, 1881 (1950).
91. Smith, D. M. and Mitchell, J., *Anal. Chem.* **22**, 750 (1950).
92. Trozzolo, A. M. and Lieber, E., *Anal. Chem.* **22**, 764 (1950).
93. Alexander, E. R. and Dittmer, D. C., *J. Am. Chem. Soc.* **73**, 1665 (1951).
94. Bournot, K., *Pharmazie* **6**, 390 (1951).
95. Buchanan, R. H., *Australian J. Applied Sci.* **2**, 276 (1951).
96. Chaney, A. and Astle, M. J., *J. Org. Chem.* **16**, 57 (1951).
97. Dorfman, L. M. and Salsburg, Z. W., *J. Am. Chem. Soc.* **73**, 255 (1951).
98. Krause, W., *Pharm. Zentralhalle* **90**, 218 (1951).
99. Montes, A. L. and Grandolini, E. A. C., *Anales direc., nacl. quím. (Buenos Aires)* **4**, 9 (1951).
100. Perret, J. J., *Helv. Chim. Acta* **34**, 1531 (1951).

101. Raley, J. H., Porter, L. M., Rust, F. F. and Vaughan, W. E., *J. Am. Chem. Soc.* **73**, 15 (1951).
102. Shostakovskii, F., Prilezhaeva, E. N. and Uvarova, N. I., *Zhur. Anal. Khim.* **6**, 348 (1951).
103. Barker, P. F. and Perry, H. M., *Perfumery Essent. Oil Record* **43**, 357 (1952).
104. Drozdov, N. S. and Materanskaya, N. P., *Myasnaya Ind. SSSR* **23**, No. 3, 73 (1952).
105. Dvořák, K., Trekoval, J., Buzková, V. and Treybal, K., *Sbornik Celostatní Pracovní Konf. Anal. Chemiků* **1**, 313 (1952).
106. de Miranda, H. and Lemmons, J. F., *Perfumery Essent. Oil Record* **43**, 226 (1952).
107. Sawamura, M., *Koryo* (*Aromatics*) No. 21, 40 (1952).
108. Feuell, A. J. and Skellon, J. H., *Analyst* **78**, 135 (1953).
109. Haslam, J. and Soppet, W. W., *J. Appl. Chem.* (*London*) **3**, 328 (1953).
110. Stakheeva-Kaverzneva, E. D. and Salova, A. S., *Zhur. Anal. Khim.* **8**, 365 (1953).
111. Johnston, V. D., *Mfg. Chemist* **25**, 337 (1954).
112. Ruzhentseva, A. K. and Pervacheva, T. D., *Zhur. Anal. Khim.* **9**, 304 (1954).
113. Satterfield, C. N., Wilson, R. E., LeClair, R. M. and Reid, R. C., *Anal. Chem.* **26**, 1792 (1954).
114. Fowler, L., Kline, H. R. and Mitchell, R. S., *Anal. Chem.* **27**, 1688 (1955).
115. Metcalfe, L. D. and Schmitz, A. E., *Anal. Chem.* **27**, 138 (1955).
116. Siggia, S. and Stahl, C. R., *Anal. Chem.* **27**, 1975 (1955).
117. Higuchi, T. and Barnstein, C. H., *Anal. Chem.* **28**, 1022 (1956).
118. Maute, R. L. and Owens, M. L., *Anal. Chem.* **28**, 1312 (1956).
119. Mital, H. C. and Gaind, K. N., *J. Pharm. Pharmacol.* **8**, 37 (1956).
120. Petrova, L. N. and Novikova, E. N., *Zhur. Priklad Khim.* **29**, 783 (1956).
121. Sasuga, H., *Kogyo Kagaku Zasshi* **59**, 1117 (1956).
122. Siggia, S., *Anal. Chem.* **28**, 1481 (1956).
123. Ströle, U., *Makromol. Chem.* **20**, 19 (1956).
124. Balis, E. P., *Aptechnoe Delo* **6**, 55 (1957).
125. Berka, A., *Chemie* (*Prague*) **9**, 528 (1957).
126. Buděšinský, B., Mňouček, K., Jančík, F. and Kraus, E., *Chem. Listy* **51**, 1819 (1957).
127. Kolusheva, A. and Morozova, A., *Farmatsiya* (*Sofia*) **7**, No. 2, 27 (1957).
128. Pesez, M., *Bull. soc. chim. France* 417 (1957).
129. Buděšinský, B., *Chem. Listy* **52**, 2292 (1958).
130. Esposito, G. G. and Swann, M. H., *Anal. Chem.* **30**, 1643 (1958).
131. Petrova, L. N. and Novikova, E. N., *Trudy Vsesoyuz. Nauch.-Issledovatel. Inst. Sintet. i Natural. Dushistykh Veshchestv* No 4, 78 (1958).

132. Petrova, L. N. and Novikova, E. N., *Trudy Vsesoyuz. Nauch.-Issledovatel. Inst. Sintet. i Natural. Dushistykh Veshchestv* No. 4, 76 (1958).
133. Terent'ev, A. P., Obtemperanskaya, S. I. and Buzlanova, M. M., *Zavodskaya Lab.* **24**, 814 (1958).
134. Buděšinský, B. and Körbl, J., *Mikrochim. Acta* 922 (1959).
135. Fritz, J. S., Yamamura, S. S. and Bradford, E. C., *Anal. Chem.* **31**, 200 (1959).
136. Hennart, C. and Merlin, E., *Chim. anal.* **41**, 287 (1959).
137. Inczédy, J. and Sztrókay, J., *Pharmazie* **14**, 96 (1959).
138. Klimova, V. A. and Zabrodina, K. S., *Izvest. Akad. Nauk SSSR, Otdel Khim Nauk* 175 (1959).
139. Klimova, V. A. and Zabrodina, K. S., *Izvest. Akad. Nauk SSSR, Otdel Khim. Nauk* 1343 (1959).
140. Lebedeva, Z. I. and Markova, I. G., *Med. Prom. SSSR* **13**, 44 (1959).
141. Maurel, A. and Gastaud, J. M., *Chim. anal.* **41**, 469 (1959).
142. Nigam, I. C., Dhingra, D. R. and Gupta, G. N., *Perfumery Essent. Oil Record* **50**, 297 (1959).
143. Noguchi, M. and Kitajima, M., *Nippon Kagaku Zasshi* (*J. Chem. Soc Japan, Pure Chem. Sect.*) **80**, 1274 (1959).
144. Petrova, L. N., Novikova, E. N. and Skvortsova, I. B., *Zhur. Priklad Khim.* **32**, 1407 (1959).
145. Schulek, E. and Maros, L., *Magyar Kem. Folyoirat* **65**, 195 (1959); *Acta Chim. Acad. Sci. Hung.* **19**, 473 (1959).
146. Buděšinský, B. and Körbl, J., *Mikrochim. Acta* 697 (1960).
147. Gyenes, I., *Magyar Kem. Folyoirat* **66**, 55 (1960).
148. Klimova, V. A. and Zabrodina, K. C., *Zhur. Anal. Khim.* **15**, 726 (1960).
149. Matsubara, Y., Wakabayashi, S. and Morita, M., *J. Chem. Soc. Japan, Ind. Chem. Sect.* **63**, 1250 (1960).
150. Sikorska, D. and Hetnarska, K., *Chem. Anal.* (*Warsaw*) **5**, 1063 (1960).
151. Chwaliński, S. and Skorupski, W., *Chem. Anal.* (*Warsaw*) **5**, 1005 (1960).
152. Hennart, C. and Merlin, E., *Chim. anal.* **43**, 28 (1961).
153. Hennart, C., *Anal. Chim. Acta* **25**, 201 (1961).
154. Ruch, J. E., Johnson, J. B. and Critchfield, F. E., *Anal. Chem.* **33**, 1566 (1961).
155. Siggia, S. and Hanna, J. G., *Anal. Chem.* **33**, 896 (1961).
156. Bellen, Z. and Sekowska, B., *Chem. Anal.* (*Warsaw*) **6**, 201 (1961).
157. Bhalerao, V. R., Endres, J. E. and Kummerow, F. A., *J. Am. Oil Chemists' Soc.* **38**, 689 (1961).
158. Bukstab, Z. I. and Distanova, L. Ya., *Masloboino-Zhirovnaya Prom.* **27**, No. 11, 29 (1961).
159. Vakhtel, M. I. and Chernyakina, A. F., *Plasticheskie Massy* No. 2, 65 (1961).
160. Mikhlin, E. D., Gurvich, A. I. and Chukaeva, V. N., *Tr. Vses. Nauchn.-Issled. Vitamin. Inst.* **8**, 103 (1961).

161. Angelova, G., *Iz. Inst. po Obshcha Neorg. Khim., Bulgar. Akad. Nauk* **9**, 137 (1962).
162. Klyuev, Yu. P., Bel'kevich, P. I. and Goncharova, L. A., *Khim. i Genezis Torfa i Sapropelei, Akad. Nauk Belorussk. SSR, Inst. Torfa* 246 (1962).
163. Kumar, R. N., Bhat, G. N. and Kuloor, N. R., *Current Sci.* (*India*) **31**, 491 (1962).
164. Langmaier, F., *Kožařstvi* **12**, 140 (1962).
165. Pollak, F. G. and Lóránt, B., *Seifen, Öle, Fette, Wachse* **88**, 399 (1962).
166. Samoilov, S. M., Andrievskii, V. N. and Kotlyarevskii, I. L., *Izv. Akad. Nauk SSSR, Otd. Khim. Nauk* No. 2 201 (1962).
167. Skvortsova, A. B., Petrova, L. N. and Novikova, E. N., *Zhur. Anal Khim.* **17**, 896 (1962).
168. Belcher, R. and Fleet, B., *J. Chem. Soc.* 5720 (1963).
169. D'Hollander, R. and Antecinis, M., *Bull. Soc. Chim. Belge* **72**, 77 (1963).
170. Ömböly, C., *Acta Pharm. Hung.* **33**, 25 (1963).
171. Ruzhentseva, A. K. and Larina, P. N., *Med. Prom. SSSR* **17**, No. 1, 42 (1963).
172. Sihtola, H. and Neimo, L., *Paperi Puu* **45**, 543, 547 (1963).
173. Přibyl, M. and Slovák, Z., *Z. Anal. Chem.* **202**, 112 (1964).

50. Iodate and iodine pentoxide

Reagent. The potassium salt has been the iodate, always used as solid or in aqueous solution.

Reactions and materials titrated. Iodate reagent functions through its oxidizing properties. The organic compounds determined may undergo this oxidation. Or iodide present (in acid solution) may be oxidized to iodine which then reacts with the organic compound in another way.

Classification is, as usual, based on the reaction which the organic compound undergoes:

1. Oxidation. It is convenient to distinguish two types of determination here:

(i) Oxidation of the organic compound according to the equation

$$2\,IO_3^- + 12\,H^+ + 10\,\epsilon \rightarrow I_2 + 6\,H_2O$$

followed in some cases by:

$$I_2 + 2\,\epsilon \rightarrow 2\,I^-$$

so that the overall oxidation is:

$$IO_3^- + 6H^+ + 6\,\epsilon \rightarrow I^- + 3\,H_2O$$

A great variety of compound classes has been determined in this way, the most frequent examples being of carboxylic acids, hydrazine derivatives, ascorbic acid and the 'oxidation values' or 'reducing power' of various materials like sewage and urine.

Iodine pentoxide oxidizes according to the change:

$$I_2O_5 + 10\,H^+ + 10\,\epsilon \rightarrow I_2 + 5\,H_2O$$

and has been used for volatile organic compounds like ethanol, ethyl iodide, cyclopropane, and ethers.

(ii) Determination of acids, ranging from pure acids to the acid content of wines, fats, 'lac', etc. Iodide present is oxidized in amounts equivalent to the acid present, following the equation:

$$IO_3^- + 5\,I^- + 6\,H^+ \rightarrow 3\,I_2 + 3\,H_2O$$

This has been much used as an alternative, often more accurate, to titration of acids with alkali reagents. The liberated iodine can be titrated with thiosulphate with high accuracy. In many cases, excess thiosulphate is already present and the conclusion is an iodine back titration. These examples are given also under the reagent heading of Thiosulphate.

2. Ion/ion combination with I_3^-, derived from IO_3^-/I^-/acid, as in the determination of caffeine and theobromine

$$\text{Base} + H^+ + I_3^- \rightarrow (\text{Base.H})I_3 \text{ (precipitate)}$$

Iodate has been used in some Cu(II) reagents for determination of reducing sugars and has the purpose of oxidizing Cu(I) formed in the reaction. Unreacted iodate is then determined at the end. These examples are not included here, primarily because the iodate is used to oxidize an inorganic material.

Reaction conditions. For reactions of type 1(i), an acid solution is used, nearly always sulphuric acid which may be concentrated. Reactions of type 1(ii) require iodide in excess and those of type 2 need acid and iodide. Iodide pentoxide oxidations have been mostly at *ca* 200°, whereas iodate oxidations have been carried out at various temperatures.

Subsequent treatment and final titration stage. (i) In about one-third of the examples, unused reagent has been back titrated, employing one of the following three techniques:

1. Any iodine reaction product was boiled out, I^- added and the liberated iodine titrated with thiosulphate.

2. Back titration in the presence of conc. HCl/CCl_4, with iodine to the I^+ formation, shown by the end-point of disappearance of iodine colour from the CCl_4.

3. Back titration with thiosulphate of unused iodine formed in reactions of type 2.

(ii) Titration of iodine formed in reactions of type 1 (ii) and in some of the oxidations of type 1 (i) with iodate and with iodine pentoxide. Both thiosulphate and arsenite have been used. As already mentioned, excess thiosulphate has sometimes been present from the beginning of the determination and in these cases, unreacted thiosulphate has been back titrated with iodine.

(iii) In one determination of semicarbazide, the ammonia reaction product was liberated by alkali, distilled into excess acid and the latter back titrated with alkali. In two other determinations, namely of organic carbon in soils and of aldonic acids, the CO_2 formed was absorbed in $Ba(OH)_2$ and back titrated.

Examples

Materials titrated	Reagent and reaction conditions	Subsequent treatment and final titration stage	Ref.
Formic acid, also in presence of acetic acid	+ 50% HIO_3 solution; refluxed 1h, reacting: $5\,HCOOH + 2\,HIO_3 \rightarrow I_2 + 5\,CO_2 + 6\,H_2O$	Iodine distilled into KI solution and titrated with thiosulphate	1
Glycerol	In water, + IO_3^- + conc. H_2SO_4	Iodine distilled into KI solution and titrated with thiosulphate	2
Formic acid	+ IO_3^-/H_2SO_4; 30 min/*ca* 100°	Iodine boiled out, I^- added and titrated with thiosulphate	3
Acids in presence of salts, e.g. formic, malic, tartaric, citric, lactic, benzoic acids	+ IO_3^-/I^-; 5 min–24 h/room temp. Some heated	Titrated with thiosulphate	4
Oxalic acid	+ IO_3^- + dilute H_2SO_4; warmed	Iodine boiled out, I^- added and titrated with thiosulphate	5
Acetic acid from study of hydrolysis of acetic anhydride	+ IO_3^-/I^-	Titrated with thiosulphate	6

Materials titrated	Reagent and reaction conditions	Subsequent treatment and final titration stage	Ref.
Ether in, e.g., blood, air, water	Passed over I_2O_5 at 200°, giving iodine	Absorbed in KI solution and titrated with thiosulphate	7
Tartaric acid	+ IO_3^-/H_2SO_4; 30 min heating on sand bath	Diluted, iodine boiled out, I^- added and titrated with thiosulphate	8
Glycerol	+ IO_3^-/H_2SO_4; heated on sand bath	+ water, iodine boiled out, I^- added and titrated with thiosulphate	9
Ethyl iodide	Oxidized with I_2O_5 at *ca* 170°, giving iodine	Absorbed and titrated with thiosulphate	10, 12, 16, 23
Formic, citric, tartaric acids	Heated with IO_3^-/H_2SO_4	Iodine distilled out, I^- added and titrated with thiosulphate	11
Acids of pK not above 6	+ IO_3^-/I^- + excess thiosulphate; 30 min/room temp.	Back titrated with iodine	13
Acetylene	Passed into IO_3^-/H_2SO_4 at 190–200°	Iodine boiled off, I^- added and titrated with thiosulphate	14
Alkyl pyridinium iodides from determination of lower alkoxyl groups by reaction with HI and passing the alkyl iodides formed into pyridine	+ water + H_2SO_4 + IO_3^-	Liberated iodine passed into KI and titrated with thiosulphate	15
Semicarbazide from identification of semicarbazones by hydrolysis with H_2SO_4	Boiled with IO_3^-	Iodine boiled out, made alkaline and NH_3 distilled into excess H_2SO_4, back titrating with alkali	17
Naphthalene picrate, formed in determination of naphthalene	+ IO_3^-/I^-	Titrated with thiosulphate	18
Citric, tartaric acids	Heated with IO_3^-/conc. H_2SO_4	Iodine evaporated off, I^- added and titrated with thiosulphate	19
Higher fatty acids (notably unsaturated acids)	+ IO_3^-/I^- + excess thiosulphate	Back titrated with iodine	20
Xanthane, xanthone, xanthydrol, dixanthydrylurea, xanthylphenylacetamide and other similar compounds	Heated with IO_3^-/H_2SO_4	Iodine distilled out, I^- added and back titrated with thiosulphate	21

Materials titrated	Reagent and reaction conditions	Subsequent treatment and final titration stage	Ref.
Dixanthydryl-urea from determination of urea by precipitation with xanthydrol	Centrifuged precipitate + IO_3^- + H_2SO_4; 2–3 min boiling	Iodine boiled out, I^- added and titrated with thiosulphate	22
Picric acid, unused from reaction with, in determination of naphthalene	+ IO_3^-/I^-	Titrated with thiosulphate	24
'Acid number' of fats	In isopropanol, + IO_3^-/I^- + excess thiosulphate; 2·5 h/55–60°	+ excess iodine and back titrated with thiosulphate	25
Caffeine	+ IO_3^-/I^- + H_2SO_4; 1 h/room temp., giving periodide precipitate	Filtered and aliquot of filtrate titrated with thiosulphate	26
Theobromine/Na salicylate	+ IO_3^-/NaCl/HCl/ acetic acid; 1 h/room temp.	Filtered and titrated filtrate with thiosulphate	27
Picric acid, unused from reaction with, in determination of naphthalene	+ IO_3^-/I^-	Titrated with thiosulphate	28
Acetic acid from determination of hydroxyl groups in fatty materials by acetylation and hydrolysis of the acetyl products	+ IO_3^-/I^-	Titrated with thiosulphate	29
Ethanol in air, blood, urine, etc.	Carried over I_2O_5 at 180°, giving iodine and some HI	Absorbed in KI and titrated	30
Acetic acid from determination of acetyl groups by distillation with *p*-toluenesulphonic acid	+ IO_3^-/I^-; 20 min/*ca* 35°	Titrated with ithosulphate	31
Cyclopropane in air, water, blood	Carried over I_2O_5 on asbestos at *ca* 200°, giving iodine	Titrated with thiosulphate	32
Maleic acid from hydrolysis of the anhydride, unused from reaction with, in determination of conjugated olefine groups	+ IO_3^-/I^- + excess thiosulphate; 2 h with intermittent shaking	+ excess iodine and back titrated with thiosulphate	33

Materials titrated	Reagent and reaction conditions	Subsequent treatment and final titration stage	Ref.
Naphthalene picrate from determination of naphthalene by precipitation	+ IO_3^-/I^-	Titrated with thiosulphate	34
Hydrazine derivatives, e.g. semicarbazide hydrochloride or aminoguanidine	+ IO_3^-/H_2SO_4; 3 min/room temp.	+ I^- and titrated with thiosulphate	35
'Oxidation equivalent' of organic compounds, e.g. valine, sucrose, acetanilide	+ at least 100% excess IO_3^- + H_2SO_4; 20–40 min/185°	+ some $NaHCO_3$ to reduce acidity, + I^- and titrated with thiosulphate	36
'Oxygen consumption' of sewage	+ IO_3^-/65–80% H_2SO_4 at 200°	+ I^- and titrated with thiosulphate	37
Acetic acid from determination of acetyl groups by distillation with acid	+ IO_3^-/I^-; 2–2·5 h/room temp.	Titrated with thiosulphate	38
Some organic acids, e.g. glycollic and dibasic acids	+ IO_3^-/I^-	Titrated potentiometrically with thiosulphate	39
Dixanthydrylurea from determination of urea by reaction with xanthydrol	+ IO_3^-/H_2SO_4/a crystal of Na tungstate; 30 min/200° in a sealed tube	Iodine distilled into KI and titrated with thiosulphate	40
Acid content of certain fats	Method of ref. 25 (gave high results if peroxides present)		41
Acidity of wines	+ IO_3^-/I^- + excess thiosulphate; 24 h/room temp.	Titrated with iodine	42
Acetic acid (micro)	+ IO_3^-/50% H_2SO_4; 12–14 h/185°	+ I^- and titrated with thiosulphate	43
Divinyl ether in blood	Aerated through I_2O_5 on pumice at *ca* 200°	Iodine absorbed in KI solution and titrated with thiosulphate	44
Formic acid (standardization)	+ IO_3^-/I^-	Titrated with thiosulphate	45
Acids with no free amino groups	Method of ref. 13		46
Oxygen consumption of sewage	Method of ref. 37		47

Materials titrated	Reagent and reaction conditions	Subsequent treatment and final titration stage	Ref.
Ascorbic acid in grapes	+ IO_3^-/I^- + HCl; 1 h/room temp.	Titrated with thiosulphate	48
Citrates, tartrates	Heated with IO_3^-/H_2SO_4 until H_2SO_4 fumes were evolved (10–15 min)	Iodine boiled out, I^- added and titrated with thiosulphate in presence of $CHCl_3$	49
Ascorbic acid	+ I^- + H_2SO_4 + IO_3^-	Immediately titrated with thiosulphate potentiometrically	50
Trichloro-, tribromo- and monobromoacetic and sulphanilic acids	+ IO_3^-/I^-. Studied influence of IO_3^- and I^- concentration and of reaction time	Titrated with thiosulphate	51
Acid value of 'lac'	In 95% ethanol, + IO_3^-/I^- + excess thiosulphate. Shaken until clear solution	+ excess iodine and back titrated with thiosulphate	52
Carboxyl groups in cellulosic materials	+ IO_3^-/I^- + NaCl + excess thiosulphate; 24 h/room temp.	Back titrated with iodine	53
Fatty acids	In ethanol, + IO_3^-/I^- + excess thiosulphate	Titrated with iodine	54
Caffeine	+ IO_3^-/I^- + acid, giving precipitate of periodide	Filtered and filtrate titrated with thiosulphate	55
Isoniazid	+ IO_3^- + H_2SO_4	Titrated iodine formed with thiosulphate	56
Reducing power of urine	+ IO_3^- + H_2SO_4; 30 min/92–94°	+ I^- and titrated with thiosulphate	57
Cellulose	Heated with IO_3^-/H_2SO_4 (compared with bichromate oxidation)	Iodine boiled out, I^- added and titrated with thiosulphate	58
Isoniazid	+ IO_3^-/acid	Titrated iodine formed with thiosulphate	59
2,4-Dinitrophenylhydrazine; also unused from reaction with, in determination of carbonyl compounds	+ IO_3^- + conc. HCl	+ CCl_4 and titrated with iodine to permanent colour in the CCl_4 layer	60

Materials titrated	Reagent and reaction conditions	Subsequent treatment and final titration stage	Ref.
'Oxidation values' of non-volatile organic compounds, e.g. carboxylic acids and salts, sugars	+ *ca* 50% excess IO_3^- + H_3PO_4, heated to 80–240° until no more iodine evolved	Iodine absorbed in arsenite and back titrated with iodine	61
Semicarbazide, unused from reaction with, in determination of glyoxal + glyoxalic acid	+ acetic acid + IO_3^-; 2 min/room temp.	+ I^- and titrated with thiosulphate	62
K hydrogen tartrate, from determination of tartaric acid in wine	Dissolved in a little hot water, + $CaCl_2$, cooled and IO_3^-/I^- added; 20 min in dark	Titrated with thiosulphate	63
Acetic acid from determination of acetyl groups by heating with *p*-toluenesulphonic acid	+ IO_3^-/I^- + excess thiosulphate; 20 min/room temp.	Back titrated with iodine	**64**
Thiourea	+ IO_3^- + HCl + $HgCl_2$	Back titrated with As(III) amperometrically	65
Picric acid, unused from reaction with, in determination of nicotine	+ IO_3^-/I^-; 10 min/room temp. in the dark	Titrated with thiosulphate	66
Ascorbic acid	+ IO_3^-	Titrated with thiosulphate	67
Reaction product from determination of phthvazide by refluxing with H_2SO_4	+ IO_3^- + $CHCl_3$; 3 min shaking	Aqueous layer + I^- and titrated with thiosulphate	68
Carboxylic acid groups in cellulosic materials	+ IO_3^-/I^- + NaCl + excess thiosulphate; 1 h/60°	Titrated with iodine	69
Reaction products from determination of penicillin by treatment with NaOH	+ HCl + acetate buffer; + IO_3^-/I^-	Titrated with thiosulphate	70
Sulphanilamide	In ethanol, + HIO_3/70% ethanol, giving precipitate of the iodate	Unused reagent determined by adding I^- and titrating with thiosulphate, or by titration with NaOH to phenolphthalein	71

Materials titrated	Reagent and reaction conditions	Subsequent treatment and final titration stage	Ref.
Organic carbon in soils	+ $IO_3^-/Cr_2O_7^{2-}/H_2SO_4/H_3PO_4$; heated to 200°	CO_2 passed into NaOH, carbonate decomposed by lactic acid and CO_2 passed into $Ba(OH)_2$; back titrated with HCl to thymolphthalein	72
Unreacted semicarbazide from determination of oxidizing groups in oxidized cellulose	Filtrate, + H_2SO_4 + excess IO_3^-; 10 min	+ I^- and titrated with thiosulphate	73
Acids	Discussion of method of ref. 13		74
Indigo carmine	+ *ca* N H_2SO_4 + NaCl + excess IO_3^-, left until the blue colour had disappeared (also in HCl solution)	+ I^- and titrated with thiosulphate	75
Formates	+ excess IO_3^- + iodine; 30 min/*ca* 100°, reacting: $HCOO^- + I_2 \rightarrow H^+ + 2I^- + CO_2$, then $6H^+ + IO_3^- + 5I^- \rightarrow 3H_2O + 3I_2$	Iodine titrated with thiosulphate, H_2SO_4 added and retitrated, giving unreacted IO_3^-	76
Acid groups in the acid form of carboxymethyl cellulose	+ IO_3^-/I^-	Thiosulphate	77
Unused maleic anhydride from determination of *p*-mentha-3,8(9)-diene	Benzene solution, + water + IO_3^-/I^- + excess thiosulphate; 2 h/room temp.	+ excess iodine and back titrated with thiosulphate	78
Unused maleic anhydride after determination of diene number of dehydrated castor oil	+ IO_3^-/I^- + excess thiosulphate	+ excess iodine, then back titrated biamperometrically with thiosulphate	79
Aldonic acids	Oxidised with KIO_3 to CO_2	CO_2 absorbed in excess $Ba(OH)_2$; back titrated with HCl	80
Hydrazines (not good with aromatic hydrazines)	+ IO_3^-/acid or + HIO_3	+ I^- and titrated with thiosulphate	81
Furfuraldehyde	+ KIO_3/H_2SO_4; 30 min	Back titrated with thiosulphate	82
Acid number of oils	+ isopropanol + IO_3^-/I^- + excess thiosulphate; 90 min/80°	Back titrated with iodine	83

References

1. Béhal, A., *Ann. chim. phys.* (7) **20**, 411 (1900).
2. Chaumeil, A., *Bull. soc. chim., Paris* **27**, 629 (1902).
3. Rupp, E., *Arch. Pharm.* **243**, 98 (1905).
4. Kolthoff, I. M., *Pharm. Weekblad* **57**, 53 (1920).
5. Rosenthaler, L., *Z. anal. Chem.* **61**, 219 (1922).
6. Skrabal, A., *Monatsh.* **43**, 493 (1922).
7. Haggard, H. W., *J. Biol. Chem.* **55**, 131 (1923).
8. Strebinger, R. and Wolfram, J., *Österr. Chemiker-Ztg.* **26**, 156 (1923).
9. Strebinger, R. and Streit, J., *Z. anal. Chem.* **64**, 136 (1924).
10. Henderson, Y. and Haggard, H. W., *Am. J. Physiol.* **73**, 193 (1925).
11. Cuny, L., *J. pharm. chim.* (8) **3**, 112 (1926).
12. Henderson, Y., *Biochem. J.* **20**, 865 (1926).
13. Kolthoff, I. M., *Chem. Weekblad* **23**, 260 (1926).
14. Strebinger, R. and Wojs, A., *Z. anal. Chem.* **69**, 20 (1926).
15. Eaton, E. P. and West, E. S., *J. Biol. Chem.* **75**, 283 (1927).
16. Henderson, Y. and Haggard, H. W., *Am. J. Physiol.* **82**, 497 (1927).
17. Veibel, S., *Bull. soc. chim.* **41**, 1410 (1927).
18. Cundall, K. N., *Gas-Age Record* **62**, 393, 402 (1928).
19. Pirrone, F., *Riv. ital. essenze e profumi* 101 (1928).
20. Ruziczka, W., *J. prakt. Chem.* **123**, 61 (1929).
21. Cuny, L. and Robert, J., *J. pharm. chim.* (8) **11**, 241 (1930).
22. Cuny, L. and Robert, J., *J. pharm. chim.* (8) **11**, 337 (1930); *Bull. soc. chim. biol.* **12**, 171 (1930).
23. Henderson, Y. and Mobitz, W., *Am. J. Physiol.* **92**, 707 (1930).
24. Schläpfer, P. and Flachs, R., *J. usines gaz* **54**, 2, 25, 51 (1930).
25. Kaufmann, H. P., *Allgem. Öl Fett-Ztg.* **28**, 225, 248 (1931).
26. Mikó, G., *Magyar Gyógyszerésztud. Társaság Értesitöje* **8**, 291 (1932).
27. Mikó, G., *Magyar Gyógyszerésztud. Társaság Értesitöje* **8**, 34 (1932).
28. Pieters, H. A. J. and Smeets, G., *Het Gas* **52**, 134 (1932).
29. Fürth, O., Kaunitz, H. and Stein, H., *Biochem. Z.* **268**, 189 (1934).
30. Haggard, H. W. and Greenberg, L. A., *J. Pharm. Pharmacol.* **52**, 137 (1934).
31. Elek, A. and Harte, R. A., *Ind. Eng. Chem., Anal. Ed.* **8**, 267 (1936).
32. Robbins, B. H., *J. Pharm. Pharmacol.* **58**, 243 (1936).
33. Kaufmann, H. P., Baltes, J. and Büter, H., *Ber.* **70**, 903 (1937).
34. Seebaum, H. and Hartmann, E., *Brennstoffchemie* **18**, 464 (1937).
35. Smith, G. S., *J. Chem. Soc.* 1325 (1937).
36. Williams, R. J., Rohrman, E. and Christensen, B. E., *J. Am. Chem. Soc.* **59**, 291 (1937).
37. Dzyadzio, A. M., *Vodosnabzhenie i Sanit. Tekh.* No. 8–9, 117 (1938).
38. Suzuki, M., *J. Biochem. (Japan)* **27**, 367 (1938).
39. Balwant Singh and Sohan Singh, *J. Indian Chem. Soc.* **16**, 343 (1939).

40. Claudatus, I. and Botezatu, M., *Biochem. Z.* **300**, 325 (1939).
41. Kaufmann, H. P. and Lund, M., *Fette u. Seifen* **46**, 390 (1939).
42. Vièles, P., *Bull. soc. chim.* **6**, 1127 (1939).
43. Hurka, W., *Mikrochemie ver. Mikrochim. Acta* **30**, 228 (1942).
44. Ruigh, W. L., *Ind. Eng. Chem., Anal. Ed.* **14**, 32 (1942).
45. Alicino, J. F., *Ind. Eng. Chem., Anal. Ed.* **15**, 764 (1943).
46. Ruziczka, W., *Z. anal. Chem.* **126**, 94 (1943).
47. Johnson, D. W., Tsuchiya, H. M. and Halvorson, H. O., *Abstract 109th Meeting Am. Chem. Soc.*, p. 25, Atlantic City, 1946.
48. Nilov, G. I., *Vinodelie i Vinogradarstvo SSSR* **6**, No. 10, 10 (1946).
49. Unger, P. and Haynes, H. G., *Analyst* **71**, 141 (1946).
50. Spacu, G. and Spacu, P., *Z. anal. Chem.* **128**, 233 (1948).
51. Lalić, M. R. and Canić, V. D., *Bull. soc. chim., Belgrade* **14**, 111 (1949).
52. Kamath, N. R. and Mainkar, V. B., *Anal. Chem.* **22**, 724 (1950).
53. Nabar, G. M. and Padmanabhan, C. V., *Proc. Indian Acad. Sci.* **31A**, 371 (1950).
54. Ruziczka, W., *Chim. anal.* **32**, 33 (1950).
55. Wade, P. and Hannen, J., *J. Sci. Food Agric.* **1**, 177 (1950).
56. Kottionis, A., *Chim. Chronika (Athens)* **17**, 78 (1952).
57. Nishikaze, O., *Igaku to Seibutsugaku (Med. & Biol.)* **25**, 1 (1952).
58. Kleinert, T. and Wincor, W., *Tappi* **36**, 507 (1953).
59. Struszynski, M. and Bellen, Z., *Przemysl Chem.* **32**, 40 (1953).
60. Barke, D. J. and Cole, E. P., *J. Appl. Chem. (London)* **5**, 477 (1955).
61. Ohashi, S., *Bull. Chem. Soc., Japan* **28**, 171 (1955).
62. Salzer, F., *Z. anal. Chem.* **146**, 260 (1955).
63. Gorbach, G. and Vaupotitsch, W., *Fette, Seifen Anstrichmittel* **58**, 865 (1956).
64. Mizukami, S., Ieki, T. and Koyama, C., *J. Pharm Soc. Japan* **76**, 465 (1956).
65. Bapat, M. G. and Sharma, B., *Z. anal. Chem.* **157**, 258 (1957).
66. Gorbach, G. and Kögler, H., *Mikrochim. Acta* 572 (1957).
67. Indovina, R. and DeLeo, E., *Conserve e deriv. agrumari (Palermo)* **6**, 115 (1957).
68. Shub, M. E. and Volkova, N. S., *Aptechnoe Delo* **6**, No. 6, 59 (1957).
69. Achwal, W. B., Nabar, G. M. and Padmanabhan, C. V., *J. Sci. Ind. Research (India)* **17B**, 497 (1958).
70. Spacu, P. and Pirtea, T. I., *Analele univ. C. I. Parhon, Bucuresti, Ser. stiint. nat.* No. 20, 48 (1958).
71. Macarovici, C. G. and Dorutui, A., *Studia Univ. Babes-Bolyai*, Ser. 1. No. 2, 115 (1959).
72. Watkinson, J. H., *Analyst* **84**, 629 (1959).
73. Yamamoto, J. and Miyata, T., *Kogyo Kagaku Zasshi* **62**, 433 (1959).
74. Ruziczka, W., *Österr. Chemiker-Ztg.* **61**, 298 (1960).

75. Gopala Rao, G. and Venkateswara Rao, N., *Acta Chem. Acad. Sci. Hung.* **26**, 489 (1961).
76. Verma, R. M. and Bose, S., *J. Indian Chem. Soc.* **38**, 109 (1961).
77. Ghosh, K. G. and Balakrishna, K. J., *J. Sci. Ind. Research, India* (*B*) **21**, 194 (1962).
78. Dässler, H-G., *Pharm. Zentralhalle* **101**, 409 (1962).
79. Jedlinski, Z. and Paprotny, J., *Chem. Anal.* (*Warsaw*) **8**, 765 (1963).
80. Maros, L., Perl, I., Vajda, M. and Schulek, E., *Magyar Kem. Folyoirat* **69**, 123 (1963).
81. Marzadro, M. and De Carolis, A., *Mikrochim. Acta* 726 (1963).
82. Tikhonova, V. I., *Izv. Vysshikh. Uchebn. Zavedenii, Khim. i Khim. Tekhnol.* **6**, 744 (1963).
83. Vallant, H., *Michrochim. Acta* 93 (1963).

51. Iodides and hydriodic acid

Reagent. Either hydriodic acid (relatively concentrated such as the 57% acid or higher) used directly; or iodides (mostly sodium or potassium) in the presence of acid, which is nearly always a mineral acid (HCl or H_2SO_4) or acetic acid. Methyl and ethyl iodides have also been used in a few determinations.

Reactions and materials titrated. Almost all examples are of two types:

1. Reaction of compounds containing lower alkyl groups joined to O, N or S, with formation of volatile lower alkyl iodides; for example

$$R.O.CH_3 + HI \rightarrow R.OH + CH_3I$$

This reaction may be regarded as hydrolysis, dealkylation or even replacement.

Some related groups like $—CH_2—CH_2—O—$ react similarly but may yield ethylene in addition to ethyl iodide.

Mostly ethers have been determined in methods based on this reaction; other compound classes determined include esters; lower alcohols like ethanol; polymers based on ethylene oxide; secondary amines containing a *N*-alkyl group and sulphides like methionine which contain $S—CH_3$. Apart from this wide analytical use, the method has been used to study the constitution of materials of higher molecular weight like lignins, cellulose ethers, etc., through determination of the number of alkoxy groups present.

2. Reduction of a wide variety of functional groups. Determinations of peroxides and related compounds like peracids, hydroperoxides,

peresters, etc., have been extensively carried out. Some of these have been kinetic or decomposition studies related to the use of peroxides as polymerization catalysts.

Other functional groups and compound classes determined by reduction include: quinones; nitro, nitroso, azo, iodoso and iodoxy compounds; nitrite esters; disulphides; sulphoxides; *N*-oxides; numerous halides in which there are reactive halogen atoms joined to nitrogen (e.g. chloramines, Tillmans' reagent), to oxygen (organic hypohalites), to sulphur (sulphonyl and sulphenyl chlorides), to selenium; or to carbonyl groups (phosgene, pentabromoacetone from determination of citric acid, or compounds containing the —CO—CHBr— group derived from the bromometric determination of enols). In all cases, iodine is a reaction product;

$$R.CO.O.O.CO.R + 2\,HI \rightarrow 2\,RCOOH + I_2$$

$$OC\begin{matrix} \diagup HC{=}CH \diagdown \\ \diagdown HC{=}CH \diagup \end{matrix}CO + 2\,HI \rightarrow \underset{OH}{\underset{|}{C}}\begin{matrix} {=}HC{-}CH{=} \\ \diagdown HC{-}CH \diagup \end{matrix}\underset{OH}{\underset{|}{C}} + I_2$$

$$RNO + 4\,HI \rightarrow RNH_2 + 2\,I_2 + H_2O$$

$$RR'S{\rightarrow}O + 2\,HI \rightarrow RR'S + I_2 + H_2O$$

$$RSO_2NHBr + 2\,HI \rightarrow RSO_2NH_2 + I_2 + HBr$$

$$2\,RSCl + 2\,HI \rightarrow RS.SR + I_2 + 2\,HCl$$

$$COCl_2 + 2\,HI \rightarrow CO + I_2 + 2\,HCl$$

(References to the determination of unused percarboxylic acids and quinones from determinations of olefines and conjugated olefines respectively, are, with few exceptions, not included here; see under these two reagent headings.)

Reduction with HI has sometimes been used as a preliminary stage in the Kjeldahl nitrogen determination of compounds containing notably N—N or N—O links. Since this is generally element analysis, it is not considered here. Where it has been used to determine a nitrogen-containing compound class in absence of other nitrogen-containing compounds, examples may be included, as for nitriles (ref. 95 for example).

3. Halogen exchange in a few cases where chlorine or bromine atoms have been replaced by iodine. Some kinetic studies of reactivity differ-

ences have been carried out in this way and the data used for analysis of binary mixtures.

Where unstable iodides are thus formed, they decompose to yield iodine, e.g.

$$BrCH_2{-}CH_2Br \xrightarrow{HI} ICH_2{-}CH_2I \longrightarrow CH_2{=}CH_2 + I_2$$

4. Addition, as in determination of epoxides

$$\underset{\text{(epoxide, bridged by O)}}{RCH - CHR'} + HI \rightarrow \underset{\;OH\qquad I}{RCH - CHR'}$$

(this principle is better known with HCl or HBr reagents). Addition can also be considered to occur in the determination of certain nitrogen bases or sulphides by reaction with a lower alkyl iodide to give quaternary iodides (e.g. refs 97, 215, 254) and sulphonium iodides (ref. 195) respectively.

$$R_3N + R'I \rightarrow (R_3R'N)^+I^-$$

$$R_2S + R'I \rightarrow (R_2R'S)^+I^-$$

(This has been given also under the reagent heading of Halides (Active).)

5. Single examples are given in the tables of transesterification (determination of dimethyl sulphate by conversion into methyl iodide); of replacement (determination of phenyl mercuric acetate by conversion to phenyl mercuric iodide); and of conversion of quaternary ammonium chlorides to iodides, separable by extraction into $CHCl_3$.

Reaction conditions. For reactions of type 1, a hydriodic acid reagent of at least 57% strength is generally used. Much discussion has raged about the best reaction conditions. Prime considerations are:

(a) Solvents without traces of alkoxyl groups and which dissolve both the hydriodic acid and the sample. Phenol, acetic and propionic acids and anhydrides have been those chiefly employed but there is disagreement about their relative merits. Probably no solvent or solvent mixture is suitable for all cases. Some authors have recommended working without a solvent but this is probably practicable only with samples which are at least slightly soluble in the hydriodic acid.

(b) A temperature high enough for complete reaction within a reasonable time (for the determination of N—CH_3 groups, temperatures of well over 300° are needed) and to help drive out the alkyl iodide.

(c) Hydriodic acid, iodine and any hydrogen sulphide (from sulphur-containing materials) must be prevented from reaching the ultimate absorption vessel for the alkyl iodide. Many washing devices have been proposed.

For reactions of type 2, especially the determination of peroxides, there is a variation of opinion about the best solvents; many such as alcohols, acetone, halides and acetic acid have been used. An atmosphere of inert gas has frequently been recommended, often realized by addition of a pellet of solid CO_2 to the reaction mixture or of some $NaHCO_3$ to an acidic solvent mixture.

Subsequent treatment and final titration stage. (i) In most cases, the determination is concluded by titration of iodide, iodate or iodine. The tabulation below gives a survey of the chief principles:

Initial reaction	Subsequent treatment	End product
Formation of alkyl iodide in reactions of type 1	+ Br_2 (then unused removed with formic acid, phenol, allyl alcohol or other agent)	*Iodate*, via reactions; $RI + Br_2 \rightarrow IBr + RBr$ $IBr + 2\,Br_2 + 3\,H_2O \rightarrow HIO_3 + 5\,HBr$
	+ $AgNO_3$	*Iodide*, giving silver iodide
	+ pyridine, $(CH_3)_3N$ or aniline	Quaternary or alkylanilinium *iodide*
	combustion	*Iodine*
Reduction in reactions of type 2	—	*Iodine*
Some halogen replacements of type 3	—	*Iodine*
Some additions, reactions of type 4	—	Quaternary ammonium or sulphonium *iodides*

The final titration stages which have been used are classified here:

(a) Iodine determination. This has nearly always been by direct titration with thiosulphate. Occasionally excess thiosulphate has been used, followed by back titration with iodine. In one instance, the reaction was carried out in the presence of excess thioglycollic acid, the unused part of which was titrated with iodine. In another, a sulphur dioxide titrant was used. Arsenite appears not to have been employed as a titrant.

(b) Iodate determination. By addition of I^-/acid and titration with thiosulphate of the iodine formed.

(c) Iodide determination (unused or that formed in the reaction). Many techniques have been tried:

1. Titration with Ag^+, direct or indirect, using excess reagent and back titrating with SCN^-. In the determination of alkyl iodides from reactions of type 1 by passing into $AgNO_3$, a gravimetric method has been used as well as back titration with SCN^- of unused Ag^+, and was in fact the original principle (Zeisel, 1885–6).

2. Titration with iodate, or addition of iodate and titration of the iodine liberated.

3. Addition of Hg(OH)CN and titration of the OH^- liberated.

4. Passage through an ion exchanger, giving an equivalent amount of OH^-, titrated with acid.

5. Titration with $[(n\text{-}C_4H_9)_4N]^+OH^-$ or $NaOCH_3$ in non-aqueous solution.

6. Oxidized to iodate with a bromine reagent similar to that used to oxidize alkyl iodides; this was followed by addition of I^-/acid and thiosulphate titration as in (b) above.

(ii) Other conclusions of a determination with an iodide reagent have been:

Titration of unused hydriodic acid after addition to α-epoxides (reaction of type 4).

Distillation and titration of ammonia from reduction of nitriles with hydriodic acid and from Kjeldahl digestion of nitro compounds likewise reduced.

Distillation and titration of methylamine in determination of certain heterocyclic nitrogen compounds by ring-splitting with an alkyl iodide/alkali reagent.

Titration of unused hexamine after precipitation with measured excess base, of a quaternary iodide formed from allyl-type chlorides and iodide.

Determination using excess bromine or iodine monochloride reagents (with back titration of unused) of ethylene yielded together with ethyl iodide from ethylene oxide derivatives.

Titration with a mercury (II) reagent of the mercaptan (cysteine) derived from HI reduction of disulphide (cystine).

Examples

As mentioned above, the alkoxyl determination (reaction of type 1) has been extensively used and studied. A selection of examples but with little or no detail of reaction conditions is given below.

In the third column of the tables, the word 'thiosulphate' serves as abbreviation for 'titrated with thiosulphate'. The end-point is visual (disappearance of the yellow iodine colour or of the starch colour) unless otherwise specified.

Materials titrated	Reagent and reaction conditions	Subsequent treatment and final titration stage	Ref.
Iodosobenzoic acid	+ I^-/H_2SO_4; brief warming on water bath	Thiosulphate	1
Iodoso and iodoxy compounds	+ I^-/HCl or acetic acid	Thiosulphate	2
Quinones	In a little 95% ethanol, + I^-/HCl; *ca* 0°	Thiosulphate	3, 4
Quinones	In a little ethanol, + I^-/HCl	Thiosulphate	5
Quinones	+ I^-/H_2SO_4	+ $NaHCO_3$ + excess thiosulphate; aqueous layer titrated with iodine	6
Compounds containing *N*-chlorine atoms, e.g. hydantoin chlorides, CO—NCl, CR₂—NCl ring with >CO	In benzene, + I^-; well shaken	+ $NaHCO_3$; thiosulphate	7
Quinones	In ether, + I^-/H_2SO_4; at least 2 min/room temp.	+ water + excess thiosulphate; aqueous layer titrated with iodine	8
Compounds containing the —CO—CHBr group, from determination of enols by reaction with bromine	+ I^-; 10 min/35°	Thiosulphate	9, 10
Peracids (after removal of H_2O_2 by MnO_4^- titration)	+ I^-/H_2SO_4	Thiosulphate	11

Materials titrated	Reagent and reaction conditions	Subsequent treatment and final titration stage	Ref.
Methoxy groups	Distilled with HI, giving CH_3I	Passed in air stream over pumice heated to 800°, giving iodine; titrated with thiosulphate (see Pyrolysis, ref. 1)	12
Methoxyl groups	Distilled with HI, giving CH_3I	Passed into pyridine, giving methyl pyridinium iodide; titrated with Ag^+ to CrO_4^- indicator; also + excess Ag^+, then + excess NaCl and final titration with Ag^+ (see Part I, Silver (I), ref. 4)	13
Benzoyl peroxide	In ethanol + I^- + acid; 4 h/*ca* 100°	Thiosulphate	14
Anthradiquinone (1,4,9,10-)	In $CHCl_3$, + ethanol/water + I^-	Thiosulphate	15
Perchlorate of di *p*-anisylhydroxyl-ammonium *N*-oxide	In acetic acid, + I^-	+ water; thiosulphate	16
Oxidation value of dehydrotetrachloro-*p*-cresol, α- or β-naphthol	In moist ethanol or acetone, + drops H_2SO_4 + I^-	Thiosulphate	17
Compounds with the —CO—CHBr group, from determination of enols by reaction with bromine	+ I^- (some react rather slowly)	Thiosulphate	18
Nitrite esters from determination of lower alcohols by reaction with HNO_2	Passed through I^-/HCl	Thiosulphate	19, 20
Benzoyl peroxide	In acetone + I^-/water, weakly acidified	Thiosulphate	21
Lower alkoxyl groups	Distilled with HI, giving alkyl iodide	Passed into pyridine, giving alkyl pyridinium iodide; oxidized with IO_3^- and titrated with thiosulphate (see Iodate, ref. 15)	22
Benzoquinone, from determination of hydroquinone by oxidation with $FeCl_3$	Extract in $CHCl_3$ or benzene, + I^-/H_2SO_4	Thiosulphate	23

R

Materials titrated	Reagent and reaction conditions	Subsequent treatment and final titration stage	Ref.
Meriquinonoid salt (chloride, perchlorate, etc.) of 2,3,6,7-tetramethoxythianthrene	$+ I^- +$ acetic acid; warmed	Thiosulphate	24
Organic peroxides in oxidized linseed oil, etc.	In acetic acid, $+ I^-$; a few min/room temp.	+ water; thiosulphate	25
Peroxides in ether	+ ethanol $+ I^- +$ HCl. Nitrogen atmosphere; 1 h in dark/room temp.	Thiosulphate	26
1,2-, racemic 2,3- and meso-2,3-dibromobutanes, from addition of bromine to butenes (suggested as a method of analysis of butene mixtures)	$+ I^-$/methanol; various reaction times/60 or 75° (react at different speeds)	Thiosulphate	27
Unused peracetic acid from determination of unsaturated fatty acids and oils	$+ I^-/H_2SO_4$	Thiosulphate	28
Methoxyl and ethoxyl groups	Heated with HI/red phosphorus, giving alkyl iodide; 1 h/140°	Carried into a bromine reagent, oxidizing to IBr and then IO_3^-; $+ I^-$/acid and titrated with thiosulphate (see Bromine reagents, ref. 79)	29
Methoxyl and ethoxyl groups (micro)	Method of ref. 29 adapted to the smaller scale; 20–30 min reflux. See also Bromine reagents, ref. 80)		30
Pentabromoacetone from determination of citric acid by oxidation with $MnO_4^-/Br^-/H_2SO_4$	In 95% ethanol, $+ I^- +$ acetic acid; 3–5 min/100°, then 10–15 min/room temp.	+ water; thiosulphate	31
'Active oxygen' (peroxides) in fats	In acetic acid/$CHCl_3$, 2:1, $+ I^-$. Nitrogen atmosphere	Thiosulphate	32
$COCl_2$	$+ I^-$/acetone	Thiosulphate	33
Peroxides in oils and fats (rancidity determination)	In acetic acid, $+ I^-$; various reaction times and temperatures, depending on degree and nature of rancidity	Thiosulphate	34

Materials titrated	Reagent and reaction conditions	Subsequent treatment and final titration stage	Ref.
Methionine in proteins	Heated with HI, giving methyl iodide	Absorbed in excess $AgNO_3$, filtered and back titrated with SCN^-	35
Methoxyl groups	Heated with HI/phenol/ acetic or propionic anhydride	Determined by method of ref. 29 (see Bromine reagents, ref. 92)	36
Methoxyl and ethoxyl groups	Heated with HI/phenol in slight modification of method of ref. 29	Method of ref. 29 (see Bromine reagents, refs 95 and 176)	37, 66
2,6-Dichlorophenol-indophenol	+ I^-/dil. H_2SO_4	Thiosulphate	38
2,4,6-Tribromophenyl hypobromite, $C_6H_2Br_3.OBr$, from determination of phenol by bromination	+ I^-	Thiosulphate	39
Methoxyl, *N*-methyl groups	Heated with HI	Determined by principle of method of ref. 29 (see Bromine reagents, ref. 103)	40
Peroxides in vegetable oils	In acetic acid/$CHCl_3$, 3:2, + saturated I^- solution; *ca* 1 min/room temp.	+ water; thiosulphate	41
Peroxides in ether	+ dry ethanol + K_2CdI_4/dilute acetic acid; 1 h in dark/room temp.	Thiosulphate	42
Methionine in proteins	Slight modification of procedure of ref. 29 (see Bromine reagents, ref. 115)		43
Methyl nitrite from determination of methanol by reaction with HNO_2	Carried by CO_2 current into I^-/HCl	Thiosulphate	44, 45
$COCl_2$	Absorbed in I^-/acetone, giving iodine and also reacting; $COCl_2 + (CH_3)_2CO \rightarrow HCl + CH_3{-}C({=}CH_2){-}O{-}COCl$	$+IO_3^-$ (to react with acid formed,) + excess thiosulphate (to react with any iodoacetone formed); titrated with iodine after at least 30 min/room temp.	46

Materials titrated	Reagent and reaction conditions	Subsequent treatment and final titration stage	Ref.
Methoxyl and ethoxyl groups in vanillin, pectin, etc.	Heated with HI, giving alkyl iodide	Determined by principle of method of ref. 29 but destroyed excess bromine with phenol (see Bromine reagents, ref. 122)	47
Peroxides in autoxidized fats	In acetic acid/$CHCl_3$ or CCl_4, 2:1 + I^-; 1 min/100°	+ water; thiosulphate	48
Methoxyl groups	Slight modification of method of ref. 29 (see Bromine reagents, ref. 132)		49
1-Chloro-2-methyl- and 1-chloro-3-methylbutane	+ I^-/acetone. Various reaction times (12–60 h)/ 60°. React at different rates	+ ice/$CHCl_3$/HCl and unused I^- determined by titration with IO_3^- to decoloration of the $CHCl_3$ layer	50
Methoxyl, ethoxyl groups	Heated with HI	Alkyl iodide passed into excess $AgNO_3$ and unused back titrated	51
Methyl nitrite from determination of methanol derived from acid hydrolysis of wood methoxy groups	Carried into I^-/acid	Thiosulphate	52
Methionine in protein hydrolysates	+ HI; 6 h digestion, reducing $-SCH_3$ to $-SH$ (homocysteine)	+ excess $Na_2S_4O_6$ + NH_4OH oxidizing the homocysteine and giving $S_2O_3^{2-}$; + HCl and titrated with IO_3^- (see Tetrathionate)	53
Ascaridole	In acetic acid + I^-. Not more than 5 min/room temp.	Thiosulphate	54
Methoxyl groups	Heated with HI	Method of ref. 29 (see Bromine reagents, ref. 142)	55
Tetranitromethane	+ I^-/water or water/ alcohol (neutral solutions); 15 min–1 h/room temp. in light with shaking, reacting; $C(NO_2)_4 + 2\,I^- \rightarrow (NO_2)_2C{=}N{\overset{\nearrow O}{\underset{\searrow O^-}{}}} + NO_2^- + I_2$	Thiosulphate	56

Materials titrated	Reagent and reaction conditions	Subsequent treatment and final titration stage	Ref.
1,2-Dibromoethane	+ I^-/ethanol; 3 h reflux (not quite complete reaction)	Thiosulphate	57
2,6-Dichlorophenol-indophenol	+ I^-/dil. H_2SO_4	Thiosulphate	58
Compounds containing the —CO—CHBr— group from determination of enols (e.g. dibenzoyl-methane) with bromine	+ I^-; 5–10 min/room temp.	Thiosulphate	59
Peroxides in unsaturated fat acids	In $CHCl_3$ or CCl_4, + I^-/acetic acid. Nitrogen or CO_2 atmosphere; 1 h/room temp.	+ water; thiosulphate	60
O-Methyl and *N*-methyl groups in volatile compounds	Adaptation of method of ref. 29 (see Bromine reagents, ref. 158)		61
Lower alkoxyl groups	Note on the technique of method of ref. 29 (see Bromine reagents, ref. 162)		62
2,6-Dichlorophenol-indophenol	+ I^-/dil. H_2SO_4	Thiosulphate	63
Alcohols, polyalcohols	+ HI ($d = 1{\cdot}96$); 5 h heating, reacting: $ROH + HI \rightarrow RI + H_2O$ $RI + HI \rightarrow RH + I_2$	Thiosulphate; then titrated with NaOH to phenolphthalein. Control. ROH = HI used minus I_2 formed	64
Peroxides in unsaturated hydrocarbons, gasoline	+ I^-/water/H_2SO_4	Unused I^- extracted with water, oxidized with Fe(III) and titrated with thiosulphate	65
Lower alkoxyl groups (micro)	Slight modification of method of ref. 29 (see Bromine reagents, ref. 177)		67
N,N'-Dichlorodi-imine, from determination of *p*-diamines by reaction with hypochlorite	+ I^-/HCl	Thiosulphate	68
Nitrosobenzene	In ethanol/water, + I^-/HCl. A few min/room temp.	Thiosulphate	69
Methoxyl groups in pulp and plant materials	Method of ref. 29 (see Bromine reagents, ref. 183)		70

Materials titrated	Reagent and reaction conditions	Subsequent treatment and final titration stage	Ref.
Peroxide values of milk powder fats	Extract in $CHCl_3$/acetic acid, + saturated I^-/water; 1 min shaking/room temp.	+ water; thiosulphate	71
Ethoxyl groups in ketene acetals	Heated with HI	Technique of method of ref. 29 (see Bromine reagents, ref. 188)	72
Sulphoxide from determination of methionine by oxidation with $H_2O_2/HClO_4$	+ I^-	Thiosulphate	73
Peroxides in n-butyl ether	+ I^-/acetic acid/ $NaHCO_3$ (to give CO_2 and prevent oxygen access)	Thiosulphate	74
Lower alkyl nitrite esters from determination of lower alcohols by reaction with HNO_2	Carried into I^-/acid	Thiosulphate	75
Methoxyl, ethoxyl groups	Heated with HI	Passed into excess standard $AgNO_3$ and unused titrated with SCN^- (see Silver (I), ref. 67)	76
Lower alkoxyl groups	Modification of method of ref. 29 (see Bromine reagents, ref. 198)		77
Peroxides	In isopropanol, + I^-/acetic acid; 2–5 min boiling	Thiosulphate (hot solution titrated)	78
Peroxides in oils and fats	In $CHCl_3$/acetic acid, + I^-/water; 1 h in dark/room temp.	Thiosulphate	79
Peroxides in fish oils	+ CCl_4 or $CHCl_3$ + acetic acid + I^-; 1 min in dark/room temp.	+ dil. HCl; thiosulphate visually or potentiometrically	80
2,6-Dichlorophenol-indophenol	+ I^-/dil. H_2SO_4	Thiosulphate	81
Methoxyl groups, e.g. in lignin preparations	Slight modification of method of ref. 29 (see Bromine reagents, ref. 211)		82
Nitrite esters	+ I^-/acid; CO_2 atmosphere	Thiosulphate	83

Materials titrated	Reagent and reaction conditions	Subsequent treatment and final titration stage	Ref.
Ethanol, distilled from blood	Principle of method of ref. 29 (see Bromine reagents, ref. 214)		84
Lower alkoxyl groups	Slight modification of method of ref. 29 (see Bromine reagents, ref. 218)		85
Phenyl sulphenyl chloride C_6H_5SCl	In CCl_4 + I^-/water. A few min shaking	+ excess thiosulphate and titrated with iodine	86
Methoxyl + ethoxyl groups	Method of ref. 29		
methoxyl groups	heated with HI, giving methyl iodide	passed into trimethylamine/ethanol, giving insoluble tetramethylammonium iodide. Separated and determined by bromine oxidation as in method of ref. 29 (see Bromine reagents, ref. 227)	87
α,β-Dibromocinnamic acid from determination of cinnamic acid by bromine addition	+ I^-/ethanol; 30 min reflux, giving cinnamic acid and iodine	Thiosulphate	88
Lower alkoxyl groups	Method of ref. 29 (see Bromine reagents, ref. 231)		89
Lower alkoxyl groups	Heated with HI as in method of ref. 29, giving alkyl iodide	Carried into pyridine, excess pyridine removed under reduced pressure, water added and Hg(OH)CN, reacting with I^- giving Hg(I)CN and OH^-; titrated with H_2SO_4 (see Amines and heterocyclic bases, ref. 26)	90
2-Methyl-1,4-naphthaquinone	+ HCl + 95% ethanol + I^-	Thiosulphate	91
Benzoyl peroxide in study of styrene polymerization	In acetone/benzene/acetic acid, 4:2:1, + solid CO_2 (giving CO_2 atmosphere) + I^-; 10–15 min/room temp.	+ water; thiosulphate	92
N-Methyl groups	Heated with HI/phenol/ammonium iodide, giving methyl iodide	Determined as in method of ref. 29 (see Bromine reagents, ref. 239)	93
Methyl ester content of pectin	Method of ref. 37		94

Materials titrated	Reagent and reaction conditions	Subsequent treatment and final titration stage	Ref.
Nitriles	+ I^-/H_2SO_4; 45 min/100°, giving NH_3	Made alkaline and distilled into H_2SO_4; back titrated with alkali to Na alizarinsulphonate/indigocarmine	95
Peroxide values of oils and fats	+ $CHCl_3$/acetic acid, 1:2 + I^-/water. Inert atmosphere; 1 h in dark/room temp.	Thiosulphate	96
Trimethylamine	Passed into methyl iodide/ethanol giving insoluble tetramethylammonium iodide	Excess methyl iodide distilled off and residue titrated with Ag^+	97
Benzoyl peroxide in study of its decomposition in various solvents	Aliquot + acetic acid + I^- + solid CO_2; 5 min/room temp.	+ water; thiosulphate	98
Peroxides in edible fats	+ $CHCl_3$/acetic acid, 2:3, + I^-/water. Inert atmosphere; 2 min/77° or 1 h in dark/room temp.	+ water; thiosulphate	99
Some organic selenium compounds with Se—Hal or Se—O— links	In CCl_4, + I^-/H_2SO_4. Few min shaking	Thiosulphate	100
Active oxygen of *t*-butyl peresters (e.g. perbenzoate, perfuroate, perstearate)	In acetone/acetic acid, + I^-; 3–4 h/room temp.	Thiosulphate	101
Ethers and esters of ethylene and propylene glycols	Heated with HI; 30 min–2 h, giving mixture of ethyl iodide and ethylene or isopropyl iodide and propylene respectively	Alkyl iodide determined by absorption in $AgNO_3$ and back titration with SCN^-; olefines by absorption in bromine reagent and titrating unused (see Bromine reagents, ref. 244 and Silver (I), ref. 82)	102
Organic peroxides	+ acetic anhydride + I^- (claimed that acetic acid catalyses the I^-/air oxygen reaction); 5–20 min/room temp.	+ water; thiosulphate	103
Phenacetin	Method of ref. 85	(see Bromine reagents, ref. 255)	104

Materials titrated	Reagent and reaction conditions	Subsequent treatment and final titration stage	Ref.
Total peroxides from oxidation of propane (including H_2O_2)	+ I^-/dil. H_2SO_4; 15 min in dark/room temp.	Thiosulphate	105
Peroxides in oxidized methyl linoleate	In $CHCl_3$/acetic acid, 1:2, + I^-/methanol. Nitrogen atmosphere; 15 min/35°	+ water; thiosulphate	106
Butoxyl groups in urea/HCHO resin fibres	Method of ref. 89, with 3 h boiling (see Bromine reagents, ref. 267)		107
Organic peroxides	+ isopropanol + a little acetic acid + I^-; 5 min reflux	+ water; thiosulphate	108
'Dimalone', insect repellent of formula (CH=CH, CH–CH₂–CH bridged ring with two CH.COOCH₃ groups)	Method of ref. 29 (see Bromine reagents, ref. 276)		109
Aliphatic peracids (after titration with Ce(IV) to remove H_2O_2)	+ I^-	Thiosulphate	110
Ascaridole in chenopodium oil	+ I^-/acid	Thiosulphate	111
Pentabromoacetone from determination of citric acid by reaction with $MnO_4^-/Br^-/H_2SO_4$	+ I^-/oxalic acid; 3–5 min boiling	+ water; thiosulphate	112
Peroxides in oil, lard and butter	In $CHCl_3$ or CCl_4, + I^- + HCl + acetic acid; CO_2 atmosphere; 5 min/room temp.	+ water, thiosulphate	113
$COCl_2$ (liquid)	+ dry acetone + dry NaI; 3 min shaking; $COCl_2 + 2I^- \rightarrow CO + I_2 + 2Cl^-$; $COCl_2 + H_2O \rightarrow CO_2 + 2HCl$	Thiosulphate; acid determined by titration with NaOH to bromothymol blue/phenol red or by adding IO_3^- and re-titrating with thiosulphate	114
Peroxides, e.g. benzoyl	In acetic acid, + $NaHCO_3$ + I^-; 15 min in dark/room temp.	+ water; thiosulphate	115

$$\begin{array}{l} CH \diagup CH \diagdown CH.COOCH_3 \\ \| \quad | \quad CH_2 \quad | \\ CH \diagdown CH \diagup CH.COOCH_3 \end{array}$$

Materials titrated	Reagent and reaction conditions	Subsequent treatment and final titration stage	Ref.
Peroxides	In acetic acid/$CHCl_3$ + I^-. Nitrogen atmosphere; 1 h/room temp.	+ water; thiosulphate	116
p-Benzoquinone; also unused after reaction with in determination of dienes	+ I^-/HCl or H_2SO_4	+ water; thiosulphate	117
Peroxides	+ acetic acid + solid CO_2 + I^-; 30 min/room temp., but some with heating—then under nitrogen atmosphere	Thiosulphate	118
Di-*t*-butyl peroxide	In acetic acid + I^-. Inert atmosphere; 45 min/60°	+ water; thiosulphate	
2,2-bis-(*t*-butylperoxy) butane $\left((CH_3)_3C.O.O\right)_2C\begin{smallmatrix}CH_3\\C_2H_5\end{smallmatrix}$	in isopropanol/acetic acid + I^-. Inert atmosphere; a few min reflux	+ water; thiosulphate	119
Total peroxides	+ acetic acid + I^-; 20 min reflux	Thiosulphate	
t-butyl hydroperoxide	+ isopropanol/acetic acid, 25:1, + I^-/water; 2 min boiling	thiosulphate	120
$Si(OCH_3)_4$; $Si(OC_2H_5)_4$	Heated with HI, giving CH_3I or C_2H_5I	Alkyl iodides determined by method of ref. 29 (see Bromine reagents, ref. 294)	121
Certain *β*- and *γ*-substituted pyridine derivatives and alkaloids	+ C_2H_5I/alkali. Various times of reflux (also with $(CH_3)_2SO_4$). Yields alkyl pyridinium iodide	Steam distilled in presence of MnO_4^-, giving CH_3NH_2; titrated with H_2SO_4	122
Peroxide content of hydrocarbons, e.g. tetralin	+ 70% acetic acid + I^-	Thiosulphate	123
Cumene hydroperoxide	Emulsion + acetic acid + water + I^-; 15 min/room temp.	Thiosulphate, biamperometrically	124

Materials titrated	Reagent and reaction conditions	Subsequent treatment and final titration stage	Ref.
Peroxides from action of oxygen on styrene, vinyl acetates and methyl methacrylate	In acetic acid, + HI. Nitrogen atmosphere; 1 h/100° in closed ampoule	Thiosulphate	125
Bis-phenylacetyl peroxide in study of its decomposition $(C_6H_5CH_2CO—O—)_2$	Aliquot + acetic acid + I^- + solid CO_2. Not less than 10 min	+ water; thiosulphate	126
tert-Butyl nitrite, formed from *t*-butanol in study of decomposition of di-*t*-butyl peroxide	Method of ref. 19		127
Lauroyl peroxide in study of its decomposition in ether and benzene	Aliquot + acetic acid + I^- + solid CO_2; 15 min/75°	+ water; thiosulphate	128
Diisopropyl peroxydicarbonate $(iC_3H_7O.CO.O—)_2$	Method of ref. 92		129
Ethoxyl groups in hydroxyethyl cellulose	Heated with HI, giving $C_2H_5I + C_2H_4$	Reaction products determined by method of ref. 102 (see Bromine reagents, ref. 306)	130
Cyclohexyl hydroperoxide in study of its decomposition	+ $CHCl_3$/acetic acid, 1:1, + I^- + solid CO_2; 10 min shaking/room temp.	+ water; thiosulphate	131
Perbenzoic acid in study of its reactions with aromatic compounds	Aliquots + I^-/acid	Thiosulphate	132
Phenyl mercuric acetate	+ measured excess I^-, giving insoluble iodide	Filtered and unused I^- titrated	133
Benzoyl peroxide in study of its decomposition in aromatic solvents in presence of iodine	Aliquot (after titration of added iodine with thiosulphate) + acetic acid + I^- + solid CO_2	Thiosulphate	134
Benzoyl peroxide in study of its decomposition in CCl_4 in presence of iodine	Aliquot (after titration with thiosulphate) + acetic acid + I^- + solid CO_2. Warmed	+ water; thiosulphate	135

Materials titrated	Reagent and reaction conditions	Subsequent treatment and final titration stage	Ref.
Dimethyl sulphate in commercial samples	+ I^-/water, giving methyl iodide; 30 min/room temp., then 30 min/50°	Determined by bromine oxidation as in method of ref. 29 (see Bromine reagents, ref. 309)	136
p-Methoxy-*p*′-nitrobenzoyl peroxide in study of its decomposition in various solvents	In nitrobenzene—method of ref. 103; also in benzene/CCl_3COOH, thiosulphate + acetic acid + I^- + solid CO_2; 20 min/room temp.		137
Ethyl nitrite from determination of ethanol in mixed solvents by reaction with HNO_2	Carried by CO_2 stream into I^-/HCl	Thiosulphate	138
Alkoxyl groups in *p*-nitrophenyl dimethyl (or ethyl) monothiophosphate	Method of ref. 29 (see Bromine reagents, ref. 316)		139
Substituted benzoyl peroxides in study of their thermal decomposition	Aliquot + acetone + I^- + solid CO_2; 30 sec/room temp.	+ water; thiosulphate	140
Unreacted *N*,*N*-dichlorobenzenesulphonamide, $C_6H_5SO_2NCl_2$, in chlorination reactions	+ I^-/HCl 5 min/room temp.	Thiosulphate	141
t-Butyl perbenzoate in study of the kinetics of its decomposition	In acetic acid/ a little phosphoric acid, + I^-; CO_2 atmosphere. Not less than 2 h/room temp.	+ water; thiosulphate	142
Symmetrically substituted benzoyl peroxides in study of their decomposition	+ acetone + I^- + solid CO_2; *ca* 1 min/room temp.	+ water; thiosulphate	143
t-Butyl perbenzoates (also substituted) in study of kinetics of their decomposition	+ dioxan/$CHCl_3$/acetic acid/phosphoric acid + HI/water; CO_2 atmosphere; 30–60 min/room temp.	+ water; thiosulphate	144
Glycerol	Heated with HI/ propionic acid, giving isopropyl iodide + iodine	Alkyl iodide determined by bromine oxidation technique of method of ref. 29 (see Bromine reagents, ref. 322)	145

Materials titrated	Reagent and reaction conditions	Subsequent treatment and final titration stage	Ref.
Peroxides in fats	In $CHCl_3$ or $C_2H_4Cl_2$, + HCl or H_2SO_4 + $CHCl_3$ + *N*-dimethylaniline + I^-; 1 min/room temp.	+ water; thiosulphate	146
Determination of equivalent weight of complexes of diaryl selenoxides + mercury halides	In warm methanol, + I^-/acid	Thiosulphate	147
Terminal $-C(NO_2)_2Br$ groups	In methanol, + I^-	Thiosulphate (immediate titration)	148
Peroxides	Several procedures described, e.g.:		149
	In alcohol, + I^-; 25 min/room temp.;	+ H_2SO_4; thiosulphate	
	in water, + HCl + I^-; 6 h/room temp.;	thiosulphate	
	in water, + $NaHCO_3$ + I^-; 45 min/room temp.	titrated with arsenite	
Acetyl peroxide in study of its decomposition in acetic acid and CCl_4	Aliquot + acetic anhydride + I^-. In vacuum; 15 min/*ca* 75°	+ water; thiosulphate	150
Unused *p*-benzoquinone from determination of diene number of oils like linseed, cottonseed, palm oil	Method of ref. 117		151
Mixed acetyl–benzoyl peroxides from treatment with oxygen of benzaldehyde/acetic anhydride	Aliquot + acetic acid + I^-. Nitrogen atmosphere; 15 min/room temp.	Thiosulphate	152
Nitro, nitroso, azo compounds and oximes	+ HI. Heated to 100–300° in sealed tube, giving iodine. Control	Thiosulphate	153
Organic peroxides, e.g. tetralin hydroperoxide	+ isopropanol/acetic acid + I^-; 10 min reflux	+ water; thiosulphate biamperometrically	154
Unused benzoyl peroxide from reaction with, in determination of triphenylmethyl	In benzene, + acetic acid + I^-/water + solid CO_2; 5 min/room temp.	Thiosulphate	155

Materials titrated	Reagent and reaction conditions	Subsequent treatment and final titration stage	Ref.
Peroxides in fats	In CCl_4/*t*-butanol/ citric acid, + I^-; 15 min/room temp.	Thiosulphate	156
Enols (formyl derivatives with HCO— group)	Critical study of method with final stage in refs 9 and 10		157
Glycidic esters	+ dry ether + dry HI gas, or + 57% HI + Na_2SO_4. Heated giving acrylic ester + iodine, via reaction of the epoxide group in the esters	+ excess thiosulphate and back titrated with iodine	158
Peroxide number	Method of ref. 32		159
Butoxyl groups in HCHO/phenol intermediates	Principle of method of ref. 29 (see Bromine reagents, ref. 355)		160
Peroxides in fats	Slight modification of method of ref. 146		161
N-Cl or *N*-Br imides, e.g. -succinimides (micro)	In water, + I^-/dil. acetic acid	Thiosulphate	162
Peroxides in fat	In acetic acid/ $CHCl_3$, 2:1, + I^-. Inert atmosphere; *ca* 25 min/room temp.	Thiosulphate	163
Peroxides, e.g. benzoyl peroxide	Method of ref. 78; studied influence of water, concentrations of I^- and acetic acid		164
Peroxides in mixtures with aldehydes (also H_2O_2)	+ acetic acid + HI; 1 h/60°; also tried: + water + I^- + ammonium molybdate; 30 min/room temp.; + isopropanol/4% acetic acid + I^-; 20 min/40°, then + HCl and 30 min more	Thiosulphate; thiosulphate; thiosulphate	165
Methoxyl and ethoxyl groups	Study of methods based on principle of ref. 29 (see Bromine reagents, ref. 381)		166

Materials titrated	Reagent and reaction conditions	Subsequent treatment and final titration stage	Ref.
Organic peroxides, e.g. in rancid fats	In $CHCl_3$/acetic acid (hot solution) + I^-. Up to 30 min	Thiosulphate	167
Hydroperoxides	+ acetic acid + $NaHCO_3$ + I^-; 10 min in dark/room temp.	+ water; thiosulphate	168
Piperazine periodate, from determination of piperazine by precipitation	Dissolved in H_2SO_4 and I^- added	Thiosulphate	169
Ascaridole in chenopodium oil	+ I^-/HCl	Thiosulphate	170
Lower alkoxyl groups	Study of influence of a number of factors on method of ref. 29 (see Bromine reagents, ref. 384)		171
Butoxyl groups	Method of ref. 29; 3 h/175° (see Bromine reagents, ref. 385)		172
Sulphenyl chlorides	+ anhydrous acetic acid + I^-; 90 sec/room temp.	+ water + excess thiosulphate and back titrated with iodine	173
Peroxides	In acetic acid/$CHCl_3$ + I^-/water. Nitrogen atmosphere; 15 min/room temp.	+ water; thiosulphate	174
Tribromophenyl hypobromite from determination of phenol by bromination	+ I^-/HCl; 10–15 min/room temp.	Thiosulphate	175, 203
Methoxyl and ethoxyl groups	Study of methods based on principle of ref. 29; preferred method of ref. 37 to that of ref. 67 (see Bromine reagents, ref. 399)		176
Nitrite esters from determination of lower alcohols (methanol to amyl alcohol) by reaction with HNO_2	Carried by nitrogen current into I^-/H_2SO_4 (based on method of refs 19 and 20)	Thiosulphate	177
Methoxyl groups	Modification of method of ref. 29 (see Bromine reagents, ref. 404)		178
Peroxides in fats	Study of some iodometric methods		179

Materials titrated	Reagent and reaction conditions	Subsequent treatment and final titration stage	Ref.
N-Halogen compounds, e.g. chloramine T, *N*-chloroacetamide, *N*-chloro- and *N*-bromo-succinimide	In methanol, water, or methanol/$CHCl_3$, + acetic acid + I^-	Titrated with SO_2/pyridine/ methanol to disappearance of colour or biamperometrically	180
Peroxide number of edible oils	Compared some iodometric methods; preferred that of ref. 41		181
Hydroxyethyl groups in starch ethers	Heated with HI giving ethyl iodide + ethylene	Ethyl iodide determined by absorption in $AgNO_3$ and back titration with SCN^-; ethylene by reaction with a bromine reagent and titrating unused (see Bromine reagents, ref. 412 and Silver (I), ref. 145)	182
N-Bromoamines from reaction of amines with hypobromite	Aspirated through I^-/ acid; 15 min/room temp.	Thiosulphate	183
Peroxides	Study of several methods, including some iodometric		184
Methoxyl groups in essential oils	Recommended method of ref. 29 (see Bromine reagents, ref. 414)		185
Ethoxyl and butoxyl groups in silicon organic compounds	Improvement of method of ref. 121 (see Bromine reagents, ref. 420)		186
Alkoxyl groups (submicro)	Principle of method of ref. 29 (see Bromine reagents, ref. 424)		187
Ethylene oxide derivatives (e.g. poly-ethylene glycols, their esters and ethers)	Heated with HI, giving ethyl iodide and ethylene (modification of method of ref. 102)	Ethyl iodide determined with excess $AgNO_3$; ethylene with excess ICl/acetic acid (see Iodine chlorides, etc., ref. 91)	188
Quinone from determination of arbutin by hydrolysis to hydro-quinone and oxidation	Distilled into I^-/acid	Thiosulphate	189
Primary allyl-type chlorides in presence of isomeric tertiary type, e.g. 1-chloro-3-methyl-2-butene in presence of 2-chloro-2-methyl-3-butene	+ I^-/hexamine, giving quaternary iodide	Unused base titrated with HCl in presence of formalin	190

Materials titrated	Reagent and reaction conditions	Subsequent treatment and final titration stage	Ref.
Nitrocyclohexane	+ HI, reacting: $C_6H_{11}NO_2 + 2\,HI \rightarrow I_2 + C_6H_{10}NOH + H_2O$	Thiosulphate	191
Peroxides	+ acetic acid + I^-. Inert atmosphere; 15 h/room temp.	Thiosulphate	192
Quinone from determination of hydroquinone by oxidation with bromine	+ I^-/HCl; 15–20 min/room temp.	Thiosulphate	193
Peroxide numbers of high molecular weight petroleum compounds	In isopropanol/acetic acid, 10:1, + I^-. Inert atmosphere; 5 min boiling	+ water; thiosulphate potentiometrically	194
Organic sulphides	+ methyl iodide/methanol; 2–3 h/100° in sealed tube, giving sulphonium iodides	Unreacted methyl iodide distilled off and sulphonium iodide determined with HNO_3/ excess $AgNO_3$ and back titration with SCN^- (see Silver (I), ref. 154)	195
O- and *N*-methyl groups (submicro)	+ HI/NH_4I/phenol/$AuCl_3$; *ca* 90 min/*ca* 160° or 3 h/up to 360°, respectively	Principle of method of ref. 29 (see Bromine reagents, ref. 446)	196
Ascaridole in chenopodium oil	Study of the iodometric determination (cf refs 54, 111, 170 for example)		197
Precipitate with molybdophosphoric acid of polyethylene glycols in their determination	Method of ref. 188		198
Dialkyl- and diacyl peroxides; alkyl hydroperoxides; peracids (analysis of mixtures)	+ I^-/acid. Various solvents and conditions and after various pretreatments to remove some compound types. Total per-compounds determined in benzene or $CHCl_3$, + acetic acid/I^-; 10–15 min/room temp.	Thiosulphate	199

Materials titrated	Reagent and reaction conditions	Subsequent treatment and final titration stage	Ref.
Benzoquinone in maleic anhydride solutions from oxidation of benzene	+ I^-/acid	Thiosulphate potentiometrically	200
1,2-Epoxides	+ I^-/acid	Unused acid back titrated	201
Alkoxyl groups in silicon organic compounds	+ HI/red phosphorus/ phenol/propionic acid; 15 min reflux	Alkyl iodide determined by method of ref. 29 (see Bromine reagents, ref. 458)	202
Peroxides	Study of factors in iodometric determination (e.g. sample size, reaction time and temperature)		204
O—CH_2—CH_2—O— and —$CHCH_3$—CH_2—O— groups in polyglycols and ethers	+ HI; CO_2 atmosphere; 90 min reflux, giving first ICH_2—CH_2I, which decomposes into ethylene and iodine	Thiosulphate	205
t-Butyl peresters	In $CHCl_3$, + I^-/water + acetic acid/$FeCl_3$; 5–10 min/room temp. ($FeCl_3$ catalyses iodine liberation)	+ water; thiosulphate	206
t-Butyl hypochlorite (standardization of a solution)	Aliquot (in acetic acid) + I^-; *ca* 5 min/room temp.	Thiosulphate	207
Thiosulphonates RSO_2S^-	+ I^-/acetic acid. In CO_2 atmosphere	Thiosulphate	208
Methoxyl, ethoxyl and isopropoxyl groups in esters, acetals, ketals and silicon organic compounds	Modification of method of ref. 29 (see Bromine reagents, ref. 471)		209
Methoxyl + ethoxyl groups	+ HI + phenol + propionic anhydride; 2 h/140°, giving methyl + ethyl iodides	Carried by CO_2 current into $(CH_3)_3N$/nitrobenzene, giving insoluble $(CH_3)_4N^+I^-$ and soluble $C_2H_5(CH_3)_3N^+I^-$; former dissolved in water and determined with excess $AgNO_3$, followed by back titration with SCN^-; solution of latter + water similarly determined. Also determined total iodides by method of ref. 29 (see Bromine reagents, ref. 474)	210

Materials titrated	Reagent and reaction conditions	Subsequent treatment and final titration stage	Ref.
Peroxides in petroleum products	+ water/isopropanol/ acetic acid, 10:100:1. Nitrogen atmosphere; at *ca* 55°	Thiosulphate potentiometrically	211
Cyclohexyl nitrite	Method of ref. 83		212
Methoxyl groups in humic acid and its oxidation products (fulvic acid)	Method of ref. 29 (see Bromine reagents, ref. 478)		213
Cumene hydroperoxide	Emulsion + I^- + acetic acid + water; 15 min/room temp.	Thiosulphate biamperometrically	214
Tertiary bases, e.g. codeine, atropine, narcotine	+ methyl iodide, giving quaternary iodides	Unreacted methyl iodide evaporated off at *ca* 40°, residue dissolved in water and passed through Amberlite IRA 400 column, giving quaternary hydroxide; titrated with H_2SO_4 (see Ion exchangers, ref. 34)	215
Lower alkoxyl groups	Modification of method of ref. 29		216
Si-Methoxy or ethoxy groups	Heated with HI/phenol/ red phosphorus. *Ca* 45 min, giving alkyl iodide	Determined by principle of method of ref. 29	217
Peroxyacetic acid	+ I^- + acetic acid + ammonium molybdate; 15 min/room temp.	Thiosulphate	218
Chloramine T; also in presence of HCHO	In water, + I^- + some acetic acid; 15 min/room temp.	Thiosulphate	219
—O—CH_2—CH_2OH groups in glycol ethers	+ HI, giving ethyl iodide + ethylene	Ethyl iodide carried with CO_2 into $AgNO_3$/acetic acid and unused Ag^+ back titrated with I^- to starch (ethylene determined gas-volumetrically) (see Silver (I), ref. 171)	220
Lower alkoxyl groups	Heated with HI/red phosphorus/phenol/ propionic acid	Alkyl iodides determined by method of ref. 29	221

Materials titrated	Reagent and reaction conditions	Subsequent treatment and final titration stage	Ref.
Phosgene in air	+ I^-/acetone		222
Higher alkoxyl groups	+ HI reagent in nitrogen atmosphere; 2–4 h/120–130° in bomb. Then + red phosphorus/ acetic acid, heated 2–3 min	Alkyl iodide distilled out with added decalin and determined by method of ref. 29	223
Nitrite esters from determination of volatile alcohols in dilute aqueous solutions	Modification of method of ref. 37		224
Ethyl cellosolve (and ethylene glycol if present)	Method of ref. 205 (ethylene glycol corrected for by periodate oxidation; see Periodate and periodic acid, ref. 114)		225
N;*N'*-Dichlorodiimine from determination of *p*-phenylenediamine by reaction with hypobromite	Solution in $CHCl_3$, + I^-/ HCl	Thiosulphate	226
Methoxyl, ethoxyl or *S*-methyl groups	+ HI + xylene. Nitrogen atmosphere; up to 3 h reflux	Alkyl iodide carried into pyridine and after 2 min, titrated with $(n\text{-}C_4H_9)_4$ *N*-hydroxide/methanol/benzene potentiometrically or to azo-violet (see Amines and heterocyclic bases, ref. 93)	227
Peroxides in lipids; also *t*-butyl hydroperoxide, lauroyl peroxide, etc.	In ethanol/acetic acid/ chloroform, 5:3:2, + excess octylthioglycollate + I^-/water	Unused thioglycollate titrated with iodine	228
Primary and secondary saturated nitro compounds after treatment with KOH/80% ethanol	+ I^-/HCl; 10 min/room temp. in the dark	+ water; thiosulphate	229
1,3-Chlorobromopropane in presence of the 1,2-compound	Aliquot in acetone + NaI/acetone; 14–16 h/room temp. in dark, giving NaCl + NaBr	Dissolved precipitate in water, added HNO_3 + excess $AgNO_3$ and back titrated with SCN^-	230
Peroxides	+ $CHCl_3$/acetic acid/ trace $FeCl_3$/I^-. Nitrogen atmosphere; 5 min/room temp.	+ water; thiosulphate	231

Materials titrated	Reagent and reaction conditions	Subsequent treatment and final titration stage	Ref.
Alkoxyl groups in polymers containing alkyl acrylates and maleates	+ HI/phenol/propionic anhydride as in method of ref. 85; 3 h/150°	Alkyl iodides determined as in method of ref. 29	232
—O—CH_2—CH_2— groups, e.g. in polyethylene glycols	+ HI. Nitrogen atmosphere; 1 h/150–160°, giving ethyl iodide and iodine	Passed into I^- solution; thiosulphate	233
$COCl_2$	Passed into I^-/dry acetone	+ water; thiosulphate. Then + IO_3^- and retitrated to determine any HCl from hydrolysis	234
Derivatives of 5-nitrofurfuraldehyde	+ HI/red phosphorus/water; 90 min heating	Determined via Kjeldahl nitrogen method (see Kjeldahl nitrogen determination, ref. 18)	235
Peroxides in fats	In $CHCl_3$/acetic acid, 3:2, + saturated KI solution; 1 min shaking	+ water; thiosulphate	236
Methoxyl, ethoxyl groups (micro)	+ phenol/phosphoric acid/KI; 1 h/195–200° in nitrogen stream	Distillate absorbed in bromine/acetic acid and determined as in method of ref. 29	237
Compounds containing the —CO—CHBr— group from determination of the enol content of acetoacetic esters by reaction with bromine at −50°	+ I^-/methanol; 5 min/room temp.	Thiosulphate	238
Peroxide in a cyclobarbitone	In 90% ethanol, + I^-/ethanol; 1 h/room temp. in the dark	Thiosulphate	239
Peroxides in volatile oils	+ $CHCl_3$ or ethyl acetate /acetic acid 2:3, in inert atmosphere; + KI/water; 5–10 min in dark	+ water; thiosulphate	240
Cystine	+ HI/red phosphorus, giving cysteine	Titrated in NaOH solution with *o*-hydroxymercuribenzoic acid to thiofluorescein (see Part I, Mercury (II), ref. 87)	241
Methoxyl groups	Study of conditions of method of ref. 29—distillation time, speed of gas stream, blank values etc.		242

Materials titrated	Reagent and reaction conditions	Subsequent treatment and final titration stage	Ref.
Peroxide numbers of fats	In $CHCl_3$/acetic acid, 2:3, + saturated KI/water; 20 min in dark (compared with colorimetric and polarographic methods)	+ water; thiosulphate	243
S-Alkyl groups	Method of ref. 29 tested on methionine and ethionine (complete reaction in under 3 h); *S*-methyl and *S*-ethyl derivatives of acetic and propionic acids (complete reaction in under 6 h); and *S*-methyl and *S*-ethyl derivatives of cysteine (incomplete in 7 h even in presence of catalysts like MoO_4^{2-}, Cu and Hg salts		244
Peroxides in cured polyester resins	+ NaI + acetic acid	Thiosulphate	245
Alkoxyl groups	Method of ref. 176		246
3-Amino-6-alkyl-sulphinylpyridazines and their sulphonamide derivatives	+ KI/HCl; 5 min, liberating iodine from reaction of the —SO— group	+ ethanol + water; thiosulphate	247
Benzoquinone in mixtures with benzoic acid, benzaldehyde and maleic anhydride	In ether, + KI/water + H_2SO_4	+ excess thiosulphate and aqueous layer back titrated with iodine	248
Free polyoxyethylene glycols in oxyethylated amines (after separation in an ion exchanger)	+ aqueous HI, giving iodine	Thiosulphate	249
Free polyoxyethylene glycols in non-ionic ethylene oxide adducts	Method of ref. 233 carried out on samples separated by paper chromatography		250
Peroxide index of phospholipids	+ NaI reagent, liberating iodine	Thiosulphate	251
Peroxide numbers	+ acetic acid + saturated KI solution; 3 min/room temp.	+ water + kerosine; thiosulphate	252
Methoxyl groups in polymers and co-polymers	+ phenol + red phosphorus; warmed to 80–90°, then + HI and heated to 140–160°	CO_2 current carried out methyl iodide and determined via method of ref. 29 See Bromine Reagents ref. 515	253

Materials titrated	Reagent and reaction conditions	Subsequent treatment and final titration stage	Ref.
Mixtures of long-chain amines and their oxides	In isopropanol, + methyl iodide; 15 min/50°, giving quaternary salts with the amines	Unreacted oxides titrated with HCl/alcohol potentiometrically	254
Total peroxides in mixtures of aldehydes, H_2O_2 and organic peroxides	+ saturated KI solution + HCl/acetic acid; 30 min boiling in CO_2 atmosphere	Thiosulphate	255
Ethylene oxide in mixtures with HCHO and acetaldehyde	+ HI/saturated KI solution	Unused acid titrated with alkali	256
Benzoyl peroxide + free chlorine in CCl_4	Acetic acid + sample + KI/water in CO_2 atmosphere; 15 min in dark (free chlorine determined in a separate titration with methyl orange)	Thiosulphate	257
Peracids (e.g. peracetic) + H_2O_2	+ dilute acetic acid at 5° + KI (pH 3–5)	Titration with thiosulphate after 2 and 5–6 min noted: extrapolation to zero time gave the peracid; + ammonium molybdate catalyst and titrated further giving total	258
Ethylene oxide adducts (hydroxyethyl groups)	+ HI, density 1·7; refluxed 90 mins	Thiosulphate	259
Benzalkonium chloride and other quaternary ammonium germicides	Solution + excess iodide	Quaternary iodide extracted with $CHCl_3$ and I^- titrated with iodate	260
Amine oxides, e.g. of strychnine, *N*-benzyl-piperidine, trimethyl-amine	+ HI or in acetic acid + KI; 30 min boiling or 15 min boiling and then 30 min/room temp. in dark respectively	Thiosulphate biampero-metrically	261
Lower alkoxyl groups	Method of ref. 29 but with KI/phosphoric acid instead of with HI		262
Methoxyl groups in certain polyfunctional derivatives of sorbitol and xylitol	Method of ref. 29 after preliminary heating with phenol/red phosphorus		263

Materials titrated	Reagent and reaction conditions	Subsequent treatment and final titration stage	Ref.
Aliphatic peracids	+ $KI/TiOSO_4$ in cold water	Thiosulphate	264
Diphenoquinonedi-(4,4′-dimethylammonium) ion, $(CH_3)_2\overset{+}{N}{=}C_6H_4{=}C_6H_4{=}\overset{+}{N}(CH_3)_2$ 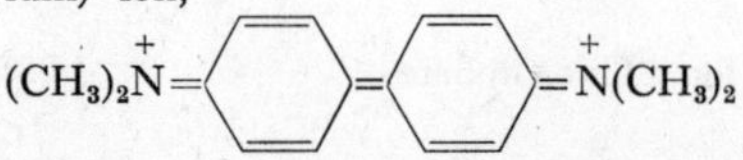	In dilute HCl, + KI; 5 min	Thiosulphate	265
Hyproperoxides	In $CHCl_3$, + KI/acetic acid/$CHCl_3$/methanol; nitrogen atmosphere; 1 h in dark	+ excess thiosulphate and back titrated with iodate	266
Peroxides	In acetic acid/$CHCl_3$, 3:2, + KI/water; 3–5 min shaking	+ water; thiosulphate	267
Nitroso compounds	In acetic acid or ethanol, + KI + HCl; 20 min	Thiosulphate	268
Cinnamic acid dibromide	In 80% methanol or acetic acid, + I^- (kinetic study)	Thiosulphate	269
Peroxide index of edible fats and oils (measure of rancidity)	Acetic acid/$CHCl_3$ + I^- + sample; boiled 4 min	+ water; thiosulphate	270
Higher alkoxyl groups (up to 26 carbon atoms, in alcohols, esters, etc.)	In propionic acid or anhydride, + 70% HI + red phosphorus; 1 h/100°	+ benzene and neutralized to thymol blue with aqueous NaOH; alkyl iodide in benzene layer refluxed 30 min with aniline giving alkylanilinium iodide; titrated with $NaOCH_3$ to the thymol blue (compare Amines and heterocylclic bases, ref. 91)	272
Easily reduced peroxides	+ NaI/isopropanol/acetic acid; 5 min reflux	}	
mainly diaryl peroxides	+ NaI/acetic acid/water; 20 min reflux	} + water; thiosulphate	273
difficulty reduced peroxides, e.g., di tert.-butyl peroxide	+ NaI/acetic acid/HCl; 50 min reflux	}	
Polyoxyethylene compounds, e.g. mono-, diethylene glycols	+ KI + 85% phosphoric acid; heated in nitrogen current; 1 h/165–170°	Iodine passed into KI solution; thiosulphate	274

References

1. Meyer, V. and Wachter, W., *Ber.* **25**, 2632 (1892).
2. Willgerodt, C., *Ber.* **26**, 1308 (1893).
3. Valeur, A., *Compt. rend.* **129**, 552 (1899).
4. Valeur, A., *Bull. soc. chim. France* **23**, 58 (1900).
5. Meyer, K. H., *Ber.* **42**, 1149 (1909).
6. Willstätter, R. and Dorogi, S., *Ber.* **42**, 2165 (1909).
7. Biltz, H. and Behrens, O., *Ber.* **43**, 1984 (1910).
8. Willstätter, R. and Majima, R., *Ber.* **43**, 1171 (1910).
9. Meyer, K. H., *Ann.* **380**, 212 (1911).
10. Meyer, K. H. and Kappelmeier, P., *Ber.* **44**, 2718 (1911).
11. D'Ans, J. and Frey, W., *Ber.* **45**, 1845 (1912).
12. Klemenc, A., *Monatsh.* **34**, 901 (1913).
13. Kirpal, A. and Bühn, T., *Ber.* **47**, 1084 (1914).
14. Vanino, L. and Herzer, F., *Arch. Pharm.* **253**, 437 (1915).
15. Dimroth, O. and Schulze, E., *Ann.* **411**, 347 (1916).
16. Meyer, K. H. and Gottlieb-Billroth, H., *Ber.* **52**, 1482 (1919).
17. Pummerer, R. and Cherbuliez, E., *Ber.* **52**, 1401, 1412 (1919).
18. Dieckmann, W., *Ber.* **55**, 2470 (1922).
19. Fischer, W. M. and Schmidt, A., *Ber.* **57**, 693 (1924).
20. Fischer, W. M. and Schmidt, A., *Ber.* **59**, 679 (1926).
21. Gelissen, H. and Hermans, P. H., *Ber.* **59**, 63 (1926).
22. Eaton, E. P. and West, E. S., *J. Biol. Chem.* **75**, 283 (1927).
23. Böck, F. and Lock, G., *Monatsh.* **53/4**, 888 (1929).
24. Fries, K., Koch, H. and Stuckenbrock, H., *Ann.* **468**, 179 (1929).
25. Marks, S. and Morrell, R. S., *Analyst* **54**, 503 (1929).
26. Van Winkle, R. and Christiansen, W. G., *J. Am. Pharm. Assoc.* **18**, 1247 (1929).
27. Dillon, R. T., Young, W. G. and Lucas, H. J., *J. Am. Chem. Soc.* **52**, 1953 (1930).
28. Smit, M. W. C., *Rec. trav. chim.* **49**, 691 (1930).
29. Vieböck, F. and Schwappach, A., *Ber.* **63**, 2818 (1930).
30. Vieböck, F. and Brecher, C., *Ber.* **63**, 3207 (1930).
31. Kometiani, P. A., *Z. anal. Chem.* **86**, 359 (1931).
32. Lea, C. H., *Proc. Royal Soc.* **108B**, 175 (1931).
33. Olsen, J. C., Ferguson, G. E., Sabetta, V. J. and Scheflan, L., *Ind. Eng. Chem., Anal. Ed.* **3**, 189 (1931).
34. Taffel, A. and Revis, C., *J. Soc. Chem. Ind. (London)* **50**, 87T (1931).
35. Baernstein, H. D., *J. Biol. Chem.* **97**, 663 (1932).
36. Bruckner, V., *Mikrochemie* **12**, 153 (1932).
37. Clark, E. P., *J. Assoc. Offic. Agr. Chem.* **15**, 136 (1932).
38. Dick, H., *Dissertation*, Frankfurt, 1932.
39. Kolthoff, I. M. and Lingane, J. J., *Pharm. Weekblad* **69**, 1147 (1932).

40. Slotta, K. H. and Haberland, G., *Ber.* **65**, 127 (1932).
41. Wheeler, D. H., *Oil & Soap* **9**, 89 (1932).
42. Green, L. W. and Schoetzow, R. F., *J. Am. Pharm. Assoc.* **22**, 412 (1933).
43. Baernstein, H. D., *J. Biol. Chem.* **106**, 451 (1934).
44. Ender, W., *Angew. Chem.* **47**, 227 (1934).
45. Ender, W., *Angew. Chem.* **47**, 257 (1934).
46. Matuszak, M. P., *Ind. Eng. Chem., Anal. Ed.* **6**, 457 (1934).
47. Nanji, H. R., *Analyst* **59**, 96 (1934).
48. French, R. B., Olcott, H. S. and Mattill, H. A., *Ind. Eng. Chem.* **27**, 724 (1935).
49. Gibson, D. T. and Caulfield, T. H., *J. Chem. Soc.* 1419 (1935).
50. Hass, H. B. and Weber, P., *Ind. Eng. Chem., Anal. Ed.* **7**, 231 (1935).
51. Palfray, C. L., *Documentat. Sci.* **4**, 1 (1935).
52. Storch, K. and Wenzel, I., *Angew. Chem.* **48**, 513 (1935).
53. Baernstein, H. D., *J. Biol. Chem.* **115**, 25 (1936).
54. Simmons, W. H., *Analyst* **61**, 179 (1936).
55. White, E. V. and Wright, G. F., *Can. J. Research* **14**, 427 (1936).
56. Krauz, C. and Štěpanek, J., *Chem. Obzor* **12**, 81 (1937).
57. Brenner, M. W. and Poland, G. L., *Ind. Eng. Chem., Anal. Ed.* **10**, 528 (1938).
58. Buck, R. E. and Ritchie, W. S., *Ind. Eng. Chem., Anal. Ed.* **10**, 26 (1938).
59. Cooper, S. R. and Barnes, R. P., *Ind. Eng. Chem., Anal. Ed.* **10**, 379 (1938).
60. Franke, W. and Jerchel, D., *Ann.* **533**, 46 (1938).
61. Furter, M., *Helv. Chim. Acta* **21**, 1144, 1151 (1938).
62. Kinsman, S. and Noller, C. R., *Ind. Eng. Chem., Anal. Ed.* **10**, 424 (1938).
63. Menaker, M. H. and Guerrant, N. B., *Ind. Eng. Chem., Anal. Ed.* **10**, 25 (1938).
64. Mitchell, H. K. and Williams, R. J., *J. Am. Chem. Soc.* **60**, 2723 (1938).
65. Panyutin, P. S. and Gindin, L. G., *Bull. acad. sci. URSS, Classe sci. math. nat., Sér. chim.* 841 (1938).
66. Clark, E. P., *J. Assoc. Offic. Agr. Chem.* **22**, 109, 622 (1939).
67. Elek, A., *Ind. Eng. Chem., Anal. Ed.* **11**, 174 (1939).
68. Herd, R. L., *J. Assoc. Offic. Agr. Chem.* **22**, 158 (1939).
69. Lobunetz., M. H. and Gortin'ska, E. N., *Univ. état. Kiev. Bull. sci., Recueil chim.* No. 4, 37 (1939).
70. Peniston, Q. P. and Hibbert, H., *Paper Trade J.* **109**, No. 17, 46 (1939).
71. Smith, J. A. B., *J. Dairy Research* **10**, 294 (1939).
72. Johnson, P. R., Barnes, H. M. and McElvain, S. M., *J. Am. Chem. Soc.* **62**, 969 (1940).
73. Kolb, J. J. and Toennies, G., *Ind. Eng. Chem., Anal. Ed.* **12**, 723 (1940).
74. Liebhafsky, H. A. and Sharkey, W. H., *J. Am. Chem. Soc.* **62**, 190 (1940).

75. Skrabal, R., *Z. anal. Chem.* **119**, 222 (1940).
76. Bürger, K. and Baláž, F., *Angew. Chem.* **54**, 58 (1941).
77. Christensen, B. E., Friedman, L. and Sato, Y., *Ind. Eng. Chem., Anal. Ed.* **13**, 276 (1941).
78. Kokatnur, V. R. and Jelling, M., *J. Am. Chem. Soc.* **63**, 1432 (1941).
79. Sabalitschka, T., *Ber.* **74**, 1040 (1941).
80. Stansby, M. E., *Ind. Eng. Chem., Anal. Ed.* **13**, 627 (1941).
81. Stravchinskii, L. R., *Lab. Prakt. USSR* **16**, No. 6, 21 (1941).
82. Bailey, A. J., *Ind. Eng. Chem., Anal. Ed.* **14**, 181 (1942).
83. Beal, G. D. and Szalkowski, C. R., *Bull. Natl. Formulary Comm.* **10**, 59 (1942).
84. Gettler, A. O. and Umberger, C. J., *J. Biol. Chem.* **143**, 633 (1942).
85. Samsel, E. P. and McHard, J. A., *Ind. Eng. Chem., Anal. Ed.* **14**, 750 (1942).
86. Böhme, H. and Schneider, E., *Ber.* **76**, 483 (1943).
87. Cooke, L. M. and Hibbert, H., *Ind. Eng. Chem., Anal. Ed.* **15**, 1100 (1943).
88. Lespagnol, A. and Merville, R., *Ann. chim. anal.* **25**, 53 (1943).
89. Houghton, A. A. and Wilson, H., *Analyst* **69**, 363 (1944).
90. Ingram, G., *Analyst* **69**, 265 (1944).
91. Zakharova, M. P. and Devyatin, V. A., *Biokhimiya* **9**, 256 (1944).
92. Cohen, S. G., *J. Am. Chem. Soc.* **67**, 17 (1945).
93. Fierz-David, H. E., Pfanner, E. and Oppliger, F., *Helv. Chim. Acta* **28**, 1463 (1945).
94. Hills, C. H., Ogg, C. L. and Speiser, R., *Ind. Eng. Chem., Anal. Ed.* **17**, 507 (1945).
95. Rose, E. L. and Ziliotto, H., *Ind. Eng. Chem., Anal. Ed.* **17**, 211 (1945).
96. Stuffins, C. B. and Weatherall, H., *Analyst* **70**, 403 (1945).
97. Wilson, H. N. and Heron, A. E., *Analyst* **70**, 38 (1945).
98. Cass, W. E., *J. Am. Chem. Soc.* **68**, 1976 (1946).
99. Lea, C. H., *J. Soc. Chem. Ind. (London)* **65**, 286 (1946).
100. McCullough, J. D., Campbell, T. W. and Krilanovich, N. J., *Ind. Eng. Chem., Anal. Ed.* **18**, 638 (1946).
101. Milas, N. A. and Surgenor, D. M., *J. Am. Chem. Soc.* **68**, 642 (1946).
102. Morgan, P. W., *Ind. Eng. Chem., Anal. Ed.* **18**, 500 (1946).
103. Nozaki, K., *Ind. Eng. Chem., Anal. Ed.* **18**, 583 (1946).
104. Green, N. and Green, M. W., *J. Am. Pharm. Assoc., Sci. Ed.* **36**, 235 (1947).
105. Kooyman, P. L. and Ghijsen, W. L., *Rec. trav. chim.* **66**, 205 (1947).
106. Lundberg, W. O. and Chipault, J. R., *J. Am. Chem. Soc.* **69**, 833 (1947).
107. Shaw, B. M., *J. Soc. Chem. Ind. (London)* **66**, 147 (1947).
108. Wagner, C. D., Smith, R. H. and Peters, E. D., *Anal. Chem.* **19**, 976 (1947).
109. Goldenson, J. and Sass, S., *Anal. Chem.* **20**, 1118 (1948).

110. Greenspan, F. G. and MacKellor, D. G., *Anal. Chem.* **20**, 1061 (1948).
111. Halpern, A., *J. Am. Pharm. Assoc., Sci. Ed.* **37**, 465 (1948).
112. Kometiani, P. A. and Sturua, G. G., *Biokhimiya* **13**, 23 (1948).
113. Mucciolo, P., Ribeiro, P. A. and Bonaldi, V., *Rev. fac. med. vet., Univ. Sao Paulo* **3**, 272 (1948).
114. Rush, C. A. and Danner, C. E., *Anal. Chem.* **20**, 644 (1948).
115. Skellon, J. H. and Wills, E. D., *Analyst* **73**, 78 (1948).
116. Skellon, J. H. and Thurston, M. N., *Analyst* **73**, 97 (1948).
117. Tamayo, M. L. and Léon, J. L., *Anal. real. soc. espan. fis. quím.* **44B**, 963 (1948).
118. Criegee, R., Schnorrenberg, W. and Becke, J., *Ann.* **565**, 7 (1949).
119. Dickey, F. H., Raley, J. H., Rust, F. F., Treseder, R. S. and Vaughan, W. E., *Ind. Eng. Chem.* **41**, 1673 (1949).
120. Dickey, F. H., Rust, F. F. and Vaughan, W. E., *J. Am. Chem. Soc.* **71**, 1432 (1949).
121. Kreshkov, A. P. and Nessonova, G. D., *Zhur. Anal. Khim.* **4**, 220 (1949).
122. Sackur, O., *Bull. soc. chim. France* **16**, 270 (1949).
123. Vaiser, V. L., *Doklady Akad. Nauk SSSR* **68**, 519 (1949).
124. Armstrong, G. P., Hall, R. H. and Quin, D. C., *J. Chem. Soc.* 666 (1950).
125. Barnes, C. E., Elofson, R. M. and Jones, G. D., *J. Am. Chem. Soc.* **72**, 210 (1950).
126. Bartlett, P. D. and Leffler, J. E., *J. Am. Chem. Soc.* **72**, 3030 (1950).
127. Bell, E. R., Rust, F. F. and Vaughan, W. E., *J. Am. Chem. Soc.* **72**, 337 (1950).
128. Cass, W. E., *J. Am. Chem. Soc.* **72**, 4915 (1950).
129. Cohen, S. G. and Sparrow, D. B., *J. Am. Chem. Soc.* **72**, 611 (1950).
130. Cohen, S. G. and Haas, H. C., *J. Am. Chem. Soc.* **72**, 3954 (1950).
131. Farkas, A. and Passaglia, E., *J. Am. Chem. Soc.* **72**, 3323 (1950).
132. Friess, S. L. and Miller, A., *J. Am. Chem. Soc.* **72**, 2611 (1950).
133. Gran, G., *Svensk Papperstidn.* **53**, 234 (1950).
134. Hammond, G. S., *J. Am. Chem. Soc.* **72**, 3737 (1950).
135. Hammond, G. S. and Soffer, L. M., *J. Am. Chem. Soc.* **72**, 4711 (1950).
136. Jureček, M., *Chem. Listy* **44**, 134 (1950).
137. Leffler, J. E., *J. Am. Chem. Soc.* **72**, 67 (1950).
138. Murakami, K., *J. Soc. Org. Syn. Chem. (Japan)* **8**, 155 (1950).
139. Reckendorfer, P., *Pflanzenschutzber.* **5**, 287 (1950).
140. Swain, C. G., Stockmayer, W. H. and Clarke, J. T., *J. Am. Chem. Soc.* **72**, 5426 (1950).
141. Takizawa, T. and Hoshiai, K., *Mem. Inst. Sci. Ind. Research, Osaka Univ.* **7**, 136 (1950).
142. Blomquist, A. T. and Ferris, A. F., *J. Am. Chem. Soc.* **73**, 3408 (1951).
143. Blomquist, A. T. and Buselli, A. J., *J. Am. Chem. Soc.* **73**, 3883 (1951).

144. Blomquist, A. T. and Berstein, I. A., *J. Am. Chem. Soc.* **73**, 5546 (1951).
145. Bradbury, R. B., *Mikrochemie ver. Mikrochim. Acta* **38**, 114 (1951).
146. Drozdov, N. and Starikova, L., *Myasnaya Ind. SSSR* **22**, No. 3, 52 (1951).
147. Gould, E. S. and McCullough, J. D., *J. Am. Chem. Soc.* **73**, 3196 (1951).
148. Klager, K., *Anal. Chem.* **23**, 534 (1951).
149. Mattner, J. and Mattner, R., *Z. anal. Chem.* **134**, 1 (1951).
150. Ross, S. D. and Fineman, M. A., *J. Am. Chem. Soc.* **73**, 2176 (1951).
151. Tamayo, M. L. and Estado, C., *Anal. real soc. españ. fis. quím.* **47B**, 815 (1951).
152. Walling, C. and McElhill, E. A., *J. Am. Chem. Soc.* **73**, 2927 (1951).
153. Aldrovandi, R. and deLorenzi, F., *Ann. chim. (Rome)* **42**, 298 (1952).
154. Abrahamson, E. W. and Linschitz, H., *Anal. Chem.* **24**, 1355 (1952).
155. Hammond, G. S., Ravve, A. and Modic, F. J., *Anal. Chem.* **24**, 1373 (1952).
156. Hartman, L. and White, M. D. L., *Anal. Chem.* **24**, 527 (1952).
157. Bokadia, M. M., *Agra Univ. J. Research* **2**, Pt. 1, 9 (1953).
158. Dullaghan, M. E. and Nord, F. F., *Mikrochim. Acta* 17 (1953).
159. Hadorn, H. and Jungkunz, R., *Mitt. Lebensm. Hyg.* **44**, 495 (1953).
160. Kantorovich, S. A. and Alegina, O. N., *Byull. Obmenu Opyt. v Lakokrasoch. Prom.* No. 4, 70 (1953).
161. Starikova, L., *Myasnaya Ind. SSSR* **24**, No. 1, 72 (1953).
162. Barakat, M. Z. and Abd El-Wahab, M. F., *Anal. Chem.* **26**, 1973 (1954).
163. Bronisz, H. and Raciborska, I., *Roczniki Państwowego Zakladu Hig.* **5**, 115 (1954).
164. Radford, A. J., *Analyst* **79**, 501 (1954).
165. Satterfield, C. N., Wilson, R. E., LeClair, R. M. and Reid, R. C., *Anal. Chem.* **26**, 1792 (1954).
166. Steyermark, A. and Loeschauer, E. E., *J. Assoc. Offic. Agr. Chem.* **37**, 433 (1954).
167. Sully, B. D., *Analyst* **79**, 86 (1954).
168. Wibaut, J. P., van Leeuwen, H. B. and van der Wal, B., *Rec. trav. chim.* **73**, 1033 (1954).
169. Wickstrøm, A. and Valseth, A., *Ann. pharm. franç.* **12**, 777 (1954).
170. American Pharm. Assoc. *National Formulary*, 10th ed., 148 (1955).
171. Belcher, R., Fildes, J. E. and Nutten, A. J., *Anal. Chim. Acta* **13**, 16 (1955).
172. Ditrych, Z., Rejková, H. and Ulbrich, V., *Chem. Listy* **49**, 869 (1955).
173. Kharasch, N. and Wald, M. M., *Anal. Chem.* **27**, 996 (1955).
174. Ricciuti, C., Coleman, J. E. and Willits, C. O., *Anal. Chem.* **27**, 405 (1955).
175. Schulek, E. and Burger, K., *Magyar Kem. Folyoirat* **61**, 359 (1955).
176. Steyermark, A., *J. Assoc. Offic. Agr. Chem.* **38**, 367 (1955).

177. v. Wacek, A. and Zeisler, F., *Mikrochim. Acta* 29 (1955).
178. Bethge, P. O. and Carlson, O. T., *Anal. Chim. Acta* **15**, 279 (1956).
179. Franzke, C., *Z. Lebensm.-Untersuch. u. Forsch.* **103**, 108 (1956).
180. Friedman, R. W., *Anal. Chem.* **28**, 247 (1956).
181. Hadorn, H., Biefer, K. W. and Suter, H., *Z. Lebensm.-Untersuch. u. Forsch.* **104**, 316 (1956).
182. Lortz, H. J., *Anal. Chem.* **28**, 892 (1956).
183. Reis, N. V., *Sbornik Nauch. Trudov Samarkand. Med. Inst.* **11**, 117 (1956).
184. Sedlaček, B. A. J., Rybin, R., Raab, J. M. and Bartoniček, M., *Roczniki Państwowego Zakladu Hig.* **7**, 293 (1956).
185. v. Schantz, M., *Farm. Aikakauslehti* **65**, 265 (1956).
186. Syavtsillo, S. V. and Bondarevskaya, E. A., *Zhur. Anal. Khim.* **11**, 613 (1956).
187. Belcher, R., Bhatty, M. K. and West, T. S., *J. Chem. Soc.* 4480 (1957).
188. Etienne, H., *Ind. chim. belge* **32**, 1175, 1287 (1957).
189. Fried, R., *Arch. Pharm.* **290**, 73 (1957).
190. Leets, K. V., Pilevskaya, A. I. and Korovkina, M. I., *USSR Patent* 106,985 Aug. 25 (1957).
191. Moldavskii, B. L. and Ivanova, I. I., *Zhur. Anal. Khim.* **12**, 274 (1957).
192. Roth, H. and Schuster, P., *Mikrochim. Acta* 840 (1957).
193. Schulek, E. and Burger, K., *Acta Pharm. Hung.* **27**, 51 (1957).
194. Sergienko, S. R., Galich, P. N. and Zpivak, L. L., *Zhur. Anal. Khim.* **12**, 139 (1957).
195. Aarna, A. Ya. and Silland, Kh. A., *Zhur. Anal. Khim.* **13**, 473 (1958).
196. Belcher, R., Bhatty, M. K. and West, T. S., *J. Chem. Soc.* 2393 (1958).
197. Böhme, H. and v. Emster, K., *Arch. Pharm.* **291/63**, 310 (1958).
198. Etienne, H., *Bull. centre Belge étude et document. eaux* (*Liège*) No. 40, 159 (1958).
199. Horner, L. and Jürgen, E., *Angew. Chem.* **70**, 266 (1958).
200. Malyshev, A. I. and Ioffe, I. I., *Zhur. Anal. Khim.* **13**, 374 (1958).
201. Mousseron, M., Jullien, J. and Peyron, A., *Parfums, cosmét., savons* **13**, No. 1, 3 (1958).
202. Nessonova, G. D. and Pogosyants, E. K., *Zavodskaya Lab.* **24**, 953 (1958).
203. Schulek, E. and Burger, K., *Z. anal. Chem.* **161**, 184 (1958).
204. Seher, A., *Fette. Seifen Anstrichsmittel* **60**, 264 (1958).
205. Siggia, S., Starke, A. C., Garis, J. J. and Stahl, C. R., *Anal. Chem.* **30**, 115 (1958).
206. Silbert, L. S. and Swern, D., *Anal. Chem.* **30**, 385 (1958).
207. Van Hall, C. E. and Stone, K. G., *Anal. Chem.* **30**, 1416 (1958).
208. Barnard, D. and Cole, E. R., *Anal. Chim. Acta* **20**, 540 (1959).
209. Favorskaya, I. A. and Auvinen, E. M., *Vestnik Leningrad Univ.* **14**, No. 16 Ser. Fiz. i Khim. No. 3, 119 (1959).

210. Makens, R. F., Lothringer, R. L. and Donia, R. A., *Anal. Chem.* **31**, 265 (1959).
211. Matthews, J. S. and Patchan, J. F., *Anal. Chem.* **31**, 1003 (1959).
212. Moldavskii, B. L. and Ivanova, I. I., *Zhur. Anal. Khim.* **14**, 378 (1959).
213. Sági, M., *Veszprémi Vegyipari Egyetem Közleményei* **3**, 47 (1959).
214. Tsuk, L. and Zollner, G., *Magyar Kem. Lapya* **14**, 417 (1959).
215. Belcher, R., Bhatty, M. K. and West, T. S., *J. Chem. Soc.* 2473 (1960).
216. Buděšinský, B. and Körbl, J., *Mikrochim. Acta* 369 (1960).
217. Fritz, G. and Burdt, H., *Z. anorg. u. allgem. Chem.* **307**, 12 (1961).
218. Havel, S., Weigner, J. A. and Sváb, J., *Chem. Pr°mysl* **10**, 579 (1960).
219. Jensen, R., Garrin, S. and Tayeau, F., *Bull. soc. chim. France* 975 (1960).
220. Kainz, G., *Mikrochim. Acta* 254 (1960).
221. Kirsten, W. J. and Nilsson, K., *Mikrochim. Acta* 983 (1960).
222. Komoda, T. and Suenaga, S., *Kôshu Eiseiin Kenkyu Hôkôku* **9**, 138 (1960).
223. Kretz, R., *Z. anal. Chem.* **176**, 421 (1960).
224. McGrew, C. and Vanetten, C. H., *J. Assoc. Offic. Agr. Chem.* **43**, 772 (1960).
225. Perepletchikova, E. M., Etlis, V. S. and Kalugin, A. A., *Zavodskaya Lab.* **26**, 154 (1960).
226. van de Pol, A., *Chem. Weekblad* **56**, 21 (1960).
227. Cundiff, R. H. and Markunas, P. C., *Anal. Chem.* **33**, 1028 (1961).
228. Dahle, L. K. and Holman, R. T., *Anal. Chem.* **33**, 1960 (1961).
229. Klimova, V. A. and Zabrodina, K. S., *Izvest. Akad. Nauk. SSSR* 176 (1961).
230. Krasnai, I. and Tóth, Z., *Magyar Kem. Folyoirat* **67**, 36 (1961).
231. Ma, T. S. and Gerstein, T., *Microchem. J.* **5**, 163 (1961).
232. Miller, D. L., Samsel, E. P. and Cobler, J. G., *Anal. Chem.* **33**, 677 (1961).
233. Obruba, K., *Mikrochim. Acta* 801 (1961).
234. Saltzman, B. E., *Anal. Chem.* **33**, 1100 (1961).
235. Egerts, V., Simanska, M. and Hillers, S., *Latvijas P.S.R. Zinatnu Akad. Vestis, Kim. Ser.* No. 1, 55 (1961).
236. Jonas, J., *J. pharm. Belg.* **16**, 187 (1961).
237. Klimova, V. A. and Zabrodina, K. S., *Izvest. Akad. Nauk SSSR Otdel. Khim. Nauk* 2234 (1961).
238. Korte, F. and Wüsten, F., *Ann.* **647**, 18 (1961).
239. Vogelenzang, E. H. and Goudswaard, A., *Pharm. Weekbl.* **96**, 761 (1961).
240. Waginaire, L. and Guillot, B., *Fette u. Seifen, Anstrichmittel* **63**, 1084 (1961).
241. Wronski, M., *Z. anal. Chem.* **184**, 193 (1961).
242. Hozumi, K. and Hazama, K., *J. Pharm. Soc. Japan* **81**, 1298 (1961).
243. Janíček, G., Pokorný, J. and Pliška, V., *Nahrung* **5**, 399 (1961).

244. Alicino, J. F., *Microchem. J. Symp. Ser.* **2**, 567 (1962).
245. Alt, B., *Kunststoffe* **52**, 133 (1962).
246. Brancone, L. M., *Microchem. J. Symp. Ser.* **2** 605, (1962).
247. Jančík, F. and Körbl, J., *Českoslov. Farm.* **11**, 305 (1962).
248. Kumar, R. N., Bhat, G. N. and Kuloor, N. R., *Current Sci.* (*India*) **31**, 491 (1962).
249. Obruba, K., *Collection Czechoslov. Chem. Communs.* **27**, 2454 (1962).
250. Obruba, K., *Collection Czechoslov. Chem. Communs.* **27**, 2968 (1962).
251. Tokes, B. and Barabas, B., *Rev. med.* (*Targa-Mures*) **8**, 376 (1962).
252. Kovacs, L., *Magyar Gyógyszerésztud. Társaság Értesitöje* **6**, 259 (1962).
253. Lebedeva, A. I. and Pisarenko, E. S., *Zhur. Anal. Khim.* **17**, 636 (1962).
254. Metcalfe, L. D., *Anal. Chem.* **34**, 1849 (1962).
255. Nettesheim, G., *Z. anal. Chem.* **191**, 45 (1962).
256. Samoilov, S. M., Andrievskii, V. N. and Kotlyarevskii, I. L., *Izvest. Akad. Nauk SSSR Otdel Khim. Nauk* No. 2, 201 (1962).
257. Shurygin, V. E., *Zavodskaya Lab.* **28**, 289 (1962).
258. Sully, B. D. and Williams, P. L., *Analyst* **87**, 653 (1962).
259. Thamm, E., *Parfüm, Kosmetik* **43**, No. 8, 285 (1962).
260. Brown, E. R., *J. Pharm. Pharmacol.* **15**, 379 (1963).
261. Höft, E. and Schultze, H., *J. Prakt. Chem.* **19**, 260 (1963).
262. Klimova, V. A. and Zabrodina, K. S., *Zhur. Anal. Khim.* **18**, 109 (1963).
263. Lebedeva, A. I. and Pisarenko, E. S., *Zhur. Anal. Khim.* **18**, 892 (1963).
264. Ledaal, T. and Bernatek, E., *Anal. Chim. Acta* **28**, 322 (1963).
265. Matrka, M., *Chem. Listy* **57**, 163 (1963).
266. Oette, K., Peterson, M. L. and McAuley, R. L., *J. Lipid Res.* **4**, 212 (1963).
267. Silles, E. and Brunner-Montes, C., *Pharm. Acta Helv.* **38**, 746 (1963).
268. Tiwari, R. D. and Sharma, J. P., *Proc. Natl. Acad. Sci., India. Sect. A* **33**, Pt. 3 379 (1963).
269. Trumbull, E. R. and Ibne-Rasa, K. M., *J. Org. Chem.* **28**, 1907 (1963).
270. Vinagre, J. and Mella, M. A., *Nutr. Bromatol. Toxicol.* **2**, 11 (1963).
271. Waginaire, L. and Guillot, B., *Perfumery Essent. Oil Record* **54**, 241 (1963).
272. Ehrlich-Rogozinski, S. and Patchornik, A., *Anal. Chem.* **36**, 840 (1964).
273. Mair, R. D. and Graupner, A. J., *Anal Chem.* **36**, 194 (1964).
274. Obruba, K., Kučerová, E. and Jureček, M., *Mikrochim. Acta* **44** (1964).

52. Iodine reagents

Reagent. Iodine in organic solvents like alcohols, hydrocarbons and halides; or in aqueous iodide solution (usually potassium iodide). This latter reagent must be used for the determinations based on reactions of ion combination (type 4 below).

Many oxidations and substitution reactions (types 1 and 2 below) require a hypoiodite reagent, prepared from iodine and an alkali or alkali buffer or salt such as carbonate, bicarbonate, borate, phosphate, citrate or acetate. The alkali component is usually a separate reagent. (In some oxidation reactions, e.g. of sugars, the sequence of addition of the iodine and alkali parts may influence the stoichiometry—see refs 106, 107 and 113 for instance.) Sometimes the components are present together in a previously mixed reagent.

The Hübl reagent of iodine/mercuric chloride is considered under Iodine chloride, and the use of iodine reagent prepared in situ from an acidified iodate/iodide mixture, is given in the section Iodate.

Reactions and materials titrated. Five principal reactions are represented in indirect titrations with iodine:

1. Oxidation, of a variety of functional groups and compound classes, including: polyphenols; aldehydes (including sugars); methyl ketones; endiols; mercaptans and other sulphur-containing compounds such as thiourea; hydrazines; purine bases. Some examples of the reaction equations are given here:

$$HCHO + I_2 + 3\,OH^- \rightarrow HCOO^- + 2\,I^- + 2\,H_2O$$

$$CH_3CO.CHO + 4\,I_2 + 7\,OH^- \rightarrow CHI_3 + C_2O_4^{--} + 5\,I^- + 5\,H_2O$$

$$CH_2{=}CH.CHO + 3\,I_2 + 4\,OH^- \rightarrow CH_2OH.COO^- + CHI_3 + 3\,I^- + 2\,H_2O$$

$$CCl_3CHO + I_2 + 2\,OH^- \rightarrow CHCl_3 + CO_2 + 2\,I^- + H_2O$$

$$CCl_3CHO + I_2 + 3\,OH^- \rightarrow CCl_3COO^- + 2\,I^- + 2\,H_2O$$

$$(CH_3)_2CO + 3\,I_2 + 4\,OH^- \rightarrow CHI_3 + CH_3COO^- + 3\,I^- + 3\,H_2O$$

$$(CH_3)_2CO + 5\,I_2 + 5\,OH^- \rightarrow 2\,CHI_3 + HCOO^- + 4\,I^- + 4\,H_2O$$

$$2\,RSH + I_2 \rightarrow RS.SR + 2\,HI$$

$$RSH + 3\,I_2 + 3\,H_2O \rightarrow RSO_3H + 6\,HI$$

$$(RO)_2PSS^- + 8\,I_2 + 20\,OH^- \rightarrow (RO)_2POO^- + 2\,SO_4^{2-} + 16\,I^- + 10\,H_2O$$

$$CS(NH_2)_2 + I_2 + H_2O \rightarrow CO(NH_2)_2 + 2\,HI + S$$

$$CS(NH_2)_2 + 4\,I_2 + 5\,H_2O \rightarrow CO(NH_2)_2 + 8\,HI + H_2SO_4$$

$C_6H_5NH.NH_2 + 2\,I_2 \rightarrow C_6H_5I + N_2 + 3\,HI$

$C_5H_4N.CONH.NH_2 + 2\,I_2 + 4\,OH^- \rightarrow C_5H_4N.COOH + N_2 + 4\,I^- + 3\,H_2O$

$C_5H_4O_3N_4 + I_2 + 2\,H_2O \rightarrow C_4H_2O_4N_2 + CO(NH_2)_2 + 2\,HI$
(uric acid) (alloxan) (urea)

$$\begin{array}{cc} -C & - & C- \\ \| & & \| \\ NOH & & NOH \end{array} + I_2 \rightarrow \begin{array}{ccc} -C & - & C- \\ \| & & \| \\ N-O & - & N \rightarrow O \end{array} + 2\,HI$$
(α-dioximes) (furoxanes)

The stoichiometry in some of these determinations depends on reaction conditions and does not always correspond to a single equation. Thus with acetone, the second equation above was proposed to account for a slightly high recovery based on the first equation alone (ref. 172). Reproducible results have then been obtained only by close adherence to the reaction conditions and control experiments have been necessary. Frequently met examples of such determinations are of sugars and of the reaction products from inactivation of penicillins by treatment with alkalies or penicillinase. Theoretically, these reaction products should react with 4 mols iodine (ref. 415):

RCONH.CH—CO—N—CH—COOH; CH—S—C($CH_3)_2$ (ring) $\xrightarrow{\text{inactivation}}$

$RCONH.CH(COOH)(CHO) + (CH_3)_2C(SH)—CH(COOH)(NH_2)$

↓ $1\,I_2$ (aldehyde part) ↓ $3\,I_2$ (thiol part)

$RCONH.CH(COOH)(COOH) + (CH_3)_2C(SO_3H)—CH(COOH)(NH_2)$

In practice, *ca* 4·5 have been found.

2. Substitution, mostly in determinations of phenols or heterocyclic hydroxy compounds. E.g.

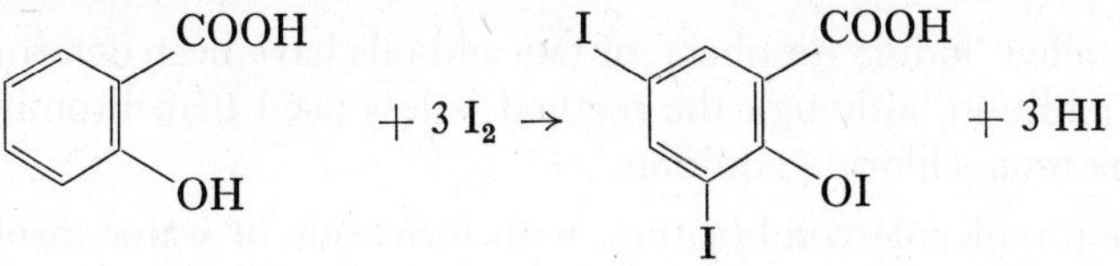

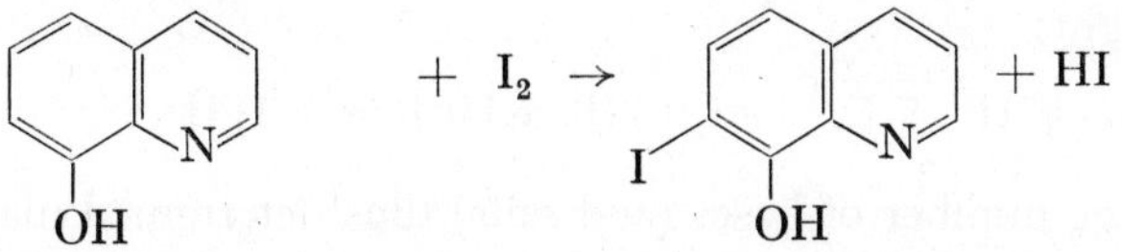

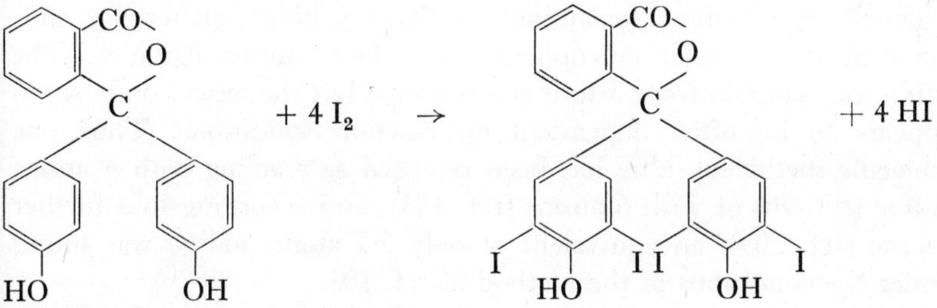

$$\text{(salicylic acid)} + 3\,I_2 \rightarrow \text{(3,5-diiodo-2-iodoxy-benzoic acid: COOH, OI, I, I)} + 3\,HI$$

$$\text{(8-hydroxyquinoline)} + I_2 \rightarrow \text{(7-iodo-8-hydroxyquinoline)} + HI$$

$$\text{(phenolphthalein)} + 4\,I_2 \rightarrow \text{(tetraiodophenolphthalein)} + 4\,HI$$

(phenolphthalein)

Propargyl alcohol and amidines have also been determined iodometrically, based on substitution reactions:

$$HOCH_2.C{\equiv}CH + I_2 + OH^- \rightarrow HOCH_2.C{\equiv}CI + I^- + H_2O$$

$$RC(=NH)NH_2 + I_2 \rightarrow RC(=NI)NH_2 \text{ or } RC(=NH)NHI + HI$$

3. Addition, in determinations of olefinic compounds such as hydrocarbons, unsaturated nitriles and carbonyl compounds and vinyl ethers. The addition is usually of one molecule iodine on to the double bond:

$$-\overset{|}{C}=\overset{|}{C}- + I_2 \rightarrow -\overset{|}{C}I-\overset{|}{C}I-$$

In presence of methanol, as with vinyl ethers, the addition of a methoxy group in postulated:

$$C_2H_5.O.CH{=}CH_2 + I_2 + CH_3OH \rightarrow C_2H_5.O.\underset{\substack{|\\OCH_3}}{CH}{-}CH_2I + HI$$

The so-called 'iodine numbers' of fats and oils have been determined by iodine addition, although the method is less used than bromine or even iodine monochloride addition.

4. Ion/ion/molecule combination, with formation of water-insoluble periodides, in determination of organic bases, usually of fairly high molecular weight:

$$\text{Base} + H^+ + I^- + n\,I_2 \rightarrow (\text{Base.H})^+[(2n + 1)\,I]^-$$

Among the large number of bases (and salts) thus determined may be mentioned: alkaloids such as morphine, atropine and caffeine; betaine; trigonelline; choline; hexamine; methylene blue; quaternary ammonium compounds; cincophene; and some sulphanilamides. The anion may contain from 3 to 9 atoms iodine but the exact composition appears to be often dependent on reaction conditions. Thus one molecule methylene blue has been reported as reacting with 4 atoms iodine (ref. 76) or with 6 atoms (ref. 183); and according to a further source (ref. 209), an equivalent of only 5·7 atoms iodine was found under the conditions of the method of ref. 183.

Under this heading may be classified the formation of periodides in the determination of polyethylene glycols ('carbowaxes') and of a diiodide from methionine.

5. Fission of metal–carbon links in determination of some metal organic compounds. A few examples are given here:

$$Ar{-}Hg{-}OOC.CH_3 + I_2 \rightarrow ArI + Hg(I)OOC.CH_3$$

$$Pb(C_2H_5)_4 + I_2 \rightarrow PbI(C_2H_5)_3 + C_2H_5I$$

$$RLi + I_2 \rightarrow RI + LiI$$

$$Zn(C_2H_5)_2 + 2I_2 \rightarrow ZnI_2 + 2C_2H_5I$$

Some compounds probably take part in more than one reaction. Thus certain polyphenolic compounds like gallic acid and tannins are probably oxidized and substituted in the phenol nucleus; 2,2,6,6-tetrabis-(hydroxymethyl)-1-cyclohexanol yields the product $CI_3(CH_2)_3.CHI.COOH$ (ref. 350); antipyrine may yield a periodide and suffer monosubstitution in the nucleus but the periodide is unstable and in alcoholic solution the only product is the 4-iodo substitution product.

Certain sulphur-containing compounds have been recently determined through their catalytic influence on the iodine/sodium azide reaction:

$$I_2 + 2\,N_3^- \rightarrow 2\,I^- + 3\,N_2$$

The iodine consumption after a definite reaction time was plotted as a function of the amount of sulphur compound and this calibration curve used for the analysis of unknown mixtures. The compounds thus determined include carbon disulphide, cystine, cysteine, penicillinamine and methionine.

Reaction conditions. The solution acidity has ranged from pH *ca* 0 (for a determination of ascorbic acid) through sensibly neutral values to pH *ca* 11. Very broadly speaking, ion/ion combination reactions have been carried out under more acid conditions and most oxidations and many substitutions in more alkaline solution.

Most materials determined are water-soluble but organic solvents have been used with hydrocarbons, in determination of unsaturation, and with some metal-organic compounds like lead tetraethyl.

Reaction temperatures have seldom been much above room temperature, on account of the comparatively high volatility of the iodine reagent. Reaction times have varied over a wide range (from a few seconds up to over 24 hours), as is to be expected from the varied types of reaction undergone by the compounds determined.

Catalysts have very rarely been employed. In the determination of olefines, some authors have used mercury salts such as the acetate, as catalysts.

As already mentioned under Reagent, the order of mixing of the reagent components and the sample may affect the stoichiometry of the reaction.

A number of reactions has been carried out in the dark or at least out of direct sunlight.

Subsequent treatment and final titration stage. The two principally used procedures depend on the easy and accurate titration of iodine:

(i) Titration of unused iodine with thiosulphate. Arsenite has been used in about ten of the examples quoted and hydrazine and ascorbic acid in one. Starch has been widely used as indicator.

In the analysis of absorbent materials like celluloses and starches, excess thiosulphate has usually been added and back titration with iodine carried out after standing for long enough to ensure that any absorbed reagent has reacted.

Alkaline iodine reagents have been neutralized or acidified before the back titration. Precipitates of reaction products (notably those of periodides mentioned under reaction 4 above) have generally been filtered or centrifuged before titrating the unused reagent.

(ii) Periodides formed in the determination of bases and other materials (reaction 4 above) have been determined by titration with thiosulphate. Titration has been facilitated by dissolving the water-insoluble product in an organic solvent like alcohol.

The above two procedures have been used in all but about a dozen of the methods tabulated below. Procedure (i) has been used in a good 90% of the references.

Other final titration stages include:

(iii) Determination of the unused part of other reagents used in combination with the iodine. For example:

Titration with acid of unused alkali from oxidations (especially of sugars) with alkali/iodine reagents.

Titration of unused acid remaining after precipitation of organic bases as periodides;

$$\text{Base} + H^+ + I^- + n\,I_2 \rightarrow (\text{Base.H})^+[(2n + 1)\,I]^- \downarrow$$

(iv) Determination of reaction products other than the periodides given under (ii). Such reaction products may be inorganic, e.g.

HI formed in mercaptan determination by reaction with iodine.

Pb(II) from determination of lead tetraethyl, using standard inorganic procedures such as precipitation with excess $Cr_2O_7^{2-}$ and iodometric back titration of the unused part, or using EDTA.

Choline periodide, precipitated in the determination of the choline, has been determined by oxidation of the I^- to IO_3^- with bromine/acetic acid reagent, followed by addition of I^-/acid and titration with thiosulphate.

Organic reaction products have also been titrated. Details are given under the reagents used but the following table gives the essentials:

Compound determined	Organic reaction product from reaction with iodine	Final titration stage
Acetone, acetaldehyde, 1,2-propylene glycol, 'Warfarin'	Iodoform	Usually with Ag(I), but also by decomposition with sunlight or with HCl giving iodine, titrated with thiosulphate

Compound determined	Organic reaction product from reaction with iodine	Final titration stage
Maltose, starch, lactose	Glucose or galactose (after treatment with HCl)	With Cu(II) or $Fe(CN)_6^{3-}$
Methyl glyoxal	Oxalate	With permanganate
Betaine	Periodide	Kjeldahl nitrogen determination

Note that iodometric titrations in organic chemistry are reviewed in ref. 403.

Examples

For economy of space in the tables below, the conclusion of the determination by titration of unused iodine with thiosulphate has been denoted by the word 'thiosulphate'.

Materials titrated	Reagent and reaction conditions	Subsequent treatment and final titration stage	Ref.
Alkaloids	+ excess iodine/I^-, giving precipitate of periodide	Filtered and aliquot of filtrate titrated with thiosulphate	1
Tannic acid in tannin	+ excess iodine; 12–15 h/room temp.	Thiosulphate	2
Phenylhydrazine; also unused from reaction with, in determination of carbonyl compounds	In water (as hydrochloride), + iodine/I^-; *ca* 1 min/room temp.	Thiosulphate	3
Acetone in methanol	+ iodine + NaOH; 15–30 sec/room temp., with shaking	+ HCl + excess thiosulphate and back titrated with iodine	4
Acetone	+ iodine + KOH. Slightly warmed; 5 min shaking	+ acid; thiosulphate	5
Phenols, e.g. phenol, β-naphthol, thymol, salicylic acid	+ NaOH; warmed to *ca* 60° and excess iodine added. *Ca* 5 min	+ H_2SO_4; thiosulphate	6, 20

Materials titrated	Reagent and reaction conditions	Subsequent treatment and final titration stage	Ref.
Tannin in hops	+ Na_2CO_3 + excess iodine; 5 min/room temp.	+ H_2SO_4 + excess thiosulphate and back titrated with iodine	7
Uric acid	Solution in excess alkali, + iodine until pale yellow; 45 min/room temp.	+ HCl; thiosulphate	8
β-Naphthol	+ NaOH + excess iodine (tested method of ref. 6 and found dependence on alkali and iodine concentrations)	+ acid + excess thiosulphate and back titrated with iodine	9
Acetone in urine	Distillate + KOH + iodine/I^-, giving iodoform precipitate	Filtered, decomposed with KOH and the I^- formed titrated with Ag(I) (see Alkalies, ref. 9)	10
Caffeine	In dilute H_2SO_4, + iodine/I^-, giving precipitate of pentaiodide	Filtered and aliquot of filtrate titrated with thiosulphate	11
Alkaloids	+ iodine/I^-, giving precipitates of periodides	Filtered; aliquot of filtrate titrated with thiosulphate, or precipitate treated with excess thiosulphate and back titrated with iodine	12, 13, 17
Thymol and carvacrol in essential oils	+ NaOH + excess iodine	Filtered, filtrate acidified; thiosulphate	14
HCHO	+ NaOH + excess iodine; 10 min/room temp.	+ H_2SO_4; thiosulphate	15
Aldoses	+ borax solution + iodine. Up to 40 h/room temp.	+ acid; thiosulphate	16
Alkaloids	+ iodine/I^- (criticized method of ref. 12)	Filtered and aliquot of filtrate titrated with thiosulphate	18, 19
Xanthates	In water, + excess iodine, with or without $NaHCO_3$; 30 min/room temp.	Thiosulphate	21

Materials titrated	Reagent and reaction conditions	Subsequent treatment and final titration stage	Ref.
Chloral	+ KOH + excess iodine (dilute KOH to prevent attack of $CHCl_3$ reaction product)	+ acid; thiosulphate	22
Betaine	In dilute HCl + saturated NaCl + iodine/I^-, giving precipitate of periodide	Derivative determined via Kjeldahl nitrogen method (see Kjeldahl nitrogen determination, ref. 1)	23
HCHO	Method of ref. 15, using *ca* 50% in excess of expected iodine amount and not adding too much acid before final titration with thiosulphate		24
HCHO	Method of ref. 15		25
Acetone	Method of ref. 4, with slow addition of iodine and 5 min/room temp.		26
Levulinic acid, as Ca salt	+ excess iodine + KOH; left until no more CHI_3 precipitated	+ HCl equivalent to the KOH; thiosulphate	27
Acetone in urine	Aspirated into KOH + excess iodine	+ HCl; thiosulphate	28
Acetone, recovered from derivative with Denigès $HgSO_4/H_2SO_4$ reagent	Distilled into NaOH + excess iodine; 15–20 min/room temp.	+ H_2SO_4; thiosulphate	29
Acetone in distillate from crude wood naphtha	+ NaOH + excess iodine; 5 min/room temp.	+ H_2SO_4; thiosulphate	30
Phenols, e.g. catechol, salicylic acid, hydroquinone, pyrogallol, gallic acid	+ excess iodine and NaOH added to disappearance of colour	+ acid; thiosulphate	31, 35
Gallic, tannic acids	+ $NaHCO_3$ + excess iodine; 18 h/room temp.	Thiosulphate	32
Acetaldehyde from determination of lactic acid by oxidation with MnO_4^-/H_2SO_4	+ alkali + excess iodine	+ acid; thiosulphate	33
Phenol in gas liquors	Distillate + NaOH + excess iodine. At 60°	+ acid; thiosulphate	34

Materials titrated	Reagent and reaction conditions	Subsequent treatment and final titration stage	Ref.
Cresols	+ Na acetate + excess iodine	Thiosulphate	36
Phenol, cresols	+ $NaHCO_3$ + excess iodine; 1 min/room temp.	Thiosulphate	37
Aldoses	+ NaOH + excess iodine; 5 min–24 h/room temp.	+ H_2SO_4; thiosulphate	38
Acetone in presence of ethanol	+ $Ca(OH)_2$ (then no reaction with alcohol) + excess iodine; slowly added during 40 min at 35°; 10 more min standing	+ H_2SO_4; thiosulphate	39
Antipyrine	In water, + $NaHCO_3$ + excess iodine; 1 h/room temp., giving iodo-substitution product	+ acetic acid + chloroform; thiosulphate	40
Aldoses	+ Na_2CO_3 + excess iodine; 30 min/room temp.	+ HCl or H_2SO_4; thiosulphate	41
Caffeine	+ acetic acid + iodine/I^- + H_2SO_4, giving precipitate of periodide	Filtered; filtrate titrated with thiosulphate	42
Glucose	+ NaOH (pH 11·9) + excess iodine. Up to 20 min/room temp.	+ H_2SO_4; thiosulphate	43
Acetone in blood (micro)	+ NaOH + excess iodine; 3 min/room temp.	+ H_2SO_4; thiosulphate	44
Glucose	Study of method of ref. 43		45
Sugars	Study of method of ref. 43		46
Acetone	Study of method of ref. 4; recommended back titration directly with thiosulphate and 5–20 min reaction time		47
Dextrose in cerebro-spinal fluid	+ Na_2CO_3 + excess iodine; 2 h/room temp.	+ HCl; thiosulphate	48
Glucose	+ NaOH + excess iodine; 10–15 min/room temp.	+ H_2SO_4; thiosulphate	49

Materials titrated	Reagent and reaction conditions	Subsequent treatment and final titration stage	Ref.
Acetone	+ KOH + excess iodine. Study of conditions	+ acid; thiosulphate	50
Mercaptans	+ iodine/I^-. Shaken at room temp.	Thiosulphate	51
Acetone in urine	Distilled into NaOH/ excess iodine; 3 min/room temp.	+ HCl; thiosulphate	52
Phenylhydrazine, unused from reaction with, in determination of furfuraldehyde	+ excess iodine	Thiosulphate	53
Acetone in blood and urine	Distilled into KOH + excess iodine; 25 min/room temp.	+ HCl; thiosulphate	54
Acetone	Method of ref. 4		55
Sugars, e.g. glucose, maltose	+ Na_2CO_3 + excess iodine; 25 min/room temp. in dark (35 min for maltose)	+ slight excess H_2SO_4; thiosulphate	56
HCHO	+ alkali + iodine (compared with other methods for HCHO)	+ acid; thiosulphate	57
Acetone in urine	+ NaOH + excess iodine; 10 min/room temp.	+ H_2SO_4; thiosulphate	58
Glucose	+ $Na_2CO_3/NaHCO_3$, pH *ca* 10, + excess iodine; 90–120 min/room temp. in dark	+ H_2SO_4; thiosulphate	59
Acetone in methanol	+ NaOH + excess iodine; 30 min/room temp. (tested on pure methanol to see if a blank was obtained)	+ H_2SO_4; thiosulphate	60
HCHO	Method of ref. 15		61
HCHO in paraformaldehyde	+ NaOH + excess iodine; 5 min/room temp.	+ HCl; thiosulphate	62

Materials titrated	Reagent and reaction conditions	Subsequent treatment and final titration stage	Ref.
HCHO in presence of methanol and formic acid	Method of ref. 62		63
Maltose, from starch	Method of ref. 43		64
Chloral	+ NaOH + excess iodine; 1 h/room temp.	+ HCl; thiosulphate	65
Antipyrine	+ Na acetate + iodine/ I^-; 20 min/room temp.	+ ethanol; thiosulphate	66
Aldoses	+ iodine, then + NaOH or Na_2CO_3; 5–10 or 20–30 min/room temp., respectively	+ HCl or H_2SO_4; thiosulphate	67
HCHO	Method of ref. 15		68
Phenylhydrazine from determination of osazones by acid hydrolysis	+ $NaHCO_3$ + excess iodine	Thiosulphate	69
Chloral hydrate	+ excess iodine, then + NaOH until pale brown; 5–10 min/room temp.	+ HCl; thiosulphate	70
Sugars, e.g. dextrose, lactose, fructose, sucrose	+ NaOH + excess iodine. Various reaction times tested/room temp.	+ H_2SO_4; thiosulphate	71
HCHO; HCHO + acetone	+ NaOH + iodine; 10 min/room temp.	+ H_2SO_4, unreacted iodine removed with thiosulphate and iodoform steam distilled out. Treated with $AgNO_3$/ethanol, giving I^-, and unused Ag(I) titrated with SCN^- (see Silver (I), ref. 23 and Nitric acid, ref. 3)	72
Olefines in fats	In alcohol, + excess iodine/alcohol + water; 3–5 min/room temp.	Thiosulphate	73
Thiosinamine from determination of allyl isothiocyanate by reaction with ammonia	+ excess iodine + H_2SO_4; 15 min/room temp.	Thiosulphate	74
Acetone; also from determination of aceto-acetic acid by acid hydrolysis	+ alkali + excess iodine	+ acid; thiosulphate	75

Materials titrated	Reagent and reaction conditions	Subsequent treatment and final titration stage	Ref.
Methylene blue	In water, + iodine/I^-, giving precipitate of a periodide	Thiosulphate, to pale blue end-point, from decomposition of the first trace of periodide after all free iodine was titrated	76
Acetone in ternary mixtures with ethanol and water	Method of ref. 4		77
Cellulose xanthate	Neutral solution + excess iodine	Thiosulphate	78
Iodine numbers	Method of ref. 73, but with ethanol containing 1–2% amyl alcohol to give better solubility properties		79
Insulin	+ phosphate buffer; pH 6·8 + excess iodine; 17 h/37°		80
Cellulose xanthate	In water, + slight excess acetic acid + excess iodine; 30 min/room temp.	Thiosulphate	81
Precipitate from determination of acetone with Nessler Hg(II) reagent	Solution in HCl + NaOH + excess iodine; 10 min/room temp.	+ HCl; thiosulphate	82
precipitate from determination of acetaldehyde with same reagent	solution in HCl + excess iodine	thiosulphate	
Acetone in derivatives of polyvalent alcohols	+ NaOH + excess iodine; 20 min/room temp.	+ HCl; thiosulphate	83
HCHO from determination of hexamine by acid hydrolysis	Distilled into excess iodine, NaOH added until yellow and left 10 min/room temp.	+ HCl; thiosulphate	84
Aldoses	+ Na_2CO_3 + excess iodine; 1–2·5 h/1°	+ HCl; thiosulphate	85
Antipyrine	Tested methods of refs 40 and 66		86
Theobromine	+ NaOH + excess iodine; 15 min/room temp.; then + HCl/NaCl and left 30 min/room temp., giving insoluble periodide	Filtered and filtrate titrated with thiosulphate	87

Materials titrated	Reagent and reaction conditions	Subsequent treatment and final titration stage	Ref.
Butanone from determination of *sec*-butanol by oxidation with $Cr_2O_7^{2-}$	+ alkali + excess iodine	+ acid; thiosulphate	88
Iodine numbers of oils	Emulsion in water/gum arabic, + iodine/I^-; 5 min/room temp.	Thiosulphate	89
Methylene blue	Studied factors influencing determination by precipitation with iodine/I^-		90
Mixtures of α, β- and β,γ-isomeric unsaturated compounds, e.g. cyclohexenylacetic acids	+ $NaHCO_3$ + excess iodine/I^-. Various times/room temp. in dark	+ $CHCl_3$ + water + HCl; thiosulphate. Interpolation gave composition of mixture	91
Iodine numbers of oils	Criticized method of ref. 89, claiming that much more than 5 min reaction time is needed		92
HCHO from determination of hexamine by hydrolysis with H_2SO_4	+ NaOH + excess iodine; 30 min/room temp.	+ H_2SO_4; thiosulphate	93
Phenol in waste liquors	Aqueous solution + alkali + excess iodine at 50–60°	+ H_2SO_4; thiosulphate	94
Acetone from determination of acetone sugars by hydrolysis with H_2SO_4	+ KOH + excess iodine. Studied reaction conditions; 4 min/room temp.	H_2SO_4; thiosulphate	95
Cincophene	In acetic acid, + excess iodine/I^-, giving $(C_{16}H_{11}NO_2)_2.HI_4$	Aliquot of filtrate titrated with thiosulphate	96
Methyl glyoxal	excess iodine + alkali; 30 min/room temp.	+ HCl; thiosulphate	97
Iodine numbers of fats	Method of ref. 73; a little HCl or $CHCl_3$ added to some		98
Iodine numbers	Method of ref. 73 compared with other iodine number determinations; at least 65% excess iodine needed		99
Lead tetraethyl	In benzene, + iodine/I^-; 2–3 min shaking at room temp.	Thiosulphate	100
Acetaldehyde, pyruvic acid, acetone, HCHO	Studied conditions for determinations with alkali/iodine; stated that excess alkali must be present		101

Materials titrated	Reagent and reaction conditions	Subsequent treatment and final titration stage	Ref.
Aldoses (micro)	+ Na_2CO_3 + 3–4 times the equivalent of iodine; 30 min/21°	+ acid; thiosulphate	102
Aldoses	Added to Na_2CO_3/iodine mixture at *ca* 0°; 2·5 h standing	+ HCl; thiosulphate	103
Dextrose in presence of fructose	+ iodine (*ca* 3 times equivalent) + carbonate/borate buffer, pH 10·6; 20 min/26–7° (claimed stoichiometric conversion to glucuronic acid)	+ H_2SO_4; thiosulphate	104
Cellulose xanthate in presence of $NaCS_3$ (also $NaCS_3$ alone after decomposing xanthate with HCl)	Added to excess iodine + dilute acetic acid; 2 min/room temp.	Thiosulphate. Xanthate amount from difference between titrations	105
Aldoses	+ excess alkali + excess iodine, added alternately in small portions during 5–6 min. Then 2 more min/room temp.	Unused alkali titrated with HCl and also back titrated with thiosulphate	106
Aldoses	Method of ref. 106 but with initial addition of iodine instead of alkali		107
Morphine in tablets or pills	Solution neutralized with HCl, + iodine/I^-; 2 min/room temp. with stirring, giving precipitate of periodide	Filtered and aliquot of filtrate titrated with thiosulphate	108
Thiosinamine from determination of allylisothiocyanate by reaction with ammonia	Filtrate + H_2SO_4 + excess iodine; 15 min/room temp.	+ benzene; thiosulphate	109
Iodine number of linseed oil	Oil + ethanol + iodine/alcohol + water; 5 min/room temp. (slight modification of method of ref. 73)	Thiosulphate	110
Choline	Neutral or weakly acid solution + iodine/I^-, giving precipitate of periodide	Centrifuged, dissolved precipitate in $CHCl_3$ or CS_2 and titrated with thiosulphate (see Part I, Thiosulphate, ref. 2)	111

Materials titrated	Reagent and reaction conditions	Subsequent treatment and final titration stage	Ref.
HCHO	In water, + NaOH + excess iodine; 1 h/room temp.	+ HCl; thiosulphate	112
Aldoses	+ excess alkali + excess iodine, added alternately in small portions, then left 20 min/room temp.	Unused alkali or iodine back titrated with acid and thiosulphate respectively	113
Chloral	Modification of method of ref. 70, using more dilute alkali; compared with other methods		114
Glucose in presence of fructose and glycine	+ $NaOH/Na_2HPO_4$ buffer, pH 11·5, + excess iodine; 1 h/room temp.	+ H_2SO_4; thiosulphate	115
Dextrose	Neutralized solution + HCO_3^-/CO_3^{2-} + excess iodine; 2 h/room temp. in dark	+ acid; thiosulphate	116
Glutathione in liver	Extract in trichloroacetic acid, + iodine; 2 min/room temp.	Thiosulphate	117
Dextrose, fructose, sucrose	+ alkali + iodine; study of factors like time, temperature, concentrations, rates of addition; for determination of dextrose in honey, recommended 10 min/20°	then + H_2SO_4; thiosulphate	118
HCHO from determination of hexamine or hexamine methylenecitrate by hydrolysis	Method of ref. 15		119
Reduced glutathione in blood	Titrated with iodine to definite blue with starch	Back titrated with thiosulphate	120
Choline in blood	Neutralized extract + iodine/I^-. Left overnight/room temp.	Precipitate filtered, dissolved in $CHCl_3$ and titrated with thiosulphate	121
Trigonelline in raw and roasted coffees	Extract + dilute HCl + iodine/I^-; 10 min/room temp., giving precipitate of periodide	Precipitate dissolved in alcohol and titrated with thiosulphate (see Part I, Thiosulphate, ref. 3)	122

Materials titrated	Reagent and reaction conditions	Subsequent treatment and final titration stage	Ref.
Caffeine	+ acetic acid + H_2SO_4 + iodine/I^- (modification of method of ref. 42, in which the H_2SO_4 was added before the iodine and not after)	Filtered and filtrate titrated with thiosulphate	123
Cellulose xanthate	+ excess iodine; in absence of oxygen	Thiosulphate	124
Choline	+ iodine/I^-	Centrifuged and precipitate titrated with thiosulphate	125
Iodine numbers of commercial lubricating oils	In acetone/ether or amyl alcohol, + ethanol + excess iodine/ethanol + water; 5 min/room temp.	Thiosulphate	126
Purines, e.g. uric acid, xanthine, guanine	+ NaOH + excess iodine, each in at least double the expected equivalent amounts; 10–15 min/room temp.	+ H_2SO_4; thiosulphate	127
Theobromine in 'diuretin' (mixed with Na salicylate)	+ excess iodine/I^-	Thiosulphate	128
Glutathione in blood, tissue	+ excess iodine; 3 min/room temp.	Thiosulphate	129
Morphine	+ iodine/I^- in excess, giving precipitate of periodide, $(C_{17}H_{10}NO_3.H)^+I_3^-$		130
Mercaptans in benzene or naphtha	+ excess iodine, giving equivalent of HI	Excess iodine removed with thiosulphate and aqueous layer titrated with NaOH to bromocresol purple or litmus	131
Ephedrine	+ NaOH + excess iodine; 30 min/60°, giving iodoform	+ acid; thiosulphate	132
Ketone bodies in blood (also from β-hydroxybutyric acid by oxidation with $Cr_2O_7^{2-}$)	Distilled into NaOH + excess iodine, lasting *ca* 50 min	+ H_2SO_4; thiosulphate	133

Materials titrated	Reagent and reaction conditions	Subsequent treatment and final titration stage	Ref.
Sugar in horse blood	Deproteinized blood + Na_2CO_3 + excess iodine; 30 min/room temp.	+ HCl; thiosulphate	134, 150
Caffeine	Extract in water, + H_2SO_4 + iodine/I^-; shaken at room temp. (slight modification of method of ref. 123)	Filtered and aliquot of filtrate titrated with thiosulphate	135
Phenols in creolin and similar products	+ alkali + iodine; 10 min/60°	+ H_2SO_4, filtered and filtrate titrated with thiosulphate	136
Acetone from determination of citric acid by reaction with MnO_4^-/acid	Distilled into alkali and iodine then added; 20 min/room temp.	+ H_2SO_4; thiosulphate	137
Aldoses	+ $NaOH/Na_2HPO_4$, pH 11·25; 30–45 min/room temp.	+ acid; thiosulphate	138
Morphine in brain	Extract + iodine/I^-	Filtered and unused iodine titrated with thiosulphate	139
Acetone from determination of butyric acid by oxidation with $Fe(III)/H_2O_2/H_2SO_4$	+ NaOH + excess iodine; 30 min/room temp.	+ HCl; thiosulphate	140
Morphine in opium	+ iodine/I^-; 3 min shaking/room temp.	Filtered and unused iodine titrated with thiosulphate	141, 207
Glucose	+ NaOH + excess iodine; 20 min/room temp.	+ H_2SO_4; thiosulphate	142
Acetone	Method of ref. 4		143
Glucose	+ HCO_3^-/CO_3^{2-} + iodine in *ca* 100% excess; 2 h/0°	+ acid; thiosulphate	144
Salicylic acid	+ excess iodine	Thiosulphate	145
Sugars	Method of ref. 118 applied in a study of clarification procedures		146
Acetone in fermented liquors	Distilled and determined by method of ref. 47		147

Materials titrated	Reagent and reaction conditions	Subsequent treatment and final titration stage	Ref.
Cysteine from determination of cystine by reduction with Zn/HCl	+ slight excess iodine/ I^-; then frozen solid	Thiosulphate	148
Iodine numbers	In ether/acetone/ethanol/ water, + iodine	+ water; thiosulphate	149
Aromatic mercuri-acetates, $Ar.Hg.OOCCH_3$	+ excess iodine, giving $ArI + Hg(I)OOCCH_3$	Thiosulphate	151
Acetone	Method of ref. 47		152
Acrolein	+ KOH + excess iodine; 30 min/room temp.	+ H_2SO_4; thiosulphate	153
Olefines in fats (micro-iodine number)	Micro-modification of method of ref. 73		154
Ephedrine	+ NaOH + excess iodine; 30 min/50°, giving iodoform	+ HCl; thiosulphate	155
Acetone in biological materials and also from acetone bodies like β-hydroxybutyric acid by oxidation with $Cr_2O_7^{2-}$	+ NaOH + excess iodine	+ acid; thiosulphate	156
Xanthates	Neutral solution + excess iodine	Thiosulphate	157
Acetone	Method of ref. 4; stated to be erratic if methanol present; formic acid said to be the chief oxidation product from the methanol		158
Glucose	+ iodine + excess NaOH; 10 min/room temp.	+ measured excess HCl, unused iodine titrated with thiosulphate and unused HCl back titrated with alkali	159
Glucose	Study of method of ref. 43		160
Betaine	+ H_2SO_4 + iodine/I^-, giving insoluble periodide	Precipitate dissolved in alcohol and titrated with thiosulphate	161

Materials titrated	Reagent and reaction conditions	Subsequent treatment and final titration stage	Ref.
Maltose, formed from starches by hydrolysis in presence of amylases	+ Na_2CO_3 (pH 9·9) + NaCl + excess iodine; 30 min/room temp. in the dark (claimed stoichiometric reaction with 1 mol iodine)	+ H_2SO_4; thiosulphate	162
Acetone from wines	+ NaOH + iodine; 10 min/room temp.	+ H_2SO_4; thiosulphate	163
Alkaloids	+ iodine/I^- + excess HCl, giving precipitates of periodides	Filtered and unused HCl in filtrate titrated with KOH to to phenolphthalein	164
Glucose	+ NaOH + excess iodine; 30–40 min/room temp.	+ H_2SO_4; thiosulphate	165
Acetone from determination of isopropanol by oxidation with $Cr_2O_7^{2-}$	Distilled into KOH + excess iodine; 15 min/room temp.	+ HCl; thiosulphate	166
Acetone from determination of citric acid by reaction with MnO_4^-/acid	Distilled into NaOH + excess iodine	+ acid; thiosulphate	167
Chlorobutanol, $(CH_3)_2C(OH)CCl_3$	+ NaOH + excess iodine; 15 min/room temp.	+ HCl; thiosulphate	168
Maltose	+ NaOH + iodine; 40 min/room temp., giving maltobionic acid	+ HCl, unreacted iodine destroyed with sulphite, heated 1–2 h/100° giving glucose; determined by titration with $Fe(CN)_6^{3-}$ (see Ferricyanide, ref. 39)	169
Acetone from biological sources	+ NaOH + excess iodine; 20 min/room temp.	+ HCl; thiosulphate	170
Zinc phenolsulphonate	in water, + Na_2CO_3 + excess iodine. Heated 15 min, then 10 min standing	+ H_2SO_4; thiosulphate	171
Acetone	Studied method of ref. 4 and found slightly above theoretical recovery (102%); suggested competing reaction yielding formate		172

Materials titrated	Reagent and reaction conditions	Subsequent treatment and final titration stage	Ref.
Phenols, e.g. β-naphthol, salicylic acid, thymol	+ excess iodine	Thiosulphate	173
Acetyl methylcarbinol in fermented media	Distillate + NaOH + excess iodine; 10–15 min/room temp.	+ H_2SO_4; thiosulphate	174
Xanthate in identification of alcohols by reaction with KOH/CS_2	+ excess iodine	Thiosulphate	175
Sugars	Method of ref. 107; various optimum reaction times worked out for different sugars, e.g. 8 min for dextrose, 15 for lactose		176
Chloral	+ NH_4OH/borate buffer, + excess iodine; 15 min/room temp.	+ HCl; thiosulphate; or titrated with arsenite without acidification	177
Acetone in air	Passed into alkali + excess iodine	+ acid; thiosulphate	178
Cincophene	+ iodine/I^-, giving precipitate of periodide	Filtered and aliquot of filtrate titrated with thiosulphate	179
Atropine	Neutral solution + large excess iodine/I^-; 2 min/room temp.	Filtered and unused iodine in filtrate titrated with thiosulphate	180
Precipitate from determination of acetone with Nessler Hg(II) reagent	Method of ref. 82		181
Methylene blue	+ Na acetate + excess iodine/I^-	Filtered and unused iodine in filtrate titrated with thiosulphate	182
p-Chlorophenol	In water, + borax + iodine; 5–10 min/room temp.	+ H_2SO_4; thiosulphate	183
Acetone from determination of isobutyric acid by oxidation with H_2O_2/H_2SO_4 or MnO_4^-	Distilled into alkali + excess iodine; 30 min/room temp.	+ acid; thiosulphate	184
Mono- and disaccharides	Critically examined method of ref. 43, stating that concentrations of reagents and reaction time must be controlled		185, 199

Materials titrated	Reagent and reaction conditions	Subsequent treatment and final titration stage	Ref.
Carotene	Aqueous suspension + excess iodine; 5 min/room temp., reacting with 1 mol reagent	Thiosulphate	186
Iodine numbers of fats and oils	In benzene, + excess iodine/benzene + $Hg(OOCCH_3)_2$/acetic acid; 10 min/room temp.	+ water; thiosulphate	187
Phenols, e.g. tyrosine, adrenaline	In water suspension + excess iodine + NaOH until decolorized + slight excess NaOH; 1–2 h/0–20°	+ H_2SO_4; thiosulphate	188
Chlorogenic acid, extracted from coffee, $(HO)_2C_6H_3CH=CH.COOC_6H_7(OH)_3$ (with COOH on the C_6H_7)	Extract + excess iodine + NaOH; 1 h/room temp. in the dark, reacting with 5 mols iodine	+ H_2SO_4; thiosulphate	189
Trigonelline phosphotungstate from determination of the former	In NaOH solution, + iodine; 1 h/room temp.	+ H_2SO_4; thiosulphate	190
Ascorbic acid in citrus juices	+ H_2SO_4 (giving pH 0·02–0·08) + excess iodine; 30 sec/room temp.	+ slight excess thiosulphate and back titrated with iodine	191
Alkaloids	+ measured excess H_2SO_4 + iodine/I^- in 2–4 times excess	Filtered and filtrate titrated with thiosulphate or with NaOH to phenolphthalein	192
Acetone from determination of acetone bodies in blood by oxidation with $Cr_2O_7^{2-}$, isolation as Hg(II) complex and acidification of last-named	Method of ref. 4		193
Acetone from determination of acetic acid by conversion to Ca salt and oxidation with H_2O_2	+ alkali + iodine, giving CHI_3	Product decomposed with conc. HCl giving iodine; thiosulphate (see Hydrochloric acid, ref. 45)	194
Salicylic acid	+ alkali + excess iodine, giving $C_6H_2I_2(OI)COONa$	+ acid; thiosulphate	195

Materials titrated	Reagent and reaction conditions	Subsequent treatment and final titration stage	Ref.
Salicylic acid from determination of aspirin by hydrolysis with NaOH	+ Na_2CO_3 + excess iodine, reacting with 3 mols iodine; 20–30 min/room temp.	+ H_2SO_4; thiosulphate	196
Thiomalic acid, cysteine, methionine in proteins	In 70–90% acetic acid + at least twice the equivalent of iodine; 1 min/room temp.	+ water; thiosulphate	197
Acetone from oxidation of ketone bodies in blood	+ alkali + excess iodine	+ H_2SO_4; thiosulphate	198
Aldoses	Studied method with iodine + NaOH, $NaHCO_3$ and Na_2CO_3, especially effect of concentrations; cf refs 186, 199		200
Glucosone	Studied method with iodine + NaOH or $NaHCO_3$; cf refs 186, 199, 200		201
Glucose	+ excess iodine; left 1 min/room temp., then NaOH added and left 'some time'	+ HCl; thiosulphate	202
Acetophenone from determination of lobeline by distillation with NaOH	+ NaOH + excess iodine; 10 min/room temp. in dark	+ H_2SO_4; thiosulphate	203
Choline	+ excess iodine/I^-; 30 min/*ca* 0°, giving periodide precipitate	Centrifuged, periodide dissolved in bromine/acetic acid, oxidizing I^- to IO_3^-; + I^- + H_2SO_4 and titrated with thiosulphate	204
'Melubrin', Na phenyl-dimethylpyrazolone aminomethanesulphon-ate	+ Na acetate (claimed better than $NaHCO_3$ or Na_2HPO_4) + excess iodine, reacting with 2 mols iodine	Thiosulphate	205
Hexamine in medicinal mixtures and prepara-tions	+ excess iodine/I^-; 5 min/room temp., giving insoluble periodide	Filtered and filtrate titrated with thiosulphate	206
Aldoses	Studied effect of structure on reaction speeds with NaOH/iodine; cf ref. 201 and previous cited there		208

Materials titrated	Reagent and reaction conditions	Subsequent treatment and final titration stage	Ref.
Methylene blue	+ Na acetate + excess iodine/I^-; (criticized method of ref. 183, saying that only 5·7 atoms iodine react and not 6)	Thiosulphate	209
Lactucin	+ excess iodine + NaOH; 15–20 min/room temp.	+ H_2SO_4; thiosulphate	210
Mercaptans in gas mixtures or aqueous solutions	Solution in $CdCl_2$, + HCl + excess iodine (reacts also with H_2S, which was separately determined)	Thiosulphate	211
Sucrose	Modification of method of ref. 43		212
Lactose	Method of ref. 169, via formation of lactobionic acid		213
Laevulinic acid	+ NaOH + excess iodine. At least 10 min/room temp. (studied factors like reagent excesses, time and temperature)	Filtered iodoform and titrated unused iodine in filtrate with thiosulphate after adding HCl	214
Free phenol in phenolic plastics	+ $NaHCO_3$ + excess iodine	+ I^-; thiosulphate	215
Betaine; choline	Neutral or acid solution + iodine/I^-/NaCl; 3 h/below 10°, giving precipitated periodides	Centrifuged, dissolved precipitate in ethanol and titrated with thiosulphate	216
Xanthate from determination of diethylene glycol monomethyl ether by reaction with KOH/CS_2	+ excess iodine	Thiosulphate	217
Thiourea	+ KOH + excess iodine; 5–10 min/room temp.	+ HCl; thiosulphate	218
Glucosamine	Method of ref. 138		219
Double lactone of *d*-mannosaccharic acid	In water, + NaOH + excess iodine. At least 10 min/room temp., giving iodoform	+ acid; thiosulphate	220

Materials titrated	Reagent and reaction conditions	Subsequent treatment and final titration stage	Ref.
Alkaloids in extract of rye grass	+ conc. phosphoric acid + iodine/I^-	Centrifuged and titrated precipitate with thiosulphate	221
Methionine	At pH 7 (phosphate buffer) + excess iodine/I^-, giving diiodide	Unreacted iodine titrated with thiosulphate, HCl added to decompose diiodide; thiosulphate	222
Acetone in blood and urine; also from determination of β-hydroxybutyric acid by oxidation with $Cr_2O_7^{2-}/H_2SO_4$	+ NaOH + excess iodine; 15 min/room temp.	+ HCl; thiosulphate	223
Lead tetraethyl	+ excess iodine/I^-	Thiosulphate	224
Aldehydes from determination of acetals in solvent mixtures by acid hydrolysis	Neutralized solution + NaOH + excess iodine; 10 min/room temp.	+ HCl; thiosulphate	225
Acetone from determination of citrate by reaction with MnO_4^-	+ KOH + excess iodine; 20 min/room temp.	+ H_2SO_4; thiosulphate	226
Acetone; also from determination of acetoacetic acid by distillation with phosphoric acid	Extract in $CHCl_3$, + water + alkali + excess iodine; 10 min/room temp. with shaking	+ HCl; thiosulphate	227
Lead tetraethyl in gasoline	+ iodine/CCl_4; 5 min/room temp.	Evaporated to dryness, organic matter oxidized with ClO_3^-/HNO_3, dissolved in water, solution neutralized, oxine added and liberated acid titrated with alkali to methyl red	228
Acetoin	+ NaOH + excess iodine; 10 min/room temp.	+ H_2SO_4; thiosulphate	229
Phenolphthalein in complex medicines	+ alkali + excess iodine; 2 h/room temp.	+ H_2SO_4; thiosulphate	230
Furfuraldehyde	+ alkali, then + excess iodine; 10–12 min/room temp.	+ H_2SO_4; thiosulphate	231

Materials titrated	Reagent and reaction conditions	Subsequent treatment and final titration stage	Ref.
Acetone from determination of citric acid by precipitation as Ba salt followed by reaction with MnO_4^-/H_2SO_4	+ NaOH + excess iodine; 10 min/room temp.	+ H_2SO_4; thiosulphate	232
2-Methylnaphthalene-1,4-diol from determination of 2-methyl-naphthaquinone by reduction with Zn/H_2SO_4	+ $NaHCO_3$ + excess iodine	+ acetic acid; thiosulphate	233
Lead tetraethyl in gasoline	+ iodine/CCl_4; 2–3 min/room temp.	Evaporated to dryness, organic matter destroyed with $HNO_3/H_2SO_4/H_2O_2$, evaporated to dryness again, dissolved Pb salt in CH_3COONH_4, added excess $Cr_2O_7^{2-}$ and back titrated iodometrically	234
Sugars in pastry pıoducts (e.g. glucose, fructose and sucrose after inversion with HCl)	+ alkali + excess iodine; 15 min/room temp.	+ H_2SO_4; thiosulphate	235
Methyl glyoxal	+ excess alkali + excess iodine. A few min/room temp.	+ HCl; thiosulphate; also oxalate reaction product precipitated as Ca salt and titrated with MnO_4^-	236
Reaction products from determination of penicillins by treatment with alkali or penicillinase	Neutralized solution + iodine; 30 min/room temp. Blank without inactivation	Thiosulphate: difference from control equivalent to penicillin	237, 408
Methylated glucoses	+ $NaHCO_3/Na_2CO_3$, pH 10·6, + excess iodine; 30–60 min/room temp. in dark	+ H_2SO_4; thiosulphate	238
Hydroquinone	In water, + $NaHCO_3$ + solid CO_2, titrated to starch end-point with iodine and 1 ml excess added	Back titrated with arsenite	239
Iodine numbers	In 96% ethanol, acetone or alcohol/ether + iodine. Based on method of ref. 73	Thiosulphate	240

Materials titrated	Reagent and reaction conditions	Subsequent treatment and final titration stage	Ref.
Reaction products from determination of penicillin G by treatment with alkali	+ excess iodine	Thiosulphate	241
Aldehyde groups in oxycellulose	+ alkali + excess iodine (method stated to be unreliable)	+ acid; thiosulphate	242
Phenols, phenolates in tar oils, benzene and toluene	+ Na_2CO_3 + excess iodine; 10 min/room temp.	+ H_2SO_4 + water; thiosulphate	243
Salicylic acid phenyl ether	In water + iodine + small amount NaOH; 1 h/room temp.	+ HCl; thiosulphate	244
Acetone	+ excess iodine + alkali + a little Mn acetate; 3 min shaking/room temp.	+ H_2SO_4; thiosulphate	245
Acetophenone from determination of lobeline by distillation in steam	Method of ref. 4		246
Reaction products from determination of colchicine by heating with HCl	+ NaOH or $Ba(OH)_2$ + excess iodine; 3 min/room temp.; control with sample without heating with HCl	+ HCl; thiosulphate	247
Invert sugar in chocolate	+ $NaHCO_3/Na_2CO_3$ + excess iodine; 90 min/room temp. in dark	+ H_2SO_4; thiosulphate	248
Reducing sugars	Studied reaction conditions; recommended pH 10·2 (CO_3^{2-}/HCO_3^-) + iodine and 30 min/room temp. (compared with Cu(II) (see ref. 136) and $Fe(CN)_6^{3-}$ (ref. 77) methods)	+ acid; thiosulphate	249
Acetone in cordite	Method of ref. 4 after initial extraction with nitrobenzene/$CHCl_3$		250
Lead tetraethyl in gasoline (micro)	+ iodine/CCl_4. Unused reagent evaporated off	Digested with $HNO_3/H_2SO_4/HClO_4$ to remove organic matter and Pb ultimately precipitated as $PbCrO_4$; dissolved in HCl, I^- added and titrated with thiosulphate	251

Materials titrated	Reagent and reaction conditions	Subsequent treatment and final titration stage	Ref.
High molecular weight quaternary ammonium compounds on textiles and paper	+ water + iodine/I^-. *Ca* 20 min/room temp., giving insoluble triiodides	Filtered, dissolved in ethanol, acidified and titrated with thiosulphate (see Part I, Thiosulphate, ref. 7)	252
Aldehydes from periodate oxidation of polysaccharides	+ Na_2CO_3 + threefold excess iodine; 30 min/room temp.	+ acid; thiosulphate	253
Lead tetraethyl in aviation gasoline	+ iodine/I^-/absolute ethanol; 5 min/room temp. with shaking in dark (based on method of ref. 224)	Thiosulphate	254
Ketones from determination of polyvinyl ketals by hydrolysis with H_3PO_4	+ NaOH + excess iodine; 15 min/room temp.	+ HCl; thiosulphate	255
Phenacetin	+ iodine/acetic acid, giving insoluble periodide	Precipitate titrated with thiosulphate	256
Phenyl glyoxal	+ excess iodine, then + excess alkali	Unused reagent titrated with thiosulphate or acid respectively	257
Unsaturation in isoprene/isobutylene copolymers	In CCl_4/CCl_3COOH + iodine/CCl_4 + $Hg(OOCCH_3)_2$/acetic acid. At least 30 min/room temp.	+ I^-; thiosulphate	258
Reaction products from determination of penicillin G by treatment with alkali	Neutralized solution + iodine; 15 min/room temp. Blank	Thiosulphate	259
Vitamin B_1	+ alkali + excess iodine; at 0°, reacting with 3 mols iodine	+ acid; thiosulphate	260
Dextrose in cane juice	+ borate/CO_3^{2-} buffer + excess iodine; 12 min/room temp. found best	+ H_2SO_4; thiosulphate	261
Chloral from determination of chlorobutanol by reaction with alkali	Distilled into alkali + iodine	+ acid; thiosulphate	262

Materials titrated	Reagent and reaction conditions	Subsequent treatment and final titration stage	Ref.
Reaction products from determination of penicillin by treatment with alkali	Neutralized with HCl, + phosphate buffer, pH 6 + excess iodine; 20 min/room temp. Blank	Thiosulphate	263
Starch extracted from plant tissues with $HClO_4$	+ alcohol/water + NaCl + iodine/I^-; 20 min/room temp., giving precipitate of a complex	Centrifuged, decomposed with NaOH/alcohol, hydrolysed with HCl and the glucose determined with Cu(II) titration (see Hydrochloric acid, ref. 71; Copper (II), ref. 143)	264
Alkyl vinyl ethers	Added to excess iodine + methanol; 10 min shaking at room temp.	Thiosulphate	265
Reaction products from determination of penicillin by treatment with alkali	Neutralized solution + iodine + phosphate buffer pH 7; 30 min/room temp. Blank	Thiosulphate	266
Reaction products from determination of penicillin by treatment with alkali	Faintly acidified solution + iodine; 15 min/30°. Blank	Thiosulphate	267
Various sugars	+ NaOH or Na_2CO_3 + iodine; Up to *ca* 3 h/room temp.	+ acid; thiosulphate	268
HCHO in hexamine	Method of ref. 15		269
Xanthate from determination of CS_2 in light oil forerunnings by reaction with benzene/ethanol/KOH	Non-aqueous layer + excess iodine + acetic acid	Thiosulphate	270
Aldoses	+ $NaHCO_3/Na_2CO_3$, pH 10·6, + iodine; 2–2·5 h/room temp.	+ H_2SO_4; thiosulphate	271
Xanthate from determination of CS_2 by reaction with ethanol/KOH	Neutralized with acetic acid to phenolphthalein, Na_2CO_3 added and + slight excess iodine	Thiosulphate	272

Materials titrated	Reagent and reaction conditions	Subsequent treatment and final titration stage	Ref.
Reaction products from determination of penicillin by treatment with alkali	Slightly acidified solution + excess iodine; 5 min/room temp. Blank	Thiosulphate	273
Phenol/*o*-cresol mixture	+ NaOH + excess iodine	+ acid; thiosulphate	274
Acetone from determination of isopropylidene groups by reaction with ozone and distillation	+ NaOH + excess iodine; 15 min/room temp.	+ acid; thiosulphate	275
Alkaloids in lupins	+ $NaHCO_3$ + excess iodine; 15 min in dark/room temp.	+ H_2SO_4; thiosulphate	276
Caffeine	+ excess iodine/I^-, giving periodide precipitate	Filtered and unused iodine in filtrate titrated with thiosulphate	277
Reaction products from determination of penicillins (Na, Ca or procaine salts) by treatment with alkali	Studied iodine consumption at various pH values from 2·0 to 6·5 and at various temperatures		278
Reaction products from determination of penicillin by treatment with alkali	Studied reaction conditions-alkali concentration, pH for iodination stage, time and temperature		279
Ascorbic acid	+ excess iodine	Thiosulphate (immediate back titration)	280
Reaction products from determination of total penicillins in industrial cultures by treatment with alkali (after extraction with butanone)	Brought to pH 4 and excess iodine added. Blank	Thiosulphate	281
Lactose (study of hydrolysis)	Method of ref. 43, compared with colorimetric method		282
Na *p*-aminosalicylate	In water, + NaOH/Na_2CO_3 + excess iodine. Reaction time selected for stoichiometry, e.g. 25 min/room temp. gave reaction with 4 I atoms	+ H_2SO_4, filtered and titrated with thiosulphate; or added $CHCl_3$ or CCl_4 and titrated without filtration	283

Materials titrated	Reagent and reaction conditions	Subsequent treatment and final titration stage	Ref.
Glucose; also sugar in blood	+ alkali + excess iodine; 6 h/room temp. or 15 min/60°	+ H_2SO_4; thiosulphate	284
Reducing sugars	Studied effect of minerals on the iodometric determination and found it to be negligible		285
Phenolphthalein in mineral oil emulsion	+ NaOH + excess iodine	+ acid; thiosulphate	286
Reaction products from determination of procaine penicillin by precipitation of the procaine with molybdo- or tungstosilicic acid, followed by treatment with alkali	Method of ref. 266		287
Resorcinol	+ acetate buffer, pH *ca* 5, + excess iodine; 1 min/room temp.	Thiosulphate	288
Phenacetin	In dilute acetic acid, + iodine/conc. HCl, giving precipitate of tetraiodo-derivative	Filtered and titrated filtrate with thiosulphate	289
Acetone	+ NaOH; 5 min/room temp.; then + iodine; 30–120 min/room temp.	+ H_2SO_4; thiosulphate	290
Hexamine	+ iodine/I^-, giving precipitate of periodide	Filtered and unused iodine in filtrate titrated with thiosulphate	291
Lead tetraethyl in aviation gasoline	+ iodine/ethanol	Reaction stopped with I^-/water; thiosulphate	292
Vinyl ethers	Method of ref. 265		293
Crotonaldehyde	In water, + NaOH + excess iodine; 45 min/room temp.	+ acid; thiosulphate	294
Propargyl alcohol	+ NaOH + excess iodine; 10 min/room temp., giving $CI{\equiv}C.CH_2OH$	+ acid; thiosulphate	295

Materials titrated	Reagent and reaction conditions	Subsequent treatment and final titration stage	Ref.
Reaction products from determination of penicillin by treatment with alkali	Neutralized solution + iodine; 10 min/room temp. Blank	Thiosulphate	296
Isoniazid	+ $NaHCO_3$ + excess iodine; 15 min/room temp., reacting with 2 mols iodine	+ HCl; thiosulphate	297
Isoniazid	+ $NaHCO_3$ + excess iodine; 20 min/room temp.	+ HCl; thiosulphate	298
Unsaturation of butyl rubber (correlated with stress–strain values)	In CCl_4 (for 1–2 h) + CCl_3COOH + iodine/CCl_4 + $Hg(OOCCH_3)_2$; 30 min/room temp., out of sunlight	+ I^-/water; thiosulphate	299
Some sulphanilamides, e.g. sulphathiazole, sulphadiazine, sulphadimezine	In dilute HCl, + iodine/I^- in 2–5 times equivalent amount, giving precipitate of periodide; 1 min/room temp.	Filtered and filtrate titrated with thiosulphate	300
Isoniazid	+ alkali + excess iodine, reacting with 2 mols iodine	+ acid; thiosulphate	301
Aldoses from aqueous plant extracts	Method of ref. 59; other substances, e.g. polyuronides may also react		302
Phenolphthalein in fat	+ NaOH + $NaHCO_3$ + excess iodine. Not more than 10 min/room temp.	+ water + I^- + HCl; thiosulphate	303
Amidines, $RC(=NH)NH_2$	In water + excess iodine + NaOH, giving $RC(=NI)NH_2$ or $RC(=NH)NHI$	Filtered, filtrate acidified with HCl and titrated with thiosulphate	304
Isoniazid in cerebrospinal fluid	+ $NaHCO_3$ + iodine excess; 10 min/room temp.	Thiosulphate	305
Caffeine in presence of aspirin and phenacetin	In water, + dilute H_2SO_4 + excess iodine/I^-	Filtered and filtrate titrated with thiosulphate	306

Materials titrated	Reagent and reaction conditions	Subsequent treatment and final titration stage	Ref.
Mannose	+ excess iodine + CO_3^{2-}; 30 min/20°	+ HCl; thiosulphate	307
Aldehyde groups in chromic oxide oxy-starches	+ $NaHCO_3/Na_2CO_3$, pH 9·7, + iodine/I^-; 2·5 h/25°	+ H_2SO_4; thiosulphate	308
Phenylhydrazine (hydrochloride)	In water, titrated with iodine to yellow and the same amount of reagent added extra; + Na_2HPO_4 and left 5 min/room temp.	+ HCl; thiosulphate	309
1,2-Propylene glycol in mixtures with ethylene glycol	+ a little HNO_3 and briefly heated; + iodine and NaOH/methanol alternately with 5 and 10 min waits respectively; finally + thiosulphate/NaOH until no change in yellow; 30 min/35–40°	Iodoform filtered, dissolved in diisopropyl ether and determined with excess Ag(I) + HNO_3, back titrating with SCN^- (see Nitric acid, ref. 13)	310
Caffeine in cola seeds (extracted with $CHCl_3$)	Evaporated extract + iodine/I^- + dilute H_2SO_4 + saturated NaCl, giving precipitate of periodide	Filtered and titrated with thiosulphate	311
Acetone from determination of citric acid by reaction with MnO_4^-	+ alkali + excess iodine	+ acid; thiosulphate	312
Methyl mercaptan, isolated from mixtures via the Hg(II) derivative and regenerated by heating with HCl	Passed into excess iodine	Thiosulphate	313
Caffeine	In water, + H_2SO_4 + iodine/I^-	Filtered and aliquot of filtrate titrated with thiosulphate	314
Guanine	+ excess iodine + NaOH; 1·5–2 h/room temp.	+ H_2SO_4; thiosulphate	315
Acetone from determination of isopropanol in dextran by oxidation with $Cr_2O_7^{2-}$	Distilled into NaOH/excess iodine (5 min distillation)	+ HCl; thiosulphate	316

Materials titrated	Reagent and reaction conditions	Subsequent treatment and final titration stage	Ref.
Phenolphthalein	In Na_2CO_3 solution, + iodine, giving tetraiodo derivative	+ HCl; thiosulphate	317
HCHO in mixtures with methanol	Method of ref. 15		318
Hexamine in resins and moulding powders	In water, + iodine/I^-, added dropwise with stirring	Filtered and filtrate titrated with thiosulphate	319
HCHO in leather (steam distilled from acid solution)	Distilled into NaOH + excess iodine; 15–20 min/room temp. in dark	+ H_2SO_4; thiosulphate	320
Reducing power of starches	+ Na_2CO_3/$NaHCO_3$, pH. 10·2, + iodine/I^-. Various times/30°	+ phosphoric acid + excess thiosulphate; 10 min, then centrifuged and titrated with iodine	321
Reaction products from determination of *N*, *N'*-dibenzylethylene-diaminedibenzyl-penicillin by treatment by alkali	Neutralized solution + iodine; 15 min/room temp. Blank	Thiosulphate	322
Caffeine in mixtures with aspirin and phenacetin (APC tablets)	Method of ref. 306		323
Tyrosine, tryptophane and methionine in mixtures in soluble proteins	+ citrate buffer, pH 6 + excess iodine; 2 h/room temp., reacting with all three + citrate buffer, pH 4; 2 h/room temp., reacting with only tryptophane and methionine	Thiosulphate; then + HCl, causing methionine periodide complex to decompose; thiosulphate again (giving methionine) + acid; thiosulphate, likewise + HCl and retitrated	324
Mercaptans	+ excess iodine; 20–30 min/room temp.	Thiosulphate	325
Glucose in invert sugar	+ Na_2CO_3 + excess iodine; 20 min/room temp.	+ HCl; thiosulphate	326
Ethyl mercaptan from determination of a sugar diethylmercaptal by reaction with HCl	Carried with CO_2 stream into iodine/ethanol; 2 h/room temp.	Thiosulphate	327

Materials titrated	Reagent and reaction conditions	Subsequent treatment and final titration stage	Ref.
Acetone from determination of isopropylidene groups by oxidation with periodate	+ NaOH + excess iodine; 10–15 min/room temp.	+ H_2SO_4; thiosulphate	328
Methionine	+ excess iodine, giving complex diiodide	Thiosulphate	329
Iodine number of vegetable oils	In CCl_4, + iodine/CCl_4 + $Hg(OOCCH_3)_2$/acetic acid; 10 min–1 h/room temp in dark	+ I^-; thiosulphate	330
Reaction products from determination of heptylpenicillin by treatment with alkali	At pH 6 (phosphate buffer) + excess iodine. Blank	Thiosulphate	331
1-Phenyl-3-pyrazolidinone ('phenidone') in photographic developers	+ H_2SO_4 (pH 0·5) + slight excess iodine; 5 min/room temp., giving the pyrazolone	Thiosulphate	332
Metol, hydroquinone	+ $NaHCO_3$ + excess iodine	Back titrated with arsenite	333
Phenylhydrazine, unused from determination of mesoxalic acid by condensation with excess	+ excess iodine	Thiosulphate	334
Thiourea; tetramethylthiourea	+ excess iodine + NaOH; 30 min/0°	Neutralized, + borax buffer and back titrated with arsenite	335
Caffeine	In water, + H_2SO_4 + excess iodine; 15 min/room temp.	Filtered and filtrate titrated with thiosulphate	336
Caffeine in coffee infusion	+ iodine/I^-	Precipitate dissolved in methanol and titrated with thiosulphate	337
2,4-Dihydroxybenzoic acid (β-resorcylic acid)	In dilute acetic acid + excess iodine; 90 min/room temp.	Thiosulphate	338
Some vinyl compounds and lactones	+ KOH + excess iodine; 25 min/25°	+ HCl; thiosulphate	339
Phenolphthalein	+ $NaHCO_3$ + excess iodine	+ H_2SO_4 + $CHCl_3$; thiosulphate	340

Materials titrated	Reagent and reaction conditions	Subsequent treatment and final titration stage	Ref.
Brilliant Green	+ dilute H_2SO_4 + excess iodine, giving an insoluble product	Filtered and filtrate titrated with thiosulphate	341
Choline	Studied the method based on precipitation of a periodide		342
4-Methyluracil	+ alkali + excess iodine; 10 min/room temp. in dark	+ H_2SO_4; thiosulphate	343
Reaction products from determination of penicillin by treatment with alkali	Studied factors like effect of pH and iodide concentration on accuracy, carrying out kinetic measurements of iodine uptake at 0–1° and at pH values from *ca* 3 to 7		344
HCHO	+ alkali + excess iodine. Not over 20 min/20°; + $HgCl_2/I^-$ also if NH_4^+ or hexamine present	+ HCl; thiosulphate	345
Acetaldehyde	+ NaOH + iodine in *ca* 8 times the equivalent amount; 10–15 min/25°	+ H_2SO_4; thiosulphate	346
Acetone in aqueous and benzene solution	Studied method of ref. 4; for aqueous solutions, added NaOH, then iodine; at least 10 min/room temp. for benzene solutions, 30 min/room temp. in dark with shaking (102% recovery with aqueous solutions)	+ H_2SO_4; thiosulphate	347
'Etazole' [*N'*-(5-ethyl-1,3,4-thiadiazol-2-yl)-sulphanilamide]	In dilute HCl, + excess iodine/I^-, giving insoluble derivative	Filtered and filtrate titrated with thiosulphate	348
Warfarin in commercial preparations	+ iodine + NaOH, giving iodoform	Separated and determined by reaction with HNO_3/excess Ag(I), back titrating with SCN^- (see Silver (I), ref. 150 and Nitric acid, ref. 17)	349
2,2,6,6-Tetrabis-(hydroxymethyl)-1-cyclohexanol	+ KOH + excess iodine; 4–6 h/room temp. in dark, converting to $CI_3.(CH_2)_3.CHI.COOH$	+ H_2SO_4; thiosulphate	350

Materials titrated	Reagent and reaction conditions	Subsequent treatment and final titration stage	Ref.
Dimethoxyborane, $BH(OCH_3)_2$ in methyl borate solutions	+ excess iodine/toluene or isopropanol	Thiosulphate	351
Unsaturation in butyl rubber	Method of ref. 258		352
Chlorogenic acid (after absorption on and elution from Wofatite L 150)	+ alkali + excess iodine	+ acid; thiosulphate	353
N'-(5-Ethyl-1,3,4-thiadiazol-2-yl)-sulphanilamide ('Etazole')	In dilute acid, + excess iodine; 5 min, giving insoluble derivative	Filtered and filtrate titrated with thiosulphate	354
Gallic acid	+ excess iodine + alkali. At least 3 h/room temp.	+ HCl; thiosulphate	355
HCHO + paraform-aldehyde	+ alkali + excess iodine; 10 min/room temp. in dark	+ H_2SO_4; thiosulphate	356, 375
Acetone	+ iodine + NaOH; 15 min/room temp.	+ H_2SO_4, unreacted iodine titrated with thiosulphate, solution neutralized with NaOH, Na acetate added and the iodoform in suspension decomposed photochemically in sunlight into iodine; titrated with thiosulphate (see Pyrolysis, ref 32)	357
Acetaldehyde	+ excess iodine + NaOH; 2 h/0°, then 1 h/20°	+ H_2SO_4; thiosulphate	358
Aldehyde groups in chemically modified cellulose	+ alkali + iodine. Studied factors like pH, I^- concentration and time	+ acid; thiosulphate	359
Lead tetraethyl in gasoline	+ iodine/alcohol; 20 min/*ca* 100°, evidently giving lead iodide	Dissolved in hot ammonium acetate, tartrate added and titrated with EDTA to chromogen black ET-OO	360
Ketones from determination of isopropanol and *sec*-butanol in fermented liquors by oxidation with $Cr_2O_7^{2-}$	+ excess iodine + alkali; 20 min/room temp.	+ H_2SO_4; thiosulphate	361

Materials titrated	Reagent and reaction conditions	Subsequent treatment and final titration stage	Ref.
Dehydroacetic acid	+ NaOH + excess iodine; 16 h/4°, giving iodoform	+ H_2SO_4; thiosulphate	362
Vinyl ethyl ether in blood	Aspirated into iodine/ methanol	Thiosulphate	363
Dichloroacetaldehyde	+ iodine + KOH; 20 min/room temp.	+ HCl + water; thiosulphate	364
Di- + trichloro-acetaldehyde	Method of ref. 364 (combined with an alkalimetric method for both or a colorimetric method for the second alone)		365
1,1-Methylenebis-isoniazid ('methazide')	+ excess iodine + NaOH; 10–15 min/room temp. in dark	+ H_2SO_4; thiosulphate	366
Reaction products from determination of dibenzyl ethylene diamine dipenicillin ('Dicillin') by treatment with alkali	At pH 4·5 + excess iodine; 20 min/room temp. Blank	Thiosulphate	367
Reaction products from determination of penicillin by treatment with NaOH	Neutralized with H_2SO_4, acetate buffer added and + iodine; 20 min/room temp. in dark. Blank	Thiosulphate	368
4-Methyl-5-hydroxy-methyluracil ('Pentoxyl')	+ NaOH + excess iodine; 15 min/room temp. in dark	+ acid; thiosulphate	369
8-Quinolinol-5-sulphonic acid	+ NaOH + excess iodine; 5 min/room temp. in dark	+ acid; thiosulphate	370
Caffeine	Observations on method of ref. 306		371
Carbowax (polyethylene glycols) surface-active agents added to edible fats	+ iodine/I^-, giving precipitate of complex	Separated, dissolved in I^-/ water and titrated with thio-sulphate (see Part I, Thiosulphate, ref. 11)	372
Vicinal dioximes	In CCl_4, + excess iodine + $Hg(OOCCH_3)_2$/ acetic acid; 30 min/room temp., giving furoxanes	+ I^-; thiosulphate	373

Materials titrated	Reagent and reaction conditions	Subsequent treatment and final titration stage	Ref.
Reducing capacity of aluminium alkyls	+ excess iodine/benzene. In nitrogen atmosphere $AlR_3 + 3 I_2 \rightarrow AlI_3 + 3 RI$	+ acetic acid; thiosulphate	374
Dialkyl- and diaryldithiophosphates	+ excess iodine, giving corresponding phosphates	Thiosulphate	376
Reaction products from determination of penicillin in fermentation media by treatment with penicillinase	At pH 6·5 + excess iodine; 25 min/room temp. Blank	Thiosulphate	377
Reaction products from determination of phenoxymethylpenicillin by treatment with NaOH	Method of ref. 237		378
1-Phenyl-3-pyrazolidinone in photographic developers	Extract in $CHCl_3$, + H_2SO_4 + iodine/$CHCl_3$ in at least 50% excess	Thiosulphate	379
Reaction products from determination of penicillin V in fermented broth samples by treatment with alkali	+ excess iodine	Thiosulphate	380, 416
Reducing sugars	Studied influence of many amino acids on the method of ref. 43 and found that all interfered		381
Plasmalogen	In $CHCl_3$/methanol, 2:1, + iodine; 30 sec/room temp.	+ ethanol; thiosulphate	382
Sugars, including sucrose after inversion	+ $NaHCO_3/Na_2CO_3$, pH 10·3, + iodine; 15–20 min/room temp.	+ H_2SO_4; thiosulphate	383
Reaction products from determination of penicillin by reaction with alkali	Studied factors affecting the accuracy of the iodometric determination		384
Caffeine in tablets	In water, + H_2SO_4 + excess iodine/I^-	Filtered and filtrate titrated with thiosulphate	385
Glucose from fruits	+ iodine + Na_2CO_3; 90 min/room temp.	+ H_2SO_4; thiosulphate	386

Materials titrated	Reagent and reaction conditions	Subsequent treatment and final titration stage	Ref.
Betaine in roots of sugar beet	Method of ref. 216		387
Thiosinamine (from determination of allyl isothiocyanate by reaction with NH_4OH)	+ HCl + acetic acid + iodine; 2 h/room temp. in dark	Thiosulphate	388
Thiomalic acid	+ conc. alkali + iodine. At least 5 min/room temp. (1 mol acid equivalent to 6 mols iodine)	+ H_2SO_4; thiosulphate	389
Organoalkalies, e.g. phenyllithium, butyllithium, amylsodium	+ iodine/ether; 3 min in nitrogen atmosphere	+ water; thiosulphate	390
Polyoxyethylene glycols	In water, + iodine/KI; 1 h/room temp., giving precipitate of complex	Centrifuged, KI + $CHCl_3$ added to precipitate and titrated with thiosulphate	391
Phenols	+ iodine + NaOH	+ acid; thiosulphate	392
Thiourea	In 10% $NaHCO_3$, + iodine	Back titrated with arsenite potentiometrically	393
Methylthioureas (mono-, di-, tri-, and tetra-)	Method of ref. 393		394
Unused 2,4-dinitrophenylhydrazine after reaction with, in determination of carbonyl compounds in foodstuffs	Filtrate + Na acetate + $CHCl_3$ + iodine; 30 min/room temp. in dark	Thiosulphate	395
Cystine	+ NaN_2 + HCl + iodine; 30 min/room temp.	Back titrated with arsenite (result obtained from a calibration curve based on known amounts of the sulphur compound)	396
Cysteine	Method of ref. 396 with 20–30 sec reaction time		397
CS_2 in industrial effluents	Method of ref. 396 at pH 5·9 and with 30 min reaction time		398
Penicillinamine from determination of penicillin G by reaction with NaOH	+ HCl and then via method of ref. 396, with 1 min reaction time		399

Materials titrated	Reagent and reaction conditions	Subsequent treatment and final titration stage	Ref.
Tannin + gallic acid in tannin-containing solutions; also gallic acid alone after precipitation of tannin with gelatine	In water, + iodine + NaOH; 15 min/room temp. in dark	+ H_2SO_4; thiosulphate	400
Plasmalogen	Method of ref. 382 with final potentiometric titration		401
Iodine values	Study of method of ref. 73		402
Paper chromatographically separated compounds, e.g. hydroquinone, metol	Dissolved in acetate buffer; + iodine	Thiosulphate	404
2-Amino-1,3,4-thiadiazole-5-thiol and its acetylation product (on the amino group)	In dilute acetic acid, + iodine/acetic acid; 1 min/room temp.	Thiosulphate	405
p-Acetylaminobenzaldehyde thiosemicarbazone ('Tibione')	+ NaOH + iodine; 10 min/2–4° in the dark	+ HCl; thiosulphate	406
Reducing sugars	+ iodine + NaOH; 20 min/15–30°	+ HCl; thiosulphate	407
Reaction products from determination of penicillin in fermented media by treatment with NaOH	+ slight excess HCl + iodine; 5 min/room temp. in the dark	Thiosulphate	409
Reaction products from determination of penicillins by treatment with NaOH	+ slight excess HCl + acetate buffer, pH 4·6 + iodine	Thiosulphate	410
Methionine	Method of ref. 396 with 30 min reaction time		411
Cysteine in protein hydrolysates	Method of ref. 396 with 20 sec reaction time		412
Cystine	Method of ref. 396 with 2 h reaction time		413
Choline in foods	Method of ref. 111		414
Reaction products from determination of penicillin by treatment with NaOH	+ excess iodine	Thiosulphate to variamine blue	415

Materials titrated	Reagent and reaction conditions	Subsequent treatment and final titration stage	Ref.
Aldehydes, acetone, aldoses, hydrazine derivatives, mercaptans, diphenols, ascorbic acid, theobromine	+ iodine + acid (HCl or H_2SO_4), alkali or near-neutral buffers (acetate, phosphate or bicarbonate)	Brought to pH 7–7·5 and back titrated with hydrazine biamperometrically or to starch	417
Bridged Diels–Alder adducts (study of configuration; *endo* forms take up 99–101% iodine; *exo* forms do not)	In acetic acid/water, + $NaHCO_3$ + iodine; 5 min/room temp.	Back titrated with arsenite	418
Formates	+ iodine + excess iodate; 30 min/*ca* 100° (see also Iodate, ref. 76)	Iodine titrated with thiosulphate, H_2SO_4 added and retitrated, giving unreacted iodate	419
Malonates	Neutral solution + iodine in *ca* 6 times theoretical amount; 20 min/100°	Thiosulphate	420
Girard T reagent (hydrazide of carboxymethyltrimethylammonium chloride); also unreacted from study of kinetics of reaction with carbonyl compounds	At pH 7–8 (phosphate buffer) + iodine	Thiosulphate	421
Unreacted 2,4-dinitrophenylhydrazine from reaction with in determination of carbonyl compounds like vanillin and acetophenone	+ iodine; 20 min	Thiosulphate ('polarization voltage titration')	422
HCHO from acid hydrolysis of polyvinyl alcohol fibres, treated with HCHO (in determination of degree of replacement of the —OH groups)	Distilled into NaOH; + iodine; 15 min in dark	+ H_2SO_4; thiosulphate	423
Reducing sugars; ascorbic acid	+ iodine/NaOH; 20 min/ 15–30°	+HCl; thiosulphate	424
5,6-Dimethylbenzimidazole	In 10% HCl, + iodine/ KI; 5 min/room temp. in the dark, giving precipitate of triiodide	Filtered and unused reagent in aliquot of filtrate titrated with thiosulphate	425, 431

Materials titrated	Reagent and reaction conditions	Subsequent treatment and final titration stage	Ref.
Glutathione in absence of cysteine	Method of ref. 396, with 15–20 sec reaction time		426
Acetone in mixtures with ethanol and butanol	Method of ref. 47		427
Zn diethyl in solution in heptane	KI + iodine/benzene + sample; nitrogen atmosphere; 5 min $Zn(C_2H_4)_2 + 2\ I_2 \rightarrow ZnI_2 + 2\ C_2H_5I$	+ acetic acid; thiosulphate	428
Quinone from oxidation of hydroquinone, derived from acid hydrolysis of arbutin in its determination	+ acid + I^-	Thiosulphate	429
Thiourea	+ NaN_3 + iodine	Thiosulphate (calibration curve relating titration with amount of thiourea)	430
2-Benzylbenzimidazole ('Dibazol')	In dilute HCl, + iodine/KI, giving precipitate of periodide	Filtered and unused iodine in filtrate titrated with thiosulphate	432
Formates	+ K hydrogen tartrate + iodine. Brought slowly to boiling (15 min) then boiled 25 min	+ I^-; thiosulphate	433
Thioglycollate (+ S^{2-} + SO_3^{2-} + $S_2O_3^{2-}$)	Sample added with stirring to H_2SO_4/water/iodine	Thiosulphate	434
Thiomalic acid	Tested method of ref. 389 and found that iodine consumption depended on factors like order of addition, temperature, time of addition and (NaOH)		435
4-Hydrazino-2-sulphodiphenyl ether hydrochloride	In dilute NaOH, + HCl + iodine; 25 min in dark	Thiosulphate	436
N-Substituted aromatic thioureas	In water or dilute acid, + $NaHCO_3$ + iodine; 20 min (claimed accurate up to concentrations of ca 1 g/litre)	Back titrated with arsenite	437

Materials titrated	Reagent and reaction conditions	Subsequent treatment and final titration stage	Ref.
Some substituted thiobarbituric acids and their salts, e.g. 5-ethyl-5-(1-methylbutyl)thiobarbituric acid	In NaOH, + iodine/I^-; 15 min/ca 100°	+ HCl + Na acetate; thiosulphate	438
Iodine numbers of oils	Method of ref. 73, using iodine generated from I^-/Ce(IV) (see Cerium (IV), ref. 59)		439
Pentamethylpiperidine tartrate ('Pempidine')	+ water + iodine; ca 15 min	Filtered and aliquot of filtrate titrated with thiosulphate	440
Acetone in mixtures with sorbose and mono- and diisopropylidene sorbose	+ iodine/alkali, yielding CHI_3	Thiosulphate	441
Mono- and disubstituted hydrazines	In water, + iodine + NaOH; 5 min (monosubstituted hydrazines gave good results, disubstituted too high)	+ HCl + I^-; thiosulphate	442
2-Chloro-10-(3-dimethylaminopropyl)phenothiazine ('Aminazine'); 2-chloro-4,6-bis(isopropylamino)-*s*-triazine ('Propazine')	In water, + iodine reagent; 10 min, giving periodides	Filtrate titrated with thiosulphate	443
Resorcinol in presence of phenol	In acetate buffer (pH 5.1), + iodine; 90 sec	Thiosulphate	444
HCHO (and numerous inorganic compounds)	Iodine reagent + sample + NaOH until colourless; 2 min	+ HCl and titrated with ascorbic acid to Tillmans' reagent as indicator ($KHCO_3$ added just before end-point)	445
HCHO in presence of HCOOH and methanol	+ iodine/NaOH; 30 min/room temp.	+ I^- + H_2SO_4; thiosulphate	446

References

1. Wagner, R., *Dingler's Polytech. J.* **101**, 40 (1862).
2. Musset, F., *Chem. News* **51**, 42 (1885).
3. v. Meyer, E., *J. prakt. Chem.* (2) **36**, 115 (1887).
4. Messinger, J., *Ber.* **21**, 3366 (1888).

5. Collischonn, F., *Z. anal. Chem.* **29**, 562 (1890).
6. Messinger, J. and Vortmann, G., *Ber.* **23**, 2753 (1890).
7. Kokazinsky, E., *Z. für deut. ges. Brauwesen* **13**, 571 (1891).
8. Kreidl, I., *Monatsh.* **14**, 109 (1893).
9. Küster, F. W., *Ber.* **27**, 1905 (1894).
10. Argenson, G., *Bull. soc. chim. Paris* (3) **15**, 1055 (1896).
11. Gomberg, M., *J. Am. Chem. Soc.* **18**, 331 (1896).
12. Kippenberger, C., *Z. anal. Chem.* **35**, 10 (1896).
13. Kippenberger, C., *Z. anal. Chem.* **35**, 659 (1896).
14. Kremers, and Schreiner, *Pharm. Rev.* **14**, 222 (1896).
15. Romijn, G., *Z. anal. Chem.* **36**, 18 (1897).
16. Romijn, G., *Z. anal. Chem.* **36**, 349 (1897).
17. Kippenberger, C., *Z. anal. Chem.* **38**, 230, 280 (1899).
18. Scholtz, M., *Z. anal. Chem.* **38**, 226, 278 (1899).
19. Scholtz, M., *Arch. Pharm.* **237**, 71 (1899).
20. Messinger, J., *J. prakt. Chem.* **61**, 237 (1900).
21. Rupp, P. and Krauss, L., *Ber.* **35**, 4157 (1902).
22. Rupp. P., *Arch. Pharm.* **241**, 327 (1903).
23. Staněk, V., *Z. physiol. Chem.* **47**, 83 (1904).
24. Auerbach, F. and Barschall, H., *Arch. Kaiserl. Gesundheitsamt.* **22**, 584 (1905).
25. Fresenius, W. and Grünhut, L., *Z. anal. Chem.* **44**, 20 (1905).
26. Keppeler, G., *Z. angew. Chem.* **18**, 464 (1905).
27. Savaré, B., *Gazz. Chim. Ital.* **36**, II 344 (1906).
28. Folin, O., *J. Biol. Chem.* **3**, 177 (1907).
29. Monimart, R., *J. pharm. chim.* (6) **26**, 392 (1907).
30. Sy, A. P., *J. Am. Chem. Soc.* **29**, 786 (1907).
31. Gardner, W. M. and Hodgson, H. H., *Proc. Roy. Soc.* **24**, 273 (1908).
32. Hinrichsen, F. W. and Kedesdy, E., *Mitt. Materialprüf. Amt., Gross. Lichterfelde West* **25**, 244, from *Chem. Zentralblatt* I, 990 (1908).
33. Jerusalem, E., *Biochem. Z.* **12**, 361, 379 (1908).
34. Skirrow, F. W., *J. Soc. Chem. Ind., London* **27**, 58 (1908).
35. Gardner, W. M. and Hodgson, H. H., *J. Chem. Soc.* **95**, 1819 (1909).
36. Pence, C., *Ind. Eng. Chem.* **4**, 518 (1912).
37. Redman, L. V., Weith, A. J. and Brock, F. P., *Ind. Eng. Chem.* **5**, 831 (1913).
38. Bland, N. and Lloyd, L. L., *J. Soc. Chem. Ind., London* **33**, 948 (1914).
39. Rakshit, J., *Analyst* **41**, 245 (1916).
40. Bougault, J., *J. pharm. chim.* (7) **15**, 337 (1917).
41. Bougault, J., *J. pharm chim.* (7) **16**, 97, 313 (1917).
42. Emery, W. O. and Spencer, G. C., *Ind. Eng. Chem.* **10**, 605 (1918).
43. Willstätter, R. and Schudel, G., *Ber.* **51**, 780 (1918).
44. Widmark, E. M. P., *Biochem. J.* **13**, 430 (1919).
45. Zablinsky, K., *Z. Verein Deut. Zuckerind.* 159 (1919).

46. Baker, J. L. and Hulton, H. F. E., *Biochem. J.* **14**, 754 (1920).
47. Goodwin, L. F., *J. Am. Chem. Soc.* **42**, 39 (1920).
48. Perrier, M., *J. pharm. chim.* **22**, 317 (1920).
49. Behre, A., *Z. Nahr. Genussm.* **41**, 226 (1921).
50. Hermans, P. H., *Chem. Weekblad* **18**, 348 (1921).
51. Kimball, J. W., Kramer, R. L. and Reed, E. E., *J. Am. Chem. Soc.* **43**, 1199 (1921).
52. Lax, H., *Biochem. Z.* **125**, 262 (1921).
53. Ling, A. R. and Nanji, D. R., *Biochem. J.* **15**, 466 (1921).
54. Pincussen, L. and Floros, K. M., *Biochem. Z.* **125**, 46 (1921).
55. Stepp, W. and Fricke, R., *Z. physiol. Chem.* **116**, 293 (1921).
56. Cajori, F. A., *J. Biol. Chem.* **54**, 617 (1922).
57. Kühl, F., *Collegium* 133 (1922).
58. Lublin, A., *Klin. Wochschr.* **1**, 894 (1922).
59. Auerbach, F. and Bodlander, E., *Z. angew. Chem.* **36**, 602 (1923).
60. Bates, H. H., Mullaly, J. M. and Hartley, H., *J. Chem. Soc.* **123**, 401 (1923).
61. Blair, E. W. and Wheeler, T. S., *Analyst* **48**, 110 (1923).
62. Borgstrom, P. and Horsch, W. G., *J. Am. Chem. Soc.* **45**, 1493 (1923).
63. Borgstrom, P., *J. Am. Chem. Soc.* **45**, 2150 (1923).
64. Josephson, K., *Ber.* **56**, 1758 (1923).
65. Kolthoff, I. M., *Pharm. Weekblad* **60**, 2 (1923).
66. Kolthoff, I. M., *Pharm. Weekblad* **60**, 194 (1923).
67. Kolthoff, I. M., *Pharm. Weekblad* **60**, 362 (1923).
68. Mach, F. and Herrmann, R., *Z. anal. Chem.* **62**, 104 (1923).
69. Nanji, D. R., *Biochem. J.* **17**, 761 (1923).
70. Rupp, E., *Pharm. Zentralhalle* **64**, 151 (1923).
71. Hinton, C. L. and Macara, T., *Analyst* **49**, 2 (1924).
72. Mach, F. and Herrmann, R., *Z. anal. Chem.* **63**, 417 (1924).
73. Margosches, B. M., Hinner, W. and Friedmann, L., *Z. angew. Chem.* **37**, 334 (1924).
74. Morvillez, F. and Meesemaecker, R., *J. pharm. chim.* **30**, 236 (1924).
75. Ljunggren, G., *Skand. Arch. Physiol.* **46**, 325 (1925).
76. Sabalitschka, T. and Erdmann, W., *Chem.-Ztg.* **49**, 561 (1925).
77. Benesch, E., *Chem.-Ztg.* **50**, 98 (1926).
78. Bernhard, R., *Kunstseide* **8**, 173, 258 (1926).
79. Brachman, G. and Morosov, A., *Oil & Fat Ind.* (*Russia*) No. 2–3, 73 (1926).
80. Brand, E. and Sandberg, M. S., *Proc. Soc. Exp. Biol. Med.* **23**, 313 (1926).
81. Faust, O., Graumann, M. and Fischer, E., *Cellulosechem.* **7**, 165 (1926).
82. Fleury, P. and Awad, Y., *J. pharm. chim.* (8) **3**, 406, 449 (1926).
83. Grün, A. and Limpächer, R., *Ber.* **59**, 695 (1926).
84. Marotta, D. and DiStefano, F., *Ann. chim. applicata* **16**, 201 (1926).

85. Pauchard, E., *J. pharm. chim.* (8) **3**, 248 (1926).
86. Borloz, A., *Helv. Chim. Acta* **10**, 543 (1927).
87. van Breukeleveen, M., *Chem. Weekblad* **24**, 206 (1927).
88. Cassar, H. A., *Ind. Eng. Chem.* **19**, 1061 (1927).
89. Fialkov, J., *Z. anal. Chem.* **70**, 227 (1927).
90. Holmes, W. C., *J. Assoc. Offic. Agr. Chem.* **10**, 505 (1927).
91. Linstead, R. P. and May, C. J., *J. Chem. Soc.* 2565 (1927).
92. Margosches, B. M. and Fuchs, K., *Z. anal. Chem.* **72**, 185 (1927).
93. Bertel, E., *Biochem. Z.* **201**, 13 (1928).
94. Dehe, H., *Chem.-Ztg.* **52**, 983 (1928).
95. Elsner, H., *Ber.* **61**, 2364 (1928).
96. Emery, W. O., *J. Am. Pharm. Assoc.* **17**, 18 (1928).
97. Fischler, F. and Boettner, R., *Z. anal. Chem.* **74**, 28 (1928); **77**, 359 (1928).
98. Lindenberg, E., *Bol. soc. chim., Sao Paulo* **1**, 92 (1928).
99. Yashkevich, S., *Masloboino-Zhirovoe Delo.* 22,31 (1928).
100. Edgar, G. and Calingaert, G., *Ind. Eng. Chem., Anal. Ed.* **1**, 221 (1929).
101. Hatcher, W. H. and Mueller, W. H., *Trans. Roy. Soc. Canada* (3) **23**, Sect. 3, 35 (1929).
102. MacLeod, M. and Robison, R., *Biochem. J.* **23**, 517 (1929).
103. Pirrone, F. and Irrera, L., *L'industria Chim.* **4**, 105 (1929).
104. Englis, D. T. and Byer, W. J., *Ind. Eng. Chem., Anal. Ed.* **2**, 121 (1930).
105. Geiger, E., *Helv. Chim. Acta* **13**, 281 (1930).
106. Kline, G. M. and Acree, S. F., *J. Research Natl. Bur. Standards* **5**, 1063 (1930).
107. Kline, G. M. and Acree, S. F., *Ind. Eng. Chem., Anal. Ed.* **2**, 413 (1930).
108. Laurence, J., *J. pharm. chim.* (8) **11**, 336 (1930).
109. Meesemaecker, R. and Boivin, J., *J. pharm. chim.* (8) **11**, 478 (1930).
110. Mikhina, E., *Masloboino-Zhirovoe Delo* No. 4–5, 28 (1930).
111. Roman, W., *Biochem. Z.* **219**, 218 (1930).
112. Signer, R., *Helv. Chim. Acta* **13**, 43 (1930).
113. Slater, C. S. and Acree, G. M., *Ind. Eng. Chem., Anal. Ed.* **2**, 274 (1930).
114. Watson, H. A., *Am. J. Pharm.* **102**, 506 (1930).
115. Dykins, F. A. and Englis, D. T., *Ind. Eng. Chem., Anal. Ed.* **3**, 21 (1931).
116. Fiehe, J. and Kordatzki, W., *Z. Untersuch. Lebensm.* **62**, 516 (1931).
117. Kühnau, J., *Biochem. Z.* **230**, 353 (1931).
118. Lothrop, R. E. and Holmes, R. L., *Ind. Eng. Chem., Anal. Ed.* **3**, 334 (1931).
119. Marotta, D. and DiStefano, F., *Ann. chim. applicata* **21**, 150 (1931).
120. Mason, H. L., *Proc. Staff Meetings, Mayo Clinic* **6**, 168 (1931).
121. Maxim, M., *Biochem. Z.* **239**, 138 (1931).
122. Nottbohm, F. E. and Mayer, F., *Z. Untersuch. Lebensm.* **61**, 202 (1931).
123. Wallrabe, G., *Apotheker-Ztg.* **46**, 341 (1931).

124. Berl, E. and Dillenius, H., *Cellulosechemie* **13**, 1 (1932).
125. Bolaffi, A., *Ann. chim. applicata* **22**, 205 (1932).
126. Galle, E. and Böhm, M., *Erdöl u. Teer* **8**, 76.91 (1932).
127. Grynberg, M. Z., *Biochem. Z.* **253**, 143 (1932).
128. Hegland, J. M. A., *Pharm. Weekblad* **69**, 1078 (1932).
129. Moncorps, C. and Schmid, R., *Z. physiol. Chem.* **205**, 141 (1932).
130. Raith, E. and Wischo, F., *Pharm. Monatsh.* **13**, 125 (1932).
131. Sampey, J. R. and Reid, F. E., *J. Am. Chem. Soc.* **54**, 3404 (1932).
132. Sanchez, J. A., *Semana med. (Buenos Aires)* II, 1183 (1932).
133. Toscano, C., *Diagnostica tec. lab. (Napoli), riv. mensile* **3**, 578 (1932).
134. Bierry, H., Gouzon, B. and Magnan, C., *Compt. rend.* **196**, 862 (1933).
135. Jermsted, A. and Østby, O., *Dansk Tids. Farm.* **7**, 117 (1933).
136. Krauer, R., *Chimica (Brasil)* **1**, 96 (1933).
137. Täufel, K. and Mayr, F., *Z. anal. Chem.* **93**, 1 (1933).
138. Dumazert, C., *Bull. soc. chim. biol.* **16**, 932 (1934).
139. Kabasawa, I., *Proc. Jap. Pharm. Soc.* 97 (1934).
140. Klinc, L., *Biochem. Z.* **273**, 1 (1934).
141. Laurence, J. and Labarre, J., *J. pharm. chim.* **20**, 353 (1934).
142. Nordlund, M., *Acta Chem. Fennica* **7B**, 95 (1934).
143. Platonov, M. S. and Plakidina, V. I., *J. Gen. Chem., USSR* **4**, 472 (1934).
144. Provvedi, F., *Ind. ital. conserve aliment.* **9**, 271 (1934).
145. Raigorods'ka, R. L. and Binova, E. S., *Farm. Zhur.* 137 (1934).
146. Saywell, L. G. and Phillips, E. P., *Ind. Eng. Chem., Anal. Ed.* **6**, 116 (1934).
147. Stahly, G. L., Osborn, O. L. and Werkman, C. H., *Analyst* **59**, 319 (1934).
148. Virtue, R. W. and Lewis, H. B., *J. Biol. Chem.* **104**, 415 (1934).
149. Zherdeva, I. and Shiryaeva, G., *Groznenskii Neftyanik* **4**, No. 6–7, 45 (1934).
150. Bierry, H., Gouzon, B. and Magnan, C., *Compt. rend. soc. biol.* **118**, 1350 (1935).
151. Bordeianu, C. V., *Ann. sci. univ. Jassy* **20**, 131 (1935).
152. Christensen, L. M. and Fulmer, E. I., *Ind. Eng. Chem., Anal. Ed.* **7**, 180 (1935).
153. Korenman, I. M., *J. Appl. Chem., USSR* **8**, 1476 (1935).
154. Ruzicka, W., *Mikrochemie* **17**, 215 (1935).
155. Sanchez, J. A., *J. pharm. chim.* **22**, 489 (1935).
156. Schmidt-Hebbel, H., *Rev. est. farm. bioquím. (Buenos Aires)* **25**, 526 (1935).
157. Shcherbakova, E. A., *Zavodskaya Lab.* **4**, 1053 (1935).
158. Sunawala, D. and Katti, M. C. T., *J. Indian Inst. Sci.* **18A**, 115 (1935).
159. Taran, E. N., *J. Appl. Chem., USSR* **8**, 562 (1935).
160. Aleshin, S. S., *J. Appl. Chem., USSR* **9**, 1729 (1936).

161. Blood, J. W. and Cranfield, H. T., *Analyst* **61**, 829 (1936).
162. Caldwell, M. L., Doebbeling, S. E. and Manian, S. H., *Ind. Eng. Chem., Anal. Ed.* **8**, 181 (1936).
163. Challe, Dubaque and Vilte, *Bull. soc. pharm. Bordeaux* **74**, 112 (1936).
164. Dietzel, R. and Paul, W., *Süddeut. Apotheker-Ztg.* **76**, 474 (1936).
165. Gubarev, E. and Puté, M., *Bull. soc. chim. biol.* **18**, 395 (1936).
166. Kemal, H., *Z. anal. Chem.* **107**, 33 (1936).
167. Kogan, A. I. and Shtipel'man, S. D., *J. Appl. Chem., USSR* **9**, 568 (1936).
168. Sinton, F. C., *J. Assoc. Offic. Agr. Chem.* **19**, 535 (1936).
169. Strepkov, S. M., *Biochem. Z.* **289**, 38 (1936).
170. Trotzkii, Yu., and Mendelson, R., *Ukr. Biokhim. Zhur.* **9**, 157 (1936).
171. Evans, M. W., *J. Assoc. Offic. Agr. Chem.* **20**, 645 (1937).
172. Haughton, C. O., *Ind. Eng. Chem., Anal. Ed.* **9**, 167 (1937).
173. Heide, A. and Stensig, S., *Dansk Tids. Farm.* **11**, 13 (1937).
174. Langlyke, A. F. and Peterson, W. H., *Ind. Eng. Chem., Anal. Ed.* **9**, 163 (1937).
175. Magidova, S. S., Divinskaya, E. K., Andreeva, E. F. and Ivashkevich, K. D., *Zavodskaya Lab.* **6**, 693 (1937).
176. Miller, H. S., *Ind. Eng. Chem., Anal. Ed.* **9**, 37 (1937).
177. Schwicker, A., *Z. anal. Chem.* **110**, 161 (1937).
178. Shur, I. V., *Klinicheskaya Med.* **15**, 220 (1937).
179. Cohen, A. I., *J. Assoc. Offic. Agr. Chem.* **21**, 95, 554 (1938).
180. Dujardin, T., *J. pharm. belg.* **20**, 571 (1938).
181. Fleury, P. and Carbon, J., *J. pharm. chim.* **28**, 102 (1938).
182. Gurmendi, G. and Guevara, J. de D., *Bol. soc. quím. Peru* **4**, 283 (1938).
183. Khaletskii, A. M. and Yanavitskaya, A. M., *Farmatsiya i Farmakol.* (*USSR*) No. 1, 17 (1938).
184. Klinc, L., *Biochem. Z.* **296**, 202 (1938).
185. Myrbäck, K. and Örtenblad, B., *Svensk Kem Tidskr.* **50**, 72 (1938).
186. Rachevskii, F. A. and Troitskii, G. V., *Lab. Prakt.* (*USSR*) No. 6, 20 (1938).
187. Scotti, G., *Olii minerali, grassi e saponi, colori e vernici* **18**, 96 (1938).
188. Slotta, K. H. and Neisser, K., *Ber.* **71**, 1611 (1938).
189. Slotta, K. H. and Neisser, K., *Ber.* **71**, 1616 (1938).
190. Slotta, K. H. and Neisser, K., *Ber.* **71**, 1987 (1938).
191. Stevens, J. W., *Ind. Eng. Chem., Anal. Ed.* **10**, 269 (1938).
192. Auguste, C., *J. pharm belg.* **21**, 935, 961 (1939).
193. Barnes, R. H. and Wick, A. N., *J. Biol. Chem.* **131**, 413 (1939).
194. Dulian, F., *Klin. Wochschr.* **18**, 1224 (1939).
195. Kobzarenko, V. S., *Akad. Nauk. USSR, Inst. Khem. Tekhnol.* (*Kiev*) 119 pp. (1939).
196. Krüger, D., *Z. anal. Chem.* **117**, 318 (1939).
197. Kuhn, R., Birkofer, L. and Quackenbush, F. W., *Ber.* **72**, 407 (1939).

198. Leites, S. M. and Odinov, A. I., *Lab. Prakt.* (*USSR*), *Sammelband* 57 (1939).
199. Myrbäck, K., *Svensk Kem. Tidskr.* **51**, 74 (1939).
200. Myrbäck, K., *Svensk Kem. Tidskr.* **51**, 149 (1939).
201. Myrbäck, K., *Svensk Kem. Tidskr.* **51**, 235 (1939).
202. Noyons, E. C., *Rec. trav. chim.* **58**, 17 (1939).
203. Tropp, M. Ya., *Ukrain. Gosudarst. Inst. Eksptl. Farm.* (*Kharkov*), *Konsul'tatsionnye Materialy* No. 5, 40 (1940).
204. Erickson, B. N., Avrin, I., Teague, D. M. and Williams, H. H., *J. Biol. Chem.* **135**, 671 (1940).
205. Evers, M. M. H., *Pharm. Weekblad* **77**, 1081 (1940).
206. Korostishevs'ka, L., *Farm. Zhur.* **13**, No. 2, 23 (1940).
207. Laurence, A. J. and Labarre, J., *Merck's Rept.* 49 (1940).
208. Myrbäck, K., *Svensk Kem. Tidskr.* **52**, 293 (1940).
209. Sabalitschka, T. and Erdmann, W., *Pharm. Helv. Acta* **15**, 162 (1940).
210. Schenk, G. and Schreber, W., *Arch. Pharm.* **278**, 185 (1940).
211. Shaw, J. A., *Ind. Eng. Chem., Anal. Ed.* **12**, 668 (1940).
212. Silin, P. M. and Sapegina, E. A., *Trudy Voronezh. Khim. Tekh. Inst.* **5–6**, 24 (1940).
213. Strepkov, S. M. and Sukhorukova, N. K., *Biokhimiya* **5**, 140 (1940).
214. Ploetz, T. and Bertels, H., *Ber.* **74**, 1456 (1941).
215. Redfarn, C. A., *Brit. Plastics* **13**, 139 (1941).
216. Reifer, I., *New Zealand J. Sci. Tech.* **22B**, 111 (1941).
217. Shupe, I. S., *J. Assoc. Offic. Agr. Chem.* **24**, 936 (1941).
218. Škramovský, S. *Časopis Českoslov. Lékárnictva* **21**, 1 (1941).
219. Dumazert, C. and Lehr, H., *Trav. mem. soc. chim. biol.* **24**, 1044 (1942).
220. Rehorst, K., *Ber.* **75**, 1644 (1942).
221. Reifer, I. and Bathurst, N. O., *New Zealand J. Sci. Tech.* **24B**, 17 (1942).
222. Lavine, T. F., *J. Biol. Chem.* **151**, 281 (1943).
223. Malan, J. R., *Onderstepoort, J. Vet. Sci. Animal Ind.* **18**, 311 (1943).
224. Widmaier, O., *Luftfahrt-Forsch.* **20**, 181 (1943).
225. Zeidler, G. and Pogranitzky, N., *Lack u. Farbenztg.* 140 (1943).
226. Bazin, S., *Ann. pharm. franç.* **2**, 14 (1944).
227. Caron, H., Raquet, D. and Flouquet, M., *Bull. soc. chim.* **11**, 549 (1944).
228. Gonick, H. and Milano, J. J., *Ind. Eng. Chem., Anal. Ed.* **16**, 4 (1944).
229. Johnson, M. J., *Ind. Eng. Chem., Anal. Ed.* **16**, 626 (1944).
230. Lespagnol, A. and Quevenne, Y., *Produits pharm.* **2**, 98 (1944).
231. Rogers, H. R., *Ind. Eng. Chem., Anal. Ed.* **16**, 319 (1944).
232. de Saint-Rat, L. and Hatey, J., *Bull. assoc. chim.* **61**, 285 (1944).
233. Jarousse, J., *Ann. pharm. franç.* **3**, 128 (1945).
234. Lykken, L., Treseder, R. S., Tuemmler, F. D. and Zahn, V., *Ind. Eng. Chem., Anal. Ed.* **17**, 353 (1945).
235. Terrier, J., *Mitt. Lebensm. Hyg.* **36**, 398 (1945).

236. Woo, S-Ch. and Chang, S-Ts., *J. Chem. Soc.* 162 (1945).
237. Alicino, J. F., *Ind. Eng. Chem., Anal. Ed.* **18**, 619 (1946).
238. Jeanloz, R., *Helv. Chim. Acta* **29**, 57 (1946).
239. Kolthoff, I. M. and Lee, T. S., *Ind. Eng. Chem., Anal. Ed.* **18**, 452 (1946).
240. Latzenhofer, J. and Ruziczka, W., *Mitt. chem. Forsch. Inst. Ind. Österreich* **1**, No. 1, 17 (1946).
241. Mundell, M., Fischbach, H. and Eble, T. E., *J. Am. Pharm. Assoc.* **35**, 373 (1946).
242. Pacsu, E., *Textile Research J.* **16**, 105 (1946).
243. Pokrovskaya, L. A., *Zavodskaya Lab.* **12**, 430 (1946).
244. Schuster, G., *Ann. chim. anal.* **28**, 146 (1946).
245. Tomoda, Y., *J. Soc. Chem. Ind. Japan* **49**, 1 (1946).
246. Uffelie, O. E., *Pharm. Weekblad* **81**, 41 (1946).
247. Uffelie, O. E., *Pharm. Weekblad* **81**, 426 (1946).
248. Vaeck, S. V., *Mededeel. Vlaam. Chem. Ver.* **8**, 179 (1946).
249. Blom, J. and Rosted, C. O., *Acta Chem. Scand.* **1**, 32 (1947).
250. Bonner, T. G., *Analyst* **72**, 434 (1947).
251. Gordon, B. E. and Burdett, R. A., *Anal. Chem.* **19**, 137 (1947).
252. Hager, O. B., Young, E. M., Flanagan, T. L. and Walker, H. B., *Anal. Chem.* **19**, 885 (1947).
253. Head, F. S. H., *J. Textile Inst.* **38**, T389 (1947).
254. Newman, L., Philip, J. F. and Jensen, A. R., *Anal. Chem.* **19**, 451 (1947).
255. Ryan, J. D. and Shaw, F. B., *U.S. Patent* 2,425,568, Aug. 12, 1947.
256. Scandarellari, G., *Boll. chim. farm.* **86**, 196 (1947).
257. Woo, S-Ch. and Wang, Ch-I., *J. Chinese Chem. Soc.* **15**, 1 (1947).
258. Gallo, S. G., Wiese, H. K. and Nelson, J. F., *Ind. Eng. Chem.* **40**, 1277 (1948).
259. Gurmandi Robles, G., *Rev. fac. farm. y bioquim., Univ. nacl. mayor San Marco (Lima)* **10**, 166 (1948).
260. Gurmandi Robles, G., *Rev. fac. farm. y bioquim., Univ. nacl. mayor San Marco (Lima)* **10**, 173 (1948).
261. Hsieh, P. T. and Wu, C. C., *Taiwan Sugar J. Quart.* **1**, No. 3/4, 41 (1948).
262. Jensen, H. and Jannke, P., *J. Am. Pharm. Assoc., Sci. Ed.* **37**, 37 (1948).
263. Pedersen, V., *Arch. Pharm. Chemi.* **55**, 625 (1948).
264. Pucher, G. W., Leavenworth, C. B. and Vickery, H. B., *Anal. Chem.* **20**, 850 (1948).
265. Siggia, S. and Edsberg, R. L., *Anal. Chem.* **20**, 762 (1948).
266. Wild, A. M., *J. Soc. Chem. Ind., London* **67**, 90 (1948).
267. Bond, C. R., *Analyst* **74**, 550 (1949).
268. Bot, G., *Magyar Kem. Lapya* **4**, 291 (1949).
269. Dorer, M. and Ozimic, M., *Farm. Glasnik* **5**, No. 9/10, 174 (1949).
270. Hansen, H., *Brennstoffchemie* **30**, 419 (1949).

271. Hirst, E. L., Hough, L. and Jones, J. K. N., *J. Chem. Soc.* 928 (1949).
272. Hofman-Bang, N. and Szybalski, W., *Acta Chem. Scand.* **3**, 926 (1949).
273. Korzybski, T. and Bagdasarian, G., *Med. Doświadczal. i Mikrobiol.* **1**, 632 (1949).
274. Leminger, O., *Chem. Obzor* **24**, 88, 100 (1949).
275. Szabó, D., *Magyar Kém. Lapya* **4**, 603 (1949).
276. Boiko, E. V., *Biokhimiya* **15**, 548 (1950).
277. Chatterjee, K. C., and Krishna Rao, P., *Indian J. Pharm.* **12**, 8 (1950).
278. Ilva, K., Johansen, O. L. and Reimers, F., *Dansk Tids. Farm.* **24**, 253 (1950).
279. Korzybski, T. and Bagdasarian, G., *Mad. Doświadczal. i Mikrobiol.* **2**, 468 (1950).
280. Lenstra, J. B., *Pharm. Weekblad* **85**, 729 (1950).
281. Pénau, H., Hagemann, G. and Saïas, E., *Ann. pharm. franç.* **8**, 100 (1950).
282. Potter, F. E., *J. Dairy Sci.* **33**, 803 (1950).
283. Pulido-Cuchi, F. and Hernandez-Gutierrez, F., *Anales real soc. españ., fis. y quím.* **46B**, 313 (1950).
284. Saeki, T., *J. Pharm. Soc. Japan* **70**, 675, 680 (1950).
285. Smirnov, V. A. and Bondarenko, A. N., *Zhur. Priklad Khim.* **23**, 972 (1950).
286. Warren, A. T., Logun, J. E. and Thatcher, R. L., *J. Am. Pharm. Assoc.* **39**, 10 (1950).
287. Wild, A. M., *Nature* **165**, 818 (1950).
288. Willard, H. H. and Wooten, A. L., *Anal. Chem.* **22**, 585 (1950).
289. Casini, A., *Ann. chim. (Rome)* **41**, 611 (1951).
290. Hayashi, K., *Research Bull. Coll. Agr. Gifu Univ.* **1**, 55 (1951).
291. Kiraev, Yu. P., *Zhur. Anal. Khim.* **6**, 127 (1951).
292. Preis, H., *Schweiz. Arch. Angew. Wiss. u. Tech.* **17**, 219 (1951).
293. Shostakovskii, M. F., Prilezhaeva, E. N. and Uvarova, N. I., *Zhur. Anal. Khim.* **6**, 348 (1951).
294. Veksler, R. I., *Trudy Kom. Anal. Khim. Akad. Nauk, SSSR* **3**, 369 (1951).
295. Yamamoto, K., Yoshimura, M. and Tanaka, M., *Bull. Chem. Soc. Japan* **24**, 151 (1951).
296. Beloff-Chain, A. and D'Accadia, F. D., *Analyst* **77**, 423 (1952).
297. Canbäck, T., *J. Pharm. Pharmacol.* **4**, 407 (1952).
298. Castel, P., Orzalesi, H. and Dubois, A., *Trav. soc. pharm. Montpellier* **12**, 73 (1952).
299. Currie, L. L., *Anal. Chem.* **24**, 1328 (1952).
300. Ibadov, A. Yu., *Aptechnoe Delo* **1**, No. 3, 11 (1952).
301. Kottionis, A., *Chim. Chronika (Athens)* **17**, 78 (1952).
302. Lüdtke, M., *Z. anal. Chem.* **136**, 415 (1952).
303. Srinavasan, M. and Bhalerao, V. R., *Current Sci. (India)* **21**, 10 (1952).
304. Stephan, F. H., *Anal. Chem.* **24**, 180 (1952).

305. Verrotti, M. and Bardelli, N., *Rass. studi psichiat.* **41**, 472 (1952).
306. Wirth, C. M. P., *Drug Standards* **20**, 226 (1952).
307. Collins, J. R., *Anal. Chim. Acta* **9**, 500 (1953).
308. Ellington, A. C. and Purves, C. B., *Can. J. Chem.* **31**, 801 (1953).
309. Endroi, P., *Magyar Kem. Folyóirat* **59**, 211 (1953).
310. Jordan, C. B. and Hatch, V. O., *Anal. Chem.* **25**, 636 (1953).
311. van Pinxteren, J. A. C. and Schallenberg-Heertjes, G., *Pharm. Weekblad* **88**, 805 (1953).
312. Ramos, M. da C. and Guimaraes, A. F., *Anais inst. vinho Porto* 9 (1953).
313. Segal, W. and Starkey, R. L., *Anal. Chem.* **25**, 1645 (1953).
314. Wolff, J. H. and Bister, F., *Z. anal. Chem.* **137**, 324 (1953).
315. Dmochowski, A. and Panusz, H., *Acta Bíochim. Polon.* **1**, 81 (1954).
316. Frisone, G. J., *Anal. Chem.* **26**, 924 (1954).
317. Gengrinovich, A. I. and Mansurkhanova, I., *Aptechnoe Delo* **3**, No. 6, 9 (1954).
318. Jost, W. D., *Plaste u. Kautschuk* **1**, 150 (1954).
319. Kasterina, T. N. and Barulina, M. V., *Khim. Prom.* No. 1, 40 (1954).
320. Mamedov, M. A., *Leskaya Prom.* **14**, No. 12, 34 (1954).
321. Meyer, K. H., van der Wyk, A. J. A. and Chen-Piao Feng, *Helv. Chim. Acta* **37**, 1619 (1954).
322. Parker, G. and Donegan, L., *J. Pharm. Pharmacol.* **6**, 167 (1954).
323. Wollish, E. G., Colarusso, R. J., Piper, C. W. and Schmall, M., *Anal. Chem.* **26**, 1753 (1954).
324. Baraud, J. and Genevois, L., *Bull. soc. chim. France* 1499 (1955); also Genevois, L. and Baraud, J., *Chim. anal.* **38**, 87 (1956).
325. Coope, J. A. R. and Maingot, G. J., *Anal. Chem.* **27**, 1478 (1955).
326. Eriksson, S. O., *Farm. Revy* **54**, 441, 456 (1955).
327. Hirase, S. and Araki, C., *Bull. Chem. Soc. Japan* **28**, 481 (1955).
328. v. Rudloff, E., *Can. J. Chem.* **33**, 1714 (1955).
329. Sakurai, H. and Kimura, T., *Ann. Rept. Takamine Lab.* **7**, 125 (1955).
330. Ubaldini, I. and Capizzi-Maitan, F., *Chim. e ind. (Milan)* **37**, 943 (1955).
331. Vladimirov, G. E., Klimov, A. N. and Zhukova, E. N., *Med. Prom. SSSR* No. 1, 19 (1955).
332. Axford, A. J., *Brit. J. Phot.* **103**, 88 (1956); *Phot. Eng.* **7**, 23 (1956).
333. Gopala Rao, G. and Sastri, T. P., *Z. anal. Chem.* **151**, 415 (1956).
334. Hiramaya, H. and Amano, T., *Ann. Rept. Shionagi Research Lab.* **6**, 55 (1956).
335. Joshi, M. K., *Anal. Chim. Acta* **14**, 509 (1956).
336. Khait, G. Ya., *Aptechnoe Delo* **5**, No. 1, 38 (1956).
337. Prange, G. and Walther, H., *Z. Lebensm.-Untersuch. u. Forsch.* **104**, 261 (1956).
338. Runti, C. and Corradina, S., *Univ. studi Trieste, Fac. sci. ist. chim.* No. 13 (1956).

339. Shostakovskii, M. F., Sedel'kovskaya, F. P. and Zelinskaya, M. O., *Izvest. Akad. Nauk SSSR, Otdel Khim. Nauk* 615 (1956).
340. Subrahmanyam, D. and Srinivasan, M., *J. Sci. Ind. Research* (*India*) **15B**, 30 (1956).
341. Vaisman, G. A. and Filenko, A. P., *Aptechnoe Delo* **5**, No. 3, 23 (1956).
342. Webster, G. R., *Biochim. et Biophys. Acta* **20**, 432 (1956).
343. Balis, E. P., *Aptechnoe Delo* **6**, 55 (1957).
344. Banfield, J. E., *J. Chem. Soc.* 2578 (1957).
345. Bose, S., *J. Indian Chem. Soc.* **34**, 497 (1957).
346. Bose, S., *J. Indian Chem. Soc.* **34**, 739 (1957).
347. Goltz, G. E. and Glew, D. N., *Anal. Chem.* **29**, 816 (1957).
348. Ibadov, A. Yu. and Beseda, G. A., *Aptechnoe Delo* **6**, 57 (1957).
349. Kámen, K., *Chem. Průmysl* **7**, 472 (1957).
350. Kamphenkel, L. and v. Hintzenstern, G., *Chem. Tech.* (*Berlin*) **9**, 704 (1957).
351. Krol, A. J., Eddy, L. B., Mackey, D. A. and Weber, A. E., *US Atomic Energy Comm. CCC*-1024-*TR*-239 (1957).
352. McNall, L. R. and Eby, L. T., *Anal. Chem.* **29**, 951 (1957).
353. Rauscher, K. and Voigt, J., *Ernährungsforsch.* **2**, 647 (1957).
354. Suprun, P. P., *Med. Prom. SSSR* **11**, No. 12, 45 (1957).
355. Turgel, E. O., *Zhur. Priklad Khim.* **30**, 819 (1957).
356. Bellen, Z., *Chim. anal.* **40**, 250 (1958).
357. Bose, S., *Anal. Chem.* **30**, 1157 (1958).
358. Bose, S., *Anal. Chem.* **30**, 1526 (1958).
359. Colbran, R. L. and Nevell, T. P., *J. Textile Inst.* **49**, T333 (1958).
360. Dmitrievskii, V. S., *Khim. i Tekhnol. Topliv i Masel* **3**, 59 (1958).
361. Genevois, L. and Lafon, M., *Chim. anal.* **40**, 156 (1958).
362. Kukal-Belohlavy, M. and Schmid, L., *Z. Lebensm.-Untersuch. u. Forsch.* **108**, 238 (1958).
363. Linde, H. W., *Anesthesiology* **19**, 254 (1958).
364. Malhotra, O. P. and Anand, V. D., *Z. anal. Chem.* **159**, 285 (1958).
365. Malhotra, O. P. and Anand, V. D., *Z. anal. Chem.* **160**, 10 (1958).
366. Merlis, V. M. and Romanova, A. S., *Med. Prom. SSSR* **12**, 51 (1958).
367. Miss, A. and Ghimpu, R., *Farmacia* (*Bucharest*) **6**, 147 (1958).
368. Miss, A. and Conu, I., *Rev. chim.* (*Bucharest*) **9**, 268 (1958).
369. Perel'man, Ya. M. and Gurevich, I. Ya., *Aptechnoe Delo* **7**, 11 (1958).
370. Velich, V., *Chem. Listy* **52**, 346 (1958).
371. Wirth, C. M. P., *Drug Standards* **26**, 85 (1958).
372. Anselmi, S., Boniforti, L. and Monacelli, R., *Chim. e ind.* (*Milan*) **41**, 421 (1959).
373. Banks, C. V. and Richard, J. J., *Talanta* **2**, 235 (1959).
374. Bartkiewicz, S. A. and Robinson, J. W., *Anal. Chim. Acta* **20**, 326 (1959).
375. Bellen, Z., *Chem. Anal.* (*Warsaw*) **4**, 13 (1959).

376. Busev, A. I. and Ivanyutin, M. I., *Zhur. Anal. Khim.* **14**, 244 (1959).
377. Ferrari, A., Russo-Alesi, F. M. and Kelly, J. M., *Anal. Chem.* **31**, 1710 (1959).
378. Kleiner, G. I. and Dendze-Pletman, B. Yu., *Med. Prom. SSSR* **13**, 42 (1959).
379. Levenson, G. I. P. and Rumens, M. G., *J. Phot. Sci.* **7**, 38 (1959).
380. Narasimhachari, V., Nayar, M. K. and Ramanarao, G., *Hindustan Antibiotics Bull.* **1**, 120 (1959).
381. Osodo, K., Shibata, S. and Shitomi, H., *J. Utilisation Agr. Products* **6**, 175 (1959).
382. Rapport, M. M. and Lerner, B., *Biochim. et Biophys. Acta* **33**, 319 (1959).
383. Šepitka, A., *Kvasný Průmysl* **5**, 13 (1959).
384. Weiss, P. J., *Antibiotics and Chemotherapy* **9**, 660 (1959).
385. Wirth, C. M. P. *Pharm. Acta Helv.* **34**, 283 (1959).
386. Osodo, K., Kazumi, H., Kotaka, M. and Shitomi, H., *Nippon Nogei Kagaku Kaishi* **33**, 166 (1959).
387. Vidal, A. A., *Rev. fac. agron., Univ. nacl. La Plata* **35**, 147 (1959).
388. Bauer-Moll, '*Die Organische Analyse*', 4th Edition, Leipzig 1960, p. 485.
389. Busev, A. I. and Fang Chang, *Vestnik Moskov. Univ. Ser. II* **15**, No. 4, 52 (1960); *Talanta* **8**, 470 (1961).
390. Clifford, A. F. and Olsen, R. R., *Anal. Chem.* **32**, 544 (1960).
391. Coppini, D. and Bertolani, G., *Boll. lab. chim. provinciali* **11**, 697 (1960).
392. Gruzdeva, N. A., *Proizv. i Ispol'z Novykh Koksokhim. Produkov, Vost. Nauchn.-Issled. Uglekhim. Inst., Sb. Statei* 96 (1960).
393. Gupta, P. C., *J. Indian Chem. Soc.* **37**, 213 (1960).
394. Gupta, P. C., *J. Indian Chem. Soc.* **37**, 629 (1960).
395. Hamann, V. and Herrmann, A., *Deut. Lebensmittelrundschau* **56**, 95, 133 (1960).
396. Kurzawa, Z., *Chem. Anal. (Warsaw)* **5**, 325 (1960).
397. Kurzawa, Z. and Suszka, A., *Chem. Anal. (Warsaw)* **5**, 327 (1960).
398. Kurzawa, Z. and Meybaum, Z., *Chem. Anal. (Warsaw)* **5**, 333 (1960).
399. Kurzawa, Z. and Suszka, A., *Chem. Anal. (Warsaw)* **5**, 897 (1960).
400. Mudzhiri, K. S. and Zhuk, I. M., *Sb. Tr. Tbilissk. Nauchn.-Issled. Khim.-Farmatsev. Inst.* **9**, 29 (1960).
401. Norton, W. T., *Biochim. et Biophys. Acta* **38**, 340 (1960).
402. Ruziczka, W., *Österr. Chem.-Ztg.* **61**, 298 (1960).
403. Ruziczka, W., *Adhäsion* **4**, 229 (1960).
404. Šimek, J., *Chem. Průmysl* **10**, 403 (1960).
405. Simionovici, R., Stoianovici, M. and Joan, C., *Rev. chim. (Bucharest)* **11**, 591 (1960).
406. Sung-Yao, Y.-W., *Yao Hsueh Hsueh Pao* **8**, 232 (1960).
407. Tomoda, M., *J. Pharm. Soc. Japan* **80**, 1696 (1960).
408. Alicino, J. F., *Anal. Chem.* **33**, 648 (1961).

409. Bethel, M. M. and Bond, C. R., *Analyst* **86**, 448 (1961).
410. Kerényi, I., *Magyar Kem. Folyoirat* **67**, 313 (1961).
411. Kurzawa, Z., *Chem. Anal.* (*Warsaw*) **6**, 399 (1961).
412. Kurzawa, Z., *Chem. Anal.* (*Warsaw*) **6**, 813 (1961).
413. Kurzawa, Z., *Chem. Anal.* (*Warsaw*) **6**, 1013 (1961).
414. Lasota, W. and Monikowski, K., *Acta Polon. Pharm.* **18**, 325 (1961).
415. Mázor, L. and Pápay, M. K., *Acta Chem. Acad. Sci. Hung.* **26**, 473 (1961).
416. Nayar, M. K. and Narasimhachari, N., *Hindustan Antibiotics Bull.* **3**, 101 (1961).
417. Panwar, K. S., Rao, S. P. and Gaur, J. N., *Anal. Chim. Acta* **25**, 218 (1961).
418. Stockmann, H., *J. Org. Chem.* **26**, 2025 (1961).
419. Verma, R. M. and Bose, S., *J. Indian Chem. Soc.* **38**, 109 (1961).
420. Verma, R. M. and Bose, S., *J. Indian Chem. Soc.* **38**, 899 (1961).
421. Wheeler, O. H., Gaind, V. S. and Rosado, O., *J. Org. Chem.* **26**, 3537 (1961).
422. Hozumi, K. and Hazama, K., *Japan Analyst* **10**, 1240 (1961).
423. Majewska, J. and Warzywoda, J., *Chem. Anal.* (*Warsaw*) **6**, 569 (1961).
424. Tomoda, M., *Kyoritsu Yakka Daigaku Kenkyu Nempo* **6/7**, 20 (1961–2).
425. Beral, H., Popescu, D. and Constantinescu, T., *Pharm. Zentralhalle* **101**, 631 (1962).
426. Kurzawa, Z. and Suszka, A., *Chem. Anal.* (*Warsaw*) **7**, 645 (1962).
427. Mehta, S. C. and Mene, P. S., *J. Sci. Ind. Res.* (*India*) **21B**, 556 (1962).
428. Novák, K., *Chem. Průmysl* **12**, 551 (1962).
429. Racz, G., Fuzi, U. and Fulop, L., *Rumanian Med. Rev.* **6**, 88 (1962).
430. Suzuki, S., *Japan Analyst* **11**, 384 (1962).
431. Beral, H., Popescu, D. and Constantinescu, T., *Rev. chim.* (*Bucharest*) **13**, 54 (1962).
432. Suprun, P. P., *Med. Prom.* (*SSSR*) **16**, No. 1, 47 (1962).
433. Verma, R. M. and Bose, S., *Anal. Chim. Acta* **27**, 176 (1962).
434. Wronski, M., *Chem. Anal.* (*Warsaw*) **7**, 851 (1962).
435. Aravamundan, A. and Rama Rao, C., *Talanta* **10**, 231 (1963).
436. Fleszar, B., *Chem. Anal.* (*Warsaw*) **8**, 757 (1963).
437. Gupta, P. C., *Analyst*, **88**, 896 (1963).
438. Jančík, F., Körbl, J. and Sulovský, J., *Czechoslovak Patent* No. 108,813, Nov. 15 1963.
439. Jungnickel, H. E. and Klinger, W., *Pharmazie* **18**, 130 (1963).
440. Koen, V., *Farmatsiya* (*Sofia*) **13**, 41 (1963).
441. Kvapil, J., Konupčik, M. and Liška, M., *Tech. Publ. Středisko Tech. Inform. Potravinar Průmyslu* No. 139,334 (1963).
442. Marzadro, M. and DeCarolis, A., *Mikrochim. Acta* 726 (1963).
443. Shakh, Ts. I. and Kagan, F. Yu., *Farmatsevt. Zh.* (*Kiev*) **18**, 13 (1963).

444. Sobczak, N., *Chem. Anal.* (*Warsaw*) **8**, 613 (1963).
445. Svehla, G., Koltai, L. and Erdey, L., *Anal. Chim. Acta* **29**, 442 (1963).
446. Szekeres, L. and Kardes, E., *Z. Anal. Chem.* **193**, 271 (1963).

53. Iodine chlorides, bromide and thiocyanate

Reagents. (a) Iodine mono- (less often tri-) chloride prepared in one of three ways, namely, from iodate/iodide/conc. HCl; from passing chlorine into an iodine solution; or from a mixture of iodine and mercuric chloride, evidently reacting as follows:

$$2\,I_2 + HgCl_2 \rightarrow HgI_2 + 2\,ICl$$

The last named, usually referred to as Hübl's reagent, is classified here rather than under Iodine by virtue of the analogy to the other iodine chloride and bromide reagents.

Recently (ref. 128), it has been claimed that iodine trichloride does not in fact contain ICl_3 but that iodate is responsible for 75% and ICl for 25% of its oxidizing power.

(b) Iodine thiocyanate, ISCN, prepared by reacting $Pb(SCN)_2$ with iodine.

(c) Iodine monobromide ('Hanuš reagent').

The reagents have usually been used in organic solvents, chiefly glacial acetic acid, halides like $CHCl_3$ and CCl_4 and ethanol. Aqueous solution has been used generally for reactions of oxidation and substitution (see below); the (iodine monochloride) reagent has then been stabilized by the presence of acid, without which it tends to hydrolyse;

$$ICl + H_2O \rightarrow HCl + HOI$$

Reactions and materials titrated. 1. Addition to olefinic bonds, accounting for about three-quarters of the examples given.

$$\text{—C=C—} + ICl \rightarrow \text{—CI—CCl—}$$

$$\text{—C=C—} + ISCN \rightarrow \text{—CI—C(SCN)—}$$

$$\text{—C=C—} + IBr \rightarrow \text{—CI—CBr—}$$

(According to ref. 127, ISCN always adds on in this way, whereas ICl may add also to form —CI—CI— or —CCl—CCl—.)
Most of the determinations are of the unsaturation of various complex mixtures, such as oils, fats, petroleum fractions, natural and synthetic rubbers, lubricating oils, etc. (the so-called 'iodine number' or 'iodine value'). Suitably modified procedures for determination of conjugated

diolefines have been the subject of vigorous, sometimes polemical discussion (see general observations on Halogen reagents for determination of unsaturation).

The determination of enols evidently depends on an initial reaction of addition, the total reaction sequence being:

$$\begin{matrix} \text{—CO—CH}_2\text{—} \\ \rightleftharpoons \\ \text{—C(OH)=CH—} \end{matrix} \xrightarrow{+\ \text{ICl}} \begin{matrix} \text{Cl} \quad\quad \text{I} \\ | \quad\quad\quad | \\ \text{—C(OH)—CH—} \end{matrix} \xrightarrow{-\ \text{HCl}} \begin{matrix} \text{—CO—CHI—} \\ \rightleftharpoons \\ \text{—C(OH)=CI—} \end{matrix}$$

It may be mentioned that, in contrast to most other halogen reagents used for determination of unsaturation (bromine, chlorine), iodine monochloride appears practically to have been used only in indirect titration.

2. Oxidation, e.g. of sulphur-containing compounds such as thiourea, sulphides, thiobarbiturates, methionine, 6-methylthiouracil. The oxidation evidently takes place according to the equation:

$$I^+ + 2\,\epsilon \rightarrow I^-$$

In more acid solution, this may be followed by:

$$I^+ + I^- \rightarrow I_2$$

giving an overall oxidation process of:

$$2\,I^+ + 2\,\epsilon \rightarrow I_2$$

Preoxidation. Preoxidation with iodine monochloride has been applied where direct oxidation of the sample component with an oxidative titrant (like iodate, Ce(IV), etc.) proceeds more slowly than the oxidation of the reaction product from the titrant (iodide, Ce(III) in the cases mentioned). The oxidation stage with the iodine monochloride, quoted above,

$$2\,I^+ + 2\,\epsilon \rightarrow I_2$$

is followed by oxidation with the titrant of the iodine with reformation of I^+, e.g.

$$I_2 + 2\,Ce^{4+} \rightarrow 2\,I^+ + 2\,Ce^{3+}$$

The preoxidation has usually been carried out in acid solution to minimize hydrolysis of the iodine monochloride (see above under Reagent).

$$ICl + H_2O \rightarrow HCl + HOI$$

The hypoiodous acid is a stronger oxidizing agent than the iodine monochloride. With substances more resistant to oxidation, however, this hydrolysis is encouraged by operating in alkaline solution, and in presence of high bromide concentration to minimize decomposition of the hypoiodite into iodide and oxygen. The solution is then acidified before the titration stage with iodate, Ce(IV), chlorite, etc.

The decision whether or not to include here methods of this pre-oxidation type, has not been easy. Where 5, 10 or more minutes reaction time has been allowed before the subsequent titration stage, it has been deemed appropriate to classify under indirect titration with iodine monochloride, and some examples are tabulated below for determination of formaldehyde, hydroquinone, glucose, thiourea and methylthiourea. Frequently, however, the preoxidation is relatively fast and titration with the oxidizing agent has followed sufficiently soon for the whole method to be considered as direct titration. The borderline is naturally very ill-defined. For the benefit of readers, a list is given here of such references in Part I where preoxidation with iodine monochloride was used.

Oxidative titrant	References
Bromate	108 (ascorbic acid)
Cerium (IV)	8 (oxalate)
	11 (oxalate)
	54 (diphenols)
	61 (hydrazines)
	70 (oxalate; hydroquinone)
Chloramine T	10 (hydroquinone; tartar emetic)
	24 (hydrazines)
Hypohalites	20 (hydrazines)
	21 (tartar emetic)
Iodate	28 (dichlorodiethyl sulphide)
	36 (sulphides)
Permanganate	115 (glucose)
Persulphate	1 (hydrazines)
	2 (hydroquinone; tartar emetic)
Vanadate	4 (hydrazines)
	5 (hydrazines)

3. Substitution, notably of phenols, aromatic amines including *p*-aminosalicylic acid, sulphanilamides and esters of *p*-aminobenzoic acid.

$$X\text{—}H + I^+ \rightarrow X\text{—}I + H^+$$

Mono-, di-, tri- and tetraiodo substitution products may be formed, as, respectively, with antipyrine; salicylic acid; phenol or aniline; and phenolphthalein.

4. 'Complex' formation, as with certain compounds of pharmaceutical importance such as spasmolytine, methadone, rivanol and methylene blue, yielding water-insoluble products.

5. Fission of the C—Pb link in the determination of lead tetraethyl, which depends on the reaction:

$$Pb(C_2H_5)_4 + 4\ ICl \rightarrow Pb(C_2H_5)_2Cl_2 + 2\ C_2H_5Cl + 2\ I_2$$

Reaction conditions. Reaction temperatures have rarely been above room temperature and occasionally near 0°. The duration has ranged from about 1 min to many hours. Conjugated olefines normally require the long reaction times and also more concentrated reagents in greater excess; these latter have sometimes been as high as 8-fold.

Mercury (II) salts have been used as catalysts in addition reactions.

Subsequent treatment and final titration stage. (a) Iodometric back titration of unreacted iodine monochloride has been used in the overwhelming majority of analyses.

$$I^+ + I^- \rightarrow I_2$$

(titrated with thiosulphate; sometimes excess added and back titrated with iodine). Where the reaction has been conducted in non-aqueous solution, it is usual to add alcohol or water first. In one case, direct titration (of IBr) was carried out with arsenite.

(b) Following the use of iodine monochloride in preoxidation, the subsequent titration has been performed with reagents like Ce(IV), chloramine T, iodate, sodium chlorite, bromate, permanganate, etc. The disappearance of iodine colour from a chloroform or CCl_4 layer has served as end-point. (In two cases a biamperometric end-point was used.)

(c) In the determinations of lead tetraethyl, the precipitate of $Pb(C_2H_5)_2Cl_2$ was dissolved in methanol and the Cl^- titrated with $Hg(ClO_4)_2$.

(d) The grouping —CO—CHI—, derived from determination of enol content by reaction with iodine monochloride, has been determined by adding iodide and titrating with thiosulphate:

$$\text{—CO—CHI—} + I^- + H^+ \rightarrow \text{—CO—CH}_2(\rightleftharpoons \text{—C(OH)=CH—}) + I_2$$

In connection with (a) above, where applied to measure the unused reagent from determination of unsaturation, substitution (yielding HCl) has often been corrected for as in bromination methods, namely, by adding iodate and retitrating with thiosulphate.

Examples

(As under some other reagents, such as Bichromate, I^-/thiosulphate in the last column has been used as an abbreviation for final titration stage (a).)

Materials titrated	Reagent and reaction conditions	Subsequent treatment and final titration stage	Ref.
Iodine number of fats and oils	In $CHCl_3$ + iodine/ $HgCl_2$/ethanol; 2–18 h/room temp.	+ water + I^-; thiosulphate	1
Iodine number of fats and oils	In $CHCl_3$ or CCl_4 + ICl/acetic acid (95%). Up to 4 h/room temp.	I^-/thiosulphate	2
Iodine number of oils	In CCl_4, + ICl/CCl_4; 10 min/room temp.; (IBr/CCl_4 reacted too slowly)	I^-/thiosulphate	3
Iodine number of fats and oils	In $CHCl_3$ + IBr/ acetic acid; 15 min/room temp.	I^-/thiosulphate	4
Iodine number of mineral oils	Method of ref. 1		5
Pure olefines, diolefines, unsaturated naphthenes, heptine, cracked gasolines	Studied methods of refs 2 and 4		6
Unsaturation of higher petroleum distillates	Method of ref. 4 gave erratic results		7
Unsaturation of petroleum products	+ IBr/CCl_4; studied reaction conditions (sample size, time, temperature) and compared with bromine reagent; considered unsatisfactory		8
Unsaturation of various petroleum products and their cracked distillates	Method of ref. 4		9
Iodine number	Exhaustive study of method of ref. 2; low results found with conjugated unsaturation or in the presence of negative groups		10

Materials titrated	Reagent and reaction conditions	Subsequent treatment and final titration stage	Ref.
Iodine number of raw rubber, gutta-percha and related materials	Dispersion in CS_2, + ICl/acetic acid; 2 h/0°	+ water/I^-; thiosulphate	11
Mixtures of α,β- and β,γ-unsaturated compounds with —COOH, —COOR or —CO—, e.g. ethyl cyclohexenyl acetates	In CCl_4, + iodine/$HgCl_2$/ethanol. In dark (results obtained by interpolation)	I^-/thiosulphate	12
Iodine number of rubber	In CCl_4, + IBr/CCl_4; 15 min/room temp. in dark	I^-/thiosulphate	13
α,β- and β,γ-unsaturated nitriles	In $CHCl_3$, + iodine/$HgCl_2$/ethanol; 1 h/room temp. (result obtained by interpolation as in method of ref. 12)	I^-/thiosulphate	14
Iodine numbers of mineral oils	Method of ref. 1 compared with that under Iodine, ref. 73		15
Unsaturation of natural rubber	Suspension in $CHCl_3$, + ICl/CCl_4. Various times/room temp.	I^-/thiosulphate	16
Eleostearic acid in tung oil	+ ICl/acetic acid reagent as in method of ref. 2; 30 min and 3 h/room temp. (difference in reagent consumption equivalent to the acid)	I^-/thiosulphate	17
Unsaturation of fats, oils, fatty acids	+ ICl/acetic acid (compared with other iodine number methods, e.g. of refs 1 and 4 above; found no substitution even after 7 days reaction; recommended minimum excess of reagent (*ca* 150% of expected amount))	I^-/thiosulphate	18
Iodine number of linoleic acid	Method of ref. 2		19
Iodine number of fats and oils	Study and discussion of method of ref. 2 (value found to depend on reaction time)		20

Materials titrated	Reagent and reaction conditions	Subsequent treatment and final titration stage	Ref.
Unsaturation of natural rubber	Suspension in $CHCl_3$, + ICl/CCl_4 in only 10–20% excess; 6 h/room temp.	I^-/thiosulphate	21
Iodine number of mineral lubricating oils	Method of ref. 2		22
Unsaturated nitriles (binary mixtures), e.g. buteno- or hexeno-nitriles (α,β- and β,γ-)	In $CHCl_3$, + iodine/$HgCl_2$/ethanol; 2 h/room temp. (composition of sample found by interpolation)	I^-/thiosulphate	23
Iodine numbers	In CCl_4, + ICl/CCl_4	I^-/thiosulphate	24
Iodine value of rubber hydrocarbons, gutta-percha, etc.	In CS_2, + ICl/acetic acid; 1–2 h/room temp.	I^-/thiosulphate	25
Iodine numbers	In CCl_4, + IBr/CCl_4; various times/room temp.	$I/^-$thiosulphate; then + iodate and retitrated with thiosulphate to correct for substitution	26
Iodine value of tung oil	+ $CHCl_3$ + ICl/acetic acid; 1 h/20° in dark (reaction extent found to depend on excess, time and temperature, but reproducible)	+ water/I^-; thiosulphate	27
HCHO	+ ICl + NaOH/KBr; 10–15 min/room temp.	+ more Br^- + HCl + CCl_4 or $CHCl_3$ and titrated with IO_3^-, IO_4^-, MnO_4^-, BrO_3^-, Ce(IV) or chloramine T to decoloration of organic layer	28
Iodine value of tung oil	Method of ref. 27, using nomograph to allow for different temperatures and reagent excesses		29
Unsaturation of hydrocarbons	In dry acetic acid/benzene, + ISCN/benzene or CCl_4; 24 h in dark	I^-/thiosulphate	30
Unsaturation of chloroprene polymers	In CCl_4, + ICl/CCl_4 in *ca* 40% excess; 4 h/room temp. in dark	I^-/thiosulphate; corrected for substitution by adding iodate and retitrating with thiosulphate, or by titration of acid formed with NaOH to methyl orange	31

Materials titrated	Reagent and reaction conditions	Subsequent treatment and final titration stage	Ref.
Unsaturation of hydrocarbons	+ $ISCN/CCl_4$; 15 h in dark	+ water; I^-/thiosulphate	32
Iodine number (micro)	Adaptation of method of ref. 1		33
Iodine number of olive oils	Compared methods of refs 1 and 4; good agreement if 15 min reaction time used for latter		34
Olefines in mineral oils	Tried method of ref. 26; recommended avoiding CCl_4 and working in the dark		35
Iodine number	In CCl_4 or $CHCl_3$, + ICl/acetic acid + Hg acetate catalyst; 3 min/room temp.	I^-/thiosulphate	36
Iodine number of marine fats	+ ICl in CCl_4/ acetic acid, 55:45; 30 min/20°	I^-/thiosulphate	37
Iodine number of conjugated olefines	Method of ref. 2, using 30 min reaction; studied influence of ratio sample: reagent		38
Iodine values, e.g. of elaidates and linoleates	Method of ref. 2		39
Allyl alcohol	Method of ref. 1		40
Iodine number of benzine	In $CHCl_3$, + iodine/ $HgCl_2$/HCl/ethanol; 1 h/room temp. in the dark	+ water/I^-; thiosulphate	41
Phenols	+ ICl/HCl (prepared from IO_3^-/I^-/conc. HCl) + HCl + water; 1–30 min/room temp.	I^-/thiosulphate	42
Iodine numbers of oils containing conjugated systems, e.g. tung oil	+ $CHCl_3$, + IBr/acetic acid in 5- to 8-fold excess; 1 h/20° gave addition to isolated double bonds; 3 h/0° gave addition to all double bonds	+ I^-/water; thiosulphate	43
Iodine number of gasoline	+ acetic acid + IBr/ acetic acid; 15 min/room temp.	+ water + Na acetate and back titrated with arsenite	44

Materials titrated	Reagent and reaction conditions	Subsequent treatment and final titration stage	Ref.
Unsaturation of butadiene and related polymers	In *p*-dichlorobenzene (brought into solution with up to 3 h heating), + $CHCl_3$ + ICl/CCl_4; 1 h/room temp. in dark	+ water + I^-/thiosulphate	45
'Partial' iodine values of fatty acids and oils	+ $CHCl_3$, + ICl/acetic acid in 2 to 2·5-fold excess; 2 min/0°	I^-/thiosulphate	46
'total' iodine values of fatty acids and oils	method of ref. 43		
Iodine number of unconjugated fats	Methods of refs 2 and 4, + Hg acetate as catalyst and 3–5 min/room temp.; compared the two		47
Unsaturation of butyl rubbers and polyiso-butylenes	In CCl_4, + ICl/acetic acid or CCl_4	+ water/ethanol/I^-; thiosulphate	48
Unsaturation, e.g. of rubber, squalene, dehydromyrcene	In $CHCl_3$ or CCl_4, + ICl/CCl_4	I^-/thiosulphate	49
sulphides	in $CHCl_3$, + ICl/acetic acid. Not less than 1 h/room temp. Also in $CHCl_3$, + ICl/CCl_4	I^-/thiosulphate	
4-Vinyl-1-cyclohexene in recycle styrene	In dioxan/acetic acid, + ICl/CCl_4; 20–30 min/0° in dark	I^-/thiosulphate	50
Unsaturation of butyl rubber	In CCl_4, + ICl/ acetic acid; 1 h/room temp. in dark	+ I^- + ethanol; thiosulphate	51
Unsaturation of natural and some synthetic rubbers	In *p*-dichlorobenzene + $CHCl_3$ + ICl_3/CCl_4; 1 h/room temp. in dark	+ water/ethanol/I^-; thiosulphate	52
Unsaturation of butadiene rubber	In dichloroethane, + ICl/acetic acid or in CCl_4, $CHCl_3$, benzene, di- or tetrachloroethane, + ICl/CCl_4; 24 h/room temp.	I^-/thiosulphate	53

Materials titrated	Reagent and reaction conditions	Subsequent treatment and final titration stage	Ref.
Methyl esters of ricinoleic, ricinelaidic and propionyl-ricinoleic acids	+ ICl/acetic acid, with and without Hg acetate (former gave greater than quantitative results, evidently due to reaction of the —OH group)	I^-/thiosulphate	54
Allyl groups in allyl esters and polyallyl esters and ethers	+ ICl/acetic acid + Hg acetate; 3 min–1 h/room temp. (tested these and three bromination procedures)	I^-/thiosulphate	55
	Compared procedures of refs 1 and 2		56
Anethole in aniseed oil	In benzene, + ICl reagent	+ I^- + excess thiosulphate and back titrated with iodine	57
Iodine number of vegetable oils	In ethanol, + iodine/$HgCl_2$/ethanol	I^-/thiosulphate	58
Unsaturation of butadiene and isoprene rubbers	In CCl_4, + IBr/CCl_4; 30 min/room temp.	+ water + I^-; thiosulphate. Then + IO_3^- and retitrated	59
Iodine number of oils and fats	In $CHCl_3$, + ICl/acetic acid + Hg acetate; 5 min/room temp.	+ I^-/water; thiosulphate	60
Unsaturation of polymers	In CS_2 or $CHCl_3$, + ICl/$CHCl_3$	I^-/thiosulphate; also determined acid formed from substitution	61
Vinyl, allyl, methallyl and other unsaturated esters of fatty acids from caproic to stearic	+ *ca* 2-fold excess ICl/acetic acid; 1 h/room temp.	I^-/thiosulphate	62
Pb tetraethyl in motor fuel or animal tissues (after preliminary extraction)	In heptane/$C_2H_2Cl_4$, + ICl/$C_2H_2Cl_4$, giving precipitate of $Pb(C_2H_5)_2Cl_2$	Precipitate dissolved in methanol and titrated with $Hg(ClO_4)_2$ to diphenyl carbazide (see Part I, Mercury (II), ref. 19)	63
Unsaturation	In CCl_4 + ICl reagent	I^-/thiosulphate	64
Unsaturation of olive oil	Method of ref. 4		65

Materials titrated	Reagent and reaction conditions	Subsequent treatment and final titration stage	Ref.
Pb tetraethyl in fuel	+ $ICl/C_2H_2Cl_4$, giving precipitate of $Pb(C_2H_5)_2Cl_2$	Dissolved in methanol/water and titrated Cl^- with $Hg(ClO_4)_2$ (see Part 1, Mercury (II), ref. 20)	66
Rubber, polyisoprene or gutta-percha, in study of their chlorination	Method of ref. 25		67
Unsaturation of butyl rubbers and certain branched olefines	In CCl_4, + various amounts of ICl/CCl_4; 1 h/room temp. (plotted total titration against initial ratio of ICl : sample, giving a discontinuity corresponding to unsaturation of the sample; addition believed to be as follows; $$\underset{+\,ICl}{—CH{=}CH—} \rightarrow —CHI—CHCl— \underset{—HI}{\rightarrow} —CH{=}CCl— \underset{+\,ICl}{\rightarrow} —CHI—CCl_2—$$ (much slower than the first addition—hence the discontinuity)	+ dilute acetic acid + I^-; thiosulphate	68
Unsaturation in higher petroleum distillates (170–270°)	Method of ref. 4, allowing for substitution by titrating the HBr formed		69
Iodine number of oils	+ ICl/acetic acid + Hg acetate; 3 min/room temp.	I^-/thiosulphate	70
Iodine numbers	Methods of refs 2 and 4, with biamperometric back titration with thiosulphate		71
Phenol and derivatives; sulphidine; streptocide; Na salicylate, etc.	+ ICl_3/HCl, giving iodo-substitution products	I^-/thiosulphate	72
Aniline (also from hydrolysis of acetanilide); novocaine; anesthesine	In water, + ICl/HCl (from IO_3^-/I^-/conc. HCl); 5 min/room temp., giving substitution products	I^-/thiosulphate	73
Sulphanilamides, e.g. sulphadimezine, streptocide, sulcimide	+ 2–4-fold excess of ICl/HCl; 20–30 min/60–80°	I^-/thiosulphate	74
p-Aminosalicylic acid and sodium salt	In dil. HCl, + ICl/HCl, giving diiodo substitution product	I^-/thiosulphate	75

Materials titrated	Reagent and reaction conditions	Subsequent treatment and final titration stage	Ref.
Iodine numbers of fats	+ emulsifier + water + ICl/HCl; 5 min/room temp.	I^-/thiosulphate	76
Iodine numbers of fats (micro)	In cellosolve, + IBr/acetic acid; 10 min/room temp.	I^-/thiosulphate	77
Conjugated olefines	+ IBr/acetic acid in *ca* 4·5-fold excess	I^-/thiosulphate	78
Unsaturation of fat	In CCl_4, $CHCl_3$ or methanol, + IBr reagent	I^-/thiosulphate; + iodate and retitrated to determine acid from substitution	79
Iodine number of fats	Emulsion in water, + iodine/$HgCl_2$/ethanol; 10–20 min/room temp.	I^-/thiosulphate	80
Acrichine (Atebrin, Mepacrine)	In water, + ICl reagent	Filtered and unused ICl determined in filtrate with I^-/thiosulphate	81
Iodine number of fats, semi-drying oils or fats	In ether, + ICl/HCl; 1 min shaking/room temp.	I^-/thiosulphate	82
Phenolphthalein	In Na_2CO_3 solution, + ICl, giving tetraiodo substitution product	I^-/thiosulphate (after acidification)	83
Many phenols	+ 3–4-fold excess ICl/HCl; 20 min/room temp.	I^-/thiosulphate	84
many aromatic amines	+ 3–4 fold excess ICl_3/HCl; 20 min/room temp.	I^-/thiosulphate	
Enols	In methanol, + ICl/methanol, evidently at *ca* −10°, + solid $NaHCO_3$ to eliminate the catalytic effect of HCl formed in the addition (compare Bromine reagents, refs 23 and 24)	Unreacted ICl removed immediately (evidently with β-naphthol or thiosulphate), I^- added and titrated with thiosulphate	85
Squalene in saponified olive oil mixtures	Method of ref. 4		86

Materials titrated	Reagent and reaction conditions	Subsequent treatment and final titration stage	Ref.
Unsaturation of fats, etc.	Method of ref. 2 considered suitable for non-conjugated olefinic constituents		87
Indene (precipitated as picrate in determination of naphthalene)	In acetic acid, + ICl reagent	I^-/thiosulphate	88
Phenols; aromatic amines	In water, dil. HCl or alcohol, + ICl_3/HCl; 30 min or more/room temp.	I^-/thiosulphate	89
Thiourea; methyl-thiourea	+ ICl + slight excess KOH; 5–15 min/room temp.	+ HCl + CCl_4 and titrated with Ce(IV), IO_3^- or MnO_4^- to disappearance of iodine colour in the CCl_4; or biampero-metrically	90
Ethylene, formed together with ethyl iodide, in determination of ethylene oxide derivatives by heating with HI	Absorbed in ICl/acetic acid	I^-/thiosulphate	91
Na salicylate, from determination of methyl salicylate by saponification	+ ICl reagent; 2 min/room temp.	I^-/thiosulphate	92
Unsaturation, e.g. in styrene	In acetic acid, ether, benzene or CCl_4, + ISCN; 1 h/room temp. (for styrene)	I^-/thiosulphate	93
Iodine number of tung oil	Method of ref. 2		94
Indene, precipitated as picrate along with naphthalene in determination of the latter in town gas	Neutralized aqueous acetone solution (from titration of the naphthalene picrate), + acetic acid + ICl/acetic acid; 20 min stirring/room temp.	I^-/thiosulphate	95
Unsaturated barbiturates, like diallyl barbiturate or Na evipanate; thiobarbiturates like Na thiopental	+ ICl/HCl	I^-/thiosulphate	96

Materials titrated	Reagent and reaction conditions	Subsequent treatment and final titration stage	Ref.
p-Aminophenylsulphonamido ethylthiadiazole ('Etazole'); sulphamethazine	In dil. HCl, + ICl/HCl or ICl_3/HCl	I^-/thiosulphate	97
Iodine numbers	Modification of method of ref. 2		98
Rivanol	In water, + ICl/HCl. Warmed 10–15 min, giving precipitate	Filtered, I^- added to filtrate and titrated with thiosulphate	99
Phenol	+ ICl/HCl; 2–5 min/room temp.	I^-/thiosulphate	100
Unsaturation of oil in emulsion	+ ICl/HCl; 5 min	I^-/thiosulphate	101
[4-(3-Methyl-1-butenylamino)butyl] guanidine benzoate ('Spherophysine benzoate')	In water, + ICl/HCl; 5 min	I^-/thiosulphate	102
Hydroquinone (and numerous inorganic materials)	+ ICl + NaOH/KBr; 10–15 min/room temp.	+ more Br^- + HCl + $CHCl_3$ or CCl_4 and titrated with Na chlorite to decoloration of the organic layer	103
Methylene blue	In water, + ICl/HCl; 15–20 min, giving precipitate	Filtered and unused ICl in filtrate determined via I^-/thiosulphate	104
Iodine value of fats	+ hot water (*ca* 80°) + ICl/HCl; 10–15 min	Cooled; I^-/thiosulphate	105
Unsaturation of naphtha	+ IBr/acetic acid + Hg acetate; 1 min/room temp.	I^-/thiosulphate	106
2-Methylamino 1-(3-hydroxyphenyl)ethanol hydrochloride	+ ICl/HCl; 5 min	I^-/thiosulphate	107
Thiourea;	In water, + ICl reagent; 30 min/room temp.	I^-/thiosulphate	108
$(C_6H_5)_2CH—C(=O)—S—CH_2CH_2N(C_2H_5)_3$ (hydrochloride)	15 min/room temp.	extracted with $CHCl_3$; unused ICl in aqueous layer determined via I^-/thiosulphate	

Materials titrated	Reagent and reaction conditions	Subsequent treatment and final titration stage	Ref.
Antipyrine	+ water + NaCl + ICl; 10 min, giving precipitate of 4-iodoantipyrine	Filtrate + I^-; thiosulphate	109
1,2-diphenyl-4-butyl-3,5-dioxopyrazolidine	as with antipyrine, but 15 min reaction		
p-Acetamidobenzaldehyde thiosemicarbazone ('Tibione')	In dilute NaOH, + boiling water + ICl/HCl; 20–30 min	I^-/thiosulphate	110
Iodine number of butter fat	In CCl_4, + ICl reagent in CCl_4/acetic acid; 1 h/room temp.	I^-/thiosulphate	111
2-Ethylcrotonylurea	+ IBr/acetic acid + Hg acetate; 30 min/room temp.	I^-/thiosulphate	112
Some sulphur-containing compounds, e.g. 6-methylthiouracil, methionine, unithiol, *p*-isopropylbenzaldehydethiosemicarbazone ('Kutizin')	+ boiling water + ICl; 15–20 min	Cooled, then I^-/thiosulphate	113
Some bases, e.g. aprophene, spasmolytine, methadone, diphenhydramine hydrochloride	In water, + ICl/HCl; 10 min/room temp., giving precipitate of complex	Filtered, aliquot of filtrate + I^-; thiosulphate	114
Glucose	+ KOH (1–2N) + ICl in at least 50% excess; 5–10 min/room temp.	+ HCl, bringing to 5–6N and titrated with Ce(IV), IO_3^- or MnO_4^- biamperometrically	115
Heptylresorcinol	+ ethanol + ICl/HCl; 1 min shaking/room temp.	I^-/thiosulphate	116
Iodine values of fatty acids and alcohols	In $CHCl_3$ or alcohol, + ICl; 5–15 min/room temp.	+ water; I^-/thiosulphate	117
Enol contents of cycloalkanones	Method of ref. 85		118
Unsaturated acids (e.g. oleic, elaidic) and iodine values of oils (e.g. sunflower, cotton-seed)	Method of ref. 82		119

Materials titrated	Reagent and reaction conditions	Subsequent treatment and final titration stage	Ref.
Unsaturation in high molecular weight fatty nitrogen derivatives (after acetylation if primary or secondary amines); quaternary ammonium chlorides	+ acetic acid or $CHCl_3$ + ICl reagent + Hg acetate; 3–5 min (30 min for last named)/room temp.	+ Na lauryl sulphate for last named; then I^-/water/ thiosulphate	120
Iodine thiocyanate index determinations on mono-, non-conjugated di- and conjugated diolefines; also mixtures (e.g. styrene or cyclohexene/limonene/ isoprene)	In benzene or ether, + ISCN reagent; 1 h for monoolefines; 15 h for non-conjugated diolefines; variable time for conjugated diolefines, depending on reagent conc.; analysed mixtures by using different concentrations and reaction times, yielding simultaneous equations	I^-/thiosulphate	121, 127
Phthalazole, sulphathiazole and its Na derivatives in pharmaceutical preparations	In dilute HCl or NaOH, + hot water + ICl/HCl; 30 min	Cooled, I^-/thiosulphate	122
3,3′,4′,5,7-Pentahydroxyflavone 3-rutinoside ('Rutin')	In alkali, + boiling water + ICl/HCl; 25 min (1 mol equivalent to 12 ICl)	I^-/thiosulphate	123
Ichthyol (mixture of ammonium salts of sulphonated hydrocarbons)	In water, + ICl/HCl. Warmed to 60–70°	I^-/thiosulphate	124
Styrene in cured polyester resins	Method of ref. 2		125
Acenaphthylene in mixtures with acenaphthene	In $CHCl_3$, + iodine/ $HgCl_2$ reagent; 2·5 h/room temp. in dark	I^-/thiosulphate	126
Acetone; HCHO	+ NaOH + ICl; 10 min	+ HCl I^-/thiosulphate	129
Olefinic bonds, e.g. in oleic acid and triolein	In $CHCl_3$ + IBr/acetic acid; 1 h in dark	+ water and I^-/thiosulphate, biamperometrically	130
Some monoamyl-substituted phenols	In ethanol, + ethanol + water + ICl; 30 min	+ water and I^-/thiosulphate	131

Materials titrated	Reagent and reaction conditions	Subsequent treatment and final titration stage	Ref.
Styrene; indene	In 90% ethanol, + ICl/ ethanol; 90 min or 5 min in light	+ water and I^-/ thiosulphate	132
2-Chloro-10-(3-dimethylaminopropyl)-phenothiazine ('Aminazine'); 2-chloro-4,6-bis-(isopropylamino)-*s*-triazine ('Propazine')	In water, + ICl; 10 min	+ $CHCl_3$ and I^-/ thiosulphate	133
Phthivazide	In NaOH, + ICl/HCl at 5°, giving precipitate of complex with ICl of iodo-substitution product	Filtered and unused determined in filtrate with I^-/thiosulphate	134
phthivazide and other derivatives of isonicotinic acid, e.g. tubazid, saluzid, larusan	In acid solution, + ICl/HCl; 10–40 min/*ca* 70°, causing oxidation	I^-/thiosulphate	
(α-Oleoyl-β-stearoyl)-phosphatidylethanolamine	In acetic acid, + IBr/ acetic acid, saturated with NaBr; 45 min/ room temp.	+ water, then I^-/thiosulphate	135

References

1. v. Hübl, B., *Dingler's Polytechnic J.* **253**, 281 (1884); *J. Soc. Chem. Ind. (London)* **3**, 641 (1884).
2. Wys, J. J. A., *Ber.* **31**, 750 (1898).
3. Marshall, A., *J. Soc. Chem. Ind. (London)* **19**, 213 (1900).
4. Hanuš, J., Z. *Untersuch. Nahr.- u. Genussm.* **4**, 913 (1901).
5. Graefe, E., Z. *angew. Chem.* **18**, 1580 (1905).
6. Faragher, W. F., Gruse, W. A. and Garner, F. H., *Ind. Eng. Chem.* **13**, 1044 (1921).
7. Waterman, H. I. and Perquin, J. N. J., *Rec. trav. chim.* **40**, 677 (1921).
8. Johansen, E. M., *Ind. Eng. Chem.* **14**, 288 (1922).
9. Morrell, J. C. and Egloff, G., *Ind. Eng. Chem.* **17**, 1259 (1925).
10. Böeseken, J. and Gelber, E. T., *Rec. trav. chim.* **46**, 163 (1927).
11. Kemp, A. R., *Ind. Eng. Chem.* **19**, 531 (1927).
12. Linstead, R. P. and May, C. J., *J. Chem. Soc.* 2565 (1927).
13. Gorgas, A., *Kautschuk* **4**, 253 (1928); *Rubber Chem. and Techn.* **2**, 362 (1929).

14. Kandiah, A. and Linstead, R. P., *J. Chem. Soc.* 2139 (1929).
15. Margosches, B. M., Krakowetz, B. and Schnabel, F., *Petroleum Z.* **25**, 1179 (1929).
16. Pümmerer, R. and Mann, F. J., *Ber.* **62**, 2636 (1929).
17. Bolton, E. R. and Williams, K. A., *Analyst* **55**, 360 (1930).
18. van Loon, J., *Chem. Umschau Fette, Öle, Wachse, Harze* **37**, 135, 257 (1930).
19. Smit, W. C., *Rec. trav. chim.* **49**, 539 (1930).
20. van Loon, J., *Verfkroniek* **4**, No. 6, 18 (1931).
21. Pümmerer, R. and Stärk, H., *Ber.* **64**, 825 (1931).
22. Casimer, E. E. and Dimitriu, N., *Ins. Géol. Roumaine, Compt. rend.* **21**, 241 (1932–3); *Petroleum Z.* **31**, No. 33, 1 (1935).
23. Letch, R. A. and Plumstead, R., *J. Chem. Soc.* 443 (1932).
24. Keffler, L. J. P. and Malden, A. M., *J. Soc. Chem. Ind.* (*London*) **52**, 242T (1933).
25. Kemp, A. R. and Mueller, G. S., *Ind. Eng. Chem., Anal. Ed.* **6**, 52 (1934).
26. Ralls, J. O., *J. Am. Chem. Soc.* **56**, 121 (1934).
27. Ho, K., Wan, C. S. and Wen, S. H., *Ind. Eng. Chem., Anal. Ed.* **7**, 96 (1935).
28. Lang, R., *Z. anal. Chem.* **106**, 12 (1936).
29. Wan, C. S. and Ho, K., *Ind. Eng. Chem., Anal. Ed.* **8**, 282 (1936).
30. Kaufmann, H. P. and Grosse-Oetringhaus, H., *Ber.* **70**, 911 (1937).
31. Klebanskii, A. L. and Rakhlina, M., *Zhur. Obshchei Khim.* (*J. Gen. Chem. USSR*) **7**, 1299 (1937).
32. Kaufmann, H. P. and Grosse-Oetringhaus, H., *Öle Kohle ver. Erdöl u. Teer* **14**, 199 (1938).
33. Kulikov, *Byull. Lakokrasochnoi Prom.* No. 12, 7 (1938).
34. Frenguelli, B. and Travaglini, R., *Olii minerali, grassi e saponi, colori e vernici* **19**, 162 (1939).
35. Hofmann, H. J., *Angew. Chem.* **52**, 99 (1939).
36. Hoffman, H. D. and Green, C. E., *Oil and Soap* **16**, 236 (1939).
37. Vossgård, A. and Björsvik, E., *Z. anal. Chem.* **115**, 195 (1939).
38. Forbes, W. C. and Neville, H. A., *Ind. Eng. Chem., Anal. Ed.* **12**, 72 (1940).
39. McCutcheon, J. W., *Ind. Eng. Chem., Anal. Ed.* **12**, 465 (1940).
40. Peregud, E. A., *Sbornik Rabot Sanit-Prom. Khim. Inst. Hig. Truda i Profzabolevanii Leningrad. Gorzdravotdela* 73 (1940).
41. Sobolev, B. N. and Golovina, M. A., *Caoutchouc & Rubber USSR* No. 4–5, 59 (1940).
42. Gengrinovich, A. I., *Farm. Zhur.* **14**, No. 2, 19 (1941).
43. v. Mikusch, J. D. and Frazier, C., *Ind. Eng. Chem., Anal. Ed.* **13**, 781 (1941).

44. Hartweg, L., *Kraftstoff* **18**, 42 (1942).
45. Kemp, A. R. and Paters, H., *Ind. Eng. Chem., Anal. Ed.* **15**, 453 (1943).
46. von Mikusch, J. D. and Frazier, C., *Ind. Eng. Chem., Anal. Ed.* **15**, 109 (1943).
47. Norris, F. A. and Buswell, R. J., *Ind. Eng. Chem., Anal. Ed.* **15**, 258 (1943).
48. Rehner, J., *Ind. Eng. Chem.* **36**, 118 (1944).
49. Bloomfield, G. F., *J. Soc. Chem. Ind. (London)* **64**, 274 (1945).
50. Laitinen, H. A., O'Brien, A. S. and Wawzonek, S., *Ind. Eng. Chem., Anal. Ed.* **17**, 769 (1945).
51. Rehner, J. and Gray, P., *Ind. Eng. Chem., Anal. Ed.* **17**, 367 (1945).
52. Wake, W. C., *Trans. Inst. Rubber Ind.* **21**, 158 (1945).
53. Kobeko, P. P. and Moskvina, E. K., *Zhur. Priklad Khim. (J. Appl. Chem. USSR)* **19**, 1143 (1946).
54. Skell, P. S. and Radlove, S. B., *Ind. Eng. Chem., Anal. Ed.* **18**, 87 (1946).
55. Boyd, H. M. and Roach, J. R., *Anal. Chem.* **19**, 158 (1947).
56. Lutz, B. E., *Anais asoc. quím. Brasil* **6**, 181 (1947).
57. Mori, D., *Riv. ital. essenze, profumi, piante offic., olii vegetali. saponi* **29**, 360 (1947).
58. Penn, A. B. K. and Wen, T-Sh., *Bull. Chungking Inst. Ind. Research* No. 2 (1947).
59. Vasil'ev, A. A., *Zhur. Obshchei Khim. (J. Gen. Chem. USSR)* **17**, 923, 929 (1947).
60. Hiscox, D. J., *Anal. Chem.* **20**, 679 (1948).
61. Lee, T. S., Kolthoff, I. M. and Mairs, M. A., *J. Polymer Sci.* **3**, 66 (1948).
62. Swern, D. and Jordan, E. F., *J. Am. Chem. Soc.* **70**, 2334 (1948).
63. Kröller, E., *Z. anal. Chem.* **129**, 6, 19 (1949).
64. Phillips, W. M. and Wake, W. C., *Analyst* **74**, 306 (1949).
65. Hadorn, H. and Jungkunz, R., *Mitt. Lebensm. Hyg.* **41**, 435 (1950).
66. Jahr, K. F., *Chem. Tech. (Berlin)* **2**, 88 (1950).
67. Kraus, G. and Reynolds, W. B., *J. Am. Chem. Soc.* **72**, 5621 (1950).
68. Lee, T. S., Kolthoff, I. M. and Johnson, E., *Anal. Chem.* **22**, 995 (1950).
69. Winward, A. and Garner, F. H., *J. Soc. Chem. Ind. (London)* **69**, 147 (1950).
70. Meyerhoffer, C. R., *Olearia* **5**, 353 (1951).
71. Duke, J. A. and Maselli, J. A., *J. Am. Oil Chemists' Soc.* **29**, 126 (1952).
72. Fialkov, Ya. A. and Kagan, F. E., *Ukrain. Khim. Zhur.* **18**, 64 (1952).
73. Gengrinovich, A. I. and Kadyrov, Ya. K., *Aptechnoe Delo* **1**, No. 1, 46 (1952).
74. Gengrinovich, A. I. and Ibadov, A. Yu., *Aptechnoe Delo* No. 3, 18 (1952).
75. Gengrinovich, A. I. and Baron, M. S., *Aptechnoe Delo* No. 4, 27 (1952).

76. Gengrinovich, A. I. and Yudevich, E. A., *Aptechnoe Delo* No. 5, 17 (1952).
77. Grunbaum, B. W. and Kirk, P. L., *Mikrochemie ver. Mikrochim. Acta* **39**, 268 (1952).
78. Veselý, V. and Cuipková, V., *Sborník Celostátní Pracovní Konf. Anal. Chemiků* **1**, 234 (1952).
79. Kamath, N. R., *Oils and Oilseeds J.* (*India*) **5**, No. 10/12, 82 (1953).
80. Kuchment, M. L., *Aptechnoe Delo* **2**, No. 6, 35 (1953).
81. Vaisman, G. A., *Aptechnoe Delo* **2**, No. 6, 25 (1953).
82. Gengrinovich, A. I., *Union Sci. Research Inst.*, *Molochnaya Prom.* **15**, No. 6, 29 (1954).
83. Gengrinovich, A. I. and Mansurkhanova, I., *Aptechnoe Delo* **3**, No. 6, 9 (1954).
84. Gengrinovich, A. I., Kagan, F. E. and Fialkov, Ya. A., *Trudy Komissii Anal. Khim.*, *Akad. Nauk SSSR*, *Otdel Khim. Nauk* **5** (8), 237 (1954).
85. Gero, A., *Anal. Chem.* **26**, 609 (1954); *J. Org. Chem.* **19**, 469, 1960 (1954).
86. Keskin, H., *Rev. fac. sci. univ. Istanbul* **19C**, 214 (1954).
87. Bolley, D. S., *J. Am. Oil Chemists' Soc.* **32**, 235 (1955).
88. Densham, A. B. and Seaton, E. M., *J. Appl. Chem.* (*London*) **6**, 101 (1956).
89. Kagan, F. E., *Ukrain. Khim. Zhur.* **22**, 94 (1956).
90. Desmukh, G. S. and Bapat, M. G., *Z. anal. Chem.* **156**, 276 (1957).
91. Etienne, H., *Ind. chim. belge* **32**, 1175, 1287 (1957).
92. Gengrinovich, A. I. and Kadyrova, Ya. K., *Aptechnoe Delo* **6**, No. 2, 68 (1957).
93. Mesnard, P. and Raby, C., 9[e] *Congr. soc. pharm. France*, *Clermont-Ferrand* 203 (1957).
94. Meyerhoffer, C. R., *Olearia* **11**, 55 (1957).
95. Mott, R. A. and Moulson, I., *J. Appl. Chem.* (*London*) **7**, 553, 557 (1957).
96. Rapaport, L. I., *Zhur. Anal. Khim.* **12**, 415 (1957).
97. Shakh, Ts. I., *Aptechnoe Delo* **6**, No. 1, 22 (1957).
98. Sulzer, H., *Mitt. Lebensm. Hyg.* **48**, 5 (1957).
99. Suprun, P. P., *Med. Prom. SSSR* **11**, No. 2, 49 (1957).
100. Erzinkyan, L. H. and Muradyan, E. H., *Izvest. Akad. Nauk. Armyan. SSSR*, *Biol. i Sel'skokhoz. Nauki* **11**, No. 8, 13 (1958).
101. Gengrinovich, A. I., *Med. Prom. SSSR* **12**, No. 4, 38 (1958).
102. Gengrinovich, A. I. and Ibadov, A. Yu., *Aptechnoe Delo* **7**, No. 2, 67 (1958).
103. Paul, R. C. and Singh, A., *J. Indian Chem. Soc.* **35**, 294 (1958).
104. Suprun, P. P., *Med. Prom. SSSR* **12**, No. 8, 38 (1958).
105. Suprun, P. P., *Aptechnoe Delo* **7**, No. 3, 48 (1958).
106. Armitrano, R., *Boll. inform. petrol* (*Buenos Aires*) No. 310, 22 (1959).

107. Gengrinovich, A. I. and Kadyrov, Ya. K., *Aptechnoe Delo* **8**, No. 5, 33 (1959).
108. Rapaport, L. I., *Aptechnoe Delo* **8**, No. 2, 63 (1959).
109. Shakh, T. I. and Kagan, F. Yu., *Farm. Zhur.* (*Kiev*) **14**, No. 5, 16 (1959).
110. Rapaport, L. I., *Farm. Zhur.* (*Kiev*) **14**, No. 2, 52 (1959).
111. Anonymous, *Milchwissenschaft* **15**, 346 (1960).
112. Otsuka, Y., *Kagaku Keisatsu Kenkyusho Hokoku* **13**, 445 (1960).
113. Rapaport, L. I. and Raznatovska, V. F., *Farm. Zhur.* (*Kiev*) **15**, 22 (1960).
114. Shakh, T. I. and Kagan, F. Yu., *Farm. Zhur.* (*Kiev*) **15**, No. 6, 18 (1960).
115. Sharma, B., *Bull. Chem. Soc. Japan* **33**, 279 (1960).
116. Gengrinovich, A. I. and Kadyrev, Ya. K., *Trudy Tashkent., Farm. Inst.* **2**, 217 (1960).
117. Babaev, V. I. and Dam'shina, N. M., *Masloboino-Zhir. Prom.* **27**, No. 10, 30 (1961).
118. Gero, A., *J. Org. Chem.* **26**, 3156 (1961).
119. Markman, A. L. and Chernenko, T. V., *Masloboino-Zhir. Prom.* **27**, No. 6, 8 (1961).
120. Milun, A. J., *Anal. Chem.* **33**, 123 (1961).
121. Mesnard, P. and Raby, C., *Bull. soc. pharm., Bordeaux* **100**, 31 (1961).
122. Shakh, T. I. and Rapaport, L. I., *Farm. Zhur.* **16**, No. 6, 12 (1961).
123. Suprun, P. P., *Med. Prom.* (*SSSR*) **15**, No. 3, 46 (1961).
124. Suprun, P. P., *Aptechnoe Delo* **10**, No. 4, 38 (1961).
125. Alt, B., *Kunststoffe* **52**, 133 (1962).
126. Balandina, V. A. and Davydova, Z. F., *Plasticheskie Massy* No. 3, 65 (1962).
127. Mesnard, P. and Raby, C., *Chim. anal.* **44**, 463 (1962).
128. Schulek, E. and Ladányi, L., *Talanta* **9**, 727 (1962).
129. Suprun, P. P., *Farmatsevt. Zh.* (*Kiev*) **17**, 37 (1962).
130. Jedlinski, Z. and Paprotny, J., *Chem. Anal.* (*Warsaw*) **8**, 765 (1963).
131. Karpov, O. N., *Zhur. Anal. Khim.* **18**, 1266 (1963).
132. Karpov, O. N. and Bystrova, R. M., *Zhur. Anal. Khim.* **18**, 1390 (1963).
133. Shakh, Ts. I. and Kagan, F. Yu., *Farmatsevt. Zh.* (*Kiev*) **18**, 13 (1963).
134. Suprun, P. P., *Farmatsevt. Zh.* (*Kiev*) **18**, 43 (1963).
135. Polyachenko, V. M. and Samokhvalov, G. I., *Zhur. Anal. Khim.* **19**, 136 (1964).

54. Iodosobenzoate (*o*-)

This reagent has been used to determine mercaptans, with which it reacts according to the equation:

$$2\,RSH + ArIO \rightarrow RS.SR + ArI + H_2O$$

Unreacted iodoso compound was then determined iodometrically by adding I^-/acid and titrating with thiosulphate:

$$ArIO + 2\,I^- + 2\,H^+ \rightarrow ArI + I_2 + H_2O$$

Four references are given here:

Materials titrated	Reagent and reaction conditions	Ref.
Mercaptans, e.g. cysteine or glutathione	Reagent in phosphate buffer, pH 7, + sample; 30 sec/room temp.	1
—SH in denatured albumin	In phosphate buffer, pH 7 + guanidine hydrochloride (denaturing agent) + reagent; 2 min/room temp.	2
reduced glutathione	as above, but 30 sec reaction	
—SH in denatured urease	as for albumin	
—SH groups in biological, pharmaceutical and toxicological analyses	Sample + phosphate buffer pH 9·1 + guanidine hydrochloride bringing pH to 7·1 + reagent; 15 min in nitrogen atmosphere; then + $CdSO_4$/NaOH and left 15 min before determining unreacted iodosobenzoate	3, 4

References

1. Hellerman, L., Chinard, F. P. and Ramsdell, P. A., *J. Am. Chem. Soc.* **63**, 2551 (1941).
2. Hellerman, L., Chinard, F. P. and Deitz, V. R., *J. Biol. Chem.* **147**, 443 (1945).
3. Merville, R., Dequidt, J. and Corteel, M. L., *Bull. soc. pharm., Lille* 57 (1959).
4. Merville, R., Dequidt, J. and Corteel, M. L., *Ann. pharm. franç.* **18**, 625 (1960).

55. Ion exchangers

Exchangers used, reactions and materials determined. Most examples are of the use of cationic and anionic exchangers, yielding acid and basic eluates, respectively. Thus determined have been principally salts of carboxylic and sulphonic acids and of organic bases like alkaloids, synthetic products and other pharmaceutical materials.

$$X—H^+ + Na^+RCOO^- \rightarrow X—Na^+ + RCOOH$$

$$X—OH^- + (Base.H^+)Cl^- \rightarrow X—Cl^- + Base + H_2O$$

Bisulphite forms $X—SO_3H^-$ have been used to separate carbonyl compounds; and Mg and Cu forms to yield Mg(II) and Cu(II) effluents by exchange with cations of alkaloids.

Three examples of the use of Al_2O_3 as a separating agent are quoted below, although this is a column chromatographic separation rather than ion exchange. Column chromatographic separations followed by titration are not considered in this book.

Reaction conditions. Most materials have been dissolved in water or water/alcohol and brought on to the exchanger in a column. No details are given here of grain size, column packing, etc.

Concluding titration stage. 1. In nearly all cases, eluted acid or base has been titrated with base or acid.

2. In the special cases mentioned above, eluted Mg^{2+} and Cu^{2+} were titrated with EDTA and the bisulphite compounds of the carbonyl compounds determined iodometrically.

3. Unchanged or unadsorbed materials have sometimes been titrated as the conclusion. Examples here are of hydroquinone and methanol (titrated with bichromate) and oxalic acid (precipitated as Ca salt and titrated with permanganate).

Examples

Materials titrated	Ion exchanger and reaction conditions	Subsequent treatment and final titration stage	Ref.
Sodium acetate from determination of acetyl groups by transesterification to ethyl acetate and hydrolysis with alkali	Wofatit K in acid form, giving acetic acid	Titrated with NaOH	1
Many alkaloid salts	In 90% ethanol; Amberlite IR-4B in base form (treatment with Na_2CO_3), giving the alkaloid bases	Titrated with HCl to methyl red/methylene blue or potentiometrically	2, 3, 6
Neutral salts, e.g. Na acetate	Dowex 2 in base form	Titrated with acid	4

Materials titrated	Ion exchanger and reaction conditions	Subsequent treatment and final titration stage	Ref.
Hexamethylene diamine dihydrochloride	Amberlite IRA-400 in base form (from NaOH)	Diamine titrated with HCl to methyl orange	5
Alkali salts of formic, acetic, citric, tartaric and benzenesulphonic acids	In water; Wofatit K and KS	Titrated eluted acid with NaOH	7
Na salts, e.g. of even higher molecular weight acids such as anthraquinonesulphonic acids; alkaloid salts, e.g. quinine hydrochloride	Permutit ES	Titrated with acid	8
Salts of local anaesthetics, e.g. of procaine and larocaine	Amberlite IRA-400	Eluted with hot ethanol and titrated with HCl	9
Salts of alkaloids and organic acids	Amberlite IRA-400	Titrated with acid	10
Hydroquinone in presence of quinone, titrated with thiosulphate	Wofatit M, absorbing the quinone monosulphurate	Hydroquinone in effluant titrated with $Cr_2O_7^{2-}$ (see Part I, Bichromate and chromic oxide, ref. 19)	11
Salts of many organic acids and bases	In water; Dowex 50	Titrated with NaOH to cresol red/thymol blue	12
Tetramethylphosphonium chloride	In water; Rohm and Haas IR 100 H, giving HCl	Titrated with NaOH	13
Ca salts, e.g. of lactic, gluconic and glycerophosphoric acids	SDV 3	Titrated with NaOH to phenolphthalein	14
Ca gluconate	Amberlite IR-120	Titrated with NaOH	15
Alkali salts of organic acids, e.g. lactates, citrates, salicylates	Amberlite IR-120. Washed with water or 75% ethanol for salicylates	Titrated with NaOH to phenolphthalein	16
Hydrochlorides of some pharmaceutical bases	In 70% ethanol; Amberlite IRA-400	Titrated with HCl to bromophenol blue or potentiometrically	17

Materials titrated	Ion exchanger and reaction conditions	Subsequent treatment and final titration stage	Ref.
Salts of quaternary ammonium bases	In water; Amberlite IRA-400 or Merck's Anionenaus-tauscher III in base form (from treatment with NaOH)	Titrated with HCl (or + HCl and back titrated with alkali)	18
Addition compounds of BBr_3 with organic bases like quinoline, α-picoline and 5-nitroquinoline	In water (evidently hydrolysing to HBr + H_3BO_3); Amberlite IR-100	Titrated acids photometrically to methyl red/methylene blue and then phenolphthalein	19
Salts of alkaloids like quinine, cocaine, atropine, ethylmorphine, ephedrine	Dowex 50 in Mg-form (from treatment with $MgSO_4$)	Mg^{2+} in effluent titrated with EDTA	20
Ba sulphonates from determination of sulphonic acids in sulphonation mixtures after removal of sulphate by precipitation with $Ba(OH)_2$	Dowex 50	Sulphonic acids titrated with NaOH to phenolphthalein	21
K acetate in saponified fish oil (with KOH/ethanol) in determination of its 'acetyl' number	Diaion BK, giving acetic acid	Titrated with KOH	22
Anionic surface-active agents	Amberlite IR-120	Titrated with alkali	23
Ethanolamine and K salts from hydrolysis in determination of equivalent weight of some esters of carboxylic, sulphonic and alkylphosphonic acids	Dowex 50 (Nalcite HCR)	Titrated with NaOH	24
Sodium salt of nicotinic acid	Pyridine form of Wofatit KPS 200, giving pyridine salt of the acid	Titrated with NaOH to phenolphthalein	25
Caffeine-Na benzoate in ampoules	SDV-3 in acid form (from treatment with HCl)	Titrated with NaOH to phenolphthalein	26
Na alginate	In water; Amberlite IR-410, then IR-120, giving alginic acid	Titrated with NaOH potentiometrically or conductometrically	27

Materials titrated	Ion exchanger and reaction conditions	Subsequent treatment and final titration stage	Ref.
K guaiacol sulphonates	Wofatite F	Titrated with alkali to methyl red	28
Na acetate + butyrate (from determination of cellulose acetate-butyrate by hydrolysis with NaOH/ethanol)	Wofatit KPS 200	Titrated with KOH to phenolphthalein	29
Na salts of acids from determination of saponification numbers by alkali hydrolysis	Amberlite IR-120 in the acid form	Titrated with KOH/ethanol potentiometrically	30
Mixtures of lactaldehyde, acetol and pyruvaldehyde	Dowex 1-X10 (in bisulphite form where Cl^- was replaced by SO_3H^- by washing with $NaHSO_3$)	Eluted with $KHSO_3$, unreacted bisulphite titrated in acid solution (pH 2·5) with iodine, $NaHCO_3$ added and combined bisulphite titrated with iodine	31
Strychnine salts	Basic Al_2O_3	Alkaloid eluted and titrated with acid	32
Barbiturates	In dimethylformamide; Amberlite IRC-50	Titrated with $NaOCH_3$/methanol–benzene to azo violet	33
Quaternary iodides from determination of tertiary amines by reaction with methyl iodide	Amberlite IRA-400 in base form	Titrated with H_2SO_4 to methyl red/methylene blue	34
Dihydrocodeine ditartrate; K guaiacol sulphonate	In water/ethanol or ethanol respectively; Amberlite IR4-400	Titrated with HCl; or + excess HCl and back titrated with NaOH	35
Oxalic acid in glucoheptonic acid lactone	MFD (Czech anionic exchanger) treated with NH_4OH	Eluted with NH_4OH and oxalate precipitated with Ca^{2+} and titrated with MnO_4^-	36
Berberine sulphate	Amberlite IRC-50 or Duolite CS-101 in Na^+ or NH_4^+ from	Eluate + HCl + excess $BaCl_2$; heated 20–30 min, methanol/NH_4OH added and titrated with EDTA to phthalein complexone	37
Salts of quinine and hydroquinine (hydrochloride, sulphate)	Activated Al_2O_3	Total base in eluate titrated with HCl to methyl red/methylene blue; hydroquinine base determined with excess bromine reagent (see Bromine reagents, ref. 497)	38

Materials titrated	Ion exchanger and reaction conditions	Subsequent treatment and final titration stage	Ref.
Some alkaloid salts, e.g. atropine sulphate or hyoscamine hydrobromide	In 96% ethanol; Al_2O_3	Eluted with NaBr/ethanol and titrated with HCl to bromocresol green or other indicators	39
Na citrate; K hydrogen tartrate	In water; Amberlite IR-120 in acid form	Titrated with NaOH to thymol blue or phenolphthalein	40
Carbonyl compounds in brandy and wine	Amberlite IRA-400 in bisulphite form	Eluted with NaCl solution, unreacted bisulphite destroyed with iodine, $NaHCO_3$ added and bisulphite liberated titrated with iodine	41
Salts of organic acids in plant material	KPS 200 in acid form	Ultimately titrated with tetramethylammonium hydroxide potentiometrically	42
Phenobarbital in elixir	Dowex 2-X8 in strongly basic form	Eluted with acetic acid/ethanol, evaporated, dissolved residue in dimethylformamide and titrated with $NaOCH_3$/ benzene/methanol	43
Sulphate and sulphonate detergents (molecular weight determination	Cation exchanger, giving H_2SO_4 or sulphonic acids	Titrated with KOH	44
Methantheline, propantheline salts	Amberlite IRA-400 in basic form	Eluate passed into excess HCl or H_2SO_4 and back titrated	45
3-Dimethylaminoisocamphane hydrobromide ('Dimecamine'); 3-methylaminoisocamphane hydrochloride ('Mecylamine')	In 80% ethanol; Amberlite IRA-400 in basic form	Eluate titrated with H_2SO_4 to methyl red/methylene blue	46
HCOONa + excess NaOH from oxidation of HCHO with H_2O_2/NaOH in determination of methanol in presence of HCHO	Cation exchange resin	Methanol in eluate determined with excess bichromate (see Bichromate and chromic oxide, ref. 253)	47
Quaternary ammonium salts	Merck III	Titrated with alkali	48
Alkaloid salts	Cation exchanger in Cu(II) form	Eluted Cu(II) titrated with EDTA to murexide	49

Materials titrated	Ion exchanger and reaction conditions	Subsequent treatment and final titration stage	Ref.
Na salts of carboxylic acids from alkaline hydrolysis of amides	Dowex 50 W-X8 in acid form	Eluted acid titrated potentiometrically with NaOH	50

References

1. Wiesenberger, E., *Mikrochemie ver. Mikrochim. Acta* **30**, 253 (1942).
2. Jindra, A., *J. Pharm. Pharmacol.* **1**, 87 (1949).
3. Jindra, A. and Pohorský, J., *J. Pharm. Pharmacol.* **2**, 269 (1950).
4. d'Ans, J. and Blasius, E., *Naturwissenschaften* **38**, 236 (1951).
5. Haslam, J. and Clasper, M., *Analyst* **76**, 33 (1951).
6. Jindra, A. and Pohorský, J., *J. Pharm. Pharmacol.* **3**, 344 (1951).
7. Wickbold, R., *Z. anal. Chem.* **132**, 241 (1951).
8. d'Ans, J., Blasius, E., Guzatis, H. and Wachtel, U., *Chem.-Ztg.* **76**, 811, 841 (1952).
9. Jindra, A. and Rentz, J., *J. Pharm. Pharmacol.* **4**, 645 (1952).
10. Rasmussen, H. B., Fuchs, D. and Lundberg, L., *J. Pharm. Pharmacol.* **4**, 566 (1952).
11. Brauer, E. and Staude, H., *Z. wiss. Phot.* **48**, 16 (1953).
12. van Etten, C. H. and Wiele, M. B., *Anal. Chem.* **25**, 1109 (1953).
13. Anderson, C. J. and Keeler, R. A., *Anal. Chem.* **26**, 213 (1954).
14. Arzamastsev, A. P., *Aptechnoe Delo* **4**, No. 3, 36 (1955).
15. Watanabe, H., *J. Chem. Soc. Japan, Pure Chem. Sect.* **76**, 1 (1955).
16. Blaug, S. M., *J. Am. Pharm. Assoc., Sci. Ed.* **45**, 274 (1956).
17. Grefsgård, B., *Medd. Norsk Farm. Selskap* **18**, 157 (1956).
18. Knabe, J., *Deut. Apotheker-Ztg.* **96**, 876, 1243 (1956).
19. Schuele, W. J., Hazel, J. F. and McNabb, W. M., *Anal. Chem.* **28**, 505 (1956).
20. Sjöstrom, E. and Rittner, W., *Z. anal. Chem.* **153**, 321 (1956).
21. Houff, W. H., Christie, D. R. and Beaumont, R. H., *Anal. Chem.* **29**, 1866 (1957).
22. Suzuki, K., *Kogyo Kagaku Zasshi* (*J. Chem. Soc. Japan, Ind. Chem. Sect.*) **60**, 1128 (1957).
23. Takahama, S. and Nishide, T., *Proc. 2nd Intern. Congr. Surface Activity* **4**, 141 (1957).
24. Baldwin, W. H. and Higgins, C. E., *Anal. Chem.* **30**, 446 (1958).
25. Howorka, K., *Pharm. Zentralhalle* **97**, 521 (1958).
26. Khvatovskaya, V. M., *Aptechnoe Delo* **7**, No. 1, 45 (1958).

27. Miyake, S., *Kogyo Kagaku Zasshi* (*J. Chem. Soc. Japan, Ind. Chem. Sect.*) **61**, 1278 (1958).
28. Pfeifer, S., *Pharmazie* **13**, 12 (1958).
29. Schröder, E., Franz, J. and Thinius, K., *Plaste u. Kautschuk* **5**, 411 (1958).
30. Swann, W. B., Zahner, R. J. and Milner, O. I., *Anal. Chem.* **30**, 1830 (1958).
31. Huff, E., *Anal. Chem.* **31**, 1626 (1959).
32. Kuntze, M. and Hädicke, M., *Pharm. Zentralhalle* **98**, 444 (1959).
33. Vincent, M. C. and Blake, M. I., *J. Am. Pharm. Assoc.* **48**, 359 (1959).
34. Belcher, R., Bhatty, M. K. and West, T. S., *J. Chem. Soc.* 2473 (1960).
35. Szymańska, A. and Sobczewska, M., *Acta Polon. Pharm.* **17**, 417 (1960).
36. Traiter, M., *Chem. Zvesti* **14**, 623 (1960).
37. Watanabe, H. *Bunseki Kagaku* **9**, 360 (1960).
38. Böhme, H., Neidlein, R. and Tauber, E., *Arch. Pharm.* **294**, 315 (1961).
39. Böhme, H., Berg, G., Stamme, H. and Tauber, E., *Arch. Pharm.* **294**, 447 (1961).
40. Richardson, M. L., *Anal. Chim. Acta* **24**, 46 (1961).
41. Maruta, S. and Suzuki, Y., *J. Chem. Soc. Japan, Ind. Chem. Sect.* **64**, 176 (1961).
42. Pohloudek-Fabini, R. and Wollmann, H., *Pharmazie* **16**, 442, 548 (1961).
43. Blake, M. I. and Siegel, F. P., *J. Pharm. Soc.* **51**, 944 (1962).
44. Desnitskii, V. M., *Masloboino Zhir. Prom.* **28**, No. 9 31 (1962).
45. Kráčmar, J. and Zýka, J., *Československ. Farm.* **11**, 459 (1962).
46. Kráčmarová, J. and Jindra, A., *Československ. Farm.* **11**, 457 (1962).
47. Légrádi, L., *Magyar Kem. Folyoirat* **69**, 117 (1963).
48. Thoma, K., Ullmann, E. and Loos, P., *Pharmazie* **18**, 414 (1963).
49. Tu, Ch-Y. and Tsang, F-H., *Yao Hsueh Hsueh Pao*, **10**, 10 (1963).
50. Bednarski, T. M. and Hume, D. N., *Anal. Chim. Acta* **30**, 1 (1964).

56. Iron (II)

Reagent. Ferrous ammonium sulphate, Mohr's salt, has been principally used, with the chloride next in frequency.

Reaction and materials titrated. All determinations are based on reduction:

$$Fe^{2+} \rightarrow Fe^{3+} + \epsilon$$

Peroxides and nitrate esters have thus been determined:

$$3\ R.O.O.R + 6\ Fe^{2+} + 6\ H^+ \rightarrow 6\ ROH + 6\ Fe^{3+}$$

$$RONO_2 + 3\ Fe^{2+} + 3\ H^+ \rightarrow ROH + 3\ Fe^{3+} + H_2O + NO$$

Reaction conditions. In acid solution, usually aqueous but with acetone or acetic acid sometimes present.

Reaction times usually below 30 min (reflux).

Often in an inert atmosphere of CO_2 or nitrogen.

Subsequent treatment and final titration stage. (i) Unused Fe(II) has been back titrated with standard oxidizing agents like MnO_4^-, $Cr_2O_7^{2-}$ or Ce(IV).

(ii) About equally frequently, Fe(III) formed in the reduction has been titrated with Ti(III), or, in one example, precipitated with measured excess SCN^- and the unused part then titrated with Hg(II).

Examples

Materials titrated	Reagent and reaction conditions	Subsequent treatment and final titration stage	Ref.
Aliphatic nitrates, e.g. mannitol hexanitrate, in presence of certain nitro compounds	In acetic acid + $FeSO_4$/H_2SO_4 + HCl. Partly evaporated	+ $MnSO_4$ and titrated with MnO_4^-	1
Peroxides in gasolines	+ $Fe(SCN)_2$ in water/acetone, 1:1, + H_2SO_4	Fe(III) titrated with Ti(III) to disappearance of red	2
Nitrate esters of ethylene glycol and glycerol	In acetic acid, + $FeCl_2$/HCl; 5 min reflux in CO_2 atmosphere	Fe(III) titrated with Ti(III) to SCN^-	3
Peroxides in hydrocarbons (gasoline, gas oil)	In 95% acetic acid, + Fe(II) ammonium sulphate in N_2 atmosphere	Unused Fe(II) titrated with $Cr_2O_7^{2-}$	4
Nitroglycerine, extracted from rocket propellant powder	+ $FeCl_2$/HCl; 10 min boiling	Titrated with Ti(III) to SCN^-	5
Monoolefinic peroxides	+ $Fe(SCN)_2$ in water/acetone, 1:1; 5 min shaking/25°	Titrated with Ti(III) to disappearance of red	6
Peroxides in gasoline oxidation products	+ $FeSO_4$ + NH_4SCN + ethanol/water/H_2SO_4	Titrated with Ti(III) to disappearance of red	7
Organic peroxides in soaps and fatty acids	In water/acetone, + Fe(II) ammonium sulphate or $Fe(ClO_4)_2$ + some H_2SO_4; 30 min	Back titrated amperometrically with $Cr_2O_7^{2-}$	8

Materials titrated	Reagent and reaction conditions	Subsequent treatment and final titration stage	Ref.
Nitrocellulose	In acetic acid, + $FeCl_2$/HCl/HBr reagent; 25–30 min boiling in CO_2 atmosphere	Titrated with Ti(III) to SCN^-	9
Nitroglycerine; nitrocellulose	+ $FeCl_2$ + acetic acid + HCl + HBr + molybdate catalyst. In N_2 or CO_2 atmosphere	Titrated with Ti(III) to SCN^-	10
Peroxide groups in coal	+ Fe(II) ammonium sulphate + ethanol; 15 min	+ excess SCN^-, filtered and unused titrated with Hg(II) to disappearance of red	11
Nitrogen content of propellants	In acetic acid/water, + HCl + $FeCl_2$/HCl + HBr; 15 min boiling	Titrated with Ti(III) to SCN^-	12
Pentaerythritol tetranitrate	In acetic acid, + HCl + $FeCl_2$; 20 min reflux in CO_2 atmosphere	Titrated with Ti(III) to SCN^-	13
Nitroglycerine	In acetic acid + $FeSO_4$ + NH_4Cl + H_2SO_4; 1 min boiling	Fe(II) excess titrated with Ce(IV) to ferroin	14
Nitrogen content of nitrocellulose	Refluxed 1–2 min in acetic acid/butyl acetate; cooled solution + Fe(II) ammonium sulphate + HCl; 1 h boiling in CO_2 atmosphere	Titrated with Ti(III) to SCN^-	15
Cellulose nitrate	In acetic acid/butyl acetate, + $FeCl_2$/HCl; 3–4 h reflux	Titrated with Ti(III) to SCN^-	16
other nitrate esters	in acetic acid, + $FeCl_2$/HCl; 5 min reflux	titrated with Ti(III) to SCN^-	
Nitrate esters of glycerol and ethylene glycol	Neutralized sample + Fe(II) ammonium sulphate/dilute H_2SO_4 + some $NaHCO_3$ evidently to give atmosphere of CO_2; 10 min boiling	Cooled and back titrated with MnO_4^-	17

References

1. Huff, W. J. and Leitch, R. D., *J. Am. Chem. Soc.* **44**, 2643 (1922).
2. Yule, J. A. C. and Wilson, C. P., *Ind. Eng. Chem.* **23**, 1254 (1931).
3. Becker, W. W., *Ind. Eng. Chem., Anal. Ed.* **5**, 152 (1933).
4. Tanner, E. M. and Brown, T. F., *J. Inst. Petroleum* **32**, 341 (1946).
5. Hirschhorn, I. S., *Anal. Chem.* **19**, 880 (1947).
6. Wagner, C. D., Smith, R. H. and Peters, E. D., *Anal. Chem.* **19**, 982 (1947).
7. Widmaier, O. and Mauss, F., *Rev. inst. franç. pétrole* **3**, 151 (1948).
8. Kolthoff, I. M. and Medalia, A. I., *Anal. Chem.* **23**, 595 (1951).
9. Shaefer, W. E. and Becker, W. W., *Anal. Chem.* **25**, 1226 (1953).
10. Tranchant, J., *Compt. rend. 27e congr. intern. chim. ind., Brussels 1954*; *Industrie chim. belge* **20**, Spec. no. 320 (1955).
11. Chalishazar, B. H. and Spooner, C. E., *Fuel* **36**, 127 (1957).
12. Grodzinsky, J., *Anal. Chem.* **29**, 150 (1957).
13. Staněk, J. and Vacek, J., *Chem. Průmysl* **8**, 361 (1958).
14. Hansen, G., *Arch. Pharm. Chemi* **66**, 93 (1959).
15. Pierson, R. H. and Julian, E. C., *Anal. Chem.* **31**, 589 (1959).
16. Marvillet, L. and Tranchant, J., *Mém. poudres* **42**, 271 (1960).
17. Shinozaki, H. and Okamoto, I., *J. Ind. Explosives Soc., Japan* **22**, 330 (1961).

57. Iron (III)

Reagent. Chloride or sulphate, the latter also as ferric alum.

Reactions and materials titrated. 1. Oxidation, e.g. of certain sulphur-containing compounds (like thiosemicarbazones, diphenylcarbazide and -carbazone); hydroquinone; oxalic acid; and cuprous acetylide (its inclusion is questionable since it may be regarded as inorganic).

$$Fe^{3+} + \epsilon \rightarrow Fe^{2+}$$

$$C_6H_4(OH)_2 + 2\,Fe^{3+} \rightarrow C_6H_4O_2 + 2\,Fe^{2+} + 2\,H^+$$
$$(COOH)_2 + 2\,Fe^{3+} \rightarrow 2\,CO_2 + 2\,Fe^{2+} + 2\,H^+$$

2. Ion/ion combination, such as in determination of sulphinates and evidently of EDTA

$$3\,RSO_2^- + Fe^{3+} \rightarrow Fe(RSO_2)_3$$

3. 'Complex formation', with some larger molecules, usually containing hydroxy groups, e.g. tocopherols, hydroxytetracycline or penicil-

lin. The reaction is complex and little understood and is the basis of empirical determinations.

Reaction conditions. Mostly in acid, aqueous solution with short reaction times and near room temperature.

Subsequent treatment and final titration stage. Two general conclusions have been adopted:

(i) Determination of unreacted Fe(III), carried out by:
titration with EDTA;
reduction with Sn(II) or Zn metal, to Fe(II) and titration with $Cr_2O_7^{2-}$;
in the majority of cases by adding I^- + acid if necessary and titrating the liberated iodine with thiosulphate.

(ii) Determination of the Fe(II) formed (in oxidation reactions of type 1), using the usual oxidizing agents: $Cr_2O_7^{2-}$ (in most cases), MnO_4^-, VO_3^- and Ce(IV) (directly and also indirectly with excess and back titration with Fe(II)).

(iii) In a single example, quinone from oxidation of hydroquinone was determined iodometrically.

Examples

Materials titrated	Reagent and reaction conditions	Subsequent treatment and final titration stage	Ref.
Cuprous acetylide	+ $Fe_2(SO_4)_3$ + H_2SO_4	Titrated Fe(II) with MnO_4^-	1
Sulphinates, RSO_2^-	+ $FeCl_3$/HCl, giving precipitate of ferric sulphinate	Filtered and unused Fe(III) reduced with $SnCl_2$/HCl or Zn/H_2SO_4 to Fe(II), then titrated with $Cr_2O_7^{2-}$ to external ferricyanide indicator	2
Hydroquinone in presence of other phenols	+ $FeCl_3$, oxidizing to quinone	Extracted with $CHCl_3$ or benzene, I^-/H_2SO_4 added and titrated with thiosulphate (see Iodides and hydriodic acid, ref. 23)	3
Vitamin E	In petroleum ether, + $FeCl_3$/alcohol, giving insoluble derivative; 10 min/room temp., then + excess NH_4OH or alkali hydroxide giving $Fe(OH)_3$. Control	Filtered precipitate dissolved in H_2SO_4, I^- added and titrated with thiosulphate	4

Materials titrated	Reagent and reaction conditions	Subsequent treatment and final titration stage	Ref.
Pyramidone	+ H_2SO_4 + Fe alum; left until the violet colour disappeared	+ excess Ce(IV) and back titrated with Fe(II) to ferroin	5
Na penicillin G	In water, + Fe(III); 5 days/room temp., giving precipitate of derivative. Control without sample	Filtered, I^-/HCl added to filtrate and titrated with thiosulphate	6
Thiosemicarbazones	+ $FeCl_3$/HCl/H_2SO_4; 30 min/60°, giving thiadiazoles	+ phosphoric acid and Fe(II) titrated with $Cr_2O_7^{2-}$ to Na diphenylamine sulphonate	7
Oxalic acid	+ Fe alum + H_2SO_4; 15–30 min in strong sunlight	+ phosphoric acid and Fe(II) titrated with Na vanadate to diphenylamine sulphonate or diphenyl benzidine	8
EDTA in biological fluids, e.g. urine	+ $FeCl_3$ + HCl; 10–15 min/room temp.	Unused Fe(III) back titrated with EDTA to sulphosalicylic acid	9
Terramycin (hydroxytetracycline)	In dilute HCl, neutralized with NaOH, + $FeCl_3$; 10 min	Titrated with EDTA with 'high frequency' end-point (first break for titration of excess Fe(III); second for titration of complex formed with the terramycin)	10
Diphenylcarbazide and -carbazone	In acetic acid, + Fe alum/dilute H_2SO_4. *Ca* 7 min (until the red colour disappeared)	+ phosphoric acid and Fe(II) titrated with $Cr_2O_7^{2-}$ to diphenylamine sulphonate	11
3-Hydroxy-2-methylpyran-4-one ('maltol') and related compounds	+ $FeCl_3$ + H_2SO_4; 7 min	Fe(II) titrated with Ce(IV) to ferroin	12
Hydroquinone	In water, + Fe alum + H_2SO_4; 5 min	+ phosphoric acid/H_2SO_4 and titrated with $Cr_2O_7^{2-}$ to diphenylamine sulphonate	13
Antipyrine	In acetate buffer, pH 3·5, + NH_4SCN + excess $FeCl_3$, giving precipitate of $Fe(C_{11}H_{13}ON_2)_3(SCN)_3$; heated to 50° to coagulate	Clear solution titrated with EDTA to determine unused Fe(III)	14

References

1. Willstätter, R. and Maschmann, E., *Ber.* **53**, 939 (1920).
2. Krishna, S. and Harnam Singh, *J. Am. Chem. Soc.* **50**, 792 (1928).
3. Böck, F. and Lock, G., *Monatsh.* **53/4**, 888 (1929).
4. Meenen, H. W., *Fette u. Seifen* **48**, 608 (1941).
5. Percs, E. and Lengyel, J., *Magyar Kem. Lapya* **4**, 536 (1949).
6. Meyer, J. and Fontanelloz, P., *Produits pharm.* **6**, 21 (1951).
7. Wollenberg, O., *Arch. Pharm.* **284**, 80 (1951).
8. Gopala Rao, G. and Aravamudan, G., *Anal. Chim. Acta* **13**, 415 (1955).
9. Bonati, F., *Ateneo parmense* **27**, 681 (1956).
10. Hochmann, K. and Bayer, I., *Z. anal. Chem.* **166**, 88 (1959).
11. Ghosh, N. N. and Ray, J. N., *J. Indian Chem. Soc.* **37**, 650 (1960).
12. Jungnickel, H. E., *Pharm. Zentralhalle* **100**, 114 (1961).
13. Bhaskara Rao, K., *Z. anal. Chem.* **185**, 286 (1962).
14. Dick, J. and Ristici, J., *Acad. Rep. Populare Romine, Baza Cercetari Stiint, Timisoara, Studii Cercetari Stiinte Chem.* **9**, No. 3-4 269 (1962).

58. Isocyanate and isothiocyanate

These reagents have been used to determine —OH and —NH— groups, with which they react fast and quantitatively to yield urethanes or substituted thioureas or ureas

$$ROH + R'N{=}C{=}O \rightarrow R'NH.COOR$$

$$RNH_2 + R'N{=}C{=}S \rightarrow R'NH.CS.NHR$$

Some examples of recent date are given here:

Materials titrated	Reagent and reaction conditions	Subsequent treatment and final titration stage	Ref.
Si—OH groups in silanols, polysiloxanes, etc.	In chlorobenzene or dioxan, + excess C_6H_5NCO. Refluxed	Unused reactant determined by adding excess isobutylamine and back titrating the unreacted part with HCl (see Amines and heterocyclic bases, ref. 69)	
Silanol groups in silicone resins	Method of ref. 1 (see Amines and heterocyclic bases, ref. 74)		2

Materials titrated	Reagent and reaction conditions	Subsequent treatment and final titration stage	Ref.
'Hydroxyl number' of unsaturated polyester resins	In acetone/chlorobenzene + excess C_6H_5NCO in chlorobenzene; 5 min/20° (reacts also with –COOH, which was determined by separate acid titration)	+ isobutylamine/same solvent and back titrated the unused with acid to bromophenol blue (see Amines and heterocyclic bases, ref. 94)	3
Amine mixtures	In dioxan, + acetic acid (to slow the reaction to a measurable rate), + excess C_6H_5NCS. Aliquots removed at various intervals (amines react at different speeds; kinetic plot gives concentration of both)	+ acetic acid (to stop reaction) and titrated with $HClO_4$/acetic acid potentiometrically	4
Tertiary amines in presence of primary and secondary	+ C_6H_5NCS + methyl isobutyl ketone; heated till dissolved, then 2 h/room temp.	Unreacted tertiary amines titrated with HCl/methyl isobutyl ketone potentiometrically	5
Hydroxyl equivalent weights of polyoxy alkylene compounds	In dimethylformamide, + C_6H_5NCO/toluene + Sn(II) octoate catalyst; 15–60 min/room temp to *ca* 100°	+ excess diisobutylamine and back titrated with $HClO_4$ (see Amines and heterocyclic bases, ref. 110)	6

References

1. Damm, K. and Noll, W., *Kolloid Ztg.* **158**, 97 (1958).
2. Noll, W., Damm, K. and Krauss, N., *Farbe u. Lack* **65**, 17 (1959).
3. Dreher, B., *Farbe u. Lack* **67**, 703 (1961).
4. Hanna, J. G. and Siggia, S., *Anal. Chem.* **34**, 547 (1962).
5. Miller, M. and Keyworth, D. A., *Talanta* **10**, 1131 (1963).
6. Reed, D. H., Critchfield, F, E. and Elder, D. K., *Anal. Chem.* **35**, 571 (1963).

59. Kjeldahl nitrogen determination

The Kjeldahl determination, based on digestion of the sample with concentrated H_2SO_4 and K_2SO_4 (to raise the boiling point of the reaction mixture) together with a catalyst like Cu(II), Hg(II) or SeO_2 (mainly to accelerate the destruction of organic matter) is a well-known procedure for the determination of nitrogen. The nitrogen is thereby converted into NH_4^+ and the procedure has been concluded by determination of this. The reaction mixture is made alkaline, the ammonia distilled into excess acid or borate and the unused acid back titrated or the borate solution titrated with acid. Colorimetric procedures, e.g. with the Nessler reagent, are also known.

Determinations of the elements do not fall within the set limits of this book. The method has, however, been used to determine certain compounds in the presence of non-nitrogen-containing materials. Where the conclusion of such determinations has been titrimetric, inclusion here is justified and some examples are tabulated below. Some authors have not made it wholly clear exactly how the determination was carried out but it is assumed that 'usual Kjeldahl determination' or equivalent expressions, imply digestion as indicated above, followed by distillation and titration.

The problem of Kjeldahl nitrogen determination on materials containing N—N or N—O links, especially nitro groups, has been extensively studied. In general, the bonds must be broken by reduction, either as a separate, preliminary stage (e.g. with HI) or by a suitable addition to the reaction mixture (e.g. of sugar). The goal of these investigations is the universal determination of nitrogen, irrespective of the type of functional group present, rather than the development of a method for, say, nitro, nitroso, or azo compounds. Accordingly, the subject is not treated here.

Examples

(Where no details are given, the 'usual procedure', as outlined in the first paragraph above, has been used.)

Materials titrated	Reagent and reaction conditions	Subsequent treatment and final titration stage	Ref.
Betaine periodide, from determination of betaine by precipitation with iodine/KI			1
Dixanthydrylurea, from determination of urea by reaction with xanthydrol			2

Materials titrated	Reagent and reaction conditions	Subsequent treatment and final titration stage	Ref.
Caffeine in coffee extracts, extracted with CCl_4 and evaporated			3
Derivatives of sulphanilamide	+ H_2SO_4 + $CuSO_4$ and heated till disappearance of brown colour then 1 h longer		4
Nitriles (after preliminary reduction with HI)	Usual method, with Cu(II) and SeO_2 catalysts	NH_3 distilled into excess H_2SO_4 and back titrated with NaOH to Na alizarinsulphonate/indigo carmine	5
Caffeine, after separation from theobromine with $CHCl_3$			6
Caffeine in coffee and tea, after extraction with $CHCl_3$			7
p-Aminosalicylate; *p*-aminosalicylic acid	Acid extracted with ether (salt first acidified), solvent evaporated; usual method, + Cu(II) and SeO_2 catalysts	Solution neutralized with NaOH, HCHO added and titrated with NaOH	8, 10
Amino acids, after paper chromatographic separation	Usual method, with Cu(II) and SeO_2 catalysts; 12 h digestion	NH_3 diffused out and titrated with HCl	9
Glycine nitranilate, from determination of former by precipitation with nitranilic acid			11
Diphenylhydantoin	+ H_2SO_4 + K_2SO_4 + HgO. Heated until colourless	+ Zn filings + $Na_2S_2O_3$ + NaOH and NH_3 distilled into excess HCl, then back titrated with NaOH to methyl red	12
Dixanthydrylurea, from determination of urea by reaction with xanthydrol	+ H_2SO_4 + K_2SO_4 + Cu(II) + H_2O_2, then + SeO_2		13
ϵ-Caprolactam and in its polymers in aqueous solutions	+ H_2SO_4 and evaporated down; then + V_2O_5 + SeO_2 + K_2SO_4 and heated 30 min	+ alkali, NH_3 distilled into H_2SO_4 and back titrated with NaOH to methyl red/methylene blue	14

Materials titrated	Reagent and reaction conditions	Subsequent treatment and final titration stage	Ref.
5-Nitrosalicylic acid, from determination of nitroguanidine by heating with H_2SO_4/salicylic acid	+ K_2SO_4 + Cu(II) + $Na_2S_2O_3$	+ water + KOH and NH_3 distilled into excess H_2SO_4; back titrated with NaOH to methyl red	15
Protein in fatty tissue			16
Ca cyanamide		NH_3 distilled into boric acid and titrated with acid	17
5-Nitrofurfuraldehyde derivatives, reduced with HI	+ H_2SO_4 + K_2SO_4 + HgO; heated until colourless		18
Amine nitrogen in plant extracts	Digested with H_2SO_4/HgO	+ conc. NaOH and distilled 15 min into boric acid; titrated with $KH(IO_3)_2$ to methyl red/methylene blue	19

References

1. Staněk, V., *Z. physiol. Chem.* **47**, 83 (1904).
2. Boivin, A., *Bull. soc. chim. biol.* **8**, 456 (1926); **10**, 684 (1928).
3. Jesser, H., *Chem.-Ztg.* **56**, 842 (1932).
4. Schulek, E. and Rozsa, P., *Z. anal. Chem.* **122**, 96 (1941).
5. Rose, E. L. and Ziliotto, H., *Ind. Eng. Chem., Anal. Ed.* **17**, 211 (1945).
6. Moores, R. G. and Campbell, H. A., *Anal. Chem.* **20**, 40 (1948).
7. Bower, R. S., Anderson, A. D. and Titus, R. W., *Anal. Chem.* **22**, 1056 (1950).
8. Grau, C. A. and Olaechea, V. P., *Rev. farm.* (*Buenos Aires*) **93**, 319 (1950).
9. Klatzkin, C., *Nature* **169**, 422 (1952).
10. Grau, C. A. and Olaechea, V. P., *Farm. chilena* **27**, 243 (1953).
11. Shimizu, W., Fujita, M. and Endo, K., *Bull. Japan Soc. Sci. Fisheries* **20**, 305 (1954).
12. Boehm, T. and Freudenberg, R., *Pharmazie* **11**, 230 (1956).
13. Hayashi, T. and Engo, T., *Takamine Kenkyujo Nempo* (*Ann. Repts. Takamine Labs.*) **8**, 136 (1956).
14. Čefelín, P. and Šittler, E., *Chem. Listy* **51**, 1320 (1957).
15. Fauth, M. I. and Stalcup, H., *Anal. Chem.* **28**, 1670 (1958).
16. Krasil'nikova, T., *Myasnaya Ind. SSSR* **31**, No. 6, 25 (1960).
17. Szucki, B. and Soczewińska, Z., *Med. Pracy* **11**, 463 (1960).

18. Egerts, V., Simanska, M. and Hillers, S., *Latvijas P.S.R. Zinatnu Akad. Vestis, Kim. Ser.* No. 1, 55 (1961).
19. Barker, A. V. and Volk, R. J., *Anal. Chem.* **36**, 439 (1964).

60. Lead (II)

Reagent. Nearly always the acetate.

Reactions and materials titrated. 1. Ion/ion combination yielding precipitates of lead salts, in determination of some carboxylic acids (notably citric acid) and of diphenols (catechol).

$$2\,RCOO^- + Pb^{2+} \rightarrow Pb(COOR)_2$$

$$C_6H_4(O^-)_2 + Pb^{2+} \rightarrow C_6H_4O_2Pb$$

2. One example of the formation of Pb—S links in determination of some sulphur-containing organic compounds. PbS and lead mercaptides $Pb(SR)_2$ are formed as insoluble reaction products.

Subsequent treatment and final titration stage. (i) In three cases, unused Pb(II) in the filtrate was determined: via precipitation as $PbSO_4$, solution in ammonium acetate and titration with ammonium molybdate to external indicator of tannin; and via direct titration with EDTA.

(ii) Via solution of the precipitate (in acetic acid, ammonium hydroxide or nitric acid) and determination of the Pb(II). Procedures used include:

1. Precipitation as $Pb(IO_3)_2$ and determination of the iodate content iodometrically.
2. Precipitation as $PbSO_4$ with measured excess H_2SO_4 and back titration with alkali.
3. Precipitation as $PbCrO_4$ and iodometric determination of the chromate.
4. Titration with EDTA (concluding with back titration using Mg(II).

(iii) Via conversion to the original acid by treatment with H_2S, HCl or H_2SO_4 and determination of this acid in one of several ways:

1. Oxidation with excess Ce(IV), MnO_4^- or IO_3^-.
2. Titration with alkali.
3. In the case of glucuronic acid, by distillation with conc. HCl, giving furfuraldehyde and determination of this with bisulphite.

Examples

Materials titrated	Reagent and reaction conditions	Subsequent treatment and final titration stage	Ref.
Tartaric acid	+ Pb acetate/acetic acid	Precipitated Pb tartrate + conc. H_2SO_4 + excess KIO_3. Heated and unused iodate determined iodometrically (see Iodate, ref. 8)	1
Glucuronic acid in urine	In ammoniacal solution, + Pb acetate	Precipitate distilled with conc. HCl, giving furfuraldehyde, then determined with bisulphite (see Bisulphite and sulphite, ref. 27)	2
Chlorogenic acid in raw coffee	Extract in water, + Pb acetate; 10 min/ *ca* 90°, then cooled in ice-water	Precipitate treated with H_2S, freed acid filtered from precipitated PbS and titrated with NaOH to bromothymol blue	3
Oxalic or citric acids in presence of other acids	+ Pb(II) reagent	Precipitate suspended in water and treated with H_2S; liberated acid determined with excess Ce(IV) (see Cerium (IV), ref. 2)	4
Malic acid in mixtures with other acids like tartaric, oxalic and succinic acids	+ Pb acetate	Pb malate dissolved in H_2SO_4 and determined with excess MnO_4^-	5
Citric acid in milk products	+ Pb acetate	Pb citrate determined with excess Ce(IV) (see Cerium (IV), ref. 11)	6
Catechol in urine	Extract in water, + pyridine/acetate buffer, pH 6·5 + Pb acetate; 1 min	Filtered, Pb derivative dissolved in acetic acid, KIO_3 added, Pb iodate filtered, H_2SO_4 + KI added to it and the liberated iodine titrated with sulphite potentiometrically	7
o-Diphenols (e.g. catechol)	+ Pb acetate reagent	Precipitate dissolved in excess H_2SO_4, boiled 5 min, ethanol added, $PbSO_4$ filtered and unreacted H_2SO_4 in filtrate titrated with NaOH to phenolphthalein	8

Materials titrated	Reagent and reaction conditions	Subsequent treatment and final titration stage	Ref.
Citric acid	+ Pb(II) reagent	Precipitate filtered, dissolved in conc. NH_4 OH, Pb precipitated as $PbCrO_4$; this product treated with HCl + I^- and titrated with thiosulphate	9
Organic sulphur-containing compounds, e.g. mercaptans, disulphides, thiocarbamates, isothiocyanates, isothioureas, etc.	In alcohol, + $Na_2Pb(OH)_4$ reagent; 30 min/room temp., giving PbS + $Pb(SR)_2$ precipitates	Filtered, unused Pb(II) in filtrate precipitated as $PbSO_4$; dissolved this in ammoninm acetate and titrated the Pb(II) with ammonium molybdate to tannin as external indicator	10
Catechol	In water at 60–70°, + Pb acetate at same temp.; 30 min	Filtered, precipitate dissolved in HNO_3, NH_4OH added to give pH 10, excess EDTA added and back titrated with $MgCl_2$ to eriochrome black T	11
Unithiol, CH_2—CH—CH_2 (SH, SH, SO_3Na)	+ excess $Pb(NO_3)_2$ in presence of 5% pyramidone solution	Unused back titrated with EDTA	12
Catechol	In water, + Pb acetate	Filtered, filtrate + Na acetate and titrated with EDTA to xylenol orange	13

References

1. Strebinger, R. and Wolfram, J., *Österr. Chem.-Ztg.* **26**, 156 (1923).
2. Haendel, M., *Rev. asoc. med. Argentina* **42**, 215 (1929).
3. Jurany, H., *Z. anal. Chem.* **94**, 225 (1933).
4. Wilkinson, J. A., Sipherd, I. R., Fulmer, E. I. and Christensen, L. M., *Ind. Eng. Chem., Anal. Ed.* **6**, 161 (1934).
5. Smolin, A. N., *Ucheniye Zapiski Moskov. Gosudarst. Pedagog. Inst.* **21**, No. 4, 125 (1940).
6. Heinemann, B., *J. Dairy Sci.* **27**, 377 (1944).
7. Baernstein, H. D., *J. Biol. Chem.* **161**, 685 (1945).
8. Fodor, G., *Acta Univ. Szeged. Chem. et Phys.* **2**, 68 (1948).
9. Glagoleva-Malikova, E. M., *Latvijas PSR Zinatnu Akad. Vestis* No. 6 (Whole No. 23) 121 (1949).

10. Lennartz, T. A. and Middeldorf, R., *Süddeut. Apoth.-Ztg.* **89**, 593 (1949).
11. Kada, Z. and Młodecka, J., *Chem. Anal. (Warsaw)* **6**, 95 (1961).
12. Shakh, Ts. I. and Kagan, F. Yu., *Farmatsevt. Zh. (Kiev)* **17**, 12 (1962).
13. Karpov, O. N., *Zhur. Anal. Khim.* **18**, 1507 (1963).

61. Lead (IV)

Reagent. The tetraacetate, $Pb(OOCCH_3)_4$, usually in acetic acid solution.

Reaction and materials titrated. Oxidation, based on the equation:

$$Pb^{4+} + 2\,\epsilon \rightarrow Pb^{2+} \text{ or}$$

$$Pb(OOCCH_3)_4 + H_2O \rightarrow Pb(OOCCH_3)_2 + 2\,CH_3COOH + O$$

Compounds determined by this oxidation procedure have been poly-alcohols and some carboxylic acids. A few typical equations are here:

$$(CH_2OH)_2 + Pb(OOCCH_3)_4 \rightarrow 2\,HCHO + Pb(OOCCH_3)_2 + 2\,CH_3COOH$$

$$CH_2OH.CHOH.CH_2OH + 2\,Pb(OOCCH_3)_4 + H_2O \rightarrow 2\,HCHO + HCOOH + 2\,Pb(OOCCH_3)_2 + 4\,CH_3COOH$$

followed by:

$$HCOOH + Pb(OOCCH_3)_4 \rightarrow CO_2 + Pb(OOCCH_3)_2 + 2\,CH_3COOH$$

$$C_6H_5CHOH.COOH + Pb(OOCCH_3)_4 \rightarrow C_6H_5CHO + CO_2 + Pb(OOCCH_3)_2 + 2\,CH_3COOH$$

$$CH_2OH.(CHOH)_4CH_2OH + 9\,Pb(OOCCH_3)_4 + 4\,H_2O \rightarrow 2\,HCHO + 4\,CO_2 + 9\,Pb(OOCCH_3)_2 + 18\,CH_3COOH$$

Reaction conditions. In acetic acid or acetic acid/water solution. Some of the oxidations are fairly long (up to 10 h) since the low stability of the reagent evidently precludes heating.

Subsequent treatment and final titration stage. (i) Unused Pb(IV) has been determined by direct titration in dilute H_2SO_4 solution with hydroquinone (to ferroin or, more usually, potentiometrically); or by addition of I^-/Na acetate and titration with thiosulphate of the liberated iodine.

(ii) In single examples, the CO_2 reaction product was absorbed in alkali and the $BaCO_3$ ultimately formed was titrated with acid; and Pb(II) formed during oxidation, titrated with EDTA.

Examples

Materials titrated	Reagent and reaction conditions	Subsequent treatment and final titration stage	Ref.
Certain glycosides (study of rates of oxidation)	In acetic acid, + Pb salt/acetic acid at 20°	Samples + I^-/Na acetate and titrated with thiosulphate	1
Ethylene glycol	As in method of ref. 1; 25–40 h/28–33°		2
Glycerol α-monochloro- and bromohydrins	+ Pb(IV) reagent. Left overnight	+ I^-/Na acetate and titrated with thiosulphate	3
α-Glycerophosphates	In water, + HCl + Pb salt/acetic acid; 6 h/room temp.	+ I^-/Na acetate and titrated with thiosulphate	4
Sugars and sugar derivatives	In acetic acid + Pb salt, oxidizing to CO_2; 8 h/40–42°	CO_2 passed into NaOH; + $BaCl_2$ and unused NaOH titrated with acid to phenolphthalein; then $BaCO_3$ titrated with acid to methyl orange (to eliminate possible error due to acetic acid carried over)	5
Formic acid	+ Pb salt + K acetate (catalyst) + acetic acid; 20–30 min/25–27°	+ I^-/Na acetate + water and titrated with thiosulphate	6
Tartaric and mandelic acids; mannitol; Ca gluconate	In water, + Pb salt/ acetic acid + a little NaOH	Back titrated potentiometrically with hydroquinone	7
Mandelic acid	In dry acetic acid + Pb salt/acetic acid; 4 h/room temp.	+ H_2SO_4 and titrated with hydroquinone to ferroin (yellow-white → orange)	8
Tartaric acid; tartrates	In 80% acetic acid + K acetate + Pb salt/acetic acid; 30 min/room temp., oxidizing to CO_2 and water	Titrated potentiometrically with hydroquinone in dil. H_2SO_4	9

Materials titrated	Reagent and reaction conditions	Subsequent treatment and final titration stage	Ref.
Numerous polyhydroxy compounds, e.g. glycol, glycerol, mannitol, Ca gluconate; acids like malic, mandelic and citric	+ acetic acid + acetate + Pb salt/acetic acid. Various reaction times (up to 10 h/room temp.)	Back titrated potentiometrically with hydroquinone in dil. H_2SO_4	10, 12
Mono- and diethylene glycol in polyoxyethylene terephthalate	In acetic acid/acetate. + Pb salt, oxidizing to HCHO	Unused determined iodometrically	11
Polyalcohols (e.g. glycol, glycerol, mannitol) and α-hydroxy acids (e.g. citric, tartaric, mandelic)	In water, + K acetate + Pb salt/acetic acid; 30 min/room temp.	+ boiling water, PbO_2 filtered and filtrate + $ZnCl_2$//NH_4Cl NH_4OH/EDTA equivalent to the Zn(II); Zn(II) set free by reaction with the Pb(II) determined in the filtrate by titration with EDTA to eriochrome black T	13
Glycerol in some preparations	Solution, + water + acetic acid/acetate + Pb salt; 30 min, giving HCHO + CO_2; suppositories dissolved in acetic acid; 45–50 min	Back titrated with hydroquinone	14
Mercaptan groups, e.g. in thiosemicarbazide	+ excess Pb salt/acetic acid, + $HClO_4$; 2 h, reacting in 1:5 molar ratio	Back titrated with hydroquinone	15

References

1. Hockett, R. C. and McClenahan, W. S., *J. Am. Chem. Soc.* **61**, 1667 (1939).
2. Seikel, M. K., *Ind. Eng. Chem., Anal. Ed.* **13**, 388 (1941).
3. Sjöberg, B., *Svensk Kem. Tidskr.* **53**, 390 (1941).
4. Wormith, D. J. and Rae, J. J., *J. Am. Chem. Soc.* **63**, 2523 (1941).
5. Abraham, S., *J. Am. Chem. Soc.* **72**, 4050 (1950).
6. Perlin, A. S., *Anal. Chem.* **26**, 1053 (1954).
7. Berka, A. and Zýka, J., *Chem. Listy* **52**, 930 (1958).
8. Berka, A., *Českoslov. Farm.* **8**, 561 (1959).
9. Berka, A., *Anal. Chim. Acta* **24**, 171 (1961).
10. Berka, A., Dvořák, V. and Zýka, J., *Mikrochim. Acta* 541 (1962).
11. Mifune, A. and Ishida, S., *J. Chem. Soc. Japan* (*Ind. Chem. Sect.*) **65**, 824 (1962).

12. Zýka, J. and Berka, A., *Microchem. J. Sym. Ser.* **2**, 789 (1962).
13. Berka, A., *Z. Anal. Chem.* **195**, 263 (1963).
14. Berka, A., Fara, M. and Zýka, J., *Českoslov. Farm.* **12**, 366 (1963).
15. Suchomelová, J. and Zýka, J., *J. Electroanal. Chem.* **5**, 57 (1963).

62. Maleic (and chloromaleic) anhydride

Reagent. Maleic anhydride in all cited cases except one, where the chloro-substituted derivative was used.

Reaction and materials titrated. The only reaction on which the analytical use of these anhydrides is based, is the addition to conjugated ethylenic systems, namely, the Diels–Alder reaction. In a few cases, it has served for the determination of individual compounds like anthracene or cyclopentadiene, but much more often the content of conjugated olefine compounds has been determined in fats, oils or other complex mixtures.

```
 |                                                      |
—C                                                   \  C     H
   \\                                                  / \   /
     C–     CH—CO                                 —C     C—CO
     |   +  ||      \O   ——————→                   ||     |     \O
     C–     CH—CO  /                              —C     C—CO  /
   //                                                  \ /   \
—C                                                   /  C     H
 |                                                      |
```

Several features of the reaction militate against its effective use in quantitative analysis. Thus in general only the *trans-trans* diolefines react with reasonable speed; substituents in the diolefine molecule can influence the speed and extent of reaction; and the competition reactions of polymerization of the diene or copolymerization with the reagent are often not negligible. It is therefore not surprising that conflicting data and opinions of the method are found in the literature.

The data obtained are often referred to as 'diene values' or 'diene numbers' (for 'pandiene numbers', see below under Reaction conditions).

The determination of the important intermediate butadiene is usually carried out by a method based on this reaction, but using a gas-volumetric principle rather than titrimetric.

It is of interest that maleic anhydride appears not to have been used for determination of hydroxyl groups, etc., as classified under Anhydrides and for which acetic and phthalic anhydrides have mostly been employed.

Reaction conditions. The reaction has been carried out in non-aqueous solution, usually in an aromatic hydrocarbon such as toluene or xylene. Acetone has also been often used.

Refluxing, sometimes several hours, or heating in a sealed vessel have generally been necessary to carry the reaction to completion or as near to it as possible.

In some determinations, small amounts of iodine have been added to the reaction mixture, in order to catalyse the isomerization from *cis-cis* or *cis-trans* isomers to the much faster reacting *trans-trans* isomers. The results from such determinations have been termed the 'pandiene values' (or numbers).

Subsequent treatment and final titration stage. (i) The conclusion when using maleic anhydride reagent appears in almost all cases to have been via determination of unused reagent. Two procedures have been used:

1. Addition of water and titration of the extracted maleic acid in the aqueous layer, using NaOH and generally with phenolphthalein indicator.

2. Addition of water + iodate/iodide/excess thiosulphate and subsequent back titration of the unreacted thiosulphate, using iodine.

(ii) In one case (ref. 30) the reaction product was extracted with alkali, acidified and titrated with bromate/bromide reagent; and in another (ref. 4) carbazole, left after removal of anthracene, was also bromometrically determined.

(iii) With chloromaleic anhydride as reagent (a single publication), the conclusion was via the tertiary halogen atom present in the adduct. This reactive atom was removed by reaction with excess $AgNO_3$ and the unused Ag(I) titrated with thiocyanate.

Examples

(Maleic anhydride has been the reagent except where stated.)

Materials titrated	Reagent and reaction conditions	Subsequent treatment and final titration stage	Ref.
Conjugated diolefines	In toluene; nitrogen atmosphere; 3 h reflux; also + iodine, then 1 h reflux	+ water + ether and titrated with NaOH to phenolphthalein	1

Materials titrated	Reagent and reaction conditions	Subsequent treatment and final titration stage	Ref.
Conjugated olefines in fats and oils	In acetone; 20 h/*ca* 100° in a sealed tube	Filtered from oily derivative and titrated with NaOH to phenolphthalein	2
Diene number of Chinese wood oil	Method of ref. 2		3
Carbazole + anthracene in crude anthracene	In xylene; 20 min reflux	+ water, xylene steam distilled out and carbazole determined in the precipitate with excess bromine reagent (see Bromine reagents, ref. 143)	4
Conjugated dienes in oils like linseed, soya oils, etc.	Method of ref. 1 gave slightly high values; suggested that some maleic anhydride reacts with —OH groups in the oil		5
Conjugated dienes	In toluene; 4 h/100° in sealed tube	Unreacted maleic (acid) titrated with NaOH	6
Conjugated dienes in fats and oils	In xylene; 15 h reflux. Or as in method of ref. 2	+ benzene + water + iodate/iodide/thiosulphate excess; after 2 h, added excess iodine and finally titrated with thiosulphate (see Iodate, ref. 33 and Thiosulphate, ref. 5)	7
Diene numbers of certain fats (semimicro)	In toluene; 1–12 h/100–130°	Evidently by method of ref. 7	8
Anthracene in oils	Method of ref. 2 (tried 2–15 h/100–130°)		9
Diene numbers	Studied methods of refs 1 and 2		10
Anthracene	In xylene; 25 min reflux	+ water and titrated with KOH to phenolphthalein	11
Pure conjugated dienes like anthracene; diene values of soybean and other vegetable oils	Methods of refs 1 and 2 studied (studied influence of —OH group—compare ref. 5)		12
Diene values of phellandrenes	In toluene. Heated to 100° in sealed tube for various periods (2–10 h)	+ water/iodate/iodide and subsequently titrated with thiosulphate	13
'Maleic values' of fats	Tested methods of refs 1 and 2, and stated that the anhydride reacts with components other than dienes, e.g. hydroxy acids, alcohols, etc.		14

Materials titrated	Reagent and reaction conditions	Subsequent treatment and final titration stage	Ref.
Diene numbers of hydrocarbons	Best in xylene; 5–30 h heating at not above 100° (to minimize polymerization and reaction between reagent and olefines)		15
Cyclopentadiene	No solvent; 1 h heating	+ iodate/iodide/excess thiosulphate and after 1 h, back titrated with excess iodine and finally with thiosulphate	16
Diene values of dehydrated castor oil	Slightly modified method of ref. 2		17
1-Pimaric acid in pine oleoresin	In n-pentane, + reagent/acetone; 4 h/20°	+ benzene, extracted with water and titrated with NaOH to phenolphthalein	18
Conjugated dienes, e.g. isoprene, cyclopentadiene	+ chloromaleic anhydride + *tert*-butyl catechol (to remove peroxides and inhibit polymerization)	+ water/acetone + HNO_3 + excess $AgNO_3$; refluxed 1 h and back titrated with SCN^- (see Silver (I), ref. 83)	19
Anthracene	Method of ref. 11, but with chlorobenzene instead of xylene as solvent		20
Pandiene numbers	Technique of method of ref. 2, but in presence of a small amount of iodine to isomerize *cis*-dienes to *trans*-		21
Anthracene in coal tar distillation products	Refluxed 45 min in xylene	Solvent distilled out and residue titrated with NaOH to ethyl orange/xylene cyanol	22
Anthracene	In dioxan; 20 min/125°	+ water and titrated with NaOH to phenolphthalein	23
Anthracene in tar oils and tar oil fractions	In xylene; 25 min reflux	+ water, xylene distilled out, and back titrated with NaOH to phenolphthalein	24
Anthracene in crude samples	In chlorobenzene; 2 h reflux at 130°	+ water and titrated aqueous phase at 55° with NaOH	25, 27, 28
Anthracene	Method of ref. 24 tried and stated that 20 min reflux sufficed		26
Conjugated dienes in cracked gasoline	In benzene; 2–3 h/40–90°	Unused back titrated with NaOH	29

Materials titrated	Reagent and reaction conditions	Subsequent treatment and final titration stage	Ref.
Cyclopentadiene	In benzene; 10 min/35°	Reaction product extracted with aqueous KOH, acidified and titrated with bromate/bromide to yellow	30
Anthracene	In xylene; 30 min reflux	+ CCl_4 + water and titrated with NaOH to cresol red/thymol blue	31
Anthracene	In chlorobenzene	Extracted with water and titrated with alkali	32
Diene numbers of monoterpenes	In benzene; 3 h/*ca* 90°	+ water, heated 15 min/*ca* 100°; maleic acid in water layer titrated with alkali	33
p-Mentha-3,8(9)-diene	In benzene; 3–4 h/*ca* 100° or 14–15 h/room temp.	+ water + iodate/iodide + excess thiosulphate; 2 h, then + excess iodine and back titrated with thiosulphate (see Iodate, ref. 78 and Thiosulphate, ref. 27)	34
Diene numbers, e.g. of dehydrated castor oil	In benzene; 12 h reflux	+ water + toluene, then + iodate/iodide + excess thiosulphate; 3 h, then + excess iodine and titrated biamperometrically with thiosulphate (see Iodate, ref. 79 and Thiosulphate, ref. 31)	35
Anthracene	In *o*-dichlorobenzene; 10 min boiling	+ water and titrated with NaOH to cresol red/thymol blue	36

References

1. Ellis, B. A. and Jones, R. A., *Analyst* **61**, 812 (1936).
2. Kaufmann, H. P. and Baltes, J., *Fette u. Seifen* **43**, 93 (1936).
3. Kaufmann, H. P. and Baltes, J., *Ber.* **69**, 2676 (1936).
4. Ardashev, B. I., *Zhur. Priklad Khim.* (*J. Appl. Chem. USSR*) **10**, 1032 (1937).
5. Bruce, R. J. and Denley, P. G., *Chem. and Ind.* (*London*) **15**, 937 (1937).
6. Dyachkov, G. and Ermolova, M., *Kautschuk and Rubber* (*USSR*) No. 3, 24 (1937).

7. Kaufmann, H. P., Baltes, J. and Büter, H., *Ber.* **70**, 903 (1937).
8. Kaufmann, H. P. and Hartweg, L., *Ber.* **70**, 2554 (1937).
9. Kaufmann, H. P., Baltes, J. and Hartweg, L., *Ber.* **70**, 2559 (1937).
10. Pelikan, K. A. and Mikusch, J. D., *Oil and Soap* **14**, 209 (1937).
11. Postovskii, I. Ya. and Khmelevskii, V. I., *Zhur. Priklad Khim.* (*J. Appl. Chem. USSR*) **10**, 759 (1937).
12. Bickford, W. G., Dollear, F. G. and Markley, K. S., *Oil and Soap* **15**, 256 (1938).
13. Goodway, N. F. and West, T. F., *J. Soc. Chem. Ind.* (*London*) **57**, 37 (1938).
14. Tyutyunnikov, B. and Ursulyak, S., *Masloiboino-Zhirovaya Prom.* **14**, No. 5, 12 (1938).
15. Grosse-Oetringhaus, H., *Petroleum Z.* **35**, 567 (1939).
16. Kirsanov, A. V., Polyakova, I. M. and Kuznetsova, Z. I., *Zhur. Priklad Khim.* (*J. Appl. Chem. USSR*) **13**, 1406 (1940).
17. Priest, G. W. and Mikusch, J. D., *Ind. Eng. Chem.* **32**, 1314 (1940).
18. Fleck, E. E. and Palkin, S., *Ind. Eng. Chem., Anal. Ed.* **14**, 146 (1942).
19. Putnam, S. T., Moss, M. L. and Hall, R. T., *Ind. Eng. Chem., Anal. Ed.* **18**, 628 (1946).
20. Ubaldini, I., Crespi, V. and Guerrieri, F., *Ann. chim. applicata* **39**, 77 (1949).
21. Mikusch, J. D., *Angew. Chem.* **62**, 475 (1950); *Z. anal. Chem.* **130**, 412 (1950).
22. Titley, A. F., Grove, J. F. and Allmark, A. J., *J. Soc. Chem. Ind.* **69**, Suppl. Vol., 523 (1950).
23. Kisfaludy, L., *Magyar Kem. Folyoirat* **58**, 312 (1952).
24. Schmidt, W., *Brennstoffchemie* **33**, 176 (1952).
25. Funakubo, E., Matsumoto, Y. and Hiroike, S., *J. Chem. Soc. Japan, Ind. Chem. Sect.* **56**, 798 (1953).
26. Funakubo, E., Matsumoto, Y. and Taniguchi, H., *J. Chem. Soc. Japan, Ind. Chem. Sect.* **57**, 143 (1954).
27. Funakubo, E. and Matsumoto, Y., *J. Chem. Soc. Japan, Ind. Chem. Sect.* **57**, 556, 562 (1954).
28. Funakubo, E., Matsumoto, Y. and Fujiura, M., *J. Chem. Soc. Japan, Ind. Chem. Sect.* **57**, 559 (1954).
29. Ichikawa, Y., Uemura, O. and Iejima, H., *J. Chem. Soc. Japan, Ind. Chem. Sect.* **57**, 367 (1954).
30. Unger, P., *Analyst* **80**, 820 (1955).
31. Takeuchi, T. and Furasawa, M., *Bunseki Kagaku* (*Japan Analyst*) **6**, 621 (1957).
32. Funakubo, E., Matsumoto, Y., Fujiura, M., Kawanishi, I. and Hiroike, S., *Brennstoffchemie* **40**, 377 (1959).
33. Hayashi, S., Yasuda, S. and Mizoguchi, K., *Nippon Kagaku Zasshi* **80**, 198 (1959).

34. Dässler, H-G., *Pharm. Zentralhalle* **101**, 409 (1962).
35. Jedlinski, Z. and Paprotny, J., *Chem. Anal.* (*Warsaw*) **8**, 765 (1963).
36. Takeuchi, T., Tanaka, T. and Furusawa, M., *Kogyo Kagaku Zasshi* **66**, 1656 (1963).

63. Manganate

This reagent appears rarely to have been used in organic analysis. Four references are given here, in which chiefly carboxylic acids are determined by oxidation with it:

Examples

Materials titrated	Reagent and reaction conditions	Subsequent treatment and final titration stage	Ref.
Formic acid in presence of oxalic and acetic acids	+ alkali + MnO_4^{2-} + H_2TeO_4; 1 h/60°	Unused reagent back titrated with arsenite	1
formic acid in absence of oxalic acid	+ alkali + MnO_4^{2-}; 45–90 min/60°	+ I^- + H_2SO_4 and the liberated iodine titrated with thiosulphate	
formic + oxalic acids	+ alkali + MnO_4^{2-}; 25 min/60°; then + MnO_4^- and heated 5–10 min longer	+ H_2SO_4 (oxalic acid then oxidized) + I^- and titrated with thiosulphate	
Carboxylic acids (e.g. lactic, malic, glycollic, pyruvic); sugars; methanol; polyalcohols; formaldehyde (tartaric, maleic and fumaric acids gave results *ca* 3% low)	In 1–3M KOH, + MnO_4^{2-}; 1–4·5 h/60°	Cooled, + H_2SO_4, left 15 min (to oxidize, e.g. oxalic acid), then + I^- and titrated with thiosulphate	2
Oxidation products from determination of tartaric, maleic and fumaric acids by treatment with MnO_4^-/H_2SO_4	Made alkaline with KOH, weighed amount K_2MnO_4 added, + KOH to bring to desired alkali concentration; 2·5 h/60°, oxidizing to CO_2 + H_2O	+ I^- + H_2SO_4 and titrated with thiosulphate	3
Formic acid	+ alkali + MnO_4^{2-}; 1 h/60°	Back titrated photometrically with As(III)	4

References

1. Polak, H. L., *Z. anal. Chem.* **176**, 34 (1960).
2. Polak, H. L., Pronk, H. F. and den Boef, G., *Z. anal. Chem.* **189**, 411 (1962).
3. Polak, H. L., Pronk, H. F. and den Boef, G., *Z. anal. Chem.* **190**, 377 (1962).
4. Polak, H. L., den Boef, G. and de Galan, L., *Z. Anal. Chem.* **198**, 321 (1963).

64. Manganese (III)

Oxalic acid has been determined by oxidation with Mn(III) and two references are given here. In each case, unused reagent was determined by titration with Fe(II).

Examples

Materials titrated	Reagent and reaction conditions	Subsequent treatment and final titration stage	Ref.
Oxalic acid; also malonic, tartaric, citric and salicylic acids	+ Mn(III) pyrophosphate + H_2SO_4; 15 min/100°. Oxalic acid oxidized to CO_2 + water; the others only partly oxidized but reproducibly	+ excess Fe(II) and finally titrated with standard Mn(III) to diphenylamine	1
Oxalic acid	Electrolytically generated Mn(III) from $MnSO_4/Fe_2(SO_4)_3/H_2SO_4$	Excess reagent coulometrically back titrated with Fe(II) by reversing the electrode polarity	2

References

1. Ishibashi, M., Shigematsu, T. and Shibata, S., *Bunseki Kagaku* (*Japan Analyst*) **8**, 380 (1959).
2. Suzuki, S., *Kogyo Kagaku Zasshi* (*J. Chem. Soc., Japan, Ind. Chem. Sect.*) **64**, 2116 (1961).

65. Manganese (IV)

The usual manganese (IV) reagent has been a suspension of MnO_2 (in one case, zinc manganite was used). It has served as an oxidizing agent, based on the reaction in acid solution:

$$MnO_2 + 4\,H^+ + 2\,\epsilon \rightarrow Mn^{2+} + 2\,H_2O$$

Lactic acid, for example, is oxidized to acetaldehyde:

$$CH_3CHOH.COOH + MnO_2 + 2\,H^+ \rightarrow CH_3CHO + CO_2 + 2\,H_2O + Mn^{2+}$$

This is the chief example of the use of MnO_2 in indirect titration of organic compounds, the acetaldehyde being distilled out and determined with bisulphite. This procedure has been an alternative to the better-known method with permanganate as oxidizing agent.

As seen in the examples below, other carboxylic acids and an organic arsenic compound have also been determined with help of the Mn(IV) reagent.

Examples

Materials titrated	Reagent and reaction conditions	Subsequent treatment and final titration stage	Ref.
Lactic acid	+ phosphoric acid + colloidal MnO_2 + $MnSO_4$ catalyst; 20 min heating	Acetaldehyde distilled into bisulphite and the combined part determined (see Bisulphite and sulphite, ref. 32)	1
Lactic acid	Method of ref. 1	(See Bisulphite and sulphite, ref. 43)	2
Cacodylates	+ MnO_2/H_2SO_4, evidently oxidizing to inorganic arsenic	Arsenic precipitated with HCl/ NaH_2PO_2, dissolved in excess iodine and back titrated with thiosulphate	3
Lactic acid in blood	+ H_2SO_4 + suspension of MnO_2; 20 min heating	Acetaldehyde distilled out and determined with bisulphite	4
Citric acid	+ bromide/bromate/ H_2SO_4 + MnO_2 suspension. At least 3 h/0°, giving pentabromoacetone	Unused bromine and MnO_2 removed with hydrazine and pentabromoacetone determined by reaction with $NaHSO_3$ giving Br^-, then titrated with Ag(I) (see Bisulphite and sulphite, ref. 72)	5

Materials titrated	Reagent and reaction conditions	Subsequent treatment and final titration stage	Ref.
Lactic acid	+ H_2SO_4 + MnO_2 + $MnSO_4$ catalyst	Acetaldehyde distilled out and determined with $NaHSO_3$	6
Mandelic acid in human bile	Extract, + H_2SO_4 + Mn(IV) reagent (Zn manganite); added slowly, oxidizing to benzaldehyde	Aldehyde steam distilled continuously into excess bisulphite, unused titrated with iodine, excess iodine added, then phosphate buffer pH 8 and back titrated with thiosulphate	7

References

1. Friedemann, T. E. and Kendall, A. I., *J. Biol. Chem.* **82**, 23 (1929).
2. Mawson, C. A. and Ritchie, A. D., *Biochem. J.* **26**, 615 (1932).
3. Babich, S., *Khim. Farm. Prom.* No. 5, 27 (1934).
4. Lauersen, F. and Wahlländer, H., *Biochem. Z.* **298**, 273 (1938).
5. Goldberg, A. S. and Bernheim, A. R., *J. Biol. Chem.* **156**, 33 (1944).
6. Lang, K. and Pfleger, K., *Mikrochemie* **36/7**, 1174 (1951).
7. Bister, F. and Wolff, J. H., *Arzneimittelforsch.* **2**, 423 (1952).

66. Mercaptans

Reagent. Dodecylmercaptan, $C_{12}H_{25}SH$, has been the most used reagent Others which have found occasional use are thioglycollate and thiophenols.

Reactions and materials titrated. 1. Addition to double bonds or epoxides, of which the determination of acrylonitrile is the most frequently encountered example:

$$CH_2{=}CH.CN + RSH \rightarrow RS.CH_2CH_2.CN$$

$$\underset{\diagdown O \diagup}{RCH{-}CHR} + R'SH \rightarrow \underset{OH\quad SR'}{RCH{-}CHR}$$

2. Reduction, in determination of peroxides and evidently of thiuram disulphides:

$$2\,RSH + R'CO.O.O.COR' \rightarrow 2\,R'COOH + RS.SR$$

$$2\,RSH + R_2'N.CS.S.S.CS.NR_2' \rightarrow 2\,R_2'NCS.SH + RS.SR$$

3. Halogen replacement in a determination of chloroacetate:

$$ClCH_2.COO^- + RS^- \rightarrow RS.CH_2COO^- + Cl^-$$

4. Fission of S—S links in determination of thiolsulphonates:

$$RSO_2.S.R' + R''SH \rightarrow RSO_2H + R'S.SR''$$

(The determination of thiuram disulphides, mentioned under 2, could also be considered as based on S—S fission.)

Reaction conditions. The addition reactions require an alkaline catalyst, usually KOH.

Reaction times have been in general short (up to *ca* 20 min).

Subsequent treatment and final titration stage. (i) In almost all cases, unreacted mercaptan has been back titrated using one of several methods:

1. With iodine or bromate in acid solution.
2. With Ag(I) reagent, potentiometrically or amperometrically.
3. With alkali in the case of a thiophenol reagent.
4. With Hg(II) to thiofluorescein indicator.

(ii) In one case, a sulphinic acid reaction product (from reaction type 4 above) was titrated with NaOH.

Examples

Materials titrated	Reagent and reaction conditions	Subsequent treatment and final titration stage	Ref.
Divinylacetylene	+ thio-*p*-cresol	Back titrated with alkali in alcoholic solution	1
Na monochloro-acetate	+ thioglycollic acid/ $NaOH/Na_2CO_3$. Boiled 1 min	+ HCl and back titrated with iodine (see Part I, Iodine, ref. 61)	2
Acrylonitrile; some α,β-unsaturated carbonyl compounds like acrylates, methacrylates, crotonates and maleates	+ dodecyl- or n-hexyl-mercaptan/ethanol or isopropanol, + alkali catalyst (KOH or tri-methylbenzylammonium hydroxide); 2–30 min/room temp.	+ acetic acid and titrated with iodine to yellow; with smaller amounts, + acetic acid + NH_4OH and titrated with $AgNO_3$ amperometrically (see Part I, Iodine, ref. 62; and Silver (I), ref. 38)	3

Materials titrated	Reagent and reaction conditions	Subsequent treatment and final titration stage	Ref.
Acrylonitrile; 1-cyano-1,3-butadiene	+ dodecylmercaptan/ dioxan or isopropanol, + KOH/isopropanol; 2 min	+ HCl + isopropanol and titrated unused mercaptan with BrO_3^-	4
Acrylonitrile in coloured solutions	+ dodecylmercaptan + basic catalyst	+ acetic acid/isopropanol and titrated with $AgNO_3$/ethanol/ isopropanol potentiometrically (see Part I, Silver (I), ref. 68)	5
Tetramethylthiuram disulphide	+ dodecylmercaptan, giving dithiocarbamate	Back titrated with iodine (see Part I, Iodine, ref. 73)	6
Thiolsulphonates, $RSO_2.SR'$	In neutral solution, + thiophenol/ethanol, giving sulphinic acid, RSO_2H	Titrated with NaOH to bromophenol blue	7
Ethylene, propylene and other epoxides	+ dodecylmercaptan/ ethanol or isopropanol, + KOH/alcohol catalyst; 20 min/room temp.	+ acetic acid + isopropanol and titrated immediately with iodine to yellow persisting for 30 sec (see Part I, Iodine, ref. 116)	8
Acrylonitrile	In methanol, + thio-glycollate; 30 sec–2 min reflux	+ NH_4OH + NH_4Cl + Na_2SO_3 and titrated with Hg(II) acetate to thio-fluorescein	9
methyl acrylate	as for acrylonitrile but NH_4OH added already with the thioglycollate and left 10 min/room temp.		
Lipide peroxides; lauroyl peroxide; *t*-butyl hydroperoxide	+ ethanol/acetic acid/ $CHCl_3$, 5:3:2, + octyl thioglycollate (dissolves lipides) + drops KI solution	Titrated with iodine to permanent yellow	10
Acrylonitrile	Modification of the method of ref. 3		11

References

1. Masuo, F. and Hattori, S., *J. Chem. Soc. Japan* **47**, 302 (1944).
2. Frenkiel, J. and Rombau, P., *Chim. anal.* **30**, 60 (1948).
3. Beesing, D. W., Tyler, W. P., Kurtz, D. M. and Harrison, S. A., *Anal. Chem.* **21**, 1073 (1949).

4. de Maldé, M., *Ann. chim. (Rome)* **42**, 437 (1952).
5. Janz, G. J. and Duncan, N. E., *Anal. Chem.* **25**, 1410 (1953).
6. Scheele, W. and Gemsch, C., *Kautschuk u. Gummi* **7**, WT 122 (1954).
7. Barnard, D. and Cole, E. R., *Anal. Chim. Acta* **20**, 540 (1959).
8. Gudzinowicz, B. J., *Anal. Chem.* **32**, 1520 (1960).
9. Wroński, M., *Chem. Anal. (Warsaw)* **5**, 823 (1960).
10. Dahle, L. K. and Holman, R. T., *Anal. Chem.* **33**, 1960 (1961).
11. Majewska, J. and Urbanowicz, S., *Chem. Anal. (Warsaw)* **6**, 841 (1961).

67. Mercury (I)

Three examples are given below of the titrimetric determination of carboxylic acids by precipitation of their mercurous salts from aqueous solution:

$$RCOO^- + Hg^+ \rightarrow RCOOHg$$

Examples

Materials titrated	Reagent and reaction conditions	Subsequent treatment and final titration stage	Ref.
Fumaric acid	In hot HNO_3 solution, + $HgNO_3$; 2–4 h/*ca* 0°	Centrifuged, precipitated salt oxidized with MnO_4^- to Hg(II), excess removed with H_2O_2 and Hg(II) finally titrated with SCN^- to Fe(III) indicator	1
Fumaric acid from determination of malic acid in green tobacco leaves by heating with NaOH	+ $HgNO_3$	Precipitate oxidized to Hg(II) and titrated with SCN^-	2
Aconitic acid in presence of itaconic acid	+ saturated $HgNO_3$ solution giving precipitate of mercurous aconitate	Precipitate added to H_2SO_4/HNO_3 (to oxidize Hg(I) to Hg(II)) and the aconitic acid titrated with MnO_4^- (see Part I, Permanganate, ref. 35)	3

References

1. Stotz, E., *J. Biol. Chem.* **118**, 471 (1937).
2. Pyatnitskii, M. P. and Yur'eva, A. F., *Biokhimiya* **14**, 196 (1949).
3. Lauer, K. and Makar, S. M., *Anal. Chem.* **23**, 587 (1951).

68. Mercury (II)

Reagent. Includes inorganic mercury compounds such as the chloride, cyanide, nitrate, perchlorate, hydroxycyanide, aminochloride or ethylenediamine tetraacetate; and organic mercury compounds like phenyl mercuric acetate, acetate and *o*-hydroxymercuribenzoate. The reagent Hg(II)/excess I^- (so-called Nessler and Mayer/Valzer reagents) contain the effective reagent HgI_4^{2-}; Hg(II)/SCN^- reagents contain $Hg(SCN)_4^{2-}$.

Reactions and materials titrated. Many different types of reaction are encountered and an attempt at classification is given here:

1. Oxidation, with formation of Hg(I) and/or Hg metal; this comprises about one-half of the examples of use of mercuric reagents, and some of the materials oxidized have been: aldehydes, including sugars and formic acid; ascorbic acid; ketoalcohols; polyphenols; sodium formaldehyde sulphoxylate; anethole; and hydrazines. It is often not wholly clear whether Hg(I), Hg metal or a mixture is formed but where the determination is concluded via the oxidation product from the organic compound (e.g. CO_2 from formic acid) or by titration back to Hg(II), this is immaterial.

2. Addition to olefinic groups and also, in a few instances, to acetylene and cyclopropane groups. These additions have been carried out with mercuric acetate and acetic acid is set free during the reaction:

$$-\overset{|}{C}=\overset{|}{C}- + Hg(OOCCH_3)_2 + H_2O \rightarrow -\overset{|}{\underset{HO}{C}}-\overset{|}{\underset{HgOOCCH_3}{C}}- + CH_3COOH$$

$$-\overset{|}{C}=\overset{|}{C}- + Hg(OOCCH_3)_2 + CH_3OH \rightarrow -\overset{|}{\underset{CH_3O}{C}}-\overset{|}{\underset{HgOOCCH_3}{C}}- + CH_3COOH$$

$$-C\equiv C- + 2\,Hg(OOCCH_3)_2 + H_2O \rightarrow -CO-C(-HgOOCCH_3)_2- + 2\,CH_3COOH$$

$$RCONHCH\left\langle\begin{matrix}CH_2\\ |\\ CH_2\end{matrix}\right. + Hg(OOCCH_3)_2 + CH_3OH \rightarrow RCONHCH\begin{matrix}\diagup OCH_3\\ \\ |\\ CH_2CH_2HgOOCCH_3\end{matrix} + CH_3COOH$$

$$CH_2{=}CH{-}CH_2OH + Hg^{2+} + H_2O \rightarrow Hg^{+}{-}CH_2{-}CHOH{-}CH_2OH + H^{+}$$

Olefines thus determined have included styrene, dehydrogenated dichloroethylbenzene, rotenone, acenaphthylene, vinyl ethers, allyl compounds and methacrylic esters. It is noteworthy that the addition method for acetylenes is the only available chemical method for di-substituted acetylene compounds apart from hydrogenation and the unreliable halogen addition.

3. A number of reactions leading to precipitation of a mercury-containing derivative in which the Hg atom may be joined to C, O, S or N or may be part of the complex HgI_4^{2-} anion. Such reactions include:

(i) Hydrogen replacement, as with mercaptans, acetylenes, amidines, barbiturates, sodium saccharine and some salts of carboxylic acids like fumaric, benzoic and salicylic. E.g.

$$2\,RSH + HgX_2 \rightarrow Hg(RS)_2 + 2\,HX \text{ or}$$

$$RSH + HgCl_2 \rightarrow RSHgCl + HCl$$

$$C_2H_2 + HgX_2 \rightarrow HgC_2 + 2\,HX$$

$$\underset{\displaystyle NH_2}{\underset{|}{RC{=}NH}} + Hg(OOCCH_3)_2 \rightarrow \underset{\displaystyle NH_2}{\underset{|}{RC{=}N{-}HgOOCCH_3}} + CH_3COOH$$

(ii) Ion/ion combination, e.g. between cations of alkaloids or other bases and reagents containing HgI_4^{2-} or other complex mercury anions. Morphine, for example (ref. 32) yields a product of formula $HgI_2.C_{17}H_{19}NO_2.HI$ (presumably $(C_{17}H_{20}NO_2)^{+}HgI_3^{-}$).

(iii) 'Complex' formation, e.g. with proteins, some olefines, thiophene and notably with acetone. The composition of these complexes tends to vary with the reaction conditions. Thus with the last-mentioned example, acetone, the following formulae have been quoted for the precipitate yielded with a $HgSO_4/H_2SO_4$ reagent and expressed as mols acetone/mols $HgSO_4$/mols HgO: 4/6/9 (ref. 7); 2/3/5 (ref. 9); 1/2/3 and 3/5/5 (from Beilstein, Band I, page 646); in another publication (ref. 39), a product containing 28% acetone was obtained, corresponding exactly to none of these formulae.

The border line between reactions of these three types is difficult to draw. Thus alkaloids and other bases appear also under certain conditions to yield products which are more complex than expected from a simple ion/ion combination.

(iv) The formation of HgS from some sulphur-containing materials like cellulose xanthates or thiourea, can be classified here.

4. One or two miscellaneous reactions which cannot be classified above, may be mentioned:

(i) Reaction with $HgCl_2$ of tetraphenylborates or triphenylcyano-borates, in the determination of these complex anions. This is a type of hydrolysis:

$$(C_6H_5)_4B^- + 4\ HgCl_2 + 3\ H_2O \rightarrow 4\ C_6H_5HgCl + H_3BO_3 + 3\ H^+ + 4\ Cl^-$$

$$(C_6H_5)_3(CN)B^- + 3\ HgCl_2 + 3\ H_2O \rightarrow$$
$$3\ C_6H_5HgCl + H_3BO_3 + HCN + 2\ H^+ + 3\ Cl^-$$

(ii) Reaction of Hg(OH)CN with alkylpyridinium iodides (strictly speaking, this is an inorganic reaction but is included here on account of the organic cation involved):

$$I^- + Hg(OH)CN \rightarrow Hg(I)CN + OH^-$$

No mention is made here of the use of Hg acetate to remove hydro-halic acid or to block —SH groups in the titration with $HClO_4$ of base hydrohalides or mercapto bases in acetic acid solvent. (See Part I, Perchloric acid.)

Reaction conditions. The wide variety of reactions means that few general remarks can be made about reaction conditions. Broadly speaking, reactions of oxidation, type 1, have been carried out at higher temperatures, often in boiling solution. On the other hand, the pre-cipitation reactions, type 3, have mostly been conducted at room temp-erature. The reaction conditions for 'complex' formation, i.e. type 3 (iii) have been empirically established and strictly observed so that the variation of composition mentioned above did not interfere.

Subsequent treatment and final titration stage. This is characterized by an exceptional diversity of methods:

(a) Determination of Hg(I) and/or Hg from oxidation reactions of type 1 above. This has been performed in several ways:

1. Excess iodine added and back titrated with thiosulphate.
2. Excess bromine added and back titrated with arsenite.

3. Directly titrated with permanganate.
4. Directly titrated with iodate.
5. Directly titrated with chloramine T.
6. Oxidized to Hg(II) with permanganate and then titrated with thiocyanate.

(b) Determination of Hg(II), either unused (then usually after filtration of a precipitated mercury salt or derivative) or from solution in acid of such a precipitate. As under (a), many techniques have been used, including:

1. Titration with thiocyanate to Fe(III) indicator.
2. Reverse titration into standard iodide solution, to end-point of first pink of HgI_2.
3. Titration with NaCl to diappearance of turbidity with nitroprusside indicator.
4. Addition of excess cyanide and back titration with Ag(I).
5. Titration with mercaptans, e.g. cysteine (potentiometrically or to nitroprusside indicator) or thioglycollic acid (to thiofluorescein indicator); or back titration with excess Na_2S, concluding by titrating the unreacted sulphide with *o*-hydroxymercuribenzoate to thiofluorescein or dithizone.
6. Complexometric determination using EDTA. For example: direct titration with EDTA; addition of excess and back titration with Zn(II), Mg(II) or sodium diethyl dithiocarbamate; addition of Zn/EDTA or Mg/EDTA and titration of the liberated Zn(II) or Mg(II) with EDTA.
7. Potentiometric titration with $HgCl_2$ of unused HgI_4^{2-} from alkaloid precipitation can be included here.

In addition to these two general principles of conclusion, a large number of further methods has been described. Most of these are classified here under two further headings, (c) and (d) below:

(c) Determination of reaction products other than the Hg(I) or Hg metal from oxidation reactions and other than the Hg(II) from precipitated organic complexes or derivatives. Some of these reaction products were separated from the reaction mixture as gas or precipitates; others were determined directly in the solution. Some examples are:

1. CO_2 from oxidation of formate, led into excess alkali reagent which was back titrated with acid.
2. HgO in the precipitated complex from determination of *tert*-butanol, filtered, dissolved in excess acid and back titrated with alkali.

3. HgS from determination of thiourea where the S^{2-} was determined by bromine oxidation and titration of unused bromine or of the HBr formed.

Examples of determinations in situ are:

4. Alkali titration of acid formed from reactions of formate, mercaptans and tetraphenylborate:

$$HCOOH + 2\,HgCl_2 \rightarrow CO_2 + 2\,HgCl + 2\,HCl$$

$$RSH + HgCl_2 \rightarrow RSHgCl + HCl$$

$$(C_6H_5)_4B^- + 4\,HgCl_2 + 3\,H_2O \rightarrow 4\,C_6H_5HgCl + H_3BO_3 + 3\,H^+ + 4\,Cl^-$$

(and triphenylcyanoborate)

5. Titration with Ag(I) of cyanide ion liberated from oxidation of sugars with $Hg(CN)_2$ reagent:

$$Hg(CN)_2 + 2\,OH^- \rightarrow Hg + H_2O + O + 2\,CN^-$$

6. Titration of acetic acid liberated from additions of mercuric acetate to unsaturated and ring compounds (see above under Reactions section 2).
7. Titration of hydroxyl ion set free from reaction of alkylpyridinium iodide with Hg(OH)CN and from antipyrine with $Hg(Cl)NH_2$.
8. Titration with Pb(II) of EDTA liberated from a Hg(II)/EDTA reagent with aldehydes and hydrazines.

(d) Back titration of the unused part of other components of the Hg(II) reagent Some examples are:

1. Iodide, in the determination of bases like morphine or vitamin B_1 which take part in reactions similar to

$$2\,(Base.H^+) + Hg^{2+} + 4\,I^- \rightarrow (Base.H^+)_2HgI_4 \text{ precipitate.}$$

The iodide was determined by addition of iodate/acid and titration of the liberated iodine with thiosulphate; or by oxidation with bromate to iodate, followed by addition of iodide/acid and titration with thiosulphate as above.

2. Acid, in the determination of alkaloids by a precipitation procedure similar to that just mentioned:

$$2\,Base + 2\,H^+ + HgI_4^{2-} \rightarrow (Base.H^+)_2HgI_4 \text{ precipitate.}$$

3. Alkali, in the determination of aldehydes or of mono-substituted acetylenes:

$$RCHO + Hg^{2+} + 2\,OH^- \rightarrow RCOOH + Hg + H_2O$$

$$2\,RC{\equiv}CH + HgI_4^{2-} + 2\,OH^- \rightarrow (RC{\equiv}C{-})_2Hg + 4\,I^- + 2\,H_2O$$

These acid and alkali titrations were carried out in the usual way.

4. Acetate, in the determination of mercaptans or unsaturated compounds:

$$2\,RSH + Hg^{2+} + 2\,CH_3COO^- \rightarrow (RS{-})_2Hg + 2\,CH_3COOH$$

$$-C{=}C- + Hg^{2+} + 2\,CH_3COO^- + CH_3OH \rightarrow -\underset{\underset{CH_3O}{|}}{C}-\underset{\underset{HgOOCCH_3}{|}}{C}- + CH_3COOH$$

The acetate was titrated in non-aqueous medium like an alcohol or glycol, using HCl titrant and indicators like thymol blue.

(e) Two other procedures of analysis completion which cannot be classified above are: titration with alkali of residual acids after oxidation of formic acid to CO_2 with Hg(II), so that the formic acid amount is given by difference from a previous titration of total acid; and determination of acetone with alkali/excess iodine, after its regeneration from a precipitated Hg(II) complex by dissolving in acid. This second example is essentially one of separation of the component to be determined.

Examples

Materials titrated	Reagent and reaction conditions	Subsequent treatment and final titration stage	Ref.
Sugar	+ $Hg(CN)_2$ + NaOH, giving Hg + CN^-; $Hg(CN)_2 + 2\,OH^- \rightarrow Hg + 2\,CN^- + H_2O + O$	CN^- titrated with Ag(I)	1
Formic acid	+ $HgCl_2$ + Na acetate; 1–1·5 h/100°	Filtered and titrated unused $HgCl_2$ with I^- (reverse titration to first pink of HgI_2)	2
HCHO in air	Passed through $HgCl_2$/I^-/alkali, giving Hg	Hg determined by adding excess iodine, acidifying and back titrating with thiosulphate	3
HCHO	+ $HgCl_2$/I^-/alkali, giving Hg	Hg determined by adding excess iodine, acidifying with HCl and back titrating with thiosulphate	4

Materials titrated	Reagent and reaction conditions	Subsequent treatment and final titration stage	Ref.
Sugars	+ $Hg(CN)_2$ + NaOH. Heated to boiling, giving Hg	Hg dissolved in HNO_3 and Hg(II) formed titrated with SCN^- to Fe(III) indicator	5
Formic acid	+ excess $HgCl_2$ + Na acetate; 15 min boiling, giving Hg and HgCl	Filtered, excess CN^- added to filtrate and back titrated with Ag(I) to turbidity with I^- indicator	6
Acetone in urine	+ $HgSO_4/H_2SO_4$; 15 min reflux, giving precipitate of complex formulated as $4(CH_3)_2CO.6HgSO_4.9HgO$	Filtered, precipitate acidified with H_2SO_4, acetone distilled and determined with alkali/ excess iodine (see Iodine reagents, ref. 29)	7
Formates, e.g. in urine	+ $HgCl_2$; 6 h/*ca* 100°, giving Hg + HgCl	Precipitate dissolved in excess iodine and back titrated with thiosulphate	8, 17
Acetone + acetoacetic acid in urine	+ $HgSO_4/H_2SO_4$; 30–45 min boiling, giving precipitate of complex formulated as $2(CH_3)_2CO.3HgSO_4.5HgO$	Precipitate dissolved in HCl, Na acetate + excess I^- added and back titrated with $HgCl_2$ to red turbidity	9
acetone + acetoacetic acid + β-hydroxy-butyric acid	+ $HgSO_4/H_2SO_4$; $Cr_2O_7^{2-}$ added to boiling solution and boiled 90 min, giving precipitate as above but with $HgSO_4$ partly replaced by $HgCrO_4$	precipitate dissolved in HCl, Na acetate + excess I^- added and back titrated with $HgCl_2$ to red turbidity	
Thiophene in commercial benzene	+ methanol + $HgSO_4/H_2SO_4$; 30 min, giving complex $C_4H_4SHg.(HgO)_2SO_4$ as precipitate	Filtered and unused Hg(II) titrated with SCN^- to Fe(III)	10
Acetaldehyde in paraldehyde	+ $HgCl_2/I^-/NaOH$; 15 min shaking, giving Hg	Filtered, dissolved in excess iodine and unused titrated with thiosulphate	11
Aldehydes, e.g. HCHO, benzaldehyde	+ $HgCl_2/I^-/NaOH$. Not less than 15 min reaction, giving Hg	+ excess iodine + HCl and back titrated with thiosulphate	12, 20

Materials titrated	Reagent and reaction conditions	Subsequent treatment and final titration stage	Ref.
Formic acid	Neutralized solution + $HgCl_2$ + excess $Ba(OH)_2$; 1 h boiling, yielding HgCl + HCl	Unneutralized $Ba(OH)_2$ titrated with HCl to phenolphthalein	13
Acetone	+ $HgSO_4/H_2SO_4$; 20 min boiling, giving insoluble complex	Filtered, dissolved in HNO_3/H_2SO_4, and titrated with NaCl to disappearance of turbidity with nitroprusside indicator	14, 22, 25
Alkaloids	+ $HgCl_2$ + I^-; 5 min/room temp. giving insoluble complex	Dissolved in HNO_3/H_2SO_4 and Hg(II) titrated as in ref. 14	15,22 25, 27
Allantoin	+ $HgCl_2/I^-/NaOH$; 12 h/room temp., giving Hg	Hg determined iodometrically as in method of ref. 12	16
Formic acid	+ $HgCl_2$	+ excess iodine and back titrated with thiosulphate	17
Formic acid	Heated with $HgCl_2$ giving HgCl precipitate	Precipitate + excess iodine and back titrated with thiosulphate	18
Formic acid in blood or urine	+ $HgCl_2$; 2 h/100°, giving HgCl	+ HCl + excess iodine and back titrated with thiosulphate	19
Acetone	+ $HgCl_2/I^-/alkali$; 20 min/room temp., giving insoluble complex	Precipitate dissolved in HCl and acetone determined with alkali/excess iodine (see Iodine reagents, ref. 82)	21
Glucose (micro)	Heated with HgI_2/I^- reagent, giving Hg	+ excess iodine and back titrated with thiosulphate	23
Formic acid in acetic acid	+ $HgCl_2$ + Na acetate; 45 min/100°	Unused $HgCl_2$ removed with I^-; + excess iodine and back titrated with thiosulphate	24
Formates	+ $HgCl_2$ + Na acetate; 2 h/100°	Precipitate dissolved in HCl, oxidized with excess bromine reagent and back titrated with arsenite to indigo carmine/styphnic acid	26

Materials titrated	Reagent and reaction conditions	Subsequent treatment and final titration stage	Ref.
Glycol, hexols	+ $HgCl_2/I^-/NaOH/$ $BaSO_4$ suspension; 45 min/100°	+ H_2SO_4 + excess iodine ($BaSO_4$ helps solution of the Hg) and back titrated with thiosulphate	28
Reducing sugars	Method of ref. 23, with addition of $BaSO_4$ for the reason given in the method of ref. 28		29, 30
Formic acid in acetic acid	Neutralized solution + $HgCl_2$ + Na acetate; 15 min boiling	Filtered and HCl liberated titrated with NaOH to phenolphthalein	31
Morphine	+ HgI_4^{2-} reagent; 5 min/room temp., giving precipitated complex	Filtered, HNO_3 added and unused HgI_4^{2-} titrated potentiometrically with $HgCl_2$	32
Alkaloids, e.g. codeine, brucine, cocaine, strychnine, narcotine, quinine, etc.	Method of ref. 32		33
Reducing sugars, e.g. glucose in urine or lactose in milk	Method of ref. 29		34
Citric acid	+ $HgSO_4/H_2SO_4$; 10 min/100°	Precipitate dissolved in acid and titrated with NaCl to disappearance of turbidity with nitroprusside indicator, as in method of ref. 14	35
arrhenal; Na salt	heated with $HgCl_2$ or $Hg(NO_3)_2$, giving precipitate	precipitate dissolved and titrated with NaCl as in method of ref. 14	
Sugars, e.g. in blood	Heated with $HgI_2/I^-/$ NaOH giving Hg; 3 min/100°	Dissolved in HNO_3/H_2SO_4, oxidized with MnO_4^- and titrated with NaCl as in method of ref. 14	36
Glucose in blood	+ $HgCl_2/I^-/NaOH$; 5 min/100°	Unused HgI_4^{2-} determined as in method of ref. 32	37
Alkaloids, e.g. atropine, hyoscamine, pilocarpine, cinchonine, sparteine	Method of ref. 32		38

Materials titrated	Reagent and reaction conditions	Subsequent treatment and final titration stage	Ref.
Acetone	+ $HgSO_4/H_2SO_4$; 10 min/boiling water bath, giving precipitate of complex containing 28% acetone	Filtered and Hg(II) in filtrate titrated with SCN^- to Fe(III)	39
Reducing power of urine	Method of ref. 23; found that concentrations of reagent and alkali and reaction time all influenced the result		40
Sparteine, novocaine	Method of ref. 15		41
Salicylates, benzoates, citrates	+ $Hg(NO_3)_2/HNO_3$	Precipitate dissolved in acid and titrated with NaCl as in method of ref. 14	42
Pyramidone	+ $HgCl_2$, giving insoluble complex (pyramidone).2 $HgCl_2$	Unused Hg(II) determined by method of ref. 6	43
Alkaloids and other bases, e.g. stovaine, novocaine, pyramidone, antipyrine, cincophene	Method of ref. 32		44
Alkaloids, aldehydes, reducing sugars	Method of ref. 32		45
Formic acid in acetic acid	Slight modification of method of ref. 31		46
Alkaloids, e.g. eserine, strychnine, geneserine	Method of ref. 15		47
HCHO in methylol derivatives of amides and ureas	+ $HgCl_2/I^-$/alkali; 10 min/100°	+ HCl + excess iodine and back titrated with thiosulphate	48, 52
Barbital	Method of ref. 25		49
Mercaptans in benzene	+ $HgCl_2$/water; 3 min shaking, giving reaction, $RSH + HgCl_2 \rightarrow RS.HgCl + HCl$	Titrated aqueous layer with NaOH to methyl red or orange	50
Thymol	+ Hg acetate/acetic acid. Heated to 100°, giving dimercuri derivative	Filtered and unused Hg(II) titrated with SCN^-	51

Materials titrated	Reagent and reaction conditions	Subsequent treatment and final titration stage	Ref.
Formic acid in mixtures with acetic and propionic acids	+ HgO; 20 min boiling; then H_3PO_4 added and 15 min further boiling; acid oxidized to CO_2	CO_2 aspirated into excess NaOH, $BaCl_2$ added and titrated with HCl to phenolphthalein	53
Acetaldehyde from determination of lactic acid by oxidation with MnO_4^-	+ $HgCl_2/I^-$/alkali	Acidified with HCl, excess iodine added and back titrated with thiosulphate	54
Volatile aldehydes in blood	Distilled into $HgCl_2/I^-$/alkali reagent, giving Hg	Determined by adding excess iodine and back titrating with thiosulphate	55
HCHO in presence of sulphite	+ $HgCl_2$ + NaOH; 15 min/room temp.	Filtered and unused Hg(II) determined with CN^-/Ag(I) titration as in method of ref. 6	56
HCHO from determination of hexamine by acid hydrolysis	+ $HgCl_2/I^-$/KOH/gum arabic; 6 min stirring	+ acetic acid + excess iodine and back titrated with thiosulphate	57
Alkaloids	+ HgI_2/I^- reagent	Filtered and unused Hg(II) titrated with SCN^-; or unused I^- determined by adding IO_3^-/H_2SO_4 and titrating the iodine with thiosulphate	58
Sugars, e.g. in urine	+ $HgCl_2/I^-$/NaOH. Heated to boiling point; glucose + fructose oxidized with 5 oxygen atoms; with Na_2CO_3 in reagent, only glucose oxidized, with 2 oxygen atoms	+ excess iodine and back titrated with thiosulphate	59
Galactose	Method of ref. 28		60
Mercaptobenzothiazole; also from determination of dibenzothiazole disulphide by reduction	In water, + $HgCl_2/I^-$/NaOH; 6 min/room temp., giving insoluble Hg derivative	+ acetic acid + excess iodine and back titrated with thiosulphate	61
Ascorbic acid	+ $HgCl_2$, giving HgCl + HCl	Titrated with alkali to phenol red or thymol blue	62

Materials titrated	Reagent and reaction conditions	Subsequent treatment and final titration stage	Ref.
α-Ketoalcohols, e.g. acetoin	In methanol, + $HgCl_2$/I^-/NaOH/$BaSO_4$. Not less than 15 min/room temp., giving Hg + HgCl	+ HCl + excess iodine and back titrated with thiosulphate	63
Sugars; furfuraldehyde	+ $HgCl_2$/I^-/Na_2CO_3. Boiled, giving Hg	+ excess iodine and back titrated with thiosulphate	64
Acetylene in liquid air	Absorbed in HgI_2/I^-/KOH, giving Hg acetylide	Dissolved in HNO_3 and Hg(II) titrated with SCN^-	65
Formic acid in pyroligneous liquor	+ Hg acetate. *Ca* 20 min circulation in closed system, giving CO_2	Absorbed in excess $Ba(OH)_2$ and back titrated with HCl to phenolphthalein	66
HCHO in presence of phenol	+ $HgCl_2$/I^-/alkali	+ excess iodine and back titrated with thiosulphate	67
HCHO, pyrogallol, gallic and tannic acids	+ $HgCl_2$/I^-/alkali	+ excess iodine and back titrated with thiosulphate	68
Opium alkaloids	Method of ref. 15		69
tert-Butanol	+ $HgSO_4$/H_2SO_4; 10 min/*ca* 100°, giving complex $C_4H_8.3\,HgSO_4.4\,HgO$	Precipitate dissolved in excess HCl and back titrated with NaOH to methyl red	70
Strychnine	+ HgI_2/I^-, giving insoluble derivative	Unused I^- in filtrate titrated with IO_3^-	71
HCHO in presence of hexamine	+ $HgCl_2$/I^-/alkali	Hg separated by centrifuging, acetic acid + excess iodine added and back titrated with thiosulphate	72
Acetone in urine	+ $HgCl_2$/I^-/alkali	Precipitate dissolved in HCl and acetone determined with alkali/excess iodine (see Iodine reagents, ref. 182)	73
Formic acid	In water, + Hg acetate + acetic acid; 10 min boiling, giving CO_2	Absorbed in NaOH, $BaCl_2$ added and back titrated to phenolphthalein	74

Materials titrated	Reagent and reaction conditions	Subsequent treatment and final titration stage	Ref.
Na formaldehyde sulphoxylate in presence of Na formaldehyde bisulphite	Oxidized with $HgCl_2$ to $HOCH_2.SO_3Na + HgCl$	HgCl filtered and determined with excess iodine and back titration with thiosulphate	75
Morphine	+ dilute H_2SO_4 + HgI_2/I^-, giving insoluble complex	Filtered, I^- in filtrate oxidized with bromine to IO_3^-; excess bromine removed with HCHO/alkali, acetic acid/I^- added and iodine titrated with thiosulphate	76
Alkaloids	In excess H_2SO_4, + HgI_2/I^-; 5 min shaking, then $BaSO_4$ added and 15 min more shaking, giving precipitate of $(Alkaloid).HI.(HgI_2)_x$	Filtered and back titrated filtrate with NaOH	77
Acetone from determination of acetone bodies in blood by oxidation with bichromate	+ bichromate + $HgSO_4/H_2SO_4$, giving precipitate of complex; 90 min reflux	Dissolved in HCl, liberated acetone distilled out and determined with alkali/excess iodine (see Iodine reagents, ref. 193)	78
Ascorbic acid	+ $HgCl_2$/HCl	HgCl formed determined with excess iodine and back titration with thiosulphate	79
Aldehydes from pyrolysis of wood	+ HgI_2/I^-/excess NaOH; 2 h/room temp.	Unused NaOH titrated with HCl to phenolphthalein	80
Acetaldehyde from determination of lactic acid by oxidation with periodate	Method of ref. 12		81
HCHO in presence of nitrite	+ $HgCl_2/I^-$/KOH	Hg filtered, dissolved in HNO_3 and titrated with SCN^-	82
Pyrethrin I	Extract + $HgSO_4/H_2SO_4$; 1 h/room temp., giving Hg(I)	HgCl precipitated with NaCl, unsaturated organic compounds extracted with acetone; precipitate + $HCl/CHCl_3$ and titrated with IO_3^-	83
Formic acid	+ $HgCl_2$	HgCl formed centrifuged, dissolved in iodine and back titrated with thiosulphate	84

Materials titrated	Reagent and reaction conditions	Subsequent treatment and final titration stage	Ref.
Methylpropene	Absorbed in HgO/ HNO_3/NaOH. Heated to *ca* 100°, giving insoluble complex (1 methylpropene ≡ 7 Hg)	Precipitate filtered, dissolved in HNO_3 and Hg(II) titrated with SCN^-	85
Na saccharine	In water, + $Hg(NO_3)_2$, giving insoluble salt	Filtered and Hg(II) in filtrate titrated with SCN^- after acidification with HNO_3	86
Pyrethrin I	Method of ref. 83 but with 15 min reaction		87
Acetone from determination of β-hydroxybutyric acid in blood by bichromate oxidation	Distilled into $HgSO_4$/ H_2SO_4. *Ca* 100 min duration	Precipitate centrifuged, dissolved in I^-/NaOH/excess iodine; after 10 min, + H_2SO_4 and titrated with thiosulphate	88
Mercaptals of some thioacids, RR′C(SR″)(SR‴), e.g. from thioglycollic acid	+ $HgCl_2$/HCl, giving RR′CO + Hg mercaptide; 30–60 min heating	Titrated with iodine	89
Alkaloids	+ $HgCl_2/I^-$, giving mercury complex	Filtered, Na_2CO_3 added to precipitate, alkaloid extracted with $CHCl_3$, aqueous layer acidified and HgI_4^{2-} titrated with Ce(IV)	90
Vitamin B_1	+ HgI_2/I^- + acid, giving insoluble complex	Filtered and I^- in filtrate determined by oxidation to IO_3^- with bromine, addition of I^-/ acid and titration with thiosulphate; or by CN^-/Ag(I) method of ref. 6	91
Alkyl pyridinium iodides from determination of alkoxyl groups by conversion to alkyl iodides with HI and absorption in pyridine	+ Hg(OH)CN, reacting with I^- giving OH^-	Titrated with H_2SO_4	92
Pentamethylene tetrazole ('Leptazole', 'Metrazole')	In phosphate buffer, pH 7·6–8, + $HgCl_2$, giving insoluble complex	Unused $HgCl_2$ determined iodometrically in filtrate	93

Materials titrated	Reagent and reaction conditions	Subsequent treatment and final titration stage	Ref.
Na arsanilate ('Atoxyl')	+ $HgCl_2$, giving insoluble salt	Unused Hg(II) in filtrate determined by reverse titration into I^- as in method of ref. 2	94
Na formate from determination of formic acid by ester formation with methanol/HCl and hydrolysis with NaOH	Method of ref. 17		95
Proteins in organic liquids	+ $HgCl_2/I^-$/acetic acid, giving insoluble products	Filtered, added excess CN^-/NH_4OH and back titrated with Ag(I)	96
HCHO from determination of $Cl.COOCH_2Cl$ by alkali hydrolysis	Method of ref. 12		97
HCHO in presence of ketones	+ $HgCl_2/I^-/NaOH$; 5 min shaking, giving Hg	+ acetic acid + methanol + excess iodine and back titrated with thiosulphate	98
Apomorphine, from determination of morphine by dehydration with H_2SO_4	Neutralized solution + $HgCl_2$ + Na acetate; 1 min boiling	+ H_2SO_4 and Hg(I) titrated with MnO_4^-	99
Styrene	+ Hg acetate/water/dioxan/a little acetic acid; 20 min shaking, giving addition product; $C_6H_5CH{=}CH_2 + Hg(OOCCH_3)_2 + H_2O \rightarrow C_6H_5CH(OH){-}CH_2{-}HgOOCCH_3 + CH_3COOH$	Unused Hg(II) converted to Hg with H_2O_2/NaOH, reaction product dissolved in HNO_3 and titrated with SCN^-	100
HCHO	+ $HgCl_2/I^-$/alkali; 5 min shaking, giving Hg or HgCl	+ acetic acid + excess iodine and back titrated with thiosulphate	101
Up to 6% acetic acid in formic acid	+ HgO; 90 min reflux, oxidizing latter to CO_2	Residual acetic acid titrated potentiometrically with NaOH	102
Theophylline	In water, + Hg acetate, giving insoluble mercury derivative	Filtered and unused Hg(II) in filtrate titrated with SCN^-	103

Materials titrated	Reagent and reaction conditions	Subsequent treatment and final titration stage	Ref.
Anethole	+ Hg acetate/acetic acid; 4–5 h reflux, giving Hg(I) and addition product $CH_3O—C_6H_4—CH(OH)—CH(OH)—CH_3$	+ excess iodine and back titrated with thiosulphate	104
Acetylenes, e.g. 1-hexyne, propargyl alcohol, 3-butyn-1-ol	In methanol, + HgI_2/I^-/methanol + excess NaOH	Unused alkali titrated with H_2SO_4 to phenolphthalein	105
Unsaturation in dehydrogenated dichloroethylbenzene	+ Hg acetate/methanol/ a little acetic acid; 1 h/50° $RCH{=}CH_2 + Hg(OOCCH_3)_2 + CH_3OH \rightarrow RC(OCH_3)—CH_2—HgOOCCH_3 + CH_3COOH$	Acetic acid formed finally determined with excess NaOH and back titration with HCl to phenolphthalein	106
Unsaturation in styrene, etc.	In CCl_4, + Hg acetate + methanol (saturated with $NaNO_3$ as catalyst); 10–15 min/room temp., with same reaction as in ref. 106	Unreacted Hg acetate converted to $HgCl_2$ with NaCl and acetic acid titrated with NaOH to phenolphthalein	107
Antipyrine	+ $Hg(Cl)NH_2$; 15 min boiling, giving equivalent of OH^- and Hg derivative	Filtered, excess HCl added and back titrated with KOH to phenolphthalein	108
$CaCl_2$ complexes of streptomycin and dihydrostreptomycin	+ $HgCl_2$/I^-/alkali; 30 min/room temp., giving Hg	Acidified with HCl, excess iodine added and back titrated with thiosulphate	109
Strychnine nitrate, quinidine sulphate	In water, + $K_2Hg(SCN)_4$, giving insoluble complexes	Filtered and SCN^- in filtrate titrated with excess $AgNO_3$	110
Isobutylene in mixtures with n-butene and butadiene	Passed into $HgSO_4$/ H_2SO_4, giving insoluble complex	Filtered, dissolved in hot HNO_3 and Hg(II) titrated with SCN^-	111
Barbiturates	In water, + $Hg(ClO_4)_2$; 15 min/room temp., with occasional shaking, giving insoluble Hg derivatives	Filtered and unused Hg(II) titrated in filtrate with SCN^-	112

Materials titrated	Reagent and reaction conditions	Subsequent treatment and final titration stage	Ref.
Rotenone	In dichloroethane, + Hg acetate/methanol/acetic acid; 25 min/room temp., with addition to the olefinic side chain: $—C=C— + Hg(OOCCH_3)_2 + CH_3OH \rightarrow —C—C(OCH_3)—HgOOCCH_3 + CH_3COOH$	+ NaCl to remove unused Hg(II), and acetic acid titrated with NaOH to phenolphthalein	113
Theophylline; theobromine	In faintly alkaline solution, + $K_2Hg(SCN)_4$ giving Hg derivative of the purine; 20 min boiling	Filtered, excess $AgNO_3$ and HNO_3 added to filtrate and back titrated with SCN^-	114
Mercaptans in ovalbumin	+ $Hg(Cl—C_6H_5COO)_2$ at pH 5·3	Unused Hg(II) reagent titrated with cysteine to external indicator of nitroprusside (see Part I, Mercaptans, ref. 1)	115
Formic acid	Heated with $HgCl_2$ or Hg acetate	Hg(I) formed titrated with iodate	116
Quinoline	+ excess $K_2Hg(SCN)_4$, giving $(C_9H_7N).Hg(SCN)_2$ precipitate	Filtered, Hg(II) precipitated from filtrate with KOH, refiltered, HNO_3 + excess $AgNO_3$ added and back titrated with SCN^-	117
Pyrazine	+ $HgSO_4/H_2SO_4$. Left overnight/room temp., giving 1:1 complex	Filtered and unused Hg(II) in filtrate titrated with SCN^-	118
Amidines	Neutral solution in water, + Hg acetate/excess Na acetate; 20 min/room temp., giving insoluble Hg derivative: $RC(=NH)NH_2 + Hg(OOCCH_3)_2 \rightarrow RC(=N—HgOOCCH_3)NH_2 + CH_3COOH$	Filtered, filtrate acidified with HNO_3 and unused Hg(II) titrated with SCN^-	119
Anethole in volatile oils	+ Hg acetate, oxidizing with formation of Hg(I)	Titrated with MnO_4^-	120

Materials titrated	Reagent and reaction conditions	Subsequent treatment and final titration stage	Ref.
Formates	+ $HgCl_2$/acetate buffer, pH 5; 30 min boiling, away from light	+ HCl + excess iodine and back titrated with thiosulphate	121
Salts of bases, e.g. quinidine sulphate; strychnine nitrate	Method of ref. 110		122
Acetylenes, $RC{\equiv}CR'$	+ Hg acetate suspension in 99% ethanol; 20–30 min shaking till dissolved, then left 2–4 h, with addition: $—C{\equiv}C— + 2\,Hg(OOCCH_3)_2 + H_2O \rightarrow$ $—CO—C(—HgOOCCH_3)_2— + 2\,CH_3COOH$	Unused Hg(II) complexed with NaCl, and titrated with NaOH to phenolphthalein	123
Mercaptans in proteins	+ excess $Cl—Hg—C_6H_4—COONa$ at pH 7·3–8·5 in phosphate buffer	Unused Hg(II) back titrated with cysteine potentiometrically	124
Methyl mercaptan in gas mixtures	Absorbed in $Hg(CN)_2$/water, giving $Hg(SCH_3)_2 + CN^-$	Filtered, excess Hg(II) added and back titrated with SCN^-	125
Olefines, e.g. vinyl and allyl acetates	+ Hg acetate/methanol; 10–30 min/*ca* 30°	+ $CHCl_3$/propylene glycol solvent and unused acetate titrated with HCl to thymol blue (see Part I, Hydrochloric acid, ref. 36)	126
Tetraphenylborates of bases from their determination by precipitation with $NaB(C_6H_5)_4$	+ $HgCl_2$, reacting: $Base.HB(C_6H_5)_4 + 4\,HgCl_2 + 3\,H_2O \rightarrow Base.HCl + 4\,C_6H_5HgCl + H_3BO_3 + 3\,HCl$	HCl titrated with alkali	127
Formates	+ $HgCl_2$ + Na acetate; 2 h/100° till no more CO_2 evolved	Precipitate of HgCl + ICl + $CHCl_3$ + HCl (giving 4–6 N conc.) and titrated with chloramine T to decoloration of the $CHCl_3$	128
Thiourea	+ $HgI_2/I^-/NaOH$; 10 min, giving HgS precipitate	Dissolved in excess bromine reagent; after 2 min, I^- added and unused bromine determined by titration with thiosulphate; or unused bromine destroyed with HgCl and HBr formed titrated with NaOH to methyl red/bromocresol green	129

Materials titrated	Reagent and reaction conditions	Subsequent treatment and final titration stage	Ref.
Triphenylcyanoborates of bases used medicinally, from their determination by precipitation with $NaB(C_6H_5)_3CN$	Precipitate + $HgCl_2$ + acetone, reacting: Base.$HB(C_6H_5)_3CN$ + 3 $HgCl_2$ + 3 $H_2O \rightarrow$ Base.HCl + 3 H_3BO_3 + 3 C_6H_5HgCl + HCN + 2 HCl	HCN boiled out and HCl titrated with alkali	130
Ascorbic acid	+ $HgCl_2$/acetate buffer, pH 3·8–4·98; 30–90 min/room temp.	HgCl filtered, dissolved in excess iodine and back titrated with thiosulphate	131
Aldehydes	+ $HgCl_2/I^-/KCl/KOH$; 1–240 min/room temp.	+ agar solution (to disperse the precipitate of Hg) + acetic acid + excess iodine; unused titrated with thiosulphate after 5 min	132
Olefines	+ Hg acetate/methanol + BF_3/methanol/ ether; 1 h/room temp. or 100°	+ NH_4OH/NH_4NO_3 buffer + measured excess Zn salt of EDTA, giving Hg—EDTA and freeing Zn(II) with the unused Hg(II); titrated with EDTA to eriochrome black T	133
Potassium tetraphenylborate	+ $HgCl_2$/NaCl, giving HCl (cf. method of ref. 127)	Titrated with NaOH to methyl red	134
Acenaphthylene in presence of acenaphthene	In CCl_4, + Hg acetate/ methanol. Warmed to 50°, cooled for 12–15 min, yielding Hg addition product and acetic acid	+ NaCl and acetic acid titrated with NaOH to phenolphthalein	135
Formate	+ $HgCl_2$ and heated until no more CO_2 evolved $HCOO^- + 2\,Hg^{2+} \rightarrow 2\,Hg^+ + H^+ + CO_2$	HgCl filtered and H^+ determined by adding excess KI and titrating with NaOH to phenolphthalein; or by adding I^-/IO_3^- and titrating with thiosulphate	136
Tetraphenylborates of bases, from their determination by precipitation with $B(C_6H_5)_4^-$ (e.g. codeine, pyramidone)	+ $HgCl_2$, giving HCl (cf. method of ref. 127)	Titrated with alkali	137

Materials titrated	Reagent and reaction conditions	Subsequent treatment and final titration stage	Ref.
Mercaptans, RSH	In methanol/benzene, 4:1, + saturated $HgCl_2$, giving RSHgCl + HCl	Titrated with KOH/methanol to bromocresol green, or as high frequency titration	138
Unsaturation in acrylic esters	+ Hg acetate/water/ dioxan/a little acetic acid; 1 h/room temp.	+ NH_4OH/NH_4Cl buffer, pH 10 + excess EDTA; back titrated with $ZnSO_4$ to eriochrome black T	139
Piperazine	In water, + $HgCl_2$; slightly warmed, giving insoluble product	Filtered and unused Hg(II) in filtrate determined by adding ammonia buffer + excess EDTA and back titrating with Mg(II) to eriochrome black T	140
Many bases, e.g. dimethylaminophenazone, metrazole, pyramidone, nicotinic acid derivatives, purines	In water, + $HgCl_2$. (Hg acetate for theophylline). Several hours/ room temp., giving precipitate of Hg derivative	Precipitate dissolved in HCl, excess EDTA added, + ammonia buffer and back titrated with Zn(II) to eriochrome black T	141
Vinyl ethers, allyl compounds and other unsaturated compounds	+ Hg acetate/dry methanol/drops acetic acid; 10 min/$-10°$ (with ethers) or 1–120 min/$-10°$ to room temp., giving Hg addition compound + acetic acid	Unused Hg(II) complexed with NaBr and acid titrated with KOH/methanol to phenolphthalein	142
Mercaptans	+ Hg acetate/methanol. Also with C_6H_5Hg acetate (to avoid interference by unsaturated compounds)	Unused acetate titrated with HCl/butanol to thymol blue or diphenylcarbohydrazide (see Part I, Hydrochloric acid, ref. 71)	143
Methacrylic esters	In methanol, + Hg acetate/methanol/$HClO_4$ (catalyst); 30 min/45°, giving addition compound	+ NaCl + ethylene glycol and acetate titrated with HCl to thymol blue	144
Pyruvic acid; 2,2-dichloropropionic acid	+ $Hg(NO_3)_2$/water; 15 min reflux. Dichloride gives pyruvic acid and reacts to give precipitate of 3,3-bis(hydroxymercuric)-3-nitrato mercuric pyruvic acid O(Hg)(Hg)C(CO.COOH)(HgNO₃) [O bridged by two Hg to C, which bears CO.COOH and $HgNO_3$]	Precipitate dissolved in KI, reacting; $C_3H_1O_7NHg_3$ + 12 KI + 3 H_2O → $CH_3COCOOK$ + 3 K_2HgI_4 + KNO_3 + 4 KOH; titrated with HCl to phenolphthalein	145

Materials titrated	Reagent and reaction conditions	Subsequent treatment and final titration stage	Ref.
2,2,3-Trichloro-propionic acid	+ Hg propionate/HNO_3; 5 min reflux, giving mixture of Hg(I) salts	Precipitate treated with KOH giving Hg_2O; ultimately filtered, dissolved in HNO_3 oxidized with MnO_4^- and Hg(II) titrated with SCN^-	145
Propyl gallate in fat	Extract in water, + Na acetate + Hg acetate, giving precipitate; 10 min reflux	Precipitate dissolved in HCl, excess EDTA added, then ammonium buffer and back titrated with $ZnSO_4$ to eriochrome black T	146
Allyl alcohol	In water, + $Hg(NO_3)_2$/HNO_3 in *ca* 20% excess; a few sec reaction time, giving $HOCH_2.CHOH.CH_2.Hg^+ + H^+$	+ NH_4OH and unreacted Hg(II) titrated with thio-glycollate to thiofluorescein	147
Strychnine salts	In HCl + $HgCl_2$/KI; 15 min/room temp., giving precipitate of complex	Filtered, filtrate boiled with KCl/$KClO_3$/HCl and Hg(II) titrated with EDTA in presence of an ammonium buffer to eriochrome black T	148
Mixtures of maleic and fumaric acids	Neutral solution + $HgSO_4$; 1 h/room temp., giving precipitate of Hg fumarate	Centrifuged and maleic acid in supernatant liquid determined with BrCl (see Bromine reagents, refs 483, 484, 498)	149, 158
Allyl chloride	In methanol, + Hg acetate/methanol + a little $HClO_4$; 15 min/room temp. $—C{=}C— + CH_3OH + Hg(OOCCH_3)_2 \rightarrow —C(OCH_3)—C(HgOCOCH_3)— + CH_3COOH$	Titrated with HCl/butanol to diphenylcarbazone; control $Hg(OOCCH_3)_2 + 2\,HCl \rightarrow HgCl_2 + 2\,CH_3COOH$ Addition product + HCl → $—C(OCH_3)—C(HgCl)— + CH_3COOH$ Titration difference → allyl chloride	150
Acetylenes	Method of ref. 105, compared with two Ag(I) methods; has the advantage of being usable in alkaline solution		151
Formates	Neutral solution + Na acetate + saturated $HgCl_2$; 40 min/100°	+ HCl, cooled, + CCl_4 and Hg(I) titrated with IO_3^- to disappearance of iodine colour from the CCl_4	152

Materials titrated	Reagent and reaction conditions	Subsequent treatment and final titration stage	Ref.
Thiourea	In NaOH solution + excess *o*-hydroxymercuribenzoic acid; boiled 30 sec	+ excess Na_2S and back titrated with *o*-hydroxymercuribenzoic acid to thiofluorescein (see Sulphides, ref. 10)	153
Styrene	In methanol, + excess $Hg(ClO_4)_2$. Refluxed 30 sec–2 min	Back titrated with thioglycollate to thiofluorescein after adding NH_4OH and methanol	154
Sulphur-containing functional groups, e.g. thioketones, disulphides, thiocyanates, isothiocyanates	+ *o*-hydroxymercuribenzoate. Boiled 5 min	Back titrated with thioglycollate to thiofluorescein	155
Thiophene	+ excess $Hg(ClO_4)_2$/ 90% methanol, containing 2·5% $HClO_4$; boiled giving mercuriated thiophene product (1 thiophene equivalent to 2 Hg^{2+})	Unreacted Hg^{2+} titrated with thioglycollate to thiofluorescein	156
Aldehydes, sugars, hydrazine derivatives like phenylhydrazine, isoniazid and semicarbazide	In water or dilute H_2SO_4, + HgO/EDTA reagent (1:1) + KOH; 15–90 min/room temp., liberating EDTA	+ HNO_3 + hexamine and EDTA titrated with $Pb(NO_3)_2$ to methylthymol blue	157
Isonicotinic acid hydrazone of 5-nitrofurfuraldehyde	In 70% ethanol, + $Hg(NO_3)_2$ + water	Filtered and unused Hg(II) in filtrate titrated with SCN^-	159
Semicarbazone of 5-nitrofurfuraldehyde	In 70% ethanol + $Hg(NO_3)_2$	Filtered and unused Hg(II) in filtrate titrated with SCN^-	160
Barbiturates	In water or ethanol, + Na acetate + Hg acetate; heated nearly to boiling	Filtered, excess EDTA and NH_4OH/NH_4Cl buffer, pH 10·4 added; unused EDTA titrated with $ZnSO_4$ to eriochrome black T	161
Isobutylene in cracking fractions	Absorbed in $HgSO_4$/ H_2SO_4; 10 min/50°, then diluted and 1 h/room temp. $\rightarrow C_4H_8(HgO.HgSO_4)_3$; also with $Hg(NO_3)_2/HNO_3$ $\rightarrow C_4H_8(HgNO_3.Hg(NO_3)_2)_2$; 1 mole isobutylene equivalent to 6 Hg(II)	Filtered, aliquot of filtrate treated with MnO_4^-, decolorized with H_2O_2 and Hg(II) titrated with SCN^- to Fe(III) indicator	162

Materials titrated	Reagent and reaction conditions	Subsequent treatment and final titration stage	Ref.
Formates	+ $HgCl_2$ + KCl (to combine with $HgCl_2$ and prevent hydrolysis) + K citrate; 20–30 min boiling, oxidizing to CO_2	CO_2 passed into $Ba(OH)_2$; back titrated with HCl to thymol blue	163, 174, 183
tert-Butanol	+ $HgSO_4/H_2SO_4$; 15 min reflux, giving precipitate of derivative formulated as $\left(O\begin{smallmatrix}Hg\\Hg\end{smallmatrix}SO_4\right)_3 C_4H_8$	Filtered, aliquot of filtrate + HNO_3 and Hg(II) back titrated with SCN^- to Fe(III)	164
Barbiturates, e.g. luminal, veronal	In ethanol, + Na acetate + $Hg(NO_3)_2$; 5–10 min/room temp., giving precipitate of derivative	Filtered, filtrate aliquot + HNO_3 and titrated with SCN^-	165
Barbiturates	+ excess $Hg(ClO_4)_2$, giving precipitate of derivative	Filtered and Hg(II) in filtrate titrated with Cu-EDTA at pH 2 to 1-(2-pyridylazo)2-naphthol; or + excess Mg-EDTA at pH 10 and back titrated at *ca* 50° with EDTA to eriochrome black T	166
Propyl gallate in lard (semimicro)	Slight modification of method of ref. 146 (15 min reflux)		167
Precipitate with tetraphenylborate from determination of non-ionic surface-active agents (polyalkylene oxides, ethers, esters)	Dissolved in dimethylformamide, Na acetate + water added and excess $Hg(NO_3)_2$; 10 min/100°, giving precipitate of complex	Centrifuged, supernatant liquid + HNO_3 and Hg(II) titrated with SCN^- to Fe(III)	168
Precipitate with tetraphenylborate from determination of 2,4-diamino-5-phenylthiazole ('Daptazole')	Solution in acetone + saturated $HgCl_2$ + excess NaOH; boiled, KI added to complex the Hg(II) and displace reaction to the right (cf. ref. 127)	Titrated with HCl to methyl red, CO_2 boiled out and finally titrated with NaOH	169
Isoniazid	+ water + Nessler reagent ($HgCl_2$/KI/alkali); 10 min/*ca* 100°	Filtered, filtrate + water/pyridine/EDTA/tartaric acid and back titrated with Na diethyldithiocarbamate to yellow brown with Cu(II) indicator	170

Materials titrated	Reagent and reaction conditions	Subsequent treatment and final titration stage	Ref.
Cyclopropylamides, $RCONH-CH<(CH_2)(CH_2)$	Method of ref. 142, with 30 min reaction time, occasionally with refluxing; react to give: $RCONH-CH(OCH_3)(CH_2CH_2-Hg-O-COCH_3)$ $(+ CH_3COOH)$		171
Some sulphur-containing compounds	+ excess *o*-hydroxymercuribenzoate + NaOH	+ excess Na_2S and back titrated with *o*-hydroxymercuribenzoate to thiofluorescein or dithizone	172
Cellulose xanthate in viscose	In $NaOH/Na_2SO_3$, heated to boiling, excess *o*-hydroxymercuribenzoic acid added and reheated to boiling	+ NH_4NO_3 + water + excess Na_2S; unused back titrated with *o*-hydroxymercuribenzoate to thiofluorescein	173
2,2-Dichloropropionate; Na monochloropropionate; Na trichloropropionate	Method of ref. 145		175
Olefine groups in acrylates	+ excess Hg(II) reagent in alkaline solution	Back titrated with EDTA	176
N-p-Toluenesulphonyl-*N'*-butylurea ('diabetamid'); *N-p*-toluenesulphonyl-*N'*-cyclohexylurea ('cycloral')	In NaOH solution, + acetic acid + Hg acetate; 10 min, giving precipitates	+ excess EDTA and back titrated with $MgSO_4$ in NH_4OH/NH_4Cl medium	177
Na salt of 5,5-diphenylhydantoin	+ excess Hg (II) reagent, yielding a precipitate of a Hg derivative	Dissolved in excess EDTA and back titrated with $ZnSO_4$ to eriochrome black T	178
Barbiturates in pharmaceuticals	In ethanol, + Na acetate + $Hg(OH)NO_3$; 10 min	Filtered; precipitate dissolved in dilute HNO_3 and titrated with SCN^-; or filtrate + hexamine and titrated with EDTA to xylenol orange	179
tert-Amylenes in C_5 olefines	+ excess $HgSO_4$ reagent, giving precipitate of formula $C_5H_{10}HgSO_4.2HgO$	+ water, and supernatant liquid titrated with SCN^-	180
Pregnin	In $CHCl_3$ + methanol, + HgI_2/KI + NaOH	Back titrated with H_2SO_4 to phenolpthalein	181

Materials titrated	Reagent and reaction conditions	Subsequent treatment and final titration stage	Ref.
2-Acetamino-1,3,4-thiadiazole-5-sulphonamide; 6-chloro-7-sulphamoyl-3,4-dihydro-1,2,4-benzothiadiazine-1,1-dioxide	In water, + $Hg(NO_3)_2$, giving precipitates of mercury derivatives, $(C_4H_6N_4)_2Hg$ and $(C_7H_8N_3O_4Cl)_2Hg$	Filtered, filtrate + HNO_3 and titrated with SCN^-	182
α-Methylstyrene	+ HgO/H_2SO_4; 2 h/room temp., giving complex	Unused Hg(II) determined by titration with SCN^-	184
dimethylphenylcarbinol	+ same reagent; 10 min/100°	similarly concluded	
N-Vinylcarbazole in its polymers	In $CHCl_3$ or $ClCH_2.CH_2Cl$, + methanol + Hg acetate; heated	+ NaCl and acetic acid liberated titrated with NaOH to phenolphthalein	185
—SH groups in sulphur-containing solid fuels	+ $HgCl_2$/ethanol; 100 h/room temp., with shaking; —SH → —SHgCl + HCl	Filtered, filtrate + NaCl and titrated potentiometrically or to methyl red with NaOH	186
Cystine	In water, + NaH_2PO_4 + Na_2SO_3 + excess *o*-hydroxymercuribenzoate $RSSR + R'HgOH + SO_3^{2-} \rightarrow RSHgR' + RSSO_3^- + OH^-$ (at pH 8)	+ NH_4OH and titrated with thioglycollate to thiofluorescein (→ pale blue)	187
K tetraphenylborate	+ $Hg(ClO_4)_2$/methanol + $HClO_4$; heated until completely dissolved	+ NH_4OH and titrated with thioglycollate to thiofluorescein	188
Mercaptosilanes ≡Si—SR	In toluene, + Hg acetate/methanol/some acetic acid; $\equiv Si{-}SR + H_2O \rightarrow \equiv Si{-}OH + RSH$; RSH then reacts with the Hg(II)	Titrated slowly with HCl/butanol to thymol blue	189
Formate from determination of formyl groups in presence of acetyl groups by hydrolysis with NaOH	Neutralized solution (with H_2SO_4), + $HgCl_2$; 1 h/*ca* 100° out of direct sunlight	+ HCl + KI + excess iodine; shaken till clear (*ca* 10 min), then back titrated with thiosulphate	190

References

1. Mertens, K. H., *Ber.* **6**, 440 (1873).
2. Portes and Ruysson, *Compt. rend.* **82**, 1504 (1877).

3. Romijn, G. and Voorthuis, J. A., *Pharm. Weekblad* **40**, 149 (1903).
4. Orloff, E. I., *J. Russ. Phys.-Chem. Ges.* **36**, 1311 (1904).
5. Glassmann, B., *Ber.* **39**, 503 (1906).
6. Denigès, G., *Bull. soc. pharm., Bordeaux*, August 1907.
7. Monimart, R., *J. pharm. chim.* **26**, 392 (1907).
8. Riesser, O., *Z. physiol. Chem.* **96**, 335 (1916).
9. van Slyke, D. D., *J. Biol. Chem.* **32**, 480 (1917).
10. Meyer, A., *Compt. rend.* **169**, 1402 (1919).
11. Stüwe, W., *Apotheker-Ztg.* **35**, 153 (1920).
12. Bougault, J. and Gros, J., *J. pharm. chim.* **26**, 5 (1922).
13. Holmberg, B. and Lindberg, S., *Ber.* **56**, 2048 (1923).
14. Ionescu, A., Spirescu, E. and Popescu, D., *Bull. soc. chim. Romania* **5**, 15 (1923).
15. Ionescu, A. and Spirescu, E., *Bull. soc. chim. Romania* **5**, 74 (1923).
16. More, J., *J. pharm. chim.* **27**, 209 (1923).
17. Riesser, O., *Biochem. Z.* **142**, 280 (1923).
18. Utkin-Ljubowzoff, L., *Biochem. Z.* **138**, 205 (1923).
19. De Eds, F., *J. Lab. Clin. Med.* **10**, 59 (1924).
20. Gros, R., *Ann. fals.* **18**, 39 (1925).
21. Fleury, P. and Awad, Y., *J. pharm. chim.* (8) **3**, 406 (1926).
22. Ionescu-Matiu, A., *J. pharm. chim.* (8) **4**, 533 (1926). *Ann. scient. Univ. Jassy* **14**, 363 (1927).
23. Baudouin, A. and Lewin, J., *Bull. soc. chim. biol.* **9**, 280 (1927).
24. Daniel, L., *J. pharm. chim.* **5**, 581 (1927).
25. Ionescu-Matiu, A., *Chimie et industrie*, Special No. 174, May 1927.
26. Oberhauser, F. and Hensinger, W., *Z. anorg. u. allgem. Chem.* **160**, 336 (1927).
27. Ionescu-Matiu, A. and Varcovici, H., *Bull. soc. chim. Romania* **10**, 5 (1928); *Bull. soc. chim. biol.* **10**, 932 (1928).
28. Fleury, P. and Marque, J., *J. pharm. chim.* **10**, 241 (1929).
29. Fleury, P. and Marque, J., *J. pharm. chim.* **10**, 292 (1929).
30. Fleury, P. and Marque, J., *J. pharm chim.* **10**, 364 (1929).
31. Fuchs, P., *Z. anal. Chem.* **78**, 125 (1929).
32. Maricq, L., *Bull. soc. chim. Belg.* **38**, 259, 265 (1929).
33. Maricq, L., *Bull. soc. chim. Belg.* **38**, 426 (1929).
34. Fleury, P. and Marque, J., *Bull. soc. chim. biol.* **12**, 58 (1930).
35. Ionescu-Matiu, A. and Popescu, A., *Chimie et industrie*, Special No. 359, March 1930.
36. Ionescu-Matiu, A. and Vitner, M., *Bull. soc. chim. biol.* **12**, 1414 (1930).
37. Maricq, L., *Bull. soc. chim. biol.* **12**, 1366 (1930).
38. Maricq, L., *Bull. soc. chim. Belg.* **39**, 496 (1930).
39. Meyer, A. and Mathey, S., *Compt. rend.* **191**, 490 (1930).
40. Pénau, H. and Tanret, G., *Bull. soc. chim. biol.* **12**, 67 (1930).

41. Ionescu-Matiu, A. and Popescu, A., *Bull. sci. pharmacol.* **38**, 71 (1931).
42. Ionescu-Matiu, A. and Popescu, A., *Bull. soc. chim. Romania* **13**, 11 (1931).
43. Machtou, R., *J. pharm. chim.* **13**, 329 (1931).
44. Maricq, L., *Bull. soc. chim. Belg.* **40**, 361 (1931).
45. Maricq, L., *Ann. bull. soc. roy. sci. med. nat., Bruxelles*, Nos. 1–2, 21, Nos. 3–4, 49 (1931).
46. Oldeman, R. G. C., *Pharm. Weekblad* **68**, 379 (1931).
47. Polonovski, M., Polonovski, M. and Cappelaere, J., *J. pharm. chim.* **14**, 328 (1931).
48. Bougault, J. and Leboucq, J., *Bull. acad. méd.* **108**, 1301 (1932).
49. Ionescu-Matiu, A. and Popescu, A., *Chimie et industrie*, Special No. 542, March 1932.
50. Sampey, J. R. and Reid, E. E., *J. Am. Chem. Soc.* **54**, 3404 (1932).
51. Bordeianu, C. V., *Z. anal. Chem.* **91**, 421 (1933).
52. Bougault, J. and Leboucq, J., *J. pharm. chim.* **17**, 193 (1933).
53. Osburn, O. L., Wood, H. G. and Werkman, C. H., *Ind. Eng. Chem., Anal. Ed.* **5**, 247 (1933).
54. Bourdeau, M., *J. pharm. chim.* **20**, 342 (1934).
55. Dupille, J. and Lachaux, M., *Bull. soc. chim. biol.* **16**, 194 (1934).
56. Eury, J., *J. pharm. chim.* **19**, 261 (1934).
57. Minatoya, S. and Nagai, I., *J. Soc. Rubber Ind., Japan* **7**, 337 (1934).
58. Gallais, F., *Bull. sci. pharmacol.* **42**, 278, 408 (1935).
59. Goswami, I. M., Das-Gupta, H. N. and Ray, K. L., *J. Indian Chem. Soc.* **12**, 714 (1935).
60. Hazard, R., Herbain, M. and Vaille, C., *J. pharm. chim.* **21**, 61 (1935).
61. Minatoya, S., Kojima, K., Aoe, I., Ebe, T. and Nagai, I., *Research Electrotech. Lab. (Tokyo)* No. 385, 33 (1935).
62. Pittarelli, E. and Pittarelli, M., *Biochim. terap. sper.* **22**, 100 (1935).
63. Schuster, G., *J. pharm. chim.* **20**, 32 (1935).
64. Goswami, M. and Das-Purkaystha, C. B., *J. Indian Chem. Soc.* **13**, 315 (1936).
65. Iol'son, L. M., Strizhevskii, I. I. and Bergel'son, A. B., *Zavodskaya Lab.* **5**, 952 (1936).
66. Weihe, H. D. and Jacobs, P. B., *Ind. Eng. Chem., Anal. Ed.* **8**, 44 (1936).
67. Ezrielev, M. and Broun, R. G., *Narodnyi Komissariat Tyazheloi Prom. SSSR, Nauch.-Issledovatel. Inst. Plasticheskikh Mass, Plasticheskie Massy, Sbornik* **2**, 254 (1937).
68. Goswami, M. and Shaha, A., *J. Indian Chem. Soc.* **14**, 208 (1937).
69. Ionescu-Matiu, A. and Ichim, C., *J. pharm. chim.* **26**, 49 (1937).
70. Lindenberg, A., *Compt. rend. soc. biol.* **125**, 135 (1937).
71. Murray, A. G., *J. Assoc. Offic. Agr. Chem.* **20**, 638 (1937).
72. Büchi, J., *Pharm. Acta Helv.* **13**, 132 (1938).

73. Fleury, P. and Carbon, J., *J. pharm. chim.* **28**, 102 (1938).
74. Reid, J. D. and Weihe, H. D., *Ind. Eng. Chem., Anal. Ed.* **10**, 271 (1938).
75. Spitzer, L., *Ann. chim. applicata* **28**, 252 (1938).
76. Wachsmuth, H., *Bull. soc. chim. biol.* **20**, 1419 (1938).
77. Auguste, C., *J. pharm. Belg.* **21**, 935, 961 (1939).
78. Barnes, R. H. and Wick, A. N., *J. Biol. Chem.* **131**, 413 (1939).
79. Rosenthaler, L., *Z. Vitaminforsch.* **9**, 342 (1939).
80. Sukhanovskii, S. I., *Lesokhim. Prom.* **2**, 37 (1939).
81. Boisson, R., *J. pharm. chim.* (9) **1**, 240 (1940).
82. Halliday, H. M. and Reade, T. H., *J. Chem. Soc.* 138 (1940).
83. Holaday, D. A. and Graham, J. J. T., *Ind. Eng. Chem., Anal. Ed.* **12**, 80 (1940).
84. Khinoi, L. M., *Sbornik Rabot. Sanit.-Prom. Khim. Inst. Higieny, Truda i Profzabolevanii Leningrad, Gorzdravotdela* 81 (1940).
85. Newton, A. and Buckler, E. J., *Ind. Eng. Chem., Anal. Ed.* **12**, 251 (1940).
86. Schulte, M. J., *Pharm. Weekblad* **77**, 1281 (1940).
87. Sherman, C. S. and Herzog, R., *Ind. Eng. Chem., Anal. Ed.* **12**, 136 (1940).
88. Weichselbaun, T. E. and Somogyi, M., *J. Biol. Chem.* **140**, 5 (1941)
89. Holmberg, B., *Arkiv Kemi Mineral. Geol.* **A15**, No. 22 (1942).
90. Reifer, I. and Bathurst, N. O., *New Zealand J. Sci Tech.* **24B**, 17 (1942).
91. Wachsmuth, H., *Natuurw. Tijdschr.* **23**, 157 (1942).
92. Ingram, G., *Analyst* **69**, 265 (1944).
93. Horsley, T. E. V., *Analyst* **71**, 308 (1946).
94. Albrand, L., *Ann. pharm. franç.* **5**, 56 (1947).
95. Bastrup, T., *Acta Pharm. Toxicol.* **3**, 303 (1947).
96. Fuà, C., *Boll. soc. ital. biol. sper.* **23**, 612 (1947).
97. Gros, R., *Ann. pharm. franç.* **5**, 459 (1947).
98. Bolle, J., Jean, H. and Jullig, T., *Mém. services chim. état.* (*Paris*) **34**, 317 (1948).
99. Ionescu-Matiu, A., Popa, I. and Monciu, L., *Ann. pharm. franç.* **6**, 26 (1948).
100. Marquardt, R. P. and Luce, E. N., *Anal. Chem.* **20**, 751 (1948).
101. Alexander, E. R. and Underhill, E. J., *J. Am. Chem. Soc.* **71**, 4014 (1949).
102. Arthur, W. J. and Struthers, G. W., *Anal. Chem.* **21**, 1209 (1949).
103. Bosly, J., *J. pharm. Belg.* (*N.S.*) **4**, 66 (1949).
104. Chauveau, J., *Bull. soc. chim. France.* 614 (1949).
105. Hanna, J. G. and Siggia, S., *Anal. Chem.* **21**, 1469 (1949).
106. Marquardt, R. P. and Luce, E. N., *Anal. Chem.* **21**, 1194 (1949).
107. Martin, R. W., *Anal. Chem.* **21**, 921 (1949).
108. Monforte, F. and D'Alcontres, G. S., *Ann. chim. applicata* **39**, 663 (1949).

109. Delaby, R. and Stephan, F., *Ann. pharm. franç.* **8**, 513 (1950).
110. Köszegi, D. and Salgó, E., *Z. anal. Chem.* **130**, 403 (1950).
111. Marushkin, M. N. and Belen'kaya, A. P., *Zhur. Anal. Khim.* **5**, 358 (1950).
112. Pedley, E., *J. Pharm. Pharmacol.* **2**, 39 (1950).
113. Hornstein, I., *Anal. Chem.* **23**, 1329, 1698 (1951).
114. Köszegi, D. and Salgó, E., *Acta Chem. Hung.* **1**, 124 (1951).
115. Macdonnell, L. R., Silva, R. B. and Feeney, R. E., *Arch. Biochem. Biophys.* **32**, 288 (1951).
116. Marconi, M., *Chimica (Milan)* **6**, 315 (1951).
117. Köszegi, D. and Salgó, E., *Z. anal. Chem.* **136**, 411 (1952).
118. Seaman, W., Woods, J. T., and Leibmann, W., *Anal. Chem.* **24**, 1949 (1952).
119. Stephan, F. H., *Anal. Chem.* **24**, 180 (1952).
120. Casparis, P. and Heiz, R., *Bull. Galenica* **16**, 29 (1953)
121. Hopton, J. W., *Anal. Chim. Acta* **8**, 429 (1953).
122. Köszegi, D. and Salgó, E., *Pharm. Zentralhalle* **92**, 157 (1953).
123. Koulkes, M., *Bull. soc. chim. France* 402 (1953).
124. Pihar, O., *Chem. Listy* **47**, 1647, 1952 (1953).
125. Segal, W. and Starkey, R. L., *Anal. Chem.* **25**, 1645 (1953).
126. Das, M. N., *Anal. Chem.* **26**, 1086 (1954).
127. Flaschka, H., Holasek, A. and Amin, A. M., *Arzneimittelforsch.* **4**, 38 (1954).
128. Balwant Singh and Sood, K. C., *Anal. Chim. Acta* **13**, 305 (1955).
129. Gutiérrez, F. N., *Anales real soc. espan., fis. y quím* **51B**, 639 (1955).
130. Schulz, E. and Goerner, H., *Arch. Pharm.* **288**, 520 (1955).
131. Suryanarayana Rao, S. V., Veereswara, R. and Gopala Rao, G., *Z. anal. Chem.* **145**, 88 (1955).
132. Ruch, J. E. and Johnson, J. B., *Anal. Chem.* **28**, 69 (1956).
133. Buděšinský, B., *Chem. Listy* **51**, 259 (1957); *Collection Czechoslov. Chem. Communs.* **22**, 1147 (1957).
134. Montequi, R., Doadrio, A. and Serrano, C., *Inform. quím. anal. Madrid* **11**, 8 (1957).
135. Soloveichik, L. S. and Nikolaeva, A. P., *Zavodskaya Lab.* **23**, 916 (1957).
136. Bose, O., *J. Indian Chem. Soc.* **35**, 320 (1958).
137. Kranjčević, M. and Broz-Kajganović, V., *Croat. Chem. Acta* **30**, 47 (1958).
138. Ratkovics, F. and Szepesváry, P., *Magyar Kém. Folyóirat* **64**, 472 (1958).
139. Bartels, U. and Hoyme, H., *Faserforsch. u. Textiltech.* **10**, 345 (1959).
140. Erben, J., *Českoslov. Farm.* **8**, 18 (1959).
141. Helmstaedter, G., *Mitt. Deut. Pharm. Ges.* **29**, 91 (1959), published in *Arch. Pharm.* **292**, No. 6 (1959).

142. Johnson, J. B. and Fletcher, J. P., *Anal. Chem.* **31**, 1563 (1959).
143. Kundu, K. K. and Das, M. N., *Anal. Chem.* **31**, 1358 (1959).
144. Mallik, K. L. and Das, M. N., *Chem. & Ind.* (*London*) 162 (1959).
145. Marquardt, R. P. and Luce, E. N., *Anal. Chem.* **31**, 418 (1959).
146. Sedláček, B. A. J., *Z. Lebensm. Unters. u. Forsch.* **111**, 108 (1959).
147. Wronski, M., *Z. anal. Chem.* **171**, 177 (1959).
148. Wu, Ch.-F. and Hsü, J.-Ch., *Yao Hsueh Hsueh Pao* **7**, 78 (1959).
149. Burger, K. and Schulek, E., *Z. anal. Chem.* **172**, 98 (1960); *Ann. Univ. Sci. Budapest Rolando Eötvös nominatae, Sect. Chem.* **2**, 145 (1960).
150. Mallik, K. L., *Anal. Chem.* **32**, 1369 (1960).
151. Prévost, S., Chudkiewicz, W., Cadiot, P. and Willemart, A., *Bull. soc. chim. France* 1742 (1960).
152. Verma, R. M. and Bose, S., *J. Indian Chem. Soc.* **37**, 47 (1960).
153. Wronski, M., *Chem. Anal.* (*Warsaw*) **5**, 101 (1960).
154. Wronski, M., *Chem. Anal.* (*Warsaw*) **5**, 823 (1960).
155. Wronski, M., *Anal. Chem.* **32**, 133 (1960).
156. Wronski, M., *Z. anal. Chem.* **174**, 280 (1960).
157. Buděšinský, B., *Collection Czechoslov, Chem. Communs.* **26**, 781 (1961).
158. Burger, K. and Schulek, E., *Magyar Kem. Folyoirat* **67**, 33 (1961).
159. Kolusheva, A. and Nin'o, N., *Farmatsiya* (*Sofia*) **11**, 17 (1961).
160. Kolusheva, A. and Nin'o, N., *Farmatsiya* (*Sofia*) **11**, No. 5, 25 (1961).
161. Kurpiel, I., Mojejko, J. and Przyborowski, L., *Acta Polon. Pharm.* **18**, 221 (1961).
162. Markevich, S. M., Polyanski, N. G., Buzlanova, M. M. and Safronenko, E. D., *Zhur. Anal. Khim.* **16**, 489 (1961).
163. Maros, L., Pinter-Szakács, M. and Schulek, E., *Anal. Chim. Acta* **25**, 546 (1961).
164. Polyanski, N. G. and Safronenko, E. D., *Zhur. Priklad Khim.* **34**, 1376 (1961).
165. Rapaport, L. I., *Farm. Zhur.* (*Kiev*) **16**, No. 1, 21 (1961).
166. Roushdi, I. M., Abdine, A. and Ayad, A., *J. Pharm. Pharmacol.* **13**, Suppl. 153T (1961).
167. Sedláček, B. A. J., *Z. Lebensm. Unters, u. Forsch.* **114**, 127 (1961).
168. Seher, A., *Fette u. Seifen, Anstrichmittel* **63**, 617 (1961).
169. Sztark, W., *Dissertationes Pharm.* **13**, 57 (1961).
170. Tatsuzawa, M., *Bunseki Kagaku* **10**, 129 (1961).
171. Theivaigt, J. G., *Anal. Chem.* **33**, 1391 (1961).
172. Wronski, M., *Chem. Anal.* (*Warsaw*) **6**, 869 (1961).
173. Wronski, M., *Z. anal. Chem.* **183**, 361 (1961).
174. Maros, L., Pintér-Szakács, M. and Schulek, E., *Magyar Kem. Folyoirat* **67**, 531 (1961).
175. Garratt, D. C., *Analyst* **87**, 367 (1962).
176. Philipp, B. and Bartels, U., *Acta Chim. Acad. Sci. Hung.* **32**, 19 (1962).

177. Popa, I. and Voicu, A., *Farmacia (Bucharest)* **10**, 399 (1962).
178. Przyborowski, L., *Ann. Univ. Mariae Curie-Sklodowska, Lublin-Polonia, Sect.* D **17** 25 (1962).
179. Rapoport, L. I. and Berzina, A. E., *Farmatsevt. Zh. (Kiev)* **17**, 25 (1962).
180. Buzlanova, M. M., Kozhikohova, N. A. and Polyanskii, N. G., *Zhur. Anal. Khim.* **18**, 1125 (1963).
181. Gavrilin, G. F. and Perel'man, Ya. M., *Med. Prom. SSSR* **17**, 48 (1963).
182. Kolusheva, A. and Nin'o, N., *Farmatsiya (Sofia)* **13**, 21 (1963).
183. Maros, L., Perl, I., Vajda, M. and Schulek, E., *Magyar Kem. Folyoirat* **69**, 123 (1963).
184. Polyanskii, N. G., Markevich, S. M., Safronenko, E. D. and Buzlanova M. M., *Tr. Komis. po Anilit. Khim., Akad. Nauk SSSR, Inst. Geo-khim. i Analit. Khim.* **13**, 93 (1963).
185. Ponomarev, Yu. P., Dmitrieva, V. N. and Bezuglyi, V. D., *Zhur. Anal. Khim.* **18**, 654 (1963).
186. Prilezhaeva, E. N., Fedorovskaya, N. P.. Miesserova, L. V., Domanina, O. N. and Khaskina, I. M., *Tr. Inst. Goryuch. Iskop., Akad. Nauk SSSR* **21**, 159 (1963).
187. Wronski, M., *Z. Anal. Chem.* **192**, 294 (1963).
188. Wronski, M., *Chem. Anal. (Warsaw)* **8**, 299 (1963).
189. Berger, A. and Magnuson, J. A., *Anal. Chem.* **36**, 1156 (1964).
190. Kan, M., Suzuki, F. and Kashiwagi, H., *Microchem. J.* **8**, 42 (1964).

69. Metals

Reagents. Zinc has been principally used, both as pure metal and as amalgam. Next in frequency of use appears to be sodium, also often as amalgam. (It is sometimes not clear whether sodium itself is the reagent, or sodium alkoxides, in cases where sodium/alcohol has been used; the same reference then appears also under Alkalies.)

Other metals which have found occasional use are: aluminium; nickel (Raney type); Devarda's alloy (copper/aluminium/zinc, 50/45/5); iron; and cadmium. Single examples are given of the use of tin and magnesium. It is surprising that tin has not been more frequently used.

Reaction and materials titrated. All determinations are based on reduction or reductive hydrolysis. Functional groups and substance classes thus determined are tabulated below, together with the principal reaction product:

Group or Class	Product
—NO_2; —NO; —N=N— (especially aromatic nitro compounds)	—NH_2
Some nitrogen-containing compounds like nitrate and nitrite esters, urethanes, tetrazine and isoniazid	Amines
Some sulphur-containing compounds, like vitamin B_1 or thiodan	H_2S or SO_3^{2-}
Disulphides, e.g. cystine	Mercaptans
Many halides, e.g. $CHCl_3$, CHI_3, chloral, DDT, dichloro- and dibromoethane, chloramphenicol	Hal^-
Quinones, e.g. benzoquinone, menadione, anthraquinone	Phenols
Pyruvic acid	Lactic acid

Reaction conditions. Most determinations have been done in acid solution, except those using sodium and some with zinc for which neutral or even alkaline solution have been needed.

Reaction times and temperatures have varied very widely.

Subsequent treatment and final titration stage. (a) Conclusion via determination of excess reagent is impracticable, since the reactions of reduction are often complex and, further, the unused metal must be brought into solution to permit its titrimetric determination. In fact, only ref. 1 shows such a conclusion, unused Zn being dissolved in Fe(III) and the Fe(II) formed titrated with permanganate.

(b) All other conclusions have been via a suitable reaction product and those tabulated above under Reaction and materials titrated have been determined by the standard titration procedures below:

Reaction Product	Determination
Amines	Chiefly by titration with nitrite or bromine reagents (aromatic primary amines) or by perchloric acid. Also by precipitation as oxalates and subsequent titration with alkali or bromate. *p*-Phenylenediamine was determined with excess NaOCl.
NH_3	Absorbed in acid and back titrated with alkali
H_2S or SO_3^{2-}	Titrated directly or indirectly with iodine

Reaction Product	Determination
Mercaptans	Titrated directly or indirectly with iodate, iodine, silver (I), mercury (II) or, in one case of thiosalicylic acid, with a diazonium salt reagent
Hal⁻	Mostly by direct or indirect titration with silver (I) or mercury (II). Fluoride was titrated with Th(IV) and iodide also by oxidation to iodate with bromine and titration with thiosulphate after addition of iodide/acid
Phenols	Titrated with oxidizing agents, e.g. halogens, permanganate, bichromate or Ce(IV)
Lactic acid	Oxidized to acetaldehyde with permanganate or manganese dioxide, and the aldehyde determined with bisulphite

Examples

Materials titrated	Reagent and reaction conditions	Subsequent treatment and final titration stage	Ref.
Nitro compounds	+ NH_4Cl + measured amount Zn. *Ca* 30 min/room temp., then heated	ZnO + unreacted Zn filtered, dissolved in $Fe_2(SO_4)_3$ and formed Fe(II) titrated with MnO_4^-	1
p-Nitrotoluene in nitrotoluene mixtures	+ HCl/water + Fe filings; 6 h reflux	*p*-Toluidine precipitated with oxalic acid and titrated with alkali (see Carboxylic acids, ref. 1)	2
Benzoquinone	+ Zn dust + acid, reducing to hydroquinone	Filtered, $NaHCO_3$ added to filtrate and titrated with iodine (see Part I, Iodine, ref. 20)	3
Thioacetic acid	Reduced with Zn to acetic acid + ZnS	Titrated with MnO_4^-, oxidizing according to the equation: $3\,ZnS + 8\,MnO_4^- + H_2O \rightarrow 3\,ZnO_2 + 8\,MnO_2 + 3\,SO_4^{2-} + 2\,OH^-$	4
N-Nitrosodimethylamine from determination of dimethylamine in methylamine mixtures by reaction with HNO_2	+ Zn + HCl. A few min boiling, giving dimethylamine $2\,(CH_3)_2N.NO + 4\,H \rightarrow 2\,(CH_3)_2NH + N_2O + H_2O$	Made alkaline and distilled into excess acid, back titrating with alkali	5

Materials titrated	Reagent and reaction conditions	Subsequent treatment and final titration stage	Ref.
p-Nitroaniline	Reduced with Zn/acid	*p*-Phenylenediamine determined with excess NaOCl and back titration with arsenite (see Chlorine reagents, ref. 4)	6
Aromatic nitro compounds	+ Zn dust + HCl; 1 h with some heating	Amines titrated with nitrite to external I^-/starch (see Part I, Nitrite, ref. 4)	7
Anthraquinone	+ hot NaOH + Zn dust; 5 min. Several treatments, giving oxyanthranol	Filtered and titrated with MnO_4^- (see Part I, Permanganate, ref. 19)	8
Thiuram disulphides	In alcohol, + Mg filings + H_2SO_4. Boiled *ca* 50 min	CS_2 formed distilled into KOH/ethanol and the xanthate determined iodometrically (see Alcohols, ref. 6)	9
$CHCl_3$	+ 95% ethanol + Na; 30 min reflux	+ HNO_3 + excess $AgNO_3$ and back titrated with SCN^-	10
Cystine	+ Zn dust + HCl; 30 min	Filtered and cysteine titrated with IO_3^- in presence of I^- (see Part I, Iodate, ref. 4)	11
CHI_3	Heated with Zn + alcoholic NaOH	I^- formed titrated with $AgNO_3$ potentiometrically	12
Pyruvic acid	+ Zn + H_2SO_4 + trace $CuSO_4$, giving lactic acid	Heated with H_2SO_4 giving acetaldehyde, then determined with bisulphite	13
Pyruvic acid	+ Zn + NaH_2PO_4	Lactic acid oxidized with MnO_2 or MnO_4^- to acetaldehyde; determined with $NaHSO_3$	14
Nitroglycerine	+ Devarda's alloy + alkali	Ammonia distilled into excess H_2SO_4 and back titrated with NaOH to Na alizarin sulphonate	15
Pyruvic acid	+ Zn/Cu couple (from Zn dust + $CuSO_4$) + H_2SO_4; 5 min, giving lactic acid	Lactic acid oxidized with MnO_4^- to acetaldehyde; distilled and determined with bisulphite	16
Aromatic nitro and nitroso compounds	Modification of method of ref. 7		17

Materials titrated	Reagent and reaction conditions	Subsequent treatment and final titration stage	Ref.
Dithiosalicylic acid	+ Zn dust in neutral solution; 30 min boiling	+ Na_2CO_3 and titrated with diazonium salt (see Part I, Diazonium salts, ref. 7)	18
p-Chloronitrobenzene in presence of the *o*-isomer	In ether, + Zn dust + HCl; 15 min boiling	+ alkali, amines extracted with ether, evaporated and *p*-chloroaniline precipitated with oxalic acid and total amine titrated with bromate (see Carboxylic acids, ref. 12)	19
Cystine in urine	Urine (after removal of interfering substances) + Zn + HCl; 30 min/room temp.	Filtered and cysteine determined with excess iodine and back titration with thiosulphate (see Iodine reagents, ref. 148)	20
Aromatic nitro compounds	Fused with Zn or Al, + alkali, giving NH_3	Absorbed in excess H_2SO_4 and back titrated with alkali	21
m-Dinitrobenzene	In methanol, + HCl + Zn/Hg, giving *m*-phenylenediamine	Titrated with BrO_3^-/Br^- (see Part I, Bromate, ref. 34)	22
Nitrosalicylic acid	+ HCl + Na/Hg, giving aminosalicylic acid	Titrated with nitrite to external I^-/starch (see Part I, Nitrite, ref. 26)	23
Nitrobenzene	Shaken with Zn/Hg until colourless, giving aniline	Titrated with BrO_3^-/Br^- (see Part I, Bromate, ref. 35)	24
Naphthalene-1,5- or -1,6-disulphonic acids	+ Na/Hg; 14 h, eliminating the 1- and the 5-SO_3H groups, yielding sulphite	Titrated with iodine	25
Naphthalene-1-sulphonic acid	Method of ref. 25 (2-acid not reduced)		26
m-Nitrobenzene-sulphonic acid; nitro-naphthalene sulphonic acid	+ HCl + Zn/Hg, giving amines	Titrated with BrO_3^-/Br^- or nitrite (see Part I, Bromate, ref. 37; and Nitrite, ref. 30)	27
Nitrotoluenes	+ HCl + Zn/Hg, giving toluidines	Titrated with BrO_3^-/Br^-; *o*-toluidine titrated also with nitrite (see Part I, Bromate, ref. 38; and Nitrite, ref. 31)	28
Nitronaphthalene	In acetic acid, + HCl + Zn/Hg; shaken until light yellow	+ ice + HCl and titrated with nitrite (see Part I, Nitrite, ref. 32)	29

Materials titrated	Reagent and reaction conditions	Subsequent treatment and final titration stage	Ref.
Chloral	+ Zn + $(NH_4)_2SO_4$, yielding Cl^-	Titrated argentometrically	30
Nitrobenzene	+ HCl + Zn/Hg in the cold	+ excess BrO_3^-/Br^- and back titrated via I^-/thiosulphate (see Bromine reagents, ref. 159)	31
Nitrobenzene	Reduced on Cd in a Jones reductor	Determined with excess BrO_3^-/Br^- and iodometric back titration (see Bromine reagents, ref. 165)	32
p-Nitrophenol	+ HCl + Zn until colourless	+ HCl + KBr and titrated with nitrite (see Part I, Nitrite, ref. 34).	33
Nitrobenzoic and -cinnamic acids	+ Zn/Hg, giving amines	Titrated with nitrite or using excess BrO_3^-/Br^- and back titration via I^-/thiosulphate (see Bromine reagents, ref. 181 and Part I, Nitrite, ref. 36)	34
Nitrobenzaldehydes	+ HCl + Zn/Hg	Amines titrated as in ref. 34 (see Bromine reagents, ref. 181 and Part I, Nitrite, ref. 37)	35
Dichloroethane in air	Absorbed in ethanol, Na added and refluxed 2 h	+ HNO_3 and Cl^- titrated with $Hg(NO_3)_2$ to nitroprusside	36
Cystine	+ HCl + Zn; 30 min	Cysteine titrated with IO_3^- in presence of I^-/acid	37
Azo compounds, e.g. methyl red or congo red	+ $NaHSO_3$ + Zn; 5 min, reducing to amines evidently via formation of dithionite: $Zn + 4\,NaHSO_3 \rightarrow ZnSO_3 + Na_2SO_3 + Na_2S_2O_4 + 2\,H_2O$; then $3\,RN{=}NR + 2\,Na_2S_2O_4 + 8\,H_2O \rightarrow 6\,RNH_2 + 4\,NaHSO_4$	+ acetic acid and left 10 min; then + $NaHCO_3$ and titrated with iodine	38
Disulphides	In a hydrocarbon, e.g. benzene, + Zn + acetic acid. Up to 3 h reflux	Benzene layer + excess $AgNO_3$ and back titrated with SCN^- (see Silver (I), ref. 65)	39
Dehydroascorbic acid	+ Zn + sulphosalicylic acid	Titrated with Tillmans' reagent	40

Materials titrated	Reagent and reaction conditions	Subsequent treatment and final titration stage	Ref.
2-Methyl 1,4-naphtho-quinone (Menadione)	In acetic acid, + HCl + Zn, reducing to the diphenol	Titrated with Ce(IV) to ferroin (see Part I, Cerium (IV), ref. 19)	41
Disulphides	Refluxed with Zn/acetic acid, giving mercaptans	Titrated with $AgNO_3$	42
2-Methyl 1,4-naphtho-quinone	In methanol, + H_2SO_4 + Zn powder; 30 min/room temp. in dark	Diluted, filtered, + $NaHCO_3$ + excess iodine; then + acetic acid and titrated with thiosulphate (see Iodine reagents, ref. 233)	43
Tetrazine, $C_2H_2N_4$	+ NaOH + Devarda's alloy, yielding NH_3	Steam distilled into excess H_2SO_4 and back titrated with NaOH to methyl red	44
DDT deposits on fruit, vegetables or vegetation	Extract, e.g. in benzene or pentane, + iso-propanol + Na; 2 h reflux, converting the 5 Cl atoms to Cl^-	+ HNO_3 + excess $AgNO_3$ and back titrated with SCN^-	45
Disulphides	Solution in water/ethanol/H_2SO_4 run through a reductor containing Zn/Hg. *Ca* 50°	+ excess NH_4OH and titrated with $AgNO_3$ ampero-metrically (see Part I, Silver (I), ref. 27)	46
DDT in milk	Evaporated extract with ethanol/ether/Skelly-solve B, + isopropanol + Na; 2 h reflux	+ water + ethanol + HNO_3 and titrated potentiometrically with $AgNO_3$; or via method of ref. 45	47
Nitro compounds, e.g. nitro- and *m*-dinitro-benzene, nitrobenzoic and nitrocinnamic acid	+ HCl + Zn/Hg (some + methanol); 3–5 min until decolor-ized	+ BrO_3^-/Br^- excess, then + I^- and back titrated with thio-sulphate (see Bromine reagents, ref. 279)	48
Chlordan and some other halogen-containing insecticides like analogues of DDT, toxaphene	Method of ref. 47		49
Diphenyl disulphide	+ acetic acid + Zn; 16 h/room temp., giving thiophenol	Titrated with iodine (see Part I, Iodine, ref. 63)	50

Materials titrated	Reagent and reaction conditions	Subsequent treatment and final titration stage	Ref.
DDT in soils	Partly evaporated extract with benzene/isopropanol, 2:1, + isopropanol + Na. Refluxed, converting all Cl to Cl^-	+ excess $AgNO_3$ and back titrated with SCN^- potentiometrically	51
Cystine	+ dilute H_2SO_4 + Na/Hg; 30 min, giving cysteine	Added to NH_4OH/NH_4NO_3 and titrated with $AgNO_3$ amperometrically (see Part I, Silver (I), ref. 47)	52
p-Chlorophenyl glyceryl ether, $CH_2OH.CHOH.CH_2O.C_6H_4Cl(p)$	+ amyl alcohol + Na	Cl^- determined with excess $AgNO_3$ and back titration with SCN^-	53
p-Chloroacetanilide in phenacetin	+ ethanol + NaOH + Raney Ni; 10 min boiling, converting Cl to Cl^-	+ water + HNO_3 + Na citrate and titrated with $Hg(NO_3)_2$ to diphenylcarbazone	54
Parathion	In ether, + water + HCl + acetic acid + Zn dust. Warmed on water bath until most ether had evaporated, and the $—NO_2$ group reduced to $—NH_2$	+ Br^- and titrated with $NaNO_2$ to external I^-/starch (see Part I, Nitrite, ref. 64)	55
Organic halides	+ alkali + Raney Ni; 3 procedures, some with preliminary standing; 1·5–2 h reflux	+ HNO_3 + excess $AgNO_3$ and titrated with SCN^-	56
Nitro compounds (aromatic)	+ KOH/alcohol + Raney Ni type of paste; 1–2 h boiling	Filtered, Br^- + HCl added and amine titrated with nitrite to I^-/starch (see Part I, Nitrite, ref. 65)	57
Na monofluoroacetate	Refluxed with Na + isoamyl alcohol	+ ethanol + HCl and brought to pH 2·6–2·7 with chloroacetate buffer; titrated F^- with $Th(NO_3)_4$ to alizarin red	58
Dinitrodibenzyldisulphonic acid; 4,4′-dinitrostilbene-2,2′-disulphonic acid	+ acetic acid + Fe powder; 1 h/100°, giving amines	Titrated with $NaNO_2$ (see Part I, Nitrite, ref. 70)	59

Materials titrated	Reagent and reaction conditions	Subsequent treatment and final titration stage	Ref.
Dibromoethane in anti-knock mixtures	+ ethanol + Zn; 1 h reflux	+ HNO_3 + excess $AgNO_3$ and back titrated with SCN^-	60
DDT	In benzene/petrol ether + Na suspension + isoamyl alcohol. Refluxed 1 h	Cl^- determined argento-metrically	61
Cystine	+ H_2SO_4 + Zn/Hg in CO_2 atmosphere; 2–3 min, giving cysteine	Titrated with iodate	62
Disulphides in mixtures with mercaptans (after extraction of the latter with excess acrylo-nitrile and removal of unused acrylonitrile with water)	In acetic acid + iso-propanol passed through Zn/Hg reductor as in method of ref. 46; at room temp. to 60° (higher temp. for higher sulphides)	Mercaptans titrated with $AgNO_3$ potentiometrically (see Part I, Silver, ref. 66)	63
Dimethyl disulphide	+ acetic acid + Zn; 3 h reflux	Methyl mercaptan determined with excess $AgNO_3$ and back titration with SCN^- (see Silver (I), ref. 122)	64
Vitamin B_1	+ H_2SO_4 + Zn/Hg, in CO_2 atmosphere, giving H_2S	Absorbed in $CdSO_4$, excess iodine + HCl added and back titrated with thiosulphate	65
Nitroglycerine in tablets	In water/alcohol + NaOH + Al + a little $CuSO_4$, giving NH_3	Distilled into excess H_2SO_4 and back titrated with alkali to methyl orange	66
Aromatic nitro compounds	+ HCl + acetic acid + Zn dust; 20–30 min refluxed	+ Br^- and titrated with $NaNO_2$ to external I^-/starch (see Part I, Nitrite, ref. 81)	67
N-Nitrosodimethyl-amine from determina-tion of dimethylamine in mixtures of methyl-amines by treatment with nitrite/acid	+ conc. HCl + Zn; 20–25 min, giving evidently dimethyl-hydrazine	+ conc. HCl and titrated with IO_3^- potentiometrically or to disappearance of brown iodine colour (see Part I, Iodate, ref. 42)	68
Di Na salt of *N*-methyl-3,5-diiodo-pyridone-4-dicarboxylic acid	In water/acetic acid + Zn dust; 1 h reflux, yielding I^-	Filtered, filtrate + bromine/acetate/acetic acid, converting I^- to IO_3^-; after 10 min, unused bromine removed with HCOOH, I^-/H_2SO_4 added and iodine titrated with thiosulphate	69

Materials titrated	Reagent and reaction conditions	Subsequent treatment and final titration stage	Ref.
Tetraiodophenolphthalein	As in method of ref. 69, but refluxed 30 min	Filtrate + conc. HCl + KCN and titrated with IO_3^- until blue with starch disappeared (to I^+ formation)	70
Disulphides	+ acetic acid + Zn; 3 h/100°	Volatile mercaptans carried into excess $AgNO_3$; back titrated with SCN^- (see Silver (I), ref. 134)	71
Nitro compounds (aliphatic and aromatic); nitroso compounds (aromatic)	+ HCl + Cd in CO_2 atmosphere. Control	Cd(II) in solution titrated with EDTA to eriochrome black T	72
2-Methyl-1,4-naphthoquinone	In acetic acid + HCl + Zn filings; 30 min in dark	Decanted and titrated diphenol with Ce(IV) to ferroin (see Part I, Cerium (IV), ref. 49)	73
Dithioglycollic acid	+ HCl + Zn or Zn/Hg	Thioglycollic acid formed titrated with iodine (see Part I, Iodine, ref. 88)	74
Nitro derivatives of dichlorobenzenes	Reduced with Zn dust to amines	Titrated with nitrite to Tropeolin 00 (see Part I, Nitrite, ref. 96)	75
Chloramphenicol	+ dil. H_2SO_4 + Zn dust; 10 min reflux, giving Cl^-	Filtered and titrated with $AgNO_3$	76
Chloramphenicol	+ HCl + Zn dust	Amine titrated with $NaNO_2$ in presence Br^- at below 27° using I^-/starch indicator (see Part I, Nitrite, ref. 98)	77
Chloramphenicol	+ HCl + Zn; 45 min/100°	+ HCl + excess BrO_3^-/Br^-; then + I^- and back titrated with thiosulphate (see Bromine reagents, ref. 423)	78
Halogen-containing organic acids (after paper chromatographic separation)	+ absolute ethanol + Na; 2 h reflux	+ water + HNO_3 and titrated with $AgNO_3$ to eosin	79
Di-*p*-chlorophenyl disulphide	+ ethanol + H_2SO_4 + Zn/Hg; 1 h/*ca* 70°	Filtered and mercaptan titrated with iodine (see Part I, Iodine, ref. 98)	80

Materials titrated	Reagent and reaction conditions	Subsequent treatment and final titration stage	Ref.
Isoniazid	+ KOH + Zn/Cu couple, yielding 2 equivalents of NH_3	Distilled into excess H_2SO_4 and back titrated with NaOH to methyl red/methylene blue	81
2-Methyl-1,4-naphthoquinone bisulphite	In acetic acid + H_2SO_4 + Zn dust; 30 min reflux, then 1 h standing	Filtered and diphenol titrated with Ce(IV) to ferroin	82
Mixtures of 2-nitro- and 3-nitrotoluene	+ H_2SO_4 + Zn, giving amine mixture	Titrated with $NaNO_2$, giving total amine; and with bromate, substituting in 2 and 3 positions respectively; combination of both titrations gave the composition (see Part I, Nitrite, ref. 103)	83
Nitroglycerine	In ethanol, + alkali + Raney Ni; boiled 15 min	Ammonia distilled into excess acid and back titrated with alkali	84
Dichloro- and dibromoethane in ethyl fluid	Refluxed with butanol/Na	Cl^- or Br^- determined with excess $AgNO_3$ and back titration with SCN^-	85
Amyl nitrate from determination of the nitrite by oxidation with MnO_4^-	Method of ref. 84		86
Cholinium chloride	+ NaOH + Raney Ni; 25 min boiling, giving trimethylamine	Distilled into excess HCl and back titrated with alkali to methyl red/methylene blue	87
Disulphides in petroleum and its products	+ acetic acid + Zn; 3–4 h reflux; or + methanol + acetic acid + Zn; 30 min/room temp. or + KOH + Zn dust + methanol	+ water and organic layer ultimately titrated with $AgNO_3$ potentiometrically (see Part I, Silver (I), ref. 134)	88
Disulphides in petroleum naphtha	+ isooctane + acetic acid + Zn; 3 h reflux in nitrogen atmosphere	+ NH_4OH and titrated potentiometrically with $AgNO_3$ (see Part I, Silver (I), ref. 136)	89
Nitrotoluenesulphonic acids, derived from determination of toluenesulphonic acids by nitration	In water, reduced with HCl/Zn dust, then 10–15 min boiling	Filtered, HCl + Br^- added and titrated with $NaNO_2$ to Tropeolin 00	90

Materials titrated	Reagent and reaction conditions	Subsequent treatment and final titration stage	Ref.
Some iodine-containing compounds, e.g. Na monoiodomethane sulphonate or Ca iodobehenate ('Sajodin')	+ H_2SO_4 + Zn dust; 10 min/100°, converting iodine to I^-	Filtered, excess $AgNO_3$ added and back titrated with SCN^-	91
Chloramphenicol	Reduced with HCl/Zn	Amine titrated with $NaNO_2$ to Tropeolin 00	92
Alkyl disulphides	+ ethanol + acetic acid + HCl + Zn; 30 min	Mercaptan products titrated with iodine (see Part I, Iodine, ref. 110)	93
Thiodan, $C_9H_6O_3Cl_6S$	In ethanol, + HCl + Zn; 45 min, giving H_2S	Aspirated into Cd acetate/Na acetate + excess iodine; slowly acidified with H_2SO_4; back titrated with thiosulphate	94
Hg-containing pharmaceuticals	+ Sn/Hg, giving Sn(II)	Titrated with $Cr_2O_7^{2-}$ to diphenylamine/HCl	95
Urethanes	+ NaOH + Raney Ni + 3–4% Al. Boiled 30 min, giving NH_3	Distilled into excess HCl and back titrated with alkali	96
Dibenzyl disulphide	In ethanol/HCl/H_2SO_4, + Zn/Hg; 20 min/65°, giving benzyl mercaptan	Titrated with iodine to yellow-green (see Part I, Iodine, ref. 120)	97
Quinone, oxidized from hydroquinone derived from acid hydrolysis of arbutin	Reduced to hydroquinone with Zn/H_2SO_4	Titrated with $Ce(SO_4)_2$ to ferroin (see Part I, Cerium (IV), ref. 80)	98
Trichlorobenzene, from determination of BHC by treatment with KOH/alcohol	Extract in petroleum ether, + Na/butanol; petroleum ether distilled off and heated further	Cl^- determined with excess Ag^+ and back titration with SCN^-	99
Chloramphenicol	Refluxed with Zn/HCl, reducing the —NO_2 group to —NH_2	Titrated with $NaNO_2$ (see Part I, Nitrite, ref. 141)	100
DDT; BHC	In 96% ethanol, + Zn dust + dilute H_2SO_4; 15 min boiling	Cl^- determined with excess $AgNO_3$, back titrating with SCN^-	101
Chloramphenicol	In warm conc. HCl, + KBr + Zn	Cooled and titrated with nitrite, using starch/I^- as external indicator	102

Materials titrated	Reagent and reaction conditions	Subsequent treatment and final titration stage	Ref.
Disulphides	In ethanol, + Zn + H_2SO_4; heated to 55° and shaken 30 min, giving mercaptans	Neutralized to bromophenol blue and titrated with Hg(II) to diphenylcarbazone (see Part I, Mercury (II), ref. 90)	103
Pentaerythritol tetranitrate; mannitol hexanitrate	In ethanol, + NaOH + $CuSO_4$ + Devarda's alloy, giving NH_3	Passed into excess H_2SO_4 and back titrated with alkali	104
Trityl phenyl sulphide	+ Zn/Hg, reducing to triphenylmethane and thiophenol	Latter titrated with $AgNO_3$ amperometrically	105
Pentachlorophenol	Heated with K in a closed tube, giving KCl	Dissolved in water and Cl^- titrated with $AgNO_3$ conductometrically	106
Isoniazid in mixtures with Na *p*-aminosalicylate	Suspension in water, + conc. HCl + Zn/Cu couple, giving NH_3	Distilled into H_2SO_4 and back titrated with NaOH	107
1,2-Dibromo-3-chloropropane in nematocides	In butane, + polyoxyethylene glycol 400 + Na; 1 h reflux	+ isopropanol/water, treated with H_2O_2 and ultimately titrated with Ag^+	108
Alkaloids of celandine root (*Chelidonium majus*)	Extract in ethanol, + H_2SO_4 + acetic acid + Zn dust; 1 h/ca 100° giving tertiary amine	Filtered, filtrate + alkali, extracted with ether, extract evaporated down and titrated with $HClO_4$/acetic acid + anhydride to crystal violet	109
Diphenoquinonedi-(4,4′-dimethylammonium) ion	+ Zn powder; mixed until solution colourless	Filtered and filtrate titrated potentiometrically with Ce(IV), bromine or bichromate	110

References

1. Green, A. G. and Wahl, A. R., *Ber.* **31**, 1080 (1898).
2. Glasman, B., *Ber.* **36**, 4260 (1903).
3. Wieland, H., *Ber.* **43**, 715 (1910).
4. Tarugi, N. and Sottile, C., *Chem.-Ztg.* **35**, 1068 (1911).
5. Weber, F. C. and Wilson, J. B., *J. Biol. Chem.* **35**, 385 (1918).
6. Callan, T. and Henderson, J. A. R., *J. Soc. Chem. Ind.* (*London*) **38**, 408T (1919).

7. Callan, T., Henderson, J. A. R. and Strafford, N., *J. Soc. Chem. Ind. (London)* **39**, 86T (1920).
8. Nelson, O. A. and Senseman, C. E., *J. Ind. Eng. Chem.* **14**, 956 (1922).
9. Callan, T. and Strafford, N., *J. Soc. Chem. Ind. (London)* **43**, 1T (1924).
10. Nicloux, M., *Compt. rend. soc. biol.* **91**, 1282 (1924).
11. Okuda, Y., *J. Chem. Soc. Japan* **45**, 1, 18 (1924).
12. Jánský, K., *Časopis českého Lékárnictva* **8**, 215 (1928).
13. Krishna, B. H., *Proc. 15th Indian Sci. Congress* 104 (1928).
14. Kendall, A. I. and Friedemann, T. E., *J. Infectious Diseases* **47**, 176 (1930).
15. Caron, H. and Raquet, D., *J. pharm. chim.* **12**, 109 (1930).
16. Wendel, W. B., *J. Biol. Chem.* **94**, 717 (1932).
17. Ueno, S. and Sekiguchi, H., *J. Soc. Chem. Ind., Japan* **36**, Suppl. binding 410 (1933).
18. Ershov, A. P., *Anilinokrasochnaya Prom.* **4**, 303 (1934).
19. Mizuch, K. G. and Savchenko, A. Ya., *Anilinokrasochnaya Prom.* **4**, 204 (1934).
20. Virtue, R. A. and Lewis, H. B., *J. Biol. Chem.* **104**, 415 (1934).
21. Alekseevskii, E. V. and Gol'braikh, Z. E., *Zhur. Priklad Khim. (J. Appl. Chem. USSR)* **9**, 1535 (1936).
22. Lobunets, M. M., *Univ. état Kiev, Bull. sci. Recueil chim.* **2**, No. 2, 69 (1936).
23. Lobunets, M. M., *Univ. état Kiev, Bull. sci. Recueil chim* **2**, No. 2, 81 (1936).
24. Per'e, M. I. and Lobunets, M. M., *Univ. état Kiev, Bull sci. Recueil chim.* **2**, No. 2, 73 (1936).
25. Terent'ev, A. P. and Terent'eva, E. M., *Sci. Repts. Moscow State Univ.* No. 6, 190 (1936).
26. Terent'ev, A. P. and Terent'eva, E. M., *Sci. Repts. Moscow State Univ.* No. 6, 207 (1936).
27. Lobunets, M. M., *Univ. état Kiev, Bull. sci. Recueil chim.* No. 3, 71 (1937).
28. Per'e, M. I., *Univ. état Kiev, Bull sci. Recueil chim.* No. 3, 37 (1937).
29. Per'e, M. I. and Lobunets, M. M., *Univ. état Kiev, Bull sci. Recueil chim.* No. 3, 43 (1937).
30. Schwicker, A., *Z. anal. Chem.* **110**, 161 (1937).
31. Gordon, B. and Dakhnov, V., *Neftyance Khoz.* **19**, No. 9, 53 (1938).
32. Lobunets, M. M., *Zavodskaya Lab.* **7**, 872 (1938).
33. Shcherbachev, K. D., *Org. Chem. Ind. USSR* **5**, 753 (1938).
34. Lobunets, M. M., *Univ. état Kiev, Bull. sci. Recueil chim.* No. 4, 23 (1939).
35. Lobunets, M. M., *Unvi. état Kiev, Bull sci. Recueil chim.* No. 4, 41 (1939).

36. Mel'nikov, F. F. and Senilov, B. V., *Lab. Prakt.* (*USSR*) **14**, No. 9–10, 18 (1939).
37. Sato, M., Hirano, T. and Kan, T., *J. Agr. Chem. Soc. Japan* **15**, 783 (1939).
38. Zaraus, V. L., *Bol. soc. quím. Peru* **5**, 124 (1939).
39. Bell, R. T. and Agruss, M. S., *Ind. Eng. Chem., Anal. Ed.* **13**, 297 (1941).
40. Goldshtein, B. I. and Volkenzon, D. V., *Biochem. J.* (*Ukraine*) **17**, 219 (1941).
41. Rosin, J., Rosenblum, H. and Mack, H., *Am. J. Pharm.* **113**, 434 (1941).
42. Ball, J. S., *U.S. Bur. Mines Rept. Investigations* 3591 (1942).
43. Jarousse, J., *Ann. pharm. franç.* **3**, 128 (1945).
44. Mester, L., *Magyar Kem. Folyoirat* **51/3**, 32 (1945–7).
45. Carter, R. H. and Hubanks, P. E., *J. Assoc. Off. Agr. Chem.* **29**, 112 (1946).
46. Kolthoff, I. M., May, D. R., Morgan, P., Laitinen, H. A. and O'Brien, A. S., *Ind. Eng. Chem., Anal. Ed.* **18**, 442 (1946).
47. Carter, R. H., *Anal. Chem.* **19**, 54 (1947).
48. Lobunets, N., *Z. anal. Chem.* **128**, 279 (1948).
49. Carter, R. H., Wells, R. W., Radeleft, R. D., Smith, C. L., Hubanks, P. E. and Mann, H. D., *J. Econ. Entomol.* **42**, 116 (1949).
50. Harnish, D. P. and Tarbell, D. S., *Anal. Chem.* **21**, 968 (1949).
51. Koblitsky, L. and Chisholm, R. D., *J. Assoc. Off. Agr. Chem.* **32**, 781 (1949).
52. Kolthoff, I. M. and Stricks, W., *J. Am. Chem. Soc.* **72**, 1952 (1950).
53. Stross, P. and Stuckey, R. E., *J. Pharm. Pharmacol.* **2**, 549 (1950).
54. Hald, J., *Acta Pharm. Intern.* **2**, 87 (1951).
55. O'Keeffe, K. and Averell, P. R., *Anal. Chem.* **23**, 1167 (1951).
56. Ruzhentseva, A. K. and Kolpakova, V. V., *Zhur. Anal. Khim.* **6**, 223 (1951).
57. Ruzhentseva, A. K. and Goryacheva, N. S., *Doklady Akad. Nauk SSSR* **81**, 849 (1951).
58. Engo, K. and Nomura, K., *Ann. Repts. Takamine Lab.* **4**, 170 (1952).
59. Inukai, K. and Maki, Y., *Repts. Govt. Ind. Research Inst., Nagoya* **1**, 101 (1952).
60. Randi, M., *Chim. e ind.* (*Milan*) **34**, 143 (1952).
61. Vastagh, G., Vastagh, E. and Gervay, V., *Arch. Pharm.* **283**, 165 (1952).
62. Yoshimura, C. and Matsuoka, M., *J. Chem. Soc. Japan, Pure Chem. Sect.* **73**, 786 (1952).
63. Earle, T. E., *Anal. Chem.* **25**, 769 (1953).
64. Segal, W. and Starkey, R. L., *Anal. Chem.* **25**, 1645 (1953).
65. Yoshimura, C., *J. Chem. Soc. Japan, Pure Chem. Sect.* **74**, 992 (1953).
66. Shraiber, M. S. and Rubinshtein, B. A., *Aptechnoe Delo* **3**, No. 5, 46 (1954).

67. Wolthius, E., Kolk, S. and Schaap, L., *Anal. Chem.* **26**, 1238 (1954).
68. Alekseev, N. F. and Dvinyanina, M. P., *Zavodskaya Lab.* **21**, 1166 (1955).
69. Boehm, T., Freudenberg, R. and Horsch, G., *Pharmazie* **10**, 226 (1955).
70. Boehm, T., Freudenberg, R. and Horsch, G., *Pharmazie* **10**, 227 (1955).
71. Coope, J. A. R. and Maingot, G. J., *Anal. Chem.* **27**, 1478 (1955).
72. Budesinský, B., *Chem. Listy* **50**, 1931 (1956); *Collection Czechoslov. Chem. Communs.* **22**, 1141 (1957).
73. Hahn, I., Scheunert, A. and Seel, H., *Pharmazie* **11**, 91 (1956).
74. Pesez, M., *Ann. fals. et fraudes* **49**, 403 (1956).
75. Spryskov, A. A. and Erykalov, Yu. G., *Zhur. Anal. Khim.* **11**, 492 (1956).
76. Vaisman, G. A. and Kislaya, M. D., *Aptechnoe Delo* **5**, No. 4, 19 (1956).
77. Wang, T.-H., *Yao Hsüeh Hsüeh Pao* (*Acta Pharm. Sinica*) **4**, 201 (1956).
78. Awe, W. and Stohlmann, H., *Arzneimittelforsch.* **7**, 495 (1957).
79. Hashmi, M. H., *Anal. Chim. Acta* **17**, 225 (1957).
80. Higgins, D. J. and Stephenson, W. H., *Analyst* **82**, 435 (1957).
81. Mitchell, B. W., Haugas, E. A. and McRoe, C. S., *J. Pharm. Pharmacol.* **9**, 42 (1957).
82. Perlotto, T., *Farmaco* (*Pavia*), *Ed. prat.* **12**, 286 (1957).
83. Portnov, M. A. and Tomilov, B. I., *Zhur. Anal. Khim.* **12**, 402 (1957).
84. Simonyi, I. and Tokár, G., *Acta Pharm. Hung.* **27**, 17 (1957).
85. Tagliavini, G., *Chim. e ind.* (*Milan*) **39**, 902 (1957).
86. Tokár, G. and Simonyi, I., *Acta Pharm. Hung.* **27**, 20 (1957).
87. Bayer, I. and Katona, K., *Acta Pharm. Hung.* **28**, 216 (1958).
88. Hubbard, R. L., Haines, W. E. and Ball, J. S., *Anal. Chem.* **30**, 91 (1958).
89. Karchmer, J. H. and Walker, M. T., *Anal. Chem.* **30**, 85 (1958).
90. Spryskov, A. A., *Izvest. Vysshikh Ucheb. Zavedenii, Khim. i Khim. Tekhnol.* No. 6, 42 (1958).
91. Suprun, P. P., *Med. Prom. SSSR* **12**, No. 11, 39 (1958).
92. Vasiliev, R., Madgearu, M., Albu-Radulescu, M. and Woinarovsky, V., *Lucrarile prezentate conf. natl. farm.* (*Bucharest*) 155 (1958).
93. Jaselskis, B., *Anal. Chem.* **31**, 928 (1959).
94. Riemschneider, R. and Hilscher, J.-C., *Z. anal. Chem.* **165**, 278 (1959).
95. Timoshenko, M. I., *Uchenya Zapiski, Pyatigorskii Farm. Inst.* **3**, 148 (1959).
96. Tóth, Z. and Krasznai, I., *Magyar Kem. Folyoirat* **65**, 289 (1959).
97. Klouček, B., Jehlička, V. and Gasparič, J., *Chem. Průmysl* **10**, 624 (1960).
98. Rácz, G., Fuzi, J. and Fulop, L., *Acta Pharm. Hung.* **30**, 212 (1960).
99. Shibasaki, T., *Bunseki Kagaku* **9**, 544 (1960).
100. Srivastava, S. K., Ray, G. K. and Mukerji, B., *J. Sci. Ind. Research* (*India*) **19B**, 456 (1960).

101. Suprun, P. P., *Aptechnoe Delo* **9**, No. 3, 19 (1960).
102. Bouw, P. S., Ie, T. S., Bulhasrin and Abdul Kadir, *Suara Pharm. Madjalah* **6**, No. 3 65 (1961).
103. Gregg, D. C., Bouffard, P. E. and Barton, R., *Anal. Chem.* **33**, 269 (1961).
104. Shraiber, M. S. and Tsarenko, N. Ya., *Med. Prom.* (*SSSR*) **15**, No. 3, 40 (1961).
105. Tarantelli, T., *Ann. chim.* (*Rome*) **51**, 1174 (1961).
106. Volina, T. L., *Nauchn. Tr. Vses. Nauchn.-Issled. Inst. Tsellyulozz.-Bumazhn. Prom.* No. 47, 112 (1961).
107. Lee, K.-T. and Ho, Y.-H., *J. Pharm. & Pharmacol.* **14**, 123 (1962).
108. Barberá Gayoso, C. and Rafols Rovira, J. M., *Quím. e Ind., Bilbao* **9**, 96 (1962).
109. Domagalina, E. and Ochyńska, J., *Chem. Anal.* (*Warsaw*) **8**, 225 (1963).
110. Matrka, M., *Chem. Listy* **57**, 163 (1963).

70. Molybdenum (III)

One example of indirect titration with this strong but rarely used reducing agent is given here:

Materials titrated	Reagent and reaction conditions	Subsequent treatment and final titration stage
Nitro and nitroso compounds, e.g. picric acid and cupferron	+ excess Mo(III) in CO_2 atmosphere	Unused back titrated with Fe(III) alum to methylene blue indicator

Reference

Gapchenko, M. V., *Zavodskaya Lab.* **10**, 245 (1941).

71. Molybdenum (VI) and tungsten (VI)

Reagent. In almost all cases, the heteropoly acids molybdo-phosphoric and -silicic and tungsto-phosphoric and -silicic acids have been used. Three examples of the use of molybdate are included here.

Reactions and materials titrated. 1. Oxidation yielding lower valency states of molybdenum and tungsten (so-called 'molybdenum blue'). Materials thus determined have been principally polyhydroxy-compounds like polysaccharides (dextrin, inulin), sugars, polyphenols and dihydroxyacetone. Mercaptans like glutathione have been determined and also uric acid.

2. Complex formation with many bases (mostly alkaloids) and, in one example, surface-active polyglycols, yielding precipitates usually of variable and complex composition.

Subsequent treatment and final titration stage. (i) Methods based on reactions of type 1 have been concluded by oxidative titration to disappearance of the blue colour, with permanganate or ferricyanide reagents.

(ii) Following reactions of type 2, ignition and gravimetric determination has probably been the most used method. In the majority of the examples below, titrimetric conclusions have depended on release of the original material from the precipitate so that the reagent has served essentially as a separating agent.

Techniques adopted have been:

1. Addition of alkali, distillation of the base and titration with acid.
2. Addition of alkali/excess iodine (with trigonelline) and subsequent back titration of unused iodine.
3. Determination of the penicillin moiety of the precipitate via successive treatment with alkali and iodine excess.
4. Reaction of polyglycols with hydriodic acid to yield ethyl iodide, determined via bromine oxidation to iodate.

Conclusions which depended on determination of the heteropoly acid part of the precipitate have been:

1. Solution of precipitate in excess alkali and back titration with acid.
2. Reduction with sodium amalgam to 'molybdenum blue' and titration as under (i) with permanganate.

Examples

Materials titrated	Reagent and reaction conditions	Subsequent treatment and final titration stage	Ref.
Nicotine	Extract in HCl, + tungstosilicic acid; 24–48 h/room temp.	Centrifuged, precipitate distilled with MgO and nicotine in distillate titrated with H_2SO_4 to alizarinsulphonic acid	1

Materials titrated	Reagent and reaction conditions	Subsequent treatment and final titration stage	Ref.
Dihydroxyacetone	+ molybdophosphoric acid; 15 min boiling, giving 'molybdenum blue'	Titrated with MnO_4^- to disappearance of blue	2
Fructose; sucrose; insulin	+ molybdophosphoric acid; 10 min/100°	+ dilute H_2SO_4 and titrated with MnO_4^- to disappearance of blue	3
Dihydroxyacetone in blood, urine, etc.	+ molybdophosphoric acid; 15 min/100° (method of ref. 2)	Titrated with MnO_4^- to disappearance of blue	4
Nicotine	In dilute H_2SO_4, + tungstosilicic acid, giving precipitate	Precipitate + alkali, nicotine distilled and titrated with HCl to methyl red	5
Nicotine	+ tungstosilicic acid	Precipitate dissolved in excess NaOH and unused back titrated with HCl to methyl red	6
Fructose in blood	+ molybdophosphoric acid reagent; 25 min boiling	Titrated with MnO_4^- to disappearance of blue	7
Inulin	Extract, + molybdophosphoric acid reagent; 90 min/100°	Titrated with MnO_4^- to pale rose colour	8
Dextrin	+ ammonium molybdate; 3 h/100°	Titrated with MnO_4^- to disappearance of blue	9
Nicotine in organs	Precipitated with tungstosilicic acid	Precipitate heated with lime, nicotine distilled into excess HCl and the acid back titrated	10
Trigonelline	In water, + a little H_2SO_4 + tungstophosphoric acid. Boiled, then cooled to 0°	Precipitate dissolved in NaOH, excess iodine added and after 1 h, unused titrated with thiosulphate	11
Fructose	+ molybdophosphoric acid; 90 min/100°	+ H_2SO_4 and titrated with MnO_4^-	12
Uric acid in blood or urine	+ molybdophosphoric acid	Titrated with $Fe(CN)_6^{3-}$/KOH to disappearance of blue	13
Glutathione	+ tungstophosphoric acid + Na_2CO_3	Titrated with $Fe(CN)_6^{3-}$ to disappearance of blue	14

Materials titrated	Reagent and reaction conditions	Subsequent treatment and final titration stage	Ref.
Polyphenols	+ tungstophosphoric acid + Na_2CO_3	Titrated with $Fe(CN)_6^{3-}$ to disappearance of blue	15
Fructose in blood	+ ammonium molybdate	Titrated with MnO_4^- to disappearance of blue	16
Alkaloids, e.g. strychnine, cocaine, atropine	In neutral or slightly acid solution, + tungstophosphoric acid	Centrifuged, precipitate reduced with Na/Hg and titrated with MnO_4^-	17
Sugars (micro)	+ molybdophosphoric acid	Titrated with MnO_4^- to disappearance of blue	18
Uric acid in urine	+ tungstophosphoric acid + alkali	Titrated with $Fe(CN)_6^{3-}$ to original colour	19
Surface-active polyglycols	+ HCl to make slightly acid + $CaCl_2$ + molybdophosphoric acid. Left overnight	Precipitate treated with HI, giving ethyl iodide; determined by reaction with bromine giving iodate (see Iodide and hydriodic acid, ref. 198)	20
Tributyl phosphate (after heating with H_2SO_4/H_2O_2)	+ HNO_3 + ammonium molybdate; 2 min shaking/60°	Filtered, excess NaOH added and back titratred with HCl	21

References

1. Bertrand, G. and Javillier, M., *Bull. soc. chim. France* (4) **5**, 241 (1909).
2. Campbell, W. R., *J. Biol. Chem.* **67**, 59 (1926).
3. Campbell, W. R. and Hanna, M. I., *J. Biol. Chem.* **69**, 703 (1926).
4. McClellan, W. E., *J. Biol. Chem.* **76**, 481 (1928).
5. Nagy, V. L., *Magyar Gyógyszerésztud. Társaság Ertesitöje* **8**, 240 (1932); *Biochem. Z.* **249**, 404 (1932).
6. Nagy, L. and Dickmann, S., *Magyar Gyógyszerésztud. Társaság Értesitöje* **9**, 210 (1933).
7. Stöhr, R., *Z. physiol. Chem.* **222**, 261 (1933).
8. Strepkov, S. M., *Biochem. Z.* **288**, 301 (1936).
9. Strepkov, S. M., *Botan. Arch.* **38**, 294 (1936).
10. Bodnár, J. and Nagy, V. L., *Deut. Z. Ges. gerichtl. Med.* **30**, 231 (1938).
11. Slotta, K. H. and Neisser, K., *Ber.* **71**, 1987 (1938).
12. Chizhova, K. H., *Khlebopekarnaya Prom.* No. 9–10, 27 (1939).
13. Ionescu-Matiu, A. and Popescu, A., *Bull. soc. chim. biol.* **21**, 264 (1939).

14. Ionescu-Matiu, A. and Popescu, A., *Bull. acad. méd. Roumanie* **4**, 385 (1939).
15. Ionescu-Matiu, A., Popescu, C. and Popescu, A., *J. pharm. chim.* **30**, 49 (1939).
16. Vengerova, F. M., *Lab. Prakt.* (*USSR*), *Sammelband* 53 (1939).
17. Ionescu-Matiu, A., Popescu, C. and Ghiorghiu, A., *Produits pharm.* **3**, No. 7, 295 (1948).
18. Carles, J., *Bull. soc. chim. biol.* **35**, 365 (1953).
19. Mais, L., *Laboratornoe Delo* **3**, No. 5, 41 (1957).
20. Etienne, H., *Bull. centre belge étude et document. eaux* (*Liège*) No. 40, 159 (1958).
21. Malinowski, J. and Rozmarynowicz, M., *Chem. Anal.* (*Warsaw*) **3**, 67 (1958).

72. Nickel (II)

Reagent and reaction conditions. Various salts have been used (chloride, sulphate, nitrate, acetate, etc.).

Ni(II) has frequently been used as the reagent for the second stage of a determination; in some cases, however, the reagent has contained the reagents for both first and this second stage (e.g. together with CS_2, hydroxylamine or SCN^-—see below) (see also under these reagent headings).

Reaction and materials titrated. Ion/ion combination involving Ni^{2+} or a complex ion containing it, has been the reaction for determining some organic anions. The products are difficultly soluble in water and usually soluble in organic solvents like $CHCl_3$. Amongst such anions can be mentioned: dithiocarbamates; xanthates; alkyl sulphates; dioxime anions; cyanide (from cyanohydrins); and *O,O*-dimethyl hydrogen phosphorodithioates.

$$2\,RNH\text{—}CS\text{—}S^- + Ni^{2+} \rightarrow (RNH\text{—}CS\text{—}S)_2Ni$$

$$2\,RO\text{—}CS\text{—}S^- + Ni^{2+} \rightarrow (RO\text{—}CS\text{—}S)_2Ni$$

$$2\,ROSO_3^- + 4\,NH_3 + Ni^{2+} \rightarrow (ROSO_3)_2[Ni(NH_3)_4]$$

$$2\begin{array}{l} RC{=}NOH \\ \quad| \\ RC{=}NO^- \end{array} + Ni^{2+} \rightarrow \begin{array}{ccccc} & & O\text{—}H\text{—}O & & \\ RC{=}N & & & & N{=}CR \\ | & & Ni & & | \\ RC{=}N & & & & N{=}CR \\ & & O\text{—}H\text{—}O & & \end{array}$$

$$RCHOH—CN \rightleftharpoons RCHO + H^+ + CN^-, \text{ followed by:}$$

$$Ni^{2+} + 4\,CN^- \rightarrow Ni(CN)_4^{2-}$$

In the determination of pyramidone, complex formation between Ni^{2+} and the base probably takes place, giving the cation $Ni(Pyramidone)_2^{2+}$ (as poorly soluble thiocyanate).

Dithiocarbamates, xanthates and dioximes are sometimes intermediate products in the determination of primary and secondary amines, of primary and secondary alcohols and of diketones (or monoximes of diketones) respectively. These amines, alcohols and diketones have also been determined directly using a composite reagent containing Ni(II) (see above under Reagent).

Subsequent treatment and final titration stage. (i) Unused reagent component has been back titrated in about half the examples given, and generally Ni(II) with EDTA; in another, unused SCN^- from precipitation of a complex thiocyanate was back titrated with Ag(I).

(ii) Ni(II) in the reaction product has been determined, usually with EDTA (direct titration to murexide, or using excess and back titrating with Ni(II)); in one case the Ni(II) was set free by reaction with Ag(I).

(iii) The organic moiety of the reaction product has also been determined; e.g. dithiocarbamate by titration with Hg(II) or dimethylphosphorodithioate with excess iodine.

Examples

Materials titrated	Reagent and reaction conditions	Subsequent treatment and final titration stage	Ref.
Secondary amines in presence of primary and tertiary	In benzene or isopentanol, + CS_2 + $NiSO_4$	Ni salt from the primary amine extracted with $NaOH/NH_4OH$; that from the secondary amine decomposed with HNO_3 or, with small amounts, treated with $AgNO_3$; liberated Ni(II) then titratred with EDTA to murexide	1
Xanthate from determination of ethanol in aqueous solution by reaction with CS_2/KOH	+ some acetic acid, CO_2 passed through for 40 min; then + Ni acetate, giving Ni xanthate; 10–15 min	Filtered, precipitate dissolved in NH_4OH and Ni(II) titrated with EDTA to murexide	2

Materials titrated	Reagent and reaction conditions	Subsequent treatment and final titration stage	Ref.
Dithiocarbamate from determination of monomethylamine in presence of other methylamines, by reaction with CS_2/NaOH	In neutral solution, + Ni(II) reagent	Dissolved in NH_4OH, + excess EDTA and back titrated with Ni(II) to murexide	3
Sulphates of long chain primary alcohols	In water, + 2-fold excess $NiCl_2$ + NH_4OH; 10 min, giving insoluble $Ni(NH_3)_4$ salt	Filtered and unused Ni(II) in filtrate titrated with EDTA to murexide	4, 6
Hexamethyleneimine in presence of hexamethylenediamine	In water, + CS_2/benzene + Ni(II) reagent	Benzene layer shaken with $AgNO_3/NH_4OH$ and the liberated Ni(II) titrated with EDTA to murexide	5
Xanthates; Na diethyldithiocarbamate	+ $Ni(NO_3)_2$ + $CHCl_3$; 1 min shaking, giving Ni salts, soluble in the $CHCl_3$	$CHCl_3$ layer + acetate buffer and titrated with Hg acetate to diphenyl carbazone	7
Cyanohydrins	+ $NiSO_4$; 15 min shaking with water-insoluble cyanohydrins	+ NH_4OH and back titrated unused Ni(II) with EDTA to murexide	8
Biacetyl	+ hydroxylamine hydrochloride + Ni acetate + Na acetate; 4 h reflux, giving Ni dimethyl glyoxime precipitate	+ NH_4OH, filtered and titrated unused Ni(II) with EDTA to murexide	9
O,O-Dialkyl hydrogen phosphorodithioates and their Na salts in technical products	+ saturated $NiSO_4$, giving Ni salts	+ excess iodine until yellow and back titrated with thiosulphate	10
Pyramidone	In water, + excess NH_4SCN + $Ni(NO_3)_2$, giving precipitate of complex	Filtered, filtrate acidified with HNO_3 and unused SCN^- titrated with Ag(I) to eosin	11
Biacetyl monoxime	Method of ref. 9		12
Vicinal dioximes	+ NH_4OH + excess Ni acetate; boiled a few min, then left 1 h, giving precipitates of Ni dioxime derivatives	Filtered and Ni(II) in filtrate titrated with EDTA to murexide	13

Materials titrated	Reagent and reaction conditions	Subsequent treatment and final titration stage	Ref.
Vicinal dioximes from determination of α-diketones by reaction with hydroxylamine	Method of ref. 13		14
Na salt of 5,5-diphenyl-hydantoin ('hydantional')	+ excess Ni(II) reagent	Precipitate titrated with EDTA to murexide	15

References

1. Nebbia, L. and Guerrieri, F., *Chim. e ind.* (*Milan*) **35**, 896 (1953).
2. Arikawa, Y. and Kato, T., *Technol. Repts. Tohoku Univ.* **19**, 104 (1954); Arikawa, Y., *Bunseki Kagaku* (*Japan Analyst*) **4**, 94 (1955).
3. Nebbia, L. and Guerrieri, F., *Chim. e ind.* (*Milan*) **37**, 198 (1955).
4. Gautier, J. A. and Renault, J., *Chim. anal.* **39**, 189 (1957).
5. Nebbia, L. and Guerrieri, F., *Chim. e ind.* (*Milan*) **39**, 672 (1957).
6. Renault, J. and Gautier, J. A., *Bull. soc. chim. France* 208 (1957).
7. Bičovský, K. and Bičovská, P., *Collection Czechoslov. Chem. Communs.* **24**, 3099 (1959).
8. Berther, C., Kreis, K. and Buchmann, O., *Z. anal. Chem.* **169**, 184 (1959).
9. Hennart, C. and Merlin, E., *Chim. anal.* **41**, 287 (1959).
10. Bátová, V. and Veselá, Z., *Sborník Prác. Výzkum. Ustav. Agrochem. Technol., Bratislava* **1**, 85 (1961).
11. Dick, I. and Ristici, J., *Farmacia* (*Bucharest*) **9**, 525 (1961).
12. Hennart, C. and Merlin, E., *Chim. anal.* **43**, 28 (1961).
13. Hennart, C. and Vieillet, F., *Anal. Chim. Acta* **25**, 150 (1961).
14. Hennart, C., *Anal. Chim. Acta* **25**, 201 (1961).
15. Przyborowski, L., *Ann. Univ. Mariae Curie-Sklodoswska, Lublin-Polonia, Sect.* D **17**, 25 (1962).

73. Ninhydrin

Reagent. Ninhydrin and the analogous compound, perinaphthindane-2,3,4-trione hydrate

$C_6H_4(CO)_2C(OH)_2$ $\qquad$ $C_{10}H_6(CO)_2C(OH)_2$

Reaction and materials titrated. Oxidation, in determination of α-amino acids:

$$\begin{matrix}-CO \\ -CO\end{matrix}\!\!>C(OH)_2 + RCH(NH_2)COOH \rightarrow$$

$$\begin{matrix}-CO \\ -CO\end{matrix}\!\!>CHOH + RCHO + CO_2 + NH_3$$

Reaction conditions. In aqueous solution at a regulated pH value, usually on the acid side of neutral. Reaction temperature has usually been the boiling point of the solution.

Subsequent treatment and final titration stage. Determinations have been concluded via a reaction product. The colorimetric methods depend on formation of a coloured product by further reaction of the secondary alcohol and ammonia with an additional molecule of ninhydrin. Titration methods depend on determination of one of the last three products in the equation above, namely:

(i) CO_2, absorbed in $Ba(OH)_2$, then back titrated with acid; or in benzylamine reagent, subsequently titrated with sodium methoxide.

(ii) NH_3, titrated with acid.

(iii) The aldehyde, absorbed in bisulphite and by titration with iodine either of unused or of combined bisulphite.

Examples

Materials titrated	Reagent and reaction conditions	Subsequent treatment and final titration stage	Ref.
Leucine	+ $(NH_4)_2SO_4$ + citric acid + ninhydrin; 15 min boiling	Aldehyde distilled into $NaHSO_3$ and unused part titrated with iodine (see Bisulphite and sulphite, ref. 47)	1
Amino acids, e.g. alanine, valine, leucine, isoleucine	+ $(NH_4)_2SO_4$ or KH_2PO_4/NaCl + citric acid + ninhydrin; 30 min boiling	Aldehyde distilled into $NaHSO_3$ and unused titrated with iodine (see Bisulphite and sulphite, ref. 54)	2
Amino acids	In water + saturated KH_2PO_4 solution + ninhydrin/water; 15 min/110–115°	CO_2 carried into $Ba(OH)_2$ and back titrated with HCl to thymol blue	3

Materials titrated	Reagent and reaction conditions	Subsequent treatment and final titration stage	Ref.
Amino acids (determination of purity of those isolated from protein digests)	+ citrate buffer + ninhydrin; Up to 30 min/*ca* 90°	CO_2 carried by nitrogen stream into $Ba(OH)_2$ and back titrated with HCl to phenolphthalein	4
Amino acids	In water, + citrate buffer, pH 2·5 + ninhydrin; 8 min	Excess ninhydrin precipitated with H_2S, filtered and NH_3 aerated into boric acid; titrated with H_2SO_4	5
Amino acids, e.g. alanine	Modification of method of ref. 2, using 75 min distillation procedure	(See Bisulphite and sulphite, ref. 78)	6
Alanine	+ KH_2PO_4 + NaCl + ninhydrin; 1 h distillation	Aldehyde distilled into $NaHSO_3$ and combined part titrated with iodine (see Bisulphite and sulphite, ref. 81)	7
Amino acids in pure solution and in blood, urine, etc.	In water, + citrate buffer, pH 2·5 or 4·7 + perinaphthindane-2,3,4-trione; 50 min/140–150°	Aldehyde carried into $NaHSO_3$, unused part destroyed with iodine, $NaHCO_3$ added and released bisulphite titrated with iodine	8
Amino acids	+ citrate buffer, pH 4·7, + perinaphthindane-2,3,4-trione; 6–15 min, depending on the acid	CO_2 absorbed in $Ba(OH)_2$ and back titrated with HCl to phenolphthalein	9
Amino acids	+ citrate buffer, pH 4·7, + perinaphthindane-2,3,4-trione or its *m*-nitro-derivative	+ conc. NaOH and NH_3 distilled into water or boric acid and titrated with H_2SO_4	10
Amino acids	+ KH_2PO_4 + NaCl + ninhydrin; 45 min up to 4 h/*ca* 100° in nitrogen current	Aldehyde distilled into $NaHSO_3$ and the combined part determined iodometrically (see Bisulphite and sulphite, ref. 140)	11
Amino acids, e.g. valine, glycine, alanine	+ buffer (usually citrate, pH 2·5) + ninhydrin. Heated to 100°	CO_2 carried by nitrogen into benzylamine/dioxan/ethanol and titrated with $NaOCH_3$ to thymol blue	12
α-Amino acids, e.g. glycine, alanine, leucine, serine, methionine, phenylalanine, tyrosine, lysine, histidine, glutamic acid	In citrate buffer; + ninhydrin; 10–15 min, giving CO_2	Passed into $Ba(OH)_2$ solution covered with a pentane layer and back titrated with HCl to thymol blue	13, 14

References

1. Laine, T., *Suomen Kemistilehti* **11B**, 28 (1938).
2. Virtanen, A. L., Laine, T. and Toivonen, T., *Z. physiol. Chem.* **266**, 193 (1940).
3. Christensen, B. E., West, E. S. and Dimick, K. P., *J. Biol. Chem.* **137**, 735 (1941).
4. van Slyke, D. D., MacFadyen, D. A. and Hamilton, P., *J. Biol. Chem.* **141**, 671 (1941).
5. MacFadyen, D. A., *J. Biol. Chem.* **153**, 507 (1944).
6. Virtanen, A. L. and Rautanen, N., *Suomen Kemistilehti* **19B**, 56 (1946).
7. Roine, P. and Rautanen, N., *Acta Chem. Scand.* **1**, 854 (1947).
8. Moubasher, R., *J. Biol. Chem.* **175**, 187 (1948).
9. Moubasher, R. and Sina, A., *J. Biol. Chem.* **180**, 681 (1949).
10. Moubasher, R., Sina, A., Awad, W. I. and Othman, A. M., *J. Biol. Chem.* **184**, 693 (1950).
11. Hunter, I. R. and Potter, E. F., *Anal. Chem.* **30**, 293 (1958).
12. Patchornik, A. and Shalitin, Y., *Anal. Chem.* **33**, 1887 (1961).
13. Maros, L., Molnár-Perl, I., Vajda, M. and Schulek, E., *Anal. Chim. Acta* **28**, 179 (1963).
14. Maros, L., Molnár-Perl, I., Vajda, M. and Schulek, E., *Magyar Kem. Folyoirat* **69**, 123 (1963).

74. Nitric acid

Reagent and reaction conditions. In only 5 of the examples below has a simple aqueous nitric acid reagent been used. Otherwise, it has been a component of the reagent, mixed with $AgNO_3$, H_2SO_4, HCl or oxidizing agents like chlorate or persulphate.

Most reactions have required heating. Solvents like acetone or ethanol have been used to improve miscibility of reagent and sample.

Reactions, materials titrated, subsequent treatment and final titration stage. 1. Nitration, with a HNO_3/H_2SO_4 reagent, in determination of benzene. The *m*-dinitrobenzene formed was determined with Ti(III).

2. Oxidation and/or esterification (presumably) in determination of propylene glycol. This preliminary stage is claimed to improve the yield of iodoform in the subsequent analytical stage of reaction with iodine/alkali (ref. 13).

3. Breakage of C—metal links in determination of, e.g. lead, bismuth and mercury organic compounds. The Pb(II), Bi(III) and Hg(II)

formed have been determined by standard inorganic procedures such as titration with EDTA.

4. Acid catalysis of reactions, such as:

(a) Fission of C—halogen links giving halide ions (notably of C—I in iodoform determination, of which 8 examples are quoted below). The halide ion has then been argentometrically titrated. Usually a mixed $HNO_3/AgNO_3$ reagent has been used and the unused Ag(I) back titrated with SCN^-. (These references are given also under the reagent Silver (I).) Only relatively rarely has the acid hydrolysis been a separate stage, with subsequent addition of the silver reagent.

Over half the given examples are of this type.

(b) Hydrolysis of urea or dicyandiamide (followed evidently by ammonium salt formation and with concluding alkali titration of the unused acid); of B—OCH_3 groups, giving methanol, subsequently determined by Ce(IV) oxidation; and of —SO_3H groups, yielding H_2SO_4, then determined by precipitation with benzidine.

Examples

Materials titrated	Reagent and reaction conditions	Subsequent treatment and final titration stage	Ref.
Iodoform	In ethanol/ether, + a few drops HNO_3 + excess $AgNO_3$. Heated	Unused Ag(I) titrated with SCN^- to Fe(III)	1
Iodoform	In ethanol/ether + HNO_3 + excess $AgNO_3$. Heated until no more smell of HNO_3	Unused Ag(I) titrated with SCN^-	2
Iodoform formed in determination of formaldehyde and acetone by reaction with iodine/NaOH	Steam distilled into $HNO_3/AgNO_3$ excess/ ethanol; 90 min reflux	Unused Ag(I) titrated with SCN^-	3
Azidodithiocarbonate groups, —$SCSN_3$	In water, + a few drops HNO_3 + excess $AgNO_3$; 2 h/room temp.	Unused Ag(I) titrated with SCN^-	4
Benzene in air	Aspirated through HNO_3/H_2SO_4 reagent, giving *m*-dinitro-benzene. *Ca* 1 h/room temp.	Made alkaline, the dinitro-benzene steam distilled out and determined with excess Ti(III), back titrating with Fe(III) (see Titanium (III), ref. 22)	5, 7

Materials titrated	Reagent and reaction conditions	Subsequent treatment and final titration stage	Ref.
Iodoform	In ethanol, + HNO_3 + excess $AgNO_3$; 2–3 h/room temp.	Unused Ag(I) titrated with SCN^-	6
Iodoform	In ether, + HNO_3 + $AgNO_3$/ethanol. Boiled 15 min	Unused Ag(I) titrated with SCN^-	8
Iodoform	In ether/ethanol, 1:3, + HNO_3 + excess $AgNO_3$. Warmed until no more smell of HNO_3	Unused Ag(I) titrated with SCN^-	9
Lead tetraethyl in gasoline	+ 40% HNO_3 containing 6% $KClO_3$. Several minutes shaking	Evaporated, dissolved residue in hot water, precipitated Pb(II) as chromate; dissolved in HCl/I^- and the liberated iodine titrated with thiosulphate	10
Tetraiodopyrrole; iodoform in ointments	+ HNO_3/HCl, 1:2; 3 min boiling	AgI precipitated with $AgNO_3$/NH_4OH, precipitate dissolved in excess KCN and titrated with $AgNO_3$ to opalescence	11
β,β′-Dichlorodiethyl ether in study of reaction with OH^- or $S_2O_3^-$	+ dilute HNO_3	Cl^- determined by adding excess Ag(I) and back titrating with SCN^- or by direct titration with Ag(I) to CrO_4^- indicator	12
1,2-Propylene glycol in mixtures with ethylene glycol	+ drops conc. HNO_3. *Ca* 20 min/50°, then 10 min standing	Treated with iodine/alkali to yield iodoform; latter determined with excess Ag(I) and back titration with SCN^- (see Iodine reagents, ref. 310)	13
Urea; dicyanodiamide	In acetone + HNO_3; 15 min/100° under pressure (latter reacts); or 2 h/120°, under pressure, reacting with both	Unused acid back titrated with NaOH	14
Methoxyl groups in methoxyborhydrides	+ HNO_3; 10 min/100°, giving methanol	Methanol determined with excess Ce(IV) and back titration with arsenite (see Cerium (IV), ref. 36)	15
Some mercurials, e.g. Hg salicylate, phenyl mercuric acetate, Na ethylmercurithiosalicylate	Heated with HNO_3/HCl (or HCl), giving Hg(II)	Organic residue extracted and Hg(II) then titrated with EDTA	16

Materials titrated	Reagent and reaction conditions	Subsequent treatment and final titration stage	Ref.
Iodoform from determination of 'Warfarin' by reaction with iodine/alkali	In ethanol, + HNO_3/ $AgNO_3$; 2–3 h/room temp.	Unused Ag(I) titrated with SCN^-	17
Organic bismuth preparations	Dissolved in HNO_3/ $CHCl_3$	+ NH_4OH and the 2-phase mixture titrated with EDTA to pyrocatechol violet or xylenol orange	18
Methoxyethyl mercuric chloride	Boiled with HNO_3/HCl	+ NH_4OH + excess KCN + a little I^- indicator and unused CN^- titrated with Ag(I) to opalescence	19
Lead tetraethyl in ethyl fluid	+ HNO_3/$AgNO_3$/ methanol	Unused Ag(I) titrated with SCN^-	20
Trichloroethylene in industrial waters	Heated with HNO_3/ $(NH_4)_2S_2O_8$, giving HCl	Absorbed in water and titrated with $AgNO_3$ potentiometrically	21
Toluenesulphonic acid isomers (as acid chlorides)	+ HNO_3/H_2SO_4 30 min	Extracted with $CHCl_3$, hydrolysed with NaOH, reduced with Zn/HCl to amines and determined by titration with NO_2^- (see Metals, ref. 90)	22
K guaiacolsulphonate	Heated with dilute HNO_3 at *ca* 100°, giving H_2SO_4	Precipitated with benzidine and precipitate titrated with NaOH to phenol red	23

References

1. Lehmann, K. B., *Pharm. Z.* 143 (1900). *Z. allgem. österr. Apotheker-Ver.* **38**, 755.
2. Gane, E. H. and Webster, M. H., *Pharm. J.* (4) **28**, 555 (1909).
3. Mach, F. and Herrmann, R., *Z. anal. Chem.* **63**, 417 (1924).
4. Browne, A. W. and Smith, G. B. L., *J. Am. Chem. Soc.* **47**, 2698 (1925).
5. Smyth, H. F., *J. Ind. Hyg. Toxicol.* **11**, 338 (1929).
6. Kunke, W. F., *J. Assoc. Offic. Agr. Chem.* **14**, 370 (1931).
7. Smyth, H. F., *J. Ind. Hyg. Toxicol.* **13**, 227 (1931).
8. Slotta, K. H. and Neissner, K., *Ber.* **71**, 1611 (1938).
9. Funck, E., *Süddeut. Apotheker-Ztg.* **79**, 622 (1939).

10. Schwartz, L., *Ind. Eng. Chem., Anal. Ed.* **15**, 499 (1943).
11. Douris, R. G., *Ann. pharm. franç.* **2**, 56 (1944).
12. Bartlett, P. D. and Lewis, E. S., *J. Am. Chem. Soc.* **72**, 405 (1950).
13. Jordan, C. B. and Hatch, V. O., *Anal. Chem.* **25**, 636 (1953).
14. Inaba, H., *Bunseki Kagaku (Japan Analyst)* **3**, 195 (1954).
15. Alexander, A. P., Bourne, P. G. and Littlehale, D. S., *Anal. Chem.* **27**, 105 (1955).
16. Iritani, H. and Tanaka, T., *J. Pharm. Soc. Japan* **77**, 106 (1957).
17. Kámen, K., *Chem. průmysl* **7**, 472 (1957).
18. Laszlovsky, J., *Acta Pharm. Hung.* **27**, 125 (1957).
19. Laubie, H., *Bull. soc. pharm., Bordeaux* **96**, 65 (1957).
20. Tagliavini, G., *Chimica e industria (Milan)* **39**, 672 (1957).
21. Deyl, Z. and Effenberger, M., *Voda* **37**, 90 (1958).
22. Spryskov, A. A., *Izvest. Vysshikh Ucheb. Zavedenii, Khim. i Khim. Tekhnol.* No. 6, 42 (1958).
23. Rozsa, P., *Acta Pharm. Hung.* **32**, 11 (1962).

75. Nitriles

Reagent. Only unsaturated nitriles appear to have been used, and in six of the seven examples given below, acrylonitrile was the reagent. Tetracyanoethylene was used in the remaining case.

Reactions and materials titrated. Addition to the double bond of the unsaturated nitrile has been the basis of all the determinations. Compounds containing 'active hydrogen' (notably mercaptans, also alcohols and fluorene) and, in one example, conjugated dienes, have been determined in this manner:

$$RSH + CH_2{=}CH.CN \rightarrow RS{-}CH_3{-}CH_2.CN$$

$$ROH + CH_2{=}CH.CN \rightarrow RO{-}CH_2{-}CH_2.CN$$

$$\text{(fluorene) } CH_2 + 2\,CH_2{=}CH.CN \rightarrow \text{(fluorene) } C(CH_2{-}CH_2.CN)_2$$

$$RCH{=}CH{-}CH{=}RCH + C(CN)_2{=}C(CN)_2 \rightarrow \text{ring: } RCH{-}CH{=}CH{-}RCH{-}C(CN)_2{-}C(CN)_2{-}$$

Final titration stage. (i) Unused reagent has been determined in two of the examples; tetracyanoethylene by titration with cyclopentadiene and acrylonitrile by reaction with sulphite and titration of the alkali formed:

$$CH_2{=}CH.CN + SO_3^{2-} + H_2O \rightarrow \underset{\substack{|\\ SO_3^-}}{CH_2}{-}CH_2.CN + OH^-$$

(ii) The reaction product 9,9-bis-(β-cyanoethyl)fluorene was determined by saponification with excess alkali and back titration of the unused; in another example, the sulphide reaction product, RS—CH_2—CH_2.CN was titrated with bromate/bromide reagent.

(iii) Unreacted materials, after removal of interfering components with the nitrile reagent, have been determined by titration. Examples are:

Disulphides, by reduction to mercaptans and titration with $AgNO_3$.

Unreacted sulphide (together with sulphide RS—CH_2—CH_2.CN) with bromate/bromide.

Thiourea with a Hg(II) reagent.

Examples

Materials titrated	Reagent and reaction conditions	Subsequent treatment and final titration stage	Ref.
Disulphides in mixtures with mercaptans	+ excess acrylonitrile + KOH; 10 min	Excess nitrile extracted with water, disulphides reduced with Zn to mercaptans and titrated with $AgNO_3$ potentiometrically (see Metals, ref. 63; Part I, Silver (I), ref. 66)	1
Mercaptans	+ excess acrylonitrile + alkali. Up to 1 h	+ Na_2SO_3 and titrated with HCl to thymolphthalein/ alizarin yellow	2
Mercaptans and sulphides in mixtures	+ excess acrylonitrile + KOH; *Ca* 2 min	+ HCl + acetic acid and titrated total sulphide with bromate/bromide to yellow, permanent for 30 sec (see Part I, Bromate, ref. 144)	3
	(in combination with iodine titration of the mercaptans alone—see Part 1, Iodine, ref. 110)		

Materials titrated	Reagent and reaction conditions	Subsequent treatment and final titration stage	Ref.
Primary and secondary alcohols	+ dioxan + excess acrylonitrile + KOH; 15 min–6 h/room temp–40°	+ Na_2SO_3 and titrated with HCl to thymolphthalein/alizarin yellow (see Bisulphite and sulphite, ref. 173)	4
1,3-Dienes	Added to excess tetracyanoethylene/CH_2Cl_2; 10 min/room temp.; with reactive samples like anthracene in presence of unreactive dienes, 20 min/—20°	Back titrated with cyclopentadiene/absolute ethanol to pentamethylbenzene as visual indicator, or photometrically (see Part I, Cyclopentadiene)	5
Thiourea in presence of thioglycollic acid	+ NaOH + excess acrylonitrile; 15 min	+ $HClO_4$ and thiourea titrated with trimercuri-acetataniline solution to *p*-dimethylaminobenzylidene rhodanine	6
Fluorene in technical products	+ acrylonitrile, giving 9,9-bis-(β-cyanoethyl)-fluorene	Product hydrolysed with excess NaOH and unused back titrated with acid	7

References

1. Earle, T. E., *Anal. Chem.* **25**, 769 (1953).
2. Obtemperanskaya, S. I., Terent'ev, A. P. and Buzlanova, M. M., *Vestnik Moskov. Univ.* **12**, *Ser. Mat. Mekh. Astron. Fiz. Khim.* No.3, 145 (1957).
3. Jaselskis, B., *Anal. Chem.* **31**, 928 (1959).
4. Obtemperanskaya, S. I., Terent'ev, A. P. and Buzlanova, M. M., *Zhur. Anal. Khim.* **16**, 372 (1961).
5. Ozolins, M. and Schenk, G. H., *Anal. Chem.* **33**, 1035 (1961).
6. Wroński, M., *Acta Chim. Acad. Sci. Hung.* **28**, 303 (1961).
7. Kretov, A. E. and Okhramovich, A. E., *USSR Patent No.* 143,590, Jan. 24 (1962). *Zhur. Priklad Khim.* **35**, 1865 (1962).

76. Nitrite

Reagent and reaction conditions. Sodium or potassium nitrite, used in acid solution.

Reactions, materials titrated, subsequent treatment and final titration stage. 1. Ester formation, in determination of lower alcohols:

$$ROH + HNO_2 \rightarrow RONO + H_2O$$

The volatile esters were carried into I^-/acid, liberating iodine, which was titrated with thiosulphate:

$$2\,RONO + 2\,H^+ + 2\,I^- \rightarrow I_2 + 2\,NO + 2\,ROH$$

2. Nitrosation reactions, which can conveniently be subdivided:

(a) Diazotization of primary aromatic amines:

$$ArNH_2 + H^+ + HNO_2 \rightarrow (ArN{\equiv}N)^+ + 2\,H_2O$$

These determinations have been concluded by back titration of unused reagent with an aromatic amine (in one case, excess of amine was used and final back titration was with nitrite).

(b) Nitrosation of secondary amines:

$$(CH_3)_2NH + HNO_2 \rightarrow (CH_3)_2N.NO + H_2O$$

The nitrosoamines were determined by reduction with Zn/acid to amines or hydrazines, followed by distillation and titration with acid, or by titration with iodate.

(c) Deamination of aliphatic —NH_2 groups as in determination of primary amines, amino acids and amides like urea:

$$X{-}NH_2 + HNO_2 \rightarrow X{-}OH + N_2 + H_2O$$

The hydroxy acids derived from amino acids have mostly been determined by a subsequent oxidation method. E.g.

Glycine → Glycollic acid: titrated with MnO_4^-.

Alanine → Lactic acid: oxidized usually with MnO_4^- to acetaldehyde, determined with bisulphite

Other amino acids → hydroxy acids: determined via use of excess Ce(IV) and back titration with Fe(II) or coulometrically

Urea → CO_2: absorbed in $Ba(OH)_2$ and titrated with acid.

Examples

Materials titrated	Reagent and reaction conditions	Subsequent treatment and final titration stage	Ref.
Mixtures of methylamines	+ acid + NO_2^-, converting primary amine to alcohol and secondary to $(CH_3)_2N.NO$	Made alkaline, tertiary amine distilled into acid and back titrated with alkali; *N*-nitroso compound + Zn/HCl, giving $(CH_3)_2NH$, similarly distilled into excess acid and back titrated (see Metals, ref. 5)	1
m-Aminophenol in presence of metol	+ HCl + excess NO_2^-, giving diazonium salt (and *N*-nitroso compound with the metol)	+ excess *m*-phenylene diamine + Na acetate and titrated unused diamine with diazonium salt (see Amines, ref. 6 and Part I, Diazonium salts, ref. 5)	2
Methanol	+ acetic acid + Na acetate + NO_2^-, giving methyl nitrite	Carried with CO_2 current into I^-/HCl and titrated the iodine liberated with thiosulphate (nitrous gases removed with urea and $NaHCO_3$) (see Iodides and hydriodic acid, ref. 19)	3
Dehydrothio-*p*-toluidinesulphonic acid and homologues (e.g. primuline); also aniline and *p*-toluidine	In NaOH, + NO_2^- + HCl + HNO_3; 10 min/0–5° or 30 min for aniline and *p*-toluidine	Unused NO_2^- back titrated with *p*-nitroaniline to external starch/I^-	4
Alcohols up to C_5	Method of ref. 3, without urea for absorbing nitrous gases (found that $NaHCO_3$ sufficed)		5
Alanine	+ acid + NO_2^-, converting to lactic acid	+ H_3PO_4 + $MnSO_4$ and MnO_4^- added to boiling solution for 20 min; acetaldehyde formed distilled into bisulphite and combined bisulphite determined iodometrically (compare Permanganate, method of ref. 32)	6
Alcohols	+ acid + NO_2^-, giving nitrite esters	Extracted with CCl_4, saponified and nitrite determined with excess MnO_4^-, back titrating iodometrically	7
Methylamines (from reaction of methanol and ammonia)	Secondary and tertiary amines determined by method based on that of ref. 1		8

Materials titrated	Reagent and reaction conditions	Subsequent treatment and final titration stage	Ref.
Alanine	+ acid + NO_2^-, giving lactic acid	Oxidized with MnO_4^-/H_2SO_4 to acetaldehyde and latter determined by reaction with bisulphite and determination of the combined bisulphite (see Permanganate, ref. 40)	9
Methanol	+ acid + NO_2^-, giving methyl nitrite (studied factors influencing the reaction)	Nitrite ester carried with CO_2 stream through $NaHCO_3$ to remove nitrous oxides, and into I^-/HCl, giving iodine; titrated with thiosulphate (see Iodides and hydriodic acid, ref. 44)	10
Methanol from determination of methoxyl groups in wood by reaction with conc. H_2SO_4	Method of ref. 10 (see Iodides and hydriodic acid, ref. 45)		11
Aniline + nitroanilines	+ HCl + NO_2^-, giving diazonium salts	+ NaOH and benzene diazonium salt titrated with β-naphthol	12
Glycine	+ acid + NO_2^-, giving glycollic acid	Oxidized with alkaline MnO_4^- to oxalic acid and the latter determined with MnO_4^-	13
Methanol from determination of methoxyl groups in wood by reaction with conc. H_2SO_4	Method of ref. 10, but after previous treatment with alkali to decompose any dimethyl sulphate from the H_2SO_4 treatment (see Iodides and hydriodic acid, ref. 52)		14
Aromatic primary amines	+ HCl + excess NO_2^-; 15 min/20–23°	Unused NO_2^- titrated with aniline or sulphanilic acid to external I^-/starch indicator	15
Glutamic acid	+ H_2SO_4 + NO_2^-; 10 min/room temp., giving hydroxyglutaric acid	Oxidized with MnO_4^- to succinic acid, precipitated with excess Ag(I), dissolved the precipitate in HNO_3 and titrated with SCN^- (see Silver ref. 52)	16
p-Cumidine in acid dyes	Diazotized in acid solution with NO_2^-	Coupled with β-naphthol 6-sulphonic acid/Na_2CO_3 (1 h/70°) and the azo compound ultimately titrated with Ti(III) (See Part I, Titanium (III), ref. 28.)	17

Materials titrated	Reagent and reaction conditions	Subsequent treatment and final titration stage	Ref.
Lower alcohols in dilute aqueous solutions	+ acetic acid + NO_2^-, giving nitrite esters	Carried with nitrogen current through KOH (to absorb nitrous oxides) and into I^-/acid; titrated with thiosulphate	18
tert-Butanol from decomposition of di-*tert*-butyl peroxide	Method of ref. 3 (see Iodides and hydriodic acid, ref. 127)		19
Ethanol in mixed solvents	+ acetic acid + NO_2^-, giving ethyl nitrite	Passed through $NaHCO_3$ to remove nitrous gases and into I^-/HCl; titrated with thiosulphate (see Iodides and hydriodic acid, ref. 138)	20
Glutamic acid	+ H_2SO_4 + NO_2^-, giving oxalic acid	Excess HNO_2 destroyed by heating and oxalic acid determined with excess Ce(IV), back titrating with Fe(II) (see Cerium (IV), ref. 24)	21
Amino acids, e.g. glycine, alanine, etc.	Method of ref. 21 (see Cerium (IV), ref. 27)		22
Dimethylamine in mixtures with other methylamines and ammonia	+ HCl + acetic acid + NO_2^-; 10 min, giving $(CH_3)_2N.NO$	Reduced with Zn/HCl to $(CH_3)_2N.NH_2$ and titrated with iodate (see Metals, ref. 68; Part I, Iodate, ref. 42)	23
Alcohols up to C_5	+ NO_2^- + acetic acid gradually added, giving nitrite esters	Nitrite esters passed through $NaHCO_3$ into I^-/HCl and titrated with thiosulphate (see Iodides and hydriodic acid, ref. 177)	24
Urea	+ acid + NO_2^-, giving CO_2	Absorbed in $Ba(OH)_2$ and back titrated with acid	25
Aromatic amines	+ HCl + Br^- + NO_2^-	Unused NO_2^- titrated with *p*-nitroaniline or *p*-toluidine to external I^-/starch or biamperometrically	26
4-Acetamido-*N*-lauroyl-1-naphthalene-sulphonamide ('PANS')	+ HCl + Br^- + NO_2^-; 15 min/0°	Unreacted NO_2^- titrated with sulphanilic acid to I^-/starch	27
Glutamic acid	+ H_2SO_4 + NO_2^-, giving hydroxyglutaric acid	+ excess Ce(IV) at the boiling point and coulometrically back titrated (see Cerium (IV), ref. 53)	28

Materials titrated	Reagent and reaction conditions	Subsequent treatment and final titration stage	Ref.
Amino acids, e.g. alanine, norleucine, glutamic acid	In water, + H_2SO_4 + NO_2^-. Boiled until the solution no longer gave colour with I^-/starch (3 min/80–100°)	+ excess vanadate and back titrated with Fe(II) (see Vanadate, ref. 20)	29
1-Naphthol-5-sulphonic acid	In water, + $NaNO_2$ + inorganic acid at 30–35°	+ excess (*p*-sulphophenyl) methylpyrazolone and unused titrated with nitrite	30
Methanol from determination of methoxyl end-groups in paraformaldehyde by hydrolysis with NaOH	Modification of method of ref. 5		31

References

1. Weber, F. C. and Wilson, J. B., *J. Biol. Chem.* **35**, 385 (1918).
2. Ermen, W. F. A., *Chem. & Ind.* (*London*) **42**, 538 (1923).
3. Fischer, W. M. and Schmidt, A., *Ber.* **57**, 693 (1924).
4. Lee, H. R. and Jones, D. O., *Ind. Eng. Chem.* **16**, 930, 948 (1924).
5. Fischer, W. M. and Schmidt, A., *Ber.* **59**, 679 (1926).
6. Kendall, A. I. and Friedemann, T. E., *J. Infectious Diseases* **47**, 171 (1930).
7. Ponndorf, W., *Z. anal. Chem.* **80**, 401 (1930).
8. Briner, E. and Gandillon, J., *Helv. Chim. Acta* **14**, 1283 (1931).
9. Fürth, O., Scholl, R. and Herrmann, H., *Biochem. Z.* **251**, 404 (1932).
10. Ender, W., *Angew. Chem.* **47**, 227 (1934).
11. Ender, W., *Angew. Chem.* **47**, 257 (1934).
12. Terent'ev, A. P. and Shchetinina, L. A., *Anilinokrasochnaya Prom.* **4**, 359 (1934).
13. Rapaport, S., *Biochem. Z.* **281**, 30 (1935).
14. Storch, K. and Wenzel, I., *Angew. Chem.* **48**, 513 (1935).
15. Phillips, J. and Lowy, A., *Ind. Eng. Chem., Anal. Ed.* **9**, 381 (1937).
16. Arhimo, A. A. and Laine, T., *Suomen Kemistilehti* **12B**, 18 (1939).
17. Jablonski, C. F., *J. Assoc. Off. Agr. Chem.* **22**, 771 (1939).
18. Skrabal, R., *Z. anal. Chem.* **119**, 222 (1940).
19. Bell, E. R., Rust, F. F. and Vaughan, W. E., *J. Am. Chem. Soc.* **72**, 337 (1950).
20. Murakami, K., *J. Soc. Org. Syn. Chem.* (*Japan*) **8**, 155 (1950).
21. Takahashi, T., Kimoto, K. and Minami, S., *J. Chem. Soc. Japan, Ind. Chem. Sect.* **55**, 805 (1952).

22. Takahashi, T., Kimoto, K. and Minami, S., *J. Chem. Soc. Japan, Ind. Chem. Sect.* **56**, 417 (1953).
23. Alekseev, N. F. and Dvinyanina, M. P., *Zavodskaya Lab.* **21**, 1166 (1955).
24. v. Wacek, A. and Zeisler, F., *Mikrochim. Acta* 29 (1955).
25. Gullstrom, D. K. and Demkovich, P. A., *J. Agr. Food Chem.* **7**, 26 (1959).
26. Goupil, R., *Chim. anal.* **42**, 300 (1960).
27. Ch-Ch. Hsiao and L-Ch. Wu, *Yao Hsueh Hsueh Pao (Acta Pharm. Sinica)* **8**, 229 (1960).
28. Takahashi, T. and Sakurai, H., *J. Chem. Soc. Japan, Ind. Chem. Sect.* **63**, 608 (1960).
29. Rao, S. P., Rathi, H. S. and Gaur, J. N., *Anal. Chim. Acta* **25**, 136 (1961).
30. Brodman, F. and Teodorescu, L., *Rev. Chim. (Bucharest)* **14**, 346 (1963).
31. Přibyl, M. and Slovák, Z., *Z. Anal. Chem.* **202**, 23 (1964).

77. Nitrophenols

Reagent. Picric acid in almost every case; there are single examples of the use of nitranilic and picrolonic acids. (The latter has a heterocyclic nucleus but it is convenient to include it here.)

Reactions and materials titrated. 1. Ion/ion combination with formation of water-insoluble salts for determination of bases like hexamine, nicotine, antipyrine, aniline, purine and other alkaloids, sulphonium and quaternary ammonium compounds.

2. Formation of water- or alcohol-insoluble molecular complexes in the determination of aromatic compounds, principally hydrocarbons. This is the principle of the usual method of determination of naphthalene in coal gas and other materials. The method has been the subject of polemical discussion and only a selection of references is given here. Insoluble complexes are also formed in the determination of dicyanodiamide and hypoxanthine using a picric acid/silver nitrate reagent (see also under Silver (I)).

Reaction conditions. Mostly carried out in water and often at lower temperature in order to reduce solubility of the products formed.

Subsequent treatment and final titration stage. (i) Determination of the unused reagent after separation (usually by filtration) of the precipitated reaction product. Techniques adopted for this include:

1. Titration with alkali, generally to indicators like phenolphthalein or *m*-cresol purple, or potentiometrically.

2. Addition of iodate/iodide and titration with thiosulphate of the iodine liberated.

3. Addition of excess Ti(III) and back titration of the unused part with Fe(III) or, in one case, with V(II).

4. Titration with methylene blue in the presence of a solvent immiscible with water, taking as end-point the first appearance of blue in the aqueous layer.

(ii) Determination of the precipitated reaction product via the picric acid moiety. The same four methods under (i) have all been used.

In the few examples quoted of the precipitation of a complex with silver picrate, the silver content of the product was determined by dissolving it in nitric acid and titrating with thiocyanate.

The precipitate formed by reaction of glycine with nitranilic acid was determined by Kjeldahl digestion and distillation.

(iii) Determination of the original material, so that the picric acid served for separation. Two examples are given:

1. Treatment of precipitated nicotine picrate with alkali, distillation of the nicotine and titration with acid.

2. Titration of the picrates of strong bases (e.g. quaternary ammonium or sulphonium, also of quinine) with perchloric acid/glacial acetic acid.

Examples

Materials titrated	Reagent and reaction conditions	Subsequent treatment and final titration stage	Ref.
Naphthalene, acenaphthene, *α*- and *β*-naphthols	+ picric acid/water (heated in first 3 cases)	Filtered and unused titrated with $Ba(OH)_2$ to phenolphthalein	1
Some nitrogen-containing bases	+ picric acid/water	Precipitate of picrate + ethanol + HCl + excess $TiCl_3$, heated and back titrated with Fe(III)	2
Naphthalene in gas	+ picric acid/water; several hours on water-bath	Method of ref. 2	3

Materials titrated	Reagent and reaction conditions	Subsequent treatment and final titration stage	Ref.
Naphthalene in gas	Passed through picric acid/water	Precipitate boiled with excess NaOH, then excess picric acid added and finally titrated with NaOH to litmus	4
Naphthalene and other aromatic compounds	+ picric acid/water	Precipitate treated with excess $TiCl_3$ and back titrated with Fe(III)	5
Quinine alkaloids	+ picric acid/HCl	Filtered and unreacted picric acid determined with excess $TiCl_3$ and back titration with Fe(III) (see Titanium (III), ref. 5)	6
Dicyanodiamide in presence of cyanamide in mixed manures	In weakly acid solution, + $AgNO_3$ + picric acid; 2 min stirring, then 30 min/0°, → precipitate of complex $C_6H_2(NO_2)_3OAg.C_2H_4N_2$	Filtered and determined gravimetrically or by dissolving in HNO_3 and titrating the Ag(I)	7
Hexamine	+ picric acid/water. Heated a few min, then 30 min/room temp.	Filtered and filtrate titrated with NaOH to methyl red	8
Naphthalene	+ picric acid/water	Precipitate dissolved in benzene, water added and titrated with NaOH to Na alizarinsulphonate; solution extracted with benzene and any indene determined bromometrically	9
Hexamine, e.g. small amounts in wine	+ picric acid/water; 5 min/room temp.	Filtered and unused titrated with NaOH to phenolphthalein	10
Antipyrine; pyramidone	In water, + picric acid/water	Filtered and filtrate titrated with NaOH to phenolphthalein	11
Naphthalene and indene in gas	Method of ref. 9		12
Nicotine in tobacco	Distillate + picric acid/water; 2 h in the cold	Filtered and precipitate titrated with NaOH to phenolphthalein	13
Naphthalene in gas	Passed through picric acid/water	Filtered and filtrate titrated with alkali	14

Materials titrated	Reagent and reaction conditions	Subsequent treatment and final titration stage	Ref.
Naphthalene in gas	Passed through picric acid/water	Precipitate + IO_3^-/I^- and liberated iodine titrated with thiosulphate (see Iodate and iodine pentoxide, ref. 18)	15
Antipyrine	In water, + picric acid/ 90% ethanol; 10 min/room temp.	Filtered and filtrate titrated with NaOH to phenolphthalein	16
Naphthalene	+ picric acid/water	Filtered and precipitate titrated with NaOH	17
Hexamine	Method of ref. 10 stated to be unreliable		18
Antipyrine + pyramidone; former alone after treatment with H_2O_2 which converts latter to non-picrate forming products	In water, + picric acid/ water	Filtered and filtrate titrated with NaOH to phenolphthalein	19
Naphthalene in oils	+ picric acid/water; 2 h/100°, then cooled	Filtered and unused titrated with NaOH	20
Naphthalene in coal distillation products	+ picric acid/water	Filtered; filtrate + IO_3^-/I^- and titrated with thiosulphate (see Iodate and iodine pentoxide, ref. 24)	21
Naphthalene in gas	Passed through picric/ acid/water	Filtered and titrated precipitate with NaOH	22
Nicotine from tobacco	Ether extract + picric acid; 2 h in the cold	Filtered and precipitate titrated with NaOH to phenolphthalein, adding a little toluene near the end-point to facilitate its observation	23
Naphthalene in mixtures with tetralin	+ saturated picric acid/ water at not above 25–28°	Filtered, precipitate dissolved in warm water and titrated with KOH to phenolphthalein	24
Naphthalene in tar, tar oil and gas	+ picric acid/water (critical study of best conditions)	Filtered and determined unused reagent by titration with KOH to phenolphthalein or Na alizarinsulphonate, or by adding IO_3^-/I^- and titrating with thiosulphate (see Iodate and iodine pentoxide, ref. 28)	25

Materials titrated	Reagent and reaction conditions	Subsequent treatment and final titration stage	Ref.
Naphthalene	+ 1·2% picric acid/ water	Filtered, precipitate dissolved in hot water and titrated with alkali to phenolphthalein	26
Antipyrine	+ picric acid	Precipitate dissolved in water and titrated with alkali	27
Naphthalene in poultry lice powders	Distilled into picric acid/water (saturated solution). Left several hours in refrigerator	Precipitate boiled with ethanol + excess NaOH and back titrated with acid to phenol-phthalein	28
Naphthalene in gas	+ picric acid/water at 4–7° as in method of ref. 30	Filtered, precipitate boiled with water and titrated with alkali to phenolphthalein	29, 34
Naphthalene in gas	+ picric acid/water at 4–7°	Filtered, precipitate heated with water and titrated with NaOH to phenolphthalein	30
Aromatic content of aviation gasoline	+ picric acid; 5 min shaking	Filtered and dissolved picric acid titrated with NaOH to phenolphthalein	31
Naphthalene	+ picric acid/water at 0°	Filtered and filtrate or pre-cipitate titrated with alkali	32
Naphthalene	+ picric acid/water; best at 12°		33
Naphthalene in motor benzene	+ saturated picric acid/ water at 0°	Titrated with alkali	35
Haemoglobin	+ picric acid/alcohol; 10 min boiling, then 1 h standing	Filtered and unused titrated with methylene blue in $CHCl_3$/ water to first blue in the water (see Part I, Dyes, ref. 13)	36
Naphthalene	Critical review of picric acid procedures		37
Naphthalene in tar oils	Distilled into cooled picric acid/water	Filtered, precipitate boiled with water and titrated with alkali	38
Naphthalene	+ picric acid	Filtered and precipitate titrated with NaOH to phenol-phthalein, or determined by adding IO_3^-/I^- and titrating with thiosulphate (see Iodate, ref. 34)	39

Materials titrated	Reagent and reaction conditions	Subsequent treatment and final titration stage	Ref.
Naphthalene	+ *ca* 4 times expected amount of picric acid solution; 5 min/shaking	Filtered and unused titrated with alkali to phenolphthalein	40
Antipyrine; pyramidone	In water, + picric acid/water	Filtered and unused titrated with NaOH	41
Naphthalene in coal tar	Vaporized out and determined by method of ref. 17		42
Hydrocarbons like naphthalene, and acenaphthene; bases like nicotine, dibenzylamine, *p*-bromoaniline	+ picric or picrolonic acid reagent	Precipitate titrated with methylene blue in $CHCl_3$/water to first blue in water (see Part I, Dyes, ref. 16)	43
Naphthalene	Slight modification of method of ref. 38		44
Acridines, e.g. acridine, proflavine, euflavine, acriflavine	+ picric acid	Precipitate titrated with methylene blue as in method of refs 36 and 43	45
Adenine; guanine	In water, + Na picrate	Precipitate titrated in hot water with NaOH to phenol red	46
Hypoxanthine	In water, + Na picrate + HNO_3; heated to 100° and excess $AgNO_3$ added; 5 min/100°, giving precipitate of argentipicrate	Precipitate dissolved in HNO_3 and titrated with SCN^- to Fe(III) indicator	47
Nicotine in tobacco preparations	+ picric acid	Precipitate dissolved in excess NaOH and back titrated with HCl	48
Aromatic content of aviation oil	+ solid picric acid; 5 min shaking/20–30°	Filtered, water added to filtrate and titrated with slight excess NaOH and final HCl titration to *m*-cresol purple	49
Dicyanodiamide	+ picric acid/$AgNO_3$, giving the complex $C_6H_2(NO_2)_3OAg.C_2H_4N_4$	Precipitate dissolved in HNO_3 and titrated with SCN^- to Fe(III) indicator (also gravimetric)	50
Naphthalene in absorbing oil	Volatilized with warm air into picric acid/water at 18–27°	Filtered and filtrate titrated with NaOH to methyl red	51

Materials titrated	Reagent and reaction conditions	Subsequent treatment and final titration stage	Ref.
Nicotine	+ picric acid/water; 1–2 h/*ca* 0°	Unused titrated in water/ $CHCl_3$ or $C_2H_4Cl_2$ with methylene blue to first blue in water (see Part I, Dyes, ref. 26)	52
Naphthalene in tar	In a little acetone, + saturated picric acid/ water; 2 h/room temp.	Filtered, precipitate boiled with water and titrated hot with NaOH	53
Alkaloids	In ethanol, + picrolonic acid/ethanol; 4 h/room temp.	Unused acid titrated potentiometrically with NaOH	54
Thiouronium halides from determination of tertiary alcohols by conversion with HCl or HBr to alkyl halides and reaction with thiourea	+ picric acid/water, giving precipitate of picrate; 30 min/room temp.	Precipitate dissolved in acetic and titrated with $HClO_4$/acetic acid to disappearance of yellow or to crystal violet indicator (see Part I, Perchloric acid, ref. 62)	55
Naphthalene in triethylene glycol	+ picric acid/acetone	Filtered and precipitate titrated with NaOH	56
Glycine in protein hydrolysates	In absolute ethanol, + nitranilic acid/ absolute ethanol. Left overnight/*ca* 0°	Filtered and nitrogen determined in precipitate by the Kjeldahl method (see Kjeldahl nitrogen determination, ref. 11)	57
Naphthalene, anthracene, aniline, *p*-toluidine	+ picric acid	Precipitate determined with excess VSO_4 and back titration with $Cr_2O_7^{2-}$ to phenosafranine (see Vanadium (II), ref. 3)	58
Naphthalene in gas	Passed through picric acid/water (concentration depended on temperature)	Precipitate dissolved in neutral $CHCl_3$ and titrated with NaOH to lacmoid; corrected for indene by determination with ICl (see Iodine chlorides, etc., ref. 88)	59
Sulphonium bromides from determination of equivalent weights of dialkyl sulphides by reaction with *p*-bromophenacyl bromide	In water, + saturated picric acid/water, giving sulphonium picrate precipitate	Precipitate titrated in acetic acid with $HClO_4$/acetic acid, to crystal violet (see Part I, Perchloric acid, ref. 161)	60

Materials titrated	Reagent and reaction conditions	Subsequent treatment and final titration stage	Ref.
Naphthalene in gas	Passed through saturated picric acid/water at 0°	Dissolved precipitate in acetic acid, brominated indene and other unsaturated picrates, re-crystallized from aqueous picric acid (only the naphthalene picrate is precipitated) and titrated with alkali	61
Naphthalene in waste water from coking plants	Distilled into picric acid	Filtered and filtrate titrated with NaOH	62
Nicotine in tobacco	Distillate from extract, + picric acid/water; 2–3 h/*ca* 0°	Filtered and picric acid in filtrate determined by adding IO_3^-/I^- and titrating with thiosulphate	63
Naphthalene; indene	+ picric acid/water (also discussed the reaction and compared the method with a German one)	Precipitate dissolved in acetone and titrated with NaOH to bromothymol blue; + acetic acid + ICl/acetic acid and unused determined iodometrically (to correct for indene) (see Iodine chlorides, etc., ref. 95)	64
Nicotine isolated from tobacco smoke	+ picric acid	Filtered, precipitate treated with alkali, the nicotine distilled out and titrated with HCl	65
Naphthalene in coke oven gas	Passed through picric acid	Filtrate + IO_3^-/I^- and titrated with thiosulphate	66
Quaternary ammonium salts	+ picric acid/dilute HCl; 1 h (sometimes longer)/100°	Filtered and precipitate titrated in acetic acid with $HClO_4$/acetic acid to crystal violet or malachite green (see Part I, Perchloric acid, ref. 242)	67
Quinine	+ picric acid/dilute H_2SO_4; 1 h/room temp., giving precipitate of quinine picrate	Dissolved in acetic acid and titrated with $HClO_4$/acetic acid to crystal violet (see Part I, Perchloric acid, ref. 295)	68
Naphthalene in gas	Study of factors (temperature, concentrations, etc.) influencing the determination by precipitation as picrate	Precipitate titrated with NaOH	69
Naphthalene in effluents	Extract in ether, + picric acid	Precipitate filtered and titrated with NaOH	70

References

1. Küster, F. W., *Ber.* **27**, 1101 (1894).
2. Sinnatt, F. S., *Proc. Chem. Soc.* **21**, 297 (1905).
3. Sinnatt, F. S., *J. Gas Lighting* **58**, 288 (1906).
4. Gair, C. J. D., *J. Soc. Chem. Ind. (London)* **26**, 1263 (1907).
5. Knecht, E. and Hibbert, E., *Ber.* **40**, 3819 (1907).
6. Kleinstück, M., *Pharm. Zentralhalle* **53**, 643, 680, 705 (1912).
7. Harder, R. N., *Ind. Eng. Chem.* **12**, 1107 (1920).
8. Kollo, C. and Lascar, O., *Bull. soc. chim. Romania* **3**, 3 (1921).
9. Brown, R. L. and Berger, H. G., *Ind. Eng. Chem.* **16**, 917 (1924).
10. Kollo, C. and Angulescu, B. N., *Bull. soc. chim Romania* **8**, 17 (1926).
11. Borloz, A., *Helv. Chim. Acta* **10**, 543 (1927).
12. Fulweiler, W. H., Jordan, C. W. and Ward, A. L., *Proc. Am. Gas Assoc.* 1418 (1927).
13. Pfyl, B. and Schmitt, O., *Z. Untersuch. Lebensm.* **54**, 60 (1927).
14. Powell, A. R., *Proc. Am. Gas Assoc.* 1421 (1927).
15. Cundall, K. N., *Gas-Age Record* **62**, 393, 402 (1928).
16. Rae, J., *Pharm. J.*, **121**, 575 (1928).
17. Schläpfer, P. and Flachs, R., *Monat. Bull. schweiz. Verein Gas Wasserfach* **8**, 224, 250, 283, 302 (1928).
18. Bordeianu, C. V., *Ann. Sci. Univ. Jassy* **15**, 380 (1929).
19. Erikson, S., *Svensk Farm. Tids.* **34**, 1 (1930).
20. Matt, M. C., *Chemist-Analyst* **19**, 15 (1930).
21. Schläpfer, P. and Flachs, R., *J. usines gaz* **54**, 2, 25, 51 (1930).
22. Tweedy, S., *Colliery Guardian* **140**, No. 3620, 1843 (1930).
23. Staikov, T. S., *Ann. univ. Sofia* **9**, 301 (1931).
24. Brückner, H., *Gas u. Wasserfach* **75**, 573 (1932).
25. Pieters, H. A. J. and Smeets, G., *Het Gas* **52**, 134 (1932).
26. Pieters, H. A. J. and Mannens, M. J., *Het Gas* **52**, 313 (1932).
27. Dózsa, A., *Magyar Gyógyszerésztud. Társaság Ertesitöje* **9**, 476 (1933).
28. Binnington, D. S. and Geddes, W. F., *Ind. Eng. Chem., Anal. Ed.* **6**, 461 (1934).
29. Pieters, H. A. J., Penners, K. and Hartman, A., *Het Gas* **54**, 430 (1934).
30. Seebaum, H. and Oppelt, W., *Gas u. Wasserfach* **77**, 280 (1934).
31. Dobryanskii, A. F. and Tikhonov-Dubrovskii, N. T., *Azerbaidzhanskoe Neftyanoe Khoz.* No. 5, 84 (1935).
32. Funk, V., *Gas u. Wasserfach* **78**, 263 (1935).
33. Munch, A. P. W. and Heukers, R. T., *Chem. Weekblad* **32**, 411 (1935).
34. Pieters, H. A. J., Penners, K. and Geel, W., *Chem. Weekblad* **32**, 268 (1935); *Het Gas* **55**, 237 (1935).
35. Zwieg, W. and Kossendey, F., *Gas u. Wasserfach* **78**, 602 (1935).
36. Bolliger, A., *Australian J. Exp. Biol. Med. Sci.* **14**, 97 (1936).

37. Dellmeier, W., *Chemiker-Ztg.* **60**, 449 (1936).
38. Gehle, H., *Brennstoffchemie* **18**, 459 (1937).
39. Seebaum, H. and Hartmann, E., *Brennstoffchemie* **18**, 460 (1937).
40. Anisimov, S. B. and Polozov, N. F., *Khim. Tverdogo Topliva* **7**, 982 (1938).
41. Vaisman, G. A. and Korostichevs'ka, L. G., *Farm. Zhur.* **11**, No. 1, 20 (1938).
42. Abder-Halden, C. and Francillon, D., *J. usines gaz* **63**, 146 (1939).
43. Bolliger, A., *Analyst* **64**, 416 (1939).
44. Starchenko, I. I. and Druzhinin, G. M., *Zavodskaya Lab.* **8**, 1185 (1939).
45. Bolliger, A., *Quart. J. Pharm. Pharmacol.* **13**, 1 (1940).
46. Hitchings, G. H. and Fiske, C. H., *J. Biol. Chem.* **141**, 827 (1941).
47. Hitchings, G. H., *J. Biol. Chem.* **143**, 43 (1942).
48. Mohr, W., *Rev. brasil. quim.* **20**, 283 (1945).
49. Gambrill, C. M. and Martin, J. B., *Ind. Eng. Chem., Anal. Ed.* **18**, 689 (1946).
50. Korinfskii, A. A., *Zavodskaya Lab.* **12**, 418 (1946).
51. Reichardt, B. E. and White, D. L., *Ind. Eng. Chem., Anal. Ed.* **18**, 286 (1946).
52. Drozdov, N. S. and Materanskaya, N. P., *Zhur. Anal. Khim.* **2**, 17 (1947).
53. Perna, F. and Pelcík, J., *Paliva a voda* **28**, 260 (1948).
54. Rimattei, F. and Otta, E., *Congr. assoc. franc. avancement sci. Tunis* 1951, *Tunisie méd.* **39**, 886 (1951).
55. Schotte, L. and Veibel, S., *Acta Chem. Scand.* **7**, 1357 (1953).
56. Diviš, I., *Paliva* **34**, 87 (1954).
57. Shimizu, W., Fujita, M. and Endo, K., *Bull. Japan. Soc. Sci. Fisheries* **20**, 305 (1954).
58. Witry-Schwachtgen, G., *Inst. Grand-Ducal Luxembourg, Sect. Sci. nat. phys. et math., Arch.* **22**, 87 (1955).
59. Densham, A. B. and Seaton, E. M., *J. Appl. Chem. (London)* **6**, 101 (1956).
60. Veibel, S. and Nielsen, B. J., *Acta Chem. Scand.* **10**, 1488 (1956).
61. Creusot, L. and Pommel, G., *Compt. rend. ind. gen., 74me Cong., Bordeaux* 1957, 151.
62. Faingol'd, S. G. and Senkovskaya, S. I., *Koks i Khim.* No. 8, 32 (1957).
63. Gorbach, G. and Kögler, H., *Mikrochim. Acta* 572 (1957).
64. Mott, R. A. and Moulson, I., *J. Appl. Chem. (London)* **7**, 546, 553, 557 (1957).
65. Mathur, S. P., *Agra Univ. J. Research* **7**, 97 (1958).
66. Gruzdeva, N. A., Khokhlova, L. A. and Shevchenko, V. G., *Koks i Khim.* No. 2, 43 (1959).
67. Howorka, K. and Hädicke, M., *Pharm. Zentralhalle* **98**, 538 (1959).
68. Hädicke, M. and Howorka, K., *Pharm. Zentralhalle* **99**, 312 (1960).
69. Iványi, G. and Róna, V., *Magyar Kem. Lapya* **15**, 568 (1960).
70. Shirma, G. B., *Gigiena i Sanit.* **26**, No. 7, 61 (1961).

78. Nitrosobenzene

This reagent has been used to study rubber unsaturation via the reaction:

$$
\text{—}CH_2\text{—}C(CH_3){=}CH\text{—}CH_2\text{—} + 2\,C_6H_5NO \rightarrow \text{—}CH{=}C(CH_3)\text{—}\underset{\underset{\underset{C_6H_5}{|}}{\overset{\|}{NO}}}{C}\text{—}CH_2\text{—} + C_6H_5NHOH
$$

An example with titrimetric conclusion is given:

Materials titrated	Reagent and reaction conditions	Subsequent treatment and final titration stage
Unsaturation of butyl rubbers and polyisobutylenes	In benzene, + nitrosobenzene/benzene. At room temp. in the dark in nitrogen atmosphere, with various reaction times	Product precipitated with excess acetone, filtered and its nitrogen content determined via the Kjeldahl method (after initial reduction with phosphorus/HI)

Reference

Rehner, J., *Ind. Eng. Chem.* **36**, 118 (1944).

79. Ozone

This reagent has been used to determine olefinic groups or compounds, leading via ozonide formation to acids, aldehydes or ketones which have then been titrated. Three examples are given:

Materials titrated	Reagent and reaction conditions	Subsequent treatment and final titration stage	Ref.
Isopropylidene groups, $\text{—}C{=}C(CH_3)_2$	In acetic acid, + ozone, giving acetone and the corresponding aldehyde	Partly neutralized with NaOH, aldehyde oxidized with MnO_4^- acetone distilled out and determined with iodine/alkali, back titrating with thiosulphate	1

Materials titrated	Reagent and reaction conditions	Subsequent treatment and final titration stage	Ref.
d-Pimaric acid (a resin acid)	In CCl_4, + 3–5% ozone/oxygen mixture for 2 h	Product decomposed with steam, giving formic acid and HCHO; distilled out and former titrated with NaOH, latter determined with H_2O_2/excess alkali (see Hydrogen peroxide, ref. 17)	2
Isopropylidene groups	In acetic acid, + ozone/oxygen (minimum amount of water desirable, since it slows the ozonization reaction)	Ozonides hydrolysed, acetone distilled and determined with alkali/excess iodine (see Iodine reagents, ref. 275)	3

References

1. Kuhn, R. and Roth, H., *Ber.* **65**, 1285 (1932).
2. Komshilov, N. P., *Lesokhim. Prom.* **3**, No. 6, 25 (1940).
3. Szabó, D., *Magyar Kem. Lapya* **4**, 603 (1949).

80. Per-carboxylic acids

Reagents. Per-acetic, -benzoic, -camphoric, -furoic, -trifluoroacetic and -phthalic (mono-) acids have all been used. An example is classified here of analysis with benzoyl peroxide.

Reactions and materials titrated. 1. Addition with epoxide formation, in determination of olefines:

$$\mathrm{RCH{=}CHR + R'COOOH \rightarrow \underset{\diagdown O \diagup}{RCH{-}CHR} + R'COOH}$$

Pure compounds such as cyclohexene, oleic and elaidic acids, pinene and other hydrocarbons have been thus determined; the unsaturation of oils, polymers such as synthetic rubbers, etc. and other materials has been determined by a similar technique. This constitutes the most usual example of the use of the per-compounds in organic analysis.

2. C—C fission in an example of determination of carbonyl compounds:

$$\mathrm{2\,RCOR' + 2\,CF_3COOOH \rightarrow RCOOR' + R'COOR + 2\,CF_3COOH}$$

3. A type of addition reaction (to a free radical) evidently occurs in the example of use of benzoyl peroxide, namely for determination of triphenylmethyl. The stoichiometric relation is triphenylmethyl: benzoyl peroxide, 2:1, although various reaction products are formed (benzoic acid, tetraphenylmethane and triphenylmethyl benzoate).

4. Oxidation, of sulphides and sulphoxides

$$R{-}S{-}R \xrightarrow{RCOOOH} R{-}\underset{\downarrow\atop O}{S}{-}R \xrightarrow{RCOOOH} R{-}\underset{\swarrow\ \searrow\atop O\quad O}{S}{-}R$$

Reaction conditions. Determinations have been in organic solvents, usually chloroform or ether, but also ethyl acetate, acetic acid, dichloroethane or benzene.

Long reaction times (24 or more hours) have sometimes been necessary to ensure complete reaction.

Subsequent treatment and final titration stage. All determinations have been based on back titration of unreacted per-compound, via addition of iodide and acid (acetic or dilute sulphuric) and titration with thiosulphate of liberated iodine.

Examples

I^-; thiosulphate in the last column is used as abbreviation for the final stage mentioned above.

Materials titrated	Reagent and reaction conditions	Subsequent treatment and final titration stage	Ref.
Unsaturated hydrocarbons, e.g. terpenes	In $CHCl_3$ or ether, + perbenzoic acid	+ I^- + H_2SO_4; thiosulphate	1
Unsaturated fatty acids and esters: vegetable oils	+ peracetic acid/acetic acid in *ca* 2-fold excess; 16 h/room temp.	+ I^- + H_2SO_4; thiosulphate (see Iodides and hydriodic acid, ref. 28)	2
'Oxygen number' of polyterpenes	+ perbenzoic acid/ $CHCl_3$; 6–96 h/10–13°	+ I^-; thiosulphate	3
Olefines, e.g. limonene, pinene, unsaturated acids	+ percamphoric acid/ $CHCl_3$; 30 min/room temp.	+ I^-; thiosulphate	4
Olefines, e.g. pinene, safrole, isosafrole, isoeugenol, cholesterol, etc.	+ perfuroic acid/ $CHCl_3$	+ I^-; thiosulphate	5

Materials titrated	Reagent and reaction conditions	Subsequent treatment and final titration stage	Ref.
Sulphides, sulphoxides and olefines like pinene and cinnamyl alcohol	+ monoperphthalic acid/ether in 2–3-fold excess; 24 h/–15 to +10°	+ ether + I^-; thiosulphate after 10 min	6
Oleic, elaidic acids; vegetable oils	In ether, + monoperphthalic acid; 1–2 days/20° (study of reaction)	I^-; thiosulphate	7
Unsaturation of drying oils	+ perphthalic acid/ethyl acetate	I^-; thiosulphate	8
'Oxygen numbers' of resin acids and oils	+ perbenzoic acid/ $CHCl_3$. At 0°	Samples taken every 15 min, + I^-; thiosulphate and continued until constant	9
Unsaturation, e.g. of tung oil; oleic and linoleic acids	+ perphthalic acid/ethyl acetate in *ca* 2-fold excess; 6 h	I^-; thiosulphate	10
Unsaturation of synthetic rubber	In $CHCl_3$ + perbenzoic acid	I^-; thiosulphate	11
Internal olefine groups in polymers	+ perbenzoic acid/ $CHCl_3$ in *ca* 25% excess. At 6°; various times	+ I^-; thiosulphate; 17–24 h part of the curve extrapolated	12
Olefines	+ perbenzoic acid/benzene (study of rate of reaction in structure determination; found that inner double bonds were attacked faster than terminal bonds)	+ I^-; thiosulphate	13
Triphenylmethyl	In benzene, + benzoyl peroxide in nitrogen atmosphere. At least 15 min	+ acetic acid + I^-; thiosulphate	14
Unsaturation	In $CHCl_3$ + perbenzoic acid/ $CHCl_3$	Aliquots at intervals + I^- + dil. H_2SO_4; thiosulphate (until constant values)	15
	also at −15° + monoperphthalic acid/ether at −15° in 2–3-fold excess; 24 or more h/−15 to +10°	+ ether + I^-/water; thiosulphate	

Materials titrated	Reagent and reaction conditions	Subsequent treatment and final titration stage	Ref.
Aldehydes and ketones	+ pertrifluoroacetic acid/dichloroethane; 30 min or more/25–50°	+ I^- + dil. H_2SO_4; thiosulphate	16
Olefines, e.g. oleic acid	In benzene, + perbenzoic acid (kinetic studies)	Aliquot + I^-/acetic acid + a little $CHCl_3$ and titrated with thiosulphate as fast as iodine liberated (to eliminate error due to possible addition of iodine to the olefinic bonds)	17

References

1. Nametkin, S. S. and Bryssova, L., *J. prakt. Chem.* **112**, 169 (1926).
2. Smit, M. W. C., *Rec. trav. chim.* **49**, 691 (1930).
3. Ruzicka, L., Silbermann, H. and Furter, H., *Helv. Chim. Acta* **15**, 482 (1932).
4. Milas, N. A. and Cliff, I. S., *J. Am. Chem. Soc.* **55**, 352 (1933).
5. Milas, N. A. and McAlevy, A., *J. Am. Chem. Soc.* **56**, 1219 (1934).
6. Böhme, H., *Ber.* **70**, 379 (1937).
7. Böhme, H. and Steinke, G., *Ber.* **70**, 1709 (1937).
8. Khvostov, I. V. and Lubman, A. M., *USSR Patent* 67,121, Sept. 20, 1946.
9. Brus, G. and Martin, G., *Congr. tech. intern. ind. peintures inds. assoc.* **1**, 317 (1947).
10. Khvostov, G. V., *Zhur. Anal. Khim.* **2**, 281 (1947).
11. Kolthoff, I. M. and Lee, T. S., *J. Polymer Sci.* **2**, 206 (1947).
12. Saffer, A. and Johnson, B. L., *Ind. Eng. Chem.* **40**, 538 (1948).
13. Eimers, E., *Ann.* **567**, 116 (1950).
14. Hammond, G. S., Ravve, A. and Modic, F. J., *Anal. Chem.* **24**, 1373 (1952).
15. Houben-Weyl, '*Methoden der Organischen Chemie*', 4th Edition, *Analytische Methoden*, Georg Thieme Verlag Stuttgart, p. 309 (1953).
16. Hawthorne, M. F., *Anal. Chem.* **28**, 540 (1956).
17. Schmalz, E. O. and Geiseler, G., *Z. anal. Chem.* **190**, 233 (1962).

81. Perchloric acid

Reagent. Nearly always in glacial acetic acid.

Reactions, materials titrated and final titration stage. 1. 'Neutralization' in determination of organic bases. Perchloric acid is widely used as a direct titrant of bases. Sometimes, principally when a poorly soluble compound is to be determined, excess reagent has been used, back titrated after a suitable interval. The usual back titrant has been the alkali metal salt of a carboxylic acid (Na and K acetate; K hydrogen phthalate). Organic bases like triethylamine or quaternary or guanidine bases have also been used. End-point determination has been potentiometric or with the usual colour indicators.

2. Dehydration (catalytic action) of certain alcohols and ethers, yielding olefines. E.g.

$$CH_3.C(C_6H_5)_2OH - H_2O \rightarrow CH_2{=}C(C_6H_5)_2$$

The olefines were then titrated with bromate/bromide reagent.

Examples

Materials titrated	Reagent and reaction conditions	Subsequent treatment and final titration stage	Ref.
Pharmaceutical bases	+ $HClO_4$/acetic acid	Back titrated with Na acetate/acetic acid potentiometrically or to indicators like malachite green, crystal violet, α-naphtholbenzein, cochineal red	1
Amines in hydrocarbon polymerization feed	+ $HClO_4$/diethyl cellosolve; 3–4 h/−78°	Hydrocarbons evaporated and residue titrated with diphenylguanidine in diethyl cellosolve to methyl red	2
Sulphates of streptomycin and dihydrostreptomycin	+ $HClO_4$ + ethylene glycol	Most SO_4^{2-} precipitated with benzidine and then back titrated with KH phthalate to crystal violet	3
4-Benzylphenyl carbamate ('Diphenan'); urethane	In acetic acid + $HClO_4$; 30 min/100°	Back titrated with triethylamine to BZL blue	4
Alkali salts of organic acids	+ $HClO_4$/acetic acid	Back titrated with Na acetate/acetic acid potentiometrically or to indicators	5
Basic groups in ion exchange resins, e.g. amines, phosphonates, carboxylates	+ $HClO_4$/acetic acid; 24 h/90–100°	Filtered and titrated with Na acetate to crystal violet or oracet blue B	6

Materials titrated	Reagent and reaction conditions	Subsequent treatment and final titration stage	Ref.
Organic bases; amino hydrohalides	+ $HClO_4$/acetic acid; 3–10 min stirring	Back titrated with Na acetate to crystal violet (Hg acetate added in hydrohalide determinations)	7
Bases of soaps in lubricating grease	In toluene, + isopropanol/ethylene glycol, 7:5, + $HClO_4$; 15 min	Back titrated with KOH/alcohol to thymol blue	8
Na salts of organic acids; quaternary halides (e.g. Na benzoate and cinnamate; glycine; trimethylphenylammonium iodide)	In acetic acid, + $HClO_4$/acetic acid	Back titrated with Na acetate/acetic acid to crystal violet	9
Tetraethylthiuram disulphide ('Antabuse')	In $CHCl_3$ + acetic anhydride + Hg acetate and titrated with $HClO_4$ to green-yellow with Gentian violet	Back titrated with K acetate to blue	10
Tetraphenylborate of dimethyl ethyl *o*-bromobenzylammonium in determination of *p*-toluenesulphonate salt of it by precipitation	+ slight excess $HClO_4$	Back titrated with Na acetate to methyl violet	11
Some α-methylbenzohydryl ethers (antihistamines)	In acetic acid, + $HClO_4$ (70% aqueous solution)/acetic acid, dehydrating to olefines	Olefines titrated with bromate/bromide	12
1,1-Diphenylethanol; 1-(*p*-bromophenyl)-1-phenylethanol	Method of ref. 12		13
KNa tartrate	+ $HClO_4$/acetic acid; 20 min stirring	Back titrated with K acetate/acetic acid potentiometrically	14
Many salts of organic (and inorganic) acids	In butanone, + $HClO_4$	Titrated potentiometrically with tetraethylammonium hydroxide, giving 2 breaks, for unused acid and for the organic (or inorganic) acid	15, 16
Alkaloids (semimicro)	+ $HClO_4$/acetic acid in excess	Back titrated with Na acetate to indicators or potentiometrically	17

References

1. Spengler, H. and Kaelin, A., *Hundert Jahre Schweiz. Apoth'-Ver.* 1843–1943, p. 543 (1943).
2. Keen, R. T., *Anal. Chem.* **23**, 1706 (1951).
3. Penau, H., Saias, E. and Ferdet, J., *Ann. pharm. franç.* **11**, 740 (1953).
4. Ekeblad, P., *Svensk Farm. Tids.* **58**, 557 (1954).
5. Blake, M. J., *J. Am. Pharm. Assoc.* **46**, 163 (1957).
6. Ficken, G. E. and Lane, E. S., *Anal. Chim. Acta* **16**, 207 (1957).
7. Belcher, R., Berger, J. and West, T. S., *J. Chem. Soc.* 2877 (1959).
8. Buehler, F. A., *Am. Chem. Soc., Div. Petrol. Chem. Preprint* **4**, No. 3, 33 (1959).
9. Serrano Berges, L., *Inf. Quim. Anal.* **14**, 41 (1960).
10. Bayer, I. and Posgay, E., *Pharm. Zentralhalle* **100**, 56 (1961).
11. Gyenes, I., *Magyar Kem. Folyoirat* **67**, 162 (1961).
12. Jančik, F., Körbl, J. and Buben, F., *Českoslov. Farm.* **10**, 416 (1961).
13. Körbl, J. and Jančik, F., *Českoslov. Farm.* **10**, 419 (1961).
14. Richardson, M. L., *Anal. Chim. Acta* **24**, 46 (1961).
15. Kreshkov, A. P., Yarovenko, A. N. and Zel'manova, I. Ya., *Doklady Akad. Nauk SSSR* **143**, 348 (1962).
16. Kreshkov, A. P., Yarovenko, A. N. and Zel'manova, I. Ya., *Zhur. Anal. Khim.* **17**, 780 (1962).
17. Miana, G. A. and Ikram, M., *Pakistan J. Sci. Ind. Res.* **5**, 201 (1962).

82. Periodates and periodic acid

Reagent. Sodium or potassium meta- or paraperiodate, or the corresponding acids (which may be used directly or formed *in situ* from the salt and an acid like sulphuric). There is one example of a quaternary ammonium periodate reagent, used in non-aqueous solution.

Reactions and materials titrated. 1. Oxidation according to the schemes:

$$IO_4^- + 2\,H^+ + 2\,\epsilon \rightarrow IO_3^- + H_2O$$

or, rarely,

$$IO_4^- + 8\,H^+ + 8\,\epsilon \rightarrow I^- + 4\,H_2O,$$

followed by:

$$7\,I^- + IO_4^- + 8\,H^+ \rightarrow 4\,I_2 + 4\,H_2O$$

Almost all examples are of the specific oxidation of the —C(OH)—C(OH)— group, following the first oxidation scheme. Materials thus titrimetrically determined include: α-glycols; glycerol and higher polyalcohols up to mannitol, sorbitol and inositol; sugars; higher carbohydrates; glycerides. The method has proved valuable for the determination of compounds containing the α-glycol group in the presence of β-, γ- or other dihydroxy compounds. With polyalcohols, the end-groups are oxidized to aldehyde groups and the inner groups to formic acid;

$$\begin{array}{l} \text{R.CHOH} \\ \quad | \\ (\text{CHOH})_n \\ \quad | \\ \text{R.CHOH} \end{array} + (n-1)\,IO_4^- \rightarrow \begin{array}{l} \text{R.CHO} \\ \\ \quad + \\ \\ \text{R.CHO} \end{array} \quad n\,HCOOH + H_2O + (n-1)\,IO_3^-$$

α-Keto alcohols, α-diketone, α-amino alcohol and α-diamino groups are similarly specifically oxidized. The amines, typified by the amino acids serine and threonine and by the ethanolamines and ethylenediamine, yield ammonia as a reaction product, e.g.

$$CH_3CH(OH).CHNH_2.COOH + IO_4^- \rightarrow$$
$$CH_3CHO + CHO.COOH + NH_3 + IO_3^-$$

followed by: $CHO.COOH + IO_4^- \rightarrow HCOOH + CO_2 + IO_3^-$

$$HOCH_2.CH_2NH_2 + IO_4^- \rightarrow 2\,HCHO + NH_3 + IO_3^-$$

$$H_2NCH_2.CH_2NH_2 + H_2O + IO_4^- \rightarrow 2\,HCHO + 2\,NH_3 + IO_3^-$$

$$(HOCH_2.CH_2)_3N + 3\,IO_4^- \rightarrow 6\,HCHO + NH_3 + 3\,IO_3^-$$

Other compounds determined by oxidation based on one of the equations above include: formic, lactic and pyruvic acids, oxidized to CO_2, acetaldehyde and acetic acid respectively; compounds containing isopropylidene groups, yielding acetone; hydrazines; streptomycin; and sulphur-containing compounds like thiourea, thiobarbiturates and dithiocarbamates, where the sulphur is usually oxidized to sulphate.

2. Ion/ion combination in a single example of formation of a water-insoluble periodate, namely, that of piperazine.

Reaction conditions. Acid, near-neutral and alkaline solution have been used. (Strongly acid solution may lead to unwanted side-reactions, e.g. with glucosides.)

Reaction temperature and time depend on the material oxidized but most α-glycols and polyalcohols react completely within an hour at room temperature. In studies of the oxidation of polysaccharides, the progress of oxidation over a period of several days has been followed.

Subsequent treatment and final titration stage. (i) Determination of unused IO_4^-, using one of the following techniques:

1. Reaction with iodide at pH *ca* 4·7–7 (acetate, phosphate, bicarbonate, borate-containing solution)

$$IO_4^- + 2\,I^- + 2\,H^+ \rightarrow IO_3^- + I_2 + H_2O$$

Occasionally the iodine has been titrated with arsenite after a 10–20 min reaction time. More usually, iodide + excess arsenite have been added and the unreacted arsenite titrated with iodine.

2. Direct titration with Fe(II) (ref. 90) or hydrazine (ref. 94).
3. Periodic acid can be titrated as a monobasic acid to pH *ca* 5·5 and as a dibasic acid to pH *ca* 10 (a less well defined end-point but better at lower temperature, near 0°).

$$H_5IO_6 + OH^- \rightarrow H_4IO_6^- + H_2O$$

$$H_4IO_6^- + OH^- \rightarrow H_3IO_6^{2-} + H_2O$$

Similarly, NaH_4IO_6 can be titrated as a monobasic acid with a pH inflection near 10. These titrations have been used to determine unused periodic acid or monosodium paraperiodate.

(ii) Determination of IO_3^- formed and unused IO_4^-, by adding I^- and acid if necessary.

$$IO_3^- + 5\,I^- + 6\,H^+ \rightarrow 3\,I_2 + 3\,H_2O$$

$$IO_4^- + 7\,I^- + 8\,H^+ \rightarrow 4\,I_2 + 4\,H_2O$$

The periodate used in the oxidation reaction is obtained by difference from a control titration without sample.

(iii) Titration with alkali of the formic acid formed with polyalcohols containing three or more adjacent C—OH groups. Unused periodate is usually first destroyed with ethylene or propylene glycol. This permits determination of such compounds in presence of dihydroxy compounds, which yield no formic acid.

(iv) Distillation of HCHO formed from terminal —CH_2OH groups, followed by determination using sulphite or bisulphite, cyanide or alkali/H_2O_2; in another procedure, glycine has been used to react with the formaldehyde and allow acetaldehyde present to be determined. (Further details are under these reagent headings.)

(v) Distillation of acetaldehyde formed from terminal $CH_3.CH(OH)$— groups, followed by determination as with HCHO, using sulphite or bisulphite reagents, hydroxylamine hydrochloride and mercury (II). (As with formaldehyde, further details of these final stages are given under the relevant reagent headings.)

(vi) Distillation of ammonia from the amino-compounds and titration with acid.

(vii) Absorption of CO_2 reaction product in $Ba(OH)_2$ and back titration with acid.

Some other concluding stages, of which only one example appears to exist are:

Titration with thiocyanate of unused silver, after periodate oxidation in presence of measured excess silver nitrate, part of which is precipitated by the iodate formed.

Determination with iodine/alkali of acetone, formed by oxidation with periodate/some permanganate in the determination of isopropylidene groups.

Titration of iodine, resulting evidently from oxidation of formic acid.

Some general or review articles, wholly or partly on the subject of periodate determinations are refs 48, 65, 80, 84 and 116.

Examples

Materials titrated	Reagent and reaction conditions	Subsequent treatment and final titration stage	Ref.
Polyalcohols in aqueous solution	+ $K_4I_2O_9$/dil. H_2SO_4; 2–3 h/room temp. Control	+ KI and titrated with thiosulphate	1
Butane-2,3-diol	+ KIO_4/dil. H_2SO_4; 2 h boiling, giving acetaldehyde	Aspirated into neutralized hydroxylamine hydrochloride and titrated HCl liberated (see Hydroxylamine, ref. 25)	2
α-Glycerophosphates	+ $NaIO_4$ or KIO_4/dil. H_2SO_4; 10 min/room temp.	+ $NaHCO_3$ + I^- + excess arsenite; back titrated with iodine after 10–15 min	3

Materials titrated	Reagent and reaction conditions	Subsequent treatment and final titration stage	Ref.
HCOOH, also in presence of acetic acid	+ KIO_4; 2 h reflux, giving iodine	+ $CaCO_3$ and titrated with thiosulphate	4
Glycerol in wines	Method of ref. 6		5
Glycerol in presence of sugars	+ KIO_4, $K_3H_2IO_6$ or $Na_3H_2IO_6$/dil. H_2SO_4; 15 min/room temp.	+ $NaHCO_3$ + I^- + excess arsenite and back titrated with iodine after 15 min	6, 7
Inositol	+ $Na_3H_2IO_6/H_2SO_4$; 24 h/room temp.	+ $NaHCO_3$ + I^- + excess arsenite and back titrated with iodine	8
Glycerol, penta-erythritol	Neutral solution, + KIO_4 or $NaIO_4$; 20 min/room temp., giving formic acid	Titrated with alkali to methyl red	9
Polyhydroxy compounds, e.g. glucose, sorbitol, mannitol, galactose	+ excess IO_4^-	At pH 4·4–7 (acetate buffer) + I^- and iodine from unused periodate titrated with thiosulphate	10
Sugar in blood serum	+ KIO_4/H_2SO_4; 20 min/100°	+ K_2HPO_4 + I^- and titrated with thiosulphate	11
Glycerol in wine	Studied and slightly modified method of ref. 6		12
α,α'-Trehalose	Neutral solution, + $NaIO_4$; 27 h/room temp., giving formic acid (study of oxidation)	Titrated with NaOH to methyl red	13
Glycerol, e.g. in presence of ethylene glycol or diethylene glycol	+ H_5IO_6; 40–80 min/room temp. Controls	Titrated with NaOH to methyl red or potentiometrically to pH 5·5 and 10; also + I^- and iodine titrated with thiosulphate. Combined with bichromate oxidation (see Bichromate, ref. 96), this analysed mixtures	14
Tartaric acid	+ HIO_4, giving glyoxylic, then formic acid	+ I^- + measured excess HCl, titrated with thiosulphate and then with KOH to phenolphthalein	15
Lactic acid	+ $NaIO_4/H_2SO_4$; 30 min boiling, giving acetaldehyde	Distilled into Hg(II) reagent and Hg + Hg(I) determined iodometrically (see Mercury (II), ref. 81)	16

Materials titrated	Reagent and reaction conditions	Subsequent treatment and final titration stage	Ref.
pyruvic acid	+ KIO_4; refluxed giving acetic acid	unused determined with arsenite	
Ethylene glycol in presence of diethylene glycol	+ $Na_2H_3IO_6/H_2SO_4$; 2 h/room temp., giving HCHO	Neutralized, excess NaOH + H_2O_2 added. After 1 h/room temp., excess H_2SO_4 added and back titrated with NaOH to cresol red (see Hydrogen peroxide, ref. 20)	17
Polyhydroxy compounds	+ $NaIO_4/H_2SO_4$; 1 h/room temp.	+ $KHCO_3$ + I^- + excess arsenite and back titrated with iodine after 10 min; also determined HCOOH + HCHO with excess bromine (see Bromine reagents, ref. 200)	18
Methylpentoses in presence of pentoses	+ alanine + $NaHCO_3$ + HIO_4; 1 h/room temp., giving acetaldehyde	Aldehyde carried by CO_2 stream into $NaHSO_3$ and iodometrically determined (see Bisulphite and sulphite, ref. 56)	19
Threonine	+ $NaHCO_3$ + arsenite + HIO_4 (giving pH 7), yielding acetaldehyde	Aerated into $NaHSO_3$ and addition compound determined iodometrically (see Bisulphite and sulphite, ref. 59)	20
Compounds with —CHOH—$CHNH_2$ group, e.g. hydroxylysine, serine, threonine, β-hydroxyglutamic acid	+ HIO_4/alkali + K_2CO_3, giving ammonia. *Ca* 7 min/room temp.	Aerated into excess standard acid and back titrated with NaOH to alizarin red; or absorbed in boric acid and titrated with acid to bromocresol green	21
Glycerol	+ $NaIO_4/H_2SO_4$; 1 h/room temp., giving formic acid. Control	Excess IO_4^- destroyed with ethylene glycol and acid titrated with alkali to pH 8·1. Control titrated to pH 6·5	22
Glycerol	+ KIO_4; 2 h/room temp., giving formic acid	Titrated with NaOH to methyl red	23
glycerol + ethylene glycol + propylene glycol	same treatment, giving formic acid, HCHO and acetaldehyde	formic acid similarly determined; HCHO determined with excess KCN and back titration of unused; total aldehydes by reaction with sulphite and titration of the alkali produced (see Cyanide, ref. 11 and Bisulphite and sulphite, ref. 61)	

Materials titrated	Reagent and reaction conditions	Subsequent treatment and final titration stage	Ref.
Propylene glycol in air	Passed through $NaIO_4/H_2SO_4$; 15 min/*ca* 0°	+ $NaHCO_3$ + I^- + excess arsenite and back titrated with iodine after 15 min	24
Threonine from protein hydrolysis	+ Na_3PO_4/HIO_4 (pH 7); 4–5 h/room temp., giving acetaldehyde	Diffused into bisulphite and addition compound determined iodometrically (see Bisulphite and sulphite, ref. 66)	25
Glycerol + 2,3-butylene glycol	+ KIO_4; 3 h/room temp., giving formic acid, HCHO and acetaldehyde	Unused KIO_4 filtered, acid titrated with NaOH to methyl red, HCHO and total aldehydes determined as in ref. 23 (see Cyanide, ref. 12 and Bisulphite and sulphite, ref. 68)	26
Ethylene glycol, propylene glycol and glycerol in cosmetics	+ KIO_4; 1 h/room temp., giving formic acid, HCHO and acetaldehyde	Acid titrated with NaOH to methyl red; unused IO_4^- by adding $NaHCO_3$ + I^- + excess arsenite and titrating with iodine; total aldehydes by reaction with $NaHSO_3$ and iodometric titration of the addition compound; acetaldehyde in the same way after removal of HCHO with glycine (see Bisulphite and Sulphite, ref. 71)	27
2,3-Butylene glycol in fermentations	+ dil. H_2SO_4, boiled and KIO_4 gradually added; 5 min boiling after conclusion of addition; also + KIO_4/H_2SO_4; 10 min/100°. Control	Acetaldehyde formed distilled into $NaHSO_3$ and addition compound determined iodometrically (see Bisulphite and sulphite, ref. 73) + NaH_2PO_4 + I^- and iodine titrated thiosulphate	28
Ethanolamine; serine	+ HIO_4/alkali/borate (pH 9·6); *Ca* 7 min distillation	Distilled out ammonia into excess acid, added IO_3^-/I^- and titrated with thiosulphate	29
α-Monoglycerides	In 97–98% ethanol + $NaIO_4$; 15–20 h in dark/room temp.	Neutralized, $NaHCO_3$ + I^- + excess arsenite added and back titrated with iodine	30
Monoglycerides in fats, etc.	+ HIO_4/acetic acid; 30 min/room temp.	+ I^- and titrated with thiosulphate. Control	31

Materials titrated	Reagent and reaction conditions	Subsequent treatment and final titration stage	Ref.
Ethanolamine	+ $NaIO_4/H_2SO_4$, giving HCHO and ammonia; 5 min/room temp.	Determined unreacted IO_4^- by method of ref. 3	32
Ethylene + propylene glycols	+ $NaIO_4/H_2SO_4$; 15 min/100°	+ $NaHCO_3$ + I^- + excess arsenite and titrated with iodine	33
propylene glycol	+ glycine + $NaIO_4$/ H_2SO_4; 15 min/100°, giving HCHO (reacts with the glycine) + acetaldehyde	acetaldehyde carried by CO_2 stream into $NaHSO_3$ and addition compound determined iodometrically (see Bisulphite and sulphite, ref. 77)	
Saponified fatty esters of ethylene glycol and glycerol	Method of ref. 31		34
Glycerol in port wine	Neutral solution, + $HIO_4/NaHCO_3$; 20 min/room temp.	+ I^- + excess arsenite and titrated with iodine. Control	35
Polyalcohols from reduction with Al/ H_2SO_4 in determination of their nitrate esters (e.g. of mannitol, erythritol, inositol)	+ HIO_4/H_2SO_4; 1 h/room temp. (24 h for inositol)	+ $NaHCO_3$ + I^- + excess arsenite and titrated with iodine after 10 min	36
Carbohydrates	Study of IO_4^- oxidation under different conditions (no. of mols formic acid formed, etc.)	Unused IO_4^- destroyed with glycol and formic acid titrated with NaOH to methyl red; also IO_3^- formed determined by adding I^- and titrating with thiosulphate	37
Monoglycerides in fats and oils	In acetic acid/$CHCl_3$, 2:1, + HIO_4/acetic acid/water; 2 min/room temp. Control	+ I^- and titrated with thiosulphate	38
Glycerol in presence of ethylene and propylene glycols	Neutral solution, + KIO_4; 1 h/room temp.	Unused IO_4^- destroyed with propylene glycol (10 min reaction) and formic acid titrated with NaOH to bromocresol purple	39
Glycerol + propylene glycol	+ H_5IO_6; 1 h/room temp. Control	Titrated with NaOH potentiometrically; then + acetic acid + I^- and titrated with thiosulphate	40

Materials titrated	Reagent and reaction conditions	Subsequent treatment and final titration stage	Ref.
Ethanolamines	$+ HIO_4$; 5 min/room temp. (study of reactions)	Ammonia formed distilled and titrated; unused IO_4^- determined iodometrically; combined with acid titration → determination of all 3 amines	41
Glycerol in fermentation residues	$+ HIO_4$/water	HCHO continuously distilled into sulphite and determined by titrating the alkali formed (see Bisulphite and sulphite, ref. 87)	42
Ca glucuronate	$+ KIO_4/H_2SO_4$; 2·5 h/36°	$+ NaHCO_3 + I^- +$ excess arsenite and titrated with iodine after 15 min	43
Dihydroxyamino-alkanes (aminoglycols)	Emulsion in water, $+ KIO_4$; 20 min/room temp. (study of periodate oxidation)	$+$ borate buffer $+ I^-$ and titrated with arsenite	44
Polyhydroxy compounds (e.g. mannitol, sugars)	$+ IO_4^-$ at pH 4·2–4·5; 3, 10, 20 and 30 h/room temp.	Unused IO_4^- destroyed with ethylene glycol and formic acid titrated with alkali to phenol red	45
Glycerol in wine	$+ KIO_4$ or $K_2H_3IO_6$	HCHO formed determined with bisulphite (see Bisulphite and sulphite, ref. 89) also $+ NaHCO_3 + I^-$ and titrated with arsenite	46
End-group determination on amylose, amylopectin and maltose	In neutral NaCl, $+ NaIO_4$. Up to 25 h (48 for maltose)/room temp.	Unused IO_4^- destroyed with glycol and formic acid titrated with $Ba(OH)_2$ to methyl red	47
Sugars (pentoses, rhamnose)	In water, $+ NaIO_4$. Mostly 20–40 min/100°	Unused IO_4^- destroyed with ethylene glycol and formic acid titrated with alkali to methyl red	49
Tartaric acid in wine, must (separated as Ca racemate)	$+ IO_4^-$/acetate buffer, pH 4·7; 15 min/100°; also in phosphate buffer, pH 7; 3 h/100°	$+ NaHCO_3 + I^- +$ excess arsenite and titrated after 20 min with iodine	50
Glucose and condensation products with β-ketonic compounds	Neutral solution $+ NaIO_4$ (as in method of ref. 49)	Formic acid titrated with alkali to phenol red/bromothymol blue	51

Materials titrated	Reagent and reaction conditions	Subsequent treatment and final titration stage	Ref.
Hydroxyethylcellulose	+ $Na_3H_2IO_6$/acetate buffer. Various reaction times in study of oxidation	+ I^- + excess arsenite and titrated with iodine	52
Glycerol	+ KIO_4	Unused IO_4^- destroyed with propylene glycol and formic acid titrated with NaOH to bromocresol purple	53, 61
Ethylene glycol from hydrolysis of ethylene halohydrins	Method of ref. 27, slightly modified	HCHO distilled into $NaHSO_3$ and addition product determined iodometrically (see Bisulphite and sulphite, ref. 96)	54
Streptomycin; dihydrostreptomycin	+ KIO_4; 1 h/45–50°	+ $NaHCO_3$ + I^- + excess arsenite and titrated with iodine after 20 min	55
Ethylene oxide	+ HIO_4/dil. $HClO_4$; 1 h/room temp. Control	+ $NaHCO_3$ + I^- + excess arsenite and titrated with iodine after 10–15 min	56
Chloralose	In ethanol, + $NaIO_4$/dil. H_2SO_4; 15 min/room temp. Control	+ $KHCO_3$ + I^- + excess arsenite and titrated with iodine after 15 min.	57
Dextran	+ $NaIO_4$; up to 96 h/room temp.	Unused IO_4^- destroyed with ethylene glycol and formic acid titrated with NaOH to phenolphthalein	58
Glycerol in wine	+ IO_4^-/H_2SO_4; 15 min/room temp.	+ $NaHCO_3$ + I^- and titrated after 5 min with arsenite	59
Phenyl-β-D-glucopyranosylsulphones	+ $NaIO_4$. Left overnight/room temp. (study of oxidation)	Formic acid titrated potentiometrically with NaOH; also extracted 8 h with ethyl acetate and unused IO_4^- in aqueous layer determined by adding $NaHCO_3$ + I^- + excess arsenite and titrating with iodine after 10 min	60
p-Acetylaminobenzaldehyde thiosemicarbazone	+ $NaIO_4$/HCl. Control	+ I^- and titrated with thiosulphate	62

Materials titrated	Reagent and reaction conditions	Subsequent treatment and final titration stage	Ref.
α-Glycols	In water + $NaIO_4$; 20 min/room temp. Control	Cooled to 0° and titrated unused reagent with NaOH to thymolphthalein/α-naphtholbenzein; $NaIO_4 + 2H_2O \rightleftharpoons NaH_4IO_6$ $NaH_4IO_6 + NaOH \rightarrow Na_2H_3IO_6 + H_2O$	63
Glycerol	Neutral solution, + KIO_4; 30 min in dark/room temp.	Unused IO_4^- removed with ethylene glycol and formic acid titrated with NaOH to phenolphthalein	64
End-groups of polysaccharides	In NaCl solution, + $NaIO_4$; 30 h/2°	Unused IO_4^- destroyed with ethylene glycol and formic acid titrated with NaOH to bromocresol purple or potentiometrically; also unused IO_4^- determined by adding $NaHCO_3 + I^-$ + excess arsenite and titrating with iodine	66
Hydroxylysine in proteins	+ HIO_4/NaOH/K_2CO_3, giving ammonia	Ammonia carried with air into boric acid and titrated with HCl	67
Glycerol	In water, + KIO_4/H_2SO_4; 10 min/room temp. Control	+ I^- + HCl and titrated with thiosulphate	68
Some thiobarbituric acid derivatives	+ HIO_4/conc. HCl; 10–15 min/room temp.	+ I^- and titrated with thiosulphate	69
Inositol	+ IO_4^-; 2·5 h/50°	+ phosphate buffer + I^- and titrated with thiosulphate	70
Glycerol + propylene glycol in desiccating ointment	+ KIO_4/neutral solution	Formic acid titrated with NaOH after removal of excess IO_4^- with propylene glycol (measure of glycerol)	71
	+ KIO_4/acid	unused IO_4^- determined by adding I^- after neutralization and titrating with arsenite	
Methyl ester of dihydroxystearic acid in castor oil	In acetic acid, + HIO_4/acetic acid; 10 min/15–20°. Control	+ I^- + $CHCl_3$ and titrated with thiosulphate	72

Materials titrated	Reagent and reaction conditions	Subsequent treatment and final titration stage	Ref.
Glycerol in fermentation solutions (after absorption on alumina and elution)	Neutral solution, + KIO_4; 7 min/room temp.	Unused IO_4^- removed by 5 min reaction with ethylene glycol and formic acid titrated with NaOH to phenolphthalein	73
7-(Dihydroxypropyl)-theophylline ('Glyophyllin')	In water, + HIO_4; 15 min/room temp., giving HCHO + theophylline 7-aldehyde	+ $KHCO_3$ + excess arsenite + I^- and back titrated with iodine after 15 min	74
Piperazine	+ ether + hexamine/ethanol + excess HIO_4, giving insoluble periodate; 10 min/10°	Precipitate dissolved in H_2SO_4, I^- added and titrated with thiosulphate (see Iodides and hydriodic acid, ref. 169)	75
Glycerol	+ KIO_4/H_2SO_4; 5–10 min/room temp. Control	Unused IO_4^- destroyed with propylene glycol, then titrated with NaOH to bromocresol purple; also + I^- and titrated with thiosulphate	76
Glycerol in mixtures with trimethylene glycol and water	Method of ref. 64		77
Isopropylidene groups —$C=C(CH_3)_2$, e.g. in mesityl oxide, certain terpenes	In water (+ pyridine or dioxan if necessary), + K_2CO_3 (giving pH 7·2–7·5) + $NaIO_4$ + a little $KMnO_4$. Up to *ca* 18 h/room temp., giving acetone	Reaction stopped with arsenite/NaOH and acetone distilled and determined with iodine/alkali (see Iodine reagents, ref. 328)	78
o-threo-1-(*p*-Nitrophenyl)-2-aminopropane-1,3-diol (from analysis of chloramphenicol by hydrolysis)	+ IO_4^- at pH 7–7·5; 10 min/room temp.	Unused determined by adding I^-/excess arsenite and titrating with iodine after 15 min	79
Technical monoglycerides	Aliquot in $CHCl_3$/pyridine/acetic acid, + KIO_4/H_2SO_4/acetic acid; 30 min in dark/room temp. Control	+ I^- and titrated with thiosulphate	81
Polyhydroxy, α-dihydroxy and α-diketone compounds	In water, + HIO_4/$AgNO_3$ reagent (giving insoluble $AgIO_3$); 10 min to 24 h/room temp.	Filtered and unused Ag^+ in filtrate determined by titration with SCN^- (see also Silver (I), ref. 146)	82

Materials titrated	Reagent and reaction conditions	Subsequent treatment and final titration stage	Ref.
Sorbitol	+ KIO_4/H_2SO_4; 20 min/100°. Control	+ I^- and titrated with thiosulphate	83
Mono- and diethanol-amine	In ethanol, + $NaHCO_3$ + KIO_4; 15 min/room temp. Control	+ I^- + excess arsenite and titrated with iodine after 15 min	85
End-group determina-on glycogens	+ $NaIO_4$ at pH 5·8; Various times/18–20°	Unused IO_4^- destroyed with ethylene glycol and formic acid titrated with NaOH to methyl red or potentiometrically; also unused IO_4^- determined by adding I^- in near neutral solution and titrating with arsenite	86
Water-insoluble α-glycols	In ethanol, + HIO_4/ ethyl acetate/acetic acid/ triethylamine; 75 min in dark/room temp.	+ $NaHCO_3$ + excess arsenite and titrated with iodine	87
Mono- and dihydrazino-phthalazines	+ HIO_4/HCl	+ I^- and titrated with thio-sulphate	88
Many organic com-pounds, e.g. sulphur-containing like thiourea, dithiocarbamates	+ HIO_4/HCl; 20–30 min/room temp.	+ I^- and titrated with thio-sulphate	89
Tartaric acid	+ acetic acid + KOH (approx. equivalent amount) + KIO_4; 4 h/room temp.	+ H_2SO_4 and titrated with $FeSO_4$ potentiometrically	90
Tartaric acid, mannitol, Ca gluconate	+ acetate buffer, pH 4·8 + KIO_4; 4 h/room temp.	+ H_2SO_4 + excess $FeSO_4$ and back titrated with KIO_4 to diphenylamine sulphonic acid	91
2-(*p*-Chlorophenyl)-3-methylbutane-2,3-diol ('Phenaglycodol')	+ HIO_4/acetic acid; 2 h in dark/room temp. Control	+ I^- and titrated with thio-sulphate	92
α-Glycol content of epoxy resins (water-insoluble)	In $CHCl_3$, + trimethyl-benzyl ammonium periodate/methanol; 2·5 h/0°. Control	+ water + H_2SO_4 + I^- and titrated with thiosulphate	93

Materials titrated	Reagent and reaction conditions	Subsequent treatment and final titration stage	Ref.
Various organic substances	Oxidized with excess IO_4^-	Unused IO_4^- titrated with hydrazine sulphate in presence of $NaHCO_3$, borax or Na acetate	94
Desoxy sugar derivatives	In water or ethanol/ water, + $NaIO_4$. Up to 4 h/room temp. (study of periodate oxidation)	Formic acid titrated with NaOH to methyl red; unused IO_4^- determined by adding $NaHCO_3/I^-$ and titrating with arsenite	95
End-groups in glycogen	+ $NaIO_4$ + methyl α-D-glucoside standard; 48 h/3°. Controls	Unused IO_4^- destroyed with ethylene glycol and formic acid titrated with $Ba(OH)_2$ potentiometrically; also + I^- + excess thiosulphate and back titrated with iodine	96
O-Carbamoylnoviose (from action of trifluoroacetic acid on novobiocin)	Aliquot + IO_4^-; 1 h in dark/room temp.	+ $NaOH/NaHCO_3$ + I^- + excess arsenite and back titrated with iodine after 15 min	97
Penta-substituted glycerols	In water or ethanol, + HIO_4/dil. H_2SO_4. Up to 35 h	+ I^- and titrated with thiosulphate	98
α-Glycols and polyhydroxy compounds, e.g. ethylene glycol, glycerol, mannitol	In water, + HIO_4, giving 2 mols HCHO; 10 min/room temp.	+ Na_2SO_3 to destroy IO_3^- and unused IO_4^- and to form bisulphite compound with the HCHO; unused SO_3^{2-} destroyed with iodine and KCN added, giving cyanohydrin and SO_3^{2-} equivalent; latter titrated with iodine after acidification (see Bisulphite and sulphite, refs 150 and 151; Cyanide, refs 32 and 33)	99, 100
Glucose	In water, + $Na_3H_2IO_6$/ H_2SO_4; 1 h/room temp.	As in refs 99 and 100 (see Bisulphite and sulphite, ref. 152; Cyanide, ref. 34)	101
Tartaric acid	In water, + ethanol/ H_3PO_4 + HIO_4; 30 min/room temp., giving glyoxalic acid	Glyoxalic acid determined by procedure of refs 99 and 100 (see Bisulphite and sulphite, refs 153, 155 and 166; Cyanide, refs 35, 36 and 46)	102, 103, 113

Materials titrated	Reagent and reaction conditions	Subsequent treatment and final titration stage	Ref.
3-(2-Tolyloxy)- and 3-(2-methoxy)-propane-1,2-diol	+ HIO_4; 10 min/room temp.	Unused titrated with arsenite	104
Fructose	In water + H_3PO_4 + $Na_3H_2IO_6$ + ethanol + H_2SO_4; 30 min/room temp.	As in refs 99 and 100 (see Bisulphite and sulphite, refs 158 and 161; Cyanide, refs 38 and 41)	105, 108
Glycerinaldehyde	+ HIO_4/H_2SO_4; 1 h/room temp., giving HCHO	As in refs 99 and 100 (see Bisulphite and sulphite, refs 159 and 162; Cyanide, refs 39 and 42)	106, 109
Serine, threonine	+ IO_4^-/alkali solution; 3–5 min; then + acetic acid and left 60 min, giving HCHO or CH_3CHO respectively, + HCOOH, CO_2 and NH_3 E.g. $HOCH_2.CHNH_2.COOH + IO_4^- \rightarrow CHO.COOH + HCHO + NH_3 + IO_3^-$, followed by: $CHO.COOH + IO_4^- \rightarrow HCOOH + CO_2 + IO_3^-$	1. aldehyde determined as in refs 99 and 100 2. + $NaHCO_3$ + I^- and titrated with arsenite 3. + $NaHSO_3$ to reduce IO_3^- and unused IO_4^- and to combine with the aldehyde, and NH_3 distilled and titrated with acid 4. + glycine to combine with the aldehyde, ammonia distilled and titrated (as before, see also under Bisulphite and sulphite, refs 160, 163 and 165; Cyanide, refs 40, 43 and 45)	107, 110 111
Polyalcohols, e.g., ethylene glycol, glycerol, mannitol	+ 20% HIO_4; 10–20 min	HCHO determined as in methods of refs 99 and 100	112
glucose, arabinose	as for polyalcohols, but 30–60 min	as above	112
fructose	+ HIO_4 + H_3PO_4 + 40–50% ethanol	as above	112
Ethylene glycol in ethyl cellosolve	+ $Na_3H_2IO_6/H_2SO_4$; 10 min/room temp. Control	+ I^- and titrated with thiosulphate	114
End group determination on glycogens (study of rates of oxidation)	Method of ref. 86		115

Materials titrated	Reagent and reaction conditions	Subsequent treatment and final titration stage	Ref.
Ethanolamines, ethylenediamine	+ IO_4^-/alkali ($NaHCO_3$); 20–60 min/room temp. or boiling, giving HCHO and NH_3	1. HCHO determined as in refs 99 and 100 2. NH_3 distilled out and titrated with acid (see Bisulphite and sulphite, refs 170, 171 and 182; Cyanide, refs 47, 48 and 50)	116, 117, 123
Aldonic and sugar di-carboxylic acids, serine, threonine, glyoxalic acid, tartaric acid	Oxidized with HIO_4 to CO_2 and HCHO	CO_2 absorbed in excess $Ba(OH)_2$ under a pentane layer and back titrated with HCl to thymol blue; HCHO determined by method of refs 99 and 100	118, 130, 131, 132
Some methylglucosides; melibiose; maltose; galactose; sucrose	Study of oxidation with various HIO_4 concs. and reaction times from 5 min to 10 h	+ I^-/acetic acid and titrated with thiosulphate	119
Free ethylene glycol in its polyesters	HIO_4/96% methanol, + sample in $CHCl_3$/ ethanol, 9:1; 30 min/warm water-bath	+ water + I^-/$NaHCO_3$ and back titrated with arsenite	120
Oxazolines	Study of periodate oxidation at various pH values (0 to 8)	+ $NaHCO_3$ + excess arsenite and back titrated with iodine after 15 min	121
Glycerol in fruit pastilles	Based on method of ref. 73		122
Glycerol in injection solutions	+ KIO_4; 10 min	+ excess arsenite + $KHCO_3$ + KI and back titrated with iodine	124
Hydroxyamino acids and peptides containing terminal hydroxyamino groups	+ conc. K_2CO_3 + HIO_4; 2·5–3 h, giving NH_3	Diffused into boric acid and titrated with H_2SO_4	125
Mono- and diethanol-amine in scrubbing solutions	+ H_2SO_4 + HIO_4; 1 min	+ Na_2CO_3 + arsenite and back titrated with iodine after 10 min	126
Glycerol in wine	+ KIO_4/H_2SO_4; 10 min	+ water/H_2SO_4/KI and titrated with thiosulphate	127
Glycerol	+ HIO_4 at room temp.	Unused reagent titrated iodometrically	128

Materials titrated	Reagent and reaction conditions	Subsequent treatment and final titration stage	Ref.
Glycerol in pharmaceutical preparations	Neutralized solution, + KIO_4 + Na_2SO_4; 5 min	+ 50% isopropanol and formic acid titrated with NaOH to bromoscresol purple	129
Glycol monomers in linear polyesters	+ excess KIO_4	HCHO determined as in method of refs 99 and 100	133

References

1. Malaprade, L., *Bull. soc. chim. France* **43**, 683 (1928).
2. Brockmann, M. C. and Werkmann, C. H., *Ind. Eng. Chem., Anal. Ed.* **5**, 206 (1933).
3. Fleury, P. and Paris, R., *J. pharm. chim.* **18**, 470 (1933).
4. Stainier, C. and Massart, J., *Congr. pharm.* (*Liège* 1934) 186 (1935).
5. Fatôme, M., *Ann. fermentations* **1**, 291 (1935).
6. Fleury, P. and Fatôme, M., *J. pharm. chim.* **21**, 247 (1935).
7. Fleury, P. and Fatôme, M., *Ann. fermentations* **1**, 285 (1935).
8. Fleury, P. and Joly, M., *J. pharm. chim.* **26**, 341, 397 (1937).
9. Malaprade, L., *Bull. soc. chim. France* (5), **4**, 906 (1937).
10. Rappaport, F., Reifer, I. and Weinmann, H., *Mikrochim. Acta* **1**, 290 (1937).
11. Rappaport, F. and Reifer, I., *Klin. Wochschr.* **16**, 1392 (1937).
12. Ferré, L. and Michel, A., *Ann. fals.* **31**, 85 (1938).
13. Jackson, E. L. and Hudson, C. S., *J. Am. Chem. Soc.* **61**, 1530 (1939).
14. Allen, N., Charbonnier, H. Y. and Coleman, R. M., *Ind. Eng. Chem., Anal. Ed.* **12**, 384 (1940).
15. Arragon, G., *Compt. rend.* **211**, 558 (1940).
16. Boisson, R., *J. pharm. chim.* (9) **1**, 240 (1940).
17. Tappi, G. and Bertolina, G., *Ricerca sci.* **11**, 1001 (1940).
18. Fleury, P. and Courtois, J., *Ann. chim. anal. chim. appl.* **23**, 117 (1941).
19. Nicolet, B. H. and Shinn, L. A., *J. Am. Chem. Soc.* **63**, 1456 (1941).
20. Shinn, L. A. and Nicolet, B. H., *J. Biol. Chem.* **138**, 91 (1941).
21. v. Slyke, D. D., Hiller, A. and MacFadyen, D. A., *J. Biol. Chem.*, **141**, 681 (1941).
22. Bradford, P., Pohle, W. D., Gunther, J. K. and Mehlenbacher, V. C., *Oil & Soap* **19**, 189 (1942).
23. Hoepe, G. and Treadwell, W. D., *Helv. Chim. Acta* **25**, 353 (1942).

24. Puck, T. T., *Science* **95**, 178 (1942).
25. Winnick, T., *J. Biol. Chem.* **142**, 461 (1942).
26. Hoepe, C., *Helv. Chim. Acta* **26**, 1931 (1943).
27. Shupe, I. S., *J. Assoc. Offic. Agr. Chem.* **26**, 249 (1943).
28. Johnson, M. J., *Ind. Eng. Chem., Anal. Ed.* **16**, 626 (1944).
29. Artom, C., *J. Biol. Chem.* **157**, 585 (1945).
30. Ivanoff, N., *Bull. mat. grasses inst. colonial, Marseille* **29**, 45 (1945).
31. Pohle, W. D., Mehlenbacher, V. C. and Cook, J. H., *Oil & Soap* **22**, 115 (1945).
32. Fleury, P. and Guitard, H., *Bull. soc. chim. biol.* **28**, 651 (1946).
33. Reinke, R. C. and Luce, E. N., *Ind. Eng. Chem., Anal. Ed.* **18**, 244 (1946).
34. Troy, A. and Bell, A. C., *Am. Perfumer* **48**, No. 7, 54 (1946).
35. Vasioncelles y Lencastre, A. de Q., *Anais inst. vinho Porto* No. 7, 31 (1946).
36. Balatre, P. and Ardaens, A., *Ann. pharm. franç.* **5**, 457 (1947).
37. Halsall, T. G., Hirst, E. L. and Jones, J. K. N., *J. Chem. Soc.* 1427 (1947).
38. Handschumaker, E. and Linteris, L., *J. Am. Oil Chemists' Soc.* **24**, 143 (1947).
39. Newburger, S. H. and Bruening, D. F., *J. Assoc. Offic. Agr. Chem.* **30**, 651 (1947).
40. Pohle, W. D. and Mehlenbacher, V. C., *J. Am. Oil Chemists' Soc.* **24**, 155 (1947).
41. Courtois, J. and Grandchamp, M., *Ann. pharm. franç.* **6**, 453 (1948).
42. Elving, P. J., Warshowsky, B., Shoemaker, E. and Margolit, J., *Anal. Chem.* **20**, 25 (1948).
43. Fleury, P., Courtois, J. and Wickström, A., *Ann. pharm. franç.* **6**, 338 (1948).
44. Mead, J. F. and Bartron, E. A., *J. Am. Chem. Soc.* **70**, 1286 (1948).
45. Meyer, K. H. and Rathgeb, P., *Helv. Chim. Acta* **31**, 1540 (1948).
46. Peynaud, E., *Ann. fals. et fraudes* **41**, 384 (1948).
47. Potter, A. L. and Hassid, W. Z., *J. Am. Chem. Soc.* **70**, 3488 (1948).
48. Fleury, P., Courtois, J. and Grandchamp, M., *Bull. soc. chim. France* 88 (1949).
49. Hirst, E. L. and Jones, J. K. N., *J. Chem. Soc.* 1659 (1949).
50. Poux, C., *Ann. fals et fraudes* **42**, 439 (1949).
51. Aparicio, F. J. L. and Román, V. S., *Anales real soc. españ. fis. y quim.* **46B**, 645 (1950).
52. Cohen, S. G. and Haas, H. C., *J. Am. Chem. Soc.* **72**, 3954 (1950).
53. Colson, R., *Oléagineux* **5**, 701 (1950).
54. Cowan, H. D., McCabe, C. L. and Warren, J. C., *J. Am. Chem. Soc.* **72**, 1194 (1950).

55. Delaby, R. and Stephan, F., *Ann. pharm. franç.* **8**, 513 (1950).
56. Eastham, A. M. and Latremouille, G. A., *Can. J. Research* **28B**, 264 (1950).
57. Fleury, P. and Jolly-Collin, J., *Ann. pharm. franç.* **8**, 15 (1950).
58. Jeanes, A. and Wilham, C. A., *J. Am. Chem. Soc.* **72**, 2655 (1950).
59. Thaler, H. and Roos, W., *Z. anal. Chem.* **131**, 24 (1950).
60. Bonner, W. A. and Drisko, R. W., *J. Am. Chem. Soc.* **73**, 3699 (1951).
61. Colson, R., *Ind. parfum.* **6**, 115 (1951).
62. Sandri, G., *Ann. chim. applicata* **41**, 135 (1951).
63. Dal Nogare, S. and Oemler, A. N., *Anal. Chem.* **24**, 902 (1952).
64. Erskine, J. W. B., Strouts, C. R. N., Walley, G. and Lazarus, W., *Analyst* **78**, 630 (1953).
65. Fleury, P., *Chim. anal.* **35**, 197 (1953).
66. Morrison, M., Kuyper, A. C. and Orten, J. M., *J. Am. Chem. Soc.* **75**, 1502 (1953).
67. Ramachandran, L. K., *J. Sci. Ind. Research* (*India*) **12B**, 9 (1953).
68. Resnikov, I. G. and Farber, E. L., *Masloboino-Zhirovaya Prom.* **18**, No. 5, 13 (1953).
69. Sandri, G. and Lambardi, F., *Atti accad. sci. Ferrara* **30**, 27 (1953).
70. Böhm, P. and Richarz, G., *Z. physiol. Chem.* **298**, 110 (1954).
71. Griffin, J. C. M., *J. Assoc. Offic. Agr. Chem.* **37**, 874 (1954).
72. Kamath, N. R., Kane, J. G. and Sreenivasan, B., *Current Sci.* (*India*) **23**, 262 (1954).
73. Sporek, K. and Williams, A. F., *Analyst* **79**, 63 (1954).
74. Wickstrøm, A. and Valseth, A., *Ann. pharm. franç.* **12**, 576 (1954).
75. Wickstrøm, A. and Valseth, A., *Ann. pharm. franç.* **12**, 777 (1954).
76. Hintermaier, A., *Fette, Seifen, Anstrichmittel* **57**, 11 (1955).
77. Lazarus, W. and Newlove, T. H., *Analyst* **80**, 276 (1955).
78. v. Rudloff, E., *Can. J. Chem.* **33**, 1714 (1955).
79. Valseth, A. and Wickstrøm, A., *Medd. Norsk Farm. Selskap.* **17**, 345 (1955).
80. Fouillouze, G., *Lyon Pharm.* **7**, 231 (1956).
81. Hartman, L., *Analyst* **81**, 67 (1956).
82. Pesez, M., *Bull. soc. chim. France* 148 (1956).
83. Adcock, L. H., *Analyst* **82**, 427 (1957).
84. Auterhoff, H. and Lohmann, V., *Deut. Apotheker-Ztg.* **97**, 904 (1957).
85. Kubias, J., *Chem. Listy* **51**, 2275 (1957).
86. Manners, D. J. and Archibald, A. R., *J. Chem. Soc.* 2205 (1957).
87. Reddaway, R. J. B., *Analyst* **82**, 506 (1957).
88. Sandri, G. C., *Boll. chim. farm.* **96**, 431 (1957).
89. Sandri, G. C., *Atti accad. sci. Ferrara* **35**, 17 (1957–8).
90. Berka, A. and Zýka, J., *Českoslov. Farm.* **7**, 141 (1958).
91. Berka, A. and Zýka, J., *Chem. Listy* **52**, 930 (1958).

92. Cerri, O., *Boll. chim. farm.* **97**, 261 (1958).
93. Stenmark, G. A., *Anal. Chem.* **30**, 381 (1958).
94. Berka, A. and Zýka, J., *Českoslov. Farm.* **8**, 136 (1959).
95. Cleaver, A. J., Foster, A. B., Hedgley, E. J. and Overend, W. G., *J. Chem. Soc.* 2578 (1959).
96. Fales, F. W., *Anal. Chem.* **31**, 1898 (1959).
97. Forist, A. A., Theal, S. and Struck, W. A., *Anal. Chem.* **31**, 100 (1959).
98. Henry-Basch, E. and Fréon, P., *Compt. rend.* **248**, 2597 (1959).
99. Maros, L. and Schulek, E., *Magyar Kem. Folyoirat* **65**, 361 (1959).
100. Maros, L. and Schulek, E., *Acta. Chim. Acad. Sci. Hung.* **20**, 359 (1959).
101. Maros, L. and Schulek, E., *Acta Chim. Acad. Sci. Hung.* **21**, 91 (1959).
102. Schulek, E., Molnár-Perl, I. and Maros, L., *Magyar Kem. Folyoirat* **65**, 363 (1959).
103. Schulek, E., Molnár-Perl, I. and Maros, L., *Acta Chim. Acad. Sci. Hung.* **20**, 443 (1959).
104. Waaler, T. and Paulssen, R. B., *Medd. Norsk Farm. Selskap.* **21**, 97 (1959).
105. Maros, L. and Schulek, E., *Magyar Kem. Folyoirat* **66**, 197 (1960).
106. Maros, L., Molnár-Perl, I. and Schulek, E., *Magyar Kem. Folyoirat* **66**, 319 (1960).
107. Maros, L., Molnár-Perl, I. and Schulek, E., *Magyar Kem. Folyoirat* **66**, 321 (1960).
108. Maros, L. and Schulek, E., *Acta Chim. Acad. Sci. Hung.* **22**, 359 (1960).
109. Maros, L., Molnár-Perl, I. and Schulek, E., *Acta Chim. Acad. Sci. Hung.* **24**, 67 (1960).
110. Maros, L., Molnár-Perl, I. and Schulek, E., *Acta Chim. Acad. Sci. Hung.* **24**, 213 (1960).
111. Maros, L., Molnár-Perl, I. and Schulek, E., *Ann. Univ. Sci. Budapest Rolando Eötvös nominatae, Sect. Chem.* **2**, 237 (1960).
112. Maros, L. and Schulek, E., *Ann. Univ. Sci. Budapest Rolando Eötvös nominatae, Sect. Chem.* **2**, 247 (1960).
113. Schulek, E. and Maros, L., *Ann. Univ. Sci. Budapest Rolando Eötvös nominatae, Sect. Chem.* **2**, 243 (1960).
114. Perepletchikova, E. M., Etlis, V. S. and Kalugin, A. A., *Zavodskaya Lab.* **26**, 154 (1960).
115. Manners, D. J. and Wright, A., *J. Chem. Soc.* 2681 (1961).
116. Maros, L., Molnár-Perl, I. and Schulek, E., *Acta Chim. Acad. Sci. Hung.* **26**, 467 (1961).
117. Maros, L., Molnár-Perl, I. and Schulek, E., *Magyar Kem. Folyoirat* **67**, 203 (1961).
118. Maros, L., Molnár-Perl, I. and Schulek, E., *Magyar Kem. Folyoirat* **67**, 527 (1961).

119. Guernet, M., *Bull. soc. chim. France* 1752 (1961).
120. Mlejnek, O. and Sečkářová, H., *Chem. zvesti* **15**, 760 (1961).
121. Wehrmeister, H. L., *J. Org. Chem.* **26**, 3821 (1961).
122. Lloyd, W. J. W., *Analyst* **87**, 62 (1962).
123. Maros, L., Molnár-Perl, I. and Schulek, E., *Acta Chim. Acad. Sci. Hung.* **30**, 119 (1962).
124. Paulssen, R. B. and Waaler, T., *Pharm. Acta Helv.* **37**, 125 (1962).
125. Okudo, H., Noguchi, S., Fujii, S. and Yamamura, Y., *Tokushima J. Exp. Med.* **9**, 137 (1962).
126. Scheirer, D. E., Ellis, G. C. and Theurer, K., *Proc. Gas Conditioning Conf.* 87, 1962.
127. Smirnova, A. P. and Eskina, N. A., *Vinodelie i Vinogradarstvo SSSR* **22**, No. 8 15 (1962).
128. Ghimicescu, G., Ghimicescu, C. and Dumbrava, E., *Acad. R. P. R., Stud. Cercet. Chim.* **11**, 103 (1963).
129. Ludwicki, H. and Sobiczewska, M., *Farm. Polska* **19**, 228 (1963).
130. Maros, L., Molnár-Perl, I. and Schulek, E., *Acad. Chim. Acad. Sci. Hung.* **35**, 1 (1963).
131. Maros, L., Molnár-Perl, I., Vajda, M. and Schulek, E., *Anal. Chim. Acta* **28**, 179 (1963).
132. Maros, L. Molnár-Perl, I., Vajda, M. and Schulek, E., *Magyar Kem. Folyoirat* **69**, 123 (1963).
133. Maros-Greger, K. and Vancso-Szmercsanyi, I., *Magyar Kem. Folyoirat* **69**, 228 (1963).

83. Permanganate

Reagent. Almost always aqueous $KMnO_4$ solution.

Reactions and materials titrated. Oxidation of numerous functional groups and compound classes:

1. Hydroxy compounds, such as alcohols (especially the lower aliphatic alcohols), polyalcohols (like glycerol, sugars and related compounds) and phenols.

2. Carboxylic acids, especially formic and oxalic; hydroxy and keto acids may be included here, exemplified by the frequently encountered determinations of lactic and citric acids, and, also, some examples of determination of tartaric, malic and malonic acids.

3. Aldehydes like formaldehyde and benzaldehyde.

4. Some olefines such as methyl α-chloroacrylate and maleic and fumaric acids.

5. A miscellaneous group of nitrogen-containing compounds, including quinine, pyramidone, choline, aminoantipyrine, benzocaine, isothiocyanates and hydrazobenzene.

Apart from these determinations of functional groups or individual compounds, standardized oxidation with permanganate has been used to measure 'oxidizability' or oxygen consumption of coals, tannins, waters, etc., or the unsaturation of materials like drying oils.

The reaction products vary with the nature of the material and with the conditions. More vigorous conditions usually lead to formation of carbon dioxide and water. A few notable exceptions where a stable intermediate is formed (and frequently determined as the concluding stage of the determination) are listed below:

Lactic acid, $CH_3.CHOH.COOH + O \rightarrow CH_3CHO + CO_2 + H_2O$

Citric acid, $C_6H_8O_7 + O \rightarrow (CH_3)_2CO + 3\,CO_2 + H_2O$

Citric acid $+ O + 5\,Br_2 \rightarrow CHBr_2.CO.CBr_3 + 3\,CO_2 + H_2O + 5\,HBr$

Cresols, $C_6H_4(OH)CH_3 + 13\,O \rightarrow CH_3COOH + 5\,CO_2 + 2\,H_2O$

Propionic acid, $C_2H_5COOH + 3\,O \rightarrow CH_3COOH + CO_2 + H_2O$

[8-hydroxyquinoline, with N and OH] $+ 8\,O \rightarrow$ [pyridine-2,3-dicarboxylic acid: N, —COOH, —COOH] $+ 2\,CO_2 + H_2O$

Hydrazobenzene,

$$C_6H_5.NH.NH.C_6H_5 + O \rightarrow C_6H_5.N{=}N.C_6H_5 + H_2O$$

Some large cations, e.g. of quaternary ammonium detergents, yield sparingly soluble permanganates, so that there is the possibility of their determination in ion/ion combination reaction analogous to that with bichromate. No example has been found in the literature, possibly because of the probability of disturbing side reactions with the more strongly oxidizing permanganate reagent.

Reaction conditions. Oxidations have been carried out in acid, neutral or alkaline solution, based on the following equations:

Acid (H_2SO_4) solution;

$$MnO_4^- + 8\,H^+ + 5\,\epsilon \rightarrow Mn^{2+} + 4\,H_2O$$

Neutral or alkaline solution;

$$MnO_4^- + 2\,H_2O + 3\,\epsilon \rightarrow MnO_2\downarrow + 4\,OH^-$$

or

$$MnO_4^- + \epsilon \rightarrow MnO_4^{2-}$$ (the manganate ion is then removed as insoluble $BaMnO_4$ by addition of Ba^{2+}; this prevents its further participation in the oxidation)

Higher temperature has been used with materials which are more resistant to oxidation or where a volatile reaction product was separated by distillation.

Subsequent treatment and final titration stage. (i) Determination of unused permanganate, using one of the following procedures:

1. Titration with oxalate, or addition of measured excess oxalate followed by final permanganate titration.

2. Titration with Fe(II) reagent or, as with oxalate, addition of excess and final titration with permanganate.

3. Addition of iodide (and acid where the reaction was carried out in neutral or alkaline solution) and titration of the iodine liberated, using thiosulphate.

4. Titration with formate in alkaline solution.

5. Titration with hydrogen peroxide.

6. Titration with arsenite or, as under 1 and 2 above, addition of excess arsenite and titration with permanganate.

7. In one example, titration with thiourea.

(ii) Determination of a reaction product, including:

1. Acetaldehyde, from lactic acid; this has usually been done with bisulphite or with alkali/excess iodine.

2. Acetone from citric acid (also from isobutyric acid), determined iodometrically with alkali/excess iodine.

3. Pentabromoacetone, from citric acid by oxidation in the presence of bromide; the equivalent of bromide ions has usually been set free

by treatment with reagents like sodium sulphide, and the determination concluded argentometrically.

4. Oxalic acid from glycerol, propionic and lactic acids; it has been directly titrated with permanganate or first precipitated as the calcium salt and then subjected to permanganate titration.

5. Certain aliphatic amines, notably the methylamines, formed from alkylpyridines, choline or pyramidone; these were determined acidimetrically.

6. CO_2 from oxidation of oxalic acid and methanol.

Single examples of three further conclusions are:

Argentometric titration of Br^- from tribromophenol.
Titration with acid of ammonia obtained by reduction of nitrate ion from permanganate treatment of amyl nitrite.
Titration with alkali of benzoic acid from permanganate oxidation of benzaldehyde.

Examples

Materials titrated	Reagent and reaction conditions	Subsequent treatment and final titration stage	Ref.
Formic acid	+ alkali/excess MnO_4^-	+ H_2SO_4 and unused titrated with Fe(II)	1
Ethanol	+ dilute H_2SO_4/excess MnO_4^-; 1½–2 days/room temp.	Unused titrated with oxalic acid	2
phenol	+ alkali/MnO_4^-	+ H_2SO_4 and unused titrated with oxalic acid	
Glycerol	+ KOH/MnO_4^-, giving oxalic acid on heating	Decolorized with SO_2 and titrated with MnO_4^- after acidification with H_2SO_4	3
Glycerol	+ KOH/MnO_4^-; 30 min boiling, giving oxalic acid	Decolorized with SO_2, MnO_2 filtered and oxalate precipitated as Ca salt; precipitate acidified and titrated with MnO_4^-	4
Formic acid	+ alkali/MnO_4^- excess; boiled 10 min.	+ excess oxalic acid + H_2SO_4 and back titrated with MnO_4^-	5

Materials titrated	Reagent and reaction conditions	Subsequent treatment and final titration stage	Ref.
Formic acid	Heated with alkali/ excess MnO_4^-	+ H_2SO_4 + excess oxalic acid and back titrated with MnO_4^-	6
Lactic acid	Boiled with alkali/MnO_4^-, giving oxalic acid	Decolorized with H_2O_2, oxalate precipitated as Ca salt, H_2SO_4 added to precipitate and titrated with MnO_4^- (see Calcium (II), ref. 1)	7
Phenol	+ Na_2CO_3 + excess MnO_4^-; 5 min boiling	+ H_2SO_4 and unused titrated with oxalic acid	8
HCHO	+ H_2SO_4 + excess MnO_4^-; 10 min shaking/room temp.	Unused titrated with H_2O_2	9
Humus in soil	+ H_2SO_4 + MnO_4^-; boiled 40–50 min	Back titrated with oxalic acid	10
Bi tartrate, precipitated in determination of tartrate	+ hot dilute H_2SO_4 and titrated with a slight excess of MnO_4^-	Back titrated with oxalic acid	11
HCHO HCOOH	+ H_2SO_4 + excess MnO_4^-; 1 h/room temp. + same reagent; 6 h/room temp.	Unused determined with excess oxalic acid and back titration with MnO_4^-	12
Phthalonic acid	+ H_2SO_4 + MnO_4^-	Unused titrated with Fe(II)	13
Lactic acid in organs and animal fluids	+ H_2SO_4; MnO_4^- added gradually to boiling solution, giving acetaldehyde	Distilled into alkali/excess iodine and unused determined with thiosulphate (see Iodine reagents, ref. 33)	14
Malonic acid	+ H_2SO_4 + MnO_4^-; 10 min/80–90°, giving formic acid; made alkaline, and heated a few min to oxidize to CO_2	+ H_2SO_4 + excess oxalic acid and back titrated with MnO_4^-	15
Lactic acid	+ H_2SO_4; MnO_4^- added gradually to boiling solution, giving acetaldehyde	Distilled into bisulphite and unused titrated with iodine (see Bisulphite and sulphite, ref. 8)	16
Tribromophenol from determination of salicylic acid by reaction with bromine water	+ MnO_4^-, giving Br^-	Filtered and Br^- determined with excess Ag(I) and back titration with SCN^-	17

Materials titrated	Reagent and reaction conditions	Subsequent treatment and final titration stage	Ref.
Coumarin	Neutralized solution + $ZnSO_4$ (catalyst of oxidation and gives better coagulated precipitate) + excess MnO_4^-; 10 min boiling	Filtered, excess oxalic acid added, then H_2SO_4 and back titrated with MnO_4^-	18
Citric acid	+ H_3PO_4; MnO_4^- added gradually to the boiling solution, giving acetone	Distilled into $HgSO_4/H_2SO_4$ reagent; boiled 45 min, giving an acetone/Hg complex. Filtered, dissolved in HCl and Hg(II) determined by titration with I^-	19
Lactose	Method of ref. 21		20
Glucose; starch after acid hydrolysis	+ Na_2CO_3 + MnO_4^-. Brought to 95° in 2 min, then 2 min at that temp.	+ H_2SO_4 + excess oxalic acid and back titrated with MnO_4^-	21
Lactic acid; also in blood, urine, etc.	+ H_2SO_4; MnO_4^- added gradually to boiling solution	Acetaldehyde aerated into bisulphite and combined bisulphite determined iodometrically (see Bisulphite and sulphite, ref. 12)	22
Ethanol (micro)	Heated with alkali + MnO_4^-, giving CO_2	+ acid + excess oxalic acid and back titrated with MnO_4^-	23
Lactic acid in animal organs	MnO_4^- added to boiling acid solution	Acetaldehyde distilled into bisulphite and unused titrated with iodine (see Bisulphite and sulphite, ref. 18)	24
Lactic acid	Similar technique to method of ref. 24; claimed priority		25
Lactic acid	+ H_2SO_4 + $MnSO_4$; MnO_4^- added during *ca* 15 min to the boiling solution	Acetaldehyde passed into bisulphite and combined determined iodometrically (see Bisulphite and sulphite, ref. 25)	26
Benzaldehyde in cherry-laurel water	+ H_2SO_4 + excess MnO_4^-; 1 h reaction time	+ excess Fe(II) and back titrated with MnO_4^-	27
Maleic, fumaric acids	+ H_2SO_4 + excess MnO_4^-, giving CO_2	+ excess oxalate and back titrated with MnO_4^-	28
Lactic acid in urine	+ H_2SO_4 + $MnSO_4$; boiling solution titrated with MnO_4^-	Acetaldehyde distilled into bisulphite and unused back titrated with iodine	29

Materials titrated	Reagent and reaction conditions	Subsequent treatment and final titration stage	Ref.
Lactic acid	$+ H_2SO_4 + MnSO_4$; boiling solution titrated with MnO_4^-	Acetaldehyde distilled into bisulphite and combined bisulphite determined iodometrically (see Bisulphite and sulphite, ref. 26)	30
Glycerol	$+ H_2SO_4 +$ excess MnO_4^-; 2 h/100°	Unused titrated in hot solution with oxalic acid	31
Lactic acid	$+ H_3PO_4 + MnSO_4$; MnO_4^- added to boiling solution during 20 min	Acetaldehyde distilled into bisulphite and combined bisulphite determined iodometrically	32
Ethanol in dilute aqueous solutions	+ excess MnO_4^- solution + conc. H_2SO_4, giving hot solution; 1 min.	+ excess oxalic acid, heated and back titrated with MnO_4^-	33
Lactic acid in tanning extracts	$+ H_2SO_4 + MnSO_4$ and MnO_4^- added to hot solution, giving acetaldehyde	Distilled into bisulphite and combined part determined iodometrically (see Bisulphite and sulphite, ref. 28)	34
Lactic acid	$+ H_2SO_4 +$ excess MnO_4^-; 15 min/100°, giving acetic acid	+ excess oxalic acid and back titrated with MnO_4^-	35
Lactic acid in muscles	Method of ref. 35		36
Lactic acid	$+ H_2SO_4 + MnSO_4$; MnO_4^- added to hot solution, giving acetaldehyde	Distilled into bisulphite and unused titrated with iodine (see Bisulphite and sulphite, ref. 30)	37
Tartrates	+ NaOH + excess MnO_4^-; 30 min/100°	$+ H_2SO_4 +$ excess oxalic acid and back titrated with MnO_4^-	38
Citric acid	$+ H_2SO_4 + Br^- + MnO_4^-$, giving pentabromoacetone	Filtered, dissolved in ethanol, acetic acid/I^- added and iodine liberated titrated with thiosulphate (see Iodide and hydriodic acid, ref. 31)	39
Lactic acid from determination of alanine by reaction with nitrite	$+ H_2SO_4$ and hot solution titrated with MnO_4^-, giving acetaldehyde	Distilled into bisulphite and combined part determined iodometrically	40

Materials titrated	Reagent and reaction conditions	Subsequent treatment and final titration stage	Ref.
Lactic acid in vegetable tan liqueurs	+ H_2SO_4 + $MnSO_4$ and MnO_4^- added to hot solution	Acetaldehyde distilled into bisulphite and combined part determined iodometrically (see Bisulphite and sulphite, ref. 32)	41
Propionic acid in presence of formic and acetic acids	+ Na_2CO_3 + MnO_4^-; 4 h/100°, giving oxalic acid	Excess MnO_4^- destroyed with ethanol, MnO_2 filtered and oxalate precipitated as Ca salt; titrated with MnO_4^- in H_2SO_4 solution (see Calcium (II), ref. 6)	42
Lactic acid in muscle	Method of ref. 32		43
Quinine in solutions, tablets and ampoules	+ H_2SO_4 + excess MnO_4^-	+ excess oxalic acid and back titrated with MnO_4^-	44
Pyramidone in presence of antipyrine, caffeine, phenacetin and acetanilide	In water, + NaOH + excess MnO_4^-, giving dihydroxypyramidone	+ I^- + H_2SO_4 and liberated iodine titrated with thiosulphate to starch	45
Formic acid in fruit juices and syrups	+ Na_2CO_3 and MnO_4^- added to boiling solution; 1 min boiling or 45 min/room temp.	+ $ZnSO_4$ and unused titrated with arsenite	46
Benzyl alcohol	+ MnO_4^-; 1 h/room temp., giving benzoic acid	Decolorized with SO_3^{2-}, acidified and the benzoic acid extracted with $CHCl_3$; evaporated and titrated with alkali	47
Lactic acid in meats, etc.	+ H_2SO_4 + $MnSO_4$ + MnO_4^- (or colloidal MnO_2); 15 min heating	Acetaldehyde distilled into bisulphite and combined part determined iodometrically	48
Lactic acid	+ alkali + excess MnO_4^-, giving oxalic acid	Precipitated as Ca salt from acetic acid solution and titrated with MnO_4^- (see Calcium (II), ref. 7)	49
Ca oxalate from determination of urine oxalic acid	+ acid + $MnSO_4$ + excess MnO_4^-; 3 min/room temp.	+ I^- and titrated with thiosulphate to starch	50
Citric acid	+ phosphate buffer, pH 1·9–2·3; MnO_4^- gradually added, giving acetone	Distilled into NaOH, excess iodine added and unused determined iodometrically (see Iodine reagents, ref. 138)	51

Materials titrated	Reagent and reaction conditions	Subsequent treatment and final titration stage	Ref.
Lactic acid	+ $MnSO_4/MnO_4^-$, giving acetaldehyde	Distilled into Nessler-type Hg(II) reagent, acidified, and Hg(I) determined by adding excess iodine and back titrating with thiosulphate (see Mercury (II), ref. 54)	52
Coumarin, extracted from plant materials by steam distillation	+ excess MnO_4^-; 10 min heating	Filtered, excess oxalic acid added, then H_2SO_4 and back titrated with MnO_4^-	53
Phenol, cresols	+ H_2SO_4 + MnO_4^-. Heated to 80°, giving CO_2 and CO_2 + acetic acid respectively	Unused MnO_4^- determined by adding I^- and titrating with thiosulphate; acetic acid distilled out and titrated with KOH to phenolphthalein or dimethylaminoazobenzene	54
Citric acid	+ $Br^-/H_2SO_4/MnO_4^-$; 10 min/room temp., giving pentabromo-acetone	MnO_2 removed with Fe(II) the pentabromoacetone extracted, with petroleum ether/Na_2S solution, giving Br^-; aqueous layer acidified, H_2S boiled out and Br^- determined with excess Ag(I) and back titration with SCN^-	55
Methanol	+ $NaOH/MnO_4^-$; 4 min/room temp., giving CO_2 and MnO_4^{2-}	+ Ba(II) to precipitate MnO_4^{2-} and prevent further oxidation by it; unused MnO_4^- titrated with Na formate, adding a little Ni(II) as catalyst near the end	56
acetone, fumaric acid, erythritol	+ $NaOH/MnO_4^-/Ba(II)$; a few min/room temp., giving CO_2 and precipitate of $BaMnO_4$	+ excess oxalic acid + H_2SO_4 and back titrated with MnO_4^-	
Acrolein	+ MnO_4^- + H_2SO_4; 15 min/*ca* 100°	+ excess oxalic acid and back titrated with MnO_4^-	57
Oxidizability of water and effluents	+ NaOH + $BaCl_2$ + MnO_4^-; 10 min/room temp.	Unused titrated with formate	58
Butyl and amyl alcohols	+ H_2SO_4 + MnO_4^-; 35 min/room temp. in the dark	+ excess oxalate, heated to 80–90° and back titrated with MnO_4^-	59

Materials titrated	Reagent and reaction conditions	Subsequent treatment and final titration stage	Ref.
Ethanol	+ alkali/MnO_4^-; 20 min/*ca* 100°	+ acid/I^- and titrated with thiosulphate	60
Lactic acid	+ H_2SO_4 + $MnSO_4$ + MnO_4^-; *ca* 60 min distillation at 90°	Acetaldehyde distilled into bisulphite and combined part determined iodometrically (see Bisulphite and sulphite, ref. 43)	61
Citric acid	Method of ref. 51 (see Iodine reagents, ref. 167)		62
Oxalates	+ MnO_4^- + $MnSO_4$ + H_2SO_4; 10 min/room temp.	+ I^- and titrated with thiosulphate to starch	63
Chloral	+ Na_2CO_3 + MnO_4^-; 20 min/room temp.	+ HCl/I^- and titrated with thiosulphate	64
Ethylene glycol	+ alkali + MnO_4^-; 90 min/room temp., then acidified and left 4 h (giving CO_2)	+ I^- and titrated with thiosulphate	65
Ethanol in saliva	+ NaOH + MnO_4^-. Heated to 100°	+ acid/I^- and titrated with thiosulphate	66
Isobutyric acid	+ MnO_4^-, giving acetone	Distilled out and determined with iodine/alkali (see Iodine reagents, ref. 185)	67
Lactic acid	+ H_2SO_4 + $MnSO_4$ + MnO_4^-, giving acetaldehyde	Distilled into bisulphite and unused titrated with iodine (see Bisulphate and sulphite, ref. 49)	68
Lactic acid (submicro)	+ acid + $MnSO_4$ + MnO_4^-, giving acetaldehyde	Distilled into bisulphite and combined part titrated with iodine (see Bisulphite and sulphite, ref. 52)	69
Oxidation index of coals	Pyridine extract of powdered coal + NaOH + MnO_4^-; 1 h boiling	Filtered and unused titrated with oxalic acid	70
Paraldehyde in 10 N H_2SO_4 solution	Slightly over titrated with MnO_4^- at 20° in CO_2 atmosphere	+ excess Fe(II) and back titrated with MnO_4^-	71
Derivatives of catechol, e.g. tannin, in tea	Recommended method of ref. 56		72

Materials titrated	Reagent and reaction conditions	Subsequent treatment and final titration stage	Ref.
Unsaturation of drying oils	In acetic acid, + MnO_4^- + an emulsifier; 1 h/room temp.	+ excess Fe(II) and back titrated with MnO_4^-	73
Oxygen consumption of potable water	+ excess MnO_4^-	Unused titrated at the boiling point with oxalic acid	74
Unsaturated compounds in cyclopropane	Passed into MnO_4^-	+ excess oxalic acid at 90° and back titrated with MnO_4^-	75
Citrate	Method of ref. 51	(see Iodine reagents, ref. 226)	76
Citric acid	+ H_2SO_4 + Br^-; MnO_4^- added gradually, giving pentabromoacetone	Treated with Na_2S, giving Br^-; determined with excess Ag(I) and back titration with SCN^-	77
Citric acid	+ H_2SO_4 + Br^- + MnO_4^-; 10 min/room temp., then 10 min/0°, giving pentabromoacetone	Excess MnO_4^- removed with H_2O_2 and determined by reaction with Na_2S giving Br^- and titration with excess Ag(I) (principle of method of ref. 55) (see Sulphides, ref. 4)	78
Ba citrate, precipitated in determination of citrate	+ acetic acid + MnO_4^-, giving acetone	Distilled out and determined with alkali/excess iodine (see Iodine reagents, ref. 232)	79
Citric acid in milk, cheese	Method of ref. 55		80
Formate from determination of chloral by alkali hydrolysis	+ Na_2CO_3 + MnO_4^-	+ H_2SO_4 + excess oxalic acid and back titrated with MnO_4^-	81
p-Aminobenzenesulphonamide	+ Br^- + H_2SO_4 + MnO_4^-; 10 min/room temp. in the dark	+ I^- and titrated with thiosulphate	82
Citric acid	Tested method of ref. 78 (and also a colorimetric method based on formation of pentabromoacetone)		83
HCHO, methanol, formic acid (in addition to inorganic materials)	Method of ref. 56 but preferred back titration with oxalate		84
Oxygen consumption of waters	+ excess MnO_4^-; 3, 10, 15 and 30 min/27°	+ I^- and titrated with thiosulphate; result from extrapolation to 4 h reaction	85

Materials titrated	Reagent and reaction conditions	Subsequent treatment and final titration stage	Ref.
Citric acid	+ NaOH + MnO_4^-; 15–24 h/room temp.	Unused titrated with formate (*cf*. ref. 56) or arsenite	86
Lactic acid in sugar; also after isolation as methyl lactate and hydrolysis	Method of ref. 7		87
Tannins; tanning agents	+ excess MnO_4^-; 10 min/room temp. (studied conditions—reaction time, temp., etc.)	+ I^- and titrated with thiosulphate	88
Ethanol in blood	Diffused into KOH/ MnO_4^-; 2–3 h/room temp. in the dark	+ $BaCl_2$ (to precipitate manganate) and unused titrated with thiourea to disappearance of pink	89
HCHO, formic acid	+ Na_2CO_3 + MnO_4^-; 20–30 min/room temp.	+ H_2SO_4 + excess Fe(II) and back titrated with MnO_4^-	90
Ca gluconate	+ excess MnO_4^-; 30 min/near boiling point	Unused titrated with oxalic acid at *ca* 80°	91
Lactic acid in milk	+ H_2SO_4 and MnO_4^- added dropwise	Acetaldehyde distilled into bisulphite and combined part determined iodometrically (see Bisulphite and sulphite, ref. 95)	92
Choline in biological material	+ MnO_4^-; 10–45 min distillation, giving trimethylamine	Final distillation into excess acid and back titration with alkali	93
Maleic acid	+ H_2SO_4 + MnO_4^-; 2–3 min/room temp.	+ I^- and titrated with thiosulphate	94
Lactic acid in fermented drinks	+ H_2SO_4 + $MnSO_4$; MnO_4^- added gradually, giving acetaldehyde	Distilled into bisulphite and combined part determined iodometrically (see Bisulphite and sulphite, ref. 100)	95
Glucose	+ MnO_4^-. Heated to 50–80°	+ excess oxalic acid and back titrated with MnO_4^-	96
Aminoantipyrine from determination of 1-phenyl-2,3-dimethyl-4-(*p*-aminophenylsulphonamido)-5-pyrazolone	Method of ref. 45		97

Materials titrated	Reagent and reaction conditions	Subsequent treatment and final titration stage	Ref.
Citric acid	$+ Br^- + H_3PO_4 + MnO_4^-$; 10 min/not above 22°, giving pentabromo-acetone	Unused MnO_4^- destroyed with H_2O_2; treated with Na_2S giving Br^- which was ultimately determined by adding solid $AgIO_3$, giving $AgBr + IO_3^-$; I^-/acid added and titrated with thiosulphate (see Sulphides, ref. 6)	98
Methyl α-chloro-acrylate in the atmosphere	Passed through MnO_4^-	+ excess oxalic acid and back titrated with MnO_4^-	99
Lactic acid in wine, grape juice, etc.	$+ H_3PO_4 + MnSO_4$ and MnO_4^- slowly added to hot solution; 20 min distillation	Acetaldehyde distilled into $NaHSO_3$ and combined part determined iodometrically (see Bisulphite and sulphite, ref. 102)	100
Oxine; 8-hydroxy-quinaldine	$+ H_2SO_4 + MnO_4^-$; 15 min/room temp., giving pyridine carboxylic acids	$+ I^-$ and titrated with thiosulphate	101
Ethanol in blood	$+ H_3PO_4 + MnO_4^-$, oxidizing to CO_2; up to 40 min/not over 60°	Back titrated with Fe(II) to barium diphenylamine sulphonate	102
4,4′-Dinitrostilbene-2,2′-disulphonic acid	Neutralized solution + MnO_4^-; 2 min/0°	$+ I^-/H_2SO_4$ and titrated with thiosulphate	103
Benzocaine	In dilute H_2SO_4, $+ Br^- + H_2SO_4 + MnO_4^-$; 5 min/room temp.	$+ I^-$ and titrated with thiosulphate	104
Glycerol	$+ NaOH + MnO_4^-$; 15–20 min/room temp.	$+ H_2SO_4$ + excess oxalic acid and back titrated with MnO_4^-	105
Glycerol, phenol, salicylic acid, methanol	Method of ref 56, using back titration with formate but potentiometrically		106
Some alcohols and aldehydes, e.g. methanol, ethanol, butanol, HCHO, acetaldehyde, benzaldehyde, also acids like tartaric and malic	$+ NaOH + MnO_4^-$; 10 min/45° (based on method of ref. 56)	$+ BaCl_2$ to precipitate MnO_4^{2-} and unused MnO_4^- titrated with formate potentiometrically	107

Materials titrated	Reagent and reaction conditions	Subsequent treatment and final titration stage	Ref.
Products from determination of pyridine derivatives by methylation with NaOH/ dimethyl sulphate	Steam distilled in presence of MnO_4^-, giving methylamine	Methylamine in distillate titrated with H_2SO_4	108
Citric acid after isolation as Ba salt	+ MnO_4^-, giving acetone	Distilled and determined with alkali/excess iodine (see Iodine reagents, ref. 312)	109
Lactic acid in heavy corn steep liquor	+ H_3PO_4 + $MnSO_4$; MnO_4^- added continuously and acetaldehyde distilled	Distilled into bisulphite and combined part determined iodometrically (see Bisulphite and sulphite, ref. 111)	110
K hydrogen phthalate from determination of phthalic anhydride	+ H_2SO_4 + MnO_4^-; 3 min	+ I^- and titrated with thiosulphate	111
Some hydroxy acids, e.g. tartaric, citric, salicylic	+ alkali + MnO_4^-. Studied catalytic effect of many cations and found Ca^{2+} best	+ H_2SO_4 + excess Fe(II) and back titrated with MnO_4^-	112
Ca oxalate from determination of oxalic acid in blood plasma, serum or red cells by precipitation	Solution in HCl, + H_2SO_4 + $MnSO_4$ + MnO_4^-	+ I^- and titrated with thiosulphate	113
Tartrate in cyanide baths	+ H_2SO_4 + $MnSO_4$ + MnO_4^-; 5 min boiling	+ I^- and titrated with thiosulphate	114
Lactic acid in wine	+ H_2SO_4 + MnO_4^-; 5–10 min heating	Acetaldehyde distilled into bisulphite and combined part determined iodometrically (see Bisulphite and sulphite, ref. 128)	115
Pyramidone	In water, + MnO_4^-, then + NaOH, giving dihydroxypyramidone	Boiled with alkali, distilled the dimethylamine formed into excess acid, concluding with back titration with alkali (see Alkalies, ref. 340)	116
Lactic acid in blood	+ H_2SO_4 + MnO_4^-, giving acetaldehyde	Distilled into bisulphite and combined part determined iodometrically (see Bisulphite and sulphite, ref. 134)	117

Materials titrated	Reagent and reaction conditions	Subsequent treatment and final titration stage	Ref.
'Permanganate numbers' of tannins	In water, + H_2SO_4 + MnO_4^-; 10 min/room temp. with shaking	+ I^- and titrated with thiosulphate	118
Methyl thiouracil	+ HCl + Br^- + MnO_4^-; 1 h/room temp. in the dark	+ excess arsenite and back titrated with MnO_4^- to methyl red	119
Amyl nitrite	In ethanol, + H_2SO_4 + MnO_4^-; 15 min/room temp. with shaking giving NO_3^-	Reduced with Raney Ni/alkali, the ammonia distilled into excess HCl with concluding back titration with alkali	120
Lactic acid in fish meat	Heated with MnO_4^-, giving acetaldehyde	Distilled into bisulphite and unused determined iodometrically (see Bisulphite and sulphite, ref. 137)	121
Volatile reducing matter in fish	Aspirated into MnO_4^-	+ I^- and titrated with thiosulphate	122
Pyramidone in 'pyributal'	+ NaOH + MnO_4^-. Boiled giving dimethylamine	Distilled into excess acid and back titrated with alkali	123
Alcohol in fish and egg products	+ excesss MnO_4^-	+ I^- and titrated with thiosulphate	124
Hydrazobenzene	In benzene or xylene, + NaOH + MnO_4^-; 10 min/room temp. with shaking, giving azobenzene	+ I^- + acid and titrated with thiosulphate	125
Lactic acid in beer	Heated with H_2SO_4/MnO_4^- reagent, giving acetaldehyde	Distilled into bisulphite and combined part determined iodometrically (see Bisulphite and sulphite, ref. 144)	126
Organic matter in water (mostly fulvic acids)	+ dil. H_2SO_4 + MnO_4^-; 30 min/100°	+ excess oxalate and back titrated with MnO_4^-	127
Glycerol; polyethylene oxide groups in plasticizers [—CH_2—CH_2—O—]$_x$	+ $KMnO_4$/KOH; 1 h reflux	+ H_2SO_4 + $MnSO_4$ + excess oxalic acid and back titrated with MnO_4^-	128
Volatile reducing substances in food (fish meat)	+ MnO_4^-; 40 min	+ I^- and titrated with thiosulphate	129

Materials titrated	Reagent and reaction conditions	Subsequent treatment and final titration stage	Ref.
Aldehyde groups in in cellulose	+ dilute H_2SO_4 + MnO_4^-; 30 min/0°	+ excess ferrous ammonium sulphate and back titrated with MnO_4^-	130
Maleic acid and anhydride from oxidation of naphthalene to give phthalic anhydride	(after extraction of naphthaquinone from aqueous solution using benzene) + MnO_4^- + H_2SO_4; 30 min/room temp.	+ I^- and titrated with thiosulphate	131, 132
Lactic acid in juices	+ $MnSO_4$ + phosphoric acid + MnO_4^-, giving acetaldehyde; distilled 5 min	Aldehyde distilled into $NaHSO_3$ and unused part determined by iodine titration	133
Methanol, ethanol	+ MnO_4^-/H_2SO_4; studied effect of time, temperature, catalysts (Mn(II) molybdate) and reaction products	+ I^- and titrated with thiosulphate	134
Oxalic acid	Oxidized to CO_2 with MnO_4^-	CO_2 absorbed in $Ba(OH)_2$, kept from contact with air by a layer of pentane; back titrated with HCl to thymol blue	135, 142, 143
Allyl and butyl isothiocyanates	Diffused from aqueous solution into MnO_4^-/NaOH, taking 2 h	+ I^-/H_2SO_4 and titrated with thiosulphate	136
Some hydroxy acids and phenols (e.g. lactic, citric, malic, salicylic)	+ MnO_4^- in H_2SO_4 or NaOH medium, + Cu (II) catalyst, giving CO_2	Back titrated with Fe (II)	137
Tannins and dyestuffs in dry wines	Completely oxidized by boiling with MnO_4^- reagent (combined with determination after removal of tannins and dyestuffs with active carbon, difference yielding their amount)	+ H_2SO_4 + I^- and titrated with thiosulphate	138
Alcohol in blood	Distillate after deproteinization + MnO_4^- + H_2SO_4; 2 min/ca 100°	+ excess oxalic acid and back titrated with MnO_4^-	139
Methanol in blood (after preliminary distillation)	+ MnO_4^-/H_2SO_4; 40 min/room temp., then heated to boiling, oxidizing to CO_2	CO_2 absorbed in $Ba(OH)_2$ and back titrated with oxalic acid to phenolphthalein	140

Materials titrated	Reagent and reaction conditions	Subsequent treatment and final titration stage	Ref.
Methylene blue (used to determine absorption capacity of soil)	In water, + H_2SO_4 + excess MnO_4^- at the boiling point	Immediately back titrated with oxalic acid	141

References

1. Péan de St. Gilles, *Ann. de chim. et de phys.* (3) **55**, 388 (1859).
2. Lalieu, *Manuel d'Oxalimetrie*, Brussels 1881.
3. Benedikt, R. and Zsigmondy, R., *Chem.-Ztg.* **9**, 975 (1885).
4. Fox, W. and Wanklyn, J. A., *Chemical News* **53**, 15 (1886).
5. Klein, *Arch. Pharm.* **225**, 524 (1887).
6. Jones, C., *J. Am. Chem. Soc.* **17**, 539 (1895).
7. Ulzer, F. and Seidel, H., *Monatsh.* **18**, 138 (1897).
8. Tocher, J. F., *Pharm. J.* **66**, 360 (1901).
9. Vanino, L. and Seitter, E., *Z. anal. Chem.* **40**, 587 (1901).
10. Istcherekoff, W., *J. exper. Landwirtschaft* **5**, 55 (1903).
11. Chapman, A. C. and Whitteridge, D., *Analyst* **29**, 163 (1904).
12. Grossmann, H. and Aufrecht, A., *Ber.* **39**, 2455 (1906).
13. Boswell, M. C., *J. Am. Chem. Soc.* **29**, 230 (1907).
14. Jerusalem, E., *Biochem. Z.* **12**, 361 (1908).
15. Cameron, A. T. and McEwan, B. C., *Chem.-Ztg.* **34**, 736 (1910).
16. Fürth, O. and Charnass, D., *Biochem. Z.* **26**, 199 (1910).
17. Lagrange, A., abstract in *Z. anal. Chem.* **51**, 264 (1912).
18. Obermayer, E., *Z. anal. Chem.* **52**, 172 (1913).
19. Willaman, J. J., *J. Am. Chem. Soc.* **38**, 2193 (1916).
20. Adriano, F. T., *Phillipine J. Sci.* **17**, 213 (1920).
21. Quisumbing, F. A., *Phillipine J. Sci.* **16**, 581 (1920).
22. Clausen, S. W., *J. Biol. Chem.* **52**, 263 (1922).
23. Klever, H. W. and Glaser, F., *Mitt. Chem. Tech. Inst., Tech. Hochschule Karlsruhe* No. 1, 13 (1923).
24. Hirsch-Kaufmann, H., *Z. physiol. Chem.* **140**, 25 (1924).
25. Meyerhof, O., *Z. physiol. Chem.* **141**, 316 (1924).
26. Friedemann, T. E., Cotonio, M. and Shaffer, P. A., *J. Biol. Chem.* **73**, 335 (1927).
27. Morvillez, F. and Défossez, M., *J. pharm. chim.* **6**, 204 (1927).
28. Sabalitschka, H. and Tietz, H., *Continental Met. and Chem. Eng.* **2**, 232 (1927).
29. Warkany, J., *Biochem. Z.* **184**, 474 (1927).
30. Lehnartz, E., *Z. physiol. Chem.* **179**, 1 (1928).

31. Ravenna, A., *Zymologica* **3**, 174 (1928).
32. Friedemann, T. E. and Kendall, A. I., *J. Biol. Chem.* **82**, 23 (1929).
33. Rozman, B. Y., *Zhur. Priklad. Khim.* **2**, 191 (1929).
34. Simskaya, A., *Vestnik Kozhevennoi Prom. Torgov.* 700 (1929).
35. Ernst, E. and Horváth, G., *Biochem. Z.* **224**, 135 (1930).
36. Ernst, E. and Takács, I., *Biochem. Z.* **224**, 145 (1930).
37. Lampitt, L. H. and Bogod, M., *Chimie et industrie*, Spec. No. 510 (1930).
38. Richert, P. H., *Ind. Eng. Chem., Anal. Ed.* **2**, 273 (1930).
39. Kometiani, P. A., *Z. anal. Chem.* **86**, 359 (1931).
40. Fürth, O., Scholl, R. and Herrmann, H., *Biochem. Z.* **251**, 404 (1932).
41. Highberger, J. H. and Youel, D. L., *J. Am. Leather Chem. Assoc.* **27**, 343 (1932).
42. McNair, J. B., *J. Am. Chem. Soc.* **54**, 3249 (1932).
43. Mawson, C. A. and Ritchie, A. D., *Biochem. J.* **26**, 615 (1932).
44. Papavassiliou, M. J., *J. pharm. chim.* **15**, 167 (1932).
45. Schulek, E. and Menyhárth, P., *Magyar Gyógyszerésztud. Társaság Értesitöje* **8**, 399 (1932). *Z. anal. Chem.* **89**, 426 (1932).
46. v. Szelenyi, G., *Z. Untersuch. Lebensm.* **63**, 534 (1932).
47. Callaway, J. and Reznek, G., *J. Assoc. Offic. Agr. Chem.* **16**, 285 (1933).
48. Friedemann, T. E. and Graeser, J. B., *J. Biol. Chem.* **100**, 291 (1933).
49. Hartmann, B. G. and Hillig, F., *J. Assoc. Offic. Agr. Chem.* **16**, 435 (1933).
50. Maugeri, S., *Z. physiol. Chem.* **217**, 138 (1933).
51. Täufel, K. and Mayr, F., *Z. anal. Chem.* **93**, 1 (1933).
52. Bourdeau, M., *J. pharm. chim.* **20**, 342 (1934).
53. Duncan, I. J. and Dustman, R. B., *Ind. Eng. Chem., Anal. Ed.* **6**, 210 (1934).
54. Miklashevskaya, V., *Khim. Tverdovo Topliva* **5**, 553 (1934).
55. Pucher, G. W., Vickery, H. B. and Leavenworth, C. S., *Ind. Eng. Chem., Anal. Ed.* **6**, 190 (1934).
56. Stamm, H., *Angew. Chem.* **47**, 791 (1934); **48**, 710 (1935).
57. Korenman, I. M., *Zhur. Priklad Khim.* **8**, 1476 (1935).
58. Stamm, K., *Angew. Chem.* **48**, 150 (1935).
59. Alekseeva, M. V., *J. Gen. Chem., USSR* **5**, 1324 (1936).
60. Friedemann, T. E. and Klaas, R., *J. Biol. Chem.* **115**, 47 (1936).
61. Hinsberg, K. and Ammon, R., *Biochem. Z.* **284**, 343 (1936).
62. Kogan, A. I. and Shtipel'man, S. D., *J. Appl. Chem. USSR* **9**, 568 (1936).
63. Renaudin, J., *J. pharm. chim.* **23**, 447 (1936).
64. Schwicker, A., *Z. anal. Chem.* **110**, 161 (1937).
65. Cuthill, R., *Analyst* **63**, 26, 259 (1938).
66. Friedemann, T. E., *Proc. Soc. Exp. Biol. Med.* **37**, 686 (1938).
67. Klinc, L., *Biochem. Z.* **296**, 202 (1938).

68. Urinson, A. P., *J. Physiol.* (*USSR*) **25**, 748 (1938).
69. McCready, R. M., Mitchell, H. K. and Kirk, P. L., *Mikrochemie* **28**, 23 (1939).
70. Olin, H. I., Conrad, P. L., Krouse, M. and Whitson, R. E., *Ind. Eng. Chem., Anal. Ed.* **11**, 489 (1939).
71. Zavarov, G. V., *Zavodskaya Lab.* **8**, 171 (1939).
72. Barua, D. N. and Roberts, E. A. H., *Biochem. J.* **34**, 1524 (1940).
73. Knowles, G., Lawson, J. C. and McQuillan, T., *J. Oil Colour Chem Assoc.* **23**, 4 (1940).
74. Koshkin, M. L. and Karasik, R. M., *Med. Exptl.* (*Ukraine*) No. 4, 9 (1940).
75. Bell, F. K. and Krantz, J. C., *J. Am. Pharm. Assoc.* **30**, 50 (1941).
76. Bazin, S., *Ann. pharm. franç.* **2**, 14 (1944).
77. Krebs, H. A. and Eggleston, L. V., *Biochem. J.* **38**, 426 (1944).
78. Pucher, G. W., *J. Biol. Chem.* **153**, 133 (1944).
79. de Saint-Rat, L. and Hatey, J., *Bull. assoc. chim.* **61**, 285 (1944).
80. Sjöström, G. and Emilsson, E., *Svensk Kem. Tidskr.* **57**, 187 (1945).
81. Harrington, T., Boyd, T. H. and Cherry, G. W., *Analyst* **71**, 97 (1946).
82. Kalinowski, K., *Ann. Univ. Mariae Curie-Sklodawska, Lublin-Polonia, Sect. AA* **1**, 1 (1946).
83. Breusch, F. L. and Tulus, R., *Biochim. et Biophys. Acta* **1**, 77 (1947).
84. Heredia, P., *Arch. farm. y bioquím, Tucumán* **3**, 173 (1947).
85. Cameron, W. M., *Inst. Sewage Purif., J. & Proc.* Pt. 1, 228 (1948).
86. Heredia, P. A. and Bianchi, F., *Arch. farm. y bioquím. Tucumán* **4**, 99 (1948).
87. Hummel, V., *Listy Cukrovar* **64**, 229 (1948).
88. Kubelka, V. and Gložič, B., *Tech. Hlíd. Kožel.* **24**, 10, 51, 78 (1949).
89. Macleod, L. D., *J. Biol. Chem.* **181**, 323 (1949).
90. Molotkova, A. S. and Zolotukhin, V. K., *Zavodskaya Lab.* **15**, 1284 (1949).
91. Sas, F. E. R., Hernández-Gutiérrez, P., and Cofino Castillo, M., *Anales real soc. españ. fis y quím.* **45B**, 1277 (1949).
92. Arkawa, T., *Hirosaki Med. J.* **1** (1), 33 (1950).
93. Cotte, J. and Kahane, E., *Bull. soc. chim. France* 639 (1950).
94. Ioffe, I. I., *Zavodskaya Lab.* **16**, 1252 (1950).
95. Peynaud, E. and Charpentie, Y., *Ann. fals. et fraudes* **43**, 246 (1950).
96. Saeki, T., *J. Pharm. Soc., Japan* **70**, 690 (1950).
97. Schulek, E. and Rózsa, P., *Acta Pharm. Intern.* **1**, 127 (1950).
98. Hargreaves, C. A., Abrahams, M. D. and Vickery, H. B., *Anal. Chem.* **23**, 467 (1951).
99. Haslam, J., Whettem, S. M. A. and Soppet, W. W., *Analyst* **76**, 628 (1951).
100. Koch, J. and Bretthauer, G., *Z. anal. Chem.* **132**, 346 (1951).

101. Phillips, J. F. and O'Hara, F. J., *Anal. Chem.* **23**, 535 (1951).
102. Gottwald, E. and Voigt, G. E., *Deut. Z. ges. gerichtl. Med.* **41**, 164 (1952).
103. Inukai, K. and Maki, Y., *Rept. Gov. Ind. Research. Inst., Nagoya* **1**, 101 (1952).
104. Kalinowski, K. and Smajkiewicz, A., *Farm. Polska* **8**, 371 (1952).
105. Marconi, M., *Chimica* (*Milan*) **7**, 336 (1952).
106. Balwant Singh, Apar Singh and Gurdas Singh, *J. Indian Chem. Soc.* **30**, 488 (1953).
107. Balwant Singh, Apar Singh and Nahan, R. K., *Research Bull. East Panjab Univ.* No. 33, 93 (1953).
108. Kahane, E. and Sackur, O., *Ann. pharm. franç.* **11**, 175 (1953).
109. Ramos, M. da C. and Guimaraes, A. F., *Anais inst. vinho Porto* 9 (1953).
110. Smith, R. J., *Anal. Chem.* **25**, 505 (1953).
111. Struszyński, M., Bellen, Z. and Bellen, N., *Przemysl Chem.* **9**, 243 (1953).
112. Zolotukhin, V. K. and Molotkova, A. S., *Trudy Komissii Anal. Khim. Akad. Nauk SSSR, Otdel Khim. Nauk* **5** (**8**), 179 (1954).
113. Grott, J. V., *Acta Gastro-Enterol. Belg.* **18**, 772 (1955).
114. Ohlweiler, A. and Meditsch, J. O., *Chemist-Analyst* **44**, 19 (1955).
115. Sapondzhyan, S. O. and Gevorkyan, K. S., *Vinodelie i Vinogradarstvo SSSR* **16**, No. 8, 10 (1956).
116. Yavorskii, N. P. and Romanyuk, Yu. F., *Aptechnoe Delo* **5**, No. 5, 27 (1956).
117. Drzhevetskaya, I. A., *Laboratornoe Delo* **3**, No. 4, 21 (1957).
118. Gložič, B., *Leder* **8**, 57 (1957).
119. Kalinowski, K., Bersztel, J., Fecko, J. and Zwierzchowski, Z., *Acta Polon. Pharm.* **14**, 77 (1957).
120. Tokár, G. and Simonyi, I., *Acta Pharm. Hung.* **27**, 20 (1957).
121. Trawinska, J., *Ann. Univ. Mariae Curie-Sklodowska, Lublin-Polonia*, Sect. DD **12**, 41 (1957).
122. Wittfogel, H. and Gebhardt, R., *Arch. Lebensm.* **8**, 241 (1957).
123. Blažek, J., *Československ. Farm.* **7**, 576 (1958).
124. Hillig, F., *J. Assoc. Offic. Agr. Chem.* **41**, 776 (1958).
125. Reiss, R., *Z. anal. Chem.* **164**, 402 (1958).
126. Silbereisen, K. and Kremkow, C., *Brauerei, Wiss. Beil.* **11**, 128 (1958).
127. Wilson, A. L., *J. Appl. Chem.* (*London*) **9**, 510 (1959).
128. Schröder, E., *Plaste u. Kautschuk* **7**, 167 (1960).
129. Tomiyama, T., Oyama, S. and Fujino, S., *Nippon Suisan Gaku Kaishi* **26**, 520 (1960).
130. Usmanov, K. U. and Perlina, R. V., *Uzbekh. Khim. Zhur.* No. 3, 20 (1960).

131. Bellen, Z., *Chem. Anal.* (*Warsaw*) **6**, 531 (1961).
132. Bellen, Z., *Acta Chim. Acad. Sci. Hung.* **26**, 422 (1961).
133. Šepitka, A. and Zradulová, E., *Listy Cukrovar* **77**, 16 (1961).
134. Sharp. J., *Anal. Chim. Acta* **25**, 139 (1961).
135. Maros, L., Schulek, E., Molnár-Perl, I. and Pinter-Szakács, M., *Anal. Chim. Acta* **25**, 546 (1961).
136. Nakamura, T., *Japan Analyst* **10**, 296 (1961).
137. Frei, V., *Českoslov. Farm.* **11**, 397 (1962).
138. Korablev, A. I. and Trofimenko, B. S., *Sadovodstvo, Vinogradarstvo i Vinodelie Moldavii* No. 1, 37 (1962).
139. Krasnova, A. I., Vishnyak, Yu. I. and Kamolov, S. K., *Laboratornoe Delo* **8**, No. 9 52 (1962).
140. Kubalski, J. and Rusiecki, W., *Acta Polon. Pharm.* **19**, 333 (1962).
141. Wojtas, R., *Chem. Anal.* (*Warsaw*) **7**, 1177 (1962).
142. Maros, L., Molnár-Perl, I., Vajda, M. and Schulek, E., *Magyar Kem. Folyoirat* **69**, 123 (1963).
143. Maros, L., Molnár-Perl, I., Vajda, M. and Schulek, E., *Anal. Chim. Acta* **28**, 179 (1963).

84. Persulphate

In the small number of examples given below, persulphate has usually been a component of a mixed reagent. The reactions have been oxidations with one exception, in which a complex silver persulphate was precipitated.

Many organic bases form poorly soluble (in water) persulphates. Its rare use as a precipitation titrant is doubtless to be attributed, as with permanganate, bichromate, periodate and others, to the powerful oxidizing properties which tend to oxidation side reactions with the sample.

Examples

Materials titrated	Reagent and reaction conditions	Subsequent treatment and final titration stage	Ref.
CHI_3	Heated with dry $S_2O_8^{2-}$, yielding iodine	Absorbed in KI solution and titrated with thiosulphate	1
CCl_3CHO	$+ S_2O_8^{2-} + MnO_4^-$, yielding chlorine	Passed through KI solution and titrated with thiosulphate	1

Materials titrated	Reagent and reaction conditions	Subsequent treatment and final titration stage	Ref.
Protein in cereal products	Digested with H_2SO_4/ $CuSO_4$ until organic matter charred; then + $K_2S_2O_8$ and heated until the persulphate decomposed	+ alkali and NH_3 distilled into H_2SO_4, back titrating with NaOH to methyl red	2
α,α'-Dipyridyl; *o*-phenanthroline	+ excess $AgNO_3$ + $S_2O_8^{2-}$, giving precipitate of complex with divalent Ag $[Ag(Base)_2]\,S_2O_8$ (see also under Silver (I), ref. 96)	Filtered and titrated unused Ag(I) in the filtrate with SCN^-; or reduced precipitate with SO_2, added HNO_3 and titrated with SCN^-	3
$CCl_2{=}CHCl$ in industrial waters	+ $(NH_4)_2S_2O_8$ + HNO_3, giving HCl	Absorbed in water and titrated with $AgNO_3$ potentiometrically	4
Organic substances in aqueous solution, e.g. glucose, lower alcohols, acetic acid, aromatic acids	+ Ag_2SO_4 + H_2SO_4 + $K_2S_2O_8$ in 100–200% excess. Heated, giving CO_2	CO_2 absorbed in $Ba(OH)_2$ covered with a pentane layer and back titrated with HCl to thymol blue	5
Organic matter in waste water	Aliquot + drops H_2SO_4 + $K_2S_2O_8$ + $AgNO_3$ catalyst; 30 min/70–75° after slowly warming up	CO_2 evolved absorbed in NaOH, $BaCl_2$ added and back titrated with HCl to phenolphthalein	6
Organic substances in aqueous solution	+ $Ag_2S_2O_8$/2% H_2SO_4, oxidizing to CO_2	CO_2 absorbed and determined as in method of ref. 5	7
Volatile organic matter in aluminate liquors	Method of ref. 7		8

References

1. Brunner, H., *Schweiz. Wochenschr. für Chem. u. Pharm.* **35**, 280 (1897).
2. Robinson, R. J. and Shellenberger, J. A., *Ind. Eng. Chem., Anal. Ed.* **4**, 243 (1932).
3. Cavicchi, G., *Ann. chim. (Rome)* **40**, 149 (1950).
4. Deyl, Z. and Effenberger, M., *Voda* **37**, 90 (1958).
5. Maros, L., Pintér-Szakács, M. and Schulek, E., *Anal. Chim. Acta* **27**, 172 (1962).

6. Leibnitz, E., Behrens, V., Koll, H. and Richter, H., *Chem. Tech. (Berlin)* **14**, 33 (1962).
7. Maros, L., Pintér-Szakács, M. and Schulek, E., *Magyar Kem. Folyoirat* **68**, 213 (1962).
8. Maros, L. and Zsindely, S., *Magyar Kem. Folyoirat* **68**, 357 (1962).

85. Phenols

Five examples are given, two of the use of phenol and three of the use of salicylic acid. The former was used to determine methylol groups in resins via condensation and subsequent titration of the water with Karl Fischer reagent:

$$RCH_2OH + HO{-}C_6H_5 \rightarrow (RCH_2{-})(HO{-})C_6H_4 + H_2O$$

Salicylic acid has been used to determine nitrate esters and nitroguanidine via hydrolysis with H_2SO_4 to HNO_3 and nitration of the phenol to yield 5-nitrosalicylic acid, then determined by Ti(III)

$$RONO_3 \rightarrow HNO_3 \rightarrow (HO{-})(HOOC{-})C_6H_3{-}NO_2$$

Other phenols like picric acid are considered under the heading Nitrophenols.

Examples

Materials titrated	Reagent and reaction conditions	Subsequent treatment and final titration stage	Ref.
Nitroguanidine; cellulose nitrate	+ H_2SO_4 + acetic acid + salicylic acid (latter material left 20 min in H_2SO_4 alone if % nitrogen exceeded 13); 15–30 or 20 min/room temp., respectively	Diluted and the nitrosalicylic acid determined by reduction with excess $TiCl_3$ and back titration with Fe(III) (see Titanium (III), ref. 49)	1

Materials titrated	Reagent and reaction conditions	Subsequent treatment and final titration stage	Ref.
Methylol groups in resols	+ benzene + dioxan + methanol + phenol + *p*-toluenesulphonic acid (catalyst); 24 h/room temp.	Water titrated with Karl Fischer reagent	2
Methylol groups in phenol resins	+ xylene + phenol + BF_3 catalyst; 3 h/60°	Cooled, ethylene glycol/pyridine, 4:1 added and titrated with Karl Fischer reagent	3
Nitroguanidine	+ H_2SO_4 + acetic acid + salicylic acid; 1 h/room temp.	Nitrosalicylic acid determined with excess Ti(III) and back titration with Fe(III) (see Titanium (III), ref. 55)	4
	also + conc. H_2SO_4 + salicylic acid; 15 min/room temp.	nitrosalicylic acid determined by Kjeldahl nitrogen method (see Kjeldahl nitrogen determination, ref. 15)	
Cellulose nitrate	In conc. H_2SO_4; 5 min, then + salicylic acid; 10–15 min/room temp., giving 5-nitrosalicylic acid	Nitrosalicylic acid determined by reaction with excess Ti(III) and back titration with Fe(III) (see Titanium (III), ref. 62)	5

References

1. Stalcup, H. and Williams, R. W., *Anal. Chem.* **27**, 543 (1955).
2. Vašta, M. and Ulbrich, V., *Chem. Listy* **49**, 1311 (1955).
3. Stenmark, G. A. and Weiss, F. T., *Anal. Chem.* **28**, 260 (1956).
4. Fauth, M. I. and Stalcup, H., *Anal. Chem.* **30**, 1670 (1958).
5. Mullen, J. D., *Anal. Chim. Acta* **20**, 16 (1959).

86. Phosphoric acid

(See general remarks under Acids)

Reagent. As aqueous solution ranging from the *ca* 85% solution to dilute solution.

Reactions and materials titrated. Phosphoric acid possesses the two useful properties of:

(i) Involatility, so that none is carried over in a subsequent distillation process (see below);

(ii) Negligible tendency to take part in side reactions like oxidation, reduction, etc.

It is used in one of two rôles as an acid reagent:

1. Ion/ion combination reactions in determination of salts of strong bases and weak organic acids, e.g. alkali acetates, xanthates or dithiocarbamates:

$$CH_3COO^- + H^+ \rightarrow CH_3COOH$$

$$RO.\underset{\underset{S}{\|}}{C}.S^- + H^+ \rightarrow RO.\underset{\underset{S}{\|}}{C}.SH \rightarrow ROH + CS_2$$

$$H_2N.\underset{\underset{S}{\|}}{C}.S^- + H^+ \rightarrow H_2N.\underset{\underset{S}{\|}}{C}.SH \rightarrow NH_3\,(+\text{ more }H^+) + CS_2$$

2. As a catalyst in several types of reaction:

(a) Mostly hydrolysis, e.g. of esters, especially acetates; acetals and ketals; condensation products between —NH_2 and —CO— groups, like formaldehyde resins, azines, oximes, hydrazones and hexamine. Some typical reactions are given:

$$RO.COCH_3 + H_2O \rightarrow ROH + CH_3COOH$$

$$C_6H_5NH.COOC_3H_7 + H_2O \rightarrow C_6H_5NH.COOH + C_3H_7OH$$

$$\downarrow$$

$$C_6H_5NH_2\,(+\text{ acid}) + CO_2$$

$$RCH{=}NOH + H_2O \rightarrow RCHO + NH_2OH\,(+\text{ acid})$$

$$(CH_2)_6N_4 + 6\,H_2O \rightarrow 6\,HCHO + 4\,NH_3\,(+\text{ acid})$$

(b) Depolymerization, e.g. of metaldehyde,

$$(CH_3CHO)_4 \rightarrow 4\,CH_3CHO$$

(c) Dehydration, e.g. of pentoses, yielding furfuraldehyde:

$$\begin{array}{l} HO\diagup CH_2.CHOH \\ \quad\;\; HOCH.CHOH \\ \quad\;\; \mid \\ \quad\;\; CHO \end{array} - 3\,H_2O \rightarrow \begin{array}{l} O\diagup CH{=}CH \\ \;\;\diagdown C{=}CH \\ \quad\;\; \mid \\ \quad\;\; CHO \end{array}$$

(d) Transesterification, using an alcohol/phosphoric acid reagent. An example of this, used for the determination of formates, is given under Alcohols, ref. 12.

Reaction conditions. Nearly always at reflux temperature in a distillation procedure which isolates a reaction product.

An entrainer like toluene or xylene has sometimes been added to help this isolation by distillation.

Subsequent treatment and final titration stage. In all cases, a reaction product has been isolated by a gas current or distillation, and titrimetrically determined. The principal reaction products have been: carbonyl compounds (e.g. formaldehyde, acetaldehyde, furfuraldehyde); acetic acid; and carbon disulphide. Standard procedures have been used for the final stage, such as:

Carbonyl compounds:	oxidation with iodine/alkali, hydrogen peroxide/ alkali or Ag(I) addition of bisulphite condensation with hydrazine
Acetic acid:	titration with alkali
Carbon disulphide:	reaction with alkali/alcohol, giving xanthate, then titrated iodometrically

Examples

Materials titrated	Reagent and reaction conditions	Subsequent treatment and final titration stage	Ref.
Acetates	Distilled with phosphoric acid/water, 1:1	Distillate titrated with NaOH to litmus	1
Azines, oximes, hydrazones of aromatic aldehydes	Heated with conc. phosphoric acid	Aldehyde distilled out and determined with excess hydrazine sulphate, back titrating unused hydrazine iodometrically (see Hydrazines, ref. 6)	2
Acetates	Distilled with phosphoric acid + xylene carrier	Distillate titrated with NaOH to phenolphthalein	3
Cellulose acetate	Heated with phosphoric acid	Acetic acid distilled and titrated with $Ba(OH)_2$	4

Materials titrated	Reagent and reaction conditions	Subsequent treatment and final titration stage	Ref.
Acetate in lead acetate	+ phosphoric acid + a little Zn dust	Acetic acid distilled and titrated with NaOH to phenolphthalein	5
Cellulose xanthate	Aqueous solution, + phosphoric acid	CS_2 formed aerated into KOH/ethanol and xanthate titrated iodometrically	6
Sodium acetate	Slow distillation with dilute phosphoric acid	Distilled into excess alkali, slight excess H_2SO_4 added, CO_2 boiled out and finally titrated to phenolphthalein	7
HCHO in HCHO/urea/butanol resins	Distilled with *ca* 40% phosphoric acid	Distilled into H_2O_2/alkali to determine the HCHO (see Hydrogen peroxide, ref. 18)	8
n-butanol in the resins	refluxed 1 h with *ca* 40% phosphoric acid + *m*-phenylenediamine (to react with the HCHO)	butanol distilled out and determined with excess $Cr_2O_7^{2-}$ (see Bichromate and chromic oxide, ref. 100)	
HCHO in resins	Distilled with phosphoric acid	Distilled into $NaHSO_3$ and determined combined bisulphite iodometrically (see Bisulphite and sulphite, ref. 57)	9
Pentoses in plant material	Distilled with phosphoric acid, giving furfuraldehyde	Furfuraldehyde determined with $NaHSO_3$ (see Bisulphite and sulphite, ref. 75)	10
HCHO or hexamine in food	+ dilute phosphoric acid + toluene; slowly heated and then distilled	HCHO in aqueous layer of distillate determined iodometrically	11
Pentoses	Distilled with 85% phosphoric acid, giving furfuraldehyde	Distilled into $NaHSO_3$ and combined part determined iodometrically (see Bisulphite and sulphite, ref. 76)	12
Polyvinyl acetal ketal in resins (safety glass)	Hydrolysed by heating with phosphoric acid; *ca* 1 h slow distillation	Aldehyde + ketone determined in distillate with $NaHSO_3$; ketones by reaction with iodine/alkali; aldehydes with Ag(I) reagent (see Bisulphite and sulphite, ref. 82; Iodine reagents, ref. 255)	13

Materials titrated	Reagent and reaction conditions	Subsequent treatment and final titration stage	Ref.
Isopropyl *N*-phenyl carbamate	In water, + 85% phosphoric acid/conc. sulphuric acid, *ca* 10:1. *Ca* 45 min boiling, giving CO_2	Passed into excess NaOH, CO_3^{2-} precipitated with $BaCl_2$ and back titrated with HCl to phenolphthalein	14
Acetates; acetyl groups	Heated with phosphoric (or sulphuric) acid, giving acetic acid	Distilled into $BaCO_3$ slurry, dissolved Ba^{2+} determined by precipitation with excess $Cr_2O_7^{2-}$ and iodometric titration of the unused part	15
Metaldehyde	Distilled with dilute phosphoric acid giving acetaldehyde	Distilled into $NaHSO_3$ and determined iodometrically	16
Acetal in wines	Heated 30 min with phosphoric acid, giving acetaldehyde	Distilled into $NaHSO_3$ and determined iodometrically	17
Thiuram disulphides; dithiocarbamates	+ pyridine/90% phosphoric acid, giving CS_2	+ KOH/alcohol and the xanthates formed titrated with iodine (see Alcohols, ref. 51)	18
Acetate in metal carboxylates (e.g. Ag, Cd, UO_2, K, Tl)	Distilled with phosphoric acid at *ca* 120–130°	Distillate titrated with NaOH/ 95% ethanol to bromothymol blue	19

References

1. Fresenius, R., *Z. anal. Chem.* **5**, 315 (1866).
2. Lautenschläger, L., *Arch. Pharm.* **256**, 81 (1918).
3. Pickett, O. A., *J. Ind. Eng. Chem.* **12**, 570 (1920).
4. Berl, E., Rueff, G. and Wahlig, W., *Chemiker-Ztg.* **55**, 861 (1931).
5. Han, J. E. S. and Chu, T. L., *Ind. Eng. Chem., Anal. Ed.* **3**, 379 (1931).
6. Fock, W. H., *Kunstseide* **17**, 117 (1935).
7. Hurd, C. B. and Fiedler, W., *Ind. Eng. Chem., Anal. Ed.* **9**, 116 (1937).
8. Levenson, J. J., *Ind. Eng. Chem., Anal. Ed.* **12**, 332 (1940).
9. Nitschmann, H. and Hadorn, H., *Helv. Chim. Acta* **24**, 237 (1941).
10. Meissner, R., *Biochem. Z.* **317**, 17 (1944).
11. Wendland, G., *Z. Untersuch. Lebensm.* **87**, 220 (1944).
12. Heines, V., *Arch. Biochem.* **11**, 531 (1946).
13. Ryan, J. D. and Shaw, F. B., *U.S. Patent No.* 2,425,568, Aug. 12 (1947).

14. Gard, L. N., *Anal. Chem.* **23**, 1685 (1951).
15. Köszegi, D. and Simonyi, J., *Acta Chim. Acad. Sci. Hung.* **5**, 33 (1954).
16. Schomberg, M., *Compt. rend. acad. agr. France* **40**, 271 (1954).
17. Cortés, I. M. and Salcedo, M. de C., *Anales real. soc. españ., fis. y quím.* (*Madrid*) **51B**, 85 (1955).
18. Roth, H. and Beck, W., *Mikrochim. Acta* 845 (1957).
19. Anderson, H. H., *Anal. Chem.* **34**, 1340 (1962).

87. Physical methods

This section includes methods where a conclusion by titration has followed a purely physical separation of the components of the sample. The principal methods of physical separation are: distillation (fractional and azeotropic after addition of an extra component); extraction; precipitation; and absorption and adsorption techniques. Many analytical procedures include a physical separation stage which follows chemical treatment of the sample (giving, for example, a volatile or insoluble reaction product). Examples of this type are not included here. The massive chapters of chromatography, including vapour phase chromatography, of counter-current extraction and of analytical fractional distillation are also not considered here. In any case, the separated components have then been determined more usually by other methods than titration (e.g. light absorption or thermal conductivity). Books, monographs and even a specialist literature (e.g. journals of chromatography) cover these subjects and render superfluous a detailed treatment here.

A small selection of examples is given below, mostly concerning comparatively simple mixtures (2 or 3 components).

Examples

Materials titrated	Separation principle and conditions	Subsequent treatment and final titration stage	Ref.
Mixtures of volatile fatty acids	Aqueous solution distilled without column and successive portions of distillate collected	These portions titrated with alkali and the titrations added up to give 'characteristic sums' for each acid; binary mixtures determined by interpolation	1

Materials titrated	Separation principle and conditions	Subsequent treatment and final titration stage	Ref.
Mixtures of fatty acids	Partitioned between water and ether	Acid in each layer titrated with alkali, giving partition coefficients, characteristic for each acid; mixtures analysed by interpolation	2
Binary mixtures of fatty acids	Distilled half of the aqueous solution	Titrated the distillate; interpolated data to determined binary mixtures	3
amine mixtures	distilled half of the aqueous solution	titrated distillate with H_2SO_4 to congo red; interpolated likewise	
Mixtures of fatty acids	Partitioned between water and diisopropyl ether; 1 min shaking	Aqueous phase titrated with KOH to phenolphthalein; unextracted aqueous solution also titrated, thus giving the partition coefficient; binary mixtures analysed by interpolation	4
Isopropanol in ethanol (1 to 20%)	Shaken with *ca* 30% NaOH at reasonably constant temperature	Upper alcohol layer titrated with H_2SO_4 to methyl red; result read from previously prepared calibration curve	5
Formic, acetic and propionic acids in mixtures	Partitioned between water and diethyl ether	Aqueous phase titrated with NaOH to phenolphthalein; unextracted aqueous solution also titrated as in method of ref. 4; result obtained by interpolation together with independent determination of formic acid by oxidation with HgO to CO_2, measured gas-volumetrically	6
Ternary mixtures of fatty acids	Partitioned between water and diethyl ether in two different proportions	Aqueous layers and unextracted aqueous solution titrated with NaOH to phenolphthalein and result obtained from a nomogram	7
Rotenone, extracted and dissolved in 80% dichloroacetic acid	Cooled to 0° and cold water added, giving precipitate of the rotenone/dichloroacetic acid solvate (1:1)	Filtered, dissolved in $CHCl_3$, water added and titrated with alkali to phenolphthalein	8

Materials titrated	Separation principle and conditions	Subsequent treatment and final titration stage	Ref.
Mixtures of lower fatty acids (C_1 to C_4)	Distilled azeoptropically with benzene and toluene; benzene/formic acid azeotrope distils first, then benzene/acetic acid, then toluene/propionic acid, toluene/isobutyric acid and lastly toluene/butyric acid	Successive fractions titrated with NaOH to phenolphthalein	9
Fatty acid mixtures from determination of cellulose mixed esters (acetate, propionate, butyrate) by saponification and acidification	Partitioned between water and butyl acetate	Aqueous layer and unextracted aqueous solution titrated with NaOH to phenolphthalein; interpolation gave analyses of the mixtures	10
Ethylamine hydrochlorides in presence of NH_4Cl	Extracted with $CHCl_3$ in a Soxhlet extractor	Extract evaporated and titrated with $AgNO_3$	11
Higher aliphatic amines (C_{12}–C_{18}) in presence of the corresponding secondary amines	(+alkali if present as salts) and distilled	Distilled into excess HCl and back titrated to methyl red	12
Organic acids (identification)	Partitioned between water and diethyl ether	Aqueous layer and unextracted aqueous solution titrated with NaOH to phenolphthaliene and acid identified via the partition coefficient	13
Nicotine in tobacco leaf	(+ some KOH) + ethylene glycol and distilled out as azeotrope	Distillate + water titrated with H_2SO_4 to methyl red/ methylene blue	14
Binary and ternary mixtures of lower fatty acids	Partitioned between water and diisopropyl ether; 2–3 min shaking at thermostatically controlled temperature	Aqueous layer and unextracted aqueous solution titrated with NaOH to phenolphthalein and results obtained by interpolation	15
Free fatty acid in metal stearates	Extracted with acetone	Evaporated extract and titrated with alkali (or residue weighed)	16
Atropine in mixtures with degradation products	Basic impurities carried out with superheated benzene at 82–85°	Residue titrated with *p*-toluene-sulphonic acid to dimethyl yellow	17

Materials titrated	Separation principle and conditions	Subsequent treatment and final titration stage	Ref.
Alkaloids in tobacco	(+ $Ba(OH)_2$) and extracted with $CHCl_3$/ benzene	Extract titrated with $HClO_4$/ acetic acid to crystal violet (see Part I, Perchloric acid, ref. 106)	18
Formic acid in presence of acetic acid	+ $CHCl_3$ + salicylic acid and formic acid/ $CHCl_3$ azeotrope distilled out	Distillate + water + methanol and titrated potentiometrically with NaOH/methanol	19
Volatile fatty acids	Method of ref. 1 claimed unsuitable for identification of the acids		20
Mixtures of furfuraldehyde and 5-hydroxymethylfurfuraldehyde	Partitioned between dilute HCl and $CHCl_3$, 1: 4 ratio	Aqueous layer titrated with bromine reagent before and after extraction; ratio of values gave the aldehyde proportion (see Bromine reagents, ref. 448)	21
Some mixtures of organic bases, e.g. benzylamine/ tribenzylamine	One component carried out by superheated organic vapours (e.g. acetonitrile, $CHCl_3$, butanone, benzene)	Distillate and residue titrated with $HClO_4$	22

References

1. Duclaux, E., *Ann. de l'école normale supérieure* **2**, 270 (1865); *Ann. chim phys.* (5) **2**, 289 (1874).
2. Behrens, W. U., *Z. anal. Chem.* **69**, 97 (1926).
3. Virtanen, A. I. and Pulkki, L., *Ann. Acad. Sci. Fennicae* **29A**, No. 25 (1927).
4. Werkman, C. H., *Ind. Eng. Chem., Anal. Ed.* **2**, 302 (1930).
5. Archibald, F. M. and Beamer, C. M., *Ind. Eng. Chem., Anal. Ed.* **4**, 18 (1932).
6. Osburn, O. L., Wood, H. G. and Werkman, C. H., *Ind. Eng. Chem., Anal. Ed.* **5**, 247 (1933).
7. Osburn, O. L., Wood, H. G. and Werkman, C. H., *Ind. Eng. Chem., Anal. Ed.* **8**, 270 (1936).
8. Jones, H. A., *Ind. Eng. Chem., Anal. Ed.* **10**, 684 (1938).
9. Schicktanz, S. T., Steele, W. I. and Blaisdell, A. C., *Ind. Eng. Chem., Anal. Ed.* **12**, 320 (1940).
10. Malm, C. J., Nadeau, G. F. and Genung, L. B., *Ind. Eng. Chem., Anal. Ed.* **14**, 292 (1942).

11. Hierneis, J., *Angew. Chem.* **56**, 126 (1943).
12. Ralston, A. W. and Hoerr, C. W., *Ind. Eng. Chem., Anal. Ed.* **16**, 459 (1944).
13. Spatt, C. and Schneider, F., *Ind. Eng. Chem., Anal. Ed.* **16**, 479 (1944).
14. Palfray, L., Sabetay, S. and Libmann-Matayer, G., *Compt. rend.* **224**, 1566 (1947).
15. Tsai, K. R. and Ying Fu, *Anal. Chem.* **21**, 818 (1949).
16. Cheremisinoff, P. N., *Chemist-Analyst* **39**, 88 (1950).
17. Gyenes, I., *Magyar Kem. Folyoirat* **59**, 12 (1953).
18. Cundiff, R. H. and Markunas, P. C., *Anal. Chem.* **27**, 1650 (1955).
19. Warner, B. R. and Raptis, L. Z., *Anal. Chem.* **27**, 1783 (1955).
20. Soleil, J. and Hirt, G., *Compt. rend.* **244**, 2059 (1957).
21. Bethge, P. O., *Svensk Papperstidn.* **61**, 565, 856 (1958).
22. Gyenes, I., *Acta Chim. Acad. Sci. Hung.* **26**, 403 (1961).

88. Potassium (I)

Tartaric and phthalic acids have been determined by ion/ion combination to give precipitates of salts:

$$HOOC(CHOH)_2COO^- + K^+ \rightarrow HOOC(CHOH)_2COOK$$

$$C_6H_4(COOH)(COO^-) + K^+ \rightarrow C_6H_4(COOH)(COOK)$$

The reactions have usually been carried out in alcoholic or aqueous-alcoholic solution to lower the solubility of the salts.

The tartrates have been determined by acidimetric titration of the salt with alkali to phenolphthalein or litmus (in one case by adding iodate/iodide and titrating with thiosulphate). Other methods have been via oxidation with excess permanganate and via titration with $HClO_4$/acetic acid, both for K hydrogen phthalate.

Examples

Materials titrated	Reagent and reaction conditions	Subsequent treatment and final titration stage	Ref.
Tartaric acid in yeasts, tartar	Extract with HCl, + K_2CO_3 + acetic acid + ethanol	Precipitate titrated with alkali to litmus	1

Materials titrated	Reagent and reaction conditions	Subsequent treatment and final titration stage	Ref.
Tartaric acid in tartar	Extract with HCl, + K_2CO_3. Boiled 20 min, filtered and filtrate + acetic acid + alcohol. *Ca* 15 min stirring	Precipitate boiled with water and titrated with KOH to litmus	2
Tartaric acid in presence of other acids, e.g. in wine or fruit juices	+ K acetate + acetic acid + 90% ethanol; 15–18 h	Precipitate dissolved in hot water and titrated with NaOH to litmus	3
Tartaric acid	+ formic acid/KOH buffer, pH 3·27. Overnight/18°	Precipitate titrated with NaOH to phenolphthalein	4
Tartaric acid in wine	Wine + KCl + K acetate/acetic acid + 96% ethanol; at 0°	Precipitate boiled with water and titrated with NaOH to litmus	5
Total phthalic anhydride in oil-modified alkyd resins	+ KOH/absolute ethanol; 4–6 h/55°, some longer	+ ether, filtered and titrated residue with $HClO_4$/acetic acid to methyl violet	6
Phthalic anhydride	+ KOH/alcohol; 15 min/70–75°	+ ether, neutralized to phenolphthalein with oleic acid and determined with excess MnO_4^-, back titrating iodometrically (see Permanganate, ref. 111)	7
Tartaric acid in raw materials	Aliquot of an extract, + acetic acid + 90–95% ethanol + KCl; 2–3 h in the cold	Precipitated titrated in hot solution with NaOH to phenolphthalein	8
Tartaric acid in wine (micro)	+ KCl + K acetate + acetic acid + ethanol; 2–3 h/*ca* 0°	Dissolved in hot water and ultimately determined by adding IO_3^-/I^- and titrating with thiosulphate (see Iodate and iodine pentoxide, ref. 63)	9
Tartaric acid in wine and must	At pH 3·5–3·8 + K^+ reagent; some + ethanol; 4 h/2°	Dissolved in hot water and titrated with NaOH	10
Total tartrates in plant products	Extract in dry ethanol, + KOH + acetic acid. Overnight in refrigerator	Precipitate titrated with alkali	11

Materials titrated	Reagent and reaction conditions	Subsequent treatment and final titration stage	Ref.
Tartaric acid in wine	+ acetic acid + KCl + 96% ethanol; 15 h/5°, giving precipitate of KH tartrate	Filtered, precipitate dissolved in hot water and titrated to phenolphthalein with NaOH	12
Tartaric acid in wine, lees and crude cream of tartar	+ K acetate + KCl + water + acetic acid + ethanol; 15 min shaking, giving KH tartrate	Precipitate dissolved in water and titrated with NaOH	13
Tartaric acid in wine	+ acetic acid + KCl + KNa tartrate + K oxalate + 96% ethanol; 2 h/8°, then 30 min/100°	Precipitate titrated with NaOH	14

References

1. Goldenberg, *Z. anal. Chem.* **47**, 57 (1908).
2. Carles, P., *Z. anal. Chem.* **52**, 702 (1913).
3. Bernhäuser, E., *Österr. Chem.-Ztg.* **31**, 4 (1928).
4. Täufel, K. and Marloth, B. W., *Z. anal. Chem.* **80**, 161 (1930).
5. Berg, P. and Schmechel, S., *Z. Untersuch. Lebensm.* **64**, 348 (1932).
6. Goldberg, A. I., *Ind. Eng. Chem., Anal. Ed.* **16**, 198 (1944).
7. Struszyński, M., Bellen, Z. and Bellen, N., *Przemysl Chem.* **9**, 243 (1953).
8. Korotkevich, A. V. and Bekirova, L. M., *Sadovodstvo, Vinogradarstvo i Vinodelie Moldavii* **10**, No. 2, 45 (1955).
9. Gorbach, G. and Vaupotitsch, W., *Fette, Seifen, Anstrichmittel* **58**, 865 (1956).
10. Nègre, E., Dugal, A. and Evèsque, J. M., *Ann. inst. natl. recherche agron.*, Ser. E **7**, 31 (1958).
11. Lewis, Y. S., Neelakantan, S. and Bhatia, D. S., *Food Sci., Mysore* **10**, 49 (1961).
12. Diemair, W. and Maier, G., *Z. Lebensm.-Untersuch-Forsch.* **117**, 465 (1962).
13. Mokhnachev, I. G., *Vinodelie i Vinogradarstvo SSSR* **23**, No. 1 23 (1963).
14. Schneyder, J. and Pluhar, G., *Mitt. (Klosterneuburg), Ser. A, Rebe Wein* **13**, 40 (1963).

89. Pyrolysis

Reaction conditions. A somewhat miscellaneous collection of analyses is included here. As implied by the heading, they have been carried out at higher temperature, ranging from *ca* 250° to 1000° and higher.

In most cases, the sample + oxygen (air), hydrogen (coal gas) or other additions such as methane or ethanol has been aspirated or swept by a carrier gas (air itself in the determination of organic materials in air; nitrogen where exclusion of oxygen was desired) through a tube or vessel, generally of quartz, at the required temperature.

Catalysts have been frequently used, such as copper, phosphoric acid and, above all, platinum. Cupric and ferric oxides have been also used, functioning possibly partly as catalysts, partly as participants in the oxidation reaction.

An example of oxidation at room temperature with oxygen gas has been included here for convenience; likewise an example of photochemical decomposition of iodoform into iodine.

Reactions, materials determined, subsequent treatment and final titration stage. At high temperatures, reactions like oxidation, reduction, decarboxylation, dehydration and dehalogenation are among the most frequently occurring. Several of these may occur simultaneously or consecutively. Except in one or two more clearly defined instances (then usually at less high temperatures), it is pointless to attempt any classification here according to reaction as has been done in other parts of this book.

The following table is an attempt to summarize briefly the examples of more than single occurrence.

Materials determined	Main reaction	Subsequent treatment and final titration stage
Halides, e.g. lower aliphatic halides (methyl chloride and bromides) insecticides and other agents (DDT, chloropicrin, aldrin, etc.)	Oxidation and dehalogenation, giving HHal and/or Hal_2 Also reduction giving HHal	(i) Any Hal_2 converted to Hal^- by reduction with sulphite, arsenite, formate, etc., and Cl^- determined by: 1. Titration with Ag^+ (direct or with SCN^- back titration) 2. Titration with Hg(II) 3. Oxidation of Br^- with OCl^- to BrO_3^- (ii) Hal_2 absorbed in KI solution and the iodine formed titrated with thiosulphate
Salts or carboxylic acids (usually alkali and alkaline earth salts)	Oxidation to carbonate, oxide, etc.	CO_3^{2-} titrated with acid; metal determined by a standard inorganic method, e.g. Bi(III) with EDTA

Materials determined	Main reaction	Subsequent treatment and final titration stage
Carboxylic acids	Decarboxylation to CO_2	Absorbed in excess $Ba(OH)_2$ and back titrated with acid
Ethanol	Dehydration to ethylene	Absorbed in excess bromine and back titrated iodometrically
Sulphur-containing compounds like methionine, sulphonamides and ichthyol (ichthammol)	Oxidation to SO_2 or SO_3	Any SO_2 oxidized to SO_3 and the H_2SO_4 or SO_4^{2-} titrated with alkali, Ba^{2+} or Pb^{2+}

Examples

Materials titrated	Reaction conditions	Subsequent treatment and final titration stage	Ref.
Methyl iodide from determination of methoxyl groups by reaction with HI	Pumice at 800°, giving iodine + some HI	Absorbed in KI solution and titrated with thiosulphate; + iodate and retitrated (to determine HI)	1
Methyl chloride in air	Furnace at 1000°, giving chlorine + HCl	Absorbed in Na_2CO_3/arsenite (to convert chlorine to Cl^-); + HNO_3 + $AgNO_3$, filtered and back titrated with SCN^- to Fe(III) indicator	2
Na acetate	Ignited to the carbonate	Titrated with HCl	3
Methyl chloride in air	Burnt with natural gas in a special burner; 1 h–90 min combustion	Vapours brought into contact with NH_3, the NH_4Cl absorbed in water and determined with excess $AgNO_3$, back titrating with SCN^-	4
CCl_4 in moist air	Heated to 1000–1100° in a silica tube	Gases absorbed in NaOH/Na_2SO_3; nearly neutralized with HNO_3 and Cl^- titrated with $AgNO_3$ to CrO_4^{2-}	5
Numerous halides in air, e.g. $CHCl_3$, chlorobenzene, propylene chloride, tetrachloroethylene, trichloroethylene, etc.	Method of ref. 5		6

Materials titrated	Reaction conditions	Subsequent treatment and final titration stage	Ref.
Na acetate	Ignited to the carbonate	Titrated with HCl	7
Chloropicrin (CCl_3NO_2) in treated grain	Carried through tube at 300–400°, giving chlorine, oxides of nitrogen and HCl	Passed through KI solution and titrated with thiosulphate	8
Chloropicrin in grain	Carried over a hot copper coil, reacting: $2\,CCl_3NO_2 \rightarrow 2\,CO_2 + N_2 + 3\,Cl_2$ or $2\,CCl_3NO_2 + O_2 \rightarrow 2\,CO_2 + 2\,NO + 3\,Cl_2$	Chlorine absorbed in KI solution and titrated with thiosulphate	9
Chlorine-containing compounds	Silica at 900°	Absorbed in NaOH; any NaOCl reduced to chloride with sulphite, then Cl^- titrated with $AgNO_3$ to chromate	10
Volatile halides in blood	Aspirated through silica tube containing Pt gauze at 900°	Products dissolved in NaOH/Na_2SO_3 and Cl^- determined by standard procedures like Ag(I) titration	11
Methyl bromide; CCl_3CN	Passed with air/H_2O_2 through silica tubes containing Pt filaments at dull redness	Absorbed in alkali; Br^- determined by adding acetic acid and titrating with $AgNO_3$ to eosin; Cl^- determined by $AgNO_3$ titration to CrO_4^{2-}	12
DDT spray deposits (extracted with acetone or benzene)	Burnt with hydrogen or coal gas, giving HCl	Absorbed in alkali + arsenite; Cl^- determined by adding excess $AgNO_3$ and back titrating with SCN^-	13
Methyl bromide in the atmosphere	Quartz tubes at 900–1000°	Passed into NaOH; Br^- determined by oxidation with OCl^-/H_3PO_4 at the boiling point to bromate, determined subsequently by adding I^-/acid and titrating with thiosulphate	14
Organic selenium compounds	Burnt in hydrogen/oxygen flame; 15–45 min, giving SeO_2	+ water + KI + H_2SO_4 and titrated with thiosulphate	15
Volatile halides	Heated in Pt tube	Products absorbed in alkali/arsenite and Cl^- determined by a standard procedure such as Ag titration	16

Materials titrated	Reaction conditions	Subsequent treatment and final titration stage	Ref.
Organic halide vapours	Absorbed on carbon and oxidized on silica at 950°	Absorbed in $NaHCO_3/Na_2SO_3$ and Cl^- determined with excess $AgNO_3$ and back titration with SCN^-	17
Tetrachloroethane in air	Oxidized on heated Pt in a quartz tube	Absorbed in alkali/arsenite and back titrated with HCl to methyl red/bromocresol green	18
Small amounts of methyl bromide	Combustion as in method of ref. 12	Br^- oxidized with OCl^- to BrO_3^-, excess destroyed with formic acid, I^-/acid added and titrated with thiosulphate; or Br^- titrated electrometrically with $AgNO_3$	19
Chlorinated hydrocarbons in industrial atmospheres	Passed over heated Pt	Gas mixture passed into arsenite, and the HCl determined with alkali	20
Alkali and alkaline earth salts of carboxylic acids	Ignited to carbonate	Dissolved in excess alkali and back titrated with HCl (alkaline earths) or H_2SO_4 (alkalies)	21
p-Aminosalicylic acid	Heated, yielding 3-aminophenol + CO_2	CO_2 passed through $Ba(OH)_2$ and back titrated with acid	22
Ethanol in blood	Aspirated through pumice/phosphoric acid at 280–300°, giving ethylene	Passed through bromine/CCl_4 and unused determined with I^-/thiosulphate (see Bromine reagents, ref. 298)	23
Halogenated hydrocarbons in caffeine-free coffee and in cereals treated with insecticides	Pyrolysed in air current at 900°	Reaction products absorbed in Na_2CO_3/arsenite; HNO_3/$AgNO_3$ added, filtered and unreacted Ag titrated with SCN^-	24
Chlorine-containing pesticides, e.g. aldrin, dieldrin	Burnt in a quartz tube containing CuO at 700–800°, in oxygen or air	Reaction products passed into Na_2CO_3, HNO_3 added and Cl^- titrated with $AgNO_3$ amperometrically	25
Tetrachloroethylene in fruit	Removed by air current and pyrolysed, giving HCl	Absorbed in Na_2CO_3/arsenite, brought to pH 3 with HNO_3 and titrated with $Hg(NO_3)_2$ to diphenylcarbazone	26

Materials titrated	Reaction conditions	Subsequent treatment and final titration stage	Ref.
Ethanol in blood	Distilled in nitrogen over pumice/pyrophosphate at 280–300°, giving ethylene (maintained that the dehydration is not quantitative)	Carried into bromine solution and unused iodometrically determined	27
Dichloroethane in treated grain	Passed over Fe_2O_3/ asbestos at 600°	Cl^- determined with excess $AgNO_3$ and SCN^- back titration	28
chloropicrin, also in treated grain	passed with hydrogen over Ni, giving NH_3	absorbed in excess acid and back titrated with alkali	
Methyl bromide absorbed by foods	Passed with air through quartz tube at 1000°	Reaction products passed into $NaOH/H_2O_2$, giving Br^-; titrated with $AgNO_3$ to brilliant yellow as absorption indicator	29
Trichloroethylene in air	Mixed with ethanol and burnt	Reaction products aspirated into $AgNO_3$ and unused back titrated	30
Halogenated hydrocarbons	Absorbed on Si gel, desorbed and pyrolysed	Passed into Na_2CO_3/Na formate and Cl^- determined with excess Ag^+ and back titration with SCN^-	31
Iodoform from determination of acetone by reaction with iodine/ NaOH	Suspension decomposed photochemically in sunlight to iodine	Titrated with thiosulphate	32
Methyl esters of fatty acids (from hydrolysis of fats and esterification of the acids with methanol) after separation by gas chromatography	Ignited to CO_2 on CuO at 800°	Absorbed in $BaCl_2/H_2O_2$/ ethanol/water and coulometrically titrated with OH^- to potentiometric end-point	33
p-Phenylene dilithium	In dry ether; oxygen passed through for 3 min, giving $LiOOC_6H_4OOLi$, reacting with the original substance to yield $LiOC_6H_4OLi$	Hydrolysed to hydroquinone with H_2SO_4 and titrated with Ce(IV) potentiometrically (see Part I, Cerium (IV), ref. 69)	34
Bismuth camphorcarboxylate	Heated to 475–550°	Residue dissolved in HNO_3, NH_4OH added and titrated with EDTA to pyrocatechol violet	35

Materials titrated	Reaction conditions	Subsequent treatment and final titration stage	Ref.
Chloropicrin; dichloroethane	Passed over Fe_2O_3 at 600° in mixture with air	Absorbed in $NaOH/Na_2SO_3$ and Cl^- titrated with $AgNO_3$	36
Methionine	Ignited at 600–700° to SO_2	Oxidized with H_2O_2 to H_2SO_4 and titrated with NaOH	37
Ichthyol (ichthammol)	Passed with air stream through red-hot quartz tube, giving SO_3	Carried into water, then titrated with $Ba(ClO_4)_2$ to indicator of torin/methylene blue	38
Methyl bromide in air	Burnt in a column with a Pt spiral, giving bromine	Absorbed in KI solution and titrated iodine	39
Uronic acids, polyuronides	Thermally decarboxylated in nitrogen current at 130–140°; conditions studied and comparison made with the more usual decarboxylation in conc. HCl	CO_2 absorbed in alkali and back titrated (also gravimetric)	40
Dichloroethane in waste waters	Heating with air to 900° in quartz tube	Products absorbed in NaOH and Cl^- titrated with Hg(II) to diphenylcarbazide	41
Aldrin in fertilizers	Burnt in oxygen atmosphere in closed flask in the fold of platinum gauze	Absorbed in H_2O_2 in the flask, HNO_3 added and Cl^- titrated amperometrically with $AgNO_3$	42
Dibromo derivatives from determination of rubber unsaturation by reaction with bromine	Combustion in oxygen, yielding bromine	Absorbed in NaOH and ultimately titrated Br^- with $Hg(NO_3)_2$	43
Some easily decarboxylated acids, e.g. *p*-aminosalicylic and acetonedicarboxylic acids	Heated in a solution of dilute H_2SO_4 (ca 30 min distillation)	CO_2 absorbed in $Ba(OH)_2$ solution under a pentane layer; back titrated with HCl to thymol blue	44, 45
p-Aminosalicyclic acid	Decarboxylated as in method of refs 44 and 45 to yield CO_2 and *m*-aminophenol	1. CO_2 determined as in method of refs 44 and 45 2. aliquot of residual solution $+ BrO_3^-/Br^- + H_2SO_4$, yielding tribromophenol + NH_3; unused bromine removed with sulphite and NH_3 distilled into excess HCl; back titrated with alkali to methyl red 3. aliquot + excess $BrO_3^-/Br^-/H_2SO_4$; after 20 min, KI added and titrated with thiosulphate (see Bromine reagents, ref. 538)	46

Materials titrated	Reaction conditions	Subsequent treatment and final titration stage	Ref.
Sulphonamides	Burnt in an oxygen-filled flask containing a Pt wire and some NaOH solution	Sulphate formed titrated with $Pb(NO_3)_2$ to pink of dithizone, after adding HNO_3/acetic acid/acetone	47

References

1. Klemenc, A., *Monatsh.* **34**, 901 (1913).
2. Martinek, M. J. and Marti, W. C., *Ind. Eng. Chem., Anal. Ed.* **3**, 408 (1931).
3. Zemlyanitzuin, V. P., *J. Chem. Ind.* (*Moscow*) **8**, 629 (1931).
4. Patty, F. A., Schrenk, H. H. and Yant, W. P., *Ind. Eng. Chem., Anal. Ed.* **4**, 259 (1932).
5. Olsen, J. C., Smyth, H. F., Ferguson, G. E. and Scheflan, L., *Ind. Eng. Chem., Anal. Ed.* **8**, 260 (1936).
6. Smyth, H. F., *Ind. Eng. Chem., Anal. Ed.* **8**, 379 (1936).
7. Hurd, C. B. and Fiedler, W., *Ind. Eng. Chem., Anal. Ed.* **9**, 116 (1937).
8. Sosedov, N. I. and Drozdova, Z. B., *Mukomol'e* **13**, No. 6, 7 (1938).
9. Muromski, M., *Lab. Prakt.* (*USSR*) **14**, No. 11, 30 (1939).
10. Winteringham, F. P. W., *J. Soc. Chem. Ind.* (*London*) **61**, 190 (1942).
11. Moran, H. E., *J. Ind. Hyg. Toxicol.* **25**, 243 (1943).
12. Lubatti, O. F. and Harrison, A., *J. Soc. Chem. Ind.* (*London*) **63**, 140 (1944).
13. Fahey, J. E., *J. Assoc. Offic. Agr. Chem.* **28**, 152 (1945).
14. Williams, D., *Ind. Eng. Chem., Anal. Ed.* **17**, 295 (1945).
15. McCullough, J. D., Campbell, T. W. and Krilanovich, N. J., *Ind. Eng. Chem., Anal. Ed.* **18**, 638 (1946).
16. Alford, W. C., *J. Ind. Hyg. Toxicol.* **29**, 396 (1947).
17. Danner, C. E. and Goldenson, J., *J. Ind. Hyg. Toxicol.* **29**, 218 (1947).
18. Goldenson, J. and Thomas, J. W., *J. Ind. Hyg. Toxicol.* **29**, 14 (1947).
19. Russell, J., *J. Soc. Chem. Ind.* (*London*) **66**, 22 (1947).
20. Setterlind, A. N., *What's new in Ind. Hyg.* **4**, No. 1, 9 (1947).
21. Siggia, S. and Maisch, M., *Anal. Chem.* **20**, 235 (1948).
22. Fontl, P., *Royal Australian Chem. Inst., J. and Proc.* **16**, No. 1, 248 (1949).
23. Schifferli, E., *Folia Med.* (*Naples*) **32**, 562 (1949).
24. Deshusses, J. and Desbaumes, P., *Mitt. Lebensm. Hyg.* **41**, 381 (1950).
25. Agazzi, E. J., Peters, E. D. and Brooke, F. R., *Anal. Chem.* **25**, 237 (1953).
26. Deshussses, J. and Desbaumes, P., *Mitt. Lebensm. Hyg.* **46**, 233 (1955).

27. Paulus, W. and Malloch, H. J., *Deut. Z. Ges. Gerichtl. Med.* **44**, 589 (1955).
28. Zakharenko, G. A. and Vodaturskii, G. A., *Trudy Odessk. Tekhnol. Inst.* No. 5, 46 (1955).
29. Desbaumes, P. and Deshusses, J., *Mitt. Gebiete Lebensm. u. Hyg.* **47**, 550 (1956).
30. Dettori, G., *Rass. med. ind.* **25**, 35 (1956).
31. Peterson, J. E., Hoyle, H. R. and Schneider, E. J., *Am. Ind. Hyg. Assoc. J.* **17**, 429 (1956).
32. Bose, S., *Anal. Chem.* **30**, 1157 (1958).
33. Liberti, A., Cartoni, G. P. and Pallotta, U., *Ann. chim.* (*Rome*) **48**, 40 (1958).
34. Clifford, A. F. and Olsen, R. R., *Anal. Chem.* **31**, 1860 (1959).
35. Pujol, J. M. and Gavaldá, L., *Galenica Acta* (*Madrid*) **13**, 411 (1960).
36. Zakharenko, G. A., *Zhur. Priklad Khim.* **34**, 1103 (1961).
37. Kurzawa, Z., *Chem. Anal.* (*Warsaw*) **6**, 1013, 1025 (1961).
38. Mandák, M. and Struhár, M., *Českoslov. Farm.* **10**, 456 (1961).
39. Egorov, N. V., *Zavodskaya Lab.* **28**, 811 (1962).
40. Anderson, D. M. W., Garbutt, S. and Smith, J. F., *Talanta* **9**, 689 (1962).
41. Sokolov, V. P. and Lobashov, K. A., *Zavodskaya Lab.* **28**, 285 (1962).
42. Wilson, H. N. and Phillipson, M., *Analyst* **87**, 441 (1962).
43. Darovskikh, G. T. and Trofimov, G. A., *Kauchuk i Rezina* **22**, 49 (1963).
44. Maros, L., Molnár-Perl, I., Vajda, M. and Schulek, E., *Anal. Chim. Acta* **28**, 179 (1963).
45. Maros, L., Molnár-Perl, I., Vajda, M. and Schulek, E., *Magyar Kem. Folyoirat* **69**, 123 (1963).
46. Schulek, E., Maros, L. and Molnár-Perl, I., *Talanta* **10** 561 (1963).
47. Špringer, V. and Majer, J., *Českoslov. Farm.* **12**, 6 (1963).

90. Quinones

Reagent. In all cases, *p*-benzoquinone has been used.

Reaction and materials titrated. In all except one case, conjugated dienes have been determined via the Diels–Alder addition reaction:

```
     |                                        |/
     C—          CO                           C         CO
    //         /    \                      /    \     /    \
 —C          CH      CH                 —C       CH        CH
  |       +  ‖       ‖      ——→          ‖       |         ‖
 —C          CH      CH                 —C       CH        CH
    \\         \    /                      \    /     \    /
     C—          CO                           C         CO
     |                                        |\
```

The reaction occurring in the determination of thebaine is probably oxidation.

Reaction conditions. In non-aqueous solution, usually ethanol or benzene.

Most reaction times have been comparatively long, even at reflux temperatures.

Subsequent treatment and final titration stage. Unreacted quinone has been determined in all examples by adding iodide/acid and titrating with thiosulphate.

Examples

Materials titrated	Reaction conditions	Subsequent treatment and final titration stage	Ref.
Thebaine in opium	In 95% ethanol; 10 min/40–50°	Product dissolved out with $CHCl_3$ and excess quinone determined iodometrically	1
Conjugated dienes like 2,3-dimethylbutadiene, 1,3-dimethylhexadiene, phellandrenes	Evidently in acetone or xylene; 15–20 h/*ca* 100°	+ I^-/HCl or H_2SO_4 and titrated with thiosulphate (see Iodides and hydriodic acid, ref. 117)	2
Diene numbers of fats and oils	Method of ref. 2 (see Iodides and hydriodic acid, ref. 151)		3
Menthofurane, e.g. in peppermint oil	In ethanol; 18 h/20°	+ I^-/acid and titrated with thiosulphate	4
Diene numbers, e.g. of vitamins A_1 and D_2	In ethanol or ethanol/benzene (large excess reagent). Heated to 100° in sealed tube	+ I^-/HCl and titrated with thiosulphate	5
Vitamins A_1 and D_2	In benzene, + hydroquinone (*ca* 20–25-fold excess of reagent); 12 h/100°	+ water/I^- + $NaHCO_3$ + excess iodine (to react with the hydroquinone); titrated with thiosulphate, HCl added and retitrated with thiosulphate after 10–15 min	6

References

1. Kanevskaya, S. I., Yaskine, D. Z. and Mitryagina, S. F., *Zhur. Priklad Khim.* (*J. Appl. Chem. USSR*) **18**, 374 (1945).

2. Tamayo, M. L. and León, J. L., *Anales real soc. españ. fis y quím.* **44B**, 963 (1948).
3. Tamayo, M. L. and Estada, C., *Anales real soc. españ. fis y quím.* **47B**. 815 (1951).
4. Ohloff, G., *Arch. Pharm.* **285**, 353 (1952).
5. Tamayo, M. L., *Fette u. Seifen* **54**, 539 (1952).
6. Tamayo, M. L. and Leal, B. I., *Anales real soc. españ. fis y quím.* **50B**, 721 (1954).

91. Selenium dioxide

Reagent and reaction conditions. SeO_2 (sometimes selenious acid) in acid solution (HCl or H_2SO_4 or acetic acid).

Reaction and materials titrated. Oxidation, based on the reaction:

$$SeO_2 + 4\ H^+ + 4\ \epsilon \rightarrow Se + 2\ H_2O$$

Ascorbic acid, hydrazine derivatives and sulphur-containing compounds like thiourea have been determined in this way:

$$2\ CH_2OH.CHOH.CH.\underset{|__________O____________CO__|}{C(OH)=C(OH)} + SeO_2 \rightarrow 2\ CH_2OH.CHOH.CH.\underset{|__O___CO__|}{CO.CO} + Se + 2\ H_2O$$

$$RCONHNH_2 + SeO_2 \rightarrow RCOOH + Se + H_2O + N_2$$

$$4\left(CS(NH_2)_2 \rightleftharpoons NH_2\text{—}\underset{\underset{NH}{\|}}{C}\text{—}SH\right) + SeO_2 \rightarrow 2\ NH_2\text{—}\underset{\underset{NH}{\|}}{C}\text{—}S\text{—}S\text{—}\underset{\underset{NH}{\|}}{C}\text{—}NH_2 + Se + 2\ H_2O$$

also

$$2\left(CS(NH_2)_2 \rightleftharpoons NH_2\text{—}\underset{\underset{NH}{\|}}{C}\text{—}SH\right) + 3\ SeO_2 \rightarrow 2\ NH_2\text{—}\underset{\underset{NH}{\|}}{C}\text{—}SO_3H + 3\ Se$$

and

$$CS(NH_2)_2 + 2\,SeO_2 \rightarrow CO(NH_2)_2 + 2\,Se + SO_3$$

$$2\ {-}N{=}\overset{|}{C}{-}SH + 3\,SeO_2 \rightarrow 2\ {-}N{=}\overset{|}{C}{-}OH + 2\,SO_2 + 3\,Se$$

Final titration stage. Excess reagent has been determined by adding I^- and titrating the iodine with thiosulphate.

Examples

Materials titrated	Reagent and reaction conditions	Subsequent treatment and final titration stage	Ref.
Thiourea	Solution + SeO_2 + H_2SO_4	Coagulated Se with NaCl, filtered, I^- + H_2SO_4 added and titrated with thiosulphate	1
Isoniazid	In acetic acid, + SeO_2/H_2O; 30 min reflux	Filtered, I^- + H_2SO_4 added and titrated with thiosulphate	2
$-N{=}\overset{\vert}{C}{-}SH$ group, as for example in thiosemicarbazones	In dilute NaOH, + SeO_2 + acetic acid; 4 h boiling	Filtered, I^- + H_2SO_4 added and titrated with thiosulphate	3
Ascorbic acid in pharmaceutical preparations	+ SeO_2 + H_2SO_4	+ I^- and titrated with thiosulphate	4
Ascorbic acid	+ SeO_2 reagent	Filtered, I^- + H_2SO_4 added and titrated with thiosulphate	5
Isoniazid	+ SeO_2	Filtered, I^- added and titrated with thiosulphate	6
Thiourea	+ SeO_2 in 3–5N HCl; 15–30 min boiling	Unused SeO_2 determined iodometrically; Se also determined (gravimetrically)	7
Condensation products of isoniazid with carbonyl compounds like veratraldehyde, furyl-2 methyl ketone, etc.	+ dilute H_2SO_4 + SeO_2; 30 min reflux	Filtered, I^- added and titrated with thiosulphate to starch	8

References

1. Werner, A. E. A., *Analyst* **65**, 286 (1940).
2. Franchi, G., *Farm. sci. e tec.* (*Pavia*) **7**, 640 (1952).
3. Franchi, G., *Ann. chim.* (*Rome*) **42**, 701 (1952).
4. Smulkowski, J., *Farm. Polska* **11**, 132 (1953).
5. Franchi, G., *Il Farmaco* (*Pavia*), *Ed. sci.* **9**, 95 (1954).
6. Akiyama, T., Fujiwara, M. and Ichida, H., *Bull. Kyoto Coll. Pharm.* **4**, 18 (1956).
7. Joshi, M., *Chem. Listy* **50**, 1928 (1956).
8. Franchi, G. and Pacini, C., *Boll. chim. farm.* **99**, 578 (1960).

92. Silver (I)

Reagent. Usually aqueous or aqueous alcoholic silver nitrate. Other reagents occasionally used include: sulphate; perchlorate; acetate; oxide (as solid or prepared *in situ* from the nitrate and alkali); benzoate (also prepared *in situ* from nitrate and sodium benzoate); sodium argentocyanide; nitrophenate (from shaking silver oxide and the nitrophenol); lactate; bromide.

The most familiar reagent, especially suitable for oxidation reactions, is that first described by Tollens (ref. 1), in which silver oxide, formed from the nitrate and alkali, is dissolved in the minimum amount of ammonium hydroxide.

Silver nitrate has also been used in mixed reagents with a further component which takes part directly in the analytical reaction. Examples of such components are: picric acid; persulphate; periodate; magnesium (II); nitric acid; and excess ammonium hydroxide. For convenience, the methods based on use of these double reagents are classified also under the second component.

Reactions and materials titrated. Several reactions are represented, although the distinction between them is not always clear.

1. Hydrogen replacement in ≡CH (mostly the example of acetylene itself); —SH (e.g. xanthates, mercaptans, thiouracils); =NH (e.g. cyanamide, dicyanodiamide, saccharine, sulpha-drugs like sulphathiazole, purines, barbituric acid derivatives); —OH (e.g. enols, purines, barbituric acid derivatives),

$$RC{\equiv}CH + 2\,AgNO_3 \rightarrow RC{\equiv}CAg.AgNO_3 + HNO_3$$

$$CN.NH_2 + 2\,AgNO_3 \rightarrow CN.NAg_2 + 2\,HNO_3$$

$$RSH + AgNO_3 \rightarrow RSAg + HNO_3$$

The reaction leads to the formation of free acid, together with a silver derivative of the organic compound which is generally insoluble in the medium used.

2. Ion/ion combination, usually with formation of insoluble silver salts. Typical examples are with certain carboxylates (e.g. succinates), tetraphenylborates, reineckates, dithiocarbamates, azidothiocarbonates, alkyl arsenates, sulphonamides, sulphonium chlorides and the halides of nitrogen bases like alkaloids; these last two examples are essentially determination of halide ions.

In neutral or alkaline solution, the materials given under reaction type 1 can be considered to react also by ion/ion combination of Ag^+ with xanthate, barbiturate, mercaptide, etc. anions. The distinction is arbitrary. Where free acid is formed (and determined as the final stage of the method—see below) the reaction is better regarded as hydrogen replacement.

In one example (ref. 185), a quaternary ammonium bromide was converted by Ag_2O into the soluble hydroxide.

3. Oxidation, such as with aldehydes, sugars, hydrazines and anti-oxidants. Silver metal is then liberated:

$$RCHO + 2\,Ag^+ + H_2O \rightarrow RCOO^- + 3\,H^+ + 2\,Ag \text{ or}$$

$$RCHO + 3\,Ag^+ + H_2O \rightarrow RCOOAg + 3\,H^+ + 2\,Ag$$

$$RCONHNH_2 + 4\,Ag^+ + H_2O \rightarrow RCOOH + N_2 + 4\,Ag + 4\,H^+$$

4. Dehalogenation in reactions with organic halides which yield the silver halide. Such halides contain a labile halogen atom (e.g. lower alkyl iodides, phosgene, compounds with a tertiary halogen atom like Diels–Alder adducts with chloromaleic anhydride).

$$RI + AgNO_3 \rightarrow AgI + RNO_3$$

$$COCl_2 + 2\,Ag^+ + H_2O \rightarrow 2\,AgCl + CO_2 + 2\,H^+$$

There is no sharp distinction between this reaction and ion/ion combination with halide salts, mentioned under 2.

5. 'Complex' formation, as with hexamine or nicotinamide, where an insoluble product is yielded which does not appear to be the result of simple ion/ion combination.

6. Replacement of sulphur by oxygen, with formation of silver sulphide. This is the basis of determination of a number of organic sulphur compounds such as thiobenzophenone, thiobarbiturates, thioureas, thioamides, thionic esters:

$$(C_6H_5)_2CS + 2\,Ag^+ + H_2O \rightarrow (C_6H_5)_2CO + Ag_2S + 2\,H^+$$

$$\underset{\underset{S}{\|}}{RC}.OR' + 2\,Ag^+ + H_2O \rightarrow \underset{\underset{O}{\|}}{RC}.OR' + Ag_2S + 2\,H^+$$

Under more vigorous reaction conditions, the reactions mentioned under 1 or 2 above may be followed by further change yielding silver sulphide. Xanthates and mercaptans readily undergo this, so that conditions must be carefully controlled.

7. The reactions with the mixed reagents given above under Reagent, are considered under the headings of the second component; the following table gives the essentials:

Reagent	Reaction
Ag(I) +	
Picric acid Persulphate Mg(II)	1 or 2 above, giving mixed salts of bases (first two) or uric acid (last-named)
HNO_3	4 above, giving Hal^- with halogen compounds less reactive than those participating under 4)
Periodate	Oxidation, e.g. of 1,2-glycols, with concurrent formation of iodate which thus precipitates as the silver salt
Excess ammonia	Addition to allyl isothiocyanate; $C_3H_5NCS + NH_3 \rightarrow C_3H_5NH.CS.NH_2$; the substituted thiourea reacts further with Ag(I) yielding Ag_2S and $C_3H_5C(NH_2){=}NH$.

With these last three examples, there is thus an initial reaction with the extra reagent component. The sample could equally well be treated with the component in a separate analysis stage (this is in fact done in some cases) and it is only for convenience that the Ag(I) part of the reagent is present from the beginning.

Reaction conditions. Few general observations can be made when such a variety of reactions is used. The majority are carried out at or near room temperature and in aqueous solution. Where the final analytical stage is the titration of acid from reactions of hydrogen replacement, it is important that the reaction medium be sensibly neutral or contain a known amount of base.

Subsequent treatment and final titration stage. The first three methods given below account for about 90% of the final stages. This is explained above all by the comparatively easy and accurate methods which are available for determination of Ag(I) by titration.

(a) Determination of unused Ag(I), usually after filtration of a silver derivative or reaction product. This has been carried out by one of the standard inorganic procedures, namely, direct titration with thiocyanate, chloride, iodide or cyanide (with the first named titrant predominating); or indirectly with these same reagents, concluding with a back titration with Ag(I). Back titration of unused Ag(I) has been carried out also with dodecyl mercaptan, glutathione and with thioacetamide. $K_2Ni(CN)_4$ has also been used, liberating Ni(II), then determined with EDTA.

(b) Determination of the silver in a reaction product, which has been brought into solution in nitric or sulphuric acid. This includes metallic silver, formed in oxidation reactions. The techniques of (a) above are available, and mostly used has been the thiocyanate titration. An interesting special case is the direct titration of colloidal silver reaction product with iodine (ref. 31).

(c) Titration of acid liberated from hydrogen replacement reactions of type 1 under Reactions. This has been carried out by organic bases like diethylamine and tris(hydroxymethyl)methylamine, but much more often with alkali. Although direct titration predominates, there are examples of use of excess base (present from the beginning or added after reaction with the silver reagent) followed by a back titration with acid. Generally excess Ag(I) is removed with chloride before the titration is performed.

(d) Determination of the original organic compound after its regeneration from the silver-containing precipitated derivative. The silver reagent serves as a separation agent in such cases. Examples are:

Uric acid, precipitated by the Ag(I)/Mg(II) reagent, regenerated with acid and titrated with permanganate or bichromate;

glutathione, precipitated as silver derivative, regenerated with HCl and determined with excess bromate;

cyanamide, precipitated as silver derivative, dissolved in NH_4Cl/excess acid and the unneutralized acid titrated with alkali.

(e) Determination of organic reaction products, e.g. formate from formaldehyde (via oxidation with Hg(II)) and butyric acid from butyraldehyde (via oxidation to acetone, followed by iodometric or other determination).

(f) Determination of inorganic reaction products, amongst which may be quoted:

OH^- from determination of tetraethylammonium bromide by conversion with Ag_2O

CN^- from determination of thiourea with $NaAg(CN)_2$:

$$CS(NH_2)_2 + 2\,NaAg(CN)_2 + 2\,NaOH \rightarrow H_2N.CN + Ag_2S + 2\,H_2O + 4\,NaCN$$

Br^- from determination of thiourea with AgBr;

Ni(II) from reaction with Ag(I) of the nickel dithiocarbamate of hexamethyleneimine in determination of the latter with a CS_2/Ni(II) reagent.

The CN^- and Br^- were titrated with Ag(I) and the Ni(II) with EDTA.

(g) As last example may be mentioned a differential procedure for aldehydes in presence of ketones. The carbonyl content was determined with hydroxylamine before and after treatment with an Ag(I) reagent; the aldehyde content was thus given by the difference.

Examples

Materials titrated	Reagent and reaction conditions	Subsequent treatment and final titration stage	Ref.
Theobromine, caffeine	+ $AgNO_3/NH_4OH$. Heated until no more ammonia evolved, giving insoluble silver derivatives	Filtered and unused Ag(I) titrated with SCN^- to Fe(III)	2
Hydrazines	+ $AgNO_3$/KOH/ NH_4OH. Boiled, giving silver	Unused Ag(I) determined by titration with CN^-	3

Materials titrated	Reagent and reaction conditions	Subsequent treatment and final titration stage	Ref.
Reducing sugars	+ $AgNO_3/NH_4OH$; 10 min/100°	Filtered, acidified with acetic acid and the unused Ag(I) titrated with NaCl according to Gay-Lussac's method	4
Acetylenes	+ $AgNO_3$/alcohol, reacting: $C_2H_2 + 3\,AgNO_3 \rightarrow 2\,HNO_3 + Ag_2C_2.AgNO_3$	Nitric acid titrated with alkali	5
2,5-Dihydroxyphenyl-acetic acid (homo-gentisic acid)	+ $AgNO_3/NH_4OH$; 5 min/room temp.	Unused Ag(I) determined by adding excess CN^- and back titrating with Ag(I) to I^-	6
Succinic acid in presence of lactic and tartaric acids	Neutral solution + $AgNO_3$, giving insoluble succinate	Precipitate + excess Cl^- and back titrated with Ag(I) to chromate	7
Allyl isothiocyanate	In ethanol, + $AgNO_3$ + NH_4OH; 24 h/room temp.	+ HNO_3 and unused Ag(I) titrated with SCN^- to Fe(III)	8
Furfuraldehyde from pentosans and pentoses by acid distillation	+ $AgNO_3$/NaOH/ NH_4OH; some min/ 60–70° or 30 min/room temp., giving pyromucic acid	Filtered and unused Ag(I) determined by titration with SCN^-	9
Uric acid	+ $AgNO_3/MgSO_4$ reagent, giving insoluble magnesium silver salt	Precipitate treated with H_2S, regenerating the uric acid; titrated with MnO_4^-	10
Disodium methyl arsenate	In water + neutral $AgNO_3$	Unused Ag(I) titrated with Cl^- to chromate	11
$CaCN_2$; cyanamide	+ $AgNO_3/NH_4OH$. Slightly warmed with shaking, giving Ag_2CN_2	Filtered and unused Ag(I) titrated with SCN^-	12
Allyl isothiocyanate	+ NH_4OH + $AgNO_3$; 1 h/100°	Filtered, acidified with HNO_3 and unused Ag(I) titrated with SCN^-	13
Fatty acids and their salts	Neutralized solution + $AgNO_3$, giving insoluble salts	Filtered and unused Ag(I) determined by titration with SCN^-	14
Iodoform	In ethanol/ether, + $AgNO_3/HNO_3$. Warmed until no more smell of HNO_3	Unused Ag(I) titrated with SCN^-	15

Materials titrated	Reagent and reaction conditions	Subsequent treatment and final titration stage	Ref.
Uric acid in urine	+ Ag/Mg reagent, giving precipitate of AgMg urate	Uric acid regenerated from precipitate by treatment with H_2SO_4; Ag_2SO_4 filtered and solution titrated with MnO_4^-	16
Cyanamide	+ $AgNO_3$ + NH_4OH, giving Ag_2CN_2	Unused Ag(I) titrated by a standard method	17
Acetylene in ethylene	Absorbed in 5% $AgNO_3$, giving Ag_2C_2 and HNO_3	+ excess alkali + NaCl, filtered and back titrated with HCl to methyl orange	18
Dicyanodiamide in presence of cyanamide in mixed manures	In weakly acid solution, + $AgNO_3$ + picric acid; 2 min stirring, then 30 min/0°, giving precipitate of complex of silver picrate and dicyanodiamide, $C_6H_2(NO_2)_3OAg.C_2H_4N_4$	Filtered and determined gravimetrically or by dissolving in HNO_3 and titrating the Ag(I)	19
Acetylene	Passed into $AgNO_3$	HNO_3 formed titrated with alkali	20
	(unsatisfactory results found, evidently depending on the conditions)		
Acetaldehyde in presence of acetone	+ $AgNO_3$/alkali/ NH_4OH. *Ca* 12 h reaction time	Unused Ag(I) determined by titration with SCN^-	21
Ca cyanamide, $CaCN_2$	+ CH_3COOAg + NH_4OH	Ag_2CN_2 precipitate dissolved in NH_4Cl/H_2SO_4, shaken 10 min and back titrated with NaOH to methyl orange	22
Iodoform formed in determination of acetaldehyde and acetone by reaction with iodine/ NaOH	Steam distilled into $AgNO_3/HNO_3$/ethanol; 90 min reflux	Unused Ag(I) titrated with SCN^-	23
HCHO	+ $AgNO_3$ + saturated Na_2CO_3/water; 5 min/room temp.	+ H_2SO_4 and unused Ag(I) titrated with Cl^- potentiometrically	24
Azidodithiocarbonate groups, —$SCSN_3$	In water + a few drops HNO_3 + excess $AgNO_3$; 2 h/room temp., giving $AgSCSN_3$	Unused Ag(I) titrated with SCN^-	25

Materials titrated	Reagent and reaction conditions	Subsequent treatment and final titration stage	Ref.
1-Heptyne in oil	+ 5% $AgNO_3$ in 95% ethanol; 6 h/room temp.	Filtered, unused Ag(I) precipitated with Cl^- and HNO_3 formed titrated with NaOH to phenolphthalein	26
Mercaptans in naphtha	+ $AgNO_3$. Shaken vigorously	+ excess SCN^-, shaken well, excess $AgNO_3$ added and finally titrated with SCN^- to Fe(III)	27
Theobromine	Neutral solution + $AgNO_3$	HNO_3 liberated titrated with NaOH to phenol red	28
Acetylenic alcohols	+ slight excess CH_3COOAg	Filtered and filtrate titrated with NaOH to phenolphthalein	29
Iodoform	In ethanol, + $AgNO_3$ + HNO_3; 2–3 h/room temp.	Unused Ag(I) titrated with SCN^-	30
Aldehydes	+ $AgNO_3$/NaOH; some + SiO_2 or $MgSO_4$ to give greater Ag_2O surface. Mostly 10–15 min/room temp. but some heated on water-bath	Unused Ag_2O dissolved in H_2SO_4; excess I^- added and back titrated with $AgNO_3$ to starch/iodine indicator. Also on micro-scale, the colloidal Ag titrated with iodine to starch	31
Glucose in leather and tanning solutions	+ $AgNO_3/NH_4OH$	+ excess KCl/acetic acid and back titrated with Ag(I) to chromate	32
Theobromine in pharmaceutical preparations	Method of ref. 28		33
Theobromine	+ $AgNO_3/NH_4OH$	Acidified with acetic acid, filtered and unused Ag(I) in filtrate titrated with SCN^-	34
Theobromine	Method of ref. 28 compared with iodometric method (considered less good)		35
Esters of thion acids, R.C(=S).OH	In alcohol, + $AgNO_3$; 12 h/room temp. in the dark, giving Ag_2S	Precipitate dissolved in HNO_3 and Ag(I) titrated with SCN^-	36

Materials titrated	Reagent and reaction conditions	Subsequent treatment and final titration stage	Ref.
Theobromine	In water, + $AgNO_3/NH_4OH$; 15 min boiling	Filtered and unused Ag(I) titrated in filtrate with SCN^-	37
Hexamine	+ excess $AgNO_3$. Shaken	Filtered and unused Ag(I) titrated with SCN^-	38
HCHO	+ $AgNO_3/NH_4OH$	Silver precipitate dissolved in HNO_3 and Ag(I) titrated with SCN^-	39
Allyl isothiocyanate in mustard flour	+ $NH_4OH/AgNO_3$; 1 h/80°	Filtered and unused Ag(I) titrated with SCN^-	40
2-Mercaptobenzo-thiazole	In NH_4OH, + $AgNO_3$, giving precipitate of Ag derivative	Unused Ag(I) titrated with SCN^- or with Cl^- to dichloro-fluorescein	41
Potassium xanthates	In water, + slight excess $AgNO_3$, giving silver xanthates which further react to give Ag_2S, etc. if too long a delay	Immediately + excess SCN^- and back titrated with $AgNO_3$ to disappearance of red with Fe(III)	42
Mercaptans in hydro-carbon solvents, e.g. naphtha, benzene, heptane, octane	Slight modification of method of ref. 27		43
Acetylene	Passed through $AgNO_3$	Filtered and unused Ag(I) titrated with SCN^-	44
Butyraldehyde in mixtures	+ Ag_2O/alkali, giving butyric acid	Distilled into H_2O_2/H_2SO_4/Fe alum, giving acetone; deter-mined iodometrically, with hydroxylamine or colori-metrically	45
Glutathione in biological material	+ Ag lactate, giving insoluble Ag derivative	+ HCl + excess BrO_3^-/Br^- with iodometric determination of the unused (see Bromine reagents, ref. 138)	46
Thiourea	+ NH_4OH + $AgNO_3$; 2 min/room temp., giving Ag_2S	Filtered and unused Ag(I) titrated in filtrate with SCN^-	47

Materials titrated	Reagent and reaction conditions	Subsequent treatment and final titration stage	Ref.
Theophylline	+ $AgNO_3/NH_4OH$; 15 min/100°, giving insoluble Ag derivative	Precipitate dissolved in HNO_3 and titrated with SCN^-	48
HCHO in dilute solutions	+ $AgNO_3$ + HCl + NaOH, added in succession with shaking after each addition; 10 min/room temp. at end	Ag precipitate filtered, dissolved in HNO_3 and titrated with SCN^-	49
Hydrochlorides of opium alkaloids, e.g. methyl- and ethyl-morphines	+ $AgNO_3$ + a little HNO_3. Heated to coagulate the AgCl	Unused Ag(I) titrated with SCN^-	50
Iodoform	In ether, + $AgNO_3$/ethanol + HNO_3; 15 min boiling	Unused Ag(I) titrated with SCN^-	51
Succinic acid from determination of glutamic acid by reaction with HNO_2, followed by oxidation with MnO_4^-	+ Ag reagent, giving insoluble Ag succinate	Dissolved in HNO_3 and titrated with SCN^-	52
2,5-Dihydroxy-phenylacetic acid ('Alkaptan')	+ $AgNO_3/NH_4OH$/oxalic acid; 5 min/room temp., then + $CaCl_2$ giving Ag (carried down by the calcium oxalate)	Centrifuged, dissolved in HNO_3 and titrated with SCN^-	53
Iodoform	+ $AgNO_3/HNO_3$/ethanol/ether. Warmed until no further smell of HNO_3	Unused Ag(I) titrated with SCN^-	54
Uric acid in urine or blood	+ $AgNO_3$/Mg(II) reagent, giving precipitate of silver magnesium urate	Dissolved in acid and titrated with bichromate to external indicator of leucomethylene blue	55
Hexamine in medicinal mixtures	In water + $AgNO_3$, giving insoluble product $2(CH_2)_6N_4.3AgNO_3$	Filtered and unused Ag(I) titrated with SCN^-	56
Acetylene in air	+ $AgNO_3/NH_4OH$, giving Ag_2C_2	Filtered and unused Ag(I) titrated in filtrate with SCN^- after adding HNO_3	57

Materials titrated	Reagent and reaction conditions	Subsequent treatment and final titration stage	Ref.
Tartaric acid	Solution + $AgNO_3$/ $NaOH/NH_4OH$; 2 h/50–60°, giving silver	Precipitate dissolved in HNO_3 and titrated with SCN^-	58
Thiourea in presence of SCN^-	+ $NaAg(CN)_2$ reagent + NaOH; 10–15 min boiling; $CS(NH_2)_2 + 2\,NaAg(CN)_2 + 2\,NaOH \rightarrow NH_2CN + Ag_2S + 2\,H_2O + 4\,NaCN$	Filtered and titrated with Ag(I) to opalescence with I^- indicator	59
Theobromine in 'diuretin'	+ $AgNO_3/NH_4OH$; 15 min/100°	Filtered and unused Ag(I) in filtrate titrated with SCN^-	60
Benzoyl-, toluyl- and chlorobenzoylbenzoic acids	+ $AgNO_3$; 15–50 min/room temp.	Filtered and unused Ag(I) titrated in filtrate with SCN^-	61
Oxalic, succinic acids	+ $AgNO_3$, giving insoluble salts	Filtered and unused Ag(I) titrated with SCN^-	62
Acetylene	Method of ref. 44		63
Theobromine	Modification of method of ref. 28		64
Mercaptans; also from determination of disulphides by reduction with Zn/acetic acid	+ $AgNO_3$; 1 min shaking	Unused titrated with SCN^-	65
HCHO in presence acetaldehyde	+ $AgNO_3/NH_4OH$ reagent of ref. 39, giving $HCOO^-$	$HCOO^-$ determined with $HgCl_2$/excess $Ba(OH)_2$ and back titration of unused OH^-	66
Lower alkyl iodides from determination of alkoxyl groups by reaction with HI	Absorbed in $AgNO_3$/ alcohol giving $AgI.AgNO_3$ precipitate	+ HNO_3, boiled and back titrated with SCN^-	67
Mercaptans in refinery caustic scrubbing solutions	+ $AgNO_3$	Unused Ag(I) titrated with SCN^-	68
Mercaptans in gasoline, naphtha, etc.	Method of ref. 27		69
Theophylline	Neutralized solution + $AgNO_3$, giving HNO_3	Titrated with NaOH to phenolphthalein	70

Materials titrated	Reagent and reaction conditions	Subsequent treatment and final titration stage	Ref.
Carboxyl groups in cellulose	+ Ag *o*-nitrophenate; 24–72 h/room temp.	Unused Ag(I) titrated with SCN^-	71
Carboxyl groups in modified starches	+ Ag_2O/*o*-nitrophenol/ water; 18 h/room temp.	Ag(I) in supernatant liquid titrated with SCN^- after addition of HNO_3	72
Hypoxanthine	In water, + Na picrate + HNO_3 + $AgNO_3$; 5 min/100°, giving an insoluble argentipicrate	Dissolved in HNO_3 and titrated with SCN^-	73
Sodium diethyl-barbiturate	+ $AgNO_3$. Shaken at room temp., giving insoluble Ag derivative	Filtered and unused Ag(I) in filtrate titrated with SCN^-	74
Ethylacetylene from determination of 1-butene by bromination and treatment with C_2H_5OK	+ $AgNO_3/NH_4OH$, giving insoluble Ag acetylide	Filtered and unused Ag(I) titrated with SCN^-	75
Theobromine	Method of ref. 28		76
Mercaptans in natural gas	+ $AgNO_3$, giving Ag_2S	+ NaCl excess and back titrated with $AgNO_3$	77
Theobromine, theophylline	Neutralized solution + $AgNO_3$, giving HNO_3	Titrated with NaOH to phenol red or bromothymol blue respectively	78
Sulphapyridine	+ $AgNO_3$, giving insoluble derivative	Heated nearly to boiling, filtered and unused Ag(I) titrated with SCN^- after acidification with HNO_3	79
Dicyanodiamide	+ $AgNO_3$/picric acid, giving the complex $C_6H_2(NO_2)_3OAg.C_2H_4N_4$	Determined gravimetrically or dissolved in HNO_3 and titrated the Ag(I) with SCN^-	80
Mercaptans in gasoline	+ Ag_2SO_4, giving H_2SO_4	Titrated with alkali; also unused Ag(I) determined with SCN^-	81
Ethyl or isopropyl iodide from determination of ethylene or propylene glycol ethers or esters by reaction with HI	Carried into $AgNO_3$/ ethanol	Unused Ag(I) titrated with SCN^-	82

Materials titrated	Reagent and reaction conditions	Subsequent treatment and final titration stage	Ref.
Adduct of chloromaleic anhydride with conjugated olefines in determination of latter	+ $AgNO_3$; 1 h reflux	Filtered and unused Ag(I) titrated with SCN^-	83
Sodium *N*-acetyl-2-hydroxyarsanilate ('Arsonine')	Neutral solution + $AgNO_3$, giving insoluble product	Filtered and unused Ag(I) in filtrate titrated with SCN^-	84
4-Propyl-2-thiouracil	In acetone, + $AgNO_3$/water, giving HNO_3	Titrated with NaOH to bromothymol blue	85
Nicotinamide	+ $AgNO_3$ giving an insoluble complex; 20 min boiling, then 30–40 min/room temp.	Filtered, filtrate acidified with HNO_3 and titrated with SCN^-	86
Barbiturates	+ $AgNO_3$ + Na acetate + $CaCO_3$; 2–3 min boiling, giving insoluble Ag derivatives	Filtered and unused Ag(I) titrated in filtrate with SCN^- after adding HNO_3	87
Thiamine (vitamin B_1)	+ $AgNO_3/HNO_3$; 20 min/room temp., giving AgCl	Unused Ag(I) titrated with SCN^-	88
Carboxyl groups in cellulose and oxidized cellulose	+ Ag_2O/*o*-nitrophenol; 18 h/room temp.	Unreacted Ag(I) titrated with SCN^-	89
Aminophylline in medicinal preparations	+ $AgNO_3/NH_4OH$, giving insoluble Ag derivative	Dissolved in HNO_3 and Ag(I) titrated with SCN^-	90
Theobromine in cocoa materials	At pH 6·4, + $AgNO_3$, giving HNO_3	Titrated with NaOH potentiometrically	91
Succinic acid in biological nutrient media	Neutral extract + $AgNO_3$ + ethanol; 2 h/room temp. in dark	Filtered and unused Ag(I) in filtrate titrated with SCN^-	92
Ethyl and vinyl acetylenes in C_4 hydrocarbon gases	Passed into $AgNO_3$/alcohol	+ water and titrated with NaOH to methyl red/methylene blue	93
Theobromine	Neutral solution + $AgNO_3$	Titrated with alkali	94
Sodium *p*-amino-salicylate	In water, + $AgNO_3$, giving insoluble salt	Filtered and unused Ag(I) titrated in filtrate with SCN^-	95

Materials titrated	Reagent and reaction conditions	Subsequent treatment and final titration stage	Ref.
α,α'-Dipyridyl; *o*-phenanthroline	+ excess $AgNO_3$ + $S_2O_8^{2-}$ giving $[Ag(Base)_2]S_2O_8^{2-}$ precipitates containing Ag(II)	Filtered and titrated Ag(I) in filtrate with SCN^-; or reduced precipitate with SO_2, added HNO_3 and titrated with SCN^-	96
Ethyl iodide from reaction of HI with hydroxyethylcellulose	Method of ref. 82		97
Acetylenes with a free H atom	In water or ethanol + C_6H_5COOAg suspension. At least 12 min shaking/room temp., giving benzoic acid	Filtered and titrated with NaOH to phenolphthalein	98
Aldehydes in presence of ketones	+ Ag_2O + water or water/dioxan; 1 h/*ca* 60° with shaking at times, giving acids	+ excess NaOH, filtered and filtrate back titrated with HCl to phenolphthalein	99
Aldehydes	In water or 50% iso-propanol passed through column of Ag_2O, giving Ag salts of corresponding carboxylic acids	Eluate titrated with SCN^-	100
Propylthiouracil	Neutralized solution + $AgNO_3$, giving HNO_3	Titrated with NaOH to bromothymol blue	101
Aldehydes in presence of ketones	+ Ag_2O/alkali, converting to acids	Carbonyl groups determined with hydroxylamine before and after treatment with the Ag_2O (see Hydroxylamine, ref. 95)	102
Acetylenic alcohols	+ $AgNO_3/NH_4OH$	Unused Ag(I) titrated with SCN^- or precipitate dissolved in HNO_3 and Ag(I) likewise titrated	103
Sodium citrate	In water/acetone, + $AgNO_3$, giving insoluble Ag citrate. Boiled and left 1 min	Filtered and Ag(I) in filtrate titrated with SCN^-	104
α-Naphthylthiourea	+ $AgNO_3/NH_4OH$, giving Ag_2S	Unused Ag(I) titrated with SCN^-	105
Pyridine-2-aldehyde	+ $AgNO_3$/NaOH/ $MgSO_4$ as in method of ref. 31	Unused Ag_2O dissolved in H_2SO_4 and titrated with I^-	106

Materials titrated	Reagent and reaction conditions	Subsequent treatment and final titration stage	Ref.
Many organic S-containing compounds, e.g. mercaptans, xanthates, thiocyanates, thiosemicarbazones, methylthiouracil	In ethanol + NaOH + $AgNO_3$ + NH_4OH in some cases, giving Ag_2S	Filtered, HNO_3 added and Ag(I) titrated with SCN^-	107
p-Acetylaminobenzaldehyde thiosemicarbazone	+ $AgNO_3$; 10–15 min boiling, giving Ag_2S	Dissolved in HNO_3 and titrated with SCN^-	108
Vinylacetylene in chloroprene	+ $AgNO_3$/ethanol/excess NH_4OH. Shaken a few min	Unused NH_4OH titrated with HCl to methyl orange	109
Sodium methyl arsenate	+ $AgNO_3$, giving insoluble Ag salt	Filtered and unused Ag(I) titrated with SCN^-	110
Betaine reineckate from determination of betaine	+ $AgNO_3$, giving insoluble Ag reineckate + betaine nitrate	Filtered and titrated with NaOH to methyl red	111
Acetylenes in butadiene	Passed into $AgNO_3$/alcohol	Titrated with NaOH to methyl red/methylene blue	112
—C≡CH group in acetylenic amines	In ethanol, + $AgNO_3$/ethanol/ethylenediamine	Titrated with NaOH to thymolphthalein	113
Methantheline bromide (2-diethylaminoethyl-9-xanthenecarboxylate methobromide)	+ $AgNO_3$/HNO_3	Unused Ag(I) titrated with SCN^-	114
Ethyl and vinyl acetylenes in butadiene and C_4 hydrocarbon fractions	Passed through $AgNO_3$/98% methanol	Titrated progressively with NaOH/methanol, to methyl red/methylene blue; original acetylenes liberated from the Ag derivatives by adding KBr, and determined bromometrically (to determine each) (see Bromine reagents, ref. 346)	115
Isoniazid	+ $AgNO_3$/NH_4OH; 2 min/50°, then 15 min/room temp., giving Ag, N_2 and isonicotinic acid	Filtered and Ag(I) in filtrate titrated with SCN^-	116

Materials titrated	Reagent and reaction conditions	Subsequent treatment and final titration stage	Ref.
Sodium *p*-amino-salicylate	In water, + $AgNO_3$ + ethanol. Shaken a few min	Filtered and unused Ag(I) titrated with SCN^-	117
Theobromine in cocoa	Neutralized solution + $AgNO_3$	Titrated with NaOH to pH 7·4	118
Thiourea	+ $AgBr/NH_4OH$/ water, giving Ag_2S and liberating Br^-	Titrated coulometrically with Ag(I) to a potentiometric end-point	119
Unused tetraphenyl-borate from determination of potassium by precipitation	+ $AgNO_3$	Unused Ag(I) titrated with SCN^-	120
Thiobarbituric acid derivatives	+ $AgNO_3/NH_4OH$, giving Ag_2S; 20 min/100°	Dissolved in HNO_3 and Ag(I) titrated with SCN^-	121
Methyl mercaptan from determination of methyl disulphide by reduction with Zn/acetic acid	+ $AgNO_3$	Unused titrated with SCN^-	122
Aldehydes	+ $AgNO_3/NaOH/$ NH_4OH. Shaken, left 5–120 min/room temp.	Unused Ag(I) titrated potentiometrically with I^-	123
Theophylline in presence of theobromine	In NH_4OH, + $AgNO_3$; 30 min/100°, giving the mono-silver derivative	Filtered and unused Ag(I) titrated with SCN^-	124
Aminophylline in tablets with sodium phenobarbital	In NH_4OH, + $AgNO_3$; 15 min/100°	Precipitate dissolved in HNO_3 and titrated with SCN^-	125
Thiofalicaines (β-piperi-dinoethyl alkylthio-*o*-cresol ketone hydro-chlorides (alkyl = n-propyl and isoamyl)	In water, + a little HNO_3 + $AgNO_3$	Unused Ag(I) titrated with with SCN^-	126
Cyanamide	+ $AgNO_3$/alkali/ NH_4OH; 5 min shaking	Filtered, precipitate dissolved in HNO_3 and titrated with SCN^-	127

Materials titrated	Reagent and reaction conditions	Subsequent treatment and final titration stage	Ref.
Ca malate, fumarate and succinate; also last-named alone after oxidation of the others with MnO_4^-	In ethanol/water, + $AgNO_3$, giving insoluble Ag salts	Unused Ag(I) titrated with SCN^-	128
Maleic hydrazide	+ Na acetate + $AgNO_3$	Filtered, filtrate acidified with HNO_3 and titrated with SCN^-	129
Tetraphenyl borates of potassium and alkaloids from their determination by precipitation; also unused $(C_6H_5)_4B^-$ after filtration	Solution in acetone + water + $AgNO_3$ + a little ether	Unused titrated with SCN^-	130
Aldehydes in presence of ketones; also from determination of acetals by acid hydrolysis	+ $AgNO_3$ + NaOH; 15 min shaking/room temp.; then + more NaOH and 10 more min	+ H_2SO_4, filtered from Ag metal and unused Ag(I) titrated with SCN^-	131
Acetylenic groups, $—C\equiv CH$	+ $AgNO_3$ or $AgClO_4$/ water	Titrated with alkali to methyl purple	132
Sodium *p*-amino-salicylate	+ 2-fold excess $AgNO_3$, giving insoluble Ag salt; 10 min/room temp.	Unused Ag(I) titrated with SCN^-	133
Mercaptans from determination of disulphides by reduction with Zn/acetic acid	Passed into $AgNO_3$	Unused Ag(I) titrated with SCN^-	134
Gaseous mercaptans	+ $AgNO_3$ + acetone/ $CdSO_4$ (to remove H_2S)	Washed out with acetone, NH_4OH/NH_4NO_3 added and titrated with dodecylmercaptan potentiometrically	135
Mercaptans in gases	Passed into $AgNO_3$	Unused titrated with SCN^-	136
Thiobenzophenone; xanthenethione	Hot solution in ethanol + $AgNO_3$/ethanol; 5–10 min, giving Ag_2S; $Ar_2CS + 2\,Ag^+ + H_2O \rightarrow Ar_2CO + Ag_2S + 2\,H^+$	Filtered and unused Ag(I) titrated with SCN^-	137
Sulphamethylthiazole ('Ultraseptyl') in presence of alkaloid salts	+ NH_4OH + $AgNO_3$; 30 min/room temp., giving insoluble derivative	Dissolved in HNO_3 and Ag(I) titrated with SCN^-	138

Materials titrated	Reagent and reaction conditions	Subsequent treatment and final titration stage	Ref.
5,5-Dialkylthio-barbituric acids	+ $AgNO_3/NH_4OH$ giving insoluble salt	Filtered and unused Ag(I) titrated with SCN^- after acidification with H_2SO_4	139
5-Sulphanilylamino-3,4-dimethylisoxazole ('Gantrisin')	In water/ethanol + borax + $AgNO_3$, giving precipitate	Filtered, HNO_3 added and unused Ag(I) titrated with SCN^-	140
6-Mercaptopurine	+ $AgNO_3/NH_4OH$, giving insoluble derivative	Filtered, HNO_3 added and unused Ag(I) titrated with SCN^-	141
Phthalylsulphathiazole	In NH_4OH, + $AgNO_3$; 15 min shaking, then tartaric acid added, shaken and left 1 h. Gives mono-Ag derivative	Filtered and unused Ag(I) titrated with SCN^-	142
Acetylene in presence of acetaldehyde	Passed into $AgNO_3$, giving HNO_3	Unused Ag(I) precipitated with Cl^- and HNO_3 titrated with NaOH to methyl red	143
Methyl pentynol	In ethanol, + $AgNO_3/NH_4OH$; 6–24 h/room temp., giving insoluble Ag derivative	Filtered, HNO_3 added and unused Ag(I) titrated with SCN^-	144
Ethyl iodide from determination of hydroxyethyl groups in low substituted starch ethers, by reaction with HI	Passed into $AgNO_3$/ethanol	Unused Ag(I) titrated with SCN^-	145
α-Glycols, α-diketones, polyhydroxy compounds	In water, + $AgNO_3/HIO_4$; 10 min–24 h/room temp., giving $AgIO_3$ precipitate) (see also Periodate and periodic acid, ref. 82)	Filtered and unused Ag(I) titrated with SCN^-	146
α-Naphthylthiourea	+ $AgNO_3$, giving Ag_2S and HNO_3 $C_{10}H_7NHCSNH_2 + 2\,AgNO_3 + H_2O \rightarrow C_{10}H_7NHCONH_2 + Ag_2S + 2\,HNO_3$	Unused Ag(I) precipitated with Cl^- and HNO_3 titrated with alkali	147
Acetylene	+ $AgNO_3$/acetate buffer, pH 4–5. Not less than 10 min/room temp.	Unused Ag(I) titrated with HCl potentiometrically	148

Materials titrated	Reagent and reaction conditions	Subsequent treatment and final titration stage	Ref.
Theophylline	+ $AgNO_3$ + NH_4OH/ NH_4NO_3; 15 min boiling in dark	Unused Ag(I) titrated with SCN^-	149
Iodoform from determination of 'Warfarin' by reaction with iodine/ alkali	In ethanol, + $AgNO_3$/ HNO_3; 2–3 h/room temp.	Unused Ag(I) titrated with SCN^-	150
Tetraphenylborates of alkaloids from their determination by precipitation with $NaB(C_6H_5)_4$;	Solution in acetone, + $AgNO_3$, giving precipitate of $AgB(C_6H_5)_4$	Unused Ag(I) titrated with SCN^-	151
also unused $NaB(C_6H_5)_4$ from this precipitation	+ $AgNO_3$	unused Ag(I) titrated with SCN^-	
Extract in CS_2 of Ni salt of dithiocarbamate of hexamethyleneimine in its determination by reaction with CS_2/Ni reagent	+ $AgNO_3$/NH_4OH, giving water-insoluble Ag dithiocarbamate	Aqueous layer separated and liberated Ni(II) titrated with EDTA to murexide	152
Lead tetraethyl in ethyl fluid	+ $AgNO_3$/HNO_3/ methanol	Unused Ag(I) titrated with SCN^-	153
Sulphonium iodides from determination of sulphides by reaction with CH_3I	+ $AgNO_3$, giving AgI	Unused Ag(I) titrated with SCN^-	154
Aldehydes in shale oil	+ Ag(I) reagent, giving acids	Unused Ag(I) precipitated with Cl^- and acid titrated with diethylamine/dioxan/water	155
2-Phenylindane-1,3-dione	+ $AgNO_3$, giving insoluble Ag derivative	Unused Ag(I) titrated with SCN^- potentiometrically	156
Acetylene	+ neutral $AgNO_3$/ acetone	Liberated HNO_3 titrated with alkali to methyl red	157
Acetylenes (including alcohols, esters, ethers, halides and heterocyclics)	+ $AgNO_3$/pyridine	Titrated with NaOH/ methanol to thymolphthalein	158
2-Acetamido-1,3,4-thiadiazole-5-sulphonamide ('Acetazolamide')	+ $AgNO_3$/NH_4OH; 5 min/100°, giving precipitate of Ag derivative	Filtered and Ag(I) in filtrate titrated with SCN^-	159

Materials titrated	Reagent and reaction conditions	Subsequent treatment and final titration stage	Ref.
5-Hydroxymethyl-4-methyluracil ('Pentoxyl')	3/4 neutralized with NaOH, then + $AgNO_3$ + solid Na oxalate	Titrated with NaOH potentiometrically or to phenolphthalein	160
Mercaptans in presence of CS_2 in hydrocarbon mixtures	+ $AgNO_3$; CS_2 blown out in nitrogen current	Back titrated with dodecylmercaptan/isopropanol	161
Acetylenes	In methanol, + $AgClO_4$/methanol	Liberated $HClO_4$ titrated with 'tris' to thymol blue/alphazurine	162
HCHO in presence of hexamine	+ $AgNO_3$ + NaOH + NH_4OH + sample; 5 min/room temp.	Back titrated with KI potentiometrically	163
Tetramethylthiuram disulphide	In dioxan, + $AgNO_3$; 20 min/50–70°	Filtered and unused Ag(I) in filtrate titrated with SCN^-	164
Sulphathiazole; methylsulphathiazole	In ethanol, + $AgNO_3$ giving precipitate of Ag derivative	Unused Ag(I) in filtrate titrated with SCN^-	165
Reaction products from determination of tolbutamide by treatment with alkali	Neutralized solution (with acetic acid) from alkali treatment, + $AgNO_3$; 3 min shaking, giving precipitate	Filtered and Ag(I) in filtrate titrated with SCN^-	166
Thiosinamine from determination of allyl isothiocyanate by reaction with ammonia	+ $AgNO_3/NH_4NO_3$; 5 min shaking, giving Ag_2S	Filtered, HNO_3 added to filtrate and unused Ag(I) titrated with SCN^-	167
Xanthates	+ Na acetate + $AgNO_3$; boiled, giving first Ag xanthate, then Ag_2S	Unreacted Ag(I) titrated with thioacetamide potentiometrically	168
3-Semicarbazidobenzamide ('Cryogenine')	In water, + $AgNO_3$	Filtered and unreacted Ag(I) in filtrate titrated with SCN^-	169
6-(4-Carboxybutylthio)-purine	In dilute HNO_3 + $AgNO_3$; stirred giving Ag derivative precipitate	Filtered, Ag(I) in filtrate titrated with SCN^-	170
Ethyl iodide from determination of $—OCH_2CH_2OH$ groups in glycol ethers by reaction with HI	Passed into $AgNO_3$/acetic acid	Back titrated with KI with starch/iodine indicator (gives blue only when I^- present in solution)	171

Materials titrated	Reagent and reaction conditions	Subsequent treatment and final titration stage	Ref.
Piperazonium adipate	In water, + $AgNO_3$. Cooled to 2°, giving precipitate of disilver adipate	Filtered and unused Ag(I) titrated with SCN^-	172
Saccharine	+ $AgNO_3$ at pH below 6, giving precipitate of Ag derivative	Filtered and Ag(I) in filtrate titrated with SCN^-	173
Acetylenes	Compared two silver methods (using $AgNO_3$ and Ag benzoate) with a mercury method		174
Nordihydroguaiaretic acid in lard	Extract in methanol, + $AgNO_3$ + Na acetate; 10 min reflux, giving metallic Ag	Filtered, Ag metal dissolved in HNO_3, NH_4OH/NH_4Cl + $K_2Ni(CN)_4$ + excess EDTA added and back titrated with $ZnSO_4$ to eriochrome black T	175
Butylhydroxyanisole (antioxidant) in pig fat	Heated 15 min with $AgNO_3$ reagent, giving precipitate of metallic Ag	Ag determined by technique of ref. 175	176
Vinylacetylene	+ $AgNO_3/NH_4OH$	Filtered, filtrate acidified and unreacted Ag(I) titrated with SCN^-	177
Citrate	+ $AgNO_3$/15–20% ethanol, giving precipitate of Ag citrate	Filtered and Ag(I) in filtrate back titrated with SCN^-	178
2-Benzylbenzimidazole hydrochloride ('Dibazol') in presence of papaverine hydrochloride	+ ethanol + NH_4OH + $AgNO_3$; 10–15 min, giving precipitate of Ag derivative	Filtered and unreacted Ag(I) titrated with SCN^-	179
Acetaldehyde; also from determination of paraldehyde by depolymerization with H_2SO_4	+ $AgNO_3/NaOH/NH_4OH$; 15 min/room temp., giving Ag metal	Unused Ag(I) titrated with KI potentiometrically or with SCN^- after filtration and addition of HNO_3	180
Acetaldehyde in presence of acetone	Method of ref. 180		181
Succinic acid in sweet wines (after preliminary separation via ion exchangers)	+ $AgNO_3$ at pH 6·7, giving Ag succinate	Filtered and Ag(I) in filtrate back titrated with SCN^-	182

Materials titrated	Reagent and reaction conditions	Subsequent treatment and final titration stage	Ref.
Acetylenes	In methanol, + $AgClO_4$ in dry methanol	Liberated $HClO_4$ titrated with 'tris' to C.I. acid yellow 24 (martius yellow)	183
	(micro-adaptation of method of ref. 162)		
Thiosinamine from determination of allyl isothiocyanate by reaction with ammonia	+ $AgNO_3$; 1 h/80°	Filtered and unused Ag(I) in filtrate titrated with SCN^-	184
Tetraethylammonium bromide in presence of hydrobromides of volatile amines	+ Ag_2O; 5 min, then centrifuged, volatile amines boiled out	Titrated with HCl to methyl red	185
Mercaptans	In pyridine, water, ethanol or acetone, + $AgNO_3$/pyridine; 15 min/room temp.	Titrated with alkali potentiometrically or to thymol blue or thymolphthalein	186
Saturated or unsaturated mercaptans	+ pyridine + $AgNO_3$/water; 5 min/room temp.	+ water and titrated with NaOH to phenolphthalein	187
Heptachlor in the commercial technical product	+ $AgNO_3$/acetic acid. Boiled 3 h, giving AgCl	+ HNO_3 and the unreacted Ag(I) titrated with SCN^-	188
Cyanamide after paper chromatographic separation	Sprayed with $AgNO_3$ reagent, giving Ag derivative	Dissolved in HNO_3 and Ag(I) titrated coulometrically	189
Barbiturates	In Na_2CO_3 + pyridine + $AgNO_3$, giving precipitate	Precipitate dissolved in HNO_3 and titrated with SCN^-	190
Theobromine in presence of titrated (with alkali) luminal	Neutral (to thymol blue) solution from previous titration, + excess $AgNO_3$	Titrated with NaOH to blue, giving sum of theobromine + luminal	191
Antioxydants like octyl gallate, dodecyl gallate, butylhydroxytoluene, ascorbyl palmitate	Extract, + $AgNO_3$ + Na acetate; refluxed 30 min, giving metallic Ag	Ag determined by technique of ref. 175	192
Mercaptobenzthiazole in rubber	Extract in ethanol, + $AgNO_3$	Unused Ag(I) titrated with NaCl	193

Materials titrated	Reagent and reaction conditions	Subsequent treatment and final titration stage	Ref.
Thiophenol in tar acids	+ methenol/water + excess $AgNO_3$ containing ^{110}Ag radioactive isotope	Back titrated radiometrically with SCN^-	194
Na salt of 5,5-diphenylhydantoin ('hydantional')	+ Ag^+/pyridine reagent, giving precipitate of complex	Ag in complex titrated with SCN^-	195
Sulphadimidine (sulphamethazine), *N'*-(4,6-dimethyl-2-pyrimidinyl) sulphanilamide.	In slightly ammoniacal solution, + Ag^+ reagent, giving precipitate of Ag derivative	Precipitate dissolved in HNO_3 and titrated with SCN^-	196
Some sulphonamides, e.g. sulphaphenazole	+ excess Ag^+ reagent, giving precipitate of Ag derivative	Filtered and unreacted Ag^+ titrated with SCN^- potentiometrically or to Fe(III)	197
α-Ethylisonicotinic acid thioamide	In methanol, + excess aqueous $AgNO_3$; 10 min, giving nitrile and Ag_2S and HNO_3, $R{-}CSNH_2 + 2\,AgNO_3 \rightarrow RCN + Ag_2S + 2\,HNO_3$	+ excess NaCl, filtered and titrated with NaOH to phenolphthalein	198 199
6-Mercaptopurine	In water, + NH_4OH + $AgNO_3$. Several min shaking, giving disilver derivative	Filtered, filtrate + $K_2Ni(CN)_4$, reacting with the Ag(I) to liberate Ni(II); + NH_4OH and titrated this Ni(II) with EDTA to murexide	200
Sulphonamides	In ethanol/water at 65°, + $AgNO_3$; 30 min/100°	Filtered and Ag(I) determined as in method of ref. 200	201
Heptachlor	Extract in isopropanol, + $AgNO_3$/acetic acid, giving AgCl (with one Cl atom only); 1 h reflux	Unreacted Ag(I) titrated with NaCl potentiometrically	202
Aldehydes in mixtures with H_2O_2 and organic peroxides	Method of ref. 100		203
Methylpentynol	Aspirated into $AgNO_3$/NH_4OH	Back titrated with KI potentiometrically	204

Materials titrated	Reagent and reaction conditions	Subsequent treatment and final titration stage	Ref.
Thiosemicarbazone of *p*-isopropylbenzaldehyde ('Cutisone')	Shaken in alcoholic $AgNO_3$ solution, giving precipitate of Ag derivative	Filtered and filtrate titrated with SCN^- to Fe(III)	205
Mercapto groups in homogenates from plant tissues	+ excess $AgNO_3$, giving precipitate of mercaptides	Unreacted Ag^+ titrated amperometrically with glutathione	206
Mercaptans from reduction with $LiAlH_4$ of disulphides in analysis of mixtures of mono-, di- and polysulphides	Distilled into $AgNo_3$/water/pyridine at $-10°$ (to coagulate the mercaptides)	+ water and titrated with NaOH to phenolphthalein; or filtered and titrated filtrate	207
Mercapto groups in sulphur-containing soid fuels	+ excess $AgNO_3$; shaken 100 h	Back titrated with KCl potentiometrically	208
Aldehydes in presence of acids, acetals and ketones (e.g. HCHO), other lower aliphatic aldehydes, benzaldehyde, crotonaldehyde and *p*-chlorobenzaldehyde	Aliquot in ethanol, + Ag_2O/*tert*-butylamine reagent; up to 2 h/room temp. (Control)	Filtered, filtrate + HNO_3 and excess $AgNO_3$ titrated with SCN^- to Fe(III)	209

References

1. Tollens, B., *Ber.* **15**, 1829 (1882).
2. Kunze, W. E., *Z. anal. Chem.* **33**, 27 (1894).
3. Denigès, G., *Ann. chim. phys.* (7) **6**, 427 (1895).
4. Ruoss, *Z. anal. Chem.* **35**, 153 (1896).
5. Chavastelon, R., *Compt. rend.* **124**, 1364 (1897); **125**, 246 (1897).
6. Denigès, G., *J. pharm. et chim.* (6) **5**, 50 (1897).
7. Bordas, F., Joulin, and v. Raczkowsky, S., *J. pharm. chim.* (6) **7**, 407 (1898).
8. Gadamer, J., *Arch. Pharm.* **237**, 110, 372 (1899).
9. Cormack, W., *J. Chem. Soc.* **77**, 990 (1900).
10. Folin, O. and Shaffer, P. A., *Z. physiol. Chem.* **32**, 552 (1901).
11. Falières, *J. pharm. et chim.* (6) **15**, 466 (1902).
12. Perotti, G., *Gazz. chim. ital.* **35**, II 228 (1905).
13. Kuntze, M., *Arch. Pharm.* **246**, 58 (1908).

14. Braun, K., *Seifenfabrikant* 1140 (1909).
15. Gane, E. H. and Webster, M. H., *Pharm. J.* (4) **28**, 555 (1909).
16. Kretschmer, E., *Biochem. Z.* **50**, 223 (1913).
17. Grube, G. and Krüger, J., *Z. angew. Chem.* **27**, 326 (1914).
18. Ross, W. H. and Trumbull, H. L., *J. Am. Chem. Soc.* **41**, 1180 (1919).
19. Harger, R. N., *Ind. Eng. Chem.* **12**, 1107 (1920).
20. Willstätter, R. and Maschmann, E., *Ber.* **53**, 939 (1920).
21. Stepp, W. and Fricke, R., *Z. physiol. Chem.* **116**, 293 (1921); **118**, 241 (1922).
22. Nanussi, A., *Giorn. Chim. Ind. Appl.* **5**, 168 (1923).
23. Mach, F. and Herrmann, R., *Z. anal. Chem.* **63**, 417 (1924).
24. Müller, E. and Löw, W., *Z. anal. Chem.* **64**, 297 (1924).
25. Browne, A. W. and Smith, G. B. L., *J. Am. Chem. Soc.* **47**, 2698 (1925).
26. Hill, A. J. and Tyson, F., *J. Am. Chem. Soc.* **50**, 172 (1928).
27. Borgstrom, P. and Reid, E. E., *Ind. Eng. Chem., Anal. Ed.* **1**, 186 (1929).
28. Boie, H., *Pharm. Ztg.* **75**, 968 (1930).
29. Krestinskii, V. and Kelbovska, M., *Ber.* **64**, 2371 (1931).
30. Kunke, W. F., *J. Assoc. Offic. Agr. Chem.* **14**, 370 (1931).
31. Ponndorf, W., *Ber.* **64**, 1913 (1931).
32. Rundle, A. S., *Coir tech.* **20**, 258 (1931).
33. van Giffen, H. J., *Pharm. Weekblad* **69**, 1321 (1932).
34. Goryainova, V. S., *Khim.-Farm. Prom.* **6**, 227 (1932).
35. Hegland, J. M. A., *Pharm. Weekblad* **69**, 1078 (1932).
36. Karjala, S. A. and McElvain, S. M., *J. Am. Chem. Soc.* **55**, 2966 (1933).
37. v. Miko, G., *Pharm. Monatsh.* **14**, 279 (1933).
38. v. Miko, G., *Pharm. Zentralhalle* **74**, 642 (1933).
39. Fialkov, A. and Shargorodski, S. D., *Mem. Inst. Chem., All-Ukrainian Acad. Sci.* **1**, 209 (1934).
40. Gros, R. and Pichon, G., *J. pharm. chim.* **19**, 249 (1934).
41. Ushakov, M. I. and Galanov, A. S., *Z. anal. Chem.* **99**, 185 (1934).
42. Makens, R. F., *J. Am. Chem. Soc.* **57**, 405 (1935).
43. Malisoff, W. M. and Anding, C. E., *Ind. Eng. Chem., Anal. Ed.* **7**, 86 (1935).
44. Novotný, D. F., *Collection Czechoslov. Chem. Communs.* **7**, 84 (1935).
45. Alekse'ev, S. V. and Zvyagina, S. I., *Sintet. Kauchuk* **5**, 19 (1936).
46. Hartner, F. and Schleiss, E., *Mikrochemie* **20**, 163 (1936).
47. Cuthill, R. and Atkins, C., *J. Soc. Chem. Ind., London* **56**, 5T (1937).
48. Stevens, A. N. and Wilson, D. T., *J. Am. Pharm. Assoc.* **26**, 314 (1937).
49. Heim, O., *Ind. Eng. Chem., Anal. Ed.* **10**, 431 (1938).
50. Rom, P., *Pharm. Monatsh.* **19**, 45 (1938).
51. Slotta, K. H. and Neisser, K., *Ber.* **71**, 1611 (1938).
52. Arhimo, A. A. and Laine, T., *Suomen Kemistilehti* **12B**, 18 (1939).
53. Figura, V., *Atti. accad. Lincei, Classe sci. fis. mat. nat.* **29**, 329 (1939).

54. Funck, E., *Süddeut. Apotheker-Ztg.* **79**, 622 (1939).
55. Ionescu-Matiu, A. and Popescu, A., *Bull. soc. chim. biol.* **21**, 264 (1939).
56. Kaganova, F. I. and Shul'man, A. A., *Farm. Zhur.* **12**, No. 3, 15 (1939).
57. Nifontova, M. V., *Org. Chem. Ind.* (*USSR*) **6**, 457 (1939).
58. Smolin, A. N., *Khim. Ref. Zhur.* (*Abstract*) **2**, No. 4, 79 (1939).
59. Williams, H. E., *J. Soc. Chem. Ind., London* **58**, 77 (1939).
60. Zil'berberg, A. I. and Fainshtein, B. B., *Ukrain. Gosudarst. Inst. Eksptl. Farm.* (*Kharkov*), *Konsul'tatsionnye Materialy* No. 8–9, 238 (1939).
61. Savchenko, A. Ya. and Mizuch, K. G., *Zavodskaya Lab.* **9**, 1101 (1940).
62. Smolin, A. N., *Uchenye Zapiski Moskov. Gosudarst. Pedagog. Inst.* **21**, No. 4, 125 (1940).
63. Striznevskii, I. I. and Chekhovich, M. D., *Zavodskaya Lab.* **9**, 1147 (1940).
64. Bell, C. W., *J. Am. Pharm. Assoc.* **30**, 240 (1941).
65. Bell, R. T. and Agruss, M. S., *Ind. Eng. Chem., Anal. Ed.* **13**, 297 (1941).
66. Bertolina, G., *Ann. chim. applicata* **31**, 294 (1941).
67. Bürger, K. and Baláž, F., *Angew. Chem.* **54**, 58 (1941).
68. Koons, R. D., *Refiner Natural Gasoline Mfr.* **20**, 393 (1941).
69. Schindler, H., Ayers, G. W. and Henderson, L. M., *Ind. Eng. Chem., Anal. Ed.* **13**, 326 (1941).
70. Schulek, E. and Rózsa, P., *Z. anal. Chem.* **122**, 112 (1941).
71. Sookne, A. M. and Harris, M., *J. Research Natl. Bur. Standards* **26**, 205 (1941).
72. Elizer, L. H., *Ind. Eng. Chem., Anal. Ed.* **14**, 635 (1942).
73. Hitchings, G. H., *J. Biol. Chem.* **143**, 43 (1942).
74. Kocsis, E. A. and Kovács, E., *Z. anal. Chem.* **124**, 40 (1942).
75. Russo, F., *Ann. chim. applicata* **32**, 216 (1942).
76. Kedvessey, G., *Ber. ungar. pharm. Ges.* **19**, 36 (1943).
77. Anon., *Amer. Gas J.* **162**, No. 6, 47, 60 (1945).
78. Reimers, F. and Gottlieb, K. R., *Dansk Tids. Farm.* **17**, 105 (1945).
79. Khromov-Borisov, N. V., Yurist, I. M. and Popova, L. P., *Farmatsiya* **9**, No. 1, 26 (1946).
80. Korinfskii, A. A., *Zavodskaya Lab.* **12**, 418 (1946).
81. Mapstone, G. E., *Australian Chem. Inst., J. and Proc.* **13**, 232 (1946).
82. Morgan, P. W., *Ind. Eng. Chem., Anal. Ed.* **18**, 500 (1946).
83. Putnam, S. T., Moss, M. L. and Hall, R. T., *Ind. Eng. Chem., Anal. Ed.* **18**, 628 (1946).
84. Albrand, L., *Ann. pharm. franç.* **5**, 56 (1947).
85. Canbäck, T., *Farm. Revy.* **29**, 465 (1947).
86. de Carvalho, R. R., *J. farm.* (*Lisbon*) **6**, 41 (1947).
87. Mangouri, H. A. and Milad, L., *Quart. J. Pharm. Pharmacol.* **20**, 109 (1947).
88. Sánchez, J. A., *Anales real acad. farm.* **13**, 377 (1947).

89. Davidson, G. F. and Nevell, T. P., *Textile Research J.* **39**, 75, 93 (1948).
90. Hilty, W. W. and Wilson, D. T., *J. Am. Pharm. Assoc., Sci. Ed.* **37**, 227 (1948).
91. Moores, R. G. and Campbell, H. A., *Anal. Chem.* **20**, 40 (1948).
92. Tasman, A. and Smith, L., *Rec. trav. chim.* **67**, 404 (1948).
93. Thomas, P. R., Donn, L. and Becker, H. C., *Anal. Chem.* **20**, 209 (1948).
94. Bell, C. W., *J. Am. Pharm. Assoc.* **38**, 391 (1949).
95. Matta, G. and Nunes, M. L., *Anais azevedos (Lisbon)* **1**, 112 (1949).
96. Cavicchi, G., *Ann. chim. (Rome)* **40**, 149 (1950).
97. Cohen, S. G. and Haas, H. C., *J. Am. Chem. Soc.* **72**, 3954 (1950).
98. Marszak, I. and Koulkes, M., *Bull. soc. chim. France* 364 (1950).
99. Mitchell, J. and Smith, D. M., *Anal. Chem.* **22**, 746 (1950).
100. Bailey, H. C. and Knox, J. H., *J. Chem. Soc.* 2741 (1951).
101. Berggren, A. and Kirsten, W., *Farm. Revy* **50**, 245 (1951).
102. Buchanan, R. H., *Australian J. Applied Sci.* **2**, 276 (1951).
103. Ichikizaki, L., Kindaichi, M. and Chinchun, Y., *J. Chem. Soc. Japan, Pure Chem. Sect.* **72**, 92 (1951).
104. Jeram, A. J. and Cooper, P., *Pharm. J.* **166**, 1180 (1951).
105. Losco, G. and Peri, C. A., *Chim. e ind. (Milan)* **33**, 557 (1951).
106. Mathes, W. and Sauermilch, W., *Ber.* **84**, 648 (1951).
107. Middeldorf, R., *Arzneimittelforsch.* **1**, 311 (1951).
108. Sandri, G., *Ann. chim. (Rome)* **41**, 135 (1951).
109. Strnad, F. and Klátil, M., *Chem. Listy* **45**, 220 (1951).
110. Suarez, L. R., *Anales asoc. quím. y farm., Uruguay* **51**, No. 2, 49 (1951).
111. Walker, H. G. and Erlandsen, R., *Anal. Chem.* **23**, 1309 (1951).
112. Hyzer, R. E., *Anal. Chem.* **24**, 1092 (1952).
113. Koulkes, M. and Marszak, I., *Bull. soc. chim. France* 556 (1952).
114. Matta, G. and Nunes, M. L., *Anais azevedos (Lisbon)* **4**, 161 (1952).
115. Robey, R. F., Hudson, B. E. and Wiese, H. K., *Anal. Chem.* **24**, 1080 (1952).
116. Sánchez, J. A., *Rev. asoc. bioquím. arg.* **17**, 324 (1952).
117. Boehm, T. and Horsch, G., *Pharmazie* **8**, 205 (1953).
118. Gerritsma, K. W. and Koers, J., *Analyst* **78**, 201 (1953).
119. Nakanishi, M. and Kobayishi, H., *Bull. Chem. Soc. Japan* **26**, 394 (1953).
120. Rüdorff, W. and Zannier, H., *Z. anal. Chem.* **140**, 1 (1953).
121. Sandri, G. and Lambardi, F., *Atti accad. sci. Ferrara* **30**, 27 (1953).
122. Segal, W. and Starkey, R. L., *Anal. Chem.* **25**, 1645 (1953).
123. Siggia, S. and Segal, E., *Anal. Chem.* **25**, 640 (1953).
124. Sina, A. and Khalek, M. A., *Proc. Pharm. Soc. Egypt, Sci. Ed.* **35**, No. 7, 49 (1953).
125. Bhattacharya, S. and Banerjee, S. C., *J. Proc. Inst. Chemists (India)* **26**, 33 (1954).

126. Bräuniger, H. and Spangenberg, K., *Pharmazie* **9**, 626 (1954).
127. Inaba, H. and Yanagisawa, D., *Japan Analyst* **3**, 196 (1954).
128. Lemjakov, N., *Anal. Chem.* **26**, 1227 (1954).
129. Milad, L. and El-Shehat, M., *Proc. Pharm. Soc. Egypt, Sci. Ed.* **36**, No. 6, 43 (1954).
130. Rüdorff, W. and Zannier, H., *Angew. Chem.* **66**, 638 (1954).
131. Siegel, H. and Weiss, F. T., *Anal. Chem.* **26**, 917 (1954).
132. Barnes, L. and Molinari, L. J., *Anal. Chem.* **27**, 1025 (1955).
133. Baron, M. S., *Aptechnoe Delo* **4**, No. 5, 17 (1955).
134. Coope, J. A. R. and Maingot, G. J., *Anal. Chem.* **27**, 1478 (1955).
135. Grimes, M. D., Puckett, J. E., Newby, B. J. and Heinrich, B. J., *Anal. Chem.* **27**, 152 (1955).
136. Hammer, C. G. B., *Svensk Kem. Tidskr.* **67**, 307 (1955).
137. Moreau, R. C., *Bull. soc. chim. France* 569 (1955).
138. Szabolcs, F., *Acta Pharm. Hung.* **25**, 17 (1955).
139. Wojahn, H. and Wempe, E., *Arch. Pharm.* **288**, 1 (1955).
140. Blažek, J. and Stejskal, Z., *Československ. Farm.* **5**, 27 (1956).
141. Blažek, J. and Stejskal, Z., *Československ. Farm.* **5**, 29 (1956).
142. Boehm, T. and Freudenberg, R., *Pharmazie* **11**, 231 (1956).
143. Frehden, O. and Brincoveanu, I., *Rev. Chim. (Bucharest)* **7**, 433 (1956).
144. Leal, M. and Dinez, M. H., *Rev. port. farm.* **6**, 14 (1956).
145. Lortz, H. J., *Anal. Chem.* **28**, 892 (1956).
146. Pesez, M. *Bull. soc. chim. France* 148 (1956).
147. Prat, J., Colas, A. and André, H., *Phytial-Phytopharm.* **5**, 133 (1956).
148. Šingliar, M. and Smejkal, V., *Chem. Zvesti* **10**, 70 (1956).
149. Gallo, U., *Boll. chim. farm.* **96**, 458 (1957).
150. Kámen, K., *Chem. průmysl* **7**, 472 (1957).
151. Keller, W. and Weiss, F., *Pharmazie* **12**, 22 (1957).
152. Nebbia, L. and Guerrieri, F., *Chim. e ind. (Milan)* **39**, 672 (1957).
153. Tagliavini, G., *Chim. e ind. (Milan)* **39**, 902 (1957).
154. Aarna, A. Ya. and Silland, Kh. A., *Zhur. Anal. Khim.* **13**, 473 (1958).
155. Aarna, A. Ya. and Küsler, K. P., *Trudy Tallin. Politekh. Inst.* **A**, No. 153, 108 (1958).
156. Danek, A. and Pelczar, T., *Dissertationes Pharm. (Krakow)* **10**, 225 (1958).
157. Frehden, O. and Beclereanu, M., *Rev. chim. (Bucharest)* **9**, 333 (1958).
158. Miocque, M. and Gautier, J. A., *Bull. soc. chim. France* 467 (1958).
159. Parikh, P. M. and Mukherji, S. P., *Indian J. Pharm.* **20**, 179 (1958).
160. Perel'man, Ya. M. and Gurevich, I. Ya., *Aptechnoe Delo* **7**, No. 3, 11 (1958).
161. Romováček, J. and Bednar, J., *Paliva* **38**, No. 1, 9 (1958).
162. Barnes, L., *Anal. Chem.* **31**, 1405 (1959).
163. Bellen, Z. and Sekowska, B., *Chem. Anal. (Warsaw)* **4**, 25 (1959).

164. Li, M.-F. and Li, K.-Ch., *Chung Shan Ta Hsueh Hsueh Pao Tzu K'o Hsueh* No. 3, 26 (1959).
165. Macarovici, C. G. and Dorutiu, A., *Studia. Univ. Babes-Bolyai* Ser. 1, No. 2, 115 (1959).
166. Parikh, P. M. and Mukherji, S. P., *Indian J. Pharm.* **21**, 110 (1959).
167. Fürst, W. and Poethke, W., *Pharm. Zentralhalle* **99**, 674 (1960).
168. Gavrish, A. P., *Nauchn. Tr. Khar'kovsk. Gorn. Inst.* **7**, 265 (1960).
169. Grecu, I., *Farmacia (Bucharest)* **8**, 55 (1960).
170. Jančik, F., Kakáč, B. and Buděšinský, B., *Českoslov. Farm.* **9**, 329 (1960).
171. Kainz, G., *Mikrochim. Acta* 254 (1960).
172. Kékesi, T. and Tóth, Z., *Acta Pharm. Hung.* **30**, 265 (1960).
173. Parikh, P. M. and Mukherji, S. P., *Analyst* **85**, 25 (1960).
174. Prévost, S., Chodkiewicz, W., Cadiot, P. and Willemart, A., *Bull. soc. chim. France* 1742 (1960).
175. Sedláček, B., *Fette & Seifen, Anstrichmittel* **62**, 669 (1960).
176. Sedláček, B., *Fette & Seifen, Anstrichmittel* **62**, 1041 (1960).
177. Vítovec, J. and Sádek, M., *Collection Czechoslov, Chem. Communs.* **25**, 1972 (1960).
178. Bakács-Polgár, E., Kurcz-Csiky, I. and Láng, B., *Pharm. Zentralhalle* **100**, 513 (1961).
179. Baron, M. S. and Gurfinkel, I. I., *Aptechnoe Delo* **10**, No. 3, 32 (1961).
180. Bellen, Z. and Sękowska, B., *Chem. Anal. (Warsaw)* **6**, 69 (1961).
181. Bellen, Z. and Sękowska, B., *Chem. Anal. (Warsaw)* **6**, 201 (1961).
182. Dimotaki-Kourakou, V., *Ann. fals.* **54**, 70 (1961).
183. Gutterson, M. and Ma, Z. S., *Michrochem. J.* **5**, 601 (1961).
184. Kerzner, I. L. and Ershova, M. S., *Masloboino-Zhirovaya Prom.* **27**, No. 11, 41 (1961).
185. Láng, B., *Acta Pharm. Hung.* **31**, Suppl. 27 (1961); *Pharm. Zentralhalle* **100**, 271 (1961).
186. Pellerin, E. and Gautier, J. A., *Ann. pharm. franç.* **19**, 81 (1961).
187. Saville, B., *Analyst* **86**, 29 (1961).
188. Shogan, S. M., Vol'fson, L. G. and Efimenko, I. A., *Trudy Nauchn. Inst. po Udobr. i Insektofung.* No. 171, 49 (1961).
189. Yamada, T. and Sakai, Y., *J. Electrochem. Soc. Japan* **29**, 852 (1961).
190. Fürst, W., *Pharmazie* **16**, 24 (1961).
191. Mustafaev, M. M., *Uch. Zap. Pyatigorskii Gos. Farmatsevt. Inst.* **5**, 207 (1961).
192. Sedláček, B., *Fette & Seifen, Anstrichsmittel* **63**, 1053 (1961).
193. Gordon, B. E., Melamed, E. A. and Belova, N. A., *Kauchuk i Rezina* **21**, No. 8, 53 (1962).
194. Matsushima, I., *Koru Toru (Coal Tar, Japan)* **14**, 649 (1962).
195. Przyborowski, L., *Ann. Univ. Mariae Curie-Sklodowska, Lublin-Polonia, Sect.* D 17 25 (1962).

196. Szabolcs, E., *Acta Pharm. Hung.* **32**, 145 (1962).
197. Sztark, W., *Dissertationes Pharm.* **14**, 40, 41, 41, 197 (1962).
198. Vasiliev, R., Sisman, E. and Burnea, I., *Rev. Chim.* (*Bucharest*) **13**, 557 (1962).
199. Vasiliev, R., Sisman, E. and Burnea, I., *Pharmazie* **17**, 606 (1962).
200. Hennart, C., *Talanta* **9**, 97 (1962).
201. Hennart, C., *Chim. anal.* **44**, 7 (1962).
202. Mitchell, W. G. and Barthel, W. F., *J. Assoc. Offic. Agr. Chem.* **45**, 113 (1962).
203. Nettesheim, G., *Z. anal. Chem.* **191**, 45 (1962).
204. Adams, B. G., Allen, D. and Marley, E., *Nature* **197**, 83 (1963).
205. Huang, Ch-Sh., Wang, Hs., and Wang, L-L., *Yao Hsueh Hsueh Pao* **10**, 372 (1963).
206. Laurinavicius, R., *Lietuvos TSR Mokslu Akad. Darbai, Ser.* C 111 (1963).
207. Porter, M., Saville, B. and Watson, A. A., *J. Chem. Soc.* 346 (1963).
208. Prilezhaeva, E. N., Fedorovskaya, N. P., Miesserova, L. V., Domanina, O. N., and Khaskina, I. M., *Tr. Inst. Goryuch. Iskop., Akad. Nauk SSSR* **21**, 159 (1963).
209. Mayes, J. A., Kuchar, E. J. and Siggia, S., *Anal. Chem.* **36**, 934 (1964).

93. Sodamide

Hydroxyl compounds have been determined by reaction with sodamide, liberating ammonia which was subsequently titrated with acid;

$$ROH + NaNH_2 \rightarrow RONa + NH_3$$

The sensitivity of the reagent to water, with which it also yields ammonia, has militated against the use of the method. Only two examples are given here:

Materials titrated	Reagent and reaction conditions	Subsequent treatment and final titration stage	Ref.
Phenols	Benzene or xylene + $NaNH_2$; current of dry air passed until no further ammonia evolved; then + sample in dry benzene; 90 min reaction time	NH_3 absorbed in excess H_2SO_4 and back titrated with alkali to methyl orange	1
Tertiary alcohols (identification)	Heated with $NaNH_2$ in a Zeisel-type apparatus	NH_3 determined acidimetrically	2

References

1. Schryver, S., *J. Soc. Chem. Ind. (London)* **18**, 533 (1899).
2. Palfray, L., Sabetay, S. and Garry, M., *Bull. soc. chim. France* (5) **10**, 131 (1943).

94. Sodium (I)

A standard method for determination of —COOH groups in cellulose and starch materials, is by displacement of H^+ with Na^+ or Ca^{2+}, followed by titration of the acid thus liberated:

$$X—COOH + Na^+ \rightarrow X—COONa + H^+$$

Two examples are given of the use of NaCl or NaBr for this purpose:

Materials titrated	Reagent and reaction conditions	Subsequent treatment and final titration stage	Ref.
—COOH groups in cellulose	+ excess standard $NaHCO_3$ + NaCl (10 times the amount of $NaHCO_3$); 1 h/room temp.	Filtered and titrated with HCl to methyl red	1
—COOH groups in CrO_3 oxy-starches	+ NaBr 24 h/room temp.	Titrated with NaOH to pH of blanks	2

References

1. Wilson, K., *Svensk Papperstidn.* **51**, 45 (1948).
2. Ellington, A. C. and Purves, C. B., *Can. J. Chem.* **31**, 801 (1953).

95. Sulphides

Reagent. Sodium sulphide, hydrosulphide, polysulphide and even an example of an organic sulphide (diphenyl sulphide) are grouped together here.

Reactions and materials titrated. 1. Reduction, based on the reaction:

$$S^{2-} \rightarrow S + 2\,\epsilon$$

(with the organic sulphide, this may be written:

$$R_2S + O \rightarrow R_2S{\rightarrow}O)$$

Certain azo dyes (e.g. amaranth), thiuram disulphides, per-acids and halides like pentabromoacetone have been determined by methods based on this reduction:

$$RN{=}NR' + 2\,S^{2-} + 4\,H^+ \rightarrow RNH_2 + R'NH_2 + 2\,S$$

$$R_2N.CS.S.S.CS.NR_2 + S^{2-} \rightarrow 2\,R_2N.CS.S^- + S$$

$$X{-}Br + S^{2-} + H^+ \rightarrow X{-}H + Br^- + S$$

$$RCOOOH + (C_6H_5)_2S \rightarrow RCOOH + (C_6H_5)_2S{\rightarrow}O$$

2. Ion/ion combination, as in an older method for determination of acids, using Na hydrosulphide:

$$H^+ + HS^- \rightarrow H_2S$$

3. Other reactions involve the fission of C—Hg or of C—S links in the determination of organic mercury compounds to give HgS and that of organic thiocyanates to give SCN^-, respectively,

$$2\,R{-}SCN + S^{2-} \rightarrow R_2S + 2\,SCN^-$$

Subsequent treatment and final titration stage. (i) In only one case has unreacted S^{2-} been back titrated; *o*-hydroxymercuribenzoate was used.

(ii) Reaction products determined have included:

1. SCN^- or Br^-, titrated with Ag(I), usually by using excess and back titrating with SCN^-; Br^- was determined in one method by shaking with excess $AgIO_3$, which reacts to give the yet more insoluble AgBr,

$$Br^- + AgIO_3 \rightarrow AgBr + IO_3^-;$$

the iodate thus liberated was determined iodometrically.

2. Hg(II) from the organic mercury compounds, determined by titration with dithizone.

3. Dithiocarbamates were decomposed by acid into CS_2, then determined by reaction with alkali/alcohol to give xanthate; the latter was titrated with iodine.

4. H_2S from the ion/ion combination example, separated and titrated with iodine.

(iii) Unreacted components in the reaction mixture have been determined as the final stage, e.g. tartrazine after reduction of amaranth; and other per-compounds after removal of percarboxylic acids.

Examples

Materials titrated	Reagent and reaction conditions	Subsequent treatment and final titration stage	Ref.
Certain carboxylic acids and phenols (e.g. nitrophenols)	+ NaHS solution (from passing H_2S into NaOH); 1–5 min	H_2S absorbed in KOH, neutralized with acetic acid and titrated with iodine to starch	1
Amaranth + tartrazine	$(NH_4)_2S$ solution added until colour change from red to yellow	+ tartrate, boiled and tartrazine titrated with $TiCl_3$ (see Part I, Titanium (III), ref. 20)	2
Aromatic isothiocyanates	In ethanol, + Na_2S/alcohol; 15–90 min reflux giving SCN^-	+ water + H_2SO_4, boiled to expel H_2S; + excess $AgNO_3$, filtered AgSCN and titrated unused Ag(I) in filtrate with SCN^-	3
Pentabromoacetone, from determination of citric acid by reaction with Br^-/acid/MnO_4^-	Extract in petrol ether, + Na_2S/water	+ H_2SO_4, H_2S boiled out, HNO_3 + excess $AgNO_3$ ultimately added and unused Ag(I) back titrated with SCN^- to Fe(III) indicator	4
Pentabromoacetone, from determination of citric acid by reaction with Br^-/acid/MnO_4^-	Treated with Na_2S	Br^- ultimately determined with $AgNO_3$	5
Pentabromoacetone, from determination of citric acid by reaction with Br^-/H_2SO_4/HPO_3/MnO_4^-	Ether solution + 4% aqueous Na_2S	Br^- in aqueous layer determined by adding solid $AgIO_3$, filtering and titrating iodate in the filtrate (+ I^- + acid and titrated with thiosulphate)	6

Materials titrated	Reagent and reaction conditions	Subsequent treatment and final titration stage	Ref.
Organic thiocyanates	Method of ref. 3 claimed to give unsatisfactory results		7
Tetramethyl thiuram disulphide	+ aqueous Na_2S	Dithiocarbamate decomposed with acid to give CS_2; carried into KOH/alcohol and the xanthate formed titrated with iodine (see Alcohols, ref. 48)	8
Percarboxylic acids in presence of diacyl peroxides and alkyl hydroperoxides	+ diphenyl sulphide; 10 min/room temp., reacting with the peracids only; control without the sulphide	+ I^- + acetic acid, left 10–15 min in CO_2 atmosphere and titrated with thiosulphate; difference from control equivalent to peracids (see Iodides and hydriodic acid, ref. 199)	9
Unused *o*-hydroxy-mercuribenzoate from determination of thiourea	(In alkaline solution from previous reaction), + slight excess Na_2S	Back titrated with *o*-hydroxy-mercuribenzoate to dithizone	10
Phenyl- and methyl-mercuric salts in biological material	Extract in benzene + aqueous Na_2S; 5 min shaking, giving water-soluble Hg complexes	+ dilute H_2SO_4, + MnO_4^-; heated 1 h/*ca* 100°; decolorized with NH_2OH and Hg(II) ultimately titrated with dithizone	11
Unreacted *o*-hydroxy-mercuribenzoate from determination of some organic sulphur-containing compounds	+ excess Na_2S	Back titrated with *o*-hydroxy-mercuribenzoate to thio-fluorescein or dithizone	12

References

1. Fuchs, F., *Monatsh.* **9**, 1132, 1143 (1888); **11**, 363 (1890).
2. Evenson, O. L. and Nagel, R. H., *Ind. Eng. Chem., Anal. Ed.* **3**, 260 (1931).
3. Panchenko, A. N. and Smirnov, G. S., *Zhur. Obshchei Khim.* (*J. Gen. Chem., USSR*) **2**, 193 (1932).
4. Pucher, G. W., *J. Biol. Chem.* **153**, 133 (1944).
5. Sjöström, G. and Emilsson, E., *Svensk Kem. Tidskr.* **57**, 187 (1945).
6. Hargreaves, C. A., Abrahams, M. D. and Vickery, H. B., *Anal. Chem.* **23**, 467 (1951).

7. Takiura, K. and Takino, Y., *J. Pharm. Soc. Japan* **74**, 839 (1954); also Takiura, K., Takino, Y. and Kondo, O., *J. Pharm. Soc. Japan* **74**, 843 (1954).
8. Iijima, T., *J. Soc. Rubber Ind., Japan* **29**, 14 (1956).
9. Horner, L. and Jürgens, E., *Angew. Chem.* **70**, 266 (1958).
10. Wronski, M., *Chem. Anal. (Warsaw)* **5**, 101 (1960).
11. Gage, J. C., *Analyst* **86**, 457 (1961).
12. Wronski, M., *Chem. Anal. (Warsaw)* **6**, 869 (1961).

96. Sulphonic acids

(See general remarks under Acids)

Reagent. *p*-Toluenesulphonic acid (in one example given, benzene- or naphthalenesulphonic acids) as solid or concentrated aqueous solution (in one case in acetic acid solvent).

Reactions, reaction conditions, subsequent treatment and final titration stage. The sulphonic acids have found use on account of their involatility (valuable where a reaction product is subsequently isolated by distillation) high acid strength and only slight tendency to decomposition or take part in side reactions (some authors have tried to correct for SO_2 formed).

Determinations are based on two types of reaction:

1. Ion/ion combination, as in determination of acetate

$$CH_3COO^- + H^+ \rightarrow CH_3COOH$$

After reaction at room temperature, the unused acid was back titrated with acetate.

2. As an acid catalyst in four types of reaction:

(a) Hydrolysis of *O*- or *N*-acetyl or benzoyl groups in their determination. Reflux for up to 3 hours (*O*-acyl groups are more easily hydrolyzed) has been followed by distillation of the organic acid and determination by titration with alkali or by adding iodate/iodine and titrating the iodine formed with thiosulphate.

(b) Dehydration of alcohols, especially tertiary alcohols like linalool:

$$RR'C(OH)CH_2R'' \rightarrow RR'C{=}CHR'' + H_2O$$

Following several minutes reflux, the water has been titrated with the Karl Fischer reagent; in one example, this dehydration served to remove one alcohol from the sample and the other was then determined by an acetylation procedure.

(c) Transesterification, using a sulphonic acid/lower alcohol reagent and distilling out the ester of the added alcohol. Examples of this are not given here but are to be found under Alcohols.

(d) Esterification, in determination of —OH groups using an acetic anhydride/sulphonic acid reagent.

Examples

Materials titrated	Reagent and reaction conditions	Subsequent treatment and final titration stage	Ref.
N- or *O*-acetyl groups	+ benzene- or naphthalenesulphonic acids; 1 to 26 h reflux, giving acetic acid	Distilled and acetic acid titrated with $Ba(OH)_2$ to phenolphthalein	1
Acetyl groups (micro)	+ *p*-toluenesulphonic acid	Acetic acid distilled out under reduced pressure and titrated with NaOH	2
Acetyl groups (micro)	+ *p*-toluenesulphonic acid. Refluxed 20 min (*O*-acetyl) to 90 min (*N*-acetyl)	Acetic acid distilled and titrated with alkali; SO_2 corrected for by iodometric titration	3
Acetyl groups	+ 25% *p*-toluenesulphonic acid in water. Refluxed 1 h (*O*-acetyl) to 2·5–3 h (*N*-acetyl)	Acetic acid distilled into iodine solution; titrated with thiosulphate (to allow for SO_2), iodate added and the iodine formed titrated with thiosulphate (see Iodate and iodine pentoxide, ref. 31)	4
Acetyl, benzoyl-groups (semimicro)	Method of ref. 3		5
Acetyl groups in glucoproteins	+ 25% *p*-toluenesulphonic acid	Distillate + IO_3^-/I^- and titrated with thiosulphate after 2–2·5 h (see Iodate and iodine pentoxide, ref. 38)	6
Acetyl groups	+ 25% *p*-toluenesulphonic acid	Acetic acid distilled into excess NaOH and back titrated with HCl to thymol blue or phenolphthalein or a mixture of both; corrected for SO_2 by reaction with iodine and back titration with thiosulphate	7

Materials titrated	Reagent and reaction conditions	Subsequent treatment and final titration stage	Ref.
Formyl groups	Method of ref. 4		8
N-Acetyl groups in Ba acid heparinate	+ 20% *p*-toluenesulphonic acid; 1 h/*ca* 100°	Acetic acid distilled out and titrated with alkali	9
Acetyl groups (micro)	+ solid *p*-toluenesulphonic acid; 1–3 h reflux as in method of ref. 4	Aceitc acid in distillate titrated with NaOH to phenolphthalein	10
Acetate ion in acetic acid	+ slight excess *p*-toluenesulphonic acid/acetic acid	Back titrated with Na acetate/acetic acid to bromophenol blue	11
O- and *N*-acetyl groups	+ 60% *p*-toluenesulphonic acid/water + water. Slow distillation lasting *ca* 11 h	Acetic acid in distillate titrated with NaOH	12
Acetyl groups	+ *p*-toluenesulphonic acid + Ag(I) if halide ion present; 1–3 h/*ca* 100°	Distilled into iodine, (50–60 min duration); titrated with thiosulphate (to correct for SO_2), iodate added and titrated with thiosulphate after 20 min (see Iodate and iodine pentoxide, ref. 64; Thiosulphate, ref. 18)	13
Alcohols, especially tertiary	+ *p*-toluenesulphonic acid; 5 min heating, dehydrating to olefine + water	Water titrated with Karl Fischer reagent	14
Geraniol; linalool	Method of ref. 14		15
Geraniol/citronellol mixtures	Heated with *p*-toluenesulphonic acid/xylene, dehydrating the geraniol	Citronellol determined by acetylation with acetic anhydride/pyridine (see Anhydrides, ref. 130)	16
2-Acetylamino-1,3,4-thiadiazole-5-thiol	Heated with 25% *p*-toluenesulphonic acid/water	Acetic acid distilled out and determined by adding IO_3^-/I^- and titrating with thiosulphate	17

References

1. Sudborough, J. J., *J. Chem. Soc.* **87**, 1752 (1905).
2. Pregl, F. and Soltys, A., *Mikrochemie* **7**, 1 (1929).

3. Friedrich, A. and Rapoport, S., *Biochem. Z.* **251**, 432 (1932).
4. Elek, A. and Harte, R. A., *Ind. Eng. Chem., Anal. Ed.* **8**, 267 (1936).
5. Merz, K. W. and Krebs, K. G., *Ber.* **71**, 302 (1938).
6. Suzuki, M., *J. Biochem. (Japan)* **27**, 367 (1938).
7. Hurka, W. and Lieb, H., *Mikrochemie ver. Mikrochim. Acta* **29**, 258 (1941).
8. Alicino, J. F., *Ind. Eng. Chem., Anal. Ed.* **15**, 764 (1943).
9. Wolfrom, M. L., Weisblat, D. I., Karabinos, J. V., McNeely, W. H. and McLean, J., *J. Am. Chem. Soc.* **65**, 2077 (1943).
10. Bradbury, R. B., *Anal. Chem.* **21**, 1139 (1949).
11. Young, W. G., Winstein, S. and Goering, H. L., *J. Am. Chem. Soc.* **73**, 1958 (1951).
12. Chaney, A. and Wolfrom, M. L., *Anal. Chem.* **28**, 1614 (1956).
13. Mizukami, S., Ieki, T. and Koyama, C., *J. Pharm. Soc. Japan.* **76**, 465 (1956).
14. Petrova, L. N. and Novikova, E. N., *Zhur. Khim. Anal.* **12**, 411 (1957).
15. Petrova, L. N. and Novikova, E. N., *Masloboino-Zhirovaya Prom.* **25**, 21 (1959).
16. van Os, F. H. L. and Elema, E. T., *Pharm. Weekblad* **95**, 761 (1960).
17. Simionovici, R., Stoianovici, M. and Joan, C., *Rev. chim. (Bucharest)* **11**, 591 (1960).

97. Sulphuric acid

(See general remarks under Acids)

Reagent. Usually in aqueous solution of concentration ranging from very low up to 70%. Organic solvents have been added to facilitate solubility.

Reactions and materials titrated. 1. Sulphonation, of some aromatic or heterocyclic compounds such as indigo and nitro compounds. This has generally served to improve the solubility or reduce volatility of the material to be determined but in one of the examples quoted (ref. 9), the sulphonation reaction was the basis of the quantitative determination. The potential interference of β-naphthol in titration of β-naphthylamine with nitrite was eliminated by a preliminary sulphonation (ref. 8).

Some examples of the use of mixed H_2SO_4/HNO_3 reagent can be classified here, although the reaction is one of nitration (determination of aromatic hydrocarbons, especially benzene) and is of course given under Nitric acid.

2. Ion/ion combination, yielding weak organic acids (which can be separated by distillation or extraction or in other ways, or which decompose under the conditions used); or yielding insoluble sulphates, as with lead salts of organic acids for example.

$$CH_3COO^- + H^+ \rightarrow CH_3COOH$$

$$CH_3COCH_2COO^- + H^+ \rightarrow CH_3COCH_2COOH \rightarrow CH_3COCH_3 + CO_2$$

$$CCl_3COO^- + H^+ \rightarrow CCl_3COOH \rightarrow CHCl_3 + CO_2$$

$$Pb(OOCCH_3)_2 + H_2SO_4 \rightarrow PbSO_4 + 2\ CH_3COOH$$

$$RNH.C(=S)S^- + H^+ \rightarrow RNH.C(=S)SH \rightarrow RNH_2 + CS_2$$

3. Ion/molecule combination, as in an example of determination of basic nitrogen compounds in hydrocarbons;

$$\text{Base} + H^+ \rightarrow (\text{Base.H})^+$$

4. Oxidation, which, together with decarboxylation, evidently occurs in the determination of lactates or lactic acid by heating with fairly concentrated sulphuric acid. Acetaldehyde is the reaction product:

$$CH_3CH(OH).COOH - CO_2 - 2\ H \rightarrow CH_3CHO$$

5. As an acid catalyst in five types of reaction, as occurs with the other principal strong acid catalyst, hydrochloric acid. In most cases, these two acids are interchangeable, but sulphuric acid can be used in higher concentration and is less volatile and is preferred where these features are desirable.

(a) Hydrolysis of a number of bonds; the most frequently occurring examples are tabulated below:

C—O e.g. esters, especially acetates and benzoates; ethers such as vinyl ethers; condensation products of acetone with polyhydroxy compounds; acetals; polysaccharides, such as cellulose. (This last named determination is a standard method in analyses of food and agricultural products, etc. From the very large number of possible references to such determinations, only a small number has been given for reasons of economy of space.) In the determination of nitrate esters, using a $H_2SO_4/Fe(II)$ reagent, the first stage is most probably hydrolysis of the ester to nitric acid. These methods are not referred to here, however, but are listed under Iron (II), also in Part I.

C—N Acid amides, especially of acetic acid, are the principal representatives in this group. Others comparatively frequently encountered are hexamine and other formaldehyde derivatives. Determinations of nitro compounds via $H_2SO_4/Fe(II)$ are not included here (see remark under C—O).

C=N Condensation products of carbonyl compounds, such as oximes, hydrazones, azines, semicarbazones and *N*-benzyl groups.

C≡N Nitriles.

C—S An example is hydrolysis of 2-naphthol-1-sulphonic acid.

C—Cl E.g. polyvinyl chloride, broken down to Cl^-.

C—Metal Both mercury organic compounds and some arsenicals can be included here, where inorganic Hg(II) and As(III) are reaction products.

S—N E.g. sulphonamides; dithiocarbamates may also be included here, although the initial reaction is probably ion/ion combination (see reaction type 2 above) to give the unstable dithiocarbamic acid, which readily decomposes with fission of the S—N bond.

(b) Dehydration of tertiary alcohols to olefines; also that of pentoses to give furfuraldehyde is classified here but far fewer examples are to be found than of the commoner procedure with HCl. The dehydration of morphine to apomorphine has been the initial stage in a determination of the alkaloid.

(c) Decarboxylation is also more rarely exemplified than with HCl. *N*-carboxyamino acid anhydrides have recently been determined after an initial decarboxylation stage:

$$\mathrm{RCH}\begin{matrix}\diagup \mathrm{CO{-}O} \\ \quad\quad | \\ \diagdown \mathrm{NH{-}CO}\end{matrix} \quad (+\,H_2O) \rightarrow \mathrm{RCH}\begin{matrix}\diagup \mathrm{COOH} \\ \\ \diagdown \mathrm{NH_2}\end{matrix} \quad + CO_2$$

The decarboxylation occurring during determination of lactic acid has been mentioned above under oxidation (type 4 reaction); and some of the organic acids formed from ion/ion combination (type 2 reaction) decompose with loss of CO_2 (e.g. acetoacetic and trichloracetic acids).

(d) Depolymerization, e.g. of paraformaldehyde and par(acet-)-aldehyde.

(e) Addition in one example to ethylene oxide:

$$\underset{\diagdown\,O\,\diagup}{CH_2{-}CH_2} + H_2O \rightarrow \underset{OH\quad OH}{CH_2{-}CH_2}$$

(Some examples are given of the use of a $H_2SO_4/MgBr_2$ reagent for epoxide determination; this is also addition, but of HBr. References are also given under Hydrobromic acid, where the reaction is classified rather than here.) Kjeldahl nitrogen determinations, in which sulphuric acid is the principal reagent and many of the above reactions certainly occur, are given a separate heading (p. 616).

Reaction conditions. It is evident that reaction conditions vary widely, from short reaction times at room temperature to long reflux periods. No useful generalizations can be given.

Subsequent treatment and final titration stage. (i) Back titration of unused acid, applicable to methods based on the first four reaction types, where acid is consumed. It has been used also where basic hydrolysis products are formed, which take up acid. Several examples are given of the determination of hexamine in this way (ammonia as hydrolysis product), and an example of a substituted urea.

(ii) Titration of unused reagent + acid reaction product has been done in two cases, namely in determination of sulphate esters by hydrolysis and of aromatic hydrocarbons by sulphonation:

$$2\,ROSO_3^- + 2\,H_2O \rightarrow 2\,ROH + H_2SO_4 + SO_4^{2-}$$

$$Ar.H + H_2SO_4 \rightarrow Ar.SO_3H + H_2O$$

(iii) Titration of a reaction product has been the usual conclusion and some of the more commonly occurring are given below:

1. Furfuraldehyde from reactions of type 5(b), by procedures using hydroxylamine or alkaline Cu(II).

2. Other carbonyl compounds from hydrolysis of acetals, formals and vinyl ethers, of isopropylidene and benzal groups, of hydrazones, azines and oximes; and of hexamine; also from depolymerization of aldehyde polymers and from decomposition of lactic acid. Standard procedures have been used for the determinations, e.g. with bisulphite, alkaline

Cu(II), cyanide, hydrazines, hydroxylamine, iodine/alkali, mercury (II) and silver (I) reagents.

3. Ammonia from hydrolysis of nitrogen-containing compounds, notably hexamine, amides like urea and asparagine, sulphonamides, urethanes and nitriles.

4. Other nitrogen-containing reaction products from hydrolyses have been hydrazine (determined via iodate oxidation); hydroxylamine (determined by reduction with excess Ti(III)); aniline and sulphanilic acid (determined with excess bromate); and *p*-phenetidine (titrated with nitrite).

5. Acid, derived from hydrolysis of esters and ion/ion combination reactions with salt anions (type 2 above). The acid has usually been separated by distillation or by extraction and titrated with alkali. (Nitric acid from hydrolytic determination of cellulose nitrate was reduced to ammonia, subsequently titrated with acid.) Acetate esters have often been determined in this way.

6. Reducing sugars from hydrolysis of hexosans, celluloses, hemi-celluloses and similar polysaccharides. While chiefly alkaline Cu(II) reagents have been used for this titration, iodine/alkali and ferricyanide reagents have also found some use.

7. Phenols from hydrolyses, determined by various methods, such as titration with $NaOCH_3$, with a diazonium salt, with Ce(IV) or iodine.

8. CS_2 from determination of dithiocarbamates by treatment with acid, has been determined by conversion to xanthate with alkali/alcohol and subsequent iodometric titration.

9. CO_2 from decarboxylation, via absorption in excess $Ba(OH)_2$.

10. Lower alcohols (methanol, ethanol) from hydrolysis of alkoxy groups, have been converted to nitrite esters and then iodometrically determined; or have been titrated with excess bichromate.

11. Metal cations like Hg(II) (also As(III)), derived from acid treatment of metal-containing organic compounds, have been determined by standard inorganic procedures such as titration with SCN^- or iodine in the two cases mentioned.

12. Where sulphonation has been carried out in order to reduce volatility or improve solubility, the subsequent titration stage has of course depended on the functional groups already present in the compound. Nitro compounds were thus treated and titrated with an

excess of a reducing agent like Sn(II) or Ti(III); chloramine T has also been used.

Examples

Materials titrated	Reagent and reaction conditions	Subsequent treatment and final titration stage	Ref.
Acetate in Pb acetate	+ excess H_2SO_4	Filtered and unused acid titrated with NaOH to litmus	1
O- and *N*-acetyl groups	+ H_2SO_4/water, from *ca* 1:1 up to 2:1; 0.5–3 h/100–120°, depending on whether *O*- or *N*-groups	+ NaH_2PO_4, acetic acid distilled out under reduced pressure into excess KOH and back titrated with H_2SO_4 to phenolphthalein	2
Semicarbazide, semioxamazide	Boiled with dil. H_2SO_4	Hydrazine formed determined by iodate titration	3
Pentosans	Distilled with dil. H_2SO_4, giving furfuraldehyde	Aldehyde determined with alkaline Cu(II) reagent (see Copper (II), ref. 17)	4
Acetyl groups in acetate esters of cellulose and other polyhydroxy compounds	+ 50% H_2SO_4; 24 h/room temp.	+ water, acetic acid distilled out and titrated	5
Hydrazones, azines and oximes of aromatic aldehydes	Heated with H_2SO_4/water, 1:1, giving the aldehydes	Distilled and determined with excess hydrazine sulphate (see Hydrazines, ref. 6)	6
Lactic acid, pure and in biological fluids like blood and urine	+ 50% H_2SO_4. *Ca* 50 min/140°, giving acetaldehyde	Distilled into bisulphite and determined the combined part (see Bisulphite and sulphite, ref. 12)	7
β-Naphthylamine in presence of *β*-naphthol	+ fuming H_2SO_4 at 0–5°, then poured into ice-water and boiled 15 min (sulphonates the naphthol and prevents its subsequent reaction with HNO_2)	+ HCl and titrated with nitrite to external starch/I^-	8
Benzene, toluene or xylene in gasoline	+ excess conc. H_2SO_4; 5 min/*ca* 45°	+ H_2O and titrated with NaOH to phenolphthalein	9

Materials titrated	Reagent and reaction conditions	Subsequent treatment and final titration stage	Ref.
Dithiocarbamates	Boiled with 30% H_2SO_4, giving CS_2	Passed into KOH/ethanol and the xanthate formed titrated with iodine	10
Lactic acid	Distilled with conc. H_2SO_4, giving acetaldehyde	Passed into bisulphite and the combined part titrated with iodine (see Bisulphite and sulphite, ref. 19)	11
Lactic acid	Distilled with 50% H_2SO_4, giving acetaldehyde	Distilled into hydroxylamine hydrochloride/KOH and back titrated with H_2SO_4 to methyl orange (see Hydroxylamine, ref. 6)	12
Lactic acid	Distilled with conc. H_2SO_4	Acetaldehyde distilled into bisulphite (see Bisulphite and sulphite, ref. 23)	13
Hexamine	Heated with H_2SO_4	HCHO distilled out; residue made alkaline and the NH_3 distilled into excess acid; back titrated with alkali	14
Acetyl and formyl groups in pectin	Distilled with dilute H_2SO_4	Acetic + formic acids in distillate titrated with NaOH (latter separately determined with Hg(II) reagent)	15
K or Na acetoacetate	Heated with H_2SO_4, giving acetone + CO_2	Unused acid titrated with alkali	16
Hexamine	Boiled with H_2SO_4 until no more HCHO evolved	Diluted and unused acid titrated with NaOH to methyl orange	17
Semicarbazones (for identification of carbonyl compounds via reaction with semi-carbazide)	+ 15–20% H_2SO_4 (or more conc.); 30 min reflux, giving hydrazine and ammonia (sulphates), + probably unhydrolysed semi-carbazide	Oxidized with iodate, made alkaline and NH_3 distilled into acid; unused acid titrated with alkali (see Iodate, ref. 17)	18
Acetates	+ H_2SO_4	Solution extracted with ether and titrated with $Ba(OH)_2$ to phenolphthalein (acetic acid amount calculated from known partition coefficient between ether and water)	19

Materials titrated	Reagent and reaction conditions	Subsequent treatment and final titration stage	Ref.
Hexamine in cerebro-spinal fluid	Distilled with dilute H_2SO_4 (*ca* 20 min)	HCHO in distillate determined with alkali/excess iodine (see Iodine reagents, ref. 93)	20
Condensation products of sugars with acetone	Distilled with dilute H_2SO_4	Acetone in distillate determined with alkali/excess iodine (see Iodine reagents, ref. 95)	21
Some comparatively volatile nitro compounds, e.g. nitrobenzene or nitrotoluene	+ oleum; 30 min/100°	Nitro groups then determined with excess Sn(II) (see Tin (II), ref. 9)	22
Hexamine	+ H_2SO_4; 5 min/100° in a closed flask	HCHO determined with Cu(II) reagent, Cu_2O dissolved in Fe(III) reagent and the formed Fe(II) titrated with MnO_4^- (see Copper (II), ref. 63)	23
Benzene in air	Passed through H_2SO_4/HNO_3. *Ca* 1 h, giving dinitrobenzene	Made alkaline, nitro compound distilled out and determined with excess Ti(III) reagent, titrating unused with Fe(III) (see Titanium (III), ref. 22)	24, 30
Cellulose nitroacetate (after determination of nitrate by reduction with Hg(I) to nitrogen)	+ 80% H_2SO_4. Several h/room temp.	+ phosphate, bringing to pH 3·6–3·8; acetic acid distilled and titrated with alkali to phenolphthalein	25
Acetyl groups in acetates of polyphenols	Hydrolysed with excess H_2SO_4	Acid mixture titrated with NaOH conductometrically, giving acetic acid as well as the excess reagent	26
Acetate in lead acetate	+ H_2SO_4 + 95% ethanol, giving $PbSO_4$ precipitate	Filtered, excess H_2SO_4 in filtrate precipitated with benzidine, refiltered and acetic acid titrated with NaOH to thymol blue or phenolphthalein	27
Pentosans in pulp	Distilled with 13% H_2SO_4, yielding furfuraldehyde	Distilled into excess hydroxylamine hydrochloride and titrated the HCl with alkali (see Hydroxylamine, ref. 19)	28
Hexamine + hexamine methylenecitrate	Hydrolysed with H_2SO_4	HCHO determined with alkali/excess iodine (see Iodine reagents, ref. 119)	29

Materials titrated	Reagent and reaction conditions	Subsequent treatment and final titration stage	Ref.
Paraformaldehyde	Distilled with H_2SO_4	HCHO in distillate determined with excess KCN (see Cyanide, ref. 7)	31
Nitroglycerol in drug preparations	+ H_2SO_4 + Na_2SO_4	HNO_3 distilled into NaOH, reduced to ammonia with Devarda's alloy, the NH_3 distilled into excess acid and back titrated with KOH	32
O-Isopropylidene groups	+ dilute H_2SO_4, giving acetone	Determined with alkali/excess iodine	33
Some HCHO derivatives, e.g. $(C_6H_5CONH)_2CH_2$	Boiled with dil. H_2SO_4, liberating HCHO	Determined with alkaline Hg(II) reagent with iodometric titration of the Hg(I) formed (see Mercury (II), ref. 48)	34
Acetyl and benzoyl groups (micro)	+ H_2SO_4 (or *p*-toluene-sulphonic acid); 20–90 min reflux	Partly neutralized, then acetic acid distilled out and titrated with alkali to phenolphthalein	35
Hexamine in drug mixtures	+ 50% H_2SO_4; 10–20 min/200°	HCHO distilled out, determined with excess cyanide, the unused being converted to CNBr with bromine; + I^-, giving iodine, titrated with thiosulphate (see Cyanide, ref. 8)	36, 39
Methoxyl groups in wood	+ 72% H_2SO_4; 2–3 h, giving methanol	Converted with nitrite/acid to methyl nitrite; determined iodometrically (see Nitrite, ref. 11)	37
Ethylene oxide	+ H_2SO_4 + 50% $MgBr_2$	Unreacted acid titrated with NaOH	38
Ethylurethane	+ H_2SO_4; 1 h reflux	Made alkaline and NH_3 distilled into excess acid; back titrated with NaOH	40
Methoxyl groups in wood	+ 72% H_2SO_4; 2–3 h, yielding methanol	Treated with KOH to decompose any dimethyl sulphate formed; then the methanol determined as in ref. 37 above (see Nitrite, ref. 14)	41

Materials titrated	Reagent and reaction conditions	Subsequent treatment and final titration stage	Ref.
Asparagine	+ H_2SO_4; 3 h/100°	Made alkaline, the ammonia distilled into excess acid and back titrated with alkali	42
Acetate from determination of acetyl groups by hydrolysis with alkali	+ $MgSO_4$ + a little H_2SO_4	Acetic acid distilled out and titrated with NaOH to phenol red	43
Paraldehyde	Boiled with H_2SO_4, giving acetaldehyde	Distilled into bisulphite and determined iodometrically	44
Sulphanilamide	+ H_2SO_4; 1 h reflux	Made alkaline with NaOH, NH_3 distilled into excess HCl and back titrated with NaOH to methyl red	45
Hexosans	+ H_2SO_4. Refluxed 50 min, giving glucose	Determined with alkaline $Fe(CN)_6^{3-}$ and iodometric back titration of the unused part (see Ferricyanide, ref. 48)	46
Benzene in the air	Passed through H_2SO_4/fuming HNO_3, giving dinitrobenzene	Made alkaline, dinitrobenzene distilled out in steam and determined with excess Ti(III), back titrating with Fe(III) (see Titanium (III), ref. 29)	47
Paraldehyde	In 50% ethanol, + a little conc. H_2SO_4	Acetaldehyde distilled into hydroxylamine hydrochloride and the liberated HCl titrated with NaOH to bromophenol blue (see Hydroxylamine, ref. 48)	48
Diketene	Refluxed with very dil. H_2SO_4, giving first acetoacetic acid, then acetone	Distilled into hydroxylamine hydrochloride and titrated the HCl set free	49
Sulphanilamides	+ 75% H_2SO_4. Refluxed 30 min	Diluted, made alkaline and distilled the NH_3 into excess H_2SO_4; back titrated with NaOH to methyl red	50
Hexamine in foods	Boiled with excess H_2SO_4 until no further smell of HCHO	Back titrated with NaOH to methyl orange	51

Materials titrated	Reagent and reaction conditions	Subsequent treatment and final titration stage	Ref.
Acyl groups in organic esters of cellulose	+ dilute H_2SO_4	Long, slow distillation of the organic acid, followed by titration with NaOH to phenolphthalein	52
HCHO in resins	Distilled with H_2SO_4 (also with HCl or H_3PO_4)	Distilled into bisulphite and determined combined part (see Bisulphite and sulphite, ref. 57)	53
Hexamine	Boiled with H_2SO_4 until no more HCHO evolved	NH_3 determined by adding $Ca(OCl)_2$/KBr to neutralized solution and allowing to react for 5 min; then + I^-/acetic acid and titrated with thiosulphate	54
Hexamine	Distilled with H_2SO_4	HCHO distilled into neutral sulphite and the OH^- formed titrated with acid to rosolic acid (see Bisulphite and sulphite, ref. 70)	55
Na cacodylate, $(CH_3)_2AsO_2Na$	+ H_2SO_4/Na_2SO_4. Heated 4 h	+ $NaHCO_3$ and As(III) titrated with iodine	56
Cellulosic materials, e.g. woods	+ 72% H_2SO_4; 45 min/30°, then diluted to 3% acid and heated 4·5 h/*ca* 100° or 1 h/120° under pressure	Neutralized and sugars determined with alkaline Cu(II) reagent (see Copper (II), ref. 131)	57
$ROSO_3^-$ groups in sulphated oils (also $RCOO^-$)	+ excess H_2SO_4; 1 h reflux to hydrolyse the esters	+ ether + NaCl (to separate the alcohols formed) and total acid titrated with NaOH to bromophenol blue	58
Basic nitrogen in hydrocarbon feed stocks	Passed through H_2SO_4/water/acetone	Hydrocarbon evaporated and back titrated with NaOH to methyl red	59
Dicyanodiamide	+ excess H_2SO_4; 15 min/80–85°, giving guanidine or ammonium sulphates	Back titrated unused with NaOH or $Ca(OH)_2$ potentiometrically or to methyl orange	60
2,3,5,7-Tetranitronaphthalene	+ ethanol + some drops conc. H_2SO_4; 5 min/100°, to give soluble sulphonic acid	Determined with excess Ti(III) and back titration with Fe(III) (see Titanium (III), ref. 33)	61

Materials titrated	Reagent and reaction conditions	Subsequent treatment and final titration stage	Ref.
Hexamine	+ excess H_2SO_4. Heated until all HCHO evolved (different times tested and found that 10 min sufficed)	Back titrated with NaOH	62
Acetanilide	Heated with H_2SO_4. giving aniline sulphate	Determined with excess BrO_3^- and iodometric back titration (see Bromine reagents, ref. 264)	63
Acetaldehyde	+ excess H_2SO_4 + excess Na_2SO_3 (pH *ca* 8). *Ca* 15 min/room temp.	Unused acid titrated with NaOH potentiometrically	64
acetals; vinyl ethers	+ excess H_2SO_4. Up to 30 min	+ excess sulphite and then titrated with NaOH as above (see Bisulphite and sulphite, ref. 84)	
Hexamine	Distilled with H_2SO_4	Distilled HCHO into sulphite and titrated the formed OH^- with H_2SO_4	65
Hemicelluloses	+ 3% H_2SO_4; 2 h reflux, giving sugars	Determined with alkaline Cu(II) reagent with iodometric determination of the unused part (see Copper (II), ref. 139)	66
Salts of dehydro-cholic acid	+ H_2SO_4, giving free acid	Extracted with trichloroethane, solvent evaporated and acid titrated with Na_2CO_3 to phenolphthalein	67
Salts of phenyl-quinoline carboxylic acid	+ H_2SO_4	Free acid extracted with ether and determined as in ref. 67	68
Morphine	+ conc. H_2SO_4; 30 min/100°, yielding apomorphine	Mildly oxidized with $HgCl_2$/Na acetate, acidified with H_2SO_4 and titrated with MnO_4^- (see Mercury (II), ref. 99)	69
Acetyl and butyryl groups in cellulose acetobutyrates	+ 18N H_2SO_4; 12 h/room temp.	+ Na_2HPO_4, the acids distilled out and titrated with NaOH to phenolphthalein	70
Saccharose; maltose	+ H_2SO_4; 75 min/*ca* 100°, giving glucose	Glucose determined with alkali/excess iodine and back titration with thiosulphate (see Iodine reagents, ref. 268)	71

Materials titrated	Reagent and reaction conditions	Subsequent treatment and final titration stage	Ref.
Cellulose in agricultural residues	+ 72% H_2SO_4; 5 min/55°, then diluted to 4% acid and autoclaved 25 min under 2 atm	Glucose determined with alkaline Cu(II) reagent	72
Sucrose in milk products	+ H_2SO_4 + acetic acid + Na acetate; 15 min/100°	Monosaccharides determined with alkaline $Fe(CN)_6^{3-}$ with iodometric titration of the unused part (see Ferricyanide, ref. 85)	73
Polyvinyl formal	+ 20% H_2SO_4; 1 h boiling, liberating HCHO	Distilled into hydroxylamine hydrochloride and the HCl set free titrated with alkali (see Hydroxylamine, ref. 84)	74
1-Phenyl-2,3-dimethyl-4-(*p*-aminophenylsulphonamido)-5-pyrazolone	+ 70% H_2SO_4; 30 min reflux	Sulphanilic acid determined with excess BrO_3^-; aminoantipyrine determined with MnO_4^- excess (see Bromine reagents, ref. 318; and Permanganate, ref. 97)	75
Dithiocarbamates	+ dilute H_2SO_4. *Ca* 15 min boiling, giving CS_2	Aspirated into KOH/methanol and the xanthate titrated with iodine (see Alcohols, ref. 43; and Part I, Iodine, ref. 66)	76
Isopropyl *N*-phenylcarbamate	In water, + conc. H_2SO_4/85% H_3PO_4, *ca* 1:10. *Ca* 45 min boiling, giving CO_2	Passed into excess NaOH, CO_3^{2-} precipitated with $BaCl_2$ and back titrated with HCl to phenolphthalein	77
Nitriles	+ 90% H_2SO_4; 1–2 h/95° in a sealed tube	NH_3 distilled into excess acid and unused back titrated with alkali	78
α-Naphthylurea	+ 60% H_2SO_4 and heated slowly to boiling (*ca* 1 h)	+ alkali and the α-naphthylamine steam distilled out; titrated with nitrite (Part I, Nitrite, ref. 69) or with excess BrO_3^-/Br^- (1 h reaction time and iodometric back titration)	79
N[4]-Phthaloyl-*N*[1]-thiazolylsulphanilamide (Sulphaphthalazole)	+ dilute H_2SO_4; 30–40 min reflux	Product precipitated with excess iodine and unused titrated with thiosulphate (see Iodine reagents ref. 300)	80

Materials titrated	Reagent and reaction conditions	Subsequent treatment and final titration stage	Ref.
3-(*p*-Chlorophenyl)-1,1-dimethylurea	+ dilute H_2SO_4. Refluxed 17–18 h (overnight)	Unused acid titrated with NaOH potentiometrically	81
Urea; urethane	Hydrolysed by heating with H_2SO_4	Made alkaline and NH_3 distilled into excess acid, back titrating with alkali	82
Benzoyl groups (semimicro)	+ *ca* 9N H_2SO_4; 5 h/140–150°	Benzoic acid extracted with $CHCl_3$ and titrated with sodium methylate to thymol blue	83
Methyl nitrite, formed in preparation of nitromethane	In methanol, + dilute H_2SO_4 in CO_2 or N_2 stream. A few min/room temp.	+ I^- and titrated with thiosulphate after 15 min	84
Dextrans	+ 4N H_2SO_4; 75 min/100°, giving glucose	Determined with alkaline Cu(II) reagent, with iodometric titration of the unused part	85
Acetates; acetyl groups	Heated with H_2SO_4 (or H_3PO_4), giving acetic acid	Distilled into $BaCO_3$ slurry, dissolved Ba^{2+} determined by precipitation with excess $Cr_2O_7^{2-}$ and iodometric titration of the unused part	86
2-Naphthol-1-sulphonic acid	+ H_2SO_4; 3 h reflux, giving 2-naphthol	Titrated with benzene diazonium chloride (see Part I, Diazonium salts, ref. 23)	87
Acetals	+ dilute H_2SO_4; 3 h/60°	Neutralized and aldehydes determined with excess Ag(I) reagent with back titration using SCN^- (see Silver (I), ref. 131)	88
Acetyl groups	+ H_2SO_4; 30 min/160–170°	Acetic acid distilled out and titrated with alkali	89
Cellulose nitrate	Dissolved in conc. H_2SO_4	+ alkali/ethanol/water + Devarda's alloy; NH_3 distilled into excess HCl and back titrated with alkali	90
Ethylene oxide in gas mixtures	Absorbed in 10% H_2SO_4 yielding ethylene glycol	Determined with excess $Cr_2O_7^{2-}$, back titrating via I^-/thiosulphate	91

Materials titrated	Reagent and reaction conditions	Subsequent treatment and final titration stage	Ref.
Trichloroacetate	+ H_2SO_4/dioxan/water; 1 h reflux, giving $CHCl_3 + CO_2$	Back titrated with NaOH to methyl red	92
Nitroguanidine; cellulose nitrate	+ H_2SO_4/salicylic acid; 20 min/room temp., giving 5-nitrosalicylic acid	Determined with excess Ti(III) and back titration with Fe(III) (see Titanium (III), ref. 49)	93
Mercury-containing diuretics	Dissolved in 50% H_2SO_4	Hg(II) titrated with SCN^- to Fe(III) indicator	94
Acetyl groups	+ dilute H_2SO_4 in N_2 atmosphere	Acetic acid distilled and titrated with alkali	95
Lactate	+ excess H_2SO_4 + $H_2O_2/Fe_2(SO_4)_3$ catalyst, giving CO_2, acetic acid and acetaldehyde, all expelled by 1 h boiling	Back titrated unused H_2SO_4 with NaOH to methyl orange	96
Phenacetin	Hydrolysed with H_2SO_4, giving *p*-phenetidine	Titrated with nitrite (see Part I, Nitrite, ref. 87)	97
Indigo	+ conc. H_2SO_4; 45 min/90°, giving soluble sulphonate	Determined by oxidation to isatin with excess $Cr_2O_7^{2-}$ and back titration with Fe(II) or iodometrically (see Bichromate, ref. 186)	98
K stearate from determination of Zn stearate in face powder, by reaction with KOH	Evaporated filtrate + H_2SO_4	Extracted with toluene, xylene or petroleum ether, alcohol added and titrated with KOH to phenolphthalein	99
Cyclohexanone oxime	Hydrolysed with H_2SO_4	Hydroxylamine determined with excess Ti(III) and back titration with Fe(III)	100
Glucosides of hydroxyanthraquinone	Hydrolysed with 20% H_2SO_4	Extracted with $CHCl_3$, evaporated down, dissolved in pyridine and titrated with $NaOCH_3$ potentiometrically	101

Materials titrated	Reagent and reaction conditions	Subsequent treatment and final titration stage	Ref.
Phthivazide	+ H_2SO_4; 30 min reflux	Oxidized with excess iodate, solution extracted with $CHCl_3$ and unused IO_3^- in aqueous part determined by adding I^- and titrating with thiosulphate (see Iodate and iodine pentoxide, ref. 68)	102
Acetyl groups	+ H_2SO_4/Na_2SO_4; 20–30 min/200–250°	Acetic acid distilled out and titrated	103
Dithiocarbamates	+ $H_2SO_4/Fe(CN)_6^{3-}$, giving CS_2	Converted to xanthate with KOH/alcohol and titrated with iodine	104
O- and *N*-benzal groups	Boiled with 60% H_2SO_4, yielding benzaldehyde	Steam distilled into excess 2,4-dinitrophenylhydrazine reagent and determined unused with Ti(III) (see Hydrazines, ref. 43; and Titanium (III), ref. 56)	105
Tributyl phosphate in petroleum and water	Heated with H_2SO_4/H_2O_2	+ HNO_3 + ammonium molybdate, warmed to 60°, shaken 2 min, precipitate filtered, dissolved in excess NaOH and back titrated with HCl	106
Ethylene oxide in fumigation mixtures with CF_2Cl_2	Passed into H_2SO_4/ saturated with $MgBr_2$; 15 min/room temp.	Back titrated with NaOH	107
Ethoxyl groups in organic Si and Al compounds	+ $H_2SO_4/Cr_2O_7^{2-}$ excess; 30 min reflux, hydrolysing to ethanol and then oxidizing	Unused $Cr_2O_7^{2-}$ determined with I^-/thiosulphate (see Bichromate, ref. 207)	108
Dilithium hydroquinone from determination of *p*-phenylene dilithium by oxidation with oxygen	In dry ether (from oxidation), + dilute H_2SO_4, giving hydroquinone	Aqueous layer titrated with $(NH_4)_2Ce(NO_3)_6$ potentiometrically (see Part I, Cerium (IV), ref. 69)	109
Cellulose nitrate	+ conc. H_2SO_4; 5 min, then + excess salicylic acid; 10–15 min/room temp., giving 5-nitrosalicylic acid	Determined with excess Ti(III) and back titration with Fe(III) (see Titanium (III), ref. 62)	110

Materials titrated	Reagent and reaction conditions	Subsequent treatment and final titration stage	Ref.
Adrenaline	+ dilute H_2SO_4; 10 min/100° in N_2 current (to prevent influence of phenol and metabisulphite in the official solutions)	+ borax + excess $Fe(CN)_6^{3-}$; $Fe(CN)_6^{4-}$ formed titrated after 5 min with $ZnSO_4$ biamperometrically (see Ferricyanide, ref. 115)	111
Acrylonitrile in co-polymers with methyl-vinylpyridine	+ 54% H_2SO_4; 2 h reflux	+ NaOH and NH_3 distilled into boric acid; titrated with HCl to methyl purple	112
Polyvinyl chloride	Distilled with conc. H_2SO_4	Distilled into NaOH; Cl^- determined with HNO_3/ excess $AgNO_3$ and back titration with SCN^-	113
Various dyes, e.g. indigo, metanil yellow, congo red, methylene blue, fuchsin	Heated with conc. H_2SO_4	Titrated with chloramine T to colourless (see Part I, chloramine B and T, ref. 26)	114
Paraformaldehyde	+ H_2SO_4/H_2O, 1:1, depolymerizing	HCHO determined with hydroxylamine (see Hydroxyl-amine, ref. 151)	115
Dipotassium salt of chlorendic acid	+ H_2SO_4/H_2O, 1:1	Freed acid extracted with ether and titrated with KOH/ methanol	116
Sulphonates, e.g. dodecylbenzenesulphon-ates, in presence of sulphates	+ H_2SO_4, liberating the free sulphonic acids	Extracted with butanol and titrated with NaOH to methyl orange	117
Derivatives of isoniazid, e.g. with veratraldehyde, benzaldehyde-3-sulphonic acid (Na salt), methyl 2-furyl ketone	+ H_2SO_4/SeO_2. Refluxed 30 min	Filtered, + KI and titrated with thiosulphate	118
Methacrylamide	+ H_2SO_4 + $CuSO_4$ (polymerization inhibi-tor); 1 h boiling	+ Na_2SO_3 + some Sn and the methacrylic acid distilled out; + HCHO (to combine with any HCN) and titrated with NaOH to phenolphthalein	119
Arbutin	+ 10% H_2SO_4; refluxed 1 h	Hydroquinone ultimately determined by titration with iodine	120

Materials titrated	Reagent and reaction conditions	Subsequent treatment and final titration stage	Ref.
Arbutin	Hydrolysed with H_2SO_4	Hydroquinone set free oxidized with $Cr_2O_7^{2-}$ to quinone, distilled out, reduced with Zn/H_2SO_4 and titrated with Ce(IV) (see Bichromate and chromic oxide, ref. 222; Metals, ref. 98; Part I, Cerium (IV), ref. 80)	121
Paraldehyde	Distilled with dilute H_2SO_4	Acetaldehyde determined with Ag(I) reagent (see Silver (I), ref. 180)	122
N-Carboxyamino acid anhydrides $RCH\langle^{CO-O}_{NH-CO}$ (ring)	+ acids like H_2SO_4 or HCl, giving $RCH\langle^{COOH}_{NH_2}$ + CO_2	CO_2 carried out with nitrogen into benzylamine/ethanol/dioxan and titrated with $NaOCH_3$ to thymol blue	123
Ethylene oxide	Absorbed in H_2SO_4/$MgBr_2$	Titrated with NaOH to bromocresol green	124
monoethanolamine	absorbed in dilute H_2SO_4	back titrated with NaOH to methyl red/methylene blue	
Water-soluble dithiocarbamates	Neutral solution, + excess H_2SO_4; 20 min/room temp.	Back titrated with NaOH	125
Non-protein nitrogen compounds in serum	+ conc. H_2SO_4; 15–30 min/room temp., giving NH_4^+	+ hypobromite, giving nitrogen; unused determined by adding KI and titrating with thiosulphate	126
Determination of degree of replacement of —OH groups in polyvinyl alcohol by treatment with HCHO	Hydrolysed with dilute H_2SO_4 at 50°, yielding HCHO	Distilled and determinded with alkali/excess iodine (see Iodine reagents, ref. 423)	127
Tertiary alcohols, e.g. *tert*-butanol, diphenyl carbinol	In acetic acid, + conc. H_2SO_4; 15–30 min/ca 100°, dehydrating to olefine	+ water + BrO_3^-/Br^-; left 5 min, then + KI and titrated with thiosulphate (see Bromine reagents, ref. 513)	128

Materials titrated	Reagent and reaction conditions	Subsequent treatment and final titration stage	Ref.
Ethers of 1,1-diphenylethanol and derivatives, e.g. $(C_6H_5)_2C(C_2H_5)—O—CH_2CH_2N(CH_3)_2$	Method of ref. 128	(see Bromine reagents, ref. 514)	129
Acetonitrile in trimethylchlorosilane	$+ H_2SO_4/CrO_3/CuSO_4$. Heated 10–20 min	+ water + KOH and ammonia distilled into acid; back titrated with alkali	130
1-(5-Tetrazoyl)-4-guanyltetrazene-(hydrate), N—N=C(—N=N—NH—NH—C(=NH)—NH$_2$)—NH—N (tetrazole ring)	+ dilute H_2SO_4; boiled 15 min, giving aminoguanidine + N_2+ N—N=C(—OH)—NH—N (tetrazole ring)	+HCl and titrated with BrO_3^- to methyl red or iodine/$CHCl_3$ indicator (oxidizing to $N_2 + CO_2 + NH_3$)	131
Dithiocarbamates	Decomposed with H_2SO_4 into CS_2 via method of ref. 76	CS_2 converted to xanthate with KOH/ethanol, then titrated with iodine (see Alcohols, ref. 66)	132
Salts in presence of acids (e.g. acetate, benzoate, oleate)	In methanol, + excess H_2SO_4	+ benzene or butanone and titrated potentiometrically in nitrogen atmosphere with $[(C_2H_5)_4N]$ OH in benzene/methanol	133
Some easily decarboxylated acids, e.g. acetone dicarboxylic acid	In water, added slowly to boiling dilute H_2SO_4; 25–30 min reaction	CO_2 passed into $Ba(OH)_2$ solution under pentane and back titrated with HCl to thymol blue	134 135
Carbobenzyloxy groups, $C_6H_5CH_2—OOC—$	+ 6–7 N H_2SO_4; boiled 15 min, giving CO_2	Absorbed in excess $Ba(OH)_2$ and back titrated with HCl to thymol blue	136

References

1. Fresenius, R., *Z. anal. Chem.* **13**, 30 (1874).
2. Wenzel, F., *Monatsh.* **14**, 478 (1893); **18**, 659 (1897).
3. Maselli, C., *Gazz. Chim. Ital.* **35**, I, 267 (1905).

4. Flohil, T., *Chem. Weekblad* **7**, 1057 (1910).
5. Ost, H. and Katamaya, T., *Z. angew. Chem.* **25**, 1468 (1912).
6. Lautenschläger, L., *Arch. Pharm.* **256**, 81 (1918).
7. Clausen, S. W., *J. Biol. Chem.* **52**, 263 (1922).
8. Lee, H. R. and Jones, D. O., *Ind. Eng. Chem.* **14**, 961 (1922).
9. Zaborowski, G., *Matières grasses* **14**, 6160 (1922).
10. Callan, T. and Strafford, N., *J. Soc. Chem. Ind.* (*London*) **43**, 8T (1924).
11. Collazo, J. and Supniewski, J., *Compt. rend. soc. biol.* **92**, 370 (1925).
12. Leone, P. and Tafuri, G. B., *Ann. chim. applicata* **15**, 206 (1925).
13. The Brehme and Brahdy, B., *Biochem. Z.* **175**, 348 (1926).
14. Marotta, D. and di Stefano, F., *Ann. chim. applicata* **16**, 201 (1926).
15. Nelson, E. K., *J. Am. Chem. Soc.* **48**, 2945 (1926).
16. Lorber, L., *Biochem. Z.* **181**, 366 (1927).
17. Olivieri-Mandalà, E. and Riccardi, G., *Ann. chim. applicata* **17**, 487 (1927).
18. Veibel, S., *Bull. soc. chim.* **41**, 1410 (1927).
19. Vesterberg, K. A. and Palmaer, E., *Arhiv Kemi Mineral. Geol.* **9**, No. 43 (1927).
20. Bertel, E., *Biochem. Z.* **201**, 13 (1928).
21. Elsner, H., *Ber.* **61**, 2364 (1928).
22. Wallerius, G., *Tek. Tid., Uppl. C* (*Kemi*) **58**, 33 (1928).
23. Rebagliatti, E. E., *Rev. farm.* (*Buenos Aires*) (2) **2**, 340 (1929).
24. Smyth, H. F., *J. Ind. Hyg. Toxicol.* **11**, 338 (1929).
25. Billing, W. M. and Tinsley, J. S., *Ind. Eng. Chem., Anal. Ed.* **2**, 380 (1930).
26. Torres, C., Capuchino, A. S. and Socias, L., *Anales soc. españ. fis. y quím.* **20**, 694 (1930).
27. Han, J. E. S. and Chu, T. L., *Ind. Eng. Chem., Anal. Ed.* **3**, 379 (1931).
28. Klingstedt, F. W., *Pappers-Trävarntidskr., Finland* 950 (1931).
29. Marotta, D. and di Stefano, F., *Ann. chim. applicata* **21**, 150 (1931).
30. Smyth, H. F., *J. Ind. Hyg. Toxicol.* **13**, 227 (1931).
31. Weinberger, W., *Ind. Eng. Chem., Anal. Ed.* **3**, 357 (1931).
32. Anderson, E. L., *J. Assoc. Offic. Agr. Chem.* **15**, 140 (1932).
33. Kuhn, R. and Roth, H., *Ber.* **65**, 1285 (1932).
34. Bougault, J. and LeBoucq, J., *J. pharm. chim.* **17**, 193 (1933).
35. Kuhn, R. and Roth, H., *Ber.* **66**, 1274 (1933).
36. Schulek, E. and Gervay, V., *Magyar Gyógyszerésztud. Társaság Értesitöje* **9**, 26 (1933); *Z. anal. Chem.* **92**, 406 (1933).
37. Ender, W., *Angew. Chem.* **47**, 257 (1934).
38. Lubatti, O. F., *J. Soc. Chem. Ind.* (*London*) **54**, 424T (1935).
39. Schulek, E. and Gervay, V., *Z. anal. Chem.* **102**, 271 (1935).
40. Schulek, E. and Gervay, V., *Z. anal. Chem.* **102**, 275 (1935).
41. Storch, K. and Wenzel, I., *Angew. Chem.* **48**, 513 (1935).

42. Vickery, H. B., Pucher, G. W., Clark, H. E., Chibnall, A. C. and Westall, R. G., *Biochem. J.* **29**, 2710 (1935).
43. Clark, E. P., *Ind. Eng. Chem., Anal. Ed.* **8**, 487 (1936).
44. Nitzescu, I., Georgescu, I. D. and Timus, D., *Compt. rend. soc. biol.* **121**, 1657 (1936).
45. Schulek, E. and Boldizár, I., *Z. anal. Chem.* **108**, 396 (1937).
46. Strepkow, S. M., *Biochem. Z.* **289**, 295 (1937).
47. *Air Hygiene Foundn. of America Inc. Inst. Preventive Eng. Ser. Bull.* No. 2, Pt. 1 (1938).
48. Bagnall, D. J. T., Smith, A. and Tankard, A. R., *Analyst* **64**, 857 (1939).
49. *Analytisches Laboratorium, Farbwerke Hoechst*, 1939 (from '*Methoden der Organischen Chemie*', *Analytische Methoden*, Houben-Weyl, Georg Thieme Verlag, Stuttgart; 4th Edition, 1953, p. 485.
50. Hoshall, E. M., *J. Assoc. Offic. Agr. Chem.* **22**, 748 (1939).
51. Alesi, G., *Ann. chim. applicata* **30**, 237 (1940); *Ind. ital. conserve* **15**, 45 (1940).
52. Genung, L. B. and Mallatt, R. C., *Ind. Eng. Chem., Anal. Ed.* **13**, 369 (1941).
53. Nitschmann, H. and Hadorn, H., *Helv. Chim. Acta* **24**, 237 (1941).
54. Slowick, E. F. and Kelly, R. S., *J. Am. Pharm. Assoc.* **31**, 9 (1942).
55. Rapine, M., *Ann. chim. anal.* **25**, 113 (1943).
56. da Costa, A. N., *Rev. brasil. farm.* **25**, 41, 45, 49, 53, 59 (1944).
57. Saeman, J. F., Bubl, J. L. and Harris, E. E., *Ind. Eng. Chem., Anal. Ed.* **17**, 35 (1945).
58. Burton, P. and Byrne, L. F., *J. Int. Soc. Leather Trades Chem.* **30**, 306 (1946).
59. Donn, L. and Levin, H., *Ind. Eng. Chem., Anal. Ed.* **18**, 593 (1946).
60. Berlin, A. A. and Zinov'eva, Z. A., *Zhur. Obshchei Khim.* (*J. Gen. Chem. USSR*) **17**, 43 (1947).
61. Loriente, E. and Niete, F., *Ion* **7**, 11 (1947).
62. Lucas, V., *Rev. brasil farm.* **29**, 361 (1947).
63. Robinson, E. D. and Werch, S. C., *J. Am. Pharm. Assoc., Sci. Ed.* **36**, 185 (1947).
64. Siggia, S., *Anal. Chem.* **19**, 1025 (1947).
65. de Souza, A. H., *Pubs. farm.* (*São Paulo*) **12**, No. 48, 5, 9 (1947).
66. Auernheimer, A. H., Wickerham, L. J. and Schniepp, L. E., *Anal. Chem.* **20**, 876 (1948).
67. Erdos, J. and Cordova, G., *Ciencia* (*Mexiko*) **8**, 267 (1948).
68. Erdos, J. and Zamudio, A., *Ciencia* (*Mexiko*) **8**, 268 (1948).
69. Ionescu-Matiu, A., Popa, I. and Monciu, L., *Ann. pharm. franç.* **6**, 26 (1948).
70. Soloveichik, L. S. and Balandina, V. A., *Zavodskaya Lab.* **14**, 398 (1948).

71. Bot, G., *Magyar Kém. Lapya* **4**, 291 (1949).
72. Dunning, J. W. and Dallas, D. E., *Anal. Chem.* **21**, 727 (1949).
73. Hites, E. D., Ackerson, C. W. and Volkmer, G. H., *Anal. Chem.* **21**, 993 (1949).
74. Soloveichik, L. S. and Novikova, E. M., *Zavodskaya Lab.* **15**, 418 (1949).
75. Schulek, E. and Rózsa, P., *Acta Pharm. Intern.* **1**, 127 (1950).
76. Clarke, D. G., Baum, H., Stanley, E. L. and Hester, W. F., *Anal. Chem.* **23**, 1842 (1951).
77. Gard, L. N., *Anal. Chem.* **23**, 1685 (1951).
78. Vanetten, C. H. and Wiele, M. B., *Anal. Chem.* **23**, 1338 (1951).
79. Hunold, G. A., *Arzneimittelforsch.* **2**, 124 (1952).
80. Ibadov, N. Yu., *Aptechnoe Delo* **1**, No. 3, 11 (1952).
81. Lowen, W. K. and Baker, H. M., *Anal. Chem.* **24**, 1475 (1952).
82. Rosenthaler, L., *Pharm. Ztg-Nachr.* **88**, 252 (1952).
83. Schivizhoffen, E. V. and Danz, H., *Z. anal. Chem.* **140**, 81 (1953).
84. Décombe, J., *Bull. soc. chim. France* 656 (1954).
85. Dimler, R. J., Davis, H. A., Gill, G. J. and Rist, C. E., *Anal. Chem.*, **26**, 1142 (1954).
86. Köszegi, D. and Simonyi, J., *Acta Chim. Acad. Sci. Hung.* **5**, 33 (1954).
87. Reiner, G. M., *Chimica* (*Milan*) **9**, 81 (1954).
88. Siegel, H. and Weiss, F. T., *Anal. Chem.* **26**, 917 (1954).
89. Wiesenberger, E., *Mikrochim. Acta* 127 (1954).
90. Padmanabhan, C. V. and Sundaram, S., *Current Sci.* (*India*) **24**, 403 (1955).
91. Pokrovskii, V. A. and Alishina, G. P., *Zavodskaya Lab.* **21**, 415 (1955).
92. Schneider, W. A. and Streeter, L. E., *Anal. Chem.* **27**, 1774 (1955).
93. Stalcup. H. and Williams, R. W., *Anal. Chem.* **27**, 543 (1955).
94. Theimer, E. E. and Arnow, P., *J. Am. Pharm. Assoc.* **44**, 381 (1955).
95. Buděšinský, B., *Chem. Listy* **50**, 1936 (1956).
96. Duduta, T., *Bul. stiint. tehnic. Inst. politehnic., Timisoara* (2) **1**, 305 (1956).
97. Falex, O., *Australian J. Pharm.* **37**, 7 (1956).
98. Gopala Rao, G. and Venkateswara Rao, N., *Z. anal. Chem.* **151**, 347 (1956).
99. Pokhlebalova, L. P. and Shatskaya, N. I., *Masloboino-Zhirovaya Prom.* **21**, No. 7, 27 (1956).
100. Procházka, J., Czerepko, K. and Jansa, J., *Chem. Anal.* (*Warsaw*) **2**, 92 (1957).
101. Ruggieri, R., *Boll. chim. farm.* **96**, 491 (1957).
102. Shub, M. E. and Volkova, N. S., *Aptechnoe Delo* **6**, No. 6, 59 (1957).
103. Sudo, T., Shimoe, D. and Tsujii, T., *Bunseki Kagaku* (*Japan Analyst*) **6**, 494 (1957).

104. Carloni, L., *Ricerca sci.* **28**, 1639 (1958).
105. Jureček, M. and Obruba, K., *Chem. Listy* **52**, 2066 (1958).
106. Malinowski, J. and Rozmaryowicz, M., *Chem. Anal.* (*Warsaw*) **3**, 67 (1958).
107. Affens, W. A., Haenni, E. O. and Fulton, R. A., *Anal. Chem.* **31**, 1565 (1959).
108. Bondarevskaya, E. A., Syavtsillo, S. V. and Potsepkina, R. W., *Zhur. Anal. Khim.* **14**, 501 (1959).
109. Clifford, A. F. and Olsen, R. R., *Anal. Chem.* **31**, 1860 (1959).
110. Mullen, J. D., *Anal. Chim. Acta* **20**, 16 (1959).
111. v. Pinxteren, J. A. C., *Pharm. Weekblad* **94**, 169 (1959).
112. Stafford, C. and Toren, P. E., *Anal. Chem.* **31**, 1687 (1959).
113. Usai, A. and Corazzi, L., *Rass. Chim.* **11**, 16 (1959).
114. Chernavina, M. S., *Trudy Sverdlovsk. Sel'skokhoz. Inst.* **7**, 363 (1960).
115. Chwaliński, S. and Skorupski, W., *Chem. Anal.* (*Warsaw*) **5**, 1005 (1960).
116. Esposito, G. G. and Swann, M. H., *Anal. Chem.* **32**, 680 (1960).
117. Espector, Y. J. C., *Rev. argentina Grasas y Aceites* **2**, 75 (1960).
118. Franchi, G. and Pacini, C., *Boll. chim. farm.* **99**, 578 (1960).
119. Furasawa, M., Takeuchi, T. and Inoue, I., *Kogyo Kagaku Zasshi* **63**, 1940 (1960).
120. Keller, E., *Arch. Pharm.* **293**, 1079 (1960).
121. Rácz, G., Fuzi, J. and Fulop, L., *Acta Pharm. Hung.* **30**, 212 (1960); *Farmacia* (*Bucharest*) **8**, 377 (1960).
122. Bellen, Z. and Sekowska, B., *Chem. Anal.* (*Warsaw*) **6**, 69 (1961).
123. Patchornik, A. and Shalitin, Y., *Anal. Chem.* **33**, 1887 (1961).
124. Saltzmann, B. E., *Anal. Chem.* **33**, 1100 (1961).
125. Shankaranarayana, M. L. and Patel, C. C., *Anal. Chem.* **33**, 1398 (1961).
126. Tanay, I., *Orvosi Hetilap* **102**, 606 (1961).
127. Majewska, J. and Warzywoda, J., *Chem.Anal.* (*Warsaw*) **6**, 569 (1961).
128. Körbl, J. and Jančík, F., *Czechoslovak Patent No.* 105, 606, Nov. 15, 1962.
129. Körbl, J. and Jančík, F., *Czechoslovak Patent* No. 105, 608, Nov. 15, 1962.
130. Syavtsillo, S. V., Luzkina, B. M. and Karabashkina, L. N., *Plasticheskie Massy* No. 2, 34 (1962).
131. Ballreich, K., *Z. Anal. Chem.* **195**, 274 (1963).
132. Bighi, C. and Penzo, L., *Ann. Chim.* (*Rome*) **53**, 1068 (1963).
133. Kreshkov, A. P., Jarovenko, A. N. and Zel'manova, I. Ya., *Zavodskaya Lab.* **29**, 295 (1963).
134. Maros, L., Molnár-Perl, I., Vajda, M. and Schulek, E., *Anal. Chim. Acta* **28**, 179 (1963).
135. Maros, L., Molnár-Perl, I., Vajda, M. and Schulek, E., *Magyar Kem. Folyoirat* **69**, 123 (1963).
136. Medzihradszky-Schweiger, H., *Acta Chim. Acad. Sci. Hung.* **37**, 239 (1963).

98. Sulphur trioxide

Some examples are given of the use of a sulphur trioxide/dioxan reagent which functions as a mild sulphonating agent for —OH and —NH_2 groups:

$$ROH + SO_3 \rightarrow ROSO_3H$$
$$RNH_2 + SO_3 \rightarrow RNHSO_3H$$

The determinations depend on the difference in back titration with alkali between a control:

$$H_2O + SO_3 \rightarrow H_2SO_4$$

and after reaction as above; each —OH or —NH_2 group consumes an acidic hydrogen.

Examples

Materials titrated	Reagent and reaction conditions	Subsequent treatment and final titration stage	Ref.
'Active hydrogen' in alcohols and amines	+ 1·5–2N solution of SO_3 in dioxan; 2–3 min/room temp. (longer for polyalcohols)	+ water and titrated with Na_2CO_3 to methyl orange or congo red	1
Alcohols, mono- and poly- (e.g. sugars); phenols; ketoximes and aldoximes	Method of ref. 1, with reaction times up to several hours for polyhydroxy compounds		2
Amines; unused aniline after reaction with, in determination of aromatic aldehydes	Method of ref. 1		3

References

1. Terent'ev, A. P. and Kupletskaya, N. B., *Doklady Akad. Nauk SSSR* **90**, 907 (1953).
2. Terent'ev, A. P. and Kupletskaya, N. B., *Zhur. Obshchei Khim. (J. Gen. Chem. USSR)* **26**, 451 (1956).
3. Terent'ev, A. P., Kupletskaya, N. B. and Andreeva, E. V., *Zhur. Obshchei Khim. (J. Gen. Chem. USSR)* **26**, 881 (1956).

99. Surface-active agents

Many examples are given in Part I of direct titration of anionic surface-active agents with cationic agents and vice versa. This reaction of ion/ion combination between the large anion and cation, yielding products which are poorly soluble in water but dissolving in organic solvents like chloroform, is usually sufficiently fast to permit such direct titration.

Three examples of indirect titration, using measured excess of reagent, are quoted here:

Materials titrated	Reagent and reaction conditions	Subsequent treatment and final titration stage	Ref.
Anionic agents	+ excess cationic agent (benzylpyridinium chloride)	+ $CHCl_3$ + methylene blue and back titrated with standard anionic agent (Na laurylbenzene sulphonates) until the $CHCl_3$ and water layers were equally blue (see Part I, Surface-active materials, ref. 56)	1
Surface active sulphonates, sulphates and carboxylates	+ excess quaternary ammonium agent in $CHCl_3$/water	+ thymolphthalein (giving blue derivative with excess reagent, soluble in the $CHCl_3$) and titrated with Na laurylsulphate to disappearance of blue from $CHCl_3$	2
Cation-active plasticizers in dye fibres	+ excess Na lauryl sulphate at 60°	Back titrated in $CHCl_3$/water mixture with alkyl benzyl dimethylammonium chlorides ('Dodigen 226 FD') to appearance of red in $CHCl_3$ with eosin indicator	3

References

1. Harada, T. and Kimura, W., *Yukagaku* (*J. Japan Oil Chemists' Soc.*) **9**, 124 (1960).
2. Kupfer, W., *Vorträge Originalfassung Intern. Kong. Grenzflächenaktive Stoffe* 3, Cologne, Germany **3**, 62 (1960).
3. Seidel, M., *Melliand. Textilber.* **44**, 81 (1963).

100. Tetraphenylborate

Reagent. Sodium salts, $NaB(C_6H_5)_4$ (and $NaB(CN)(C_6H_5)_3$), usually in aqueous solution.

Reaction and materials titrated. The determinations depend on ion/ion combination with formation of water-insoluble products. Many bases, mostly of higher molecular weight, have been thus determined, e.g. alkaloids, synthetic pharmaceuticals and medicinals; an example is given also of determination of nonionic surface-active agents (then evidently complex-formation)

$$\text{Base.H}^+ + B(C_6H_5)_4^- \rightarrow (\text{Base.H})[B(C_6H_5)_4]$$

Reaction conditions. Most precipitations have been carried out in weakly acid to neutral solution (pH 4 to 6). Reaction times of up to several hours have occasionally been used to ensure complete precipitation.

Subsequent treatment and final titration state. (i) Unreacted tetraphenylborate has been back titrated with Ag(I) to eosin indicator and also by using excess Ag(I) reagent and concluding with the usual thiocyanate titration to Fe(III) indicator. Other back titrants, used recently, were cetylpyridinium chloride (ref. 21) and KCl (ref. 22).

(ii) More frequently, the analysis has been concluded via the precipitate, which has the advantage over method (i) of being independent of ions like halides which react with Ag(I). Several techniques have been used, following solution of the precipitate in acetone or other solvents like acetic acid, dioxan, dimethylformamide or butanone/acetic anhydride:

1. Titration with $HClO_4$ (of the base moiety), usually to methyl violet.

2. Titration with Ag(I) to eosin, chromate or biamperometrically.

3. Reaction with $HgCl_2$, yielding HCl, subsequently titrated with alkali:

$$B(C_6H_5)_4^- + 4\,HgCl_2 + 3\,H_2O \rightarrow 4\,C_6H_5HgCl + H_3BO_3 + 3\,HCl + Cl^-$$

$$B(CN)(C_6H_5)_3^- + 3\,HgCl_2 + 3\,H_2O \rightarrow 3\,C_6H_5HgCl + H_3BO_3 + HCN + 2\,HCl + Cl^-$$

4. Reaction with excess Hg(II) and back titration with SCN^-.

Refs. 13 and 16 are to the analytical applications of tetraphenylborate.

Examples

Materials titrated	Reagent and reaction conditions	Subsequent treatment and final titration stage	Ref.
Nitrogen-containing pharmaceuticals, e.g. atropine, codeine, brucine, pilocarpine, procaine, antipyrine, pyramidone, hexamine and their salts	In acetate buffer, pH 5·6 + $NaB(C_6H_5)_4$	Filtered, precipitate dissolved in acetone, acetic acid + Br^- added and titrated with $AgNO_3$ to eosin (allowed for the Br^- added)	1
Thiofalicaines (β-piperidinoethyl alkyl-thio-*o*-cresol ketone hydrochlorides (alkyl = n-propyl and isoamyl)	In acetate buffer, + $NaB(C_6H_5)_4$. Left several hours	Precipitate filtered and dissolved in acetone, acetic acid + Br^- added and titrated as in ref. 1	2
Nitrogen bases, e.g. procaine, morphine, strychnine, sympatol, pyramidone	In neutral solution, + a little acetic acid + *ca* 1·5–2-fold excess $NaB(C_6H_5)_4$ at 70–80°; then + $AlCl_3$ and cooled	Filtered, precipitate dissolved in acetone and $HgCl_2$ + measured excess NaOH added; boiled briefly, KI added to complex excess Hg(II) and titrated with NaOH to methyl red.	3
Nitrogen bases, e.g. atropine sulphate, pyridine nitrate, pyramidone, antipyrine, hexamine, benzidine	In acetic acid + a little $Al(NO_3)_3$ (to help coagulation) + $NaB(C_6H_5)_4$	Filtered and unused reagent + excess $AgNO_3$, back titrating with SCN^-; in presence of Cl^-, precipitate in acetone, + excess $AgNO_3$, likewise back titrated (see Silver (I), ref. 130)	4
Phenothiazines; antihistamines	At pH 4–6 in acetate buffer; 25 min/room temp.	Titrated as in method of ref. 2 (see Part I, Silver (I), ref. 82)	5
Quaternary ammonium compounds	In acetate buffer, pH 4–5, + *ca* 50% excess of $NaB(C_6H_5)_4$; 30 min/60°	Precipitate filtered, dissolved in dioxan and titrated with $HClO_4$ to methyl violet (see Part I, Perchloric acid, ref. 109)	6
Nitrogen-containing medicinals	+ $NaB(CN)(C_6H_5)_3$; 2–3 h/room temp.	Filtered, dissolved precipitate in acetone, $HgCl_2$ + water added; HCN boiled out and HCl formed titrated with alkali (see Mercury (II), ref. 130)	7

Materials titrated	Reagent and reaction conditions	Subsequent treatment and final titration stage	Ref.
Organic bases	Precipitated as in method of ref. 6	Precipitate dissolved in acetic acid and titrated with $HClO_4$/ to methyl violet or Tropeolin 00 (see Part I, Perchloric acid, ref. 137)	8
Aliphatic and aromatic amines	In dilute HNO_3, H_2SO_4 or acetic acid (pH *ca* 3), + moderate excess $NaB(C_6H_5)_4$	Filtered and unused reagent determined in filtrate by adding excess $AgNO_3$ and back titrating with SCN^-	9
Atropine; hyoscyamine	+ 1·5–2-fold excess $NaB(C_6H_5)_4$ at 75°	Precipitate + $HgCl_2$ + excess NaOH, boiled, KI added to complex excess $HgCl_2$ and titrated with HCl to methyl red; CO_2 boiled out and titration concluded with NaOH	10
Alkaloids, e.g. ephedrine, atropine, strychnine	At pH 4–5, + $NaB(C_6H_5)_4$; 10 min/*ca* 40°	Filtered: (a) precipitate dissolved in acetone, $HgCl_2$ + NaOH added, boiled, then KI + HCl added and titrated with NaOH to methyl red (b) precipitate in acetone + acetic acid + a little KBr, titrated with $AgNO_3$ to eosin (c) unreacted reagent in filtrate, + excess $AgNO_3$ and back titrated with SCN^- (d) precipitate in acetone, + excess $AgNO_3$ + ether and unused Ag(I) back titrated with SCN^- (e) precipitate in acetone, titrated with $AgNO_3$ to CrO_4^- (see Part I, Silver (I), ref. 117; this part, Silver (I), ref. 151)	11
Organic bases, e.g. codeine, pyramidone	+ $NaB(C_6H_5)_4$	Precipitate treated with $HgCl_2$ and the HCl titrated with alkali (see Mercury (II), ref. 137)	12
Procaine and other local anaesthetics	Hydrochloride + citrate buffer, pH 6, + $NaB(C_6H_5)_4$; 1 h/room temp.	Filtered, precipitate dissolved in acetone and titrated with $HClO_4$/acetic acid to crystal violet	14

Materials titrated	Reagent and reaction conditions	Subsequent treatment and final titration stage	Ref.
Organic bases	+ $NaB(C_6H_5)_4$	Filtered and unused reagent titrated with Ag(I) potentiometrically	15
Alkaloids, e.g. hydrochlorides of morphine, reserpine and papaverine	At pH 5–7, + $NaB(C_6H_5)_4$	Filtered, precipitate dissolved in acetone and titrated with $AgNO_3$ biamperometrically	17
o-Bromobenzyl ethyl dimethylammonium *p*-toluenesulphonate	In water + some drops $AlCl_3$ + acetate buffer, pH 4·5, + $NaB(C_6H_5)_4$; 30 min/40–60°	Precipitate filtered, dissolved in butanone/acetic anhydride and titrated with $HClO_4$ to methyl violet	18
Non-ionic surface-active agents (polyalkylene oxides, ethers, etc.)	In water, + acetic acid + $NaB(C_6H_5)_4$; 6–8 h, some 15 h	Filtered, precipitate dissolved in dimethylformamide, Na acetate + excess $Hg(NO_3)_2$ added; 10 min/100° and unused Hg(II) titrated with SCN^- to Fe(III) (see Mercury (II), ref. 168)	19
2,4-Diamino-5-phenylthiazole ('Daptazole')	In water + acetic acid + $NaNO_2$ + $NaB(C_6H_5)_4$	Precipitate filtered, dissolved in acetone, $HgCl_2$ + excess NaOH added, boiled, KI added and titrated with HCl to methyl red; CO_2 expelled by boiling and finally titrated with NaOH	20
Organic bases in pharmaceutical preparations	At pH 7, + excess $NaB(C_6H_5)_4$, giving precipitates	Back titrated with cetylpyridinium chloride to bromophenol blue	21
Salts of sympathomimetic amine (e.g. aliphatic amines, phenylethylamines, imidazoles and benzylic alcoholamines like ephedrine)	In acetate buffer, pH 4·6, + reagent slowly added; then ca 10 min	Back titrated amperometrically with KCl	22

References

1. Schultz, O. E. and Goerner, H., *Deut. Apotheker-Ztg. ver. Süddeut. Apotheker-Ztg.* **93**, 585 (1953).
2. Bräuniger, H. and Spangenberg, K., *Pharmazie* **9**, 626 (1954).

3. Flaschka, H., Holasek, A. and Amin, A. M., *Arzneimittelforsch.* **4**, 38 (1954).
4. Rüforff, W. and Zannier, H., *Angew. Chem.* **66**, 638 (1954).
5. Bräuniger, H. and Hofmann, R., *Pharmazie* **10**, 644 (1955).
6. Gautier, J. A., Renault, J. and Pellerin, F., *Ann. pharm. franç.* **13**, 725 (1955).
7. Schultz, E. and Goerner, H., *Arch. Pharm.* **288**, 520 (1955).
8. Gautier, J. A., Renault, J. and Pellerin, F., *Ann. pharm. franç.* **14**, 337 (1956).
9. Ievinš, A. and Gudriniece, E., *Zhur. Anal. Khim.* **11**, 735 (1956).
10. van Pinxteren, J. A. C., Verlop, M. E. and Westerink, D., *Pharm. Weekblad* **91**, 873 (1956).
11. Keller, W. and Weiss, F., *Pharmazie* **12**, 19 (1957).
12. Krajcević, M. and Broz-Kajganović, V., *Croat. Chem. Acta* **30**, 47 (1958).
13. Buzás, L., *Magyar Kem. Lapya* **14**, 251 (1959).
14. Chatten, L. G., Pernarowsky, M. and Levi, L., *J. Am. Pharm. Assoc., Sci. Ed.* **48**, 276 (1959).
15. Heyrovský, A., *Collection Czechoslov. Chem. Communs.* **24**, 170 (1959).
16. Montequi, R. and Serrano, C., *Anales real acad. farm.* **26**, 107 (1960).
17. Phaf, C. W. R., *Pharm. Weekblad* **95**, 517 (1960).
18. Gyenes, I., *Magyar Kem. Folyoirat* **67**, 162 (1961).
19. Seher, A., *Fette, Seifen, Anstrichmittel* **63**, 617 (1961).
20. Sztark, W., *Dissertations Pharm., Krakow* **13**, 57 (1961).
21. Johnson, C. A. and King, R. E., *J. Pharm. Pharmacol.* **14**, 77 (1962).
22. Smith, E., Worrell, L. F. and Sinsheimer, J. E., *Anal. Chem.* **35**, 58 (1963).

101. Tetrathionate

One example of the use of this reagent in an oxidation reaction is given below:

Material titrated	Reagent and reaction conditions	Subsequent treatment and final titration stage
Homocysteine from 6 h digestion of methionine (from protein hydrolysates) with HI	+ excess $Na_2S_4O_6$ + NH_4OH, in absence of atmospheric oxygen, reacting to give thiosulphate	+ HCl and thiosulphate titrated with iodate

Reference

Baernstein, H. D., *J. Biol. Chem.* **115**, 25 (1936).

102. Thallium (I)

An example based on ion/ion combination yielding a water-insoluble product, is given:

Material titrated	Reagent and reaction conditions	Subsequent treatment and final titration stage
Tetraphenyl-borate	+ excess $TlNO_3$; 4–6 h reaction time	Filtered and unused Tl(I) titrated with iodate in presence of $CHCl_3$/conc. HCl to disappearance of iodine colour from the $CHCl_3$ layer

Reference

Sant, B. R. and Mukherji, A. K., *Talanta* **2**, 154 (1959).

103. Thallium (III)

Two examples, based on oxidation and concluding with titration of the unreacted Tl (III), are quoted below:

Materials titrated	Reagent and reaction conditions	Subsequent treatment and final titration stage	Ref.
Hydrazines, e.g. iso-niazid, semicarbazide, benzoylhydrazine	Aqueous solution, + $Tl_2(SO_4)_3/H_2SO_4$, then + NH_4OH until $Tl(OH)_3$ just began to precipitate	Solution cleared with acetic acid and titrated with EDTA to 1-(2-pyridineazo)-resorcinol	1
Hydroquinone	+ excess Tl(III) reagent	Back titrated at pH 2.1 and at 90°, using EDTA and xylenol orange as indicator	2

References

1. Berka, A., *Z. Anal. Chem.* **193**, 276 (1963).
2. Sakai, T., *Nippon Kagaku Zasshi* **85**, 30 (1964).

104. Thiocyanates (simple and complex)

Reagent. Simple thiocyanate reagents have included the potassium and ammonium salts and a number of thiocyanates of bivalent metals, such as copper, zinc, cadmium, nickel and cobalt. In most cases, these latter have been prepared *in situ* from the potassium or ammonium thiocyanate and a suitable, easily available metal salt like copper sulphate, cadmium chloride, etc.

The principal complex thiocyanate used has been the reineckate, $[Cr(NH_3)_2(SCN)_4]^-$; others used occasionally have been $Cr(SCN)_6^{3-}$ and $Hg(SCN)_4^{2-}$ (the latter behaving like a mixture of $Hg(SCN)_2$ and $2\ SCN^-$).

Reactions and materials titrated. 1. In all but four of the examples given below, the determination has been based on the formation of water-insoluble products via reactions of ion/ion or ion/molecule combination or of complex formation. Many bases and their salts have thus been determined, such as: simpler heterocyclics (pyridine, quinidine) and aromatic amines (aniline, toluidines); alkaloids and their salts, like quinine, strychnine and some purines; synthetic bases like antihistamines and phenothiazines.

The insoluble products appear to be of three types;

(a) Complexes, formulated $(Base)_x Met(SCN)_2$, where the metal is Cu, Cd, Hg or Ni; also $(Base)_x Met(SCN)_3$ with Fe(III).

(b) Reineckates or salts of other complex thiocyanate anions, in which the base cation, BH^+ appears, e.g.

$$(BH^+)[Cr(NH_3)_2(SCN)_4]^- \quad (BH^+)_2\ Co(SCN)_4^{2-} \quad (\text{or } Zn(SCN)_4^{2-})$$

$$(BH^+)_3\ Cr(SCN)_6^{3-}$$

(c) A derivative of the organic base with the metal from the complex, as in the reaction between theophylline or theobromine and $Hg(SCN)_4^{2-}$:

$$2\ C_7H_8N_4O_2 + Hg(SCN)_4^{2-} \rightarrow (C_7H_7N_4O_2)_2Hg + 4\ SCN^- + 2\ H^+$$

2. Addition to α-epoxides and to aziridinyl compounds in single examples below:

$$\text{e.g.}\quad -\overset{|}{C}-\overset{|}{C}- \text{(bridged by O)} + SCN^- + H^+ \rightarrow -\underset{OH}{\overset{|}{C}}-\underset{SCN}{\overset{|}{C}}-$$

3. Replacement of chlorine in determination of methyl chlorosilanes:

$$(CH_3)_xSiCl_{4-x} + (4-x)\ SCN^- \rightarrow (CH_3)_xSi(SCN)_{4-x} + (4-x)\ Cl^-$$

Reaction conditions. The precipitations have been carried out in aqueous solution, usually neutral, faintly alkaline or fairly acid. (The reaction of type 3 was in non-aqueous solution, since the chlorosilanes are readily hydrolysed with water.)

Most precipitations have been rapidly performed. Temperatures were almost always near room temperature.

In refs 36 and 49 the influence of reaction conditions (pH) on the precipitation of, and the reaction between organic bases and reineckate ion are discussed.

Subsequent treatment and final titration stage. (i) In about half the examples tabulated below, a component of the reagent has been back titrated after filtration of an insoluble reaction product. Such components include:

1. SCN^-, by direct titration with Ag(I) or by addition of excess Ag(I) and back titrating with SCN^- reagent. This has been the most commonly used conclusion under (i). In one example (ref. 47), SCN^- was determined by iodate titration.

2. Reineckate ion, titrated with Ag(I).

3. Cu(II), Cd(II) and Fe (III) in precipitations with mixed reagents containing SCN^-, by titration with EDTA; Cu(II) was determined also iodometrically.

4. Unreacted acid from determinations according to type 2 reactions, titrated with alkali.

(ii) The precipitated reaction product has been determined in several ways:

1. Direct determination of a complex anion, usually the reineckate. This has been done after dissolving in acetone/water by direct or indirect titration with Ag(I), back titrating with SCN^- in the indirect case.

2. Via destruction of the complex anion using hot alkali or oxidizing agents, converting into a reaction product determinable by titration. Amongst such products may be mentioned:

SCN^- (from heating with alkali/tartrate), determined by titration with Hg(II); by using excess Ag(I) and back titration with SCN^-; by oxidation with excess bromate; or by passing through an ion exchanger and titrating the acid formed (from NH_4SCN).

Cd(II) by titration with EDTA.

Original base (from heating with alkali), extracted with $CHCl_3$ and titrated with acid.

CrO_4^{2-} (from oxidation of reineckate with BrO_3^- or H_2O_2), determined iodometrically via addition of I^-/acid and titrating with thiosulphate.

3. Via double decomposition of the reineckate salt, without bringing about destruction of the anion. Examples are:

Titration with $HClO_4$.

Precipitation of the bichromate of the base, and iodometric titration of unused $Cr_2O_7^{2-}$.

Precipitation of Ag reineckate with $AgNO_3$ and titration of the nitrate of the base with NaOH.

Examples

Materials titrated	Reagent and reaction conditions	Subsequent treatment and final titration stage	Ref.
Pyridine	+ excess Cu(II) + SCN^-, giving precipitate of $Cu(C_5H_5N)_2^{2+}(SCN^-)_2$	Filtered and unused Cu(II) in filtrate determined by adding I^-/acid and titrating with thiosulphate	1
Pyridine	+ excess NH_4SCN or KSCN + slight excess Cu(II), giving precipitate as in method of ref. 1	Filtered and unreacted SCN^- titrated with Ag(I) to Fe(III) indicator	2
Toluidines	+ NH_4SCN + $CuSO_4$, giving $Cu(C_7H_8NH_2)_2^{2+}(SCN^-)_2$ precipitate	Filtered and unused SCN^- titrated with Ag(I)	3
Pyridine	+ NH_4SCN + $CuSO_4$, giving precipitate	Filtered and unused SCN^- titrated with Ag(I)	4

Materials titrated	Reagent and reaction conditions	Subsequent treatment and final titration stage	Ref.
Quinidine	Neutral solution + excess SCN^-, giving precipitate of salt	Filtered and unused SCN^- titrated with $AgNO_3$	5
Aniline	+ excess SCN^- + $CuSO_4$, giving precipitate of $Cu(C_6H_5NH_2)_2^{2+}(SCN^-)_2$	Unused SCN^- in filtrate titrated with Ag(I)	6
Alkaloids in nux vomica and quinine tinctures	+ Reinecke salt; 24 h/room temp.	Centrifuged, precipitate heated with NaOH, the liberated alkaloid extracted with $CHCl_3$/ether and titrated with acid	7
Quinidine sulphate; strychnine nitrate	In water + $K_2Hg(SCN)_4$ reagent, yielding precipitates of thiocyanate complexes	Filtered and SCN^- in filtrate titrated with Ag^+	8
Choline	+ Reinecke salt	Cr(III) of precipitate oxidized with BrO_3^- or H_2O_2 to CrO_4^{2-} and this determined iodometrically	9
Methonium compounds	+ Reinecke salt	Precipitate + excess $Cr_2O_7^{2-}$ and unused determined iodometrically. Also titrated with $HClO_4$/acetic acid (see Bichromate, ref. 161)	10
Theophylline theobromine	In faintly alkaline solution, + $K_2Hg(SCN)_4$, giving Hg derivatives of the purines; 20 min boiling	Filtered, HNO_3 + excess $AgNO_3$ added to the filtrate; back titrated with SCN^-	11
Betaine	In HCl at pH 1, + Reinecke salt/HCl at below 5°, giving precipitate of betaine reineckate	Dissolved in acetone, reineckate precipitated with $AgNO_3$, filtered and betaine nitrate titrated with NaOH to methyl red	12
Quinoline	+ excess $K_2Hg(SCN)_4$, giving precipitate of complex (Quinoline)$Hg(SCN)_2$	Filtered, Hg(II) precipitated from filtrate with KOH, refiltered, HNO_3 + $AgNO_3$ added and back titrated with SCN^-	13

Materials titrated	Reagent and reaction conditions	Subsequent treatment and final titration stage	Ref.
Bases, e.g. strychnine, procaine, lobeline, diphenylhydramine, dibucaine	In dilute HCl, + Reinecke salt; 2–24 h/room temp. or lower	Precipitate heated with alkali/tartrate, then + HNO_3 + excess $AgNO_3$ and back titrated with SCN^-	14
Certain analgetics, e.g. dolantin, polamidon, eliradon, dromoran	+ Reinecke salt, giving insoluble reineckates	Unused reineckate in filtrate titrated with $AgNO_3$	15
2-Piperidinoethyl-4-propoxyphenyl ketone hydrochloride ('Falicaine')	In water, + Reinecke salt; 1 h/*ca* 0°, giving precipitate	Dissolved in acetone, boiled 10 min with KOH/tartrate; + HNO_3 + $AgNO_3$ and back titrated with SCN^-	16
Salts of bases, e.g. quinidine sulphate; strychnine nitrate	Method of ref. 8		17
β-Piperidinoethyl alkylthio *o*-cresol ketone hydrochlorides ('thiofalicaines')	In water, + dil. H_2SO_4 + Reinecke salt. Several h/*ca* 0°	Precipitate determined as in method of ref. 16	18
Phenothiazine; antihistamines	In very dil. H_2SO_4 + Reinecke salt. Left overnight	Precipitate determined as in method of ref. 16	19
Pyramidone; isoniazid	In water + $Cd(SCN)_2$ (from Cd acetate + NH_4SCN), giving precipitate of complex	Filtered and unused Cd(II) in filtrate determined by adding NH_4 buffer, pH 10 and titrating with EDTA to eriochrome black T	20
Pyramidone	In water + pH 10 buffer + $Cd(SCN)_2$	Precipitate filtered and unused Cd(II) in filtrate titrated with EDTA	21
Isoniazid; hexamine	Method of ref. 21		22
Pyramidone in pharmaceuticals	Boiling solution in water, + $Cd(SCN)_2$ (from $CdCl_2$ + NH_4SCN); neutralized to methyl red with NaOH; 90–120 min standing	Filtered, precipitate dissolved in NH_4OH/NH_4Cl and Cd(II) titrated with EDTA to eriochrome black T	23
Pyridine or its perchlorate	At pH 5·2–5·7 + $Cu(NO_3)_2$ + excess KSCN; 1 h standing, giving insoluble complex	Filtered, excess Ag(I) added to filtrate and back titrated with SCN^-	24

Materials titrated	Reagent and reaction conditions	Subsequent treatment and final titration stage	Ref.
Dihydrostreptomycin sulphate	+ Reinecke salt; 30 min/*ca* 0°, giving 1:3 complex as precipitate	Centrifuged, precipitate boiled with NaOH/tartrate, then HNO_3 + $AgNO_3$ added and back titrated with SCN^-	25
Certain alkaloids, e.g. eserine, strychnine	+ Zn or Co thiocyanate, giving precipitate of $(Alkaloid.H^+)_2$ $[Metal(SCN)_4]^{2-}$	Precipitate dissolved in HNO_3 and SCN^- determined with Ag(I)	26
Lupin alkaloids (e.g. sparteine); strychnine alkaloids	+ Reinecke salt, at pH 3–4, giving insoluble salts, e.g. with sparteine, $[C_{15}H_{27}N_2]^+$ $[Cr(NH_3)_2(SCN)_4]^-$	Back titrated with $AgNO_3$; or decomposed precipitate with NaOH and determined the NH_3 yielded	27
Isoniazid in solutions	+ some drops dil H_2SO_4 + water + Reinecke salt	Precipitate dissolved in acetone, excess $AgNO_3$ added, + HNO_3, filtered and back titrated with SCN^-	28
Chloropromazine and other phenothiazine derivatives	In dil. H_2SO_4, + Reinecke salt; 2–12 h/0–4°	Precipitate dissolved in acetone, + water + NH_4OH and boiled 10 min; passed through Wofatit F column, giving free HCNS, titrated with KOH to methyl red/methylene blue	29
1,2-Epoxides	In water/dioxan or ethanol + HCl + saturated KSCN. Control without sample	Back titrated with NaOH to bromophenol blue	30
Alkaloids like quinine, cinchonine, brucine or strychnine	+ HCl + $K_3[Cr(SCN)_6]$, giving precipitates of composition $(Alkaloid)_3H_3$ $[Cr(SCN)_6]_{1 \text{ or } 2}$	Dissolved in acetone, excess $AgNO_3$ added, giving $Ag_3[Cr(SCN)_6]$; filtered and back titrated with SCN^-	31
Chloropromazine	In acid solution, + Reinecke salt or + $K_3[Cr(SCN)_6]$ at 70°	Precipitate dissolved in acetone/water/acid and titrated with $AgNO_3$ potentiometrically	32
Pentazole	+ HCl or HNO_3 + Reinecke salt, giving precipitate of $(C_6H_{10}N_4.H^+)$ $[Cr(NH_3)_2(SCN)_4]^-$	Dissolved in acetone, excess $AgNO_3$ added and back titrated with SCN^-; or titrated with Ag(I) potentiometrically	33

Materials titrated	Reagent and reaction conditions	Subsequent treatment and final titration stage	Ref.
Methadone; phenothiazine derivatives like diparcol or chloropromazine hydrochloride	In HCl solution + Reinecke salt; 1 h/*ca* 0°, giving precipitates of reineckates	Precipitate + HCl titrated with BrO_3^- until yellow; + I^- and back titrated with thiosulphate. Phenothiazines also by treatment of precipitate with acetone/NaOH and titration of the SCN^- with $Hg(NO_3)_2$ to diphenylcarbazone	34
Alkaloids, e.g. atropine, brucine or strychnine	Method of ref. 27		35
Promethazine ('Phenergan')	In dil. HCl, + K reineckate until solution violet; 5 min/room temp, giving (Promethazine)$_3H_3[Cr(SCN)_6]$	Dissolved in acetone/water, 1:1 and titrated potentiometrically with $AgNO_3$	37, 43
Chloropromazine ('Largactil')	As in method of ref. 37		38
Piperazine	In water, + NH_4SCN + $CdCl_2$ or $CdSO_4$; 10–15 min standing, giving precipitate $[Cd(C_4H_{10}N_2)](SCN)_2$	Filtered and SCN^- in filtrate determined by titration with $AgNO_3$	39
Piperazine	In water, + NH_4SCN + slight excess $CuSO_4$; 5–10 min standing	Filtered and SCN^- in filtrate titrated with $AgNO_3$	40
Isoniazid	In water, + NH_4SCN + slight excess $CuSO_4$; 30 min standing	Filtered and SCN^- in filtrate titrated with $AgNO_3$	41
Methyl chlorosilanes, $(CH_3)_xSiCl_{4-x}$ (x = 1, 2, or 3)	+ NH_4SCN, giving the corresponding thiocyanates	Titrated conductometrically with pyramidone	42, 48
2-[(*p*-Chlorobenzyl)-(*β*-dimethylamino-ethyl)amino]-pyridine ('Synopen')	+ Reinecke salt, giving insoluble complex	Dissolved in acetone, water added and titrated with $AgNO_3$ potentiometrically	44
Bases, e.g. chloropromazine, isoniazid, quinine, atropine, tetrahydrofurfuryl nicotinate	+ Reinecke salt, giving precipitates	Dissolved in acetone/water and titrated potentiometrically with $AgNO_3$	45

Materials titrated	Reagent and reaction conditions	Subsequent treatment and final titration stage	Ref.
Pyramidone	+ water + excess NH_4SCN + $Ni(NO_3)_2$; few min standing, giving $[Ni(C_{13}H_{17}ON_3)_2][SCN^-]_2$	Filtered, filtrate + HNO_3 and titrated with $AgNO_3$ to eosin	46
Quinine	+ dilute H_2SO_4 + $K_3[Cr(SCN)_6]$	Filtered, aliquot + NaOH, boiled 1–2 min, then + conc. HCl and titrated with IO_3^- to amaranth (orange→yellow)	47
Diphenhydramine hydrochloride ('Benadryl')	In dilute H_2SO_4, + Reinecke salt; heated to 60–70°, then cooled	Filtered, precipitate dissolved in alcohol, decomposed by heating with KBr/NaOH/ tartrate, then + acid + excess BrO_3^- until yellow; after 15 sec, + KI and titrated with thiosulphate	50
Antipyrine	+ NH_4SCN $_4$ acetic acid + excess $FeCl_3$ (at pH 3.5 with buffer if necessary), giving $[Fe(C_{11}H_{12}N_2O)_3]^{3+}(SCN^-)_3$	Heated to 50° to coagulate and aliquot of clear solution titrated with EDTA	51
N-[3-Dimenthylamino-propyl]iminodibenzyl hydrochloride ('Tofranil', 'Imipramin')	In dilute H_2SO_4, + Reinecke salt; 90 min/ca 0°	Filtered, precipitate dissolved in acetone; + water + NaOH/ tartrate and heated 10 min, then + HNO_3 + excess $AgNO_3$ and back titrated with SCN^- to Fe(III)	52
Reserpine; kanamycin	In acetic acid/water/ ethanol or water respectively, + Reinecke salt; shaken 2 min, then 2 h/ca 0°	Filtered, precipitate + KBr/ NaOH/tartrate, boiled, HCl added and titrated to yellow with BrO_3^-; after 15 sec, + KI and titrated with thiosulphate	53
Isoniazid	+ NH_4SCN + $CuSO_4$/ NH_4OH/NH_4Cl reagent, giving precipitate	Centrifuged and Cu(II) in filtrate titrated with EDTA to murexide	54
Pyramidone	+ $(NH_4)_2Cd(SCN)_4$ reagent; 10 min (principle of method of ref. 21)	Filtered, precipitate dissolved in NH_4OH, brought to pH 10 and titrated with EDTA to eriochrome black T	55
Organic bases, e.g. hexamethonium bromide, iodisan (endoiodin), dextromoramide	In dilute H_2SO_4, + Reinecke salt; 2 h/*ca* 0°	Precipitate + KBr/NaOH/tartrate and heated at 100° until solution became green; + acid + BrO_3^- until yellow, then after 15 sec, + KI and titrated with thiosulphate	56

Materials titrated	Reagent and reaction conditions	Subsequent treatment and final titration stage	Ref.
Aziridinyl compounds (with group —N—CH_2) \\/ CH_2	+ KSCN/methanol + *p*-toluenesulphonic acid/methanol/water; in nitrogen atmosphere; —N—CH_2 + SCN^- + H^+→ —$NHCH_2CH_2SCN$ \\/ CH_2	Back titrated with KOH/ methanol to various indicators, e.g. bromothymol blue	57

References

1. Spacu, G. and Creangà, C., *Bull. soc. Stiinte, Cluj* **2**, 105 (1924).
2. Spacu, G. and Voicu, O., *Bull. soc. Stiinte Cluj* **2**, 89 (1924).
3. Cismaru, D., *Bull. soc. chim. Romania* **16A**, 37 (1934).
4. Fratkin, R. L., Yuravleva, L. P. and Blankshtein, A. G., *Sborn. Robot. Chim. Otdela* 88 (1935).
5. Nonnct, R., *J. pharm. chim.* **22**, 112 (1935).
6. Spacu, G. and Dima, L., *Z. anal. Chem.* **110**, 25 (1937).
7. Del Pozo, A., *Galenica Acta* (*Madrid*) **2**, No. 1, 25 (1949).
8. Köszegi, D. and Salgó, E., *Z. anal. Chem.* **130**, 403 (1950).
9. Trusov, V. I., *Biokhimiya* **15**, 495 (1950).
10. Heyrovský, A., *Sborník Celostatní Pracovní Konf. Anal. Chemiků* **1**, 221 (1951).
11. Köszegi, D. and Salgó, E., *Acta Chim. Hung.* **1**, 124 (1951).
12. Walker, H. G. and Erlandsen, R., *Anal. Chem.* **23**, 1309 (1951).
13. Köszegi, D. and Salgó, E., *Z. anal. Chem.* **136**, 411 (1952).
14. Okazaki, K. and Kitamura, N., *J. Pharm. Soc. Japan* **72**, 1056 (1952).
15. Vogt, H. and Heemann, I., *Pharm. Zentralhalle* **91**, 311 (1952).
16. Hannig, E., *Pharmazie* **8**, 28 (1953).
17. Köszegi, D. and Salgó, E., *Pharm. Zentralhalle* **92**, 157 (1953).
18. Bräuniger, H. and Spangenberg, K., *Pharmazie* **9**, 626 (1954).
19. Bräuniger, H. and Hofmann, R., *Pharmazie* **10**, 644 (1955).
20. Buděšinský, B., *Pharmazie* **10**, 597 (1955).
21. Buděšinský, B., *Českoslov. Farm.* **4**, 71 (1955).
22. Buděšinský, B., *Českoslov. Farm.* **4**, 185 (1955).
23. Groebel, W. and Schneider, E., *Z. anal. Chem.* **146**, 191 (1955).
24. Musha, S. and Munemori, M., *J. Chem. Soc. Japan, Ind. Chem. Sect.* **58**, 393 (1955).
25. Vogt, H., *Arch. Pharm.* **288**, 20 (1955).
26. Orlova, V. I. and Portnov, A. I., *Nekotorya Voprosy Farmatsii, Sbornik Nauch. Trudov Vyssh. Farm. Ucheb. Zavedenii Ukr. SSR* 112 (1956).

27. Drabent, Z. and Podeszewski, Z., *Farm. Polska* **13**, 32, 208, 212 (1957).
28. Spacu, P. and Teodorescu, G., *Rev. chim.* (*Bucharest*) **8**, 42 (1957).
29. Howorka, K., *Pharm. Zentralhalle* **97**, 374 (1958).
30. Mousseron, M., Jullien, J. and Peyron, A., *Parfums, cosmetiques, savons* **13**, No. 1, 3 (1958).
31. Spacu, P. and Iancu, C., *Analele Univ. 'C. I. Parhon', Bucuresti, Ser. stiinte nat.* No. 20, 63 (1958).
32. Spacu, P., Antonescu, E. and Gheorghui, C., *Acad. rep. populare Romine, Studii cercetari chim.* **6**, 573 (1958).
33. Spacu, P., Albescu, I. and Gheorghiu, C., *Acad. rep. populare Romine, Studii cercetari chim.* **6**, 565 (1958).
34. Montequi, R. and Santiso, M. F., *Anales real acad. farm.* **25**, 5 (1959).
35. Podeszewski, Z., *Farm. Polska* **15**, 436 (1959).
36. Poethke, W., Gebert, P. and Müller, E., *Pharm. Zentralhalle* **98**, 389 (1959).
37. Spacu, P. and Antonescu, E., *Acad. rep. populare Romine, Studii cercetari chim.* **7**, 247 (1959).
38. Spacu, P., Antonescu, E. and Gheorghiu, C., *Rev. chim. acad. rep. populare Romine* **4**, 243 (1959).
39. Grecu, I., *Farmacia* (*Bucharest*) **8**, 261 (1960); *Rev. chim.* (*Bucharest*) **11**, 714 (1960).
40. Grecu, I. and Curea, E., *Farmacia* (*Bucharest*) **8**, 625 (1960).
41. Grecu, I. and Curea, E., *Farmacia* (*Bucharest*) **8**, 503 (1960).
42. Kreshkov, A. P. and Drozdov, V. A., *Doklady Akad. Nauk SSSR* **131**, 1345 (1960).
43. Spacu, P. and Antonescu, E., *Rev. chim.* (*Bucharest*) **11**, 243 (1960).
44. Spacu, P. and Antonescu, E., *Acad. rep. populare Romine, Studii cercetari chim.* **8**, 73 (1960).
45. Danek, A., *Acta Polon. Pharm.* **18**, 229 (1961).
46. Dick, I. and Ristici, J., *Farmacia* (*Bucharest*) **9**, 525 (1961).
47. Gonzalez Carrero, J. and Flores de Ligondes, J., *Anales Real Soc. Espan., Fis. Quim.* (*Madrid*) Ser. B, **57**, No. 12, 765 (1961).
48. Kreshkov, A. P., *Tr. Mosk. Khim.-Tekhnol. Inst.* No. 32, 333 (1961).
49. Lee, K-T., *Anal. Chim. Acta* **24**, 397 (1961)
50. Montequi, R. and de Valderrama, F., *Farm. nueva* (*Madrid*) **26**, 221 (1961).
51. Dick, J. and Ristici, J., *Acad. Rep. Populare Romine, Baza Cercetari Stiint. Timisoara, Studii Cercetari Stiinte Chim.* **9**, No. 3–4 269 (1962).
52. Domagalina, E. and Przyborowski, L., *Chem. Anal.* (*Warsaw*) **7**, 1153 (1962).
53. Montequi, R. and de Valderrama, E. F., *Anales Real Acad. Farm.* **28**, 133 (1962).
54. Tatsuzawa, M., *Bunseki Kagaku* **11**, 1055 (1962).

55. Vasiliev, R. Scintee, V., Chialda, I., Sisman, E., Fruchter, J. and Jecu, M. *Rev. Chim.* (*Bucharest*) **13**, 759 (1962).
56. Montequi, R., de Valderrama, E. F., and Collado, M. C., *Anales Real Acad. Farm.* **29**, 71 (1963).
57. Schlitt, R. C., *Anal. Chem.* **25**, 1063 (1963).

105. Thiocyanogen

Reagent. Usually in acetic acid, CCl_4 or a mixture of these two. It is generally prepared by reaction of lead thiocyanate and bromine in one of these solvents or solvent mixtures:

$$Pb(SCN)_2 + Br_2 \rightarrow PbBr_2 + (SCN)_2$$

The mixed reagent iodine thiocyanate, ISCN, is considered under Iodine, Chlorides, Bromide and Thiocyanate.

Reactions and materials titrated. 1. Addition to olefine groups in determination of unsaturation mostly in complex mixtures like fats, oils and hydrocarbon mixes such as rubber materials and petroleum products. The data are often expressed as the 'thiocyanogen number' or 'thiocyanogen value', analogous to bromine and iodine numbers or values.

$$-\overset{|}{C}=\overset{|}{C}- + (SCN)_2 \rightarrow -\overset{|}{C}(SCN)-\overset{|}{C}(SCN)-$$

The extent of addition to polyolefines (non-conjugated) usually differs from that of addition of other halogen agents like ICl or bromine; analyses of mixtures (e.g. of oleic, linoleic and linolenic acids) have been attempted via simultaneous equations derived from treatment with thiocyanogen and these other reagents.

2. Substitution in determination of phenols, enols and heterocyclic compounds like antipyrine. Phenols like α- and β-naphthols and thymol yield monothiocyanates. It is possible that addition first occurs, succeeded by elimination of HSCN. E.g.

$$\begin{array}{c} C_6H_5 \\ | \\ N \\ CH_3-N \quad CO \\ | \qquad | \\ CH_3-C{=}CH \end{array} \xrightarrow{(SCN)_2} \begin{array}{c} C_6H_5 \\ | \\ N \\ CH_3-N \quad CO \\ | \qquad | \\ CH_3-C-CH \\ | \qquad | \\ SCN \quad SCN \end{array} \xrightarrow{-HSCN} \begin{array}{c} C_6H_5 \\ | \\ N \\ CH_3-N \quad CO \\ | \qquad | \\ CH_3-C{=}C-SCN \end{array}$$

$$—CO—CH_2— \rightleftharpoons —C(OH){=}CH— \xrightarrow{(SCN)_2} —\underset{\displaystyle SCN}{\underset{|}{C}}(OH)—\underset{\displaystyle SCN}{\underset{|}{CH}}— \xrightarrow{-HSCN}$$

$$—C(OH){=}\underset{\displaystyle SCN}{\underset{|}{C}}— \rightleftharpoons —CO—\underset{\displaystyle SCN}{\underset{|}{CH}}—$$

Reaction conditions. The sensitivity of the reagent towards water requires all determinations to be carried out in dry organic solvents. Some of the reaction times are long—24 h and over—but temperatures above *ca* 25° do not appear to have been used, also presumably on account of the limited stability of the reagent.

Final titration stage. In all cases unused reagent has been determined by adding aqueous or alcoholic iodide solution and titrating the liberated iodine with thiosulphate

$$(SCN)_2 + 2\,I^- \rightarrow I_2 + 2\,SCN^-$$

Examples

The reader is referred to the many publications especially in the late twenties and the thirties by H. P. Kaufmann and co-workers, of which only a small selection has been given here.

Materials titrated	Reagent and reaction conditions	Ref.
Unsaturated compounds	(Preparative, in organic solvents, but first example of use in addition)	1
Naphthols; thymol; antipyrine	In CCl_4 (thymol in nitromethane), + $(SCN)_2/CCl_4$. Various reaction times (5, 10, 15, 25 min, etc.) until constant back titration	2
Enols, e.g. aceto-acetic ester	In CCl_4 or nitromethane + $(SCN)_2$ Values varied with time of reaction	3
Thiocyanate number	24 h reaction in the dark	4
Thiocyanate number of linseed oil	+ $(SCN)_2$ in acetic acid; various reaction times tried	5
Unsaturated hydrocarbons	+ $(SCN)_2$ in acetic acid in *ca* 3-fold excess; 10–40 h (gave complete reaction even if not necessarily stoichiometric)	6

Materials titrated	Reagent and reaction conditions	Ref.
Unsaturation of fatty oils	+ $(SCN)_2$/acetic acid in *ca* 50% excess	7
Rubber hydrocarbons	In CCl_4, + $(SCN)_2$ reagent in 50–100% excess. In dark and absence of oxygen. Various reaction times with extrapolation	8
Unsaturation of oils and fats	+ $(SCN)_2$ in *ca* 50% excess; 24 h/*ca* 20° in the dark	9
Oleic and linoleic acids	Principle of method of ref. 4	10
Thiocyanogen number of vegetable oils	Method of ref. 4	11
	Discussed usefulness of method of ref. 4 for determination of the type of unsaturated fatty acid	12
Unsaturated hydrocarbons	Method of ref. 6	13
Semimicro determination of thiocyanogen number of fats	In acetic acid/CCl_4/acetic anhydride, 6:3:1, + reagent; 4 h in dark; or 12 h if linolenic acid present	14
Unsaturation of petroleum products	Method of ref. 8	15
Thiocyanogen number of oils, e.g. olive	+ $(SCN)_2$/acetic acid. Studied influence of reaction time, varying from 1 to 30 h/room temp.	16
Linoleic and linolenic acids and their methyl esters; linseed oil unsaturation	+ $(SCN)_2$ reagent; 24 h/20°	17
Unsaturation of rubber	In CCl_4, + $(SCN)_2$/CCl_4 in nitrogen atmosphere. Various reaction times/10–12°	18
Thiocyanogen numbers of fatty acids	In acetic acid; 24 h/room temp.	19
Unsaturation of fats and oils	+ $(SCN)_2$ reagent + $HgCl_2$; found that it catalysed addition so that 5 h reaction sufficed instead of 24	20

References

1. Kaufmann, H. P., *Ber. Pharm. Ges.* **33**, 139 (1923).
2. Kaufmann, H. P. and Gaertner, P., *Ber.* **57**, 932 (1924).
3. Kaufmann, H. P. and Wolff, G., *Ber.* **57**, 934 (1924).
4. Stadlinger, H., *Pharm. Ztg.* **73**, 340 (1928).
5. Kaufmann, H. P. and Keller, M., *Z. angew. Chem.* **42**, 20 (1929).
6. Kaufmann, H. P., *Arch. Pharm.* **267**, 1 (1929).
7. Kimura, W., *J. Soc. Chem. Ind. (Japan)* **32**, 451 (1929).
8. Pummerer, R. and Stärk, H., *Ber.* **64**, 825 (1931).
9. Martin, W. C. and Stillman, R. C., *Oil and Soap* **10**, 29 (1933).
10. Godbole, N. N. and Sadgopal, *Allgem. Öl u. Fett-Ztg.* **31**, 435 (1934).
11. Ivanov, S. L., Lebedev, V. P. and Kel'tzev, P. P., *Schriften Zentral. Forschungsinst. Lebensmittelchem. USSR* **4**, 185 (1935).
12. Kraëff, A. A., *Verfkroniek* **8**, 159 (1935).
13. Krassilchik, A., *Ann. combustibles liquides* **10**, 923 (1935).
14. Kaufmann, H. P. and Hartweg, L., *Fette u. Seifen* **45**, 356 (1938).
15. Grosse-Oetringhaus, H., *Petroleum-Ztg.* **35**, 75, 112 (1939).
16. Sher, H. N. and Coysh, R. H., *Analyst* **64**, 814 (1939).
17. Painter, G. P. and Nesbitt, L. L., *Ind. Eng. Chem., Anal. Ed.* **15**, 123 (1943).
18. Rehner, J., *Ind. Eng. Chem.* **36**, 118 (1944).
19. Niemierko, W., *Acta Biol. Exptl. (Warsaw)* **14**, 199 (1947).
20. Chakrabarty, S. K., Ganguly, D. and Goswami, M. N., *J. Indian Chem. Soc., Ind. and News Ed.* **20**, 6 (1957).

106. Thiosulphate

Reagent. The readily available sodium salt has been used.

Reactions and materials titrated. 1. Addition, with ring opening, to 3- or 4-membered ring compounds like α-epoxides, ethyleneimines (aziridinyl compounds) and β-propiolactone:

$$\underset{\diagdown O \diagup}{RCH\text{—}CH_2} + S_2O_3^{2-} + H_2O \rightarrow \underset{\displaystyle |\atop OH}{RCH}\text{—}CH_2S_2O_3^- + OH^-$$

$$R\text{—}N\begin{matrix}\diagup CH_2\\ |\\ \diagdown CH_2\end{matrix} + S_2O_3^{2-} + H_2O \rightarrow R\text{—}NH\text{—}CH_2CH_2S_2O_3^- + OH^-$$

$$R_2\overset{+}{N}\langle{}^{CH_2}_{CH_2} + S_2O_3^{2-} \rightarrow R_2N{-}CH_2CH_2S_2O_3^-$$

$$\begin{matrix} CH_2{-}CH_2 \\ | \quad\quad | \\ CO{-}O \end{matrix} + S_2O_3^{2-} \rightarrow \begin{matrix} CH_2{-}CH_2S_2O_3^- \\ | \\ COO^- \end{matrix}$$

2. Replacement of other organic groups by the $-S_2O_3^-$ group, e.g. with halides, sulphenamides or sulphenyl thiocyanates:

$$RHal + S_2O_3^{2-} \rightarrow RS_2O_3^- + Hal^-$$

$$RS{-}NR_2 + S_2O_3^{2-} + 2\,H^+ \rightarrow RS{-}S_2O_3^- + R_2NH_2^+$$

$$RS{-}SCN + S_2O_3^{2-} \rightarrow RSS_2O_3^- + SCN^-$$

3. Reduction, e.g. of seleninic acids:

$$RSeO_2H + 3\,S_2O_3^{2-} + 3\,H^+ \rightarrow RSeS_2O_3^- + S_4O_6^{2-} + 2\,H_2O$$

Here again, as in 1 and 2, the $-S_2O_3^-$ group is introduced into the organic molecule.

The most prominent application of thiosulphate can be classified here, namely, in conjunction with iodate/iodide for determination of acids and also to determine phosgene or iodoform via consumption of iodine liberated with iodide/acid and in ultraviolet light respectively:

$$6\,H^+ + IO_3^- + 5\,I^- \rightarrow 3\,I_2 + 3\,H_2O$$

$$COCl_2 + 2\,I^- \rightarrow I_2 + CO + 2\,Cl^-$$

followed by the reaction:

$$I_2 + 2\,S_2O_3^{2-} \rightarrow 2\,I^- + S_4O_6^{2-}$$

(These examples are classified also under Iodate and Iodide respectively.)

Reaction conditions. Most determinations (especially those of acids) have been performed in aqueous or aqueous/alcoholic solution (the poor solubility of thiosulphate in organic solvents enforces this).

Reaction times and temperatures have varied widely.

Subsequent treatment and final titration stage. (i) Back titration of unreacted thiosulphate with iodine (in some cases, excess iodine has been added and the final titration carried out with thiosulphate). This has been the method most frequently adopted.

(ii) Determination of OH^- formed in addition reactions (type 1) by titration with acid. To avoid side reactions, the OH^- must be titrated as fast as it is formed or it must be removed from solution, e.g. by precipitation as a poorly soluble hydroxide ($Mg(OH)_2$ in one example) which is subsequently titrated.

Examples

Materials titrated	Reagent and reaction conditions	Subsequent treatment and final titration stage	Ref.
Acids of pK not above 6	+ iodate/iodide + excess thiosulphate; 30 min/room temp.	Back titrated with iodine	1
Higher fatty acids (notably unsaturated acids)	+ iodate/iodide + excess thiosulphate	Back titrated with iodine	2
'Acid number' of fats	In isopropanol, + iodate/iodide + thiosulphate; 2·5 h/55–60°	+ excess iodine and back titrated with thiosulphate	3
Phosgene	+ KI/acetone + iodate + excess thiosulphate; 30 min $COCl_2 + 2\,I^- \rightarrow CO + 2\,Cl^-$	Back titrated with iodine (allowed for added iodate)	4
Maleic acid, from hydrolysis of the anhydride, unused from reaction with, in determination of conjugated olefines	+ iodate/iodide + thiosulphate; 2 h with intermittent shaking	+ excess iodine and back titrated with thiosulphate	5
Acid content of certain fats	Method of ref. 3 (gave high results if peroxides were present)		6
Acidity of wines	+ iodate/iodide + thiosulphate; 24 h/room temp.	Titrated with iodine	7
Acids with no free amino groups	Method of ref. 1		8
Ethyleneimonium ion, e.g. from nitrogen mustards	In aqueous solution, + thiosulphate; 10 min	Titrated with iodine	9

Materials titrated	Reagent and reaction conditions	Subsequent treatment and final titration stage	Ref.
Sulphenamides, $RS.NR_2$	In ethanol or isopropanol, + thiosulphate + acetic acid; 10 min/room temp.	+ water and back titrated with thiosulphate	10
sulphenyl thiocyanates, RS.SCN	in ethyl acetate + ethanol + excess thiosulphate; 5 min/room temp.	+ water and back titrated with thiosulphate	10
sulphur piperidides, $S_x(NC_5H_{10})_2$	as sulphenamides	+ water and back titrated with thiosulphate	10
p-Nitrobenzeneseleninic acid, $NO_2—C_6H_4SeO_2H$	+ H_2SO_4 + thiosulphate	Back titrated with iodine	11
Acid value of 'lac'	In 95% ethanol, + iodate/iodide + + thiosulphate. Shaken until clear solution	+ excess iodine and titrated with thiosulphate	12
—COOH groups in cellulosic materials	+ iodate/iodide + NaCl + thiosulphate; 24 h/room temp.	Back titrated with iodine	13
Mono- and diepoxides	+ thiosulphate/50% acetone. Heated usually 10–20 min	Continuously titrated with acetic acid to phenolphthalein	14
'Acid number' of fatty acids	In ethanol, + iodate/iodide + thiosulphate	Titrated with iodine	15
β-Propiolactone	+ thiosulphate + phosphate buffer, (K_2HPO_4); 10–20 min/room temp.	Back titrated with iodine	16
Ethyleneimine derivatives	+ thiosulphate + HCl bringing to pH 4 (methyl orange); 30 min/room temp. Control	Titrated with NaOH to phenolphthalein to correct for the basicity of the material	17
Acetic acid from determination of acetyl groups by hydrolysis	+ iodate/iodide + thiosulphate; 20 min/room temp.	Titrated with iodine	18

Materials titrated	Reagent and reaction conditions	Subsequent treatment and final titration stage	Ref.
Iodoform (in study of reaction between acetaldehyde and iodide/alkali)	In ether/benzene + thiosulphate; 30–40 min in sunlight	Titrated with iodine	19
—COOH groups in cellulosic materials	+ iodate/iodide + NaCl + thiosulphate; 1 h/60°	Titrated with iodine	20
Iodoform (in study of reaction between acetone, iodine and alkali)	Method of ref 19.		21
Epoxides (basic)	In water, + acetic acid + thiosulphate; 15 min/70°	Cooled in ice and titrated with iodine	22
Ethyleneimine group	+ thiosulphate	Titrated with HCl to pH 4 potentiometrically	23
Terminal epoxides, e.g. styrene oxide	+ ethanol + thiosulphate/$MgSO_4$ reagent, pH 8·25; 15 min reflux, giving precipitate of $Mg(OH)_2$	+ water and titrated with slight excess acetic acid to methyl red/methylene blue and finally with NaOH to phenolphthalein	24
Iodoform	In ethanol + benzene/ether + thiosulphate, in ultraviolet lamplight; 1 min shaken, then 10 min until no more brown in aqueous phase	+ KI and titrated with iodine	25
Phosgene	Method of ref. 4		26
Maleic acid from hydrolysis of the unreacted maleic anhydride after reaction with, in determination of *p*-mentha-3,8(9)-diene	Aqueous layer, + iodate/iodide + excess thiosulphate; 2 h/room temp.	+ excess iodine, then back titrated with thiosulphate	27
Tris-(1-aziridinyl)phosphine sulphide ('Thio-TEPA')	Evaporated extract in $CHCl_3$, + excess thiosulphate and + HCl to methyl orange until red persisted 10–15 sec. Control	Titrated with NaOH to phenolphthalein (corrects for basicity of the material)	28

Materials titrated	Reagent and reaction conditions	Subsequent treatment and final titration stage	Ref.
Aziridinyl compounds, e.g. dipin	In water, + 20% thiosulphate and immediately titrated to methyl orange with HCl; 30 min. Control	Titrated with NaOH to phenolphthalein	29
Some halides (e.g. lower alkyl iodides; alkyl haloacetates; chloro- and bromo-acetone and acetophenone; benzyl chloride and its *p*-nitro derivative)	Chiefly in dioxan + 3–5 fold excess aqueous thiosulphate (giving *ca* 1:1 dioxan/water); 2 min–6 h/25–60°	Back titrated with iodine	30
Maleic acid from hydrolysis of unreacted anhydride after reaction with, in determination of conjugated olefine groups in, e.g. dehydrated castor oil	In water/toluene, + iodate/iodide + excess thiosulphate; 3 h/room temp.	+ excess iodine, then titrated biamperometrically with thiosulphate	31
Propylene oxide	+ excess thiosulphate	Titrated with acid	32
Acid number of oils	In isopropanol, + iodate/iodide + excess thiosulphate; 90 min/80°	Titrated with iodine	33

References

1. Kolthoff, I. M., *Chem. Weekblad* **23**, 260 (1926).
2. Ruziczka, W., *J. prakt. Chem.* **123**, 61 (1929).
3. Kaufmann, H. P., *Allgem. Öl Fett-Ztg.* **28**, 225, 248 (1931).
4. Matuszak, M. P., *Ind. Eng. Chem., Anal. Ed.* **6**, 457 (1934).
5. Kaufmann, H. P., Baltes, J. and Büter, H., *Ber.* **70**, 903 (1937).
6. Kaufmann, H. P. and Lund, M., *Fette u. Seifen* **46**, 390 (1939).
7. Vièles, P., *Bull. soc. chim.* **6**, 1127 (1939).
8. Ruziczka, W., *Z. anal. Chem.* **126**, 94 (1943).
9. Golumbic, C., Fruton, J. S. and Bergmann, M., *J. Org. Chem.* **11**, 518 (1946).
10. Foss, O., *Acta Chem. Scand.* **1**, 310 (1947).
11. Foss, O., *J. Am. Chem. Soc.* **70**, 421 (1948).

12. Kamath, N. R. and Mainkar, V. B., *Anal. Chem.* **22**, 724 (1950).
13. Nabar, G. M. and Padmanabhan, C. V., *Proc. Indian Acad. Sci.* **31A**, 371 (1950).
14. Ross, W. C. J., *J. Chem. Soc.* 2257 (1950).
15. Ruziczka, W., *Chim. anal.* **32**, 33 (1950).
16. Tyler, W. P. and Beesing, D. W., *Anal. Chem.* **24**, 1511 (1952).
17. Allen, E. and Seaman, W., *Anal. Chem.* **27**, 540 (1955).
18. Mizukami, S., Ieki, T. and Koyama, C., *J. Pharm. Soc. Japan* **76**, 465 (1956).
19. Bose, S., *J. Indian Chem. Soc.* **34**, 825 (1957).
20. Achwal, W. B., Nabar, G. M. and Padmanabhan, C. V., *J. Sci. Ind. Research* (*India*) **17B**, 497 (1958).
21. Bose, S., *Anal. Chem.* **30**, 1136 (1958).
22. Leary, J. B., *J. Am. Pharm. Assoc., Sci. Ed.* **49**, 606 (1960).
23. Lidaks, M., Licis, J. and Veiss, A., *Latvijas P.S.R. Zinatnu Akad. Vestis* No. 2, 101 (1960).
24. Sully, B. D., *Analyst* **85**, 895 (1960).
25. Verma, R. M. and Bose, S., *J. Indian Chem. Soc.* **37**, 540 (1960).
26. Saltzman, B. E., *Anal. Chem.* **33**, 1100 (1961).
27. Dässler, H-G., *Pharm. Zentralhalle* **101**, 409 (1962).
28. Raine, D. N., *J. Pharm. Pharmacol.* **14**, 614 (1962).
29. Ruzhentseva, A. K., Chivireva, A. M. and Leiferova, N. G., *Med. Prom. SSSR* **16**, 46 (1962).
30. Ashworth, M. R. F. and Winter, M., *Anal. Chim. Acta* **29**, 75 (1963).
31. Jedlinski, Z. and Paprotny, Z., *Chem. Anal.* (*Warsaw*) **8**, 765 (1963).
32. Polyanskii, N. G. and Potudina, N. L., *Zavodskaya Lab.* **29**, 802 (1963).
33. Vaillant, H., *Mikrochim. Acta* **93** (1963).

107. Thiourea

Thiourea has been used for the determination of halides by addition, yielding thiouronium salts:

$$R.Hal + CS(NH_2)_2 \rightarrow \left(R—C—S\begin{matrix}{=}NH_2 \\ {\diagdown}NH_2\end{matrix}\right)^+ Hal^-$$

In the two examples given, this was an intermediate stage in the determination of alcohols, which had previously been converted to the corresponding halides by reaction with HCl, HBr or $HCl/ZnCl_2$.

Materials titrated	Reagent and reaction conditions	Subsequent treatment and final titration stage	Ref.
Tertiary halides from determination of equivalent weight of tertiary alcohols by reaction with HCl or HBr	+ ethanol + thiourea. Refluxed 45 min–5 h	Thiouronium halide converted to picrate and titrated with $HClO_4$/acetic acid to crystal violet (see Part I, Perchloric acid, ref. 62 and Nitrophenols, ref. 55)	1
Secondary and tertiary halides from determination of alcohols by reaction with $HCl/ZnCl_2$	+ thiourea + KI; 1–3 h/*ca* 100°	Converted to 3,5-dinitrobenzoates, then determined with excess Ti(III) reagent (see Carboxylic acids and carboxylates, ref. 29; and Titanium (III), ref. 51)	2

References

1. Schotte, L. and Veibel, S., *Acta Chem. Scand.* **7**, 1357 (1953).
2. Jureček, M., Chládek, O., Chládková, R., Souček, M. and Srpová, B., *Chem. Listy* **51**, 448 (1957).

108. Tillmans' reagent

Although this reagent has been widely used as a direct titrant, especially of ascorbic acid, vitamin C, only a single example has been found of its use in indirect titration:

Materials titrated	Reagent and reaction conditions	Subsequent treatment and final titration stage
Vitamin C	+ slight excess of the Tillmans' reagent; 30 sec/room temp.	Back titrated with Fe(II) in the presence of Na oxalate

Reference

Kuhn, A., *Klin. Wochschr.* **20**, 1174 (1941).

109. Tin (II)

Reagent. Stannous chloride, generally in HCl solution.

Reaction and materials titrated. All determinations have been based on reduction according to:

$$Sn^{2+} \rightarrow Sn^{4+} + 2\,\epsilon$$

Over half the examples given are of the determination of nitro compounds. Others include azo compounds (also azo dyes), peroxides, and sulphoxides.

$$RNO_2 + 3\,Sn^{2+} + 6\,H^+ \rightarrow RNH_2 + 3\,Sn^{4+} + 2\,H_2O$$

$$RN{=}NR + 2\,Sn^{2+} + 4\,H^+ \rightarrow 2\,RNH_2 + 2\,Sn^{4+}$$

$$RS.SR + Sn^{2+} + 2\,H^+ \rightarrow 2\,RSH + Sn^{4+}$$

$$R_2S{\rightarrow}O + Sn^{2+} + 2\,H^+ \rightarrow R_2S + Sn^{4+} + H_2O$$

Reaction conditions. Most reductions have required heating and have been done in an inert atmosphere of CO_2 or nitrogen or even hydrogen.

Subsequent treatment and final titration stage. (i) Back titration of unused Sn(II) has been used in nearly every case, with iodine as the principal reagent. Numerous authors have found a dependence on the speed of iodine titration, so that standard conditions have been maintained and a control titration performed on the reagent under these same conditions.

Other back titration agents have been Fe(III) (to indigo carmine); $Cr_2O_7^{2-}$ (to external I^-/starch or to the first appearance of the colour of the originally titrated material through reoxidation); Ce(IV) (to *p*-ethoxychrysoidine); or Cu(II) (to orange yellow in presence of Br^-/acid). In one case, excess Fe(III) was added and the Fe(II) formed titrated with $Cr_2O_7^{2-}$.

(ii) In one of the examples, a reaction product was titrated, namely the mercaptan resulting from reduction of a disulphide; the titrant was Ag(I).

(iii) In one further example, the Sn(II) reduction was used to remove a component of the mixture for analysis (azo dyes). The unreduced triphenylmethane dyes could then be determined by a Ti(III) reduction.

Examples

Materials titrated	Reagent and reaction conditions	Subsequent treatment and final titration stage	Ref.
Aromatic nitro compounds, mostly with $—SO_3H$ group also	+ $SnCl_2/HCl$ reagent; warmed some min	+ Na_2CO_3 until precipitate formed had dissolved; titrated with iodine to starch	1
Nitro compounds	Principle of method of ref. 1		2
Peroxides	+ $SnCl_2$ in CO_2 atmosphere. *Ca* 5 min heating	Back titrated with iodine	3
Nitro compounds, e.g. *m*-dinitrobenzene	In ethanol + $SnCl_2/HCl$; 1·5–2 h heating in CO_2 atmosphere	Back titrated with iodine	4
Dinitrobenzene, from determination of benzene in gas by nitration with HNO_3/H_2SO_4	Evaporated ether extract, + ethanol + $SnCl_2/HCl$; 10 min/ca 100°	Diluted and aliquot titrated with iodine to starch	5
Nitro compounds	+ $SnCl_2/HCl/KBr$; 15 min boiling in CO_2 atmosphere	Back titrated to orange-yellow with strongly acid $CuSO_4/KBr$	6
Nitrotoluenes	+ $SnCl_2/HCl$. Heated to 100° Control titrated at the same rate	Diluted and titrated with iodine (maintained a steady rate of titration)	7
Nitro groups	In 95% ethanol, + $SnCl_2/HCl$; 2 h reflux in CO_2 atmosphere	Diluted and titrated with iodine	8
Nitro compounds (sulphonated first if volatile)	+ $SnCl_2$; 20 min reflux	Back titrated with iodine to starch	9
Azo compounds	+ $SnCl_2/HCl$ in CO_2 atmosphere	Back titrated with $Cr_2O_7^{2-}$ to external I^-/starch indicator	10
Mixtures of azo and triphenylmethane dyes	+ *ca* 2-fold excess $SnCl_2/HCl$; 3–12 min/80–100° or 18–24 h/room temp.	Triphenylmethane dye then determined with $TiCl_3$; total similarly determined and azo dye content got by difference	11
Methylene blue	Heated with $SnCl_2$ in CO_2 atmosphere	Back titrated with $Cr_2O_7^{2-}$ to blue	12

Materials titrated	Reagent and reaction conditions	Subsequent treatment and final titration stage	Ref.
Organic peroxides in motor fuel	Heated to 95° with $SnCl_2$ in CO_2 atmosphere	+ HCl and back titrated with $FeCl_3$/HCl to indigo carmine	13
Azo dyes	Solution in conc. H_2SO_4 + $SnCl_2$ + HCl; 45 min–2 h/100°. Soluble dyes needed 15–60 min reflux	+ a little I^-/starch and titrated with iodine or $Cr_2O_7^{2-}$	14
Nitrobenzene in mineral oils	In methanol/xylene, + at least 2-fold excess $SnCl_2$. In CO_2 atmosphere	Back titrated with iodine	15
Nitro groups	In ethanol, + H_2SO_4 + $SnCl_2$; 90 min/100° in CO_2 atmosphere	Rapidly back titrated with iodine	16
Quinones like 2-methyl-1,4-naphthoquinone	In 95% ethanol, + $SnCl_2$. Heated until colourless (1–2 min)	+ $KHCO_3$, filtered, acidified with H_2SO_4 and titrated with Ce(IV) to *p*-ethoxychrysoidine	17, 18
Sulphoxides; amine oxides	In ethanol or water, + $SnCl_2$/HCl; 45 min boiling in CO_2 atmosphere	+ conc. HCl and titrated with Fe alum to indigo trisulphonate	19
Condensation products of carbonyl compounds with *p*-nitrophenyl-hydrazine	In H_2SO_4, + $SnCl_2$; 30 min reflux or in alkali, + K stannate; 15 min reflux	Partly neutralized with $NaHCO_3$ and titrated with iodine slightly acidified, then + $NaHCO_3$ and titrated with iodine	20
Peroxides	In acetic acid, + $SnCl_2$/HCl; 1 h/room temp. in nitrogen atmosphere (benzoyl peroxide 1 h/80°)	+ excess boiling Fe alum + NH_4Cl, heated 30 sec at 70–75°, phosphoric acid/H_2SO_4 added and titrated with $Cr_2O_7^{2-}$ to diphenylamine sulphonic acid	21
Peroxides in presence of sulphoxides	Method of ref. 21		22
Some nitrofurane derivatives	In carbowax, + $SnCl_2$/HCl; 40 min in dark	+ water + $NaHCO_3$ and titrated with iodine	23
Dibenzothiazole disulphide	+ $SnCl_2$, giving mercaptobenzothiazole	Titrated with Ag(I) conductometrically or with iodine visually	24

Materials titrated	Reagent and reaction conditions	Subsequent treatment and final titration stage	Ref.
Derivatives of aromatic amines with 2,4-dinitrochlorobenzene	In acetic acid, + $SnCl_2$; 90 min/100°, to decoloration; CO_2 atmosphere	Back titrated with iodine	25
m-Nitrobenzoic acid	+ $SnCl_2$ in alkaline solution; 15 min/100° in hydrogen atmosphere	+ HCl + water and titrated with iodine	26
Some aromatic nitro and azo compounds	+ excess $SnCl_2$ reagent in CO_2 atmosphere	Back titrated iodometrically	27
Diphenoquinonedi-(4,4′-dimethylammonium) ion	+ excess $SnCl_2$ reagent in nitrogen atmosphere	Back titrated with iodine to starch	28

References

1. Limprecht, H., *Ber.* **11**, 35 (1878).
2. Claus, A. and Glassner, A., *Ber* **14**, 778 (1881).
3. v. Pechmann, H. and Vanino, L., *Ber.* **27**, 1512 (1894).
4. Young, S. W. and Swain, R. E., *J. Am. Chem. Soc.* **19**, 812 (1897).
5. Pfeiffer, *Chem.-Ztg.* **28**, 884 (1904).
6. Berry, A. J. and Colwell, C. K., *Chem. News* **112**, 1 (1915).
7. Colver, E. de W. S. and Prideaux, E. B. R., *J. Soc. Chem. Ind.* (*London*) **36**, 480 (1917).
8. Desvergnes, L., *Ann. chim. anal. chim. appl.* **2**, 141 (1920).
9. Wallerius, G., *Tek. Tid., Uppl. C.* (*Kemi*) **58**, 33 (1928).
10. Ostrozhinskaya, G., *Anilinokrasochnaya Prom.* No. 1, 18 (1933).
11. Kime, J. A., *Ind. Eng. Chem., Anal. Ed.* **5**, 151 (1933).
12. Shcherbachev, K. D., *Khim. Farm. Prom.* No. 2, 117 (1935).
13. Hock, H. and Schrader, O., *Naturwiss.* **24**, 159 (1936); *Brennstoffchemie* **18**, 6 (1937).
14. Kozlov, V. V. and Simanovskaya, A. V., *Zhur. Priklad Khim.* (*J. Appl. Chem. USSR*) **10**, 688 (1937).
15. Shikhutskaya, G., *Neftyanoe Khoz.* **18**, No. 10, 75 (1938).
16. Hinkel, L. E., Ayling, E. E. and Walters, T. M., *J. Chem. Soc.* 403 (1939).
17. Schulek, E. and Rozsa, P., *Magyar Kem. Folyoirat* **47**, 75 (1941).
18. Schulek, E. and Rozsa, P., *Ber.* **75**, 1548 (1942).
19. Glynn, E., *Analyst* **72**, 248 (1947).

20. Petit, G., *Bull. soc. chim. France* 141 (1948).
21. Barnard, D. and Hargrave, K. R., *Anal. Chim. Acta* **5**, 476 (1951).
22. Barnard, D. and Hargrave, K. R., *Anal. Chim. Acta* **6**, 23 (1952).
23. Carvajal, G., Ribas, A. and Méndez, A., *Anales escuela nacl. cienc. biol. (Mex.)* **8**, 131 (1955).
24. Lorenz, O. and Echte, E., *Kautschuk u. Gummi* **9**, WT 300 (1956).
25. Bräuniger, H. and Spangenberg, K., *Pharmazie* **12**, 491 (1957).
26. Lapin, N. N. and Slynsarev, A. T., *Zavodskaya Lab.* **23**, 1430 (1957).
27. Reichel, I. and Dobrescu, F., *Bul. Stiint. Technic. Inst. Politehnic Timisoara* **4**, 247 (1959).
28. Matrka, M., *Chem. Listy* **57**, 163 (1963).

110. Titanium (III)

Reagent. $TiCl_3$ in acid solution in most cases. The sulphate has been recommended with aromatic compounds in order to eliminate the risk of nuclear chlorination.

Reactions and materials titrated. 1. Reduction according to the equation:

$$Ti^{3+} \rightarrow Ti^{4+} + \epsilon$$

Functional groups or compound classes reduced include: nitro, nitroso and azo compounds; diazonium salts, osazones, quinones, nitrate esters, peroxides, sulphoxides and *N*-oxides. Some typical reactions undergone by the organic molecules are:

$$\text{—NO}_2 + 6\,Ti^{3+} + 6\,H^+ \rightarrow \text{—NH}_2 + 6\,Ti^{4+} + 2\,H_2O$$

$$\text{—NO} + 4\,Ti^{3+} + 4\,H^+ \rightarrow \text{—NH}_2 + 4\,Ti^{4+} + H_2O$$

$$\text{—SO—} + 2\,Ti^{3+} + 2\,H^+ \rightarrow \text{—S—} + 2\,Ti^{4+} + H_2O$$

$$\text{—CO—} + 2\,Ti^{3+} + 2\,H^+ \rightarrow \text{—CHOH—} + 2\,Ti^{4+}$$

(quinones)

$$\text{—ONO}_2 + 8\,Ti^{3+} + 8\,H^+ \rightarrow \text{—OH} + 8\,Ti^{4+} + NH_3 + 2\,H_2O$$

$$\text{—N=N—} + 4\,Ti^{3+} + 4\,H^+ \rightarrow 2\,\text{—NH}_2 + 4\,Ti^{4+} \text{ or,}$$

$$\text{—N=N—} + 2\,Ti^{3+} + 2\,H^+ \rightarrow \text{—NH—NH—} + 2\,Ti^{4+},$$

followed by benzidine transformation (ref. 64)

The equations are sometimes not exactly stoichiometric. Thus nitrate esters (the fifth example given) were found to require only 7·5 equivalents of reagent, which was explained by loss of nitric oxide (ref. 26). Nitroamines appear not always to be reduced to hydrazines with consumption of 6 equivalents of reagent. For example, nitrosoamines, —NH.NO are probably formed. The reduction of nitroglycerin has been postulated as follows:

$$\begin{array}{lclclcl} CH_2ONO_2 & & CH_2ONO_2 & & CH_2ONO_2 & & CH_2OH \\ | & & | & & | & & | \\ CHONO_2 & \rightarrow & CHONO & \rightarrow & CHOH & \rightarrow & CHOH \\ | & & | & & | & & | \\ CH_2ONO_2 & & CH_2ONO_2 & & CH_2ONO_2 & & CH_2OH \end{array} \quad \text{(ref. 39)}$$

2. One example is given of a reaction of presumably complex formation, in which a titanium derivative of tannic acid was precipitated.

Reaction conditions. Both acid and alkaline conditions have been used, the reaction proceeding faster in general in the latter.

Catalysts (see ref. 3) include hydrofluoric acid and polyhydroxy compounds, notably anions of hydroxy acids such as tartrates and citrates.

The reaction has nearly always been carried out in an inert atmosphere of nitrogen or carbon dioxide. The latter has also been generated by adding bicarbonate to acid solutions, instead of passing a current of gas through the apparatus.

In general, the reduction reaction is fast and reaction times have rarely exceeded about 10 min.

Subsequent treatment and final titration stage. (i) Back titration of unreacted Ti(III) in the majority of cases. This has been done as follows:

1. Usually with Fe(III) to SCN^- indicator; methylene blue has also been used as indicator (allowing for the quantity used) and potentiometric end-point determination.

2. With methylene blue and also other dyes like crystal scarlet and acid green, all of which function as their own indicators.

3. By adding Fe(III) and titrating the Fe(II), formed from the excess Ti(III), with an oxidizing reagent like bichromate, vanadate or Ce(IV).

(ii) Determination of an organic reaction product, e.g. aromatic amines (from Ti(III) reduction of nitro or nitroso compounds) with excess bromate/bromide, followed by iodometric back titration; or trimethylamine (from reduction of its oxide) by distillation into excess standard acid.

(iii) In one example, the Ti(III) reduction was used to remove an interfering material, namely, nitro compounds in propellants. The phthalate esters to be determined, were then extracted from the acid solution by petroleum ether and determined by saponification.

The titanometric determination of nitro compounds is reviewed in ref. 32.

Examples

Materials titrated	Reagent and reaction conditions	Subsequent treatment and final titration stage	Ref.
Nitro compounds, e.g. picric acid, *p*-nitro-aniline, dinitrobenzene-sulphonic acids; azo compounds	+ $TiCl_3$ excess, some + alcohol + HCl; 5 min boiling	Unused titrated with Fe(III) to SCN^-	1
Nitro compounds, e.g. trinitrocresol	+ $TiCl_3$ + HCl; 5 min boiling	Unused titrated with Fe(III) to SCN^-	2
azo dyes	+ tartrate		
Quinones	In water or acetic acid + excess $TiCl_3$	Unused titrated with Fe(III) to SCN^-	4
Unused picric acid from a precipitation determination of quinine alkaloids	+ HCl + excess $TiCl_3$; 10 min boiling	Unused titrated with Fe(III) to SCN^-	5
Nitro and nitroso compounds	Boiling solution + excess $TiCl_3$	+ excess methylene blue and back titrated boiling solution with $TiCl_3$ to decoloration	6
Alizarin and alizarin dyes	In ethanol, + tartrate + excess $TiCl_3$; brought to boiling	Titrated with Fe(III) to disappearance of blue-green of solution	7
Nitro compounds	In concentrated acid solution, + excess $TiCl_3$; boiled	Unused titrated with Fe(III) to SCN^-	8

Materials titrated	Reagent and reaction conditions	Subsequent treatment and final titration stage	Ref.
Aromatic nitro compounds	+ excess $Ti_2(SO_4)_3$, to avoid nuclear chlorination	Unused titrated with Fe(III) to SCN^-	9
Aromatic nitro compounds	+ $Ti_2(SO_4)_3$ to avoid nuclear chlorination	Unused titrated with Fe(III) to SCN^-	10
Nitro compounds, e.g. *p*-nitraniline	In water, ethanol or dilute acid, + H_2SO_4 + $TiCl_3$; 5 min boiling	Back titrated with Fe(III) to SCN^-	11
Diazonium salts	+ HCl + excess $TiCl_3$	Unused titrated with acid green dye after adding tartrate	12
p-nitroisodiazobenzene	+ tartrate + $TiCl_3$	unused titrated with crystal scarlet (both dyes act as their own indicator)	
Nitro compounds like picric acid derivatives and hexahydro 1,3,5-trinitro-*sym*-triazine	+ excess $TiCl_3$	Unused titrated with Fe(III) to SCN^-	13
Aromatic nitro compounds	Compared $TiCl_3$ and $Ti_2(SO_4)_3$	Unused titrated with Fe(III) to SCN^-	14
Nitroso compounds (vulcanization accelerators)	+ excess $TiCl_3$. Heated to 60–70°	Unused titrated with Fe(III) to SCN^-	15
Aromatic nitro compounds with *m*-substituent, e.g. *m*-nitrotoluene, *m*-nitrochlorobenzene	In water or ethanol, + H_2SO_4 + $TiCl_3$; 5 min or more boiling	Amine determined with excess BrO_3^-/Br^- and iodometric titration of unused (see Bromine reagents, ref. 35)	16
Glucosazone; osazones from determination of sugars with phenylhydrazine	+ excess $TiCl_3$. A few min boiling	+ HCl and back titrated with crystal scarlet	17, 18
Nitrobenzene	+ NaOH + $TiCl_3$ added until black persistent for 2 min; 5 min/room temp.	Allowed unused Ti(III) to oxidize and determined aniline with excess BrO_3^-/Br^- (see Bromine reagents, ref. 44)	19

Materials titrated	Reagent and reaction conditions	Subsequent treatment and final titration stage	Ref.
Nitro compounds, e.g. nitroanilines, picric acid, nitrobenzene and -naphthalene	+ citrate + bicarbonate (to give CO_2 with acid reagent) + excess $TiCl_3$; 2 min/room temp.	Unused titrated potentiometrically with Fe(III); or + HCl and titrated with Fe(III) to SCN^-	20
Tannic acid	In water, + $(NH_4)_2CO_3$ + excess $TiCl_3$ giving precipitate of $TiO(C_{14}H_{10}O_9)$	Filtered and unused titrated with Fe(III) to SCN^-	21
Dinitrobenzene from determination of benzene by nitration with HNO_3/H_2SO_4	+ excess $TiCl_3$	Back titrated with Fe(III) to SCN^-	22
Aromatic nitro compounds	In acetic acid + citrate + bicarbonate (to give CO_2); $TiCl_3$ added until solution dark violet; 2 min/room temp.	+ conc. HCl and titrated with Fe(III) to SCN^-	23
2,4-Dinitrotoluene (in presence of nitroglycerine previously reduced with Fe(II))	In acetic acid + *ca* twice the expected equivalent of $TiCl_3$; 5 min boiling	Back titrated with Fe(III) to SCN^-	24
Nitrobenzene in oils	+ xylene + methanol + H_2SO_4 + excess $Ti_2(SO_4)_3$; 10–20 min reflux	Unused titrated with Fe(III) to SCN^-	25
Aliphatic nitrate esters	In acetic acid + $Ti_2(SO_4)_3$; 20 min boiling	Unused titrated with Fe(III) to methylene blue	26
p-Nitro- and 2,4-dinitrophenylhydrazones	+ *ca* 1·75 times the expected equivalent of $TiCl_3$ or $Ti_2(SO_4)_3$	Unused titrated with methylene blue; or excess methylene blue added and back titrated with Ti(III)	27
Nitrobenzene in oil (up to 5%)	Method of ref. 25		28
Dinitrobenzene from determination of benzene in air by nitration	+ $TiCl_3$/HCl	Unused titrated with Fe(III) to SCN^-	29

Materials titrated	Reagent and reaction conditions	Subsequent treatment and final titration stage	Ref.
2,4-Dinitrophenyl-hydrazones of ketones and aldehydes, e.g. ascorbic acid	In methanol, + excess $TiCl_3$. Heated to *ca* 60°	Unused titrated with Fe(III) to SCN^- or with methylene blue	30
Nitroglycerine	In 95% ethanol, + $TiCl_3$; 10 min/room temp., then 10 min boiling and finally 10 min/0°	Unused titrated with Fe(III) to SCN^-	31
2,3,5,7-Tetranitro-naphthalene; picramic acid	+ excess $TiCl_3$ after 5 min/100° with ethanol/drops H_2SO_4; 15 min	Unused titrated with Fe(III) to methylene blue	33
Dinitrotoluene in smokeless powder	In acetic acid/Na acetate, + excess $TiCl_3$; 15 sec/room temp.	+ HCl and unused titrated with Fe(III) to SCN^-	34
Nitroguanidine	+ HCl + $TiCl_3$ excess; 15 min reflux	Unused titrated with Fe(III) to SCN^-	35
RDX (cyclotrimethy-lenetrinitramine)	in acetic acid, + $FeCl_2$ + HCl + *ca* 3 times equivalent of $TiCl_3$; 30 min reflux	unused titrated with Fe(III) to SCN^-	
Nitroamines, e.g. nitro-urea and nitroguanidine; some nitroso compounds	In 1:1 HCl, + $TiCl_3$; 15 min reflux; $FeSO_4$ added to some before reflux	Back titrated with Fe(III) to SCN^-	36
Saturated sulphoxides	In acetic acid, + $TiCl_3$/HCl; 1 h/80°	+ boiling Fe(III) after 30 sec, + CCl_4 (to dissolve sulphide reaction products) + H_3PO_4 and Fe(II) titrated with $Cr_2O_7^{2-}$ to diphenylamine sulphonate	37
unsaturated sulphoxides	in acetic acid, + $TiCl_3$/HCl; 1 h/80°	unused titrated with Fe(III) to SCN^-	
2,4-Dinitrotoluene in American powders	+ excess $TiCl_3$	Back titrated with Fe(III)	38
Nitroglycerine	In 70% acetic acid, + excess $Ti_2(SO_4)_3$; 10 min reflux (modification of method of ref. 31)	Unused titrated with Fe(III) to SCN^-	39

Materials titrated	Reagent and reaction conditions	Subsequent treatment and final titration stage	Ref.
Nitrobenzohydrazone, precipitated in determination of methylglyoxal	+ HCl + excess $TiCl_3$; 5 min boiling	Unused titrated with Fe(III) to SCN^-	40
Unused 2,4-dinitrophenylhydrazine from determination of carbonyl compounds by precipitation	+ excess $TiCl_3$ + HF. Heated to boiling	Unused titrated with Fe(III) to SCN^-	41 42
Sulphoxides in presence of hydroperoxides	Method of ref. 37		43
Trimethylamine oxide in fish	+ $TiCl_3$ or $Ti_2(SO_4)_3$, giving trimethylamine	Diffused into excess HCl and back titrated with NaOH to methyl red	44
Unused 4-nitro-,2,4-dinitro- and 2,4,6-trinitrophenylhydrazine from determination of carbonyl compounds by precipitation	+ excess $TiCl_3$	Unused titrated with Fe(III) to SCN^-	45
Nitroguanidine and derivatives	In 10% acetic acid + citrate (pH 3·5–4·5) + excess $TiCl_3$; 3 min/room temp.	+ HCl and titrated with Fe(III) to SCN^-	46
Nitroguanidine	+ excess $TiCl_3$ + HCl + $FeSO_4$. Refluxed (studied reactions)	Back titrated with Fe(III) to SCN^-	47
Phthalate esters in propellants, in presence of nitro compounds	In 84% acetic acid + $TiCl_3$; 5 min/60°, then 5 min/100° to reduce the nitro compounds	Esters extracted with petroleum ether and determined by saponification (see Alkalies, ref. 314)	48
5-Nitrosalicylic acid from determination of cellulose nitrate and nitroguanidine by reaction with salicylic acid/H_2SO_4	+ excess $TiCl_3$; 1 min boiling	Unused titrated with Fe(III) to SCN^-	49
Chloramphenicol	In water, + $TiCl_3$ + HCl+$NaHCO_3$(→CO_2) 5 min gentle boiling	Unused titrated with Fe(III) to SCN^-	50

Materials titrated	Reagent and reaction conditions	Subsequent treatment and final titration stage	Ref.
Alkylthiouronium 3,5-dinitrobenzoates from determination of secondary and tertiary alcohols by conversion to chlorides with HCl/$ZnCl_2$, followed by reaction with thiourea/KI and then with Na 3,5-dinitrobenzoate	In ethanol, + citrate + excess $TiCl_3$; 2 min/room temp.	+ HCl and titrated with Fe(III) to SCN^-	51
Sulphoxides	+ $TiCl_3$ excess; 1 h/80°	+ excess Fe(III)/$(NH_4)_2SO_4$, then + H_2SO_4 + H_3PO_4; sulphides extracted with *n*-butanol and CCl_4 and Fe(II) in aqueous phase titrated with $Cr_2O_7^{2-}$ to diphenylamine sulphonate	52
Mono-, di- and trinitro compounds	+ polyphosphate + excess $TiCl_3$	Unused titrated with Ce(IV), VO_4^{3-} or $Cr_2O_7^{2-}$ to diphenylamine sulphonate, indigo carmine or methylene blue	53
Nitroguanidine	Extract, + Na acetate (pH 5) + excess $TiCl_3$; 3 min/room temp.	Unused titrated with Fe(III) to SCN^-	54
Nitroguanidine	+ NaOH/Na acetate, pH *ca* 11·5, + excess $TiCl_3$. Also method of ref. 49. Compared with other methods	Back titrated with Fe(III) to SCN^-	55
Unused 2,4-dinitrophenylhydrazine from reaction with benzaldehyde, yielded in determination of benzal groups by hydrolysis	+ excess $TiCl_3$ + HCl + HF; 30 min boiling	Unused titrated with Fe(III) to SCN^-	56
Nitroguanidine	+ NaOH + Na acetate, pH 11·5, + excess $TiCl_3$; 3 min/room temp.	+ HCl and titrated with Fe(III) to SCN^-	57
Cyclotrimethylene trinitroamine (RDX)	In acetic acid/HCl, + citrate + excess $TiCl_3$; 30 min reflux	Back titrated with Fe(III) to SCN^-	58

Materials titrated	Reagent and reaction conditions	Subsequent treatment and final titration stage	Ref.
2,4-Dinitrophenylhydrazones of carbonyl compounds separated by paper chromatography	Extract from cut-out strips in acetic acid, + Na acetate + excess $TiCl_3$; 5–10 min/50°	+ HCl and unused titrated with Fe(III) to SCN^-	59
N-oxides, e.g. of pyridine and related compounds	In water, + NH_4SCN (for complex formation in some cases) + excess $TiCl_3$; 5–60 min/room temp.	Unused titrated with Fe(III)	60
Nitroso and nitro compounds (micro)	In 95% ethanol, + Na acetate; $TiCl_3$ added to colour change; 3 min/room temp.	+ HCl and titrated with Fe(III) to SCN^-	61
5-Nitrosalicylic acid from determination of cellulose nitrate by reaction with salicylic acid/H_2SO_4	+ excess $TiCl_3$; 45–50 min/room temp.	Back titrated with Fe(III) to SCN^-	62
Peroxides in essential oils	+ *tert*-butanol + $TiCl_3$ + H_2SO_4; 10 min/room temp.	Unused titrated with Fe(III) to methylene blue	63
Azo, nitro, nitroarylhydrazines and diazonium compounds	+ some ethanol, in acetate buffer, + $TiCl_3$; also in HCl for determination of azo compounds in presence of nitro compounds; 3–10 min/room temp.	+ HCl and unused titrated with Fe(III) to SCN^- as in method of ref. 61	64
Nitro compounds; also mixtures with nitrate esters	In acetic acid, + $TiCl_3$ reagent; 5 min reflux, in CO_2	Unused titrated with Fe(III) to SCN^-	65
gem-Dinitro and trinitro compounds	In acetic acid, + $TiCl_3$ reagent; 10 min reflux in CO_2	Unused titrated with Fe(III) to SCN^-	66
Organic peroxides	In acetone + Na acetate/water + $TiCl_3$ in nitrogen atmosphere; 5 min	+ HCl and unused titrated with Fe(III) to SCN^-	67

Materials titrated	Reagent and reaction conditions	Subsequent treatment and final titration stage	Ref.
Benzoquinone; 2-methyl-1,4-naphthoquinone	In acetic acid, + $Ti_2(SO_4)_3$	Back titrated with $Ce(SO_4)_2$ photometrically at 290 or 320 mu respectively; titration equalled distance between the 2 breaks	68
Nitro compounds	In acetic acid or ethanol, + dilute H_2SO_4 + $Ti_2(SO_4)_3$; mostly with 30 min reflux, some only 10–15 min, some 1 h; nitrogen atmosphere	Unused titrated with Fe(III) to SCN^-	69
Nitro compounds	In acetic acid, + citrate catalyst + Ti sulphate reagent; 1 min, then warmed 1 min; nitrogen atmosphere	+ H_2SO_4 and back titrated with Fe(III) to SCN^-	70

References

1. Knecht, E. and Hibbert, E., *Ber.* **36**, 1554 (1903).
2. Knecht, E. and Hibbert, E., *Ber.* **40**, 3820, 3822 (1907).
3. Piccard, J., *Ber.* **42**, 4341 (1909).
4. Knecht, E. and Hibbert, E., *Ber.* **43**, 3455 (1910).
5. Kleinstück, M., *Pharm. Zentralhalle* **53**, 643, 680, 705 (1912).
6. Salvaterra, H., *Chem.-Ztg.* **38**, 90 (1914).
7. Knecht, E. and Hibbert, E., *J. Soc. Dyers Colourists* **31**, 241 (1915).
8. van Duin, C. F., *Chem. Weekblad* **16**, 1111 (1919).
9. Callan, T., Henderson, J. A. R. and Strafford, N., *J. Soc. Chem. Ind.* (*London*) **39**, 86T (1920).
10. van Duin, C. F., *Rec. trav. chim.* **39**, 578 (1920).
11. English, F. L., *Ind. Eng. Chem.* **12**, 994 (1920).
12. Knecht, E. and Thompson, L., *J. Soc. Dyers Colourists* **36**, 215 (1920).
13. Rathsburg, H., *Ber.* **54**, 3183 (1921).
14. Callan, T. and Henderson, J. A. R., *J. Soc. Chem. Ind.* (*London*) **41**, 157T (1922).
15. Callan, T. and Strafford, N., *J. Soc. Chem. Ind.* (*London*) **43**, 1T (1924).
16. Francis, A. W. and Hill, A. J., *J. Am. Chem. Soc.* **46**, 2498 (1924).
17. Knecht, E. and Hibbert, E., *J. Chem. Soc.* 1537 (1924).
18. Knecht, E. and Hibbert, E., *J. Chem. Soc.* 2009 (1924).
19. Kolthoff, I. M., *Chem. Weekblad* **22**, 558 (1925).

20. Kolthoff, I. M. and Robinson, C., *Rec. trav. chim.* **45**, 169 (1926).
21. Kirshna, S. and Nathu Ram, *Ber.* **61**, 771 (1928).
22. Smyth, H. F., *J. Ind. Hyg.* **11**, 338 (1929).
23. Maruyama, S., *Sci. Papers Inst. Phys.-Chem. Research, Tokyo* **16**, 196 (1931).
24. Becker, W. W., *Ind. Eng. Chem., Anal. Ed.* **5**, 151 (1933).
25. Anding, C. E., Zieber, B. and Malisoff, W. M., *Ind. Eng. Chem., Anal. Ed.* **6**, 41 (1934).
26. Oldham, J. W. H., *J. Soc. Chem. Ind., London* **53**, 263T (1934).
27. MacBeth, A. K. and Price, J. R., *J. Chem. Soc.* 151 (1935).
28. Kurtz, S. S., Headington, C. E. and Zieber, B., *Ind. Eng. Chem., Anal. Ed.* **8**, 1 (1936).
29. Air Hygiene Foundn. of America Inc., *Inst. Preventive Eng. Ser. Bull.* No. 2, Pt. 1 (1938).
30. Espil, L. and Genevois, L., *Bull. soc. chim. France* (5) **5**, 1532 (1938); also Espil, L. and Mandillon, G., *Compt. rend. soc. biol.* **129**, 1187 (1938).
31. Shankster, M. and Wilde, T. H., *J. Soc. Chem. Ind., London* **57**, 91T (1938).
32. Genevois, L., *Chim. anal.* **29**, 101 (1947).
33. Loriente, E. and Niete, F., *Ion* **7**, 11 (1947).
34. Butts, P. G., Meikle, W. J., Shovers, J., Kouba, D. L. and Becker, W. W., *Anal. Chem.* **20**, 947 (1948).
35. Kouba, D. L., Kicklighter, R. C. and Becker, W. W., *Anal. Chem.* **20**, 948 (1948).
36. Zimmerman, R. P. and Lieber, E., *Anal. Chem.* **22**, 1151 (1950).
37. Barnard, D. and Hargrave, K. R., *Anal. Chim. Acta* **5**, 476, 536 (1951).
38. Dalbert, R. and Tranchant, J., *Mém. poudres* **33**, 383 (1951).
39. Fainer, P., *Can. J. Chem.* **29**, 46 (1951).
40. Prey, V., Waldmann, E. and Ludwig, F., *Monatsh.* **82**, 1022 (1951).
41. Schöniger, W. and Lieb, H., *Mikrochemie ver. Mikrochim. Acta* **38**, 165 (1951).
42. Schöniger, W., Lieb, H. and Gassner, K., *Z. anal. Chem.* **134**, 188 (1951).
43. Barnard, D. and Hargrave, K. R., *Anal. Chim. Acta* **6**, 23 (1952).
44. Hjorth-Hansen, S., *Anal. Chim. Acta* **6**, 438 (1952).
45. Schöniger, W., Lieb, H. and Gassner, K., *Mikrochim. Acta* 434 (1953).
46. Sternglanz, P. D., Thompson, R. C. and Savell, W. L., *Anal. Chem.* **25**, 1111 (1953).
47. Brandt, W. W., DeVries, J. E. and Gantz, E. St. C., *Anal. Chem.* **27**, 392 (1955).
48. Grodzinski, J., *Anal. Chem.* **27**, 1765 (1955).
49. Stalcup, H. and Williams, R. W., *Anal. Chem.* **27**, 543 (1955).

50. Awe, W. and Stohlmann, H., *Arzneimittelforsch.* **7**, 495 (1957).
51. Jureček, M., Chládek, O., Chládková, R., Souček, M. and Srpová, B., *Chem. Listy* **51**, 448 (1957).
52. Legault, R. R. and Groves, K., *Anal. Chem.* **29**, 1495 (1957).
53. Suzuki, S., Muramoto, Y., Ueno, M. and Sugano, T., *Bull. Chem. Soc. Japan* **30**, 775 (1957).
54. Wegman, R. T. and Roth, M., *U.S. Dept. Com. Office, Tech. Service, PB Rept.* 129650 (1957).
55. Fauth, M. I. and Stalcup, H., *Anal. Chem.* **30**, 1671 (1958).
56. Jureček, M. and Obruba, K., *Chem. Listy* **52**, 2066 (1958).
57. Roth, M. and Wegman, R. F., *Anal. Chem.* **30**, 2036 (1958).
58. Stanek, J. and Vacek, J., *Chem. průmysl* **8**, 361 (1958).
59. Blom, L. and Caris, J., *Nature* **184**, Suppl. No. 17, 1313 (1959).
60. Brooks, R. T. and Sternglanz, P. D., *Anal. Chem.* **31**, 561 (1959).
61. Ma, T. S. and Earley, J. V., *Mikrochim. Acta* 129 (1959).
62. Mullen, J. D., *Anal. Chim. Acta* **20**, 16 (1959).
63. van Os, F. H. L. and Schollens, C., *France et ses Parfums* **3**, No. 13, 30 (1959).
64. Earley, J. V. and Ma, T. S., *Mikrochim. Acta* 685 (1960).
65. Marvillet, L. and Tranchant, J., *Mém. poudres* **42**, 271 (1960).
66. Fauth, M. I. and Roecker, G. W., *Anal. Chem.* **33**, 894 (1961).
67. Ma, T. S. and Gerstein, T., *Microchem. J.* **5**, 163 (1961).
68. Shimomura, S., *Yakugaku Zasshi* **81**, 1412 (1961).
69. Tiwari, R. D. and Sharma, J. P., *Z. anal. Chem.* **191**, 329 (1962).
70. Tiwari, R. D. and Sharma, J. P., *Anal. Chem.* **35**, 1307 (1963).

111. Vanadate

Reagent. Usually sodium, potassium or ammonium metavanadate; an example is included of the use of vanadium pentoxide.

Reaction and materials titrated. The determinations depend on oxidation:

$$VO_3^- + 4\,H^+ + \epsilon \rightarrow VO^{2+} + 2\,H_2O$$

A wide variety of materials has been determined, principally carboxylic acids (oxalic, tartaric, citric, lactic, gallic) and hydroxy compounds (glycerol, mannitol, tannins, adrenaline, gallic acid—mentioned under carboxylic acids). Most of the oxidations lead to CO_2, formic or acetic acid as end-products. A few specimen equations are given below:

$$(COOH)_2 + O \rightarrow 2\,CO_2 + H_2O$$

(tartaric acid) $C_4H_6O_6 + 4\,O \rightarrow 3\,CO_2 + HCOOH + 2\,H_2O$

(uric acid) $C_5H_4N_4O_3 + 2\,H_2O + O \rightarrow C_4H_2N_2O_4$ (alloxan) $+ 2\,NH_3 + CO_2$

(phthalocyanines) $(C_8H_4N_2)_4H_2 + 7\,H_2O + O \rightarrow$
$4\,C_8H_5O_2N$ (phthalimide) $+ 4\,NH_3$

(citric acid) $C_6H_8O_7 + O \rightarrow (CH_3)_2CO + 3\,CO_2 + H_2O$

$$RCHO + O \rightarrow RCOOH$$

Reaction conditions. In strongly acid (H_2SO_4) solution (excepting the example using V_2O_5—ref. 17), mostly with heating.

Subsequent treatment and final titration stage. (i) Unreacted vanadate titrated with Fe(II) (usually ferrous ammonium sulphate) to indicators like *N*-phenylanthranilic acid.

(ii) In a small number of cases, the VO^{2+} formed was titrated with MnO_4^- or Ce(IV).

Refs 21 and 23 are to reviews of applications of vanadate reagent in analysis.

Examples

Materials titrated	Reagent and reaction conditions	Subsequent treatment and final titration stage	Ref.
Naphthalene and naphthalene-sulphonic acids	$+ H_2SO_4 + NH_4VO_3$; 15 min/120°, oxidizing to phthalic acid	+ water and reduced vanadium titrated with MnO_4^-	1
Pyramidone	In 8–10N H_2SO_4 + vanadate	Unreacted vanadate titrated with Fe(II)	2
Tartaric, oxalic acids	+ conc. H_2SO_4 + vanadate at 100°	Unused reagent back titrated with Fe(II)	3
Indigocarmine; indigo	+ acid + $NaVO_3$; left until the blue colour disappeared (oxalic acid as catalyst)	Back titrated with Fe(II)	4
Tetraethylthiuram disulphide ('Stopetyl')	$+ HNO_3 + NH_4VO_3$, oxidizing to sulphate	Back titrated potentiometrically or conductometrically	5
Tannins	$+ H_2SO_4 + NaVO_3$; heated to 30–40°	Back titrated with Fe(II) to phenylanthranilic acid	6

Materials titrated	Reagent and reaction conditions	Subsequent treatment and final titration stage	Ref.
Citric, tartaric and malic acids	+ KVO_3 + H_2SO_4 + water; 5 min reflux, 5–6 min reflux and 25–30 min/80° respectively	Back titrated with Fe(II) to phenylanthranilic acid	7
Na oxalate	+ vanadate + H_2SO_4 (giving evolution of heat); 3–10 min (standardization of vanadate in reality)	+ water and titrated with Fe(II) to blue of VO^{2+}, then phenylanthranilic acid added and titration concluded to this indicator	8
5,7-Dibromooxine; metal oxinates	+ NH_4VO_3 + H_2SO_4; 1 h/100°	Back titrated with Fe(II)	9
Phthalocyanines; Cu phthalocyanines and their sulphonic acids	+ phosphoric acid + 2–10N H_2SO_4 + $NaVO_3$; 5–60 min/100°	Back titrated with Fe(II)	10
Isoniazid in aqueous solution	In water, + $NaVO_3$ + H_2SO_4; 1 min	Back titrated with Fe(II) to phenylanthranilic acid	11
2,5- and 2,7-naphthalenedisulphonic acids	(after separation of Cu electrolytically), + at least 70% H_2SO_4 + HVO_3; 15 min/100°, giving phthalic acid	V(IV) titrated with MnO_4^-	12
Lactic acid	+ $NaVO_3$ + H_2SO_4; 10 min/100° (studied oxidation of polyalcohols and other acids also)	+ further H_2SO_4 and titrated with Fe(II) to phenylanthranilic acid	13
Glycerol	+ NH_4VO_3 + H_2SO_4; 1 h/100°	+ further H_2SO_4 and titrated as in ref. 13	14
Uric acid	+ H_2SO_4 + $NaVO_3$; 15 min/room temp.	Back titrated with Fe(II) to phenylanthranilic acid	15
'Analgin'	+ H_2SO_4 + NH_4VO_3; 10 min	Unreacted vanadate titrated with Fe(II) to phenylanthranilic acid	16
Butyllithium (n- and *tert*-)	In heptane + weighed amount V_2O_5; 10 min in argon atmosphere	+ H_2SO_4 + boiling water and titrated hot with Ce(IV) potentiometrically	17
Various organic compounds, e.g. acids, alcohols, aldehydes, ketones	+ NH_4VO_3 + H_2SO_4. A few min to several hours/*ca* 100°	Back titrated with Fe(II) to phenylanthranilic acid	18

Materials titrated	Reagent and reaction conditions	Subsequent treatment and final titration stage	Ref.
Pyramidone; tannin	Method of ref. 18, with 90 min/100°		19
Hydroxy acids from determination of amino acids by reaction with nitrite/acid	+ $NaVO_3$ in 12N H_2SO_4; 50 min reflux	Back titrated with Fe(II) to phenylanthranilic acid or potentiometrically	20
Adrenaline	+ excess NH_4VO_3; 9 min/*ca* 100°	+ H_2SO_4 and back titrated with Fe(II) to phenylanthranilic acid	22
p-Phenylenediamine	+ H_2SO_4(1–6N) + $NaVO_3$; 5 min	Back titrated with Fe(II)	24

References

1. Calcott, W. S., English, F. L. and Downing, F. B., *Ind. Eng. Chem.* **16**, 27, 1190 (1924).
2. Cherkasov, V. M. and Petrova, V. A., *Zhur. Anal. Khim.* **5**, 305 (1950).
3. Gopala Rao, G. and Gowda, H. S., *Current Sci.* (*India*) **21**, 188 (1952).
4. Gopala Rao, G. and Sastri, M. N., *Current Sci.* (*India*) **21**, 189 (1952).
5. Parrák, V., *Farmácia* **22**, No. 11–12, 19 (1953).
6. Suranova, Z. P., *Trudy Odessk. Univ. Sbornik Khim. Fakul'teta* **3**, 73 (1953).
7. Suranova, Z. P., *Trudy Odessk. Gosudarst. Univ. in I.I. Mechnikova, Sbornik Khim. Fak.* **4**, 65 (1954).
8. West, D. M. and Skoog, D. A., *Anal. Chim. Acta* **12**, 301 (1955).
9. Nazarenko, V. A. and Vinkovetskaya, S. Ya., *Zhur. Anal. Khim.* **11**, 572 (1956).
10. Gopala Rao, G. and Sastri, T. P., *Z. anal. Chem.* **169**, 11 (1959).
11. Gowda, H. S. and Gopala Rao, G., *Z. anal. Chem.* **165**, 36 (1959).
12. Semenchuk, O. V. and Stulova, L. M., *Trudy Vsesoyuz. Nauch.-Issledovatel. Inst. Zvukozapisi* No. 6, 139 (1959).
13. West, D. M. and Skoog, D. A., *Anal. Chem.* **31**, 583 (1959).
14. West, D. M. and Skoog, D. A., *Anal. Chem.* **31**, 586 (1959).
15. Gopala Rao, G. and Murty, B. V. S. R., *Z. Anal. Chem.* **174**, 44 (1960).
16. Nosenkova, N. G., *Trudy Sverdlovsk. Sel'skokhoz. Inst.* **7**, 369 (1960).
17. Collins, P. F., Kamienski, C. W., Esmay, D. L. and Ellestad, R. B., *Anal. Chem.* **33**, 468 (1961).

18. Eremina, Z. I. and Gurevich, V. G., *Farm. Zhur.* (*Kiev*) **16**, No. 1, 13 (1961).
19. Eremina, Z. I. and Gurevich, V. G., *Farm. Zhur.* (*Kiev*) **16**, No. 2, 17 (1961).
20. Rao, S. P., Rathi, H. S. and Gaur, J. V., *Anal. Chim. Acta* **25**, 136 (1961).
21. Berka, A., Vulterin, J. and Zýka, J., *Chemist-Analyst* **51**, 24 (1962).
22. Skibina, E. M., *Tr. Khar'kovsk. Farmatsevt. Inst.* No. 2 129 (1962).
23. Dhont, J. H., *Chem. Tech.* (*Amsterdam*) **18**, No. 1 19 (1963).
24. Sastry, T. P., *Z. Anal. Chem.* **195**, 349 (1963).

112. Vanadium (II)

General remarks. The analyses are all based on reduction according to the equation:

$$V^{2+} \rightarrow V^{3+} + \epsilon$$

Mostly nitro compounds have been determined:

$$RNO_2 + 6\,V^{2+} + 6\,H^+ \rightarrow RNH_2 + 2\,H_2O + 6\,V^{3+}$$

Some diazo compounds and triphenylmethane and other dyes have also been determined with V(II).

Conclusion has been by titration of unused reagent, usually with Fe(III) but in one quoted case with $Cr_2O_7^{2-}$.

The reagent has been prevented from air oxidation by working in an inert gas atmosphere.

Examples

Materials titrated	Reagent and reaction conditions	Subsequent treatment and final titration stage	Ref.
Nitrophenols, e.g. picric acid; nitroaniline	+ *ca* 300% excess V(II) in CO_2 atmosphere; 5 min	Back titrated with Fe alum to safranine	1
Nitro compounds like picric acid, nitro- and *m*-dinitrobenzene; *p*-nitroaniline; certain dyes like indigo and methylene blue	+ large excess VSO_4, with or without buffer. In CO_2 atmosphere. Usually boiled	Titrated with Fe alum to SCN^-	2

Materials titrated	Reagent and reaction conditions	Subsequent treatment and final titration stage	Ref.
Nitro compounds, e.g. dinitrophenylhydrazones in determination of carbonyl compounds; dinitrobenzoates from determination of —OH groups; picrates of amines or hydrocarbons; 2,4-dinitrophenyl ethers from determination of glycine	+ excess VSO_4. Various conditions	Back titrated with $Cr_2O_7^{2-}$ to phenosafranine	3
Difficultly reducible nitro compounds, e.g. nitroguanidines or 5-nitroxylene	In ethanol or dil. acetic acid, + acetate buffer; 1–5 min/room temp. In oxygen-free atmosphere	+ H_2SO_4 and titrated with Fe(III) to phenosafranine	4
E.g. methylene blue, Lauth's violet		Potentiometric back titration with Fe alum compared with that to safranine T or neutral red	5
Diazophenols or naphthols with —Cl, —COOH or —SO_3H groups	+ HCl + VSO_4; 5 min. In CO_2 or N_2 atmosphere	Back titrated with Fe alum to safranine	6
Hydroxytriphenylmethane dyes, e.g. aurin	In ethanol/H_2SO_4 (prelinary short heating), + VSO_4; 1 min. In N_2 atmosphere	Back titrated with Fe alum to safranine T or potentiometrically	7

References

1. Gapchenko, M. V. and Sheintsis, O. G., *Zavodskaya Lab.* **9**, 562 (1940).
2. Banerjee, P. C., *J. Indian Chem. Soc.* **19**, 35 (1942).
3. Witry-Schwachtgen, G., *Inst. Grand-Ducal Luxembourg, Sect. Sci. nat. phys. et math., Arch.* **22**, 87 (1955).
4. Ellis, C. M. and Vogel, A. I., *Analyst* **81**, 693 (1956).
5. Matrka, M. and Ságner, Z., *Chem. Průmysl* **9**, 526 (1959).
6. Nemodruk, A. A. and Oreshko, V. F., *Izvest. Vysshikh. Ucheb. Zavedenii, Khim. i Khim. Tekhnol.* **3**, 316 (1960).
7. Matrka, M. and Ságner, Z., *Chem. Průmysl* **11**, 135 (1961).

113. Water

Reagent and reaction conditions. The overall equation for hydrolyses is commonly written with participation of one or more molecules of water:

$$—X—Y— + H_2O \rightarrow —XH + HOY—$$

Some reactions of addition may be similarly formulated, e.g.

$$—C{\equiv}C— + H_2O \rightarrow —CO—CH_2—$$

$$—C{\equiv}N + H_2O \rightarrow —CONH_2$$

$$\underset{\diagdown O \diagup}{—C—C} + H_2O \rightarrow \underset{OH}{—C}—\underset{OH}{C—}$$

In fact, few reactions are carried out with pure water as a reagent, but make use of a catalyst. As a rough general rule, such reactions have been classified in this book under the catalytic agent and the reader is referred to the various acid reagents (notably Hydrochloric and Sulphuric acids) and basic reagents (notably Alkalies). The section here contains a small selection of examples in near-neutral solution and some others with less frequently used catalysts like BF_3, Hg(II) salts, NaI and pyridine. In the determination of amines and hydroxyl compounds using anhydride reagents, a control titration is often performed, in which a reagent sample is hydrolysed with water (usually + pyridine catalyst). Examples of this are not included in the tables below, but the use of the control titration is mentioned under Anhydrides (p. 130).

Reactions and materials titrated. 1. Hydrolysis of various bonds, e.g.

C—O in anhydrides and some esters

C—Cl in acid chlorides and some other reactive halides

S—Cl in sulphonyl chlorides

C—Metal in metal-organic compounds like Grignard reagents or metal alkyls and aryls

C≡N in nitriles (considered as hydrolysis but can be equally well regarded as addition)

2. Addition to certain multiple bonds like acetylene, isothiocyanate and, in the determination of lobeline, evidently to an olefinic link:

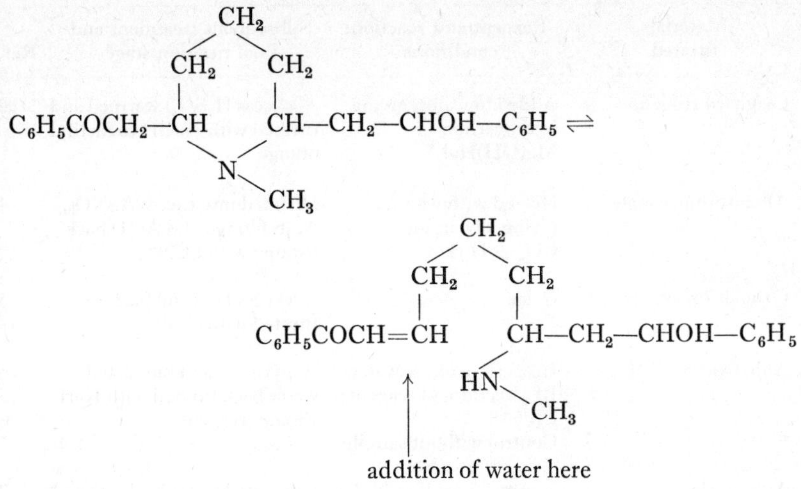

```
                  CH2
                 /   \
              CH2     CH2
               |       |
C6H5COCH2—CH          CH—CH2—CHOH—C6H5  ⇌
                 \   /
                  N
                   \
                    CH3

                                   CH2
                                  /   \
                               CH2     CH2
                                |       |
                 C6H5COCH=CH           CH—CH2—CHOH—C6H5
                            ↑         /
                            |      HN
                            |        \
                            |         CH3
                   addition of water here
```

Subsequent treatment and final titration stage. (i) Back titration of unused water, using the Karl Fischer reagent, has been used in six of the examples quoted.

(ii) More usually a reaction product has been determined, including:

1. Acids, derived from anhydride or certain ester hydrolyses, generally titrated with alkali to phenolphthalein.

2. Alkalies, derived from metal organic (Li, Mg) compounds, titrated with the usual mineral acid reagents like HCl or H_2SO_4.

3. Cl^- from hydrolysis of chlorides, using excess Ag(I) and back titrating with SCN^- (in one case, the HCl formed was alternatively titrated with alkali).

4. Carbonyl compounds, using hydroxylamine or alkaline iodine reagents.

Examples

Materials titrated	Reagent and reaction conditions	Subsequent treatment and final titration stage	Ref.
Acetic anhydride	+ water: several h at room temp. (compared many methods)	Titrated with NaOH to phenolphthalein	1
Anhydrides	+ water; 15 min/100°	Titrated with KOH to phenolphthalein	2

Materials titrated	Reagent and reaction conditions	Subsequent treatment and final titration stage	Ref.
Grignard reagents	Added to water, giving hydrocarbon + Mg(OH)Hal	+ excess H_2SO_4, warmed and titrated with NaOH to methyl orange	3
Allyl isothiocyanate	Heated with water, giving allylamine + CO_2 + H_2S	Distilled into excess $AgNO_3$, Ag_2S filtered and Ag(I) back titrated with SCN^-	4
Grignard reagents	+ ice	+ excess HCl and back titrated with alkali	5
Anhydrides	In acetic acid, + water/ BF_3/acetic acid reagent; 2 h/60°. Control without sample	+ pyridine and unreacted water back titrated with Karl Fischer reagent	6
Anhydrides	+ water/pyridine/NaI catalyst; 1 h/60°. Control without sample	Unreacted water back titrated as in ref. 6	7
Lithium alkyls	In nitrogen stream, + water	Titrated with HCl to phenolphthalein	8
Acetic anhydride, unused from determination of amines	+ water/pyridine/NaI; 30 min/60°. Control without sample	Unused water titrated with Karl Fischer reagent	9
Acetyl sulphanilyl chloride	+ water/pyridine reagent; 10 min, beginning at 0° and warming up	+ methanol and unused water titrated with Karl Fischer reagent	10
Acetic anhydride	+ water/pyridine; 1–2 min (part of study of an acetylation method for —OH groups; required a method of hydrolysing the anhydride without attacking any ester present)	Titrated with NaOH to phenolphthalein	11
Nitriles	+ water/BF_3 catalyst/ acetic acid; 2 h/80°. Control without sample	Unused water titrated at 0° with Karl Fischer reagent	12
Lobeline	Steam distilled at pH 6–7, giving acetophenone	Ketone determined with alkali/excess iodine (see Iodine reagents, ref. 246)	13
Tetraethyl pyrophosphate	Heated 17 h/50° with water, giving diethyl orthophosphate	Titrated with alkali	14

Materials titrated	Reagent and reaction conditions	Subsequent treatment and final titration stage	Ref.
Pseudo-esters of laevulinic acid	+ water. A few min/50°	Titrated with alkali	15
Acid chlorides (e.g. benzoyl, oleoyl); sulphonyl chlorides (e.g. *p*-toluene-)	+ water/pyridine. A few min/room temp. Blank with water alone, giving free Cl^-	+ HNO_3 + excess $AgNO_3$ and back titrated with SCN^-	16
Halide ethers of formula RCH_2CHXOR^1, where R = H or CH_3, X = Cl or Br and R′ = R or Ar	+ water, giving HX + RCH_2CHO + R′OH	Titrated with NaOH or $AgNO_3$	17
Imines; Schiff's bases	+ water; 10 min/*ca* 0°, giving carbonyl compounds	Neutralized with H_2SO_4 and determined with excess bisulphite, back titrating with iodine	18
Acetylenes RC≡CR′	+ water/$HgSO_4$/H_2SO_4 reagent in methanol; 1 h reflux, giving $RCOCH_2R'$	Neutralized and ketone determined with hydroxylamine reagent (see Hydroxylamine, ref. 122)	19
p-Acetamidobenzene-sulphonyl chloride in commercial product	+ water/pyridine; blank with water/ether, giving Cl^-	+ HNO_3 + excess $AgNO_3$ and back titrated with SCN^- to Fe(III) or potentiometrically	20
Acetic anhydride	+ water + catalyst (basic—pyridine; acidic—H_2SO_4)	Unused water back titrated with Karl Fischer reagent	21
Sulphonyl chlorides (e.g. *m*-benzenedi-)	+ water/pyridine/$CHCl_3$ (free acid by adding water/$CHCl_3$ only)	Titrated with NaOH to phenolphthalein	22
2-(α-phenyl-α-carbethoxymethyl)thiazolidine-4-carboxylic acid ('Leucogen')	Boiled 1 h with water, giving cysteine + ethyl α-formylphenyl-acetate	Ester distilled out and titrated with bromate potentiometrically; cysteine in residue likewise determined	23
Alkyl tin halides	+ water, or 99% ethanol, hydrolysing to Cl^-	Titrated with $AgNO_3$ to 'high frequency' end-point	24
Acid chlorides in presence of acid anhydrides and acids	+ water/pyridine/dioxan; 1 h/100°	+ excess anhydride and heated 1 h/100° to destroy excess water; + acetic or propionic acid and titrated with $HClO_4$ to metanil yellow; + Hg acetate and retitrated	25

Materials titrated	Reagent and reaction conditions	Subsequent treatment and final titration stage	Ref.
Ethyl orthoformate	+ water; boiled 2 min, yielding ethyl formate	Determined with excess bromine chloride or by treatment with excess NaOH and back titration with acid	26

References

1. Radcliffe, L. G. and Medofski, S., *J. Soc. Chem. Ind. (London)* **36**, 628 (1917).
2. Reclaire, A., *Perfumery Essent. Oil Record* **13**, 148 (1922).
3. Gilman, H., Wilkinson, P. D., Fishel, W. P. and Meyers, C. H., *J. Am. Chem. Soc.* **45**, 150 (1923).
4. Mousseron, M., *Bull. pharm. sud-est* **33**, 146 (1929); *Quart. J. Pharm. Pharmacol.* **2**, 336 (1930).
5. Houben, J., Bredler, J. and Fischer, W., *Ber.* **69**, 1766 (1936).
6. Smith, D. M., Bryant, W. M. D. and Mitchell, J., *J. Am. Chem. Soc.* **62**, 608 (1940).
7. Smith, D. M., Bryant, W. M. D. and Mitchell, J., *J. Am. Chem. Soc.* **63**, 1700 (1941).
8. Gilman, H. and Haubein, A. H., *J. Am. Chem. Soc.* **66**, 1515 (1944).
9. Mitchell, J., Hawkins, W. and Smith, D. M., *J. Am. Chem. Soc.* **66**, 782 (1944).
10. Seaman, W., Norton, A. R., Woods, J. T. and Massad, E. A., *Ind. Eng. Chem., Anal. Ed.* **16**, 517 (1944).
11. Leman, A., *Bull. soc. chim. France* **12**, 908 (1945).
12. Mitchell, J. and Hawkins, W., *J. Am. Chem. Soc.* **67**, 777 (1945).
13. Uffelie, O. F., *Pharm. Weekblad* **81**, 41 (1946).
14. Hall, S. A. and Jacobsen, M., *Agr. Chem.* **3**, No. 7, 30 (1948).
15. Langlois, D. P. and Wolff, H., *J. Am. Chem. Soc.* **70**, 2624 (1948).
16. Drahowzal, F. and Klamann, D., *Monatsh.* **82**, 470 (1951).
17. Shostakovskii, M. F. and Bogdanova, A. V., *Zhur. Anal. Khim.* **8**, 231 (1953).
18. Barrett, S. J. and Whitehurst, D. H., Unpublished data, quoted in *Organic Analysis*, Vol. 3, Interscience Publishers, p, 194 (1956).
19. Siggia, S., *Anal. Chem.* **28**, 1481 (1956).
20. Bellen, N., *Chem. Anal. (Warsaw)* **2**, 463 (1957).
21. Novikova, E. N. and Petrova, L. N., *Zhur. Anal. Khim.* **12**, 534 (1957).
22. Barker, J. F., Payne, C. M. and Maulding, J., *Anal. Chem.* **32**, 831 (1960).

23. Goryacheva, N. S. and Korchagina, V. A., *Aptechnoe Delo* **9**, 33 (1960).
24. Matsuda, H. and Matsuda, S., *Kogyu Kagaku Zasshi* **64**, 539 (1961).
25. Hennart, C. and Vieillet, F., *Chim. anal.* **44**, 61 (1962).
26. Barcza, L. and Burger, K., *Magyar Kem. Folyoirat* **69**, 178 (1963).

114. Xanthydrol

This reagent has been used to determine urea, mostly in biological fluids like blood and urine. Reaction occurs according to the following equation:

$$
\begin{array}{ccc}
O{<}^{C_6H_4}_{C_6H_4}{>}CH.OH & & \\
 & + \begin{array}{c} NH_2 \\ | \\ CO \\ | \\ NH_2 \end{array} \longrightarrow & \begin{array}{l} O{<}^{C_6H_4}_{C_6H_4}{>}CH{-}NH \\ \qquad\qquad\qquad\quad | \\ \qquad\qquad\qquad\quad CO \\ \qquad\qquad\qquad\quad | \\ O{<}^{C_6H_4}_{C_6H_4}{>}CH{-}NH \end{array} \\
O{<}^{C_6H_4}_{C_6H_4}{>}CH.OH & & \text{Dixanthydrylurea}
\end{array}
$$

The reaction has usually been carried out in methanol or acetic acid or a mixture of these, in which the product is insoluble.

The filtered or centrifuged product has been gravimetrically and titrimetrically determined. Titrimetric conclusions have been via:

(i) Oxidation with bichromate, followed by back titration with Fe(II) or $Fe(CN)_6^{4-}$ or by adding I^-/acid and titrating with thiosulphate. CO_2 from the oxidation has been determined by absorption in $Ba(OH)_2$ and back titration with acid.

(ii) Oxidation with iodate or hypobromite, with iodometric back titration as in (i).

(iii) Titration with permanganate.

(iv) Kjeldahl determination of the nitrogen content.

Examples

Reagent and reaction conditions	Subsequent treatment and final titration stage	Ref.
	Precipitate oxidized with $Cr_2O_7^{2-}/H_2SO_4$ and the CO_2 absorbed in $Ba(OH)_2$, back titrating with acid; also via Kjeldahl nitrogen determination (see Bichromate, ref. 30; Kjeldahl nitrogen determination, ref. 2)	1

Reagent and reaction conditions	Subsequent treatment and final titration stage	Ref.
	Precipitate oxidized with excess $Cr_2O_7^{2-}$ and back titrated with Fe(II) (see Bichromate, ref. 31)	2
Deproteinized urine sample + xanthydrol/methanol; 1 h	Precipitate filtered, dissolved in 50% H_2SO_4, giving fluorescent yellow solution; water added and titrated with MnO_4^- at 70–75°	3
Technique of method of ref. 3	Precipitate filtered, $Cr_2O_7^{2-}$ + H_2SO_4 added, left 2–3 min; + water + I^- and titrated with thiosulphate	4
Deproteinized (with CCl_3COOH) blood sample, + acetic acid + xanthydrol/acetic acid; 10 min	Centrifuged, precipitate dissolved in excess $Cr_2O_7^{2-}$/H_2SO_4; 15 min/room temp., KI added and back titrated with thiosulphate	5
+ acetic acid + 5% xanthydrol/methanol; 30–60 min	Centrifuged, H_2SO_4 + known weight solid KIO_3 added, boiled 2–3 min to drive off iodine, I^- added and titrated with thiosulphate (see Iodate, ref. 21 and 22)	6
Technique of method of ref. 6	Precipitate + excess $Cr_2O_7^{2-}$, heated 5 min, I^- then added and titrated with thiosulphate	7
Deproteinized fluid, + acetic acid + xanthydrol/methanol; 1 h	Centrifuged, precipitate heated with H_2SO_4/excess KIO_3 and the unused iodate determined by adding I^- and titrating with thiosulphate (see Iodate, ref. 40)	8
	Precipitate oxidized with excess $Cr_2O_7^{2-}$ and back titrated with ferrocyanide to diphenylamine indicator (see Bichromate, ref. 108)	9
Urine sample + acetic acid + xanthydrol/acetic acid; 30 min	Centrifuged, precipitate oxidized with excess hypobromite; after 5 min, I^-/HCl added and titrated with thiosulphate (see Bromine reagents, ref. 289)	10
Injection sample + acetic acid + xanthydrol/methanol-acetic acid, 1:4; 7 h	Precipitate digested with H_2SO_4/K_2SO_4 + some H_2O_2 and SeO_2, as in Kjeldahl determination (see Kjeldahl nitrogen determination, ref. 13)	11

References

1. Boivin, A., *Bull. soc. chim. biol.* **8**, 456 (1926); **10**, 684 (1928).
2. Cordebard, H., *Bull. soc. chim. biol.* **10**, 461 (1928).
3. Luck, J. M., *J. Biol. Chem.* **79**, 211 (1928).

4. Allen, F. W. and Luck, J. M., *J. Biol. Chem.* **82**, 693 (1929).
5. Fiorentino, M., *Riforma Med.* No. 38, 21 pp. (1929).
6. Cuny, L. and Robert, J., *Bull. soc. chim. biol.* **12**, 171 (1930); *J. pharm. chim.* (8) **11**, 337 (1930).
7. Cuny, L. and Robert, J., *Bull. soc. chim. biol.* **13**, No. 10, 1167 (1931); *J. pharm. chim.* **15**, 7 (1932).
8. Claudatus, I. and Botezatu, M., *Biochem. Z.* **300**, 325 (1939).
9. Thivolle, L. and Sonntag, G., *Trav. membres soc. chim. biol.* **23**, 1296 (1941).
10. Dán, S. and Braun, M., *Orvosi Hetilap* **90**, 283 (1949).
11. Hayashi, T. and Engo, T., *Takamine Kenkyujo Nempo* (*Ann. Repts. Takamine Lab.*) **8**, 136 (1956).

115. Zinc(II)

The use of Zn(II) has depended on the formation of water-insoluble Zn compounds, usually via ion/ion combination at medium pH values (up to 10). Titration of unreacted Zn(II) with EDTA has been the most-used conclusion

Examples

Materials titrated	Reagent and reaction conditions	Subsequent treatment and final titration stage	Ref.
Oxine in mixtures with sulphanilamide	Neutralized solution, + Zn acetate; shaken 5 min, then left 15 min	Filtered, Zn oxinate dissolved in HCl, excess bromate/bromide added, left 1 min and back titrated with thiosulphate after adding KI	1
Some substituted oxines (5-chloro-, 5,7-dichloro-, 5-SO_3H)	In warm alcoholic solution, + buffer, pH 10, + excess $ZnSO_4$	Unused Zn(II) titrated with EDTA to pyrocatechol violet or eriochrome black T	2
Carboxylic acid groups in pulps	+ Zn acetate solution; left overnight, giving precipitate of Zn derivative	Filtered and unused Zn(II) in filtrate titrated with EDTA at pH ca 10(NH_4OH/NH_4Cl buffer)	3
Thioacetamide	+ Zn nitrate; then + NaOH and boiled 5–10 min	ZnS filtered, filtrate + NH_4OH/NH_4Cl, giving pH 10 and titrated with EDTA to eriochrome black T	4

Materials titrated	Reagent and reaction conditions	Subsequent treatment and final titration stage	Ref.
Thiourea	+ Zn nitrate + alkali + hydroxylamine hydrochloride; boiled at least 20 min	As for thioacetamide (see previous page)	4
Barbiturates	In borate buffer, + excess $ZnSO_4$; 15 min/ *ca* 100°	Filtered, filtrate + NH_4OH/ NH_4Cl(pH 10) and titrated with EDTA to eriochrome black T; Zn(II) in precipitate also similarly determined	5
Oxine and derivatives in pharmaceutical products	In NH_4Cl/NH_4OH(pH 10) buffer, + ethanol + excess $ZnSO_4$ + $CHCl_3$	+ water and unused Zn(II) titrated with EDTA to eriochrome black T	6

References

1. Bontemps, R., *J. pharm. Belge* **7**, 553 (1952).
2. Buděšinský, B., *Českoslov. Farm.* **4**, 221 (1955).
3. Doering, H., *Das Papier* **10**, 140 (1956).
4. Lesz, K., Wieczorkiewicz, H. and Lipiec, T., *Chem. Anal.* (*Warsaw*) **6**, 1033 (1961).
5. Roushdi, I. M., Abdine, H. and Awad, A., *J. Pharm. Pharmacol.* **13**, Suppl. 153T (1961).
6. Ömböly, C. and Derzsi, E., *Acta Pharm. Hung.* **32**, 246 (1962).

SECTION 3

INDEX TO FUNCTIONAL GROUPS AND COMPOUND CLASSES

The same classification as in Part I has been adopted. This uses an alphabetical order of groups and classes, with 3 columns for the tabulation. The first column contains examples of the group or class being considered. The second contains the reagent used in the determination, arranged alphabetically within each group or class heading. In the third are given reference numbers from Section 2 under that reagent heading. The word 'many' in the third column generally implies that there are at least 10 examples in Section 2 under the particular reagent heading and that individual citation is considered to be unnecessary. Where the total number of references to the use of a reagent in Section 2 exceeds about 200 (e.g. with Alkalies, Bromine Reagents, Iodine Reagents), this arbitrarily chosen number of 10 is then relatively few and more have usually been quoted in the index.

Some general features of the index are mentioned here:

Compounds containing two functional groups have in general been classified under both of these groups, for the readers' convenience, even though the group may not take part directly in the reaction with the particular reagent. More commonly encountered complex compound classes with several functional groups (e.g. alkaloids, antibiotics, dyes, vitamins, etc.) have usually been given separate collective headings; occasionally the compounds have been included under the functional group reacting in a particular determination (e.g. azo dyes under Azo Compounds as well as under Dyes; note in particular the paragraph below on Synthetic Bases and their Salts).

Certain general headings of compound classes like Amines, Carbonyl Compounds, etc., have been used, as well as the corresponding sub-headings like Primary Amines, Secondary Amines and Tertiary Amines, or Aldehydes and Ketones respectively. Under these general headings are included references to the analysis of mixtures of the different sub-classes such as the three amine types; or to determinations applying equally to all the sub-classes, e.g. with hydrazine or hydroxylamine reagents for carbonyl compounds. The reader is naturally recommended to look under both general and sub-headings when searching for a possible method. Such alternative headings are in fact given in the alphabetical index at the front of the book (pp. xvi–xix).

Only functional groups or compound classes appear as headings in this index but an index to individual compounds for both Part I and Part II of the book is given at the end of this part (pp. 971).

Some further explanatory notes are given about the individual headings:

Ammonium Hydroxide and Salts, Substituted; includes quaternary bases and salts. Some overlap necessarily occurs with Synthetic Bases and their Salts and with the Amine classes (see below).

Aromatic Hydrocarbons; includes examples like styrene and indene, where the side chain reacts as an olefinic group (also included under Olefines).

Carboxylates, Carboxylic Acids; many methods, e.g. oxidations in acid solution, apply equally to the free acid and salt, and these examples have been included under Carboxylic Acids. Only where the method is evidently specifically intended for salts in contrast to the acids does the example appear under Carboxylates. A good instance is the determination of salts via treatment with an inorganic acid, giving the corresponding free carboxylic acid, then isolated and titrated. As previously recommended, the reader is advised to look under both headings.

Halogen-containing Compounds; includes primarily alkyl and aryl halides, polyhalides and halogen-containing insecticides. Acid chlorides, sulphonyl and sulphenyl chlorides and halide salts of bases are separately classified.

Synthetic Bases and their Salts; this is an 'overflow' or 'miscellaneous' class, chiefly of pharmaceuticals like anaesthetics, antihistamines, hypnotics etc., for which no relatively restricted class headings have been given (as, for example, for Barbiturates or Phenothiazines). A small number has indeed been classified under the reacting functional group which it contains. Thus the anaesthetic esters of *p*-aminobenzoic acid appear also under Esters and under Primary Amines. The division from Alkaloids is not sharp. Naturally occurring compounds, now principally obtained synthetically (e.g. ephedrine), are borderline cases.

Examples (no entry under this heading is equivalent to 'miscellaneous')	Reagent	References under this reagent heading
	Acetals and Ketals	
Hydrolysis products of polyvinyl acetal ketal resins	Bisulphite and Sulphite	82
Hemiacetals, hemiketals	Cyanide	14
	Hydrobromic Acid	11
	Hydrochloric Acid	4, 56
acetone derivatives of polyhydroxy compounds	Hydrochloric Acid	8
	Hydroxylamine	53, 83, 91, 95, 146, 167
butyral groups in polyvinyl butyral	Hydroxylamine	72
Lower alkoxy groups in acetals and ketals	Iodides and Hydriodic Acid	209
Polyvinyl acetal ketal in resins	Phosphoric Acid	13
acetal	Phosphoric Acid	17
	Sulphuric Acid	21, 64, 88, 127
polyvinyl formal	Sulphuric Acid	74
	Acetylenes	
Mono- and disubstituted	Alcohols	36
	Bromine Reagents	81, 166, 346, 382
acetylene	Bromine Reagents	145, 327
E.g. acetylenedicarboxylic acid	Chromium (II)	5, 11
	Copper (I)	3, 4, 5, 7, 9
Acetylene	Iodate	14
Propargyl alcohol	Iodine Reagents	295
Cuprous acetylide	Iron (III)	1
Divinylacetylene	Mercaptans	1
	Mercury (II)	65, 105, 123, 151
Acetylene	Silver (I)	18, 20, 44, 57, 63, 143, 148, 157
acetylenic alcohols	Silver (I)	29, 103, 144, 158, 204
acetylenic hydrocarbons, e.g. vinylacetylene, ethylacetylene	Silver (I)	26, 75, 93, 109, 115, 177
	Silver (I)	5, 98, 112, 113, 132, 158, 162, 174, 183
	Water	19
	Acid Chlorides	
	Alcohols	45, 55, 56, 59, 64, 65
Chlorides of oxalic acid monoesters	Alkalies	348

Examples (no entry under this heading is equivalent to 'miscellaneous')	Reagent	References under this reagent heading
	Amines	29, 37, 64, 88, 90, 92, 106
	Water	10, 16, 25
	Alcohols	
Diacetone alcohol and other keto alcohols	Alkalies	267
—OH end-groups in paraformaldehyde	Alkalies	477
	Aluminium Hydride and Borohydride	1, 2, 3, 4
Mono- and polyalcohols	Anhydrides	Many
Lower alcohols, glycols like glycerol, mannitol	Bichromate	Many
Glycerol, phenyldimethylcarbinol	Bisulphate	1, 2
Allyl alcohol	Bromine Reagents	13, 173, 317, 330, 379
glycerol	Bromine Reagents	112, 157, 160
other alcohols (methanol, isopropanol, furfuryl alcohol)	Bromine Reagents	112, 251, 325, 382, 392, 480, 503
Primary and secondary alcohols	Carbon Disulphide	3, 5
E.g. lower alcohols (methanol, ethanol) and in essential oils etc. (citronellol, isoborneol)	Carboxylic Acids and Carboxylates	5, 7, 11, 15, 24, 25, 27, 31, 33
Methanol	Cerium (IV)	22, 26, 36
glycerol	Cerium (IV)	4, 6, 8, 12, 39, 53
pentaerythritol	Cerium (IV)	13, 21, 53
other monoalcohols (lower)	Cerium (IV)	14, 20, 22
other polyalcohols	Cerium (IV)	10, 20, 21, 39, 53, 55
Glycerol	Copper (II)	18, 107, 112, 118, 151
mannitol	Copper (II)	24, 89, 107, 161
sorbitol	Copper (II)	107
Dihydroxyacetone	Ferricyanide	16
polyalcohols like inositol, mannitol, sorbitol	Ferricyanide	58
	Halides (Active)	Many
Tertiary alcohols	Hydrobromic Acid	6
eucalyptol	Hydrobromic Acid	10
Tertiary alcohols	Hydrochloric Acid	88, 108, 116
secondary alcohols	Hydrochloric Acid	108
Diacetone alcohol	Hydroxylamine	80
dihydroxyacetone	Hydroxylamine	165
Glycerol	Iodate and Iodine Pentoxide	2, 9
ethanol	Iodate and Iodine Pentoxide	30, 78
Glycol ethers (hydroxyether groups, polyethylene glycols)	Iodides and Hydriodic Acid	182, 188, 198, 205, 220, 225, 233, 249, 250, 259, 274
	Iodides and Hydriodic Acid	64, 145, 224
Chlorobutanol	Iodine Reagents	168

Examples (no entry under this heading is equivalent to 'miscellaneous')	Reagent	References under this reagent heading
acetyl methylcarbinol	Iodine Reagents	174
acetoin	Iodine Reagents	229
1,2-propylene glycol	Iodine Reagents	310
2,2,6,6-tetrabis(hydroxy-methyl)-1-cyclohexanol	Iodine Reagents	350
carbowax (polyethylene glycols)	Iodine Reagents	372, 391
'Hydroxyl number'	Isocyanate and Isothio-cyanate	3, 6
Polyalcohols, e.g. ethylene glycol, mannitol, glycerol	Lead (IV)	2, 7, 10, 12, 13, 14
hydroxy acids, e.g. mandelic, tartaric acids	Lead (IV)	7, 8, 9, 10, 11, 12, 13, 14
Methanol, polyalcohols	Manganate	2
Tertiary alcohols	Mercury (II)	70, 164, 184
glycol, hexols	Mercury (II)	28
α-keto alcohols, e.g. acetoin	Mercury (II)	63
Dihydroxyacetone	Molybdenum (VI) and Tungsten (VI)	2, 4
polyglycols	Molybdenum (VI) and Tungsten (VI)	20
1,2-Propylene glycol	Nitric Acid	13
Primary and secondary alcohols	Nitriles	4
Lower alcohols (up to C_5)	Nitrite	3, 5, 7, 10, 11, 14, 18, 19, 20, 24, 31
Substituted ethanols	Perchloric Acid	13
1,2-Glycol group, e.g. in glycols, glycerol, higher polyalcohols, tartaric acid	Periodates and Periodic Acid	Many
—C(OH)—C(NH_2)— group, e.g. in ethanolamine, serine, threonine	Periodates and Periodic Acid	Many
Methanol	Permanganate	56, 84, 106, 107, 134, 140
ethanol	Permanganate	2, 23, 33, 60, 66, 89, 102, 107, 124, 134, 139
glycerol	Permanganate	3, 4, 31, 105, 106, 128
other monoalcohols	Permanganate	47, 59, 107
other polyalcohols	Permanganate	56, 65
Lower alcohols	Persulphate	5
n-Butanol in mixtures with HCHO/urea/butanol resins	Phosphoric Acid	8
Ethanol/isopropanol mixtures	Physical Methods	5
Ethanol	Pyrolysis	23, 27
Polyhydroxy compounds, α-glycols	Silver (I)	146
Tertiary alcohols	Sodamide	2
E.g. tertiary alcohols	Sulphonic Acids	14, 15, 16

Examples (no entry under this heading is equivalent to 'miscellaneous')	Reagent	References under this reagent heading
Tertiary alcohols	Sulphuric Acid	128
	Sulphur Trioxide	1, 2
Polyalkylene oxides	Tetraphenylborate	19
Glycerol, α-hydroxy acids, etc.	Vanadate	14, 18, 20
	Aldehydes	
E.g. HCHO, glyoxal	Alkalies	3, 81, 93, 315, 319, 336, 353, 399
	Aluminium Hydride and Borohydride	3
E.g. HCHO	Amines and Heterocyclic Bases	24, 53, 83, 104
HCHO	Ammonium Hydroxide and Ammonium Salts	1, 4, 6, 8, 9, 10, 14, 16, 17, 22
E.g. acetaldehyde, benzaldehyde	Bichromate	2, 28, 101, 147, 206, 251, 256
E.g. HCHO, acetaldehyde, furfuraldehyde, benzaldehyde, glyoxal	Bisulphite and Sulphite	Many
Furfuraldehyde	Bromine Reagents	Many
HCHO	Bromine Reagents	111, 200, 455, 541
unsaturated aldehydes like acrolein, crotonaldehyde	Bromine Reagents	216, 295, 379, 466, 482, 503, 519
other aldehydes, e.g. vanillin, chloral, aminoaldehydes	Bromine Reagents	148, 152, 181, 301, 448
HCHO, acetaldehyde	Carbonyl Compounds	6, 24, 26, 28
HCHO	Cerium (IV)	45
HCHO	Chlorate	1
HCHO	Chlorine Reagents	5, 25
benzaldehyde	Chlorine Reagents	25
	Chlorite	5, 6, 7, 9
HCHO	Copper (II)	63, 124
furfuraldehyde	Copper (II)	17, 20, 85, 101
acrolein	Copper (II)	84
chloral	Copper (II)	124
E.g. HCHO	Cyanide	Many
E.g. HCHO, benzaldehyde	Halides (Active)	15, 21, 43, 55
	Hydrazines	Many
HCHO	Hydrochloric Acid	53
HCHO	Hydrogen Peroxide	Many
other aldehydes, e.g. glyoxal, acetaldehyde, vanillin	Hydrogen Peroxide	8, 19, 22, 25, 35, 36, 37, 39, 40
	Hydroxylamine	Many
Furfuraldehyde	Iodate and Iodine Pentoxide	82
HCHO	Iodine Reagents	Many
acetaldehyde	Iodine Reagents	33, 82, 101, 346, 358

Examples (no entry under this heading is equivalent to 'miscellaneous')	Reagent	References under this reagent heading
chloral	Iodine Reagents	22, 65, 70, 114, 177, 262, 365
aldehyde groups in treated polysaccharide materials, e.g. oxidized starches, celluloses	Iodine Reagents	242, 253, 308, 359
dichloroacetaldehyde	Iodine Reagents	364, 365
E.g. acrolein, crotonaldehyde, glyoxals	Iodine Reagents	97, 153, 201, 225, 231, 236, 257, 294, 417
HCHO	Iodine Chlorides, etc.	28, 129
	Ion Exchangers	31
HCHO	Manganate	2
HCHO	Mercury (II)	3, 4, 12, 48, 52, 56, 57, 67, 68, 72, 82, 97, 98, 101
acetaldehyde	Mercury (II)	11, 54, 81
furfuraldehyde	Mercury (II)	64
	Mercury (II)	12, 20, 45, 55, 80, 132, 157
Glycerinaldehyde	Periodate	106, 109
	Percarboxylic Acids	16
HCHO	Permanganate	9, 12, 84, 90, 107
benzaldehyde	Permanganate	27, 107
other aldehydes, e.g. acrolein, chloral, acetaldehyde	Permanganate	57, 64, 107, 130
HCHO in resins	Phosphoric Acid	8, 9, 11
Furfuraldehyde/5-hydroxy-methylfurfuraldehyde mixtures	Physical Methods	21
HCHO	Silver (I)	1, 24, 39, 49, 66, 163, 209
acetaldehyde	Silver (I)	21, 180, 181, 209
	Silver (I)	9, 31, 45, 99, 100, 102, 106, 123, 131, 155, 203, 209
HCHO and derivatives	Sulphuric Acid	34, 53
acetaldehyde	Sulphuric Acid	64
O- and *N*-benzal groups	Sulphuric Acid	105
	Vanadate	18

Aliphatic Hydrocarbons

Cyclopropane	Iodate	32

Alkaloids and their Salts

Lobeline	Alkalies	126
eserine	Alkalies	196

Examples (no entry under this heading is equivalent to 'miscellaneous')	Reagent	References under this reagent heading
belladonna alkaloids	Alkalies	308
	Aluminium Hydride and Borohydride	3
Nornicotine/nicotine mixtures	Anhydrides	102
Alkaloid sulphates	Barium (II)	6
Strychnine	Bichromate	34, 63
morphine	Bichromate	150, 154
brucine	Bichromate	63
choline salts	Bichromate	196
E.g. nicotine, quinine, atropine, strychnine	Bismuth (III)	2, 3, 5, 6, 9, 11, 13
Quinine	Bromine Reagents	278, 301, 350
other alkaloids (strychnine, codeine, solasodine) and salts	Bromine Reagents	301, 383, 477, 497, 516
E.g. quinine	Cadmium (II)	11, 13, 14, 18
Quinine hydrochloride	Copper (II)	175
	Dimethyl Sulphate	1, 2
Morphine	Ferricyanide	80, 116, 120, 122
E.g. morphine	Halides (Active)	12, 16, 25, 40, 41, 68
Morphine derivatives	Hydrochloric Acid	50
atropine derivatives	Hydrochloric Acid	59
colchicine	Hydrochloric Acid	65
	Iodides and Hydriodic Acid	122, 215
E.g. morphine, choline, betaine	Iodine Reagents	Many
Alkaloid salts	Ion Exchangers	2, 3, 6, 8, 10, 20, 32, 35, 37, 38, 39, 49
Betaine periodide	Kjeldahl Nitrogen Determination	1
E.g. morphine, strychnine, codeine	Mercury (II)	Many
tetraphenylborates of alkaloids	Mercury (II)	137
Alkaloids of celandine root	Metals	109
Nicotine	Molybdenum (VI) and Tungsten (VI)	1, 5, 6, 10
trigonelline	Molybdenum (VI) and Tungsten (VI)	11
	Molybdenum (VI) and Tungsten (VI)	17
Quinine alkaloids	Nitrophenols	6, 68
nicotine	Nitrophenols	13, 23, 43, 48, 52, 63, 65
	Nitrophenols	54
	Perchloric Acid	17
Quinine, choline	Permanganate	44, 93
Nicotine	Physical Methods	14
atropine	Physical Methods	17
tobacco alkaloids	Physical Methods	18

Examples (no entry under this heading is equivalent to 'miscellaneous')	Reagent	References under this reagent heading
Thebaine	Quinones	1
Hydrochlorides of opium alkaloids	Silver (I)	50
Morphine	Sulphuric Acid	69
	Tetraphenylborate	1, 3, 4, 9, 10, 12, 17
E.g. quinidine, strychnine, quinine, atropine	Thiocyanates	5, 7, 8, 9, 14, 17, 26, 27, 31, 35, 45, 47, 53
Lobeline	Water	13

Aluminium-containing Compounds

Examples	Reagent	References
Ethoxy groups in some organic aluminium compounds	Bichromate	207
Aluminium alkoxides	Hydrochloric Acid	138
Reducing capacity of aluminium alkyls	Iodine Reagents	374
Ethoxy groups in some organic aluminium compounds	Sulphuric Acid	108

Amides and Imides

Examples	Reagent	References
N-Acetyl groups	Alcohols	2, 5, 7, 16, 35
Urea and substituted ureas	Alkalies	5, 125, 248, 290, 338, 365, 386, 395, 413, 473
neostigmine bromide and methylsulphate	Alkalies	141, 371
	Alkalies	80, 103, 104, 120, 124, 136, 153, 167, 299, 306, 318, 326, 349, 354, 361, 364, 377, 395, 409, 428, 442, 459, 474, 475, 478, 479
	Aluminium Hydride and Borohydride	6
Dixanthydrylurea	Bichromate	30, 31, 108
acetanilide	Bichromate	80
4-chloroacetanilide	Bichromate	155
ϵ-caprolactam	Bismuth (III)	8
Urea	Bromine Reagents	5, 7, 29, 37, 43, 76, 303, 388, 405, 451, 494, 508, 518
substituted ureas	Bromine Reagents	75, 82, 249, 256, 289, 494
E.g. phenacetin, salicylamide	Bromine Reagents	47, 296, 329, 383

Examples (no entry under this heading is equivalent to 'miscellaneous')	Reagent	References under this reagent heading
Carbodiimide	Carboxylic Acids	35
Imides	Chlorine Reagents	2
diphenylhydantoin	Chlorine Reagents	10
urea	Chlorine Reagents	19, 22
	Halides (Active)	31, 85
Acetanilide	Hydrochloric Acid	28, 42, 84, 146
phenacetin	Hydrochloric Acid	28, 93, 122, 146
polyamides, end-groups, etc.	Hydrochloric Acid	103, 121, 132
	Hydrochloric Acid	9, 99, 120, 126, 129, 137
Dixanthydrylurea	Iodate	21, 22, 40
xanthylphenylacetamide	Iodate	21
Phenacetin	Iodides and Hydriodic Acid	104
Phenacetin	Iodine Reagents	256, 289
2-Ethylcrotonylurea	Iodine Chlorides, etc.	112
Diphenylcarbazone, diphenylcarbazide	Iron (III)	11
Dixanthydrylurea	Kjeldahl Nitrogen Determination	2, 13
diphenylhydantoin	Kjeldahl Nitrogen Determination	12
ε-caprolactam	Kjeldahl Nitrogen Determination	14
Allantoin	Mercury (II)	16
sodium saccharin	Mercury (II)	86
cyclopropylamides	Mercury (II)	171
Na salt of 5,5-diphenyl-hydantoin	Mercury (II)	178
substituted ureas	Mercury (II)	177, 182
Na salt of 5,5-diphenyl-hydantoin	Nickel (II)	15
Urea	Nitric Acid	14
Urea	Nitrite	25
Nicotinamide	Silver (I)	86
Saccharin	Silver (I)	173
Na salt of 5, 5-diphenyl-hydantoin	Silver (I)	195
N-Acetyl groups	Sulphonic Acids	1, 9, 12, 17
Urea and derivatives	Sulphuric Acid	79, 81, 82
acetyl groups in general	Sulphuric Acid	2
e.g. acetanilide, phenacetin, methacrylamide	Sulphuric Acid	34, 63, 97, 119
Urea	Xanthydrol	All 11

Amidines

Examples	Reagent	References under this reagent heading
	Iodine Reagents	304
	Mercury (II)	119

Examples (no entry under this heading is equivalent to 'miscellaneous')	Reagent	References under this reagent heading
Amines and Bases (in General)		
Primary and secondary amines	Aluminium Hydride and Borohydride	1, 3
Primary, secondary amines; mixtures of primary, secondary and tertiary amines	Anhydrides	Many
	Bromine	60, 413, 489
Mixtures of amines	Carbon Disulphide	4, 6, 7, 8, 9, 10, 11, 12
Mixtures of amines	Carbonyl Compounds	13, 15, 19, 22, 29, 34
Arylamines	Cerium (IV)	20, 29
	Chlorine Reagents	2
Amines and mixtures of the 3 classes (especially aniline and alkylanilines)	Halides (Active)	9, 18, 30, 32, 33
Weak aromatic bases	Hydrochloric Acid	36
unsaturated amines	Hydrochloric Acid	97
Mixtures of long-chain amines and their oxides	Iodides and Hydriodic Acid	254
Arylamines	Iodine Chlorides, etc.	84, 89
Mixtures of amines	Isocyanates and Isothiocyanates	4, 5
Amine nitrogen	Kjeldahl Nitrogen Determination	19
Amine mixtures	Nickel (II)	1, 5
Mixtures of the 3 amine classes	Nitrite	1, 8, 23
Nitrogen-containing bases	Nitrophenols	2
Pharmaceutical bases, etc.	Perchloric Acid	1, 2, 4, 7
amino groups in ion-exchange resins	Perchloric Acid	6
Ethanolamines	Periodates and Periodic Acid	29, 32, 41, 85, 116, 117, 123, 126
Amines in general	Physical Methods	3, 12, 22
ethylamine hydrochlorides	Physical Methods	11
Basic nitrogen compounds in hydrocarbons	Sulphuric Acid	59
non-protein nitrogen compounds in serum	Sulphuric Acid	126
Amines containing 'active hydrogen'	Sulphur Trioxide	1, 3
Amines, bases	Tetraphenylborate	Many
Amino Acids		
Glutamine	Alkalies	232
Mono sodium glutamate	Anhydrides	156
ϵ-Aminocaproic acid	Barium(II)	7
	Bichromate	151

Examples (no entry under this heading is equivalent to 'miscellaneous')	Reagent	References under this reagent heading
EDTA	Bismuth (III)	14
Tyrosine	Bromine Reagents	105
α-amino acid derivatives	Bromine Reagents	49
aromatic amino acids, e.g. aminobenzoic and salicylic acids	Bromine Reagents	181, 185, 288, 307, 335, 428
	Calcium (II)	21
α-amino acids	Carbonyl Compounds	Many
ε-aminocaproic acid	Carbonyl Compounds	33, 35
E.g. alanine, valine, leucine	Chlorine Reagents	11, 12, 14
α-amino acids	Copper (II)	23, 26, 111, 121, 128, 141, 147, 155, 174, 182, 198, 202, 217
p-aminosalicylate	Copper (II)	166
E.g. glycine	Halides (Active)	47, 71
p-Aminosalicylate	Iodine Reagents	283
tryptophane	Iodine Reagents	324
p-Aminosalicylate	Iodine Chlorides, etc.	75
EDTA	Iron (III)	9
p-Aminosalicylate, e.g.	Kjeldahl Nitrogen Determination	8, 9, 10
glycine nitranilate	Kjeldahl Nitrogen Determination	11
α-amino acids	Ninhydrin	All 14
α-amino acids, e.g. alanine, glycine	Nitrite	6, 9, 13, 16, 21, 22, 28, 29
Glycine	Nitrophenols	57
α-amino acids with —CHOH—$CHNH_2$ group like serine, threonine	Periodate	20, 21, 25, 29, 67, 107, 110, 111, 118, 125, 130, 131
Glycine	Perchloric Acid	9
Asparagine	Sulphuric Acid	42

Amine Oxides

Examples	Reagent	References
Long-chain amine oxides	Halides (Active)	77
	Iodides and Hydriodic Acid	254, 261
	Tin (II)	19
Trimethylamine oxide	Titanium (III)	44
pyridine oxide and related compounds	Titanium (III)	60

Ammonium Hydroxide and Salts, Substituted

Examples	Reagent	References
Tetramethylammonium nitrate or sulphate	Alkalies	74
neostigmine bromide or methylsulphate	Alkalies	141, 371

Examples (no entry under this heading is equivalent to 'miscellaneous')	Reagent	References under this reagent heading
Quaternary ammonium salts	Bichromate	111, 257
flavines	Bichromate	127
methonium reineckates	Bichromate	161
cetyl trimethylammonium bromide	Bichromate	169
choline salts	Bichromate	196
N,*N*′-bis-(*N*-methylquinolyl-urea)methyl sulphate	Bichromate	212
	Bichromate	257
	Bismuth (III)	10
Tetramethylammonium iodide	Bromine Reagents	227
methantheline bromide	Bromine Reagents	342
decamethylene bis(trimethyl-ammonium) iodide	Bromine Reagents	407
	Cadmium (II)	9
gallamine triiodide	Cadmium (II)	18
Acriflavine and other flavine dyes	Ferricyanide	28
phenanthridinium salts	Ferricyanide	71
quinidine diethyliodide	Ferricyanide	94
methantheline bromide	Ferricyanide	99
	Ferricyanide	72, 75, 81, 121, 129
Quaternary ammonium nitrites	Halides (Active)	59
Alkyl pyridinium iodides	Iodate	15
Quaternary ammonium halides (germicides)	Iodides and Hydriodic Acid	260
diphenoquinonedi-(4,4′-dimethylammonium) ion	Iodides and Hydriodic Acid	265
Betaine	Iodine Reagents	23, 161, 216, 387
choline	Iodine Reagents	111, 121, 125, 204, 216, 342, 414
trigonelline	Iodine Reagents	122
high molecular weight quaternary salts	Iodine Reagents	252
Quaternary ammonium chlorides	Iodine Chlorides, etc.	120
Salts	Ion Exchangers	18, 34, 45, 48
Betaine periodide	Kjeldahl Nitrogen Determination	1
Alkyl pyridinium iodides	Mercury (II)	92
Cholinium chloride	Metals	87
diphenoquinonedi-(4,4′-dimethylammonium) ion	Metals	110
Trigonelline	Molybdenum (VI), etc.	11
Flavines, e.g. proflavine, acri-flavine	Nitrophenols	45
	Nitrophenols	67

Examples (no entry under this heading is equivalent to 'miscellaneous')	Reagent	References under this reagent heading
Trimethylphenylammonium iodide	Perchloric Acid	9
dimethylethyl *o*-bromobenzyl-ammonium tetraphenylborate	Perchloric Acid	11
Choline	Permanganate	93
Betaine reineckate	Silver (I)	111
methantheline bromide	Silver (I)	114
thiofalicaines	Silver (I)	126
piperazonium adipate	Silver (I)	172
tetramethylammonium bromide	Silver (I)	185
Cation-active plasticizers	Surface Active Agents	3
	Tetraphenylborate	2, 6, 9, 12, 18
	Thiocyanates	10, 16, 50, 52, 56
Diphenoquinonedi-(4,4′-dimethylammonium) ion	Tin (II)	28
	Anhydrides	
E.g. acetic, phthalic anhydrides	Alcohols	9, 26, 34, 42, 44, 47, 61, 62
	Alkalies	33, 45, 59, 65, 88, 166, 220, 286, 296, 373, 463
E.g. acetic anhydride	Amines	Many
Acetic anhydride	Carboxylic Acids, etc.	9
Maleic anhydride	Hydrocarbons	1, 2
Uronic anhydride groups	Hydrochloric Acid	21
N-carboxyamino acid anhydrides	Hydrochloric Acid	140
Phthalic anhydride	Potassium (I)	6, 7
N-Carboxyamino acid anhydrides	Sulphuric Acid	123
E.g. acetic anhydride	Water	1, 2, 6, 7, 9, 11, 21
	Anils	
Formalaniline	Bromine Reagents	208
	Water	18
	Antibiotics and Related Compounds	
Penicillins	Alkalies	177, 185, 219, 225, 228, 231, 237, 252, 255, 260, 264, 282, 307, 324, 342, 369, 388, 393, 394, 397, 407, 411, 420, 422, 429, 432, 433, 450
Penicillin G	Bromine Reagents	367
kanamycin reineckate	Bromine Reagents	516

Examples (no entry under this heading is equivalent to 'miscellaneous')	Reagent	References under this reagent heading
Novobiocin	Carboxylic Acids	32
Penicillin	Copper (II)	173
Penicillins	Ferricyanide	84
Penicillin	Hydrogen Peroxide	30
Reaction products from treatment of penicillin with alkali	Iodate	70
Reaction products from treatment of penicillins with alkali	Iodine Reagents	237, 241, 259, 263, 266, 267, 273, 278, 279, 281, 287, 296, 322, 331, 344, 367, 368, 377, 378, 380, 384, 399, 408, 409, 410, 415, 416
Penicillin	Iron (III)	6
terramycin	Iron (III)	10
Streptomycin and dihydrostreptomycin, $CaCl_2$ complexes	Mercury (II)	109
Streptomycin and dihydrostreptomycin sulphates	Perchloric Acid	3
Streptomycin, dihydrostreptomycin	Periodates and Periodic Acid	55
Dihydrostreptomycin	Thiocyanates	25
kanamycin	Thiocyanates	53

Aromatic Hydrocarbons

Examples	Reagent	References
Anthracene	Bromine Reagents	143, 492
indene, styrene	Bromine Reagents	147, 204, 312
naphthalene	Bromine Reagents	300
acenaphthylene	Bromine Reagents	512
Naphthalene picrate	Iodate	18, 34
Acenaphthylene	Iodine Chlorides, etc.	126
styrene	Iodine Chlorides, etc.	125, 132
Anthracene	Maleic Anhydride	Many
Acenaphthylene	Mercury (II)	135
Benzene	Nitric Acid	5, 7
Fluorene	Nitriles	7
Naphthalene	Nitrophenols	Many
indene	Nitrophenols	12, 64
acenaphthene	Nitrophenols	1, 43
anthracene	Nitrophenols	58
e.g. aromatic contents	Nitrophenols	5, 31, 49
Benzene, toluene, xylenes	Sulphuric Acid	9, 24, 30, 47
Naphthalene	Vanadate	1

Arsenic-containing Compounds

Examples	Reagent	References
Diphenylarsenic chloride	Alkalies	64
Triphenylarsine	Bromine Reagents	263

Examples (no entry under this heading is equivalent to 'miscellaneous')	Reagent	References under this reagent heading
sodium *p*-aminophenylarsonate	Bromine Reagents	373
4-Hydroxy-3-acetamidophenyl arsinate	Hydrochloric Acid	117
Triphenylarsine	Hydrogen Peroxide	27
trialkylarsines	Hydrogen Peroxide	32
Cacodylates	Manganese (IV)	3
Arrhenal	Mercury (II)	35
sodium arsanilate	Mercury (II)	94
Disodium methyl arsenate	Silver (I)	11
sodium methyl arsenate	Silver (I)	110
sodium *N*-acetyl-2-hydroxy-arsanilate	Silver (I)	84
Sodium cacodylate	Sulphuric Acid	56
	Azo Compounds	
	Chromium (II)	5
	Dithionite	2, 3
	Iodides and Hydriodic Acid	153
	Metals	38
	Tin (II)	10, 11, 14, 27
	Titanium (III)	1, 2, 64
	Barbituric Acids and Salts	
E.g. bromural, carbromal	Alkalies	386, 473
E.g. unsaturated barbiturates (allyl-, etc.); hexabarbital	Bromine Reagents	247, 271, 340, 383, 430, 468
	Copper (II)	204, 219, 224
Bromine-containing compounds, e.g. bromural, carbromal	Hydrogen Peroxide	43
Unsaturated barbiturates	Iodine Chlorides, etc.	96
	Ion Exchangers	33, 43
	Mercury (II)	49, 112, 161, 165, 166, 179
	Silver (I)	74, 87, 190
	Zinc (II)	5
	Bismuth-containing Compounds	
	Nitric Acid	18
Bismuth tartrate	Permanganate	11
Bismuth camphorcarboxylate	Pyrolysis	35
	Boron-containing Compounds	
Tetraphenylborates	Bichromate	230, 238
Dimethoxyborane	Iodine Reagents	351

Examples (no entry under this heading is equivalent to 'miscellaneous')	Reagent	References under this reagent heading
Addition compounds of BBr_3 with organic bases	Ion Exchangers	19
Tetraphenylborates	Mercury (II)	127, 134, 137, 168, 169, 188
triphenylcyanoborates	Mercury (II)	130
Methoxyl groups in methoxy-borohydrides	Nitric Acid	15
Tetraphenylborates	Perchloric Acid	11
Tetraphenylborates	Silver (I)	120, 130, 151
Tetraphenylborates	Thallium (I)	

Carbamates and Urethanes

Examples	Reagent	References
Carbamates	Alkalies	207, 292, 381
urethanes	Alkalies	125, 246
meprobamate	Alkalies	455
Isopropyl *N*-arylcarbamates	Hydrochloric Acid	84, 118
meprobamate	Hydrochloric Acid	125
Urethanes	Metals	96
Urethane	Perchloric Acid	4
Isopropyl *N*-phenylcarbamate	Phosphoric Acid	14
Urethanes	Sulphuric Acid	40, 82
isopropyl *N*-phenylcarbamate	Sulphuric Acid	77

Carbonyl Compounds (in general)

Examples	Reagent	References
	Aluminium Hydride and Borohydride	1
carbonyl groups in cellulose	Aluminium Hydride and Borohydride	9
	Aluminium Isopropylate	
	Amines and Heterocyclic Bases	61, 78
	Bisulphite and Sulphite	Many
Carbonyl groups in starch	Cyanide	22, 49
	Hydrazines	Many
	Hydroxylamine	Many
	Ion Exchangers	41
	Percarboxylic Acids	16

Carboxylates

Examples	Reagent	References
Sodium acetate	Alcohols	29
	Ammonium Hydroxide and Ammonium Salts	3
Laurylamine acetate	Bichromate	178
Na, Ba acetate	Bichromate	110, 181

Examples (no entry under this heading is equivalent to 'miscellaneous')	Reagent	References under this reagent heading
Calcium pantothenate	Carboxylic Acids	28
Acetate	Copper (II)	81
gluconate	Copper (II)	192, 200
Formate	Ferricyanide	125
Calcium acetate	Hydrogen Peroxide	13
Metal naphthenates	Hydrochloric Acid	95
Disodium alkenylsuccinates	Hydrochloric Acid	147
Formates	Iodine Reagents	419, 433
malonates	Iodine Reagents	420
E.g. acetates	Ion Exchangers	Many
Calcium gluconate	Lead (IV)	7, 10, 12
tartrates	Lead (IV)	9
	Perchloric Acid	5, 6, 8, 9, 14, 15
Acetates	Phosphoric Acid	1, 3, 5, 7, 15, 19
Alkali and alkaline earth salts	Pyrolysis	3, 7, 21
bismuth camphorcarboxylate	Pyrolysis	35
Acetates	Sulphonic Acids	11
Acetates	Sulphuric Acid	1, 19, 27, 43, 86, 133
	Sulphuric Acid	16, 67, 68, 92, 99, 116, 133

Carboxylic Acids

E.g. acetic, lactic, oxalic acids	Alcohols	19, 22, 33, 37, 41, 46, 50
	Alkalies	15, 239, 298, 335, 403, 404, 457, 463
	Aluminium Hydride and Borohydride	3, 4, 5, 8
Chrysanthemum monocarboxylic acid	Amines	50
	Amines	64, 108
Free lauric acid in lauroyl chloride	Ammonium Hydroxide and Ammonium Salts	19
Citric acid	Barium (II)	1, 2
tartaric acid	Barium (II)	4
succinic acid	Barium (II)	5
E.g. formic acid; hydroxyacids like lactic, β-hydroxybutyric; polycarboxylic acids like tartaric, phthalic	Bichromate	Many
Tartaric acid	Bismuth (III)	1
Formic acid	Bromine Reagents	15, 16, 19, 27, 54, 76, 101, 104, 200, 205, 225, 262, 357, 507, 520, 541

Examples (no entry under this heading is equivalent to 'miscellaneous')	Reagent	References under this reagent heading
salicylic acid	Bromine Reagents	10, 26, 31, 86, 87, 90, 116, 118, 163, 174, 282, 301, 325, 375, 383, 442, 461, 467
p-hydroxybenzoic acid	Bromine Reagents	168, 206, 215, 428, 462
unsaturated acids, e.g. oleic, cinnamic, fumaric, maleic, acrylic, crotonic, sorbic	Bromine Reagents	21, 51, 63, 70, 120, 125, 154, 184, 216, 228, 300, 348, 354, 358, 421, 445, 469, 483, 484, 498, 503, 536
other non-olefinic acids	Bromine Reagents	52, 101, 240, 380, 401
E.g. oxalic, tartaric acids	Calcium (II)	Many
d-Tartaric acid	Carboxylic Acids	3, 4, 6, 8, 22
aconitic acid	Carboxylic Acids	18, 19, 20
Hydroxy- and polycarboxylic acids like oxalic, tartaric, malic, lactic; some aromatic acids	Cerium (IV)	Many
E.g. citric, tartaric, mandelic acids; carboxylic acid groups in starches, celluloses, etc.	Copper (II)	107, 123, 129, 152, 170, 191, 193, 199, 200
Tartaric acid	Copper (III)	
Glucuronic acid	Ferricyanide	27, 68, 73
Uronic acids and salts	Hydrochloric Acid	10, 15, 26, 29, 64, 81, 94, 115, 124
other sugar acids	Hydrochloric Acid	39, 55
Butyric acid	Hydrogen Peroxide	10
isobutyric acid	Hydrogen Peroxide	12
Acids of pK *ca* 6 and lower; oxidizable acids like formic, hydroxy- and polycarboxylic acids	Iodate	Many
Cincophene	Iodine Reagents	96, 179
Oxalic acid	Iron (III)	8
Citric acid	Lead (II)	4, 6, 9
other acids like tartaric, oxalic, malic, glucuronic, chlorogenic	Lead (II)	1, 2, 3, 4, 5
E.g. formic, mandelic, tartaric acids	Lead (IV)	6, 7, 8, 9, 10, 12, 13
Formic, hydroxy- and poly-carboxylic acids	Manganate	All 4
Oxalic acid	Manganese (III)	1, 2
other hydroxy- and poly-carboxylic acids	Manganese (III)	1
Lactic acid	Manganese (IV)	1, 2, 4, 6
other hydroxy- and poly-carboxylic acids	Manganese (IV)	5, 7

Examples (no entry under this heading is equivalent to 'miscellaneous')	Reagent	References under this reagent heading
Fumaric acid	Mercury (I)	1, 2
aconitic acid	Mercury (I)	3
Formic acid	Mercury (II)	Many
citric acid	Mercury (II)	35, 42
chloropropionic acids	Mercury (II)	145, 175
fumaric acid	Mercury (II)	149, 158
	Mercury (II)	9, 42, 44, 141, 145
Tartaric acid	Periodates and Periodic Acid	15, 50, 90, 91, 102, 103, 113, 118, 130, 131, 132
glyoxalic acid	Periodates, etc.	118, 130, 131, 132
formic acid	Periodates and Periodic Acid	4
lactic, pyruvic acids	Periodates and Periodic Acid	16
Lactic, citric acids	Permanganate	Many
formic acid	Permanganate	1, 5, 6, 12, 46, 81, 84, 90
tartaric acid	Permanganate	11, 38, 107, 112, 114
oxalic acid	Permanganate	50, 63, 113, 135, 142, 143
maleic acid	Permanganate	28, 94, 131, 132
fumaric acid	Permanganate	28, 56
salicylic acid	Permanganate	106, 112, 137
other acids	Permanganate	13, 15, 42, 67, 91, 107, 111, 137
Acetic, aromatic acids	Persulphate	5
Volatile and lower aliphatic acids	Physical Methods	Many
Tartaric acid	Potassium (I)	1, 2, 3, 4, 5, 8, 9, 10, 11, 12, 13, 14
p-Aminosalicylic acid	Pyrolysis	22, 44, 45, 46
uronic acids	Pyrolysis	40
acetone dicarboxylic acid	Pyrolysis	44, 45
Succinic acid	Silver (I)	7, 52, 62, 92, 128, 182
carboxyl groups in starches, celluloses	Silver (I)	71, 72, 89
substituted benzoic acids (e.g. *p*-aminobenzoic and salicylic acids)	Silver (I)	61, 95, 117, 133
citric acid	Silver (I)	104, 178
	Silver (I)	6, 14, 53, 58, 62, 128
Carboxyl groups in cellulose, etc.	Sodium (I)	Both
	Sulphides	1
Lactic acid	Sulphuric Acid	7, 11, 12, 13, 96
trichloroacetic acid	Sulphuric Acid	92
easily decarboxylated acids	Sulphuric Acid	134, 135
	Thiosulphate	Many
Tannic acid	Titanium (III)	21

Examples (no entry under this heading is equivalent to 'miscellaneous')	Reagent	References under this reagent heading
Hydroxy- and polycarboxylic acids	Vanadate	3, 7, 8, 13, 18, 20
Carboxylic acid groups in pulp	Zinc (II)	3
	Conjugated Hydrocarbons	
Butadiene	Bromine Reagents	38, 41
4-vinyl-1-cyclohexene	Bromine Reagents	248, 292
cyclopentadiene, isoprene	Bromine Reagents	147, 487
sorbic acid	Bromine Reagents	536
	Iodine Chlorides, etc.	38, 45, 78, 121, 127
4-vinyl-1-cyclohexene	Iodine Chlorides, etc.	50
E.g. in fats and oils	Maleic Anhydride	Many
1,3-Dienes	Nitriles	5
Dienes, etc.	Quinones	2, 3, 4, 5, 6
	Cyanates and Isocyanates	
Alkyl silicon isocyanates	Alkalies	244
Hexamethylene, benzyl and cyclohexyl isocyanates	Amines	32
phenyl isocyanate	Amines	69, 74, 94, 110
isocyanate groups in general	Amines	39, 41, 49, 72, 76, 98
Isocyanate groups	Hydrochloric Acid	104
	Diazo Compounds	
Diazomethane	Carboxylic Acids	2
Diazophenols	Vanadium (II)	6
	Diazonium Salts	
	Amines	6, 111, 112
	Chromium (II)	6
Benzenediazonium chloride	Dithionite	1
	Titanium (III)	12, 64
	Disulphides	
Dibenzothiazole disulphide	Alkalies	323
	Aluminium Hydride and Borohydride	7
E.g. cystine, dixanthogen	Bisulphite and Sulphite	99, 112, 117, 124, 126, 132, 133, 139, 146, 147, 148, 168, 169, 172, 176, 177, 181, 184, 185

Examples (no entry under this heading is equivalent to 'miscellaneous')	Reagent	References under this reagent heading
E.g. cystine	Bromine Reagents	444, 459
Tetraethylthiuram disulphide	Cerium (IV)	46
Thiuram disulphides	Cyanide	26, 37
dibutyl dixanthogen	Cyanide	53
E.g. cystine	Electrolytic Reduction	1, 3
Dixanthogens	Halides (Active)	72
E.g. cystine	Iodides and Hydriodic Acid	241
E.g. cystine	Iodine Reagents	396, 413
	Lead (II)	10
Thiuram disulphides	Mercaptans	6
	Mercury (II)	155
Cystine	Metals	11, 20, 37, 52, 62
E.g. dimethyl, diphenyl, dibenzyl, etc.	Metals	9, 39, 42, 46, 50, 63, 64, 71, 74, 80, 88, 89, 93, 97, 103
Tetraethylthiuram disulphide ('Antabuse')	Perchloric Acid	10
Thiuram disulphides	Phosphoric Acid	18
Tetramethylthiuram disulphide	Silver (I)	164
Thiuram disulphides	Sulphides	8
Dibenzothiazole disulphide	Tin (II)	24
Tetraethylthiuram disulphide	Vanadate	5
	Dithiocarbamates	
	Ferricyanide	111
	Nickel (II)	3, 7
	Periodates and Periodic Acid	89
	Phosphoric Acid	18
Nickel salt of dithiocarbamate of hexamethyleneimine	Silver (I)	152
	Sulphuric Acid	10, 76, 104, 125, 132
	Dyes	
Malachite green	Alkalies	368, 391
Methylene blue	Bichromate	103, 138
indigo; indigosulphonic acid	Bichromate	186, 240
E.g. methylene blue	Chromium (II)	2, 11
Azo dyes	Dithionite	2
Flavine dyes	Ferricyanide	28
dyestuffs in wine	Ferricyanide	123
Indigo carmine	Iodate	75
Methylene blue	Iodine Reagents	76, 90, 182, 209
Brilliant green	Iodine Reagents	341
Methylene blue	Iodine Chlorides, etc.	104
Azo dyes	Metals	38
	Permanganate	138, 141

Examples (no entry under this heading is equivalent to 'miscellaneous')	Reagent	References under this reagent heading
Amaranth	Sulphides	2
E.g. indigo, fuchsine	Sulphuric Acid	98, 114
	Tin (II)	11, 12, 14
Alizarin dyes	Titanium (III)	7
Indigo, indigo carmine	Vanadate	4
	Vanadium (II)	2, 5, 7
	Enediols	
Ascorbic acid	Bromine Reagents	383, 503
Ascorbic acid	Copper (II)	186
Ascorbic acid	Dyes	3
Ascorbic acid	Ferricyanide	101, 113, 119
Ascorbic acid	Halides (Active)	23
Ascorbic acid	Iodate	48, 50, 67
Ascorbic acid	Iodine Reagents	191, 280, 417, 424
Ascorbic acid	Mercury (II)	62, 79, 131
Ascorbic acid	Selenium Dioxide	4, 5
Ascorbic acid	Tillmans' Reagent	
	Enols	
2-Nitroindane-1,3-dione (salts)	Amines	43
Enol contents	Bromine Reagents	23, 24, 32, 34, 156, 349, 504
acetylacetone	Bromine Reagents	328
aci-form of nitroethane	Bromine Reagents	313
4-butyl-1,2-diphenylpyrazolidine-3,5-dione	Bromine Reagents	431
	Copper (II)	33, 35, 138, 145
	Iodides and Hydriodic Acid	157
Enol contents of cycloalkanones	Iodine Chlorides, etc.	118
2-Phenylindane-1,3-dione	Silver (I)	156
	Thiocyanogen	3
	Epoxides and Ethyleneimines	
Ethylene and other α-epoxides	Bisulphite and Sulphite	36, 118
E.g. ethylene oxide	Hydrobromic Acid	1, 7, 8, 14
3,3-bis(chloromethyl)oxacyclobutane	Hydrobromic Acid	16
E.g. ethylene oxide	Hydrochloric Acid	Many
oxetanes	Hydrochloric Acid	109
α-epoxides	Iodides and Hydriodic Acid	201, 256
α-epoxides	Mercaptans	8
Ethylene oxide	Periodates and Periodic Acid	56
Ethylene oxide	Sulphuric Acid	38, 91, 107, 124

Examples (no entry under this heading is equivalent to 'miscellaneous')	Reagent	References under this reagent heading
α-epoxides	Thiocyanates	30
ethyleneimines (aziridines)	Thiocyanates	57
α-epoxides	Thiosulphate	14, 22, 24, 32
ethyleneimines (aziridines)	Thiosulphate	9, 17, 23, 28, 29
Esters		
Acetate esters	Alcohols	Many
Saponification numbers, etc.	Alkalies	Many
	Aluminium Hydride and Borohydride	1, 3
Allethrin	Amines	50
Propyl gallate	Bismuth (III)	12
Glycerides	Bisulphate	1
Esters of *p*-aminobenzoic acid	Bromine Reagents	97, 169, 186, 194, 210, 223, 226, 287, 296, 301, 302, 374, 383, 389, 454, 509
unsaturated esters	Bromine Reagents	70, 479, 534
ethyl formate	Bromine Reagents	523
Ethyl orthoformate	Carboxylic Acids	36
Benzyl esters; carbobenzyloxy groups	Hydrobromic Acid	13, 17
Acetates	Hydrochloric Acid	24, 28
benzoates	Hydrochloric Acid	1
ethyl *p*-aminobenzoate	Hydrochloric Acid	101
aminoalkyl esters	Hydrochloric Acid	150
Carbobenzyloxy groups	Hydrogen Gas	5
Ethyl acetate	Hydrogen Peroxide	22, 36
Esters of glycols	Iodides and Hydriodic Acid	102, 188
	Iodides and Hydriodic Acid	94, 109, 158, 209
Unsaturated esters	Iodine Chlorides, etc.	54, 55, 62
esters of *p*-aminobenzoic acid, e.g. procaine, benzocaine	Iodine Chlorides, etc.	73
Salts of esters of *p*-aminobenzoic acid	Ion Exchangers	9
α, β-Unsaturated esters	Mercaptans	3, 9
Vinyl, allyl acetates	Mercury (II)	126
acrylic acid esters	Mercury (II)	139
methacrylic esters	Mercury (II)	144
propyl gallate	Mercury (II)	146, 167
Benzocaine	Permanganate	104
Acetyl groups	Phosphoric Acid	15
cellulose acetate	Phosphoric Acid	4
Methyl esters of fatty acids	Pyrolysis	33
Gallic acid esters; ascorbyl palmitate	Silver (I)	192
Acetate, benzoate, formate esters	Sulphonic Acids	Many

Examples (no entry under this heading is equivalent to 'miscellaneous')	Reagent	References under this reagent heading
Acetate esters	Sulphuric Acid	2, 5, 15, 26, 35, 70, 86, 89, 95, 103
benzoate esters	Sulphuric Acid	35, 83
	Sulphuric Acid	15, 52, 70, 136
E.g. procaine	Tetraphenylborate	1, 3, 14
ψ-esters of laevulinic acid	Water	15
ethyl orthoformate	Water	26
	Ethers	
Methoxyl groups in pectin and paraformaldehyde	Alkalies	82, 476
Diethyl ether	Bichromate	13, 24, 36, 49, 54, 60, 90, 97, 104, 137, 147, 156, 159, 160
ethoxyl groups	Bichromate	139, 207
alkylene oxide polymers	Bichromate	217, 229, 231
paraldehyde	Bichromate	101
alkyl cellosolves	Bichromate	122
dioxan	Bichromate	134
Trioxymethylene	Bisulphite and Sulphite	4
Trifluoroethyl vinyl ether	Bromine Reagents	411
Cellulose carboxymethyl ethers	Copper (II)	229
Trioxymethylene	Cyanide	4
Ethylene oxide polymers (nonionic detergents)	Ferrocyanide	2, 3, 4, 5, 6
E.g. dibenzyl ether	Hydrobromic Acid	5
vinyl ethers	Hydrobromic Acid	11
Methoxyl, ethoxyl groups	Hydrochloric Acid	51
paraldehyde	Hydrochloric Acid	4
Vinyl ethers	Hydrogen Gas	2
Vinyl ethers	Hydroxylamine	67, 71, 77, 102, 146
Diethyl ether	Iodate	7
divinyl ether	Iodate	44
Lower alkoxyl groups	Iodides and Hydriodic Acid	Many
ethylene oxide polymers and related compounds, e.g. polyethylene glycols	Iodides and Hydriodic Acid	102, 188, 198, 205, 220, 225, 233, 249, 250, 259, 274
higher alkoxyl groups	Iodide and Hydriodic Acid	272
Alkyl vinyl ethers	Iodine Reagents	265, 293, 363
ethylene oxide polymers	Iodine Reagents	372, 391
paraformaldehyde	Iodine Reagents	356, 375
	Iodine Reagents	244, 351
Vinyl ethers	Mercury (II)	142
tetraphenylborates of ethylene oxide polymers	Mercury (II)	168
Alkylene oxide polymers (surface-active materials)	Molybdenum (VI) and Tungsten (VI)	20

Examples (no entry under this heading is equivalent to 'miscellaneous')	Reagent	References under this reagent heading
β, β′-Dichlorodiethyl ether	Nitric Acid	12
methoxyl groups in methoxy-borohydrides	Nitric Acid	15
α-Methylbenzhydryl ethers	Perchloric Acid	12
Paraldehyde	Permanganate	71
ethylene oxide polymers	Permanganate	128
Metaldehyde	Phosphoric Acid	16
Paraldehyde	Sulphuric Acid	44, 48, 122
paraformaldehyde	Sulphuric Acid	31, 115
lower alkoxyl groups	Sulphuric Acid	37, 41, 108
vinyl ethers	Sulphuric Acid	64
ethers of 1,1-diphenylethanol	Sulphuric Acid	129
alkylene oxide polymers	Tetraphenylborate	19
Halide ethers, $RCH_2—CH(X)—OR$	Water	17
Germanium-containing Compounds		
Ethyl germanium esters	Alkalies	245
Guanidines		
1-(5-Tetrazoyl)-4-guanyltetrazene	Bromine Reagents	522
Diphenyl guanidine	Carbon Disulphide	2
Aminoguanidine	Iodate	35
	Iodine Chlorides, etc.	102
Nitroguanidine	Phenols	1, 4
1-(5-Tetrazoyl)-4-guanyltetrazene	Sulphuric Acid	131
nitroguanidine	Sulphuric Acid	93
Nitroguanidine and derivatives	Titanium (III)	35, 46, 47, 54, 55, 57
Nitroguanidine	Vanadium (II)	4
Halogen-containing Compounds		
DDT	Alkalies	157, 171, 174, 178, 181, 182, 201, 204, 205, 238, 241, 256, 258, 272, 280, 287, 390
Chloral	Alkalies	1, 17, 19, 37, 44, 51, 52, 53, 70, 107, 121, 128, 179, 321, 367

Examples (no entry under this heading is equivalent to 'miscellaneous')	Reagent	References under this reagent heading
BHC	Alkalies	194, 224, 226, 240, 263, 266, 272, 320, 327, 332, 416
methyl bromide	Alkalies	54, 110, 147, 173, 230, 293, 321, 330
chloroform	Alkalies	16, 78, 83, 84, 92, 200, 321, 415, 441
iodoform	Alkalies	9, 22, 55, 63, 119, 439
monochloroacetic acid	Alkalies	149, 152, 176, 233
dichloroethane	Alkalies	123, 303, 325, 468
phosgene	Alkalies	39, 41
pentabromoacetone	Alkalies	91, 96
chlorobutanol	Alkalies	102, 150, 222, 322
dichloroacetic acid	Alkalies	168, 211
bromoform	Alkalies	200, 285
chloramphenicol	Alkalies	301, 398, 444
dichloroacetaldehyde	Alkalies	366, 367
chlorohydrins	Alkalies	189, 227
dibromoethane	Alkalies	351, 447
cyanuric chloride	Alkalies	410, 465
	Alkalies	Many
Chiefly alkyl halides, e.g. iodides, methyl bromide	Amines and Heterocyclic Bases	3, 5, 11, 20, 25, 26, 28, 42, 44, 68, 77, 81, 87, 91, 93, 109
dichloro-, dibromoethane	Amines and Heterocyclic Bases	23, 47, 87
	Amines and Heterocyclic Bases	67, 87, 92, 109
DDT	Ammonium Hydroxide and Ammonium Salts	20
Chloramphenicol	Anhydrides	124
4-Chloroacetanilide	Bichromate	155
trichlorobenzene	Bichromate	219
BHC	Bichromate	223
pentachlorophenol	Bichromate	224
Chloropicrin	Bisulphite and Sulphite	46
pentabromoacetone	Bisulphite and Sulphite	72
Lower alkyl iodides	Bromine Reagents	Many
unsaturated chlorides	Bromine Reagents	283, 372, 436
aromatic chlorides	Bromine Reagents	83, 161, 419
chloral	Bromine Reagents	152
tert-Butyl hypochlorite	Carboxylic Acids	30
Chloroform, carbon tetrachloride	Chromium (II)	4
Bromoacetylenes	Copper (I)	9
Chloral	Copper (II)	124
Chloropicrin	Dithionite	4
Ethyl bromide	Electrolytic Reduction	2

Examples (no entry under this heading is equivalent to 'miscellaneous')	Reagent	References under this reagent heading
Aldrin	Halides (Active)	67
Iodoform	Hydrochloric Acid	45, 57
chloramphenicol	Hydrochloric Acid	120
tetraiodopyrrole	Hydrochloric Acid	57
Organophosphorus chloridates	Hydrofluoric Acid	
DDT	Hydrogen Gas	1
Methyl bromide	Hydrogen Peroxide	23, 28
trichloroacetonitrile	Hydrogen Peroxide	23
bromine-containing barbiturates	Hydrogen Peroxide	43
Ethyl iodide	Iodate	10, 12, 16, 23
trichloro-, tribromo- and mono-bromoacetic acid	Iodate	51
Phosgene	Iodides and Hydriodic Acid	33, 46, 114, 222, 234
—CO—CHBr groups from bromination of enols	Iodides and Hydriodic Acid	9, 10, 18, 59, 238
2,6-dichlorophenol-indophenol	Iodides and Hydriodic Acid	38, 58, 63, 81
2,4,6-tribromophenyl hypo-bromite	Iodides and Hydriodic Acid	39, 175, 203
pentabromoacetone	Iodides and Hydriodic Acid	31, 112
N,*N*′-dichlorophenylenediimine	Iodides and Hydriodic Acid	68, 226
other *N*-halides	Iodides and Hydriodic Acid	7, 141, 162, 180, 183, 219
other *C*-halides, e.g. poly-haloalkanes	Iodides and Hydriodic Acid	27, 50, 57, 88, 190, 230, 269
phenylsulphenyl chloride	Iodides and Hydriodic Acid	86
tert-butyl hypochlorite	Iodides and Hydriodic Acid	207
Chloral	Iodine Reagents	22, 65, 70, 114, 177, 262, 365
dichloroacetaldehyde	Iodine Reagents	364, 365
chlorobutanol	Iodine Reagents	168
p-chlorophenol	Iodine Reagents	183
Glycerol halohydrins	Lead (IV)	3
Monochloroacetate	Mercaptans	2
Chloropropionates	Mercury (II)	145, 175
allyl chloride	Mercury (II)	150
DDT	Metals	45, 47, 49, 51, 61, 101
chloramphenicol	Metals	76, 77, 78, 92, 100, 102
dibromo- and dichloroethane	Metals	36, 60, 85
	Metals	10, 12, 30, 49, 53, 54, 56, 58, 69, 70, 79, 91, 99, 101, 106, 108
Iodoform	Nitric Acid	1, 2, 3, 6, 8, 9, 11, 17
tetraiodopyrrole	Nitric Acid	11
β, *β*′-dichlorodiethyl ether	Nitric Acid	12
trichloroethylene	Nitric Acid	21
Tribromophenol	Permanganate	17
chloral	Permanganate	64

Examples (no entry under this heading is equivalent to 'miscellaneous')	Reagent	References under this reagent heading
methyl α-chloroacrylate	Permanganate	99
Iodoform, chloral	Persulphate	1
trichloroethylene	Persulphate	4
Methyl bromide	Pyrolysis	12, 14, 19, 29, 39
chloropicrin	Pyrolysis	8, 9, 28, 36
dichloroethane	Pyrolysis	28, 36, 41
methyl chloride	Pyrolysis	2, 4
trichloroethylene	Pyrolysis	6, 30
tetrachloroethylene	Pyrolysis	6, 26
chiefly volatile halides and insecticides	Pyrolysis	1, 5, 6, 10, 11, 12, 13, 16, 17, 18, 20, 24, 25, 31, 32, 42, 43
Iodoform	Silver (I)	15, 23, 30, 51, 54, 150
lower alkyl iodides	Silver (I)	67, 82, 97, 145, 171
heptachlor	Silver (I)	188, 202
adduct of chloromaleic anhydride and dienes	Silver (I)	83
Pentabromoacetone	Sulphides	4, 5, 6
Polyvinylchloride	Sulphuric Acid	113
Iodoform	Thiosulphate	19, 21, 25
phosgene	Thiosulphate	4, 26
alkyl halides, haloacetate esters, halogen-substituted ketones	Thiosulphate	30
Secondary and tertiary alkyl halides	Thiourea	1, 2
Chloramphenicol	Titanium (III)	50
Halide ethers, $RCH_2—CH(X)—OR$	Water	17
alkyl tin halides	Water	24
Hydrazines		
Semicarbazones	Alkalies	125
phthivazide	Alkalies	375
Nicotinic acid hydrazide	Anhydrides	166
1,1-dimethylhydrazine	Anhydrides	169
Phenylhydrazine and hydrazones	Arsenate	Both
Isoniazid	Bichromate	176
1,4-dihydrazinophthalazine	Bichromate	215
Isoniazid	Bromine Reagents	334, 338, 351, 393, 395
cyanoacethydrazide	Bromine Reagents	472
	Bromine Reagents	531
Isoniazid	Cadmium (II)	5, 7
2-furfurylidene-1-methyl-ethylidenehydrazide ('Larucan')	Cadmium (II)	22

Examples (no entry under this heading is equivalent to 'miscellaneous')	Reagent	References under this reagent heading
Mixtures of hydrazines	Carbonyl Compounds	31
Methylhydrazine	Chlorine Reagents	24
Isoniazid	Chlorite	8
Isoniazid	Copper (II)	180, 208, 223
Phenylhydrazine	Dyes	1
Isoniazid	Ferricyanide	105
mono- and dihydrazino-phthalazine	Ferricyanide	108
semicarbazide	Ferricyanide	127
Isoniazid	Halides (Active)	48
methylhydrazine	Halides (Active)	69
Osazones	Hydrochloric Acid	5
semicarbazide and semi-carbazones, e.g. nitrofurazone	Hydrochloric Acid	11, 37, 134
isoniazid and hydrazones	Hydrochloric Acid	86, 145
Semicarbazide	Iodate	17, 35, 62, 73
isoniazid	Iodate	56, 59
aminoguanidine	Iodate	35
2,4-dinitrophenylhydrazine	Iodate	60
	Iodate	81
Phenylhydrazine	Iodine Reagents	3, 53, 69, 309, 334
isoniazid and related compounds	Iodine Reagents	297, 298, 301, 305, 366
2,4-dinitrophenylhydrazine	Iodine Reagents	395, 422
Girard T reagent derivatives	Iodine Reagents	421
	Iodine Reagents	417, 436, 442
Phthivazide	Iodine Chlorides, etc.	134
E.g. isoniazid	Mercury (II)	157, 159, 160, 170
Isoniazid	Metals	81, 107
Mono- and dihydrazinophthalazines	Periodates, etc.	88
Azines, hydrazones of aromatic aldehydes	Phosphoric Acid	2
Isoniazid	Selenium Dioxide	2, 6
condensation products of isoniazid with aldehydes	Selenium Dioxide	8
Isoniazid	Silver (I)	116
maleic hydrazide	Silver (I)	129
3-semicarbazidobenzamide	Silver (I)	169
	Silver (I)	3
Hydrazines, hydrazones, azines	Sulphuric Acid	3, 6, 18
phthivazide	Sulphuric Acid	102
isoniazid derivatives	Sulphuric Acid	118
Isoniazid, semicarbazide, benzoylhydrazine	Thallium(III)	1
Isoniazid	Thiocyanates	20, 22, 28, 41, 45, 54
p-Nitrophenylhydrazones	Tin (II)	20
Nitroarylhydrazines and hydrazones	Titanium (III)	27, 30, 41, 42, 45, 56, 59, 64

Examples (no entry under this heading is equivalent to 'miscellaneous')	Reagent	References under this reagent heading
osazones	Titanium (III)	17, 18
nitrobenzohydrazone of methylglyoxal	Titanium (III)	40
Isoniazid	Vanadate	11
Dinitrophenylhydrazones	Vanadium (III)	3
	Hydrazo Compounds	
Hydrazobenzene	Dyes	4, 5
Hydrazobenzene	Permanganate	125
	Hydroxamates	
Long-chain hydroxamic acids	Hydrochloric Acid	78
	Iodoso- and Iodoxy Compounds	
	Iodides and Hydriodic Acid	1, 2
	Isopropylidene Groups	
	Ozone	1, 3
	Periodate	78
O-Isopropylidene groups	Sulphuric Acid	33
	Ketones	
Diacetone alcohol and other ketoalcohols	Alkalies	267
α-diketones	Alkalies	419, 471
Acetone in mixtures with alcohols	Bichromate	195, 201, 205
2,2,6,6-tetrabishydroxy-methylcyclohexan-1-one	Bichromate	193
E.g. acetone	Bisulphite, etc.	2, 6, 21, 53, 60, 98, 106
Ketophenols(e.g. resaceto-phenone)	Bromine Reagents	343, 524
unsaturated ketones	Bromine Reagents	425, 503
α- and β-diketones	Bromine Reagents	376
Camphor	Carboxylic Acids	23
Diketones	Cerium (IV)	10
Acetone	Chlorine Reagents	1
Diketones	Chromium (II)	8, 11
β-Dicarbonyl compounds	Copper (II)	138

Examples (no entry under this heading is equivalent to 'miscellaneous')	Reagent	References under this reagent heading
aminoketones	Copper (II)	164
	Cyanide	14
Dihydroxyacetone	Ferricyanide	16
	Hydrazines	2, 3, 9, 12, 14, 15, 24, 37, 48
α-Diketones	Hydrogen Peroxide	34, 45, 50
	Hydroxylamine	Many
Acetone	Iodine Reagents	Many
acetophenone	Iodine Reagents	203, 246
methylglyoxal	Iodine Reagents	97, 236
laevulinic acid	Iodine Reagents	27, 214
e.g. pyruvic acid, acetoin, butanone, phenylglyoxal, etc.	Iodine Reagents	88, 101, 133, 174, 201, 229, 255, 257, 349, 361, 362,
Acetone	Iodine Chlorides, etc.	129
Acetol	Ion Exchangers	31
Acetone	Mercury (II)	7, 9, 14, 21, 22, 25, 39, 73, 78, 88
e.g. acetoin, pyruvic acid	Mercury (II)	63, 145
Pyruvic acid	Metals	13, 14, 16
Dihydroxyacetone	Molybdenum (VI) and Tungsten (VI)	2, 4
Biacetyl and monoxime	Nickel (II)	9, 12
	Percarboxylic Acids	16
	Periodates and Periodic Acid	16, 82
Acetone	Permanganate	56
Rotenone	Physical Methods	8
α-Diketones	Silver (I)	146
	Vanadate	18

Lactones

Examples	Reagent	References
Santonin	Alkalies	56, 72, 139
e.g. coumarin, narcotine	Alkalies	72, 359, 373
3-Methylchromone	Hydrazines	47
E.g. warfarin, dehydroacetic acid	Iodine Reagents	220, 339, 349, 362
Coumarin	Permanganate	18, 53
Diketene	Sulphuric Acid	49
β-Propiolactone	Thiosulphate	16

Lead-containing Compounds

Examples	Reagent	References
Lead tetraethyl	Bromine Reagents	71, 144, 219, 491, 529
Lead tetraethyl	Chlorate	4, 5
Lead tetraethyl	Hydrochloric Acid	6, 44, 62, 92, 111, 130
lead glucuronate	Hydrochloric Acid	10

Examples (no entry under this heading is equivalent to 'miscellaneous')	Reagent	References under this reagent heading
Lead tetraethyl	Iodine Reagents	100, 224, 228, 234, 251, 254, 292, 360
Lead tetraethyl	Iodine Chlorides, etc.	63, 66
Lead tetraethyl	Nitric Acid	10, 20
Lead tetraethyl	Silver (I)	153
Lead acetate	Sulphuric Acid	27
	Magnesium-containing Compounds	
Alkyl magnesium halides	Hydrochloric Acid	141
Alkyl magnesium halides	Water	3, 5
	Mercaptans	
E.g. cysteine	Anhydrides	58, 132
Silver or cadmium derivatives of glutathione	Bromine Reagents	138
1-methyl-2-mercaptoimidazole	Bromine Reagents	402
6-mercaptopurine	Bromine Reagents	432
E.g. cysteine, glutathione	Cadmium (II)	1, 2, 4
	Copper (II)	157, 194, 227
E.g. glutathione	Ferricyanide	13
cysteine	Ferricyanide	119
E.g. thiophenol	Halides (Active)	18, 51, 64, 66, 81
Mercaptobenzothiazole, Zn salt	Hydrochloric Acid	102
Mercaptans (+ aryl trityl sulphides)	Hydrogen Peroxide	46
Cysteine	Iodine Reagents	148, 197, 397, 412
glutathione	Iodine Reagents	117, 120, 129, 426
thiomalic acid	Iodine Reagents	197, 389, 435
E.g. alkyl mercaptans, thioglycollate	Iodine Reagents	51, 131, 211, 313, 325, 327, 405, 417, 434
Unithiol	Iodine Chlorides, etc.	113
E.g. in proteins	Iodosobenzoate	All 4
	Lead (II)	10, 12
	Lead (IV)	15
E.g. methyl mercaptan, 2-mercaptobenzothiazole	Mercury (II)	50, 61, 115, 124, 125, 138, 143, 186
Thioacetic acid	Metals	4
Glutathione	Molybdenum (VI) and Tungsten (VI)	14
	Nitriles	1, 2, 3, 6
In naphtha, gasoline, etc.	Silver (I)	27, 43, 65, 68, 69, 77, 81, 107, 134, 135, 136, 161, 186, 187 206, 207, 208
6-mercaptopurine	Silver (I)	141, 200

Examples (no entry under this heading is equivalent to 'miscellaneous')	Reagent	References under this reagent heading
2-mercaptobenzothiazole	Silver (I)	41, 193
glutathione	Silver (I)	46
methyl mercaptan	Silver (I)	122
6-(4-carboxybutylthio)purine	Silver (I)	170
thiophenol	Silver (I)	194
	Mercury-containing Compounds	
Ethyl mercurichloride	Alkalies	462
Mercuriacetic acid + mercuric acetate	Bromine Reagents	521
Mercuric acetate in binary acetate mixtures	Hydrocarbons	3
E.g. mercury dimethylmercaptide, methoxyethyl mercuric chloride	Hydrochloric Acid	89, 107, 110, 144
Mersalyl	Hydrogen Peroxide	41
Phenylmercuric acetate	Iodides and Hydriodic Acid	133
Mercury derivatives of acetone and acetaldehyde	Iodine Reagents	29, 82, 181
arylmercuric acetates	Iodine Reagents	151
Mercury-containing pharmaceuticals	Metals	95
E.g. phenylmercuric acetate, mercury salicylate, methoxyethylmercuric chloride	Nitric Acid	16, 19
o-Hydroxymercuribenzoate	Sulphides	10, 12
phenyl- and methylmercuric salts	Sulphides	11
Mercury-containing diuretics	Sulphuric Acid	94
	Metal Alkyls and Aryls	
Potassium phenylisopropyl	Halides (Active)	4
lithium alkyls	Halides (Active)	5, 27
Phenyllithium, butyllithium, amylsodium	Iodine Reagents	390
zinc diethyl	Iodine Reagents	428
p-Phenylenedilithium	Pyrolysis	34
Dilithium hydroquinone	Sulphuric Acid	109
Butyllithium	Vanadate	17
Lithium alkyls	Water	8
Alkyl tin halides	Water	24
	Methyl Groups	
C-Methyl groups	Bichromate	47, 59, 123, 124, 142, 166, 168, 179, 182, 184, 189, 197, 227, 228, 241

Examples (no entry under this heading is equivalent to 'miscellaneous')	Reagent	References under this reagent heading
Ethylidene groups $CH_3.CH=$	Bichromate	139
methyl groups in alkylbenzenes	Bichromate	227
N-Methyl groups	Iodides, etc.	40, 61, 93, 196
	Methylol Groups	
In formaldehyde/amine resins	Alcohols	53
Mono- and dimethylolurea	Alkalies	248
In formaldehyde/urea or thiourea resins	Cyanide	24, 51
In formaldehyde resins	Hydrochloric Acid	49
	Phenols	2, 3
5-Hydroxymethylfurfuraldehyde/ furfuraldehyde mixtures	Physical Methods	21
	Nitrate Esters	
E.g. methyl nitrate	Alkalies	62, 135, 278
Cellulose nitrate	Chromium (II)	9
E.g. glycerol, cellulose nitrates	Iron (II)	1, 3, 5, 9, 10, 13, 14, 16, 17
Glycerol nitrate	Metals	15, 66, 84
amyl nitrate	Metals	86
nitrates of pentaerythritol, mannitol	Metals	104
Cellulose nitrate	Phenols	1, 5
Cellulose nitrate/acetate	Sulphuric Acid	25, 90, 93, 110
glycerol nitrate	Sulphuric Acid	32
E.g. glycerol nitrate	Titanium (III)	26, 31, 39, 65
	Nitriles	
Trichloroacetonitrile	Alkalies	160
acrylonitrile	Alkalies	164
nicotinic, isonicotinic nitriles	Alkalies	362
	Alkalies	124, 326, 378, 426, 449, 466, 478
	Aluminium Hydride and Borohydride	6
α,β-Unsaturated nitriles, e.g. acrylonitrile	Amines and Heterocyclic Bases	61, 80, 105
α,β-Unsaturated nitriles, e.g. acrylonitrile	Bisulphite and Sulphite	120, 129, 136, 173, 180
β,γ-Unsaturated nitriles	Bromine Reagents	74, 93
β-methoxy-α-ethoxymethyl-acrylonitrile	Bromine Reagents	426
cyanoacethydrazide	Bromine Reagents	472
	Chlorine Reagents	2

Examples (no entry under this heading is equivalent to 'miscellaneous')	Reagent	References under this reagent heading
cis-1-Cyano-1,3-butadiene	Diazonium Salts	5
	Hydrochloric Acid	99
1-imino-2-cyanocyclopentane	Hydrochloric Acid	131
	Hydrogen Gas	6
Trichloroacetonitrile	Hydrogen Peroxide	23
acrylonitrile	Hydrogen Peroxide	24
	Hydrogen Peroxide	42
Acrylonitrile	Hydroxylamine	133
	Iodides and Hydriodic Acid	95
Unsaturated nitriles	Iodine Chlorides, etc.	14, 23
	Kjeldahl Nitrogen Determination	5
calcium cyanamide	Kjeldahl Nitrogen Determination	17
Acrylonitrile	Mercaptans	3, 4, 5, 9, 11
1-cyano-1,3-butadiene	Mercaptans	4
Cyanohydrins	Nickel (II)	8
Dicyanodiamide	Nitric Acid	14
Dicyanodiamide	Nitrophenols	7, 50
Trichloroacetonitrile	Pyrolysis	12
Cyanamide	Silver (I)	12, 17, 127, 189
calcium cyanamide	Silver (I)	12, 22
dicyanodiamide	Silver (I)	19, 80
Dicyanodiamide	Sulphuric Acid	60, 78
acrylonitrile	Sulphuric Acid	112
acetonitrile	Sulphuric Acid	130
	Water	12

Nitrite Esters

Examples	Reagent	References
Amyl nitrite	Chlorate	2, 3
Quaternary ammonium nitrites	Halides (Active)	59
Nitrite esters of lower alcohols	Iodides and Hydriodic Acid	19, 20, 44, 45, 52, 75, 83, 127, 138, 177, 224
cyclohexyl nitrite	Iodides and Hydriodic Acid	212
Amyl nitrite	Permanganate	120
Methyl nitrite	Sulphuric Acid	84

Nitro Compounds

Examples	Reagent	References
Aromatic nitro compounds	Alkalies	49, 97
primary and secondary nitro compounds	Alkalies	430
chloropicrin	Alkalies	146
E.g. trinitrotoluene	Bichromate	39
	Bichromate	242

Examples (no entry under this heading is equivalent to 'miscellaneous')	Reagent	References under this reagent heading
Chloropicrin	Bisulphite and Sulphite	46
Nitrophenols	Bromine Reagents	241, 391
nitroarylamines	Bromine Reagents	141, 434
	Bromine Reagents	313, 419
Primary and secondary nitroparaffins	Chlorine Reagents	20
E.g. picric acid, nitroanilines	Chromium (II)	1, 5, 8, 9, 10
Picric acid	Copper (II)	91
	Dithionite	3, 4
Chloramphenicol	Hydrochloric Acid	120
Chloropicrin	Hydrogen Gas	3
Picric acid, picrates	Iodate	18, 24, 28, 34, 66
Nitrocyclohexane	Iodides and Hydriodic Acid	191
tetranitromethane	Iodides and Hydriodic Acid	56
terminal dinitrobromomethyl groups, —$C(Br)(NO_2)_2$	Iodides and Hydriodic Acid	148
5-nitrofurfuraldehyde derivatives	Iodides and Hydriodic Acid	235
	Iodides and Hydriodic Acid	153, 229
5-Nitrosalicylic acid	Kjeldahl Nitrogen Determination	15
5-nitrofurfuraldehyde derivatives	Kjeldahl Nitrogen Determination	18
Chiefly aromatic nitro compounds	Metals	Many
E.g. picric acid	Molybdenum (III)	
4,4′-Dinitrostilbene-2,2′-disulphonic acid	Permanganate	103
Nitroguanidine	Phenols	1, 4
Chloropicrin	Pyrolysis	8, 9, 28, 36
E.g. nitrobenzene, nitrotoluenes	Sulphuric Acid	22
tetranitronaphthalene	Sulphuric Acid	61
nitroguanidine	Sulphuric Acid	93
	Tin (II)	Many
Chiefly aromatic mono- and polynitro compounds	Titanium (III)	Many
nitroamines with —$NHNO_2$ group, e.g. RDX, nitroguanidine	Titanium (III)	13, 35, 36, 46, 54, 55, 57, 58
E.g. picric acid, nitroanilines	Vanadium (II)	1, 2, 3, 4

Nitroso Compounds

Examples	Reagent	References
1-Nitroso-1-methylurea	Alkalies	365
N-Nitrosodiphenylamine	Amines and Heterocyclic Bases	84, 89
	Bichromate	242
	Chromium (II)	5, 7, 8

Examples (no entry under this heading is equivalent to 'miscellaneous')	Reagent	References under this reagent heading
Dinitrosopentamethylene-tetramine	Hydrochloric Acid	47
Nitrosobenzene	Iodides and Hydriodic Acid	69
	Iodides and Hydriodic Acid	153, 268
N-Nitrosodimethylamine	Metals	5, 68
aromatic nitroso compounds	Metals	17, 72
E.g. cupferron	Molybdenum (III)	
	Titanium (III)	6, 15, 36, 61

Olefines

Examples	Reagent	References
Unsaturation; unsaturated acids	Aluminium Hydride and Borohydride	8
α,β-Unsaturated nitriles or carbonyl compounds	Amines and Heterocyclic Bases	61, 80, 105
Rubber hydrocarbons	Bichromate	83, 117, 128
α,β-Unsaturated carbonyl compounds (chiefly furfuraldehyde)	Bisulphite and Sulphite	7, 21, 27, 33, 44, 50, 64, 75, 76, 80, 91, 120
α,β-unsaturated nitriles, e.g. acrylonitrile	Bisulphite and Sulphite	120, 129, 136, 173, 180
Determination of unsaturation ('Bromine numbers'); unsaturated hydrocarbons, acids, alcohols, esters, nitriles, etc.	Bromine Reagents	Many
Camphene	Carboxylic Acids	10, 14, 31
dicyclopentadiene	Carboxylic Acids	21
pinene	Carboxylic Acids	23
Iodine numbers of fatty oils	Cerium (IV)	59
Unsaturation, e.g. of oils, fatty acids, glycerides, rubber	Chlorine Reagents	3, 6, 7, 8, 15, 16, 17, 18, 21
Acrolein	Copper (II)	84
cis-1-Cyano-1,3-butadiene	Diazonium Salts	5
Determination of unsaturation ('Iodine or Bromine numbers')	Halides (Active)	8, 37, 42, 58, 82
aldrin	Halides (Active)	67
Olefines in hydrocarbon mixtures	Hydrobromic Acid	2
α, *p*-dimethylstyrene	Hydrobromic Acid	4
Maleic anhydride, acid	Hydrocarbons	1, 2
C_4 olefines	Hydrochloric Acid	46
α, *p*-dimethylstyrene	Hydrochloric Acid	58
unsaturated amines	Hydrochloric Acid	97
tertiary amylenes	Hydrochloric Acid	142
Vinyl ethers	Hydrogen Gas	2
Acrylonitrile	Hydrogen Peroxide	24
Vinyl ethers	Hydroxylamine	67, 71, 78, 102, 146
α,β-unsaturated carbonyl compounds (chiefly furfuraldehyde)	Hydroxylamine	17, 19, 21, 22, 53, 68, 74, 82, 87, 89, 94, 120, 132, 159

Examples (no entry under this heading is equivalent to 'miscellaneous')	Reagent	References under this reagent heading
acrylonitrile	Hydroxylamine	133
Divinyl ether	Iodate, etc.	44
Unsaturation of oils, fats, etc. ('Iodine number')	Iodine Reagents	73, 79, 89, 92, 98, 99, 110, 126, 149, 154, 187, 240, 258, 330, 402, 439
unsaturation of rubber	Iodine Reagents	299, 352
vinyl ethers	Iodine Reagents	265, 293, 363
	Iodine Reagents	91, 186, 189, 339, 353
chlorogenic acid	Iodine Reagents	189, 353
Unsaturation of oils, fats, rubbers, petroleum fractions, etc.	Iodine Chlorides, etc.	Many
unsaturated acids and esters, e.g. oleic, linoleic	Iodine Chlorides, etc.	12, 17, 18, 19, 39, 46, 54, 55, 62, 118, 119, 130
α,β-unsaturated nitriles	Iodine Chlorides, etc.	14, 23
indene (as picrate)	Iodine Chlorides, etc.	88, 95, 132
styrene	Iodine Chlorides, etc.	93, 121, 125, 127, 132
squalene	Iodine Chlorides, etc.	49, 86
	Iodine Chlorides, etc.	6, 12, 35, 38, 40, 49, 50, 57, 86, 91, 96, 112, 121, 126, 127, 130
Acrylonitrile	Mercaptans	3, 4, 5, 9, 11
divinylacetylene	Mercaptans	1
1-cyano-1,3-butadiene	Mercaptans	4
compounds containing the —C=C—CO— group	Mercaptans	3, 9
Unsaturated hydrocarbons, e.g. styrene, isobutylene	Mercury (II)	85, 100, 107, 111, 154, 162, 180, 184
unsaturated esters	Mercury (II)	126, 139, 144, 176
unsaturated ethers, e.g. vinyl ethers, anethole	Mercury (II)	104, 120, 142
	Mercury (II)	106, 107, 133, 147, 149, 150, 158, 185
Indene	Nitrophenols	12, 64
Rubber unsaturation	Nitrosobenzene	
d-pimaric acid	Ozone	2
Unsaturated hydrocarbons, acids, esters and unsaturation of oils, rubbers, etc.	Percarboxylic Acids	Many
Maleic acid and anhydride	Permanganate	131, 132
methyl α-chloroacrylate	Permanganate	99
4,4′-dinitrostilbene-2,2′-disulphonic acid	Permanganate	103
	Permanganate	57, 73, 75
Vinyl ethers	Sulphuric Acid	64

Examples (no entry under this heading is equivalent to 'miscellaneous')	Reagent	References under this reagent heading
acrylonitrile	Sulphuric Acid	112
Unsaturated hydrocarbons, acids; unsaturation of fats, oils, rubber materials	Thiocyanogen	Many
Oximes		
	Anhydrides	137
Cyclohexanone oxime	Bromine Reagents	505
Acetone oxime, dimethyl glyoxime	Chromium (II)	3
Acetone oxime	Halides (Active)	73
Cyclohexanone oxime	Hydrochloric Acid	119
Diacetyl monoxime	Hydroxylamine	152
	Iodides and Hydriodic Acid	153
Vicinal dioximes	Iodine Reagents	373
Vicinal dioximes	Nickel (II)	13, 14
diacetyl monoxime	Nickel (II)	12
Oximes of aromatic aldehydes	Phosphoric Acid	2
Cyclohexanone oxime	Sulphuric Acid	100
	Sulphuric Acid	2, 6
	Sulphur trioxide	2
Peroxides and other Per-compounds		
	Arsenic (III)	2, 3, 4, 5, 6
Ascaridole	Hydrobromic Acid	9
Peracids, peroxides, hydroperoxides, etc.	Iodides and Hydriodic Acid	Many
ascaridole	Iodides and Hydriodic Acid	54, 111, 170, 197
Peroxides, chiefly in gasoline	Iron (II)	3, 4, 6, 7, 8, 11
Lipide and lauroyl peroxides; *tert*-butyl hydroperoxide	Mercaptans	10
Percarboxylic acids	Sulphides	9
Peroxides	Tin (II)	3, 13, 21, 22
Peroxides	Titanium (III)	63, 67
Phenols and Heterocyclic Hydroxy Compounds		
Cresols	Alkalies	427
xylenols	Alkalies	440
	Aluminium Hydride and Borohydride	1, 2, 3, 4, 5
	Anhydrides	Many
Salicylic acid	Bichromate, etc.	22, 76, 129
hydroquinone	Bichromate, etc.	192, 222, 255
	Bichromate, etc.	22, 151, 183, 224
Oxine	Bismuth (III)	3

Examples (no entry under this heading is equivalent to 'miscellaneous')	Reagent	References under this reagent heading
propyl gallate	Bismuth (III)	12
Monophenols, polyphenols, nitrophenols, halogen-substituted phenols, hydroxy-substituted aromatic acids, etc.	Bromine Reagents	Many
Cresols	Calcium (II)	12
Calcium cresolates	Carboxylic Acids	13
Mono-, di- and triphenols	Cerium (IV)	20, 23, 28, 31, 41, 43, 53, 55
salicylic acid	Cerium (IV)	32, 33
aminophenols	Cerium (IV)	29
Oxine, oxinates	Chlorite	11
Nitrophenols	Chromium (II)	1
Picric acid	Copper (II)	91
β-Naphthol	Diazonium Salts	3, 4
phenols e.g., in coals, humic acids	Diazonium Salts	6, 7
Lignin hydroxyl groups	Dimethyl Sulphate	3
Diphenols	Ferricyanide	100, 124
tannins	Ferricyanide	96, 123
adrenaline	Ferricyanide	115
E.g. phenol, salicylic acid, oxine	Halides (Active)	2, 6, 11, 44, 46, 47, 53, 63, 73, 74, 79, 83, 84
Picric acid, picrates of hydrocarbons	Iodate	18, 24, 28, 34, 66
Phenol	Iodine Reagents	6, 20, 34, 37, 94, 215, 274
salicylic acid	Iodine Reagents	6, 20, 31, 145, 173, 195, 196
phenolphthalein	Iodine Reagents	230, 286, 303, 317, 340
thymol	Iodine Reagents	6, 14, 20, 173
β-naphthol	Iodine Reagents	6, 9, 20, 173
hydroquinone	Iodine Reagents	31, 239, 333, 404
gallic acid	Iodine Reagents	31, 32, 35, 355, 400
cresols	Iodine Reagents	36, 37, 274
tyrosine	Iodine Reagents	188, 324
chlorogenic acid	Iodine Reagents	189, 353
resorcinol	Iodine Reagents	288, 444
	Iodine Reagents	14, 31, 136, 183, 188, 233, 243, 288, 333, 338, 370, 392, 417
E.g. salicylates, hydroquinone	Iodine Chlorides, etc.	42, 72, 83, 84, 89, 92, 100, 103, 116, 123, 131
Hydroquinone	Ion Exchangers	11
Hydroquinone	Iron (III)	3, 13
Diphenols, e.g. catechol	Lead (II)	7, 8, 11, 13

Examples (no entry under this heading is equivalent to 'miscellaneous')	Reagent	References under this reagent heading
Salicylic acid	Manganese (III)	1
Propyl gallate	Mercury (II)	146, 167
	Mercury (II)	42, 51, 68
Substituted phenols (Cl—, NO_2—, —S—)	Metals	18, 23, 70, 106
Polyphenols	Molybdenum (VI) and Tungsten (VI)	15
Tyrosine	Ninhydrin	13, 14
m-Aminophenol	Nitrite	2
1-naphthol-5-sulphonic acid	Nitrite	30
Naphthols	Nitrophenols	1
Phenol	Permanganate	2, 8, 54, 106
salicylic acid	Permanganate	106, 112, 137
tribromophenol	Permanganate	17
cresols	Permanganate	54
oxine, 8-hydroxyquinaldine	Permanganate	101
Homogentisic acid	Silver (I)	6, 53
nordihydroguaiaretic acid	Silver (I)	175
gallic acid esters	Silver (I)	192
	Sodamide	1
	Sulphides	1
2-naphthol-1-sulphonic acid	Sulphuric Acid	87
adrenaline	Sulphuric Acid	111
	Sulphur Trioxide	2
Hydroquinone	Thallium (III)	2
Nitrophenols	Titanium (III)	1, 2, 5, 13, 20
Thymol, naphthols	Thiocyanogen	2
Dibromoxine and oxinates	Vanadate	9
adrenaline	Vanadate	22
Nitrophenols	Vanadium (II)	1, 2, 3
Oxine and substituted oxines	Zinc(II)	1, 2, 6
	Phenothiazines	
Chloropromazine reineckate	Ammonium Hydroxide and Ammonium Salts	24
	Bromine Reagents	396
Chloropromazine	Cadmium (II)	16, 18
Aminazine	Iodine Reagents	443
Aminazine	Iodine Chlorides, etc.	133
	Tetraphenylborate	5
Chloropromazine	Thiocyanates	29, 32, 34, 38, 45
promethazine	Thiocyanates	37, 43
phenothiazine	Thiocyanates	19
	Phosphorus-containing Compounds	
Tetraethyl pyrophosphate	Alkalies	213, 242, 421
dialkyl phosphites	Alkalies	328

Examples (no entry under this heading is equivalent to 'miscellaneous')	Reagent	References under this reagent heading
esters of thiophosphoric acid	Alkalies	352
some phosphorus-containing esters	Alkalies	360
some organophosphorus fluoridates and pyroesters	Alkalies	421
trichloroethyl phosphate	Alkalies	445
Some phosphorus-containing esters	Amines and Heterocyclic Bases	68
Thiophosphoric acid	Bromine Reagents	435
Menadione diphosphate (dicalcium salt)	Cerium (IV)	35
Tributyl phosphate	Hydrobromic Acid	15
Di- and trialkyl phosphites	Hydrochloric Acid	100
Organophosphorus chloridates	Hydrofluoric Acid	
Organophosphorus fluoridates and pyrophosphonates	Hydrogen Peroxide	44
triphenylphosphine	Hydrogen Peroxide	51
Dialkyl- and diarylthio-phosphates	Iodine Reagents	376
(α-Oleoyl-β-stearoyl)phosphatidylethanolamine	Iodine Chlorides, etc.	135
Tetramethylphosphonium chloride	Ion Exchangers	13
salts of glycerophosphoric acid	Ion Exchangers	14
α-Glycerophosphates	Lead (IV)	4
Parathion	Metals	55
Tributyl phosphate	Molybdenum (VI) and Tungsten (VI)	21
O,*O*-Dialkyl hydrogen phosphorodithioates	Nickel (II)	10
Phosphonate groups in ion exchange resins	Perchloric Acid	6
α-Glycerophosphates	Periodate	3
Tributyl phosphate	Sulphuric Acid	106
Tris-(1-aziridinyl)phosphine	Thiosulphate	28
Tetraethyl pyrophosphate	Water	14

Polysaccharides

Examples	Reagent	References under this reagent heading
Pectin	Alkalies	212, 273
saponins	Alkalies	372
Benzylcellulose	Anhydrides	20
Lipides	Bichromate	140
cellulose	Bichromate	11, 81, 89, 112, 136, 175, 246
starch	Bichromate	178
hemicelluloses	Bichromate	185
Esculoside	Bromine Reagents	502

Examples (no entry under this heading is equivalent to 'miscellaneous')	Reagent	References under this reagent heading
Celluronic and alginic acids	Calcium (II)	22
pectin	Calcium (II)	29
Alginic acid and Na salt	Cerium (IV)	16, 21
Cellulose carboxymethyl ethers	Copper (II)	152, 191, 229
pectins	Copper (II)	165
Starches, dextrines	Ferricyanide	64
Pentosans	Hydrobromic Acid	3, 12
Pentosans	Hydrochloric Acid	Many
e.g. cellulose, starch, dextrans, hemicelluloses, etc.	Hydrochloric Acid	19, 48, 71, 90, 94, 98, 133
Cellulose	Iodate, etc.	58
Starches	Iodine Reagents	264, 321
Na alginate	Ion Exchangers	27
Dextrin, inulin	Molybdenum (VI) and Tungsten (VI)	9
End-groups in polysaccharides, e.g. dextrans, amylose	Periodates and Periodic Acid	47, 66, 86, 96, 115
dextrans	Periodates and Periodic Acid	58
Pentosans	Sulphuric Acid	4, 28
cellulosic materials, e.g. woods	Sulphuric Acid	57, 72
e.g. dextrans, glucosides, hemicelluloses	Sulphuric Acid	46, 66, 85, 101
	Primary Amines	
Primary amino alkyl alkoxysilanes	Alkalies	380
E.g. aniline	Anhydrides	1, 42
Rivanol	Bichromate	79
flavines	Bichromate	127
laurylamine acetate	Bichromate	178
Cystamine	Bisulphite and Sulphite	172
Aniline and salts	Bromine Reagents	44, 82, 124, 150, 159, 172, 207, 264, 303, 333
xylidines	Bromine Reagents	131, 136, 192
p-aminosalicylic acid and salts	Bromine Reagents	288, 307, 335
toluidines	Bromine Reagents	82, 140, 199
other aromatic amines	Bromine Reagents	35, 55, 60, 82, 141, 165, 224, 279, 288, 303, 318, 423, 459, 489, 501, 538, 543, 545
esters of *p*-aminobenzoic acid, e.g. procaine, benzocaine, panthesin	Bromine Reagents	97, 169, 186, 194, 210, 223, 226, 287, 296, 301, 302, 374, 383, 389, 454, 509
	Carbonyl Compounds	12, 18, 20, 23

Examples (no entry under this heading is equivalent to 'miscellaneous')	Reagent	References under this reagent heading
p-Toluidine	Carboxylic Acids	1
p-chloroaniline	Carboxylic Acids	12
aniline	Carboxylic Acids	16
melamine	Carboxylic Acids	26
Aromatic primary amines	Cerium (IV)	29, 55
aminophenols	Cerium (IV)	29
sodium *p*-phenylenediamine-sulphonate	Cerium (IV)	29
β-naphthylamine	Cerium (IV)	55
p-Diamines	Chlorine Reagents	4, 9, 23
Aniline	Chlorite	10
Aniline	Copper (II)	105
sodium *p*-aminosalicylate	Copper (II)	166
glucosamine hydrochloride and related compounds	Copper (II)	228
Aminoacridines	Ferricyanide	28, 69
Aniline	Halides (Active)	7, 9, 30, 33, 44
aminothiazole	Halides (Active)	38
anthranilic acid	Halides (Active)	44
benzylamine	Halides (Active)	73
Ethyl *p*-aminobenzoate	Hydrochloric Acid	101
Sodium *p*-aminosalicylate	Iodine Reagents	283
glucosamine	Iodine Reagents	219
penicillinamine	Iodine Reagents	399
Aromatic amines, e.g. aniline	Iodine Chlorides, etc.	73, 84, 89
p-aminosalicylic acid	Iodine Chlorides, etc.	75
procaine, benzocaine	Iodine Chlorides, etc.	73
Hexamethylenediamine dihydrochloride	Ion Exchangers	5
p-Aminosalicylic acid	Kjeldahl Nitrogen Determination	8, 10
Piperazine	Mercury (II)	140
Primary aromatic amines	Nitrite	2, 4, 12, 15, 17, 26
p-Bromoaniline	Nitrophenols	43
aniline, *p*-toluidine	Nitrophenols	58
acridines, e.g. acriflavine, proflavine	Nitrophenols	45
Compounds containing the —$CHNH_2$—CHOH— group, e.g. amino acids like serine, threonine, hydroxylysine; ethanolamines, aminoglycols	Periodiates and Periodic Acid	Many
ethylenediamine	Periodates and Periodic Acid	116, 117, 123
Benzocaine	Permanganate	104
Na *p*-aminosalicylate	Silver (I)	95, 113, 117
β-Naphthylamine	Sulphuric Acid	8
monoethanolamine	Sulphuric Acid	124

Examples (no entry under this heading is equivalent to 'miscellaneous')	Reagent	References under this reagent heading
Aniline	Sulphur Trioxide	3
E.g. procaine	Tetraphenylborate	1, 3, 14
Benzidine	Tetraphenylborate	4
Toluidines	Thiocyanates	3
aniline	Thiocyanates	6
p-Phenylenediamine	Vanadate	24
Proteins and Related Compounds		
Proteins, e.g. milk proteins	Alkalies	254,300,389,418,443
diketopiperazine	Alkalies	318
Proteins in insulin	Bichromate	145
Proteins	Bromine Reagents	42
Peptones	Carbonyl Compounds	11
proteins in cheese	Carbonyl Compounds	30
Peptides	Copper (II)	174
proteins	Copper (II)	214
Plasmalogen	Iodine Reagents	382, 401
Proteins	Kjeldahl Nitrogen Determination	16
Proteins	Mercury (II)	96
Haemoglobin	Nitrophenols	36
Proteins	Persulphate	2
Purines and Related Compounds		
Allophanic acid and esters	Alkalies	125
alloxan	Alkalies	167
Uric acid	Ammonium Hydroxide and Ammonium Salts	2, 7, 12, 18, 21
Theophylline + 7-(2-hydroxy-ethyl) theophylline	Anhydrides	151
Ammonium uranyl urate	Bromine Reagents	273
caffeine	Bromine Reagents	274, 291, 488, 537
6-mercaptopurine	Bromine Reagents	432
	Bromine Reagents	374, 488
theophylline, theobromine	Bromine Reagents	537
Theobromine, theophylline	Bismuth (III)	5
Diphenylhydantoin	Chlorine Reagents	10
Uric acid	Copper (I)	1, 2
Uric acid	Copper (II)	2, 8
theophylline	Copper (II)	142, 181, 207, 221
Uric acid	Ferricyanide	13
Caffeine	Iodate	26, 55
theobromine	Iodate	27
Caffeine	Iodine Reagents	11, 42, 123, 135, 277, 306, 311, 314, 323, 336, 337, 371, 385

Examples (no entry under this heading is equivalent to 'miscellaneous')	Reagent	References under this reagent heading
theobromine	Iodine Reagents	87, 128, 417
uric acid	Iodine Reagents	8, 127
guanine	Iodine Reagents	127, 315
xanthine	Iodine Reagents	127
Caffeine	Kjeldahl Nitrogen Determination	3, 6, 7
diphenylhydantoin	Kjeldahl Nitrogen Determination	12
Theophylline	Mercury (II)	103, 114
allantoin	Mercury (II)	16
theobromine	Mercury (II)	114
diphenylhydantoin, Na salt	Mercury (II)	178
	Mercury (II)	141
Uric acid	Molybdenum (IV) and Tungsten (VI)	13, 19
Diphenylhydantoin, Na salt	Nickel (II)	15
Adenine, guanine	Nitrophenols	46
hypoxanthine	Nitrophenols	47
7-(dihydroxypropyl)theophylline	Periodates and Periodic Acid	74
Theobromine	Silver (I)	2, 28, 33, 34, 35, 37, 60, 64, 76, 78, 91, 94, 118, 191
theophylline	Silver (I)	48, 70, 78, 124, 149
uric acid	Silver (I)	10, 16, 55
aminophylline	Silver (I)	90, 125
caffeine	Silver (I)	2
hypoxanthine	Silver (I)	73
6-mercaptopurine	Silver (I)	141, 200
6-(4-carboxybutylthio)purine	Silver (I)	170
diphenylhydantoin, Na salt	Silver (I)	195
Theobromine, theophylline	Thiocyanates	11
Uric acid	Vanadate	15

Pyrazolones

Examples	Reagent	References
Pyramidone	Alkalies	32, 48, 340
1-Phenyl-2,3-dimethyl-4-pyrrolidinyl-5-pyrazolone	Bichromate	213
Antipyrine	Bromine Reagents	463
Pyramidone	Cadmium (II)	5, 6, 8, 24
Picrolonic acid, picrolonates	Chromium (II)	10
Melubrin, novalgin	Cyanide	27, 29
Antipyrine	Ferrocyanide	1
Pyramidone/antipyrine mixtures	Hydrogen Peroxide	9
novalgin	Hydrogen Peroxide	47, 48
Antipyrine	Iodine Reagents	40, 66, 86

Examples (no entry under this heading is equivalent to 'miscellaneous')	Reagent	References under this reagent heading
melubrin	Iodine Reagents	205
1-phenyl-3-pyrazolidinone	Iodine Reagents	332, 379
E.g. antipyrine	Iodine Chlorides, etc.	109
Pyramidone	Iron (III)	5
antipyrine	Iron (III)	14
Pyramidone	Mercury (II)	43, 44, 141
antipyrine	Mercury (II)	44, 108
tetraphenylborate of pyramidone	Mercury (II)	137
Pyramidone	Nickel (II)	11
Antipyrine	Nitrophenols	11, 16, 19, 27, 41
pyramidone	Nitrophenols	11, 19, 41
Pyramidone	Permanganate	45, 116, 123
aminoantipyrine	Permanganate	97
1-Phenyl-2,3-dimethyl-4-(*p*-aminophenylsulphonamido)-5-pyrazolone	Sulphuric Acid	75
Pyramidone, antipyrine	Tetraphenylborate	1, 3, 4, 12
Pyramidone	Thiocyanates	20, 21, 23, 46, 55
antipyrine	Thiocyanates	51
Antipyrine	Thiocyanogen	2
Pyramidone	Vanadate	2, 19
Analgin	Vanadate	16

Quinones

Examples	Reagent	References
Camphoquinone	Bromine Reagents	360
quinhydrones	Bromine Reagents	437
Anthraquinones	Chromium (II)	5
quinone, quinhydrone	Chromium (II)	8
Anthraquinone	Hydrazines	33
	Hydroxylamine	148
Benzoquinone	Iodides and Hydriodic Acid	23, 117, 151, 189, 193, 200, 248, 429
anthradiquinone	Iodides and Hydriodic Acid	15
2-methyl-1,4-naphthoquinone	Iodides and Hydriodic Acid	91
	Iodides and Hydriodic Acid	3, 4, 5, 6, 8
2-methyl-1,4-naphthoquinone	Metals	41, 43, 73, 82
benzoquinone	Metals	3, 98
anthraquinone	Metals	8
Glucosides of hydroxyanthraquinone	Sulphuric Acid	101
E.g. 2-methyl-1,4-naphthoquinone	Tin (II)	17, 18
Alizarin and dyes	Titanium (III)	7
quinone; 2-methyl-1,4-naphthoquinone	Titanium (III)	68
	Titanium (III)	4

Examples (no entry under this heading is equivalent to 'miscellaneous')	Reagent	References under this reagent heading
Secondary Amines and Heterocyclic Bases		
N-Alkylanilines	Anhydrides	1, 2
tryptophane	Anhydrides	58
piperazine	Anhydrides	140
Carbazole	Bichromate	35
diphenylamine	Bichromate	39
atebrin	Bichromate	79, 125
Piperazine salts	Bismuth (III)	16
Diphenylamine	Bromine Reagents	47, 82, 130, 249
pyrrole and related compounds (indoles, carbazole)	Bromine Reagents	143, 401, 493
	Bromine Reagents	108, 212, 287, 390, 434, 545
Piperazine	Cadmium (II)	21
Dimethylamine, e.g.	Carbon Disulphide	1, 5
Carbazole	Carbonyl Compounds	9
ephedrine hydrochloride	Carbonyl Compounds	14
N-Methyl, *N*-ethylanilines	Chlorite	10
Piperazine	Copper (II)	201, 209
Adrenaline	Ferricyanide	115
piperazine periodate	Iodides and Hydriodic Acid	169
Metol	Iodine Reagents	333, 404
ephedrine	Iodine Reagents	132, 155
adrenaline	Iodine Reagents	188
tryptophane	Iodine Reagents	324
Atebrin	Iodine Chlorides, etc.	81
Piperazine	Mercury (II)	140
Dimethylamine	Nitrite	23
Dibenzylamine	Nitrophenols	43
Piperazine	Periodates and Periodic Acid	75
diethanolamine	Periodates and Periodic Acid	85
Piperazonium adipate	Silver (I)	172
Adrenaline	Sulphuric Acid	111
Piperazine	Thiocyanates	39, 40
Adrenaline	Vanadate	22
Selenium-containing Compounds		
	Iodides, etc.	100, 147
	Pyrolysis	15
p-Nitrobenzeneseleninic acid	Thiosulphate	11
Silicon-containing Compounds		
Ethyl silicon isothiocyanates	Alcohols	38
Alkyl silicon isothiocyanates and isocyanates	Alkalies	229, 244

Examples (no entry under this heading is equivalent to 'miscellaneous')	Reagent	References under this reagent heading
alkyl silicon iodides	Alkalies	265
primary amino alkyl alkoxy silanes	Alkalies	380
Alkoxy groups in alkoxysilanes	Anhydrides	164
mercaptosilanes	Anhydrides	168
Ethoxyl groups in some organic silicon compounds	Bichromate	207
Aryloxysilanes	Bromine Reagents	438
—Si—C_6H_5 groups	Bromine Reagents	511
Organosilyl metallic compounds	Halides (Active)	70
Aryloxysilanes with *tert*-butoxyl groups	Hydrochloric Acid	112
Lower alkoxy groups in alkoxysilanes	Iodides and Hydriodic Acid	121, 186, 202, 209, 217
Silanol groups	Isocyanate and Isothiocyanate	1, 2
Mercaptosilanes	Mercury (II)	189
Ethoxyl groups in some organic silicon compounds	Sulphuric Acid	108
Methylchlorosilanes	Thiocyanates	42, 48
Steroids and Related Compounds		
Sterols	Anhydrides	28, 61
Cholesterol, plant sterols; also as digitonides	Bichromate	42, 86, 171
Diethylstilbestrol; its esters	Bromine Reagents	220, 408, 417, 473, 495, 496
cholesterol, also as digitonide	Bromine Reagents	300, 377, 535, 542
β-sitosterol	Bromine Reagents	535
Cholesterol	Digitonin	All 5
Cholesterone	Hydroxylamine	40
Cholesterol	Percarboxylic Acids	5
Dehydrocholic acid salts	Sulphuric Acid	67
Sugars and Related Compounds		
	Anhydrides	22, 33, 36, 59, 61, 62, 66, 118
E.g. glucose, sucrose	Bichromate	18, 22, 69, 76, 80, 107, 120, 151, 157, 165, 174, 216
Mono- and disaccharides	Bromine Reagents	112, 113, 126, 268, 378, 422
E.g. dextrose	Cerium (IV)	6, 37, 52
Aldoses	Chlorite	1, 2, 3, 4, 6
Reducing sugars	Copper (II)	Many

Examples (no entry under this heading is equivalent to 'miscellaneous')	Reagent	References under this reagent heading
E.g. glucose	Cyanide	6, 15, 17, 18, 21
Glucose	Dyes	2
E.g. glucose, sucrose, lactose	Ferricyanide	Many
Aldoses	Halides (Active)	3
E.g. glucose, fructose, lactose	Hydrazines	8, 33
Pentoses	Hydrobromic Acid	3
Pentoses	Hydrochloric Acid	Many
sucrose	Hydrochloric Acid	66, 73, 128
glucose	Hydrochloric Acid	48
xylose	Hydrochloric Acid	60
	Hydrochloric Acid	135
Aldoses	Hydroxylamine	60, 148
Mono- and disaccharides	Iodine Reagents	Many
glucosamine	Iodine Reagents	219
double lactone of *d*-manno-saccharic acid	Iodine Reagents	220
methylated glucoses	Iodine Reagents	238
Glucose	Iodine Chlorides, etc.	115
Sugars and derivatives	Lead (IV)	5
	Manganate	2
E.g. glucose, lactose, galactose	Mercury (II)	1, 5, 23, 29, 30, 34, 36, 37, 45, 59, 60, 64, 157
Fructose	Molybdenum (VI) and Tungsten (VI)	3, 7, 12, 16
sucrose	Molybdenum (VI) and Tungsten (VI)	3
	Molybdenum (VI) and Tungsten (VI)	18
Pentoses, hexoses, disaccharides and related compounds like aldonic and sugar dicarboxylic acids	Periodates and Periodic Acid	Many
Glucose	Permanganate	21, 96
lactose	Permanganate	20
Glucose	Persulphate	5
Pentoses	Phosphoric Acid	10, 12
E.g. glucose	Silver (I)	4, 32
Sucrose	Sulphuric Acid	71, 73
arbutin	Sulphuric Acid	120, 121
maltose	Sulphuric Acid	71
condensation products of sugars with acetone	Sulphuric Acid	21
	Sulphur Trioxide	2

Sulphate Esters

Examples	Reagent	References
Sodium alkyl sulphates	Alkalies	154
dimethyl sulphate	Alkalies	253

Examples (no entry under this heading is equivalent to 'miscellaneous')	Reagent	References under this reagent heading
Alkyl sulphate detergents	Amines and Heterocyclic Bases	15
sulphoricinoleates	Amines and Heterocyclic Bases	40
	Amines and Heterocyclic Bases	16, 68
	Hydrochloric Acid	17, 33, 83
Dimethyl sulphate	Iodides and Hydriodic Acid	136
Sulphates of long-chain alcohols	Nickel (II)	4, 6
$ROSO_3^-$ in sulphated oils	Sulphuric Acid	58

Sulphinates

Examples	Reagent	References
Formaldehyde Na Sulphoxylate	Copper (II)	113
	Iron (III)	2

Sulphonamides and Salts

Examples	Reagent	References
Sulphonamides and sulphanilamides, e.g. Diamox, PANS	Alkalies	60, 193, 374, 377, 395, 409, 470
Sulphafurazole	Anhydrides	121
Sulphathiazoles	Bromine Reagents	213, 230, 320
sulphonamides	Bromine Reagents	238, 286, 374, 527
sulphanilamide	Bromine Reagents	151, 180
	Chlorine Reagents	13
	Copper (II)	218
Sulphonamides	Hydrochloric Acid	9, 52, 63, 77, 127
sulphapyridine	Hydrochloric Acid	61
sulphasolucin	Hydrochloric Acid	68
saccharine	Hydrochloric Acid	9
Sulphanilamide	Iodate	71
Etazole	Iodine Reagents	348, 354
sulphanilamides	Iodine Reagents	300
Sulphanilamides	Iodine Chlorides, etc.	72, 74, 97, 122
Sulphanilamide derivatives	Kjeldahl Nitrogen Determination	4
	Mercury (II)	86, 177, 182
PANS	Nitrite	27
Sulphanilamide	Permanganate	82
	Pyrolysis	47
Sulphanilamides, e.g. sulphapyridine, sulphathiazole	Silver (I)	79, 138, 140, 142, 159, 165, 196, 197, 201
Saccharine	Silver (I)	173
Sulphanilamides	Sulphuric Acid	45, 50, 75, 80

Examples (no entry under this heading is equivalent to 'miscellaneous')	Reagent	References under this reagent heading
	Sulphonates	
Aralkyl sulphonates	Alkalies	289
ichthyol	Alkalies	401
glyoxal bisulphite	Alkalies	399
Detergents like Igepon T, alkyl and aralkyl sulphonates	Amines and Heterocyclic Bases	30, 33, 38, 46, 55, 85, 96, 97, 107
Metal phenolsulphonates	Bromine Reagents	73, 84
p-Phenylenediaminesulphonate	Cerium (IV)	29
Bisulphite compounds of aldehydes (formaldehyde, acetaldehyde, glyoxylic acid)	Cyanide	Many between 28 and 50
'melubrin', 'novalgin'	Cyanide	27, 29
Aralkyl sulphonates	Hydrochloric Acid	83
Novalgin	Hydrogen Peroxide	47, 48
Glyoxal bisulphite	Hydroxylamine	145
Zinc phenolsulphonate	Iodine Reagents	171
'melubrin'	Iodine Reagents	205
Ichthyol	Iodine Chlorides, etc.	124
Benzene-, anthraquinone-, guaiacolsulphonates; detergents	Ion Exchangers	7, 8, 21, 23, 24, 28, 35, 44
Potassium guaiacolsulphonate	Nitric Acid	23
Ichthyol	Pyrolysis	38
E.g. dodecylbenzenesulphonate	Sulphuric Acid	117
Surface-active sulphonates	Surface Active Agents	1, 2
Analgin (melubrin)	Vanadate	16
	Sulphonic Acids	
J-acid/urea addition product	Alkalies	413
Naphthalenesulphonic acids	Amines and Heterocyclic Bases	18, 48
carbazole-3-sulphonic acid	Amines and Heterocyclic Bases	34
benzenesulphonic acids	Amines and Heterocyclic Bases	63
lignin sulphonic acids	Amines and Heterocyclic Bases	52
sulphonic acid groups in detergents	Amines and Heterocyclic Bases	73
sulphonated lubricating oils	Amines, etc.	60
Naphthalenesulphonic acids	Bichromate	55
indigosulphonic acid	Bichromate	186, 240
Sulphanilic acid	Bromine Reagents	303, 318
anthranilic acid-5-sulphonic acid	Bromine Reagents	185
p-aminobenzenesulphonic acid	Bromine Reagents	224

Examples (no entry under this heading is equivalent to 'miscellaneous')	Reagent	References under this reagent heading
guaiacolsulphonic acid and quinosol	Bromine Reagents	242
panthesin	Bromine Reagents	287
β-naphtholsulphonic acid	Bromine Reagents	456
1-naphthylamine-5-sulphonic acid	Bromine Reagents	501
δ-Sulphonic acids	Copper (II)	93
β-Naphthalenesulphonic acid	Hydrazines	13
o-benzenedisulphonic acid	Hydrazines	39
Sulphanilic acid	Iodate	51
indigo carmine	Iodate, etc.	75
8-Quinolinol-5-sulphonic acid	Iodine Reagents	370
Naphthalene-sulphonic acids	Metals	25, 26
1-Naphthol-5-sulphonic acid	Nitrite	30
4,4′-Dinitrostilbene-2,2′-sulphonic acid	Permanganate	103
2-Naphthol-1-sulphonic acid	Sulphuric Acid	87
Naphthalenesulphonic acids	Vanadate	1, 12
phthalocyaninesulphonic acids	Vanadate	10
indigo carmine	Vanadate	4
8-Quinolinol-5-sulphonic acid	Zinc (II)	2
	Sulphonium Salts	
	Bismuth (III)	10
Bromides	Nitrophenols	60
Iodides	Silver (I)	154
	Sulphonyl and Sulphenyl Chlorides	
Sulphonyl chlorides	Alkalies	28
Sulphonyl chlorides	Amines	106
Sulphenyl chlorides, e.g. benzenesulphenyl chloride	Iodides and Hydriodic Acid	86, 173
Toluenesulphonyl chlorides	Nitric Acid	22
	Water	10, 16, 20, 22
	Sulphones	
Dihydrochlorothiazide	Bromine Reagents	527
Phenyl β-D-glucopyranosyl sulphones	Periodates and Periodic Acid	60
	Sulphoxides	
Thionyl groups, (—C—O)(—C—O)>S→O	Alkalies	347

Examples (no entry under this heading is equivalent to 'miscellaneous')	Reagent	References under this reagent heading
Methionine sulphoxide	Iodides and Hydriodic Acid	73
3-amino-6-alkylsulphinylpyridazines	Iodides and Hydriodic Acid	247
	Percarboxylic Acids	6
	Tin (II)	19
	Titanium (III)	37, 43, 52

Sulphur-containing Compounds, Miscellaneous

Examples	Reagent	References
Esters of thiophosphoric acid	Alkalies	352
phenyl thioacetate	Alkalies	236
reineckates of aliphatic amines	Alkalies	452
	Alkalies	360
Alkyl polysulphides, R—S_x—R′	Aluminium Hydride and Borohydride	11
	Amines and Heterocyclic Bases	68
Thiophosphoric acid	Bromine Reagents	435
Sodium formaldehyde sulphoxylate	Copper (II)	113
Thiosulphonates, RSO_2S^-	Cyanide	2
Thiazine	Ferricyanide	13
Thioethoxyl groups	Hydrochloric Acid	87
Thiosulphonates, RSO_2S^-	Iodides and Hydriodic Acid	208
Etazole	Iodine Reagents	348, 354
dialkyl- and diaryldithiophosphates	Iodine Reagents	376
	Lead (II)	10
Thiolsulphonates, RSO_2SR'	Mercaptans	7
Sodium formaldehyde sulphoxylate	Mercury (II)	75
mercaptals	Mercury (II)	89
	Mercury (II)	155, 172
Thiodan	Metals	94
Thioacetic acid	Metals	4
dithiosalicylic acid	Metals	18
O,O-Dialkylhydrogenphosphorodithioates	Nickel (II)	10
Azidodithiocarbonates, —$SCSN_3$	Nitric Acid	4
—N=C(—)—SH groups	Selenium Dioxide	3
Azidodithiocarbonates	Silver (I)	25
esters of thion acids, RCSOH	Silver (I)	36
Sulphenamides, $RSNR_2$; sulphenyl thiocyanates, RS—SCN; sulphur piperidines $S_x(NC_5H_{10})_2$	Thiosulphate	10

Examples (no entry under this heading is equivalent to 'miscellaneous')	Reagent	References under this reagent heading
	Synthetic Bases and Salts	
Benzocaine	Alkalies	130
neostigmine bromide and methyl sulphate	Alkalies	141, 371
Tetracaine and ephedrine hydrochlorides	Anhydrides	161
Atebrin dihydrochloride	Bichromate	79, 125
rivanol	Bichromate	79
flavines	Bichromate	127
Antihistamines	Bismuth (III)	15
Esters of *p*-aminobenzoic acid, e.g. procaine, benzocaine, pantocaine, panthesin	Bromine Reagents	97, 169, 186, 194, 210, 223, 226, 287, 296, 301, 302, 374, 383, 389, 445, 449, 454, 509
sympatol	Bromine Reagents	108
Metrazol	Cadmium (II)	17
atebrin	Cadmium (II)	20
imipramine (tofranil)	Cadmium (II)	23
E.g. ephedrine hydrochloride, sympatol	Carbonyl Compounds	14
Aminoflavines, e.g. acriflavine	Ferricyanide	28, 69
adrenaline	Ferricyanide	115
Acaprin	Hydrochloric Acid	126
Phenazine, benzophenazine	Hydrogen Gas	4
Ephedrine	Iodine Reagents	132, 155
benzimidazoles	Iodine Reagents	425, 431, 432
adrenaline	Iodine Reagents	188
Procaine, benzocaine	Iodine Chlorides, etc.	73
atebrin	Iodine Chlorides, etc.	81
rivanol	Iodine Chlorides, etc.	99
e.g. aprophene, methadone, diphenhydramine, spasmolytine	Iodine Chlorides, etc.	114
Salts	Ion Exchangers	9, 17, 45, 46
Metrazol	Mercury (II)	93, 141
Acridines, e.g. acriflavine	Nitrophenols	45
E.g. pharmaceutical bases	Perchloric Acid	1, 7
Oxazolines	Periodates, etc.	121
Benzocaine	Permanganate	104
	Silver (I)	114, 126, 179
Adrenaline	Sulphuric Acid	111
E.g. procaine, sympatol, ephedrine, thiofalicaines	Tetraphenylborate	1, 2, 3, 5, 7, 11, 12, 14, 20, 21, 22
	Thiocyanate	10, 15, 16, 18, 19, 33, 44, 50, 52, 56
Adrenaline	Vanadate	22

Examples (no entry under this heading is equivalent to 'miscellaneous')	Reagent	References under this reagent heading
Tannins and Related Compounds		
—OH groups in tannins	Anhydrides	99
Tannins	Copper (II)	216
Tannides	Diazonium Salts	1, 2
	Ferricyanide	43, 96, 123
Tannin + gallic acid	Gelatine	
Tannic acid, tannin, gallic acid	Iodine Reagents	2, 7, 31, 32, 35, 355, 400
Gallic, tannic acids	Mercury (II)	68
propyl gallate	Mercury (II)	146, 167
Tannins, tanning agents	Permanganate	72, 88, 118, 138
Octyl, dodecyl gallates	Silver (I)	192
Tannic acid	Titanium (III)	21
Tannins	Vanadate	6, 19
Tertiary Amines and Heterocyclic Bases		
N-Hydroxyethylpiperazine	Anhydrides	140
Hexamine	Bichromate	33
atebrin	Bichromate	79, 125
quinoline	Bichromate	80
rivanol	Bichromate	79
flavines	Bichromate	127
Hexamine	Bromine Reagents	455, 486
3,3-diethyl-2,4-dioxo-tetrahydropyridine	Bromine Reagents	326
Hexamine	Cadmium (II)	7
pyridine	Cadmium (II)	10
rivanol	Cadmium (II)	15
metrazol	Cadmium (II)	17
atebrin	Cadmium (II)	20
Hexamine	Carboxylic Acids	17
melamine	Carboxylic Acids	26
Metrazol	Copper (I)	6, 8
Pyridine and salts	Copper (II)	41, 169
hexamine	Copper (II)	124
substituted aminoketones	Copper (II)	164
Certain β- or γ-substituted pyridines	Dimethyl Sulphate	1, 2
Aminoacridines, e.g. acriflavine	Ferricyanide	28, 69
Trimethylamine	Halides (Active)	34
some pyridine derivatives	Halides (Active)	40
Hexamine	Hydrochloric Acid	32
N,N'-bis-(*N*-methylquinolinyl-urea) methylsulphate ('Acaprin')	Hydrochloric Acid	126

Examples (no entry under this heading is equivalent to 'miscellaneous')	Reagent	References under this reagent heading
Phenazine, benzophenazine	Hydrogen Gas	4
Trimethylamine	Iodides and Hydriodic Acid	97
substituted pyridine derivatives	Iodides and Hydriodic Acid	122
	Iodides and Hydriodic Acid	215
Hexamine	Iodine Reagents	206, 291, 319
cincophene	Iodine Reagents	96, 179
pempidine	Iodine Reagents	440
Atebrin	Iodine Chlorides, etc.	81
rivanol	Iodine Chlorides, etc.	99
pharmaceutical bases, e.g. methadone, diphenhydramine	Iodine Chlorides, etc.	114
Addition products of BF_3 with pyridine and quinoline bases	Ion Exchangers	19
Cincophene	Mercury (II)	44
metrazol	Mercury (II)	93, 141
quinoline	Mercury (II)	117
pyrazine	Mercury (II)	118
dimethylaminophenazone, nicotinic acid derivatives	Mercury (II)	141
N-vinylcarbazole	Mercury (II)	185
Hexamine	Nitrophenols	8, 10, 18
acridines	Nitrophenols	45
α,α'-Dipyridyl, *o*-phenanthroline	Persulphate	3
Hexamine	Phosphoric Acid	11
Hexamine	Silver (I)	38, 56
α,α'-dipyridyl, *o*-phenanthroline	Silver (I)	96
Hexamine	Sulphuric Acid	14, 17, 20, 23, 29, 36, 39, 51, 54, 55, 62, 65
Hexamine	Tetraphenylborate	1, 4
Pyridine	Thiocyanates	1, 2, 4, 24
quinoline	Thiocyanates	13
hexamine	Thiocyanates	22
pentazole	Thiocyanates	33
Phthalocyanines and derivatives	Vanadate	10

Thioamides and Related Compounds

Examples	Reagent	References
S-Alkylthioureas	Alkalies	437
Thiourea	Bromine Reagents	451, 499, 526
thiosemicarbazone of *p*-acetylaminobenzaldehyde	Bromine Reagents	331
thioacetamide	Bromine Reagents	500
Thiourea and derivatives	Cadmium (II)	3, 19
thiosemicarbazones	Cadmium (II)	12, 19
Thiourea	Ferricyanide	103, 107
Thiourea	Halides (Active)	86
Thiourea	Hydrogen Peroxide	33
Thiourea	Iodate	65

Examples (no entry under this heading is equivalent to 'miscellaneous')	Reagent	References under this reagent heading
Thiourea	Iodine Reagents	218, 335, 393, 429, 430
thiosinamine	Iodine Reagents	74, 109, 388
substituted thioureas, e.g. tetramethylthiourea	Iodine Reagents	335, 394, 437
thiosemicarbazones	Iodine Reagents	406
Thioureas	Iodine Chlorides, etc.	90, 108
thiosemicarbazones	Iodine Chlorides, etc.	110, 113
Thiosemicarbazones	Iron (III)	7
Thiosemicarbazide	Lead (IV)	15
Thiourea	Mercury (II)	129, 153
Thiourea	Periodates and Periodic Acid	89
thiosemicarbazone of *p*-acetyl-aminobenzaldehyde	Periodates and Periodic Acid	62
Thiourea	Selenium Dioxide	1, 7
thiosemicarbazones	Selenium Dioxide	3
Thiourea	Silver (I)	47, 59, 119
α-naphthylthiourea	Silver (I)	105, 147
thiosinamine	Silver (I)	167, 184
thiosemicarbazones	Silver (I)	107, 108, 205
α-ethylnicotinic acid thioamide	Silver (I)	198, 199
Thioacetamide, thiourea	Zinc (II)	4

Thiobarbituric Acids and Salts

Examples	Reagent	References
	Bromine Reagents	363
	Ferricyanide	97
Thiopental	Halides (Active)	55
	Iodine	438
E.g. thiopental	Iodine Chlorides	96
	Periodate and Periodic Acid	69
	Silver (I)	121, 139

Thiocyanates and Isothiocyanates

Examples	Reagent	References
Ethyl silicon isothiocyanates	Alcohols	38
Alkyl silicon isothiocyanates	Alkalies	229, 244
Isothiocyanate groups	Amines and Heterocyclic Bases	39, 72, 76, 101
Allyl isothiocyanate	Ammonium Hydroxide and Ammonium Salts	5, 11, 13, 15, 23, 25, 26, 27
Allyl isothiocyanate	Bromine Reagents	272
Isothiocyanates	Lead (II)	10
Thiocyanates, isothiocyanates	Mercury (II)	155
Allyl, butyl isothiocyanates	Permanganate	136
Allyl isothiocyanate	Silver (I)	8, 13, 40
thiocyanates	Silver (I)	107
Isothiocyanates	Sulphides	3, 7
Allyl isothiocyanate	Water	4

Examples (no entry under this heading is equivalent to 'miscellaneous')	Reagent	References under this reagent heading
	Thioethers	
Alkyl aromatic or heterocyclic sulphides, e.g. dimethyl sulphide, phenyl benzyl sulphide, thiophene	Bromine Reagents	102, 196, 293, 321, 352, 364, 429, 457, 459, 544
methionine	Bromine Reagents	444
Dichlorodiethyl sulphide	Halides (Active)	35
	Halides (Active)	49, 54
Methionine	Hydrogen Peroxide	16, 38
aryl trityl sulphides (+ mercaptans)	Hydrogen Peroxide	46
Methionine	Iodides and Hydriodic Acid	35, 43, 53
	Iodides and Hydriodic Acid	195
S-alkyl groups	Iodides and Hydriodic Acid	227, 244
Methionine	Iodine Reagents	197, 222, 324, 329, 411
Methionine	Iodine Chlorides, etc.	113
	Iodine Chlorides, etc.	49
Thiophene	Mercury (II)	10, 156
cystine	Mercury (II)	187
mercaptosilanes (≡Si—SR)	Mercury (II)	189
Trityl phenyl sulphide	Metals	105
Methionine	Ninhydrin	13, 14
	Percarboxylic Acids	6
Methionine	Pyrolysis	37
	Thioketones (including Carbon Di- and Oxysulphide)	
Carbon disulphide	Alcohols	Many
Carbon disulphide	Amines and Heterocyclic Bases	71, 79, 99
carbon oxysulphide	Amines and Heterocyclic Bases	65
Carbon disulphide	Iodine Reagents	398
Thioketones	Mercury (II)	155
Thiobenzophenone, xanthenethione	Silver (I)	137
	Thiouracils	
	Bromine Reagents	369
6-Methylthiouracil	Iodine Chlorides, etc.	113
Methylthiouracil	Permanganate	119
4-propyl-2-thiouracil	Silver (I)	85, 101
methylthiouracil	Silver (I)	107

Examples (no entry under this heading is equivalent to 'miscellaneous')	Reagent	References under this reagent heading
	Thiouronium Salts	
Alkylthiouronium iodides	Carboxylic Acids	29
Thiouronium halides	Nitrophenols	55
Alkylthiouronium 3,5-dinitrobenzoates	Titanium (III)	51
	Uracils	
4-Methyluracil	Alkalies	396
4-Methyluracil	Bromine Reagents	476
4-Methyluracil	Iodine Reagents	343
4-methyl-5-hydroxymethyluracil	Iodine Reagents	369
4-Methyl-5-hydroxymethyluracil	Silver (I)	160
	Vitamins and Related Compounds	
Vitamin B_1	Bismuth (III)	7
Vitamin B_6	Bromine Reagents	365
Ca pantothenate	Bromine Reagents	308
Ca Pantothenate	Carboxylic Acids	28
α-Tocopherol	Cerium (IV)	19
Vitamin B_1	Ferricyanide	78, 92
Carotene	Iodine Reagents	186
vitamin B_1	Iodine Reagents	260
Vitamin E	Iron (III)	4
Vitamin B_1	Mercury (II)	91
Vitamin B_1	Metals	65
Vitamins A_1, D_2	Quinones	5, 6
Vitamin B_1	Silver (I)	88
	Xanthates	
	Arsenic (III)	1
	Copper (II)	16
	Ferricyanide	128
Cellulose xanthates	Halides (Active)	10, 29
	Halides (Active)	65
Cellulose xanthate	Hydrochloric Acid	34
	Hydrochloric Acid	7
Cellulose xanthate	Iodine Reagents	78, 81, 105, 124
	Iodine Reagents	21, 157, 175, 217, 270, 272
Cellulose xanthate	Mercury (II)	173
	Nickel (II)	2, 7
Cellulose xanthate	Phosphoric Acid	6
	Silver (I)	42, 107, 168

INDEX TO INDIVIDUAL COMPOUNDS DETERMINED BY DIRECT AND INDIRECT TITRATION

The following index covers the individual compounds specifically mentioned in the first columns of the tables of Sect. 2 in both Parts I and II. A few words of explanation and clarification about the index are given here.

The index is arranged in 3 columns. In **Column 1** the individual compounds are arranged alphabetically. Salts of acids are given under the anion; e.g. sodium acetate appears under 'Acetate'. Deviation from this principle occurs only with some salts of less commonly encountered metals, but the anion classification is also given in all cases. Trade and trivial names, apart from those which are well known like 'phenobarbital', are usually followed by the systematic name in square brackets. The compound appears then again under this systematic name. Thus 'Antabuse' is given under 'A' and also under 'T' for 'Tetraethylthiuram disulphide'. The prefixes n-, *sec*-, *tert*, *cis*-, and *trans*- have been ignored in alphabetizing, but compounds beginning with iso, bis, mono, bi (di), tri, etc., have been alphabetized under the prefix.

In **Column 2** the functional group which the individual compound contains or the compound class to which it belongs is given. These refer to the headings in Sect. 3 in Parts I and II. Several entries may appear in Column 2. Polyfunctional compounds have usually an entry for each function. Further, the headings in Sect. 3 in Part II sometimes differ from those in Part I and both or a fusion of the two are then given. Thus Part I has no heading for 'Sulphonyl chlorides' so that for the entry 'Benzenesulphonyl chloride' in Column 1, both 'Halogen-containing compounds' (for Part I) and 'Sulphonyl chlorides' (for Part II) are given in Column 2. An example of a 'fused' title is 'Ammonium hydroxides, salts, etc. which combines 'Ammonium salts, substituted' (Part I) with 'Ammonium hydroxide and salts, substituted' (Part II). This includes organic bases and salts which contain $=\overset{+}{\dot{N}}=$ with 1, 2, 3 or 4 carbon atoms linked to the nitrogen.

The recommended procedure is first to read the entry in Column 2 and to look under this entry in Sect. 3 in each part. Cross references are given in Sect. 3 to the more detailed information and original literature in Sect. 2. The individual compound sought may be quoted in the first column ('Examples') in Sect. 3 and the corresponding references in Sect. 2 can be consulted first. The reader will appreciate that, to economize space, only a limited number of specific examples could be quoted in the examples column. Moreover, he will note under 'Materials Titrated', the first column in the tables of Sect. 2, that summarized entries such as 'Amides', 'Nitro compounds', 'Carboxylic acids', etc. appear. For the same reasons of economy of space and convenience, it was not possible to enumerate under 'Materials Titrated' every titrated compound in every publication cited in Sect. 2. Some authors in developing or testing a method, titrated up to 40 or 50 members of a particular compound class, which would have occupied half-a-page of space if fully listed. The compound sought by the reader may be concealed in one of these summarized entries. He is thus advised to consult further all the references to Sect. 2 given in Sect. 3 where the first (examples) column has no entry or where the entry is preceded by 'E.g.' The example of, say, acetonitrile illustrates this. The index to individual compounds gives 'Nitriles' in Column 2 and under 'Nitriles' in Sect. 3 in Part I (p. 471) and Part II (p. 941–2), acetonitrile is in fact mentioned twice; ref. 5 under 'Lithium aluminium hydride' in Part I and ref. 130 under 'Sulphuric acid' in Part II. Other entries in Sect. 3 under 'Nitriles' ought now to be consulted. The first given, in Part II is evidently for trichloroacetonitrile—ref. 160 under 'Alkalies' in Sect. 2—and is of no direct use. The first possibly directly useful entries in Part II are refs. 124, 326, 378, etc. under 'Alkalies'. He will in fact find that acetonitrile was one of the 4 nitriles determined in ref. 378. Altogether there are 15 original sources which can be consulted in this way. It is of course possible that the method referred to for trichloroacetonitrile (and for other nitriles quoted under 'Examples' in Sect. 3) would be applicable for acetonitrile. The decision whether to consult these also, rests with the reader. He is also advised to examine the headings of Sect. 3 in the Contents (pp. xvii–xx in Part I and pp. xvi–xix in Part II). He will see a number of alternative or supplementary headings in brackets which are worth consulting. Thus when his individual compound is an aldehyde or ketone, he ought to look in Sect. 3 not only under these headings but also under 'Carbonyl compounds': or, when the compound is, say, a primary amine, to look under 'Amines and bases in general', as well as under 'Primary amines'.

Some individual compounds appear only a few times in the whole book and are often not mentioned under 'Examples' in the tables of Sect. 3. The page numbers in Parts I and II on which such compounds are mentioned, are entered in **Column 3**. (I) following the number refers to Part I and (II) to Part II. Since each page has an average of only some 12 references, this will greatly accelerate the search. It must be repeated here that Column 3 contains only those entries which are quoted by name in the 'Materials Titrated' columns of Sect. 2 in both parts. The relevant summarizing entries of 'Materials Titrated' ought to be consulted, just as mentioned in the previous paragraph, in case they contain useful examples. Some relatively rarely encountered compounds for which there was no convenient functional group or compound class heading in Sect. 3, have been given no entry in Column 2. Column 3 then always contains references to the places of citation in the book.

When the reader does not find in the index the compound in which he is interested, he can still operate in the same way, via the functional group or compound class. This will likewise lead him to the same cross-references in the third column of Sect. 3 in each part and consultation of these original articles will often uncover a titration method for his compound. Even if this fails, he will at least find methods for closely similar compounds which will probably be applicable to his particular case. This can be illustrated with the specific example of propionamide which is not in the index. Amongst the cross-references to be found to amide titration is ref. 228 under 'Perchloric acid', p. 342 in Part I. Propionamide is mentioned along with 40 other amides in this article. To save space, the entry on p. 342 under 'Materials titrated' had been abbreviated to 'Amides'. On the other hand, the summarizing entry 'Amides' for ref. 210 on p. 340 in Part I does not include propionamide. Formamide is, however, there and it is reasonable to assume that the method described could successfully be applied to propionamide.

The author would like to thank Frau H. Lentes for valuable help in the compilation of this index.